S0-CKY-192

Recent Progress in

HORMONE RESEARCH

The Proceedings of the Laurentian Hormone Conference

VOLUME 37

RECENT PROGRESS IN

HORMONE RESEARCH

Proceedings of the
1980 Laurentian Hormone Conference

Edited by

ROY O. GREEP

VOLUME 37

PROGRAM COMMITTEE

G. D. Aurbach
J. C. Beck
R. O. Greep
E. Knobil
D. T. Krieger
E. E. McGarry
M. New
B. W. O'Malley
J. E. Rall
K. Savard
N. B. Schwartz
J. L. Vaitukaitis

1981

ACADEMIC PRESS
A Subsidiary of Harcourt Brace Jovanovich, Publishers
New York London Toronto Sydney San Francisco

ACADEMIC PRESS, INC.
111 Fifth Avenue, New York, New York 10003

United Kingdom Edition published by
ACADEMIC PRESS, INC. (LONDON) LTD.
24/28 Oval Road, London NW1 7DX

LIBRARY OF CONGRESS CATALOG CARD NUMBER: Med. 47-38

ISBN 0-12-571137-9

PRINTED IN THE UNITED STATES OF AMERICA

81 82 83 84 9 8 7 6 5 4 3 2 1

CONTENTS

LIST OF CONTRIBUTORS AND DISCUSSANTS

H. Adlercreutz
A. Amsterdam
F. Auletta
G. D. Aurbach
K. L. Baird
F. C. Bartter
J. J. M. Bergeron
T. Bigos
L. Birnbaumer
M. E. Birnbaumer
H.-C. Blossey
E. M. Bogdanove
H. L. Bradlow
A. E. Broadus
L. Bullock
H. Burrows
G. Campbell
J. Carter
R. Chatterton
J. Chen
S. Cohen
P. W. Concannon
V. Cortes-Gallegos
C. E. Creutz
K. Crickard
J. F. Crigler
W. F. Crowley
G. B. Cutler
B. Dobyns
P. K. Donahoe
R. W. Downs, Jr.
B. Dupont
J. Dupre
C. Eil
J. Eng
L. E. Faber
R. Fellows
J. S. Flier
H. G. Friesen
T. Fujii
J. Geller
F. W. George
J. M. George
A. L. Goldstein
R. O. Greep
J. E. Griffin
W. W. Grody
M. M. Grumbach
C. Grunfeld
N. Hall
J. T. Harmon
L. C. Harrison
S. Hu
M. R. Hughes
I. T. Huhtaniemi
R. B. Jaffe
R. Jewelewicz
Z. Josefsberg
C. R. Kahn
F. A. Karlsson
F. J. Karsch
M. Kasuga
M. N. Khan
R. J. Khan
G. L. King
E. Knobil
D. Koritnik
W. Krawietz
G. E. Landreth
U. C. Lang
C. Lazier
M. Leshin
L. S. Levine
M. A. Levine
T. L. K. Low
J. E. McClure
G. Macdonald
T. J. McDonald
S. J. Marx
A. R. Means
R. E. Miller
B. F. Mitchell
C. Monder
I. Mowszowicz
W. R. Moyle
B. E. P. Murphy
T. Murray
F. Naftolin
Z. Naor
P. B. Naylor
M. I. New
J. Nolin

W. D. Odell
B. W. O'Malley
S. Pang
J. Parsons
B. A. Patel
C. J. Pazoles
O. H. Pearson
E. Peck
G. J. Pepe
J. M. Podskalny
M. Pollack
H. B. Pollard
B. I. Posner
M. Postel-Vinay
C. Raj
H. G. M. Raj
J. E. Rall
S. A. Reen
B. F. Rice
H. J. Ringold
B. Robaire
I. Rothchild
A. K. Roy
S. W. Ryder
P. H. Saenger
K. Savard
W. T. Schrader
M. Serón-Ferré
E. M. Shooter
R. A. Sikstrom
M. J. Singer, Jr.
S. W. Spaulding
A. M. Spiegel
B. G. Steinetz
K. Sterling
E. Straus
A. Sutter
G. B. Thurman
W. P. VanderLaan
E. Van Obberghen
A. K. Verma
R. F. Weick
N. L. Weigel
G. Weiss
J. Weisz
A. Wentz
J. D. Wilson
C. A. Winkel
C. J. Woodard
R. S. Yalow
B. A. Yankner
M. M. Zatz

PREFACE

We deeply regret the loss of Dr. Abraham White, Vice-President of the Board of Directors of the Laurentian Hormone Conference, who suffered a fatal heart attack. He has been a regular attendant and strong supporter of these Conferences from their inception, and will be greatly missed. It is with fond remembrance that we dedicate this volume to Abe. Had his death not intervened, it would have included a paper by him.

The wonders of science grow more wondrous with each passing year, and are reflected as such in this thirty-seventh annual volume of *Recent Progress in Hormone Research*. It contains the proceedings of the 1980 Laurentian Hormone Conference which was held at Mont Tremblant Lodge, August 24 to 29. There, fourteen leaders, each an expert in his or her field of special interest, provided detailed accounts of brilliant investigative endeavors and the insight gained as to the far more wondrous complex of exquisitely integrated systems that constitute the marvel of living organisms such as ourselves. The level of sophistication in hormone research as reported here is such as to suggest that researchers might already be exploring the ultimate bases of life and its ability to reproduce. That, however, is only an illusion because each new advance simply opens expanding vistas of realms yet to be explored. The critical value of these deliberations among experts in hormone research is that they help chart the course of future advances in this area of biomedical research.

It is my pleasure to convey to Drs. Melvin M. Grumbach, Gordon Macdonald, John R. Gill, Jr., Frederic C. Bartter, John Dupre, Henry Friesen, William D. Odell, and J. Edward Rall the grateful appreciation of all members of the Program Committee for their skillful chairing of the scientific sessions. The great help provided by Martha Wright in managing the logistics of the Conference, by Lucy Felicissimo and Carmen Ferrara in transcribing, on the spot, all of the taped discussions, and by the staff of Academic Press for their professional expertise and willing cooperation in the timely production of this volume is gratefully acknowledged.

Roy O. Greep

Abraham White

Memorial Tribute to Dr. Abraham White

It is my honor, but sad responsibility to open this session by paying respects to Abe White who suffered a fatal heart attack this past February while visiting Santa Barbara. Many of you are old friends of Abe who know that the Laurentian Hormone Conference was Abe's favorite meeting and Mont Tremblant his favorite meeting place. Abe was a founding member of this Conference at the first meeting held at Chesapeake Bay in 1944, and after the move to Mont Tremblant the next year he attended virtually every meeting while serving on the Board and Program Committee. Few speakers at the Laurentians escaped Abe's analytical inquiring mind and his incisive questions invariably delivered in a gentle, almost apologetic manner. I should also like to interject at this point that just as Abe was a part of this Conference, so also was his lovely wife Edna. They were an unusually devoted, loving, and caring couple. Edna could not attend this year's meeting, but I hope that she will rejoin us in future years.

Abe had an illustrious academic career following his Ph.D. at Michigan in 1931, with successive professorships at Yale, UCLA, Columbia, Yeshiva, and Stanford. Along the way, he won the Eli Lilly Prize in biochemistry in 1938, the Borden Award in 1969, and was elected to the American Academy of Arts and Sciences and the National Academy of Sciences. He also coauthored with Handler and Smith their famous text "Principles of Biochemistry."

I will not attempt to recount all of Abe's scientific achievements, but I would like to summarize briefly his important contributions to the role of hormones and the immune system. In the early 1940s, when the function of the lymphoid system was still unknown, Abe and Tom Dougherty at Yale demonstrated that the administration to rodents of the then newly purified ACTH caused thymolysis and lymphocytolysis. Similar activity was found with cortical hormone extracts, eventually attributed solely to the 11-hydroxylated steroids. White and Dougherty also first demonstrated the synthesis of antibody by lymphoid cells and its suppression by corticoids or ACTH. These were the first indications of the role of lymphoid tissues in immune phenomena and the role of the endocrine system on host immunity.

Later investigations with Sydney Roberts at UCLA established that calf thymus extracts produced lymphoid tissue hypertrophy. In the 1960s, Abe's interest in thymic extracts was rekindled when the dramatic wasting effects of neonatal thymectomy were established and when it was observed that cell-free thymic extracts reconstituted the thymectomized mouse.

At Albert Einstein College of Medicine, with Jerome Klein and Allan Goldstein, a novel assay based on tritiated thymidine incorporation into lymph nodes was developed which permitted the evaluation of potential lymphocytopoietic fractions of calf thymus extracts. This marked the beginning of a long productive collaboration with Dr. Goldstein that contributed to establishing the thymus as an endocrine gland and elucidating its hormonal role in immunity. In 1966 Goldstein and White described the preparation of an active, partially purified thymic lymphopoietic fraction from calf thymus and suggested that this fraction contained a hormone that was called "thymosin." It is particularly appropriate that Dr. Goldstein will discuss that work at this year's Conference.

In subsequent years at Syntex, Abe and Pamela Burton worked on the isolation of a fraction from human blood that exhibited thymic, hormone-like activity. Purification of this component from Cohn's Fraction IV established that the active component was associated with the purified prealbumin molecule.

As a lifelong friend of Abe's, I felt exceptionally privileged when Abe joined us at Syntex eight years ago as a Distinguished Scientist, and took the office next to mine. Describing Abe in action calls for a series of superlatives—gracious, modest, wonderful teacher, sparkling sense of humor, and, above all, his tremendous enthusiasm for science, research, music, theater, and life. He was a whirlwind of activity, and although his chronological age at death was 72, his vigor and activity belied those years. Abe died a young man, and we shall miss him.

HOWARD J. RINGOLD
Syntex Research Laboratories
Palo Alto, California

Recent Progress in

HORMONE RESEARCH

The Proceedings of the Laurentian Hormone Conference

VOLUME 37

The Role of Gonadal Steroids in Sexual Differentiation[1,2]

JEAN D. WILSON, JAMES E. GRIFFIN, FREDRICK W. GEORGE, AND MARK LESHIN

Department of Internal Medicine, The University of Texas Southwestern Medical School, Dallas, Texas

I. Introduction

Embryos of both sexes develop in an identical fashion for the first 2 months of gestation, and only thereafter does anatomical and physiological development diverge to result in the formation of the male and female phenotypes. The fundamental mechanism of sexual differentiation was elucidated by Alfred Jost (1953, 1972). He established that the castrated mammalian embryo develops as a female. Male development is induced in the embryo only in the presence of specific hormonal signals arising from the fetal testis. According to the Jost formulation—now the central dogma of sexual development—sexual differentiation is a sequential, ordered, and relatively simple process (Fig. 1). Chromosomal sex, established at the time of conception, directs the development of either ovaries or testes. If testes develop, their hormonal secretions elicit the development of the male secondary sex characteristics, collectively known as the male phenotype. If an ovary develops or if no gonad is present, anatomical development is female in character. Thus, whatever the mechanisms by which chromosomal or genetic sex is translated into gonadal sex, it is the action of the gonads as endocrine organs that is responsible for development of the sexual phenotypes.

Stimulated by this powerful paradigm, subsequent investigators have sought to identify the specific hormones that are secreted by the fetal testis, to elucidate the control mechanisms that regulate the rates of secretion of these hormones at the crucial moment in embryonic development, and to characterize—at the molecular and genetic level—the mechanisms by which the testicular hormones induce the conversion of the sexually indifferent embryo into the male phenotype. As a consequence, the origi-

[1] The Gregory Pincus Memorial Lecture.

[2] The original work described in this review was supported by grant AM03892 from the National Institutes of Health.

ISBN 0-12-571137-9

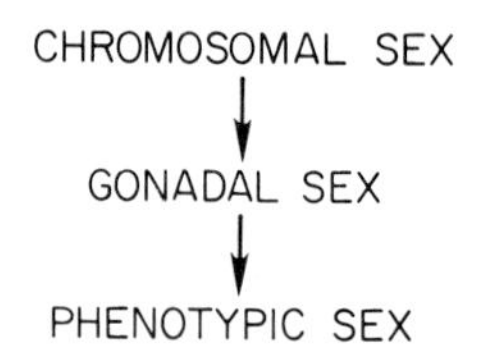

FIG. 1. The Jost model for sexual differentiation.

nal formulation of Jost has been refined and expanded, and insight has been obtained into the pathogenesis of many derangements of sexual development in humans resulting from single gene defects that impede either the formation or the cellular actions of the hormones of the fetal testis.

The purpose of this article is to describe current concepts of the processes by which the fetal gonads acquire the capacity to function as endocrine organs and of the mechanisms by which the endocrine secretions of the fetal testis modulate male development. The major focus will be on the events in the human and rabbit embryos. We will first review the anatomical events involved in the formation of the sexual phenotypes and then the factors that mediate this development.

II. Formation of the Sexual Phenotypes

As formulated by Jost (1953, 1972), the first phase of sexual development involves the establishment of chromosomal sex at the time of fertilization, the heterogametic complement (XY) being male and the homogametic state (XX) female. The second involves the development of gonadal sex. The Y chromosome carries genetic determinants that induce the indifferent gonad to differentiate as a testis. These determinants are either identical to or closely linked to the gene specifying a cell-surface antigen termed the H-Y antigen (Wachtel, 1980; Ohno, 1978).

The formation of the sexual phenotype is the direct consequence of the type of gonad formed. The temporal sequence by which chromosomal, gonadal, and phenotypic development takes place in the human embryo is shown schematically in Fig. 2. The germ cells do not originate in the embryo itself but rather in the yolk sac (Peters, 1970). By about the 10–20 mm crown–rump length stage of embryonic development, the germ cells migrate to their ultimate destination in the genital ridges of the embryo. After the migration, the gonads in male and female embryos appear identical and consist of three components—the primordial germ cells themselves, the connective tissue of the genital ridge, and a covering layer of epithelium. Histological differentiation of the gonads begins when the germ cells in the testis line up to form the so called spermatogenic cords.

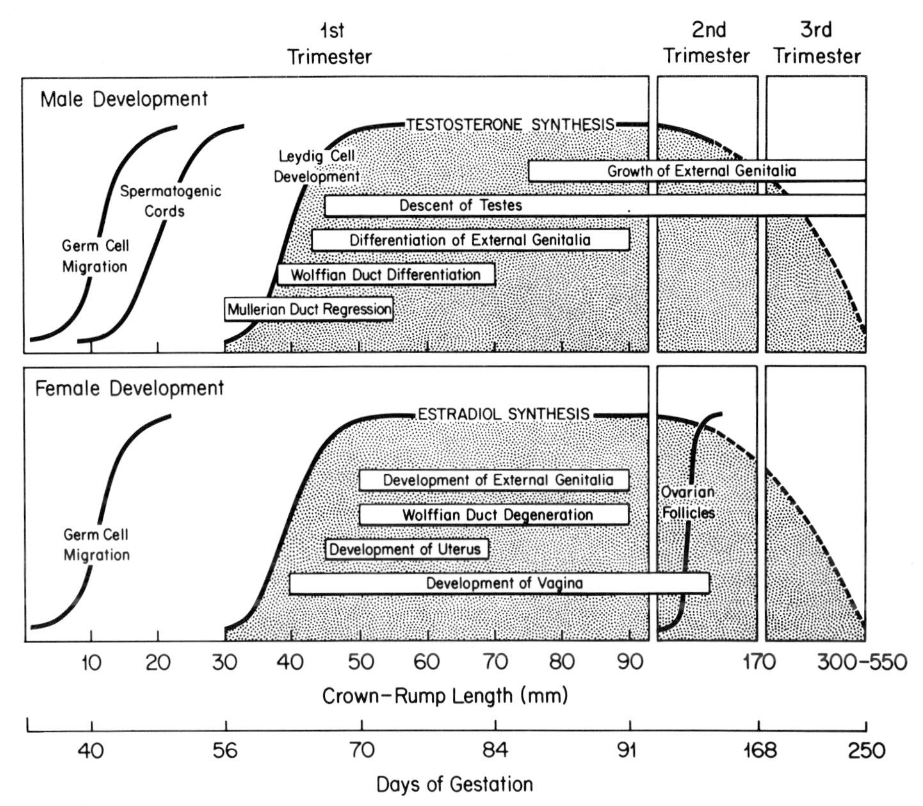

FIG. 2. The temporal relation between gonadal development, the onset of endocrine function in the gonads, and the anatomical differentiation of the internal genital tract and the external genitalia in the human embryo.

Shortly thereafter, Leydig (interstitial) cells appear in the connective tissue of the testis; these cells synthesize testosterone. In contrast to the early, rapid development of the testes, fetal ovaries show little histological development until the second third of gestation when the definitive ovarian follicles develop. Development of the definitive male and female urogenital tracts is largely accomplished between the 30 and 90 mm crown–rump stages in the human embryo. Although the timing of events in embryogenesis varies, the sequence of events in sexual differentiation is common among mammalian species, namely histologic and functional development of the fetal testis precedes male phenotypic development.

The anatomical events in the development of the male and female urogenital tracts are diagrammed schematically in Figs. 3 and 4 (Wilson, 1978, 1979). In brief, the primordial genital tract of both sexes consists of three

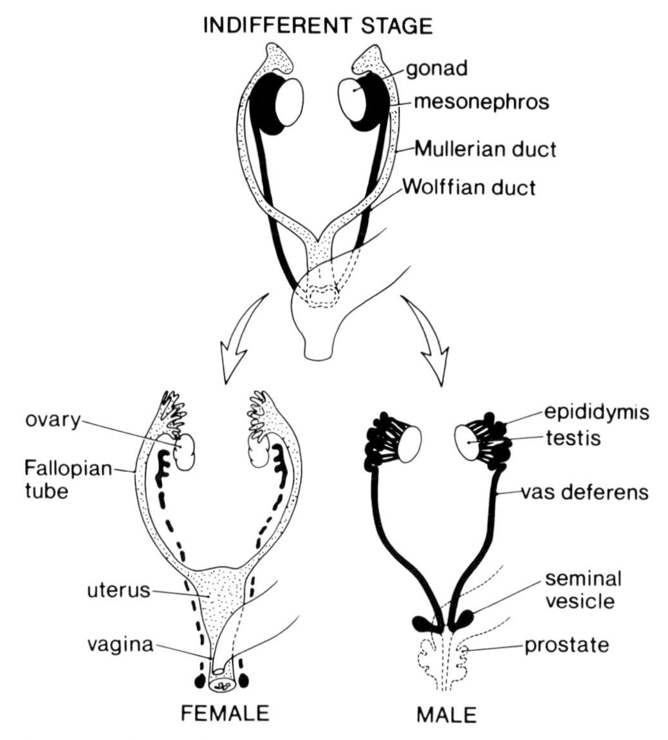

FIG. 3. Formation of the internal genital tract in male and female embryos.

components: (a) the gonads, (b) two genital duct systems (Wolffian and Müllerian), and (c) a common opening for the genital ducts and the urinary tract to the outside through the genital folds on the abdominal wall.

The process by which this primordium undergoes sexual differentiation is straightforward. The internal genital tracts in the two sexes develop from different duct systems, Wolffian and Müllerian (Fig. 3). In the male the Wolffian ducts persist, and the Müllerian ducts regress. In the female the opposite occurs, the Müllerian duct system persists, and the Wolffian ducts degenerate. The external genitalia in the two sexes develop from the genital tubercle, folds, and swellings (Fig. 4).

A. REPRODUCTIVE TRACT DEVELOPMENT

Male urogenital tract development (termed virilization) begins shortly after the formation of the spermatogenic cords of the testis (Fig. 2). The initial event is the onset of regression of the Müllerian ducts, ultimately resulting in their disappearance. Müllerian duct regression is quickly followed by

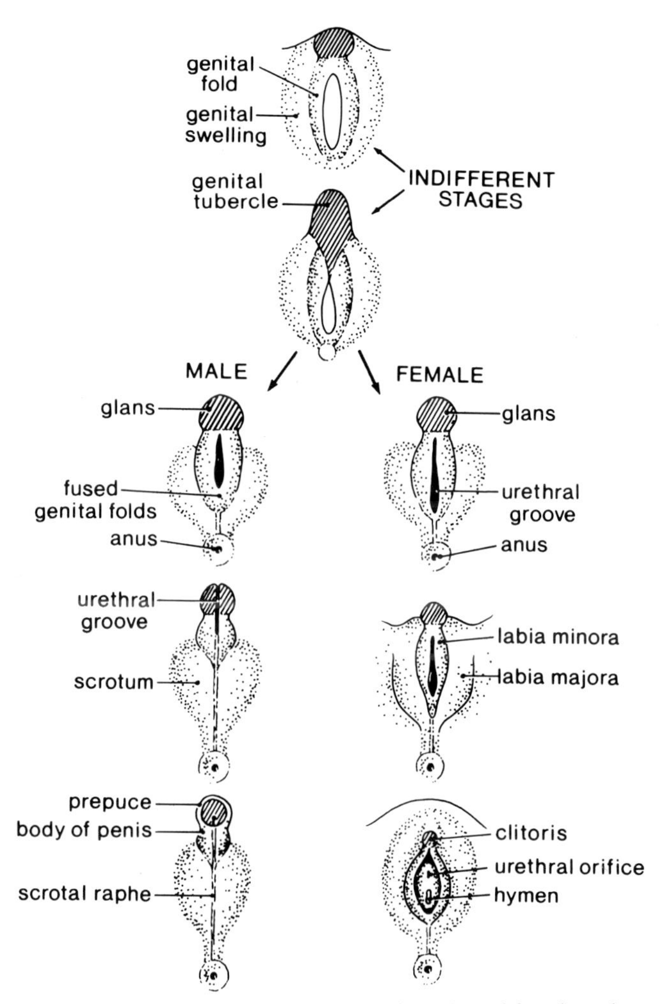

FIG. 4. Formation of the external genitalia in male and female embryos.

virilization of the Wolffian ducts (Fig. 3). The upper portion of the Wolffian duct forms the epididymis, the central portion develops a thick muscular coat to become the vas deferens, and the terminal portion gives rise to the ejaculatory duct and seminal vesicle (Fig. 3). Simultaneously, the prostate gland arises from a series of endodermal buds that appear in the lining of the primitive urethra. In the female embryo the Wolffian ducts regress, and the Müllerian ducts develop into the fallopian tubes and uterus and contribute to development of the vagina (Fig. 3).

In contrast to the internal genitalia, which develop from separate duct systems in males and females, the external genitalia of both sexes develop from common anlage. The external genitalia of the female enlarge but otherwise undergo little change from the indifferent state (Fig. 4). The genital tubercle becomes the clitoris, the adjacent genital swellings give rise to the labia majora, and the genital folds become the labia minora.

In the male, development of the external genitalia begins shortly after the onset of virilization of the Wolffian ducts (Fig. 4). The genital folds elongate and fuse to form the penis and male urethra. As a consequence of the fusion the urogenital swellings on each side of the urethral orifice form a bilobed scrotum that serves as the receptacle for descent of the testes. As the penis develops, it migrates anteriorly.

Anatomical development of the internal and external genitalia is accomplished largely by the end of the first trimester of gestation. At this time the testes remain in the abdominal cavity, and no differential growth of the male external genitalia has occurred. Thus, during the formation of the male urethra the phallus enlarges to the same extent in male and female embryos. In the latter part of gestation two final aspects of male development are completed, namely descent of the testes and accelerated growth of the genital tract. In the male embryo growth commences in the external genitalia, the prostate, and the structures derived from the Wolffian duct during the second trimester and continues until shortly before birth. Descent of the testes in man takes place over a 7-month period, beginning about the sixth week of gestation and finishing in some instances after birth.

B. BREAST DEVELOPMENT

Only one functional mammary bud develops on each side of the chest wall in the human embryo. (In many species multiple glands develop.) This bud can be recognized in the 7 mm embryo and is well differentiated by the 40 mm stage. In mid-gestation the nipple develops, and secondary epithelial buds appear. During the remainder of embryonic life ductular proliferation continues so that by the time of birth 15–25 branches are present. In embryos of some species there is clear-cut sexual dimorphism in breast development. For example, in the male rodent the excretory ducts regress under the influence of testosterone leaving the breast as an isolated island in the subcutaneous tissue (Kratochwil and Schwartz, 1976). Dimorphism of breast development has not been documented in the human embryo, however, and the breasts of boys and girls are identical prior to the onset of puberty (Pfaltz, 1949).

III. Control of Sexual Development

A. ROLE OF TESTICULAR SECRETIONS

The fact that transformation of the indifferent urogenital tract and external genitalia into the male phenotype is determined by secretions of the fetal testis was established as a result of studies of the effects of castration in the rabbit embryo (Jost, 1972). Removal of the gonads from embryos of either sex prior to the onset of phenotypic differentiation results in the development of embryos with a female phenotype. Thus, the male is the induced phenotype in that testicular secretions cause formation of the male urogenital tract whereas female differentiation is not dependent on the presence of an ovary and therefore does not require secretions from the embryonic gonad. Jost also deduced that two secretions from the fetal testis are essential for male development—Müllerian inhibiting substance and androgen (1972).

1. Müllerian Inhibiting Substance

Müllerian inhibiting substance is an incompletely characterized protein hormone that acts in the male to cause regression of the Müllerian ducts. The formation of the inhibiting substance constitutes the initial endocrine function of the embryonic testis, and Müllerian duct regression commences shortly after differentiation of the spermatogenic tubules. The inhibiting substance is a glycoprotein of about 70,000 molecular weight and is formed by the spermatogenic tubules (Blanchard and Josso, 1974; Donahoe *et al.,* 1977; Picard *et al.,* 1978). The mechanism by which the substance acts to suppress Müllerian duct development is uncertain. However, the concept that Müllerian regression is an active process (i.e., it is not just a failure of the ducts to grow as may be the case for regression of the Wolffian ducts in the female) is supported by the existence of an hereditary disorder (the persistent Müllerian duct syndrome) in which genetic and phenotypic men have fallopian tubes and uteri together with male Wolffian duct structures (Sloan and Walsh, 1976). This disorder is inherited as a recessive trait, either autosomal or X-linked. The nature of the underlying defect is uncertain, but it must reside either in a failure to produce the Müllerian inhibiting substance or inability of the tissue to respond to the hormone. A striking feature of the persistent Müllerian duct syndrome is failure of the initial phase of testicular descent—namely, transabdominal movement of the testis. This suggests that Müllerian inhibiting substance plays a crucial role in the movement of the testis into the scrotum. Such descent is essential for normal testicular function.

2. Androgen

The second developmental hormone of the fetal testis was identified by Jost to be an androgenic steroid. The principal steroid hormone formed by the testis in postnatal life is testosterone (Fig. 5). Testosterone is also the androgen formed by the testes of the rabbit and human embryos at the time of male phenotypic development (Lipsett and Tullner, 1965; Wilson and Siiteri, 1973; Siiteri and Wilson, 1974). Perhaps more importantly, not only is testosterone the major steroid formed by the fetal testes in these species, but no major unknown steroids were identified in the same experiments (Wilson and Siiteri, 1973; Siiteri and Wilson, 1974). In both species the onset of testosterone formation by the testes commences shortly after the onset of differentiation of the spermatogenic tubules and concomitant with the histological differentiation of the Leydig cells of the testis (Wilson and Siiteri, 1973; Siiteri and Wilson, 1974; George *et al.,* 1978a). Thus, testosterone serves as the principal fetal as well as the postnatal androgen in the male.

Testosterone is believed to perform at least two functions in male development. First, it probably acts locally within the testis to promote maturation of the spermatogenic tubules and the formation of sperm. Second, it is secreted into the fetal circulation where it plays an essential role in development of the male phenotype. As a circulating hormone it may also be responsible for programming in the central nervous system of those systems that regulate testicular function and certain male behavioral patterns.

The critical role of testosterone in development of the male urogenital tract was deduced from three types of embryologic and endocrine evidence: First, the fact that testosterone synthesis immediately precedes the initiation of virilization in a variety of species suggested a cause and effect relation between the two events (Lipsett and Tullner, 1965; Attal, 1969; Wilson and Siiteri, 1973; Siiteri and Wilson, 1974; Rigaudiere, 1979). Second, the administration of testosterone analogs induces male development of the internal and external genitalia in female embryos of several species

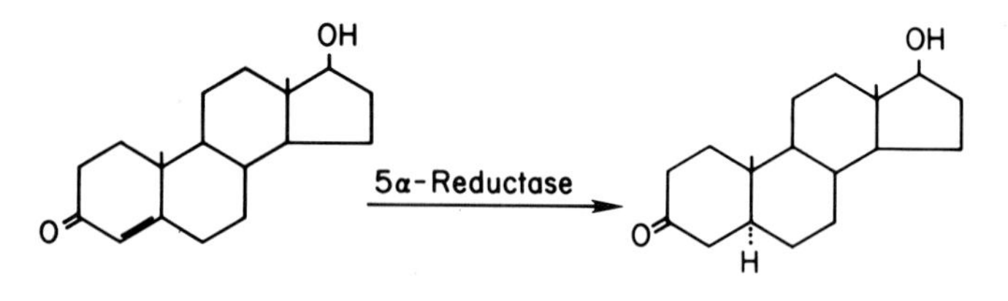

FIG. 5. Conversion of testosterone to dihydrotestosterone.

(Shultz and Wilson, 1974). Third, administration at the appropriate time in embryonic development of pharmacologic agents that inhibit the synthesis or action of androgens prevents male development (Goldman, 1970; Neumann *et al.*, 1970). There is now ample genetic evidence substantiating this concept. In man, five separate genetic defects are known to cause inadequate testosterone synthesis and incomplete virilization of the male embryo during embryogenesis (Bongiovanni, 1978; Griffin and Wilson, 1978; Wilson, 1978). Each defect involves a discrete enzyme (or enzyme complex) required for the conversion of cholesterol to testosterone (20,22-desmolase, 3β-hydroxysteroid dehydrogenase, 17α-hydroxylase, 17,20-desmolase, and 17β-hydroxysteroid dehydrogenase). In each of these disorders the virilization of the male urogenital tract is incomplete; the degree of abnormality varies, depending upon the severity of the enzymatic deficiency. Some affected males develop as phenotypic women with complete failure of virilization of the Wolffian ducts, urogenital sinus, and external genitalia. At the other extreme affected men appear normal except for mild developmental abnormalities such as hypospadias. The fact that neither fallopian tubes nor uterus is present in such patients indicates that regression of the Müllerian ducts takes place normally during embryogenesis and that Müllerian regression is independent of testosterone biosynthesis.

B. REGULATION OF TESTOSTERONE SYNTHESIS IN THE FETAL TESTIS

If male development is largely mediated by testosterone, understanding the factors that regulate testosterone synthesis during embryogenesis is essential for understanding how genetic sex is translated into gonadal sex. In the male embryo of the New Zealand rabbit, testosterone synthesis commences reproducibly during a 12-hour period between days 17 and 17.5 of gestation (Fig. 6, upper panel). In experiments that encompass this interval and the onset of phenotypic development we have done time-sequence measurements of each enzyme involved in the conversion of cholesterol to testosterone and estradiol, histological studies of the Leydig cells, studies of the LH/hCG receptor and its functional capacity, and *in vitro* studies of several types to assess the regulation of the rates of steroid hormone formation (Catt *et al.*, 1975; Milewich *et al.*, 1977; George *et al.*, 1978a,b, 1979; George and Wilson, 1980). These studies can be summarized as follows:

Prior to the onset of steroid hormone synthesis the primordial gonads of both sexes lack only two enzymes (or enzyme complexes) in the testosterone synthetic pathway—20,22-desmolase activity and 3β-

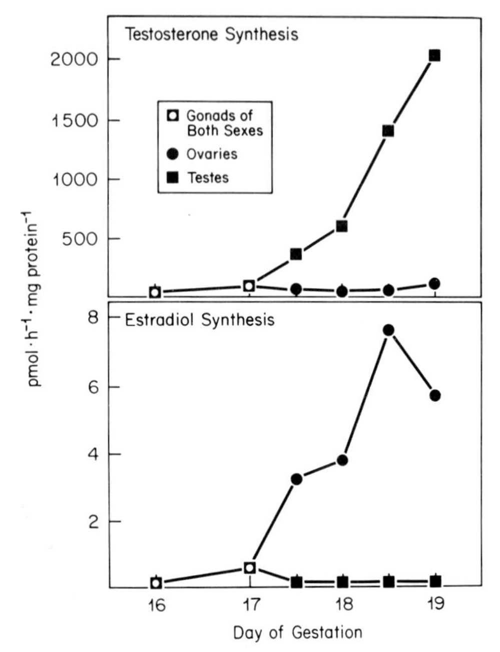

FIG. 6. Onset of endocrine function in the fetal testis and ovary of the rabbit embryo. Each gonad begins to synthesize its characteristic hormones at approximately the same time on day 17.5 (Milewich *et al.*, 1977).

hydroxysteroid dehydrogenase activity. All other enzymes required for the remaining three reactions in the conversion of cholesterol to testosterone are present in excess in both types of gonads. On approximately day 17.5 there is a rapid increase in 20,22-desmolase activity in both ovaries and testes, whereas 3β-hydroxysteroid dehydrogenase activity increases only in the testes so that by day 18 the activity is at least 50 times as great in testes as in ovaries. The appearance of this activity in the testis corresponds exactly with the onset of testosterone formation and with the transformation of the undifferentiated interstitial cells of the testis into mature Leydig cells with abundant smooth endoplasmic reticulum (George *et al.*, 1978a).

An unexpected finding in these studies was that the ovary begins to form potent estrogenic hormones at exactly the same time as the onset of testosterone synthesis in the testis (Milewich *et al.*, 1977; George *et al.*, 1978b), indeed before histological differentiation of the ovary has been recognized (Fig. 6, lower panel). Similarly the onset of endocrine function of human fetal testes and ovaries occurs simultaneously between 6 and 8 weeks of gestation (Siiteri and Wilson, 1974; George and Wilson, 1978a).

The enzymatic profile that underlies the onset of the characteristic endocrine function in the ovary and testis of the rabbit is reviewed in Fig. 7. On day 18 of gestation (at a time when histological differentiation of the testis is advanced) only two differences in the steroid hormone-synthesizing machinery can be detected between ovary and testis. First, 3β-hydroxysteroid dehydrogenase activity is greater in the testis than in the ovary; this enzyme is rate-limiting in testosterone synthesis at this stage of development in the rabbit, and thus more testosterone is synthesized in the testis than in the ovary. Second, the fetal ovary has the capacity to convert the small amount of testosterone synthesized in the tissue into estradiol whereas the testis does not. The remaining enzymes in the pathway of steroid hormone synthesis from cholesterol are equal in ovary and testis at this time. There are differences in the details of the enzymatic profiles among species, but in all cases examined to date testosterone and estrogen synthesis appear to be activated simultaneously (Milewich *et al.*, 1977; Mauleon *et al.*, 1977; George and Wilson, 1978a; George *et al.*, 1978b; Sholl and Goy, 1978). Thus, differences in the rates of a small number of enzymatic reactions in the gonads at a critical time in development have profound consequences for the further differentiation of the individual.

The question as to whether the rates of formation of the gonadal steroids are themselves regulated at the onset by other hormones is not yet resolved. Late in embryogenesis, as in the postnatal state, gonadotropins from the pituitary and/or placenta regulate the rates of estradiol and testosterone formation in the ovary and testis, primarily by control-

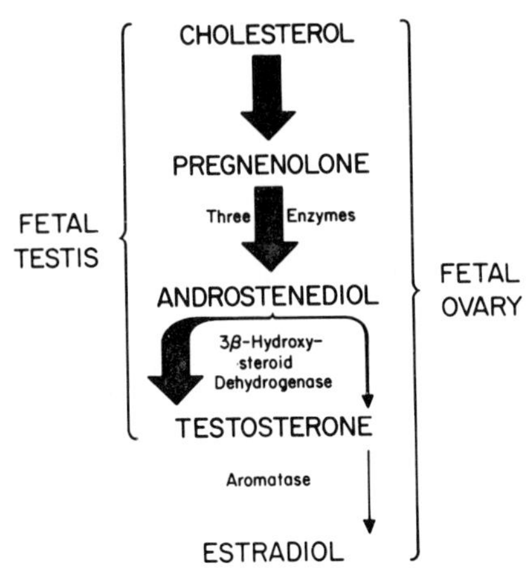

FIG. 7. Enzymatic profile of the pathway of steroid hormone synthesis in the ovary and testis of the rabbit embryo on day 18 of gestation.

ling the side-chain cleavage of cholesterol to pregnenolone, thereby regulating the availability of substrate for the formation of the hormones. In the rabbit the anterior pituitary differentiates at about the same time as the onset of testosterone synthesis in the fetal testis, suggesting the possibility that hormones from the pituitary may control testosterone synthesis at the time of its initiation (Schechter, 1970). In species such as the human in which the placenta produces large amounts of gonadotropic hormones, the onset of testosterone production could be regulated by the placental gonadotropins. A receptor for luteinizing hormone is demonstrable in rabbit testis at the time of the onset of testosterone synthesis, and from its first appearance in the Leydig cell membrane, this receptor is functionally coupled to the side-chain cleavage process by which cholesterol is converted to pregnenolone (Catt *et al.*, 1975; George *et al.*, 1979).

Other evidence is compatible with an alternative possibility, namely that the onset of testosterone synthesis is independent of the pituitary or other hormonal control. First, the endocrine differentiation of the gonads occurs in organ culture (Picon, 1967; George *et al.*, 1978a; George and Wilson, 1980). That is, day 16 rabbit embryo testes and ovaries undergo their characteristic enzymatic differentiation at the appropriate time when cultured for 2 to 4 days in synthetic media devoid of hormones (Fig. 8). Second, gonadotropin is not required for testosterone formation in the fetal rabbit testis until late in embryogenesis when cholesterol side-chain cleavage (and the availability of pregnenolone) becomes rate-limiting in

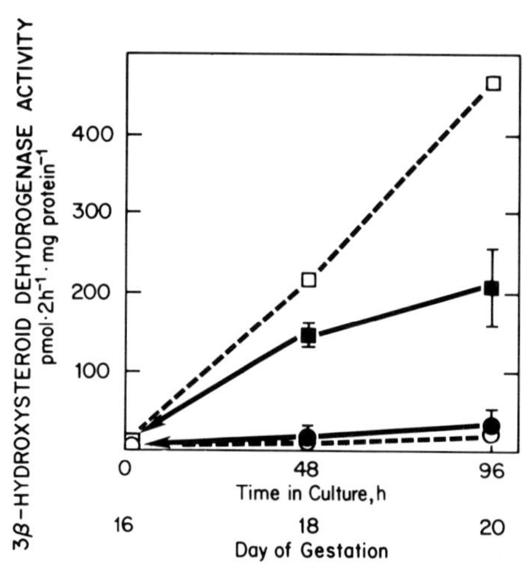

FIG. 8. Appearance of 3β-hydroxysteroid dehydrogenase in fetal rabbit testis in organ culture. □, ○, Testes and ovaries, respectively, in intact controls assayed at days 16, 18, and 20 of gestation. ■, ●, Testes and ovaries, respectively, removed from day 16 embryos and maintained for 48 or 96 hours in organ culture (George and Wilson, 1980).

the enzymatic sequence of testosterone biosynthesis (George *et al.*, 1979). These findings raise the possibility that the differentiation of the gonads as endocrine organs is controlled by factors intrinsic to the gonads themselves. If this interpretation is correct, the embryonic ovary and testis function initially as independent or autonomous endocrine organs. It also follows that sexual development occurs independently of the pituitary gland. The fact that testosterone production becomes gonadotropin-dependent late in embryogenesis indicates that the late testosterone-mediated events in male development such as growth of the male genitalia are modulated indirectly by gonadotropic hormones from the pituitary and/or placenta. This provides an explanation for the fact that males with hereditary hypogonadotropic hypogonadism often have microphallus and a high frequency of cryptorchidism but otherwise normal male anatomy (Walsh *et al.*, 1979).

C. MECHANISM OF ANDROGEN ACTION IN THE EMBRYO

The current concepts of how androgens exert their cellular actions within target tissues in postnatal life are summarized schematically in Fig. 9. Testosterone (T) is the androgen secreted by the testis and the major androgen in plasma. Testosterone enters target tissues by a passive diffusion process. Inside the cell testosterone can be converted to dihydrotestosterone (D) by the 5α-reductase enzyme (Fig. 5). Testosterone or dihydrotestosterone is then bound to the same high affinity androgen receptor protein (R) in the cytosol. The hormone–receptor complexes (TR and DR) move from cytosol to the nucleus. Inside the nucleus the steroid–receptor complexes interact with acceptor sites on the chromosomes. The character of the acceptor sites within the nucleus (i.e., whether protein or DNA)

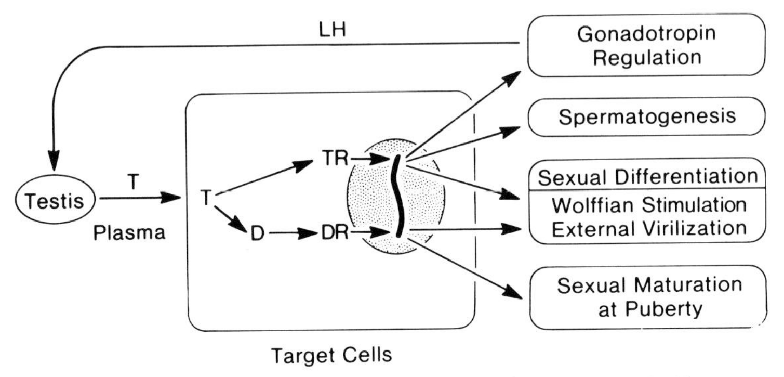

FIG. 9. Current concepts of the mechanism of action of testosterone. T, Testosterone; D, dihydrotestosterone; R, androgen receptor protein; LH, luteinizing hormone.

and their number are not resolved, but the overall result of the nuclear interaction of the hormone–receptor complexes is to increase transcription of specific structural genes with the subsequent appearance of new messenger RNA and new proteins in the cytoplasm of the cell. The reason that testosterone mediates some androgen effects and dihydrotestosterone mediates others is not clear. It may involve some subtle difference in the affinity of the receptor for the androgen or some undefined feature of the metabolism of testosterone and its local concentration in the genital tract.

As the result of studies in normal embryos and in animals and humans with single gene mutations that cause resistance to androgen action it has been established that androgens act in the embryo by the same mechanisms as in the postnatal state (Griffin and Wilson, 1980). The testosterone–receptor complex is responsible for regulation of gonadotropin secretion by the hypothalamic–pituitary system, for regulation of spermatogenesis and for virilization of the Wolffian duct during embryogenesis, whereas the dihydrotestosterone–receptor complex induces virilization of the urogenital sinus and external genitalia during embryogenesis and is responsible in large part for the maturational events at male puberty (Fig. 9).

Three types of single gene mutations have been informative in establishing the applicability of this scheme to events in the embryo (Fig. 10). Each mutation affects one of the three major processes in the pathway of normal androgen action, namely, the 5α-reductase enzyme, the androgen receptor, or the subsequent phases of hormone action. Each of these defects results in hereditary resistance to androgen action and causes incomplete

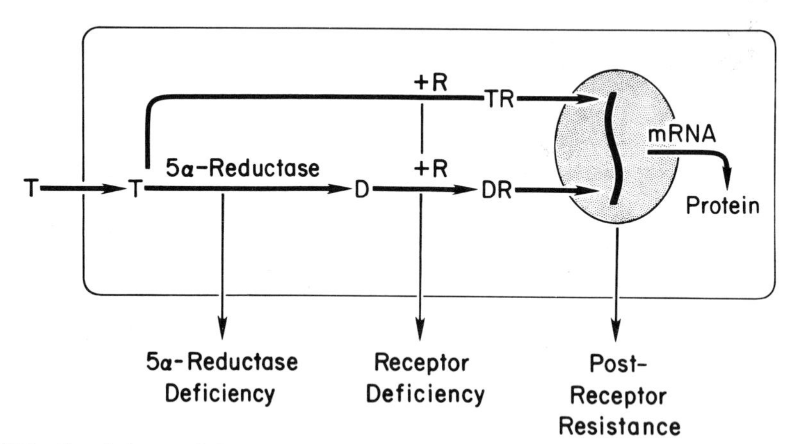

FIG. 10. Schema of the molecular biology of androgen resistance showing the three steps in the pathway of androgen action at which mutations have been identified. T, Testosterone; D, dihydrotestosterone; R, receptor; mRNA, messenger RNA.

virilization during embryogenesis (and in subsequent life) despite the fact that testosterone formation and Müllerian duct regression are normal.

1. Role of Testosterone and Dihydrotestosterone

The fact that testosterone is responsible for virilization of the Wolffian ducts and that dihydrotestosterone is responsible for virilization of the external genitalia was recognized on the basis of studies of androgen metabolism in embryos (Wilson and Lasnitzki, 1971; Wilson, 1973; Siiteri and Wilson, 1974). Namely, in the embryos of the rat, rabbit, guinea pig, and human, 5α-reductase activity is maximal in the anlage of the prostate and external genitalia prior to virilization, whereas the enzyme is virtually undetectable in the Wolffian duct derivatives until after virilization of the tissues is far advanced (Fig. 11). This deduction received genetic substantiation from studies of patients with a rare form of abnormal sexual development originally termed pseudovaginal perineoscrotal hypospadias by Nowakowski and Lenz (1961). Affected persons are 46,XY males who have an autosomal recessive disorder characterized by an external female phenotype at birth and the presence of bilateral testes and normally virilized Wolffian structures (epididymis, vas deferens, seminal vesicle, and ejaculatory duct) that terminate in a vagina (Fig. 12). At the time of expected puberty the external genitalia virilize to a variable extent, axillary and pubic hair develop normally, and testosterone production increases to the male range. Gynecomastia does not develop. This is the phenotype that would be predicted if dihydrotestosterone-mediated events in male phenotypic development were deficient but the testosterone-mediated phases were normal (Fig. 9). Direct evidence of a defect in 5α-reductase activity in this disorder was reported in 1974 in two families—one from Dallas (Walsh *et al.*, 1974) and one from the Dominican Republic (Imperato-McGinley *et al.*, 1974; Peterson *et al.*, 1977). Additional patients were described subsequently (Saenger *et al.*, 1978; Hodgins *et al.*, 1977; Fisher *et al.*, 1978; Greene *et al.*, 1978; Imperato-McGinley *et al.*, 1980). The disorder is now termed 5α-reductase deficiency and not the original anatomic designation.

In affected persons reported to date elevated ratios of plasma testosterone to dihydrotestosterone after human chorionic gonadotropin stimulation are present before puberty, and normal to elevated plasma testosterone levels and low plasma dihydrotestosterone levels are present in adults. Elevated ratios of urinary 5β-reduced to 5α-reduced steroids, decreased *in vivo* conversion of testosterone to dihydrotestosterone, diminished 5α-reductase activity in tissue biopsy specimens, and deficient or abnormal 5α-reductase activity in fibroblasts cultured from genital skin are consistent features.

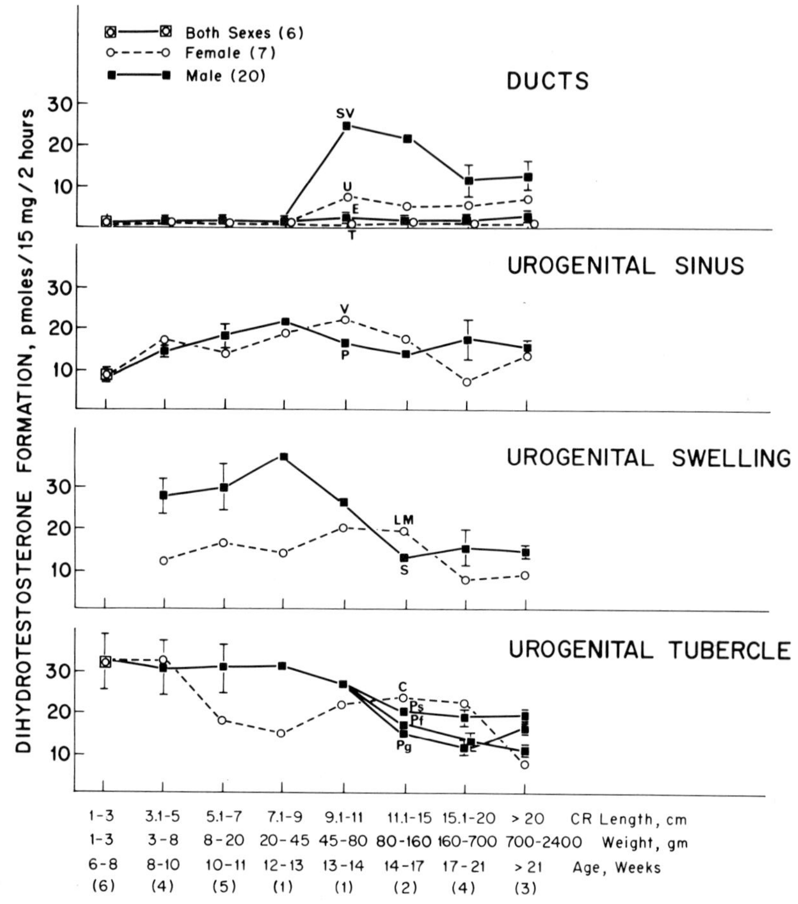

FIG. 11. Dihydrotestosterone formation in the urogenital tissues of the human embryo as a function of the age of the embryo. SV, Seminal vesicle; U, uterus; E, epididymis; T, fallopian tubes; V, vagina; P, prostate; LM, labia majora; S, scrotum; C, clitoris; Ps, shaft of penis; Pf, foreskin of penis; Pg, glans penis (Siiteri and Wilson, 1974).

Affected men have less facial and body hair and less temporal hairline recession than unaffected men from the same families. Acne has not been observed. No prostatic tissue is palpable, and no prostatic utricle can be visualized on cystoscopy. Thus, in the male temporal hairline recession, growth of facial and body hair, and development of acne as well as development of the external genitalia and prostate during embryogenesis are mediated by dihydrotestosterone.

Although plasma luteinizing hormone (LH) is elevated, it is lower than in castrated men or subjects with disorders of the androgen receptor (Wil-

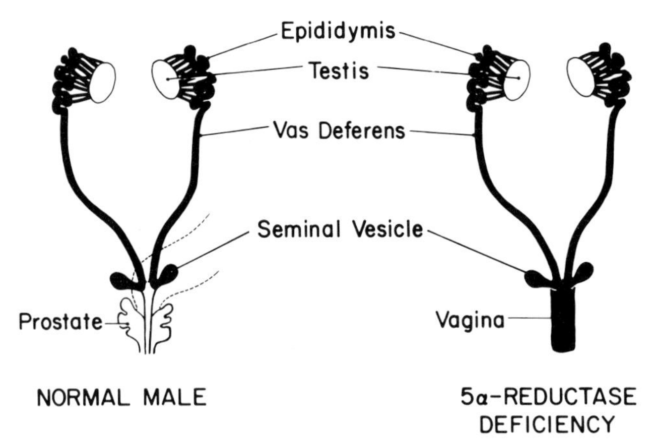

FIG. 12. Schematic diagram of the anatomy of the internal genital tract in 5α-reductase deficiency.

son and MacDonald, 1978). The relatively normal plasma levels of LH probably explains why estrogen formation is within the normal range for men and why gynecomastia is absent. In several untreated patients virilization at the time of expected puberty appears to be accompanied by a change in gender role from female to male (Imperato-McGinley *et al.*, 1979, 1980). This phenomenon has not taken place in patients castrated early and raised as females. Several subjects raised as females and given subsequent estrogen replacement therapy have made successful adjustments as women.

The deficiency in 5α-reductase is believed to be due to the homozygous state of an autosomal recessive gene that is manifest clinically only in males. Homozygous 46,XX persons have normal fertility, and heterozygous 46,XY persons are clinically normal (Peterson *et al.*, 1977).

The molecular features of the mutation have been studied in cells cultured from six subjects from four pedigrees (Table I and Fig. 13). The enzyme in normal genital skin fibroblasts has a pH optimum of 5.5; measurement of this activity has proved to be the most sensitive means to detect the enzyme deficiency (Wilson, 1975; Moore *et al.*, 1975; Moore and Wilson, 1978; Leshin *et al.*, 1978; Imperato-McGinley *et al.*, 1980). In the families from Dallas and the Dominican Republic 5α-reductase activity was markedly deficient. However, in cells cultured from patients from a Los Angeles family (Fisher *et al.*, 1978), the activity of the enzyme is in the low-normal range, despite the demonstration of a severe deficiency of the enzyme in fresh tissues from the same patients (Leshin *et al.*, 1978). In contrast to the enzyme in cells from the first families described with the disorder, the enzyme from the Los Angeles family has a normal pH op-

TABLE I

Characteristics of Residual 5α-Reductase Activity in Four Families with 5α-Reductase Deficiency[a]

Family	Activity at pH 5.5 (pmol/mg protein/hr)	K_m for Testosterone (μM)	K_m for NADPH (μM)	Stability after exposure to cycloheximide (%)
Controls (12)[b]	33(2–150)	0.08 ± 0.01[c]	40 ± 8[c]	>95
Dallas	0.2	1.80	250	>95
Dominican Republic	0.2	3.40	97	>95
Los Angeles	4.5	0.16	1760	<5
New York	0.6	2.20	425	75

[a] Data from Leshin *et al.* (1978) and Imperato-McGinley *et al.* (1980).
[b] Number of subjects
[c] Mean ± SEM.

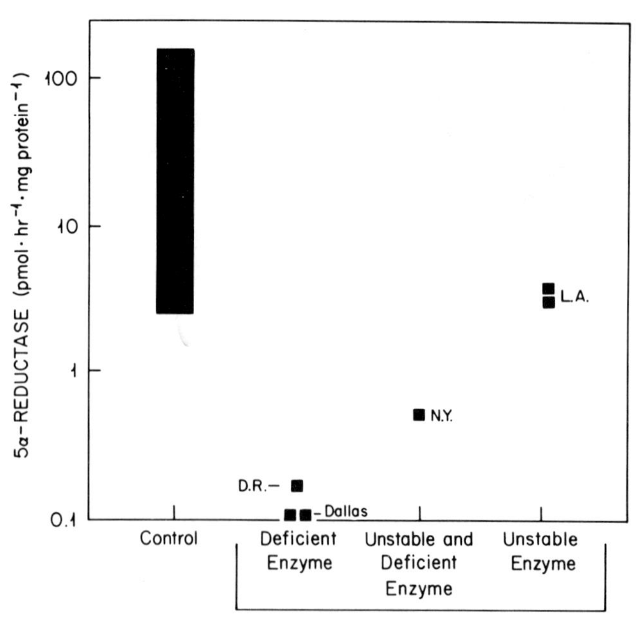

FIG. 13. 5α-Reductase activity at pH 5.5 in sonicates of genital skin fibroblasts cultured from four families with 5α-reductase deficiency. D.R., Dominican Republic; L.A., Los Angeles; N.Y., New York. (Adapted from Imperato-McGinley *et al.*, 1980.)

timum and a normal K_m for testosterone (Table I). However, affinity for reduced nicotinamide adenine dinucleotide phosphate (NADPH), the cofactor for the reaction, is decreased, and the enzyme is unstable, with a rapid turnover (Leshin *et al.*, 1978). Recently, cells from a patient from a New York family were found to have intermediate levels of 5α-reductase with intermediate stability and altered affinity for both testosterone and NADPH (Imperato-McGinley *et al.*, 1980) (Table I). Our interpretation of these results is shown schematically in Fig. 14. Namely, different structural mutations of the 5α-reductase enzyme can give rise to the disorder. Some of these mutations affect the binding of the steroid substrate to the enzyme (Dallas and Dominican Republic); others affect primarily the binding of NADPH (Los Angeles). Still other mutations affect both functions (New York). This genetic heterogeneity among families with similar clinical manifestations is similar to that noted for other inherited enzyme deficiencies, such as glucose-6-phosphate dehydrogenase deficiency (Beutler and Yoshida, 1973).

A major unresolved issue is why the external genitalia of patients with 5α-reductase deficiency virilize more at puberty than during embryogenesis. This problem is closely related to the unresolved question of why dihydrotestosterone formation is important in androgen physiology.

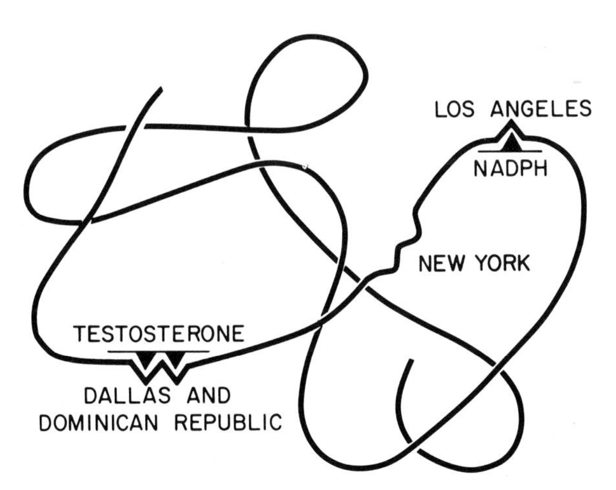

FIG. 14. Symbolic interpretation of the mutations that give rise to 5α-reductase deficiency. The polypeptide chain of the protein is indicated by the curved line to symbolize the tertiary structure of the enzyme. The binding sites for testosterone and NADPH are indicated as being at different locations on the molecule. The Dallas and Dominican Republic families are designated as having mutations that primarily affect the part of the molecule that binds testosterone while the Los Angeles family has a mutation that affects the binding of NADPH. The mutation in the New York family is represented by an abnormality that affects the binding of both substrates.

The late virilization may be due to the presence of higher levels of plasma testosterone at puberty than during embryogenesis, to the accumulation of some dihydrotestosterone in plasma as a result of the action of the residual 5α-reductase demonstrable in all patients, or to some unidentified change in molecular or endocrine function with age.

2. Role of the Androgen Receptor

Several disorders of the androgen receptor cause abnormal sexual development in man and animals.

a. The Tfm Mouse. The first such disorder to be characterized in molecular terms was the testicular feminization (*Tfm*) mutation in the mouse, an X-linked disorder in which affected males have testes and normal testosterone production but differentiate as phenotypic females (Lyon and Hawkes, 1970). No Müllerian duct derivatives can be identified, indicating that the Müllerian regression function of the testis is intact. However, there is a total failure of androgen-mediated aspects of male development in the Wolffian duct, urogenital sinus, and external genitalia. A blind-ending vagina is usually present. Such animals are resistant to the action of their own testosterone and to exogenous testosterone and dihydrotestosterone both during embryogenesis and in postnatal life (Goldstein and Wilson, 1972). Dihydrotestosterone formation is normal, but the androgen receptor protein of the cell cytosol is undetectable; consequently, the hormone cannot reach the nucleus of the cell and interact with the chromosomes (Gehring *et al.*, 1971; Bullock *et al.*, 1971; Goldstein and Wilson, 1972). Elucidation of the pathophysiology of this mutation documented the critical role of the androgen receptor in the normal embryonic action of androgen and established that the same receptor protein serves as the mediator of the actions of both testosterone and dihydrotestosterone.

b. The Human Testicular Feminization Syndromes. Analysis of the genetic abnormalities of the androgen receptor in the human has provided additional insight into the role of the androgen receptor in embryonic virilization. The most common disorder is the complete form of testicular feminization. Pettersson and Bonnier (1937) deduced from pedigree analysis that affected persons are genetic men, that the defect could be due to either an X-linked recessive defect or a sex-limited autosomal dominant mutation, and that the phenotype could result from failure of male induction in an embryo in which the fundamental trend is toward the female phenotype. The term testicular feminization was introduced by Morris (1953), who described in detail the clinical features of the disease. The disorder is the most common form of male pseudohermaphroditism

(Jagiello and Atwell, 1962) and is the cause for about 10% of all cases of primary amenorrhea (Ross and Vande Wiele, 1974).

The clinical features of the complete form of testicular feminization are uniform (Wilson and MacDonald, 1978). A phenotypic female is evaluated because of primary amenorrhea (postpubertal) or inguinal hernia (prepubertal). Breast development at the time of expected puberty, the general habitus, and the distribution of body fat are female in character; many patients have a truly feminine appearance. Axillary and pubic hair are scanty or absent. The external genitalia are unambiguously female, and the clitoris is normal. The vagina is short and blind ending. Internal genitalia are absent except for the testes, which may be in the abdomen, in the inguinal canal, or in the labia majora. Occasionally, remnants of the Müllerian or Wolffian ducts can be identified. Testicular histology is similar to that in long-standing cryptorchid testes of other causes; spermatogenesis is always absent. The karyotype is 46,XY, and there is frequently a history of similarly affected family members. About a third of the patients have negative family histories and are presumed to represent new mutations. As in the *Tfm* mouse, the gene for the disorder is X-linked (Meyer *et al.*, 1975).

About a tenth of these patients have an incomplete or partial form of testicular feminization. The incomplete disorder resembles the complete form except that there is some ambiguity of the external genitalia and some virilization as well as feminization occurs at puberty (Morris and Mahesh, 1963; Madden *et al.*, 1975). Persons with the incomplete disorder have the habitus and general appearance of women and most commonly present with primary amenorrhea. There is partial fusion of the labioscrotal folds and a variable degree of clitoromegaly. The vagina is short and blind ending. At laparotomy all derivatives of the Müllerian duct are absent. The presence of male Wolffian duct derivatives and the partial virilization of the external genitalia clearly separate the incomplete from the complete disorder. The family history in most cases is uninformative. However, in at least one family the pattern of inheritance is compatible with X-linkage. No pedigree has been reported in which the complete and incomplete forms of testicular feminization coexist in the same family.

The endocrine pathology of both the complete and incomplete forms of the disorder has been characterized in considerable detail; in brief, testosterone levels in plasma and testosterone production rates are high or within the normal range for men, levels of plasma LH are high, and estrogen production rates are higher than normal for men. Feminization is thought to result from the combined effects of androgen resistance and increased estrogen levels (Wilson and MacDonald, 1978; MacDonald *et al.*, 1980).

Androgen resistance in human testicular feminization is also due to abnormalities of the androgen receptor. Keenan and co-workers (1974, 1975) have reported that the amount of high-affinity dihydrotestosterone binding in some patients with the complete disorder is virtually undetectable—a defect analogous to that demonstrated in the *Tfm* mouse. Defective binding has been confirmed by other laboratories (Griffin *et al.*, 1976; Kaufman *et al.*, 1976). Recent evidence has suggested two types of abnormalities of the androgen receptor in testicular feminization (Griffin, 1979) (Fig. 15). Some patients with both the complete and incomplete forms of testicular feminization have partial receptor deficiency (about half normal levels of binding) under the usual assay conditions at 37°C but normal binding at 26°C. When the assay is performed at an elevated temperature (42°C) dihydrotestosterone binding (the amount of receptor) decreases to less than 20% of the levels seen at 37°C (Fig. 15). The thermal inactivation is rapidly reversed on lowering the assay temperature to

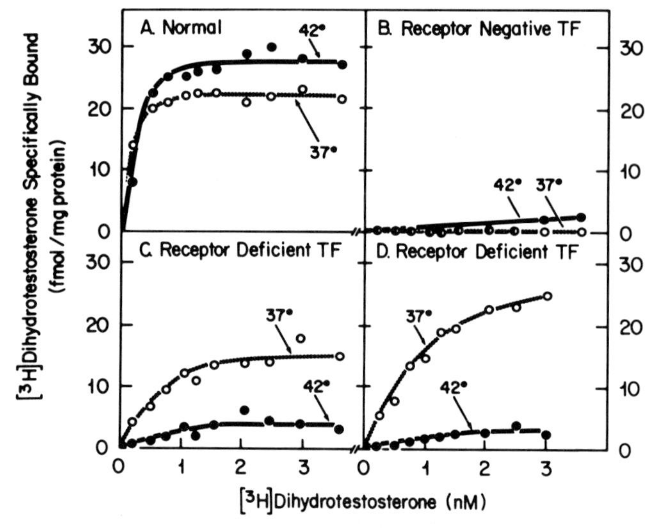

FIG. 15. Dihydrotestosterone binding at 37 and 42°C in genital skin fibroblasts derived from a normal subject, one patient with receptor negative testicular feminization (TF), and two subjects with receptor deficient testicular feminization. Specific binding of [^{3}H]dihydrotestosterone is plotted as a function of dihydrotestosterone concentration. The amount of high-affinity binding in cells from the normal subject (A) increases slightly at 42°C compared with the usual binding condition of 37°C. The specific binding in the cells from the patient with receptor negative testicular feminization (B) is virtually undetectable at both temperatures. The high-affinity dihydrotestosterone binding in the cell from the two patients with receptor deficient testicular feminization (C and D) is clearly measurable at 37°C but decreases at the higher temperature to a level that is similar to that seen in the cells from the patient with the receptor negative disorder (Griffin, 1979).

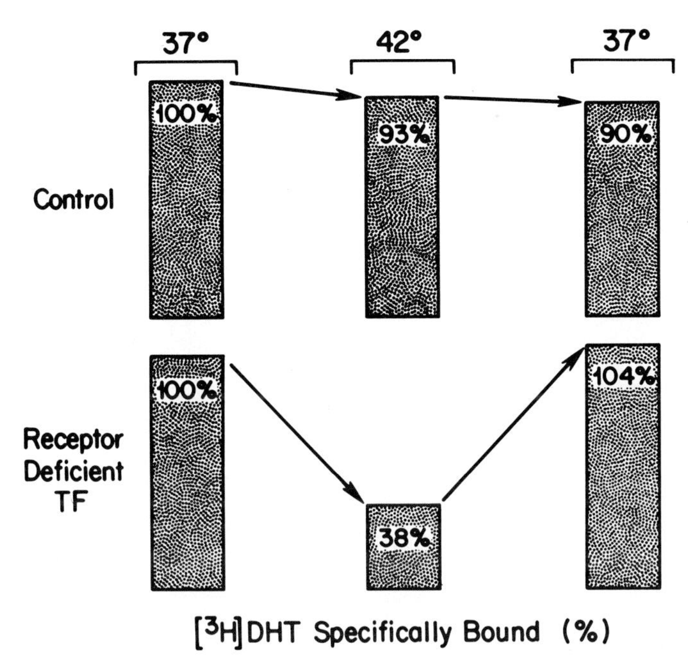

FIG. 16. Reversibility of temperature sensitivity of dihydrotestosterone in cells from a patient with receptor deficient testicular feminization. Monolayer binding of [^{3}H]dihydrotestosterone (DHT) in genital skin fibroblasts during a 45-minute incubation is shown by the bars. The amount bound at 37°C is designated as 100%. Parallel monolayers were preincubated at 37°C for 45 minutes, and binding with [^{3}H]DHT assessed at 42°C (labeled 42°). Others were preincubated for 45 minutes at 42°C, and binding with [^{3}H]DHT was assessed at 37°C (labeled 37° on right-hand side). The amount of binding in cells from a control subject did not change greatly when binding was performed at 42°C or with a 42°C preincubation prior to binding at 37°C. In contrast the amount of specific DHT binding in the cells from a patient with receptor deficient testicular feminization decreased to 38% of the basal level when the binding was assessed at 42°C. However, preincubation at 42°C followed by binding at 37°C resulted in return of the binding to the basal level (data from Griffin, 1979).

37°C—suggesting reversible alteration of the structure of the receptor at elevated temperatures (Fig. 16). In other systems thermolability has proved to be a sensitive marker for structural abnormalities in enzymes and other proteins. Among the patients with the phenotype of testicular feminization and a temperature-sensitive receptor (Fig. 17) are three pairs of siblings in whom pedigree analysis suggests X-linked inheritance. Thus, as summarized in Fig. 18, at least two different molecular abnormalities of the receptor can lead to the syndrome of testicular feminization: an unstable receptor or a lack of binding. Although unstable receptors are associated with both complete and incomplete testicular feminization, a lack

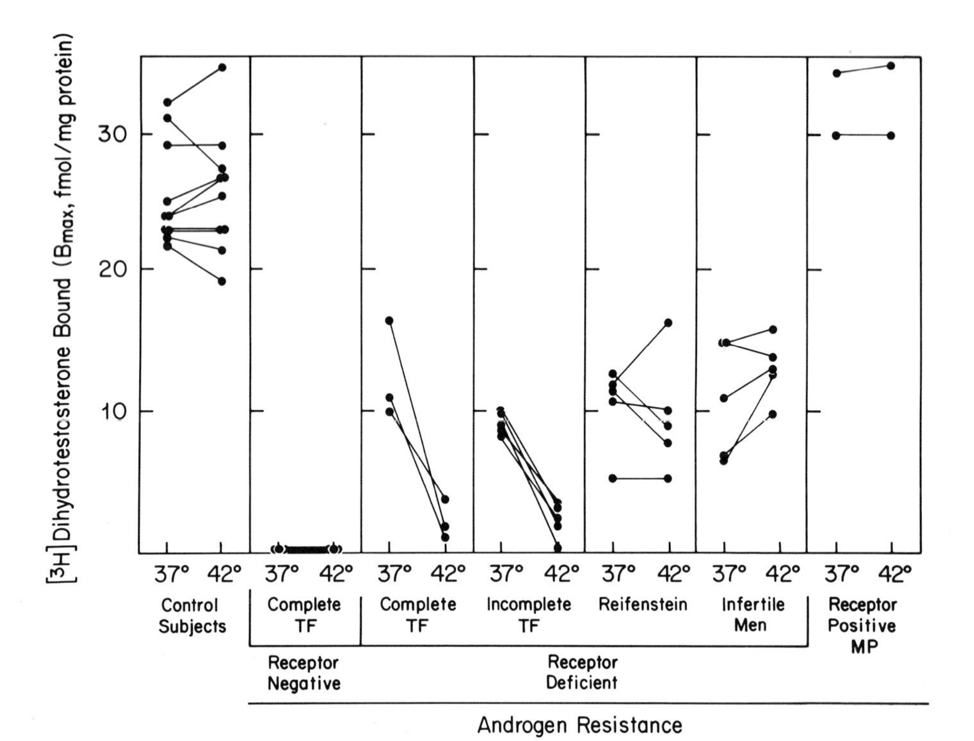

FIG. 17. Effect of elevated temperature on the amount of high-affinity dihydrotestosterone binding (B_{max}) in fibroblasts from 10 control subjects and 23 patients with androgen resistance. T.F., Testicular feminization; M.P., male pseudohermaphroditism. The B_{max} does not change greatly in cells from control subjects when the binding assay temperature is increased from 37 to 42°C. The amount of binding in the cells from three patients with complete testicular feminization is undetectable at both temperatures; these patients are designated as having a receptor negative mutation. A number of patients with a predominantly female phenotype (complete and incomplete testicular feminization) or a predominantly male phenotype (Reifenstein syndrome and infertile men) have variable (but partial) deficiency in the amount of dihydrotestosterone binding at 37°C. When the temperature of the binding assay is increased to 42°C, the amount of binding in the cells from the patients with testicular feminization decreases to about 20% of the basal level. In contrast the B_{max} in cells from patients with Reifenstein syndrome or infertility does not change consistently on increasing the assay temperature. The amount of binding in cells from two patients with male pseudohermaphroditism due to androgen resistance is normal at 37°C and not altered by increasing the assay temperature; these patients are designated as having a receptor positive mutation.

of binding has been found only in patients with the complete form of the disorder.

c. Abnormalities of the Androgen Receptor in Phenotypic Men. Other patients with hereditary abnormalities of the androgen receptor have a male phenotype. Families with such abnormalities were originally de-

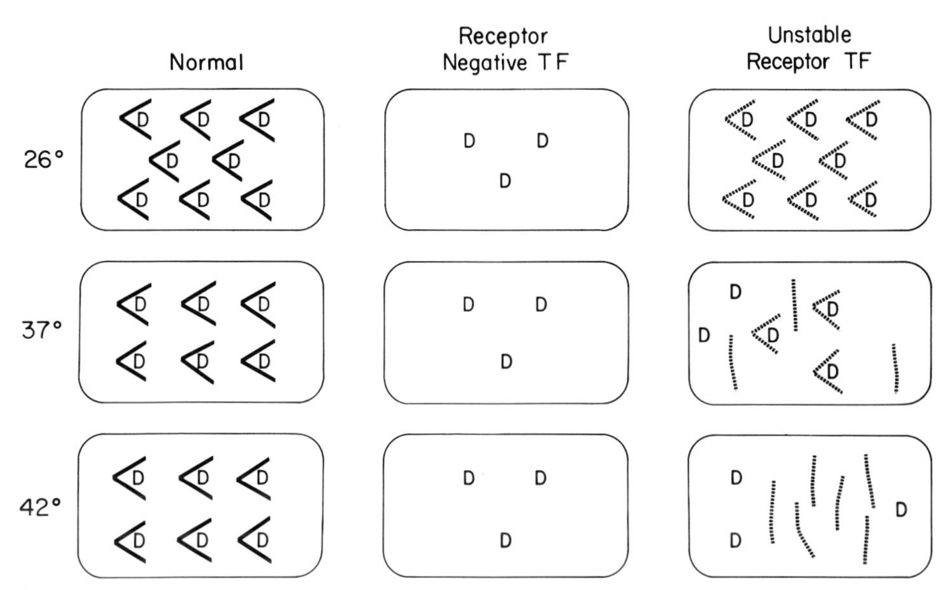

FIG. 18. Diagram of the postulated defects in receptor negative and receptor deficient (unstable receptor) testicular feminization. D, Dihydrotestosterone; TF, testicular feminization. The solid lines denote normal androgen receptor, and the dashed lines denote qualitatively abnormal receptor that is unstable. In normal cells high-affinity androgen binding is greater at 26 than at 37°C, and binding does not decrease on exposure to elevated temperature. In receptor negative testicular feminization, binding is equally low at all temperatures; either the receptor is so altered that it cannot bind androgen, or it is absent. In unstable-receptor testicular feminization androgen binding is normal at 26°C, half normal at 37°C, and nearly undetectable at 42°C (Griffin and Wilson, 1980).

scribed by Reifenstein (1947), Rosewater *et al.* (1965), Gilbert-Dreyfus *et al.* (1957), and Lubs *et al.* (1959). Each was originally assumed to be a distinct entity, but three fairly extensive pedigrees have been reported in which affected members of the same family exhibit variable phenotypes that incorporate the defects described (Walker *et al.,* 1970; Gardo and Papp, 1974; Wilson *et al.,* 1974). Since all these pedigrees are compatible with X-linkage, these syndromes probably constitute variable manifestations of a single mutation and can be termed Reifenstein syndrome.

The spectrum of defective virilization in this disorder ranges from gynecomastia and azoospermia to more severe defects such as hypospadias and even to the presence of a pseudovagina. The most common finding is a male neonate with perineoscrotal hypospadias, who is later noted to have azoospermia and gynecomastia after the time of expected puberty. Axillary and pubic hair are normal, but chest and facial hair is diminished. Temporal recession of the hairline is minimal, and the voice is prepubertal in character. Cryptorchidism is common, and on average the testes are smaller than normal. Leydig cells appear normal. The spermatogenic tubules contain both germinal and Sertoli cells, but the germinal cells do not mature beyond the primary spermatocyte stage. Some subjects have defects in Wolffian duct derivatives (such as absence or severe hypoplasia of the vas deferens), and the infertility may be due in part to these anatomic changes in the ejaculatory system as well as to defective spermatogenesis. The psychologic orientation in most subjects appears to be male, and affected men have had successful marriages. The endocrine profile is similar to that in testicular feminization, namely high plasma levels of testosterone, LH, and estradiol (Wilson *et al.,* 1974; Amrhein *et al.,* 1977).

These findings would be predicted if a patient had an abnormality in the androgen receptor that was less severe than that in testicular feminization (Fig. 10). Indeed, levels of the androgen receptor in fibroblasts cultured from patients with the typical familial disorder are only partially deficient (Griffin *et al.,* 1976; Amrhein *et al.,* 1977; Griffin, 1979) (Fig. 17). In most patients no qualitative abnormalities in the residual androgen receptor can be demonstrated (Griffin and Wilson, 1977; Collier *et al.,* 1978), and, unlike patients with testicular feminization and partial deficiency of the receptor, the residual receptors in cells from these patients are not thermolabile (Griffin, 1979) (Fig. 17).

The fact that infertility could be the only manifestation of androgen receptor abnormality in otherwise normal men has been recognized only recently. In a family study of the Reifenstein syndrome, some men were noted to be infertile but otherwise phenotypically normal; they had the same degree of androgen resistance, as manifested by the plasma levels of testosterone and luteinizing hormone, and the same degree of receptor deficiency in cultured skin fibroblasts as did their more severely affected relatives (Wilson *et al.,* 1974). Thus, some affected persons may have only mild phenotypic evidence of androgen-receptor deficiency. It was then shown that some infertile men with uninformative family histories but elevated mean plasma levels of luteinizing hormone and testosterone had a deficiency of the androgen receptor in cultured skin fibroblasts that was similar to that demonstrated in families with Reifenstein syndrome (Aiman *et al.,* 1979). Such patients have normal male external genitalia, apparently normal Wolffian duct structures, and infertility due to azoospermia or severe oligospermia. The amount of androgen receptor in genital-skin fibroblasts is on average less than half normal (Fig. 17), and in most patients the residual receptor appears to be qualitatively normal (Griffin, 1979).

To summarize, two broad classes of mutations can be identified for the disorders involving the 5α-reductase and the androgen receptor: one in which function has been abolished (enzyme activity or androgen binding is profoundly deficient) and another class in which enzymatic activity or binding is detectable but the function is qualitatively abnormal (abnormal K_m for NADPH in the case of 5α-reductase and thermolability of the androgen receptor). This latter class of mutations is of particular importance since they imply that the identified abnormalities are in fact the primary result of alterations in the genes encoding these two molecules, thus ascribing an essential role to the 5α-reductase and the androgen receptor in normal male development.

3. Presumptive Role of Nuclear Processing of the Androgen Receptor

A third category of androgen resistance was delineated by Amrhein and colleagues (1976) in a family with a phenotype similar to that in testicular feminization in which affected individuals had normal levels of 5α-reductase enzyme, normal amounts of androgen receptor, and normal nuclear localization of dihydrotestosterone in cultured fibroblasts. Thus, the defect appears to involve some late intranuclear event in androgen action (Fig. 10).

Although the first patients had the testicular feminization phenotype, subsequent patients have had a variety of abnormalities ranging from incomplete testicular feminization to phenotypes similar to that in the Reifenstein syndrome (Amrhein *et al.*, 1977; Keenan *et al.*, 1977; Collier *et al.*, 1978). The site of the molecular abnormality in these patients is still unclear. It is possible that the receptor is qualitatively abnormal but that the abnormality is too subtle to be detected by present methods. [In the two patients whom we studied no abnormality of affinity, turnover, or nuclear localization of the androgen receptor could be found (Collier *et al.*, 1978), and there was no thermolability of the androgen receptor (Griffin, 1979).] Alternatively, the defect may involve the intranuclear processing of the hormone–receptor complex. The existence of such a mutation implies the role of one or more additional proteins essential for the normal nuclear events in androgen action.

Thus, as the result of studies of these various single gene defects that result in abnormal sexual development it can be concluded that androgens act in embryonic development to produce virilization of the embryos via the same molecular processes as in the postnatal state (Fig. 9). It should be emphasized that female embryos have the same androgen receptor system and the same ability to respond to androgens as male embryos. The phenotypic difference between men and women resides only in the nature of the hormones that are produced. The female embryo exposed to androgens will virilize like the male. Such androgen exposure can come from androgen ingestion by the mother, from maternal tumors, or from overproduction within the fetus. The most common cause of female virilization in the human is congenital adrenal hyperplasia due to an autosomal recessive mutation that results in a defect in the 21-hydroxylase enzyme (Bongiovanni, 1978). In this disorder the synthesis of cortisol is deficient, and late in gestation there is a compensatory increase in the synthesis of adrenal androgen, which produces virilization of the genitalia in affected females. Likewise, the administration of androgens to pregnant rats and mice results in female offspring with virilization of the urogenital tracts (Shultz and Wilson, 1970).

D. POSSIBLE ROLE OF ESTROGENS IN EMBRYONIC DEVELOPMENT

It is of interest that in contrast to the situation in regard to testosterone synthesis and action, in which many single gene mutations have been characterized, no mutations have been identified to date that result in either deficient estrogen synthesis or resistance to estrogen action. Estrogen synthesis is activated temporarily in male and female embryos at a very early stage even before they become implanted in the wall of the uterus. Evidence suggests that estrogen action is essential for implantation and survival of the embryo (Nalbandov, 1971; Dickmann *et al.,* 1975; George and Wilson, 1978b). This raises the possibility that estrogen action is essential to life itself. If mutations occur that prevent either the synthesis or response to estrogens they may block the implantation of the embryo and thus be lethal. In contrast, androgen action is not necessary for survival of the embryo.

Later in embryogenesis estradiol formation is initiated in the embryonic ovary before definitive histological differentiation of the ovary occurs, and it is possible that the histological differentiation of the tissue may be mediated in part by a local action of estradiol analogous to the postulated role of testosterone in testicular maturation. Whether estrogen plays any other role in the subsequent development of either sex is uncertain. Embryogenesis normally takes place in a sea of hormones (steroid and nonsteroid) derived from the placenta, the maternal circulation, the fetal adrenal gland, the fetal testis, and possibly from the fetal ovary itself. It is not known whether these substances influence female phenotypic development, but it is likely that estrogens and progestins are involved in the growth and maturation of the internal genitalia of the female during the later phases of embryonic life, even if not required for their differentiation.

IV. Conclusion

The fundamental validity of the Jost formulation for sexual development is now amply documented. Genetic sex determines gonadal sex, and the gonads in turn determine the development of the sexual phenotypes through their function as endocrine organs. A striking feature of this model is its overall simplicity. As the result of a difference in the activity of only one or a few enzymes in the gonads at a critical time in development, testosterone synthesis is activated in the fetal testis. This hormone in turn causes profound developmental effects in the male that account in large part for the differences between men and women.

In at least two regards the Jost model must now be amplified. First, it is clear from the analysis of single gene mutations that genetic sex is more complex than can be explained by the constitution of the sex chromosomes alone. In the human at least one X-linked gene is essential for testicular development, and autosomal genes necessary for differentiation of the ovaries and testes have been identified in several species (reviewed by Wilson, 1978). Some of these genes influence migration of the primordial germ cells, others regulate the processing or function of the H-Y antigen system that is involved in testicular development, some code for the enzymes required for steroid hormone synthesis, and the function of the remainder is unknown. The important point is that gonadal development is determined by genes located on the autosomes as well as on the X and Y chromosomes. Second, the process by which male phenotypic sex develops depends on the expression of several gene products necessary for androgen action so that the entire process of sexual development can actually be characterized as a series of sequential interactions between the genetic machinery and regulatory factors.

We now have considerable insight into the nature of the various genes involved in this process. This fortunate circumstance is the result of the fact that aberrations at any stage of sexual development, whether due to environmental causes, chromosomal abnormalities, or single gene mutations, have profound consequences, each of which is expressed as a characteristic defect in sexual development. Investigation of the pathogenesis of such defects in man and animals has provided insight into the endocrine, molecular, and genetic determinants that regulate the normal process.

The analysis of the single gene mutations that produce abnormal sexual development in man and animals has been particularly informative in this regard. A minimum of 19 genes have been implicated in sexual differentiation in man (Wilson and Goldstein, 1975). The involvement of such a large number of genes does not imply a greater complexity for sexual differentiation than for other developmental processes but rather reflects the comparative ease with which mutant genes affecting the normal process of sexual development can be identified. Normal sexual development is essential to the survival of species but not to the life of individuals. Developmental defects in organ systems essential to life on the other hand frequently cause abnormalities that result in abortion or early death. Therefore, individuals with even the most profound abnormalities of sexual development survive, usually come to the attention of physicians, and have been the subjects of many detailed pathophysiological studies. Thus, the relatively simple mechanism that imposes male development on the indifferent embryo requires the participation of many normal genes common to both the male and female embryo.

Some fundamental issues in the embryonic development of the genital tract are still poorly understood. One relates to the mechanism by which specific tissues develop the capacity early in embryogenesis that will allow them to respond to a hormonal stimulus later in development. As the result of careful studies in the embryo, Cunha and his colleagues have established that the mechanisms that allow a tissue to respond to androgens is acquired by embryonic tissues of the urogenital tract early in embryogenesis; the mesenchyme of the embryonic urogenital tract contains the receptor mechanism that regulates the epithelial response to androgen, namely the development and proliferation of the prostatic buds (Cunha *et al.,* 1980). How the appropriate signal is transferred from mesenchyme to epithelium is unclear, and it is not known how connective tissue of the urogenital tract acquires this differentiative capacity. Another problem relates to the precise mechanisms by which the same hormonal signal is translated into different physiological effects in different tissues. For example, the diverse effects of androgen during embryogenesis include regression of the mammary duct (in the rodent at least), budding and proliferation in the urogenital sinus and Wolffian duct, fusion of cells in the urethral fold, and differential growth of the entire male genital tract late in embryogenesis. At present we have no insight into the mechanisms by which these apparently different functions are accomplished. Ultimately, these fundamental issues of embryogenesis will have to be clarified before it will be possible to understand the entire program by which the myriad of genetic determinants and hormones interact to cause the development of phenotypic sex.

REFERENCES

Aiman, J., Griffin, J. E., Gazak, J. M., Wilson, J. D., and MacDonald, P. C. (1979). *N. Engl. J. Med.* **300,** 223.

Amrhein, J. A., Meyer, W. J., III, Jones, H. W., Jr., and Migeon, C. J. (1976). *Proc. Natl. Acad. Sci. U.S.A.* **73,** 1.

Amrhein, J. A., Klingensmith, G. J., Walsh, P. C., McKusick, V. A., and Migeon, C. J. (1977). *N. Engl. J. Med.* **297,** 350.

Attal, J. (1969). *Endocrinology* **85,** 280.

Beutler, E., and Yoshida, A. (1973). *Ann. Hum. Genet.* **37,** 151.
Blanchard, M. G., and Josso, N. (1974). *Pediat. Res.* **8,** 968.
Bongiovanni, A. M. (1978). *In* "The Metabolic Basis of Inherited Disease" (J. B. Stanbury, J. B. Wyngaarden, and D. S. Fredericksen, eds), p. 868. McGraw-Hill, New York.
Bullock, L. P., Bardin, C. W., and Ohno, S. (1971). *Biochem. Biophys. Res. Commun.* **44,** 1537.
Catt, K. J., Dufau, M. L., Neaves, W. B., Walsh, P. C., and Wilson, J. D. (1975). *Endocrinology* **97,** 1157.
Cunha, G. R., Chung, L. W. K., Shannon, J. M., and Reese, B. A. (1980). *Biol. Reprod.* **22,** 19.
Dickermann, Z., Dey, S. K., and Gupta, J. S. (1975). *Proc. Natl. Acad. Sci. U.S.A.* **72,** 298.
Donahoe, P. K., Ito, Y., Price, J. M., and Hendren, W. H., III (1977). *Biol. Reprod.* **16,** 238.
Fisher, L. K., Kogut, M. D., Moore, R. J., Goebelsmann, J., Isaacs, H., Jr., Griffin, J. E., and Wilson, J. D. (1978). *J. Clin. Endocrinol. Metab.* **47,** 653.
Gardo, S., and Papp, Z. (1974). *J. Med. Genet.* **11,** 267.
Gehring, U., Tomkins, G. M., and Ohno, S. (1971). *Nature (London)* **232,** 106.
George, F. W., and Wilson, J. D. (1978a). *J. Clin. Endocrinol. Metab.* **47,** 550.
George, F. W., and Wilson, J. D. (1978b). *Science* **199,** 200.
George, F. W., and Wilson, J. D. (1980). *Nature (London)* **283,** 861.
George, F. W., Catt, K. J., Neaves, W. B., and Wilson, J. D. (1978a). *Endocrinology* **102,** 665.
George, F. W., Milewich, L., and Wilson, J. D. (1978b). *Nature (London)* **274,** 172.
George, F. W., Simpson, E. R., Milewich, L., and Wilson, J. D. (1979). *Endocrinology* **105,** 110.
Gilbert-Dreyfus, S., Sebaoun, C. A., and Belaisch, J. (1957). *Ann. Endocrinol.* **18,** 93.
Goldman, A. S. (1970). *Endocrinology* **88,** 527.
Goldstein, J. L., and Wilson, J. D. (1972). *J. Clin. Invest.* **51,** 1647.
Greene, S. A., Symes, E., and Brook, C. G. D. (1978). *Arch. Dis. Child.* **53,** 751.
Griffin, J. E. (1979). *J. Clin. Invest.* **64,** 1624.
Griffin, J. E., and Wilson, J. D. (1977). *J. Clin. Endocrinol. Metab.* **45,** 1137.
Griffin, J. E., and Wilson, J. D. (1978). *Clinics Obstet. Gynaecol.* **5,** 457.
Griffin, J. E., and Wilson, J. D. (1980). *N. Engl. J. Med.* **302,** 198.
Griffin, J. E., Punyashthiti, K., and Wilson, J. D. (1976). *J. Clin. Invest.* **57,** 1342.
Hodgins, M. B., Clayton, R. N., and London, D. R. (1977). *J. Endocrinol.* **75,** 24.
Imperato-McGinley, J., Guerrero, L., Gautier, T., and Peterson, R. E. (1974). *Science* **186,** 1213.
Imperato-McGinley, J. Peterson, R. E., Gautier, T., and Sturla, E. (1979). *N. Engl. J. Med.* **300,** 1233.
Imperato-McGinley, J., Peterson, R. E., Leshin, M., Griffin, J. E., Cooper, G., Draghi, S., Berenyi, M., and Wilson, J. D. (1980). *J. Clin. Endocrinol. Metab.* **50,** 15.
Jagiello, G., and Atwell, J. D. (1962). *Lancet* **1,** 329.
Jost, A. (1953). *Recent Prog. Horm. Res.* **8,** 379.
Jost, A. (1972). *Johns Hopkins Med. J.* **130,** 38.
Kaufman, M., Straisfeld, C., and Pinsky, L. (1976). *J. Clin. Invest.* **58,** 345.
Keenan, B. S., Meyer, W. J., III, Hadjian, A. J., Jones, H. W., and Migeon, C. J. (1974). *J. Clin. Endocrinol. Metab.* **38,** 1143.
Keenan, B. S., Meyer, W. J., III, Hadjian, A. J., and Migeon, C. J. (1975). *Steroids* **25,** 535.
Kratochwil, K., and Schwartz, P. (1976). *Proc. Natl. Acad. Sci. U.S.A.* **73,** 4041.
Leshin, M., Griffin, J. E., and Wilson, J. D. (1978). *J. Clin. Invest.* **62,** 685.
Lipsett, M. B., and Tullner, W. W. (1965). *Endocrinology* **77,** 273.

Lubs, H. A., Jr., Vilar, O., and Bergenstal, D. M. (1959). *J. Clin. Endocrinol. Metab.* **13,** 1110.
MacDonald, P. C., Madden, J. D., Brenner, P. F., Wilson, J. D., and Siiteri, P. K. (1980). *J. Clin. Endocrinol. Metab.* **49,** 905.
Madden, J. D., Walsh, P. C., MacDonald, P. C., and Wilson, J. D. (1975). *J. Clin. Endocrinol. Metab.* **41,** 751.
Mauleon, P., Bezard, J., and Terqui, M. (1977). *Ann. Biol. Anim. Biochem. Biophys.* **17,** 399.
Meyer, W. J., III, Migeon, B. R., and Migeon, C. J. (1975). *Proc. Natl. Acad. Sci. U.S.A.* **72,** 1469.
Milewich, L., George, F. W., and Wilson, J. D. (1977). *Endocrinology* **100,** 187.
Moore, R. J., and Wilson, J. D. (1976). *J. Biol. Chem.* **251,** 5895.
Moore, R. J., Griffin, J. E., and Wilson, J. D. (1975). *J. Biol. Chem.* **250,** 7168.
Morris, J. M. (1953). *Am. J. Obstet. Gynecol.* **65,** 1192.
Morris, J. M., and Mahesh, V. B. (1963). *Am. J. Obstet. Gynecol.* **87,** 731.
Nalbandov, A. V. (1971). *In* "The Biology of the Blastocyst" (R. J. Blandau, ed.), p. 383. Univ. of Chicago Press, Chicago, Illinois.
Neumann, F., von Berswordt-Wallrabe, R., Elger, W., Steinbeck, H., Hahn, J. D., and Kramer, M. (1970). *Recent Prog. Horm. Res.* **26,** 337.
Nowakowski, H., and Lenz, W. (1961). *Recent Prog. Horm. Res.* **17,** 53.
Ohno, S. (1978). *J. Am. Med. Assoc.* **239,** 217.
Peters, H. (1970). *Philos. Trans. R. Soc. London Ser. B* **259,** 91.
Peterson, R. E., Imperato-McGinley, J., Gautier, T., and Sturla, E. (1977). *Am. J. Med.* **62,** 170.
Pettersson, G., and Bonnier, G. (1937). *Hereditas* **23,** 49.
Pfaltz, C. R. (1949). *Acta Anat.* **8,** 293.
Picard, J. Y., Tran, D., and Josso, N. (1978). *Mol. Cell. Endocrinol.* **12,** 17.
Picon, R. (1967). *Arch. Anat. Microsc. Morphol. Exp.* **56,** 281.
Reifenstein, E. C., Jr. (1947). *Proc. Am. Fed. Clin. Res.* **3,** 86.
Rigaudiere, N. (1979). *Acta Endocrinol.* **92,** 174.
Rosewater, S., Gwinup, G., and Hamwi, G. J. (1965). *Ann. Intern. Med.* **63,** 377.
Ross, G. T., and Vande Wiele, R. L. (1974). *In* "Textbook of Endocrinology" (R. H. Williams, ed), 5th Ed. p. 368. Saunders, Philadelphia, Pennsylvania.
Saenger, P., Goldman, A. S., Levine, L. S., Korth-Schutz, S., Muecke, E. C., Katsumata, M., Doberne, Y., and New, M. I. (1978). *J. Clin. Endocrinol. Metab.* **46,** 627.
Schechter, J. (1970). *Gen. Comp. Endocrinol.* **14,** 53.
Schultz, F. M., and Wilson, J. D. (1974). *Endocrinology* **94,** 979.
Sholl, S. A., and Goy, R. W. (1978). *Biol. Rep.* **18,** 160.
Siiteri, P. K., and Wilson, J. D. (1974). *J. Clin. Endocrinol. Metab.* **38,** 113.
Sloan, W. R., and Walsh, P. C. (1976). *J. Urol.* **115,** 459.
Wachtel, S. S. (1980). *Biol. Reprod.* **22,** 1.
Walker, A. C., Stack, E. M., and Horsfall, W. A. (1970). *Med. J. Aust.* **1,** 156.
Walsh, P. C., Madden, J. D., Harrod, M. J., Goldstein, J. L., MacDonald, P. C., and Wilson, J. D. (1974). *N. Engl. J. Med.* **291,** 944.
Walsh, P. C., Wilson, J. D., Allen, T. D., Madden, J. D., Porter, J. C., Neaves, W. B., Griffin, J. E., and Goodwin, W. E. (1979). *J. Urol.* **120,** 90.
Wilson, J. D. (1971). *Dtsch. Ges. Endokrinol.* **17,** 11.
Wilson, J. D. (1975). *J. Biol. Chem.* **250,** 3498.
Wilson, J. D. (1978). *Annu. Rev. Physiol.* **40,** 279.
Wilson, J. D. (1979). *In* "Campbell's Urology (J. H. Harrison, R. F. Gittes, A. D. Perlmutter, T. A. Stamey, and P. C. Walsh, eds), p. 1469. Saunders, Philadelphia, Pennsylvania.

Wilson, J. D., and Goldstein, J. L. (1975). *Birth Defects Orig. Artic. Ser.* **11,** 1.
Wilson, J. D., and Lasnitsky, I. (1971). *Endocrinology* **89,** 659.
Wilson, J. D., and MacDonald, P. C. (1978). *In* "Metabolic Basis of Inherited Disease" (J. B. Stanbury, J. B. Wyngaarden, and D. S. Fredrickson, eds), p. 894. McGraw-Hill, New York.
Wilson, J. D., and Siiteri, P. K. (1973). *Endocrinology* **92,** 1182.
Wilson, J. D., Harrod, M. J., Goldstein, J. L., Hemsell, D. L., and MacDonald, P. C. (1974). *N. Engl. J. Med.* **290,** 1097.

DISCUSSION

C. Eil: In men with gynecomastia of no identifiable cause, we have measured androgen receptors in fibroblasts cultured from areolar skin and from genital skin using a similar assay to that Dr. Wilson and his colleagues have perfected. We have obtained results of normal foreskin, genital skin, and areolar skin from normal males and females and from males with gynecomastia. Looking at their binding capacities and their affinities, we were not able to detect any differences in the receptors at room temperature. We have not done similar analyses at either 37 or 42°C. Considering the results depicted graphically, the ranges for the foreskin fibroblasts, genital skin fibroblasts, and areolar skin fibroblasts overlap and there were no differences at least in this group of men with idiopathic gynecomastia in the receptor; looking at entry of dihydrotestosterone into the nucleus comparing the two groups also has proven negative.

W. F. Crowley: Dr. Wilson, would you comment on your understanding of the pathogenesis of this infertile male syndrome. Specifically, my question relates to why these men lack gynecomastia. I have always viewed the appearance of gynecomastia as a rather sensitive assay of androgen and estrogen balance. Presumably the androgen receptor defect in these men is sufficient to give them difficulty with their seminiferous tubules and with their LH regulation but not enough for gynecomastia, and I do not understand that.

Second, one of the cases that you cited in your description of these infantile men had Sertoli cells only on biopsy of his testes. The syndrome of Sertoli cell only bears some resemblance to your cases in that they often have normal to slightly elevated LHs and testosterone levels well within the normal male range. Are these two syndromes, in fact, one and the same or perhaps closely related?

J. D. Wilson: Let me address the second point first: The possibility that we have been redescribing the Sertoli cell only syndrome has been suggested by others and I find it a very interesting possibility. Only after we study a larger number of patients will we be able to resolve that issue. In regard to the first question, there are two possibilities: one is that we are not dealing with a primary gene defect. Perhaps different factors regulate the appearance of the receptor in different tissues, so that what we are dealing with is the remote consequence of a regulatory abnormality that influences the androgen receptor in a select number of tissues. The second possibility is one that intrigues me. It is possible that different amounts of receptor are necessary in different tissues for specific actions of the hormone. It is conceivable that you have to have a larger amount of the receptor in the spermatogenic tubule than you do in the external genitalia, for example. If that were the case a selective abnormality that resulted in a half normal amount of receptor could conceivably have different effects in different tissues. In that way asymmetry could occur in which there is a normal development of the external genitalia but abnormal spermatogenesis and gonadotropin regulation. I would simply say that we cannot be certain that we are dealing with the primary gene defect, and it will take additional work to explain the total pathogenesis of this disorder.

A. K. Roy: Your studies on patients with 5α-reductase deficiency showed a clearcut difference between the effects of testosterone and DHT on spermatogenesis and appearance of the secondary sexual characters at puberty. However, in most of the cases the androgen receptors are known to cross react with both DHT and testosterone. Would you like to comment on this apparent paradox?

I. Mowszowicz: Dr. Wilson has shown us very clearly the importance of both 5α-reductase and receptor as effectors of androgen action in sexual differentiation. Dr. Kuttenn in Dr. Mauvais-Jarvis's laboratory, where I also work, has developed an assay measuring the capacity of total skin homogenates to convert [^{3}H]testosterone to DHT and androstanediols. This has allowed us to measure 5α-reductase activity in genital or pubic skin of normal subjects from either sex or in patients with various disorders of androgen sensitivity. In genital skin 5α-reductase activity ranges from 400 to 1000 fmoles/mg skin; it is not different in men or women, or children of either sex. This leads us to the conclusion that the enzyme is not regulated by androgens in this area; this is confirmed by the study of androgen insensitive patients presumably due to complete or partial receptor deficiency: they have normal 5α-reductase levels in genital skin. Patients with pseudohermaphroditism due to 5α-reductase deficiency have a very low level of enzyme activity. In pubic skin in contrast, 5α-reductase activity seems to be androgen dependent: it is significantly higher in men than in women, it is low in children of both sexes, and increases in boys at puberty; in addition it is low in hypogonadal men and can be increased with treatment with T or hCG. This androgen dependency is confirmed by the study of patients with disorders of androgen sensitivity: it is barely measureable in patients with the complete form of the syndrome of testicular feminization, or in patients with 5α-reductase deficiency: in patients with pseudohermaphroditism due to receptor deficiency 5α-reductase is variable and parallels the degree of androgen insensitivity. It thus appears that in pubic skin, 5α-reductase activity is androgen dependent and is a good marker of androgen sensitivity.

We have also measured the androgen binding capacity in cytosols of human skin from different anatomical sites in men or women. Whereas androgen-binding capacity is higher in genital skin than in pubic skin, it presents no variation with either sex or age. It appears from these data that the androgen receptor in human skin cytosol is not regulated by androgen hormones. It thus seems that the androgen-dependent 5α-reductase activity might serve as an amplifier of androgen action whereas the receptor is only the transmitter of this action.

J. D. Wilson: I've been worrying about that for many years. People have spent the larger part of a decade trying to explain this important problem in androgen physiology. It's conceivable that dihydrotestosterone formation is a mechanism for concentrating androgen in target cells and that it's not necessary in the Wolffian ducts because of high concentrations of testosterone in the lumen of the Wolffian duct. It is also conceivable that there is some difference in the metabolism of the hormone, such as the fact that testosterone can be converted to estrogen but dihydrotestosterone cannot.

W. D. Odell: An alternative explanation of the variation in phenotype which you relate to amount of receptor or lability of receptor could be an alteration in the specificity of the receptor. You discussed dihydrotestosterone binding to receptor; could you tell us also about the relative bindings of dihydrotestosterone, testosterone, and other androgens?

J. D. Wilson: Insofar as we have studied the specificity of binding, we have not found major differences in the binding of testosterone compared to that of dihydrotestosterone. It is quite clear that we must continue to look for mutations that influence the specificity of binding.

B. W. O'Malley: In regard to these interesting temperature-sensitive mutants, could you summarize what other physicochemical characteristics might differ from the normal receptors? For instance, have you investigated the $t_{1/2}$ for hormone binding, salt sensitivity, DNA or nuclear binding, charge, size, sensitivity to pyridoxal phosphate and molybdate?

J. D. Wilson: They are not stabilized to the same extent by molybdate as is normal receptor. So far as we can tell, the entry into the nucleus and the turnover in those cell strains are roughly the same as controls. We do not know whether nuclear localization is equivalent to normal binding of the hormone–receptor complex to specific sites on chromatin. We are making a major attempt to study these temperature-sensitive mutants in considerable detail and to characterize them.

B. W. O'Malley: Have you done any experiments in which you mixed the temperature-sensitive and normal cytosols or made somatic cell hybrids between abnormal and normal cells or force [^{3}H]testosterone on the abnormal DHT receptor and check for altered temperature sensitivity.

J. D. Wilson: If you mix the cytosols of control and the temperature-sensitive mutant there is the expected additive effect. We have not succeeded in forming hybrids to study complementation.

J. Geller: From the data presented concerning patients with 5α-reductase deficiency, it would seem as if since they had normal sexual drive at puberty and that DHT therefore had little or nothing to do with the onset of male libido at puberty, I wonder if you feel that indeed male sexual libido is a sex hormone-mediated or regulated function that does depend upon T binding to receptor or T in some other fashion mediating its androgenic effects. The second question that I had relates to a question mark next to estrogen that you showed in a summary of androgen-mediated action. I know from your very elegant studies in the dog on BPH that estrogen certainly plays a major role in that disorder. I wonder if in the human there is any evidence that estrogen has any effect on androgen-mediated events?

J. D. Wilson: In answer to the last question, I know of no direct evidence that estrogen plays a role in the sexual behavior of male humans, and it has been very difficult to devise experiments to answer that. In regard to the first question: The fact that patients with 5α-reductase deficiency are allowed to go through a normal pubertal development also develop a male sexual drive is not necessarily evidence that sexual drive is mediated by testosterone and not by dihydrotestosterone. No patient has yet been described with total absence of the enzyme, and consequently all patients with 5α-reductase deficiency make some dihydrotestosterone at the time of puberty and have some dihydrotestosterone circulating in plasma. Until such time as we have either potent 5α-reductase inhibitors and can totally prevent this in experimental animals or until such a mutation is described in which the dihydrotestosterone formation is totally absent, I simply do not think we can answer the question. Although male sexual drive is generally believed to be mediated by the effects of hormones in the central nervous system, it is also possible that sociological and other factors may influence the apparent gender reversal in this disorder.

M. Grumbach: This was a splendid synthesis of our present state of knowledge to which you contributed so much. Would you comment on two issues? One is the influence of other hormones on the action of testosterone on androgen-sensitive target tissues, especially in relation to estrogen. In some tissues, for example, estrogen and androgen are antagonistic; whereas in other tissues estrogen may have a synergistic or potentiating effect on the action of testosterone. The studies from your group on the prostate are consistent with an augmenting effect of estrogen, and we recently suggested, based on indirect evidence, that estrogen may have a potentiating effect on androgen action on the growth of pubic hair. The second question concerns the differentiation of Wolffian duct derivatives with the complete (or severe) form of testicular feminization. Most of us who see infants and children have been able to identify at least remnants of or hypoplastic Wolffian duct derivatives, e.g., an epididymis and vas deferens, whereas their presence or at least identification has been much less common in the affected adult. What is your present view of the nature of the fetal cytosol androgen receptor in the Wolffian duct and its relation to androgen receptors in other target organs?

J. D. Wilson: I once favored the idea that there might be an embryonic receptor in the Wolffian duct that was different from that in the external genitalia. Our attempts to demonstrate that directly have not been very successful. Unpublished studies from our laboratory examining the androgen receptor directly in embryonic tissues have led us to the opposite conclusion, namely, that it is in fact the same receptor in the embryo as in the adult. I too have had the experience that some infants with the complete form of testicular feminization have persistent Wolffian duct structures in their testicular fascia. If we'd looked at normal female infants of the same age, I think they would also have some Wolffian duct remnants.

M. Grumbach: In the absence of a difference in the androgen receptor do you think that the paracrine function of testosterone, the mediation of its differentiating, stabilizing, and ipsilateral action on Wolffian duct differentiation through local vs humoral dissemination might account for the discrepancy between Wolffian duct differentiation in testicular feminization and female differentiation of the urogenital sinus and external genitalia. Local diffusion of testosterone in relatively high concentration to the Wolffian duct might lead to varying degrees of differentiation in some cases.

J. D. Wilson: Yes, I find that very attractive. But the Wolffian duct terminates in the urogenital sinus. It would be easier for me to explain a local concentration effect if not only the ejaculatory duct and seminal vesicle virilized, but a little bit of the prostate. But none of the patients with 5α-reductase deficiency has had a remnant of a prostate. It looks as if dihydrotestosterone formation is absolutely required for a prostate. I consider this problem to be the major dilemma of androgen physiology.

P. K. Donahoe: You questioned whether normal females have persistent Wolffian duct structures. We operate on a number of female infants with congenital anomalies and with incarcerated hernias; however, I don't recall seeing remnants of Wolffian ducts.

Within the last year, we had the opportunity to study two patients with persistent Müllerian duct syndrome, assaying testis fragments in an organ culture assay for Müllerian inhibiting substance. In a previously published study we noted that Müllerian inhibiting substance (MIS) was present in human infants for 2 years, after which we can no longer detect MIS in an organ culture assay. We recently had the opportunity to study an 11-month-old infant from California and a 22-month-old from Children's Hospital in Boston each having persistence of Müllerian duct structures. The 11-month-old had high levels of MIS (4+), and the 22-month-old had low levels (1+). It must be remembered that normal 22-month-old males have barely detectable levels (1+). Study of both these cases of persistent Müllerian ducts indicate that MIS is produced normally, but that probably some receptor mechanism is deficient. At least in these two specimens that are rare and very difficult to get, it appears that there is MIS, but probably receptor deficiency in the duct itself.

J. D. Wilson: I would interpret the first one as evidence of receptor deficiency and the second one as more likely being evidence of a deficiency in production of the Müllerian regression factor. Thus both forms of it must exist.

P. K. Donahoe: The normal 22-month-old has a very low level of Müllerian inhibiting substance. This patient falls in the range of normal.

J. D. Wilson: I know, but I can speculate.

M. New: Until your elegant experiments demonstrated a role for dihydrotestosterone in the differentiation of the external genitalia *in utero,* we didn't know that dihydrotestosterone was necessary for sexual differentiation. What is the evidence that dihydrotestosterone is necessary for the development of secondary sexual characteristics at puberty? I thought that the pubertal secondary sexual characteristics have been normal.

J. D. Wilson: I don't think that's true. The interpretation of the Dominican Republic pedigree is complicated because of a mixture of racial backgrounds with varying amounts of sexual and facial hair. But if you compare the affected members and their unaffected male siblings, there is a total absence of acne, an astonishing absence of temporal hair regression, and no beard development in these individuals. They do have some penile development, and they do develop some pubic and axillary hair, but they have no chest hair development. So I would argue that dihydrotestosterone is responsible for a large part of the secondary sex characteristics of male puberty. Failure of development of the anlagen of the prostate during embryogenesis could prevent its subsequent development, but there is no prostate development in any of them. Certainly the absence of this enzyme has profound consequences on prostate development. The other events may be postpubertal. Dr. Imperato-McGinley, as you may remember, has given dihydrotestosterone to one or two affected individuals in the Dominican Republic and reported that they do get temporal hair regression and beard growth.

E. Peck: Dr. Wilson, I enjoyed your talk very much; however, I'm concerned about your extrapolation of thermodynamic constants, K_d and B_{max}, in your binding analyses. That extrapolation is, in fact, invalid and is very sensitive to the ratio of specific to nonspecific binding in your sample. If this ratio varies from sample to sample as it did in the saturation analyses that I saw, you would obtain a very variable number, especially for B_{max}, but also for K_d. Since nonspecific binding is temperature sensitive, this extrapolation might abolish some determinations of specific binding when your incubation temperature is high, i.e., by elevating nonspecific binding considerably over specific. You might do well to analyze the data again using a Rosenthal solution for Scatchard analysis instead of this extrapolation which really is not legitimate.

J. D. Wilson: Well, thermodynamics aside, I have only shown a fraction of a large number of studies and have not attempted to go into detail about the receptor studies this evening. We measure specific and nonspecific binding simultaneously in every experiment. And whether you analyze this by Scatchard analysis or by a variety of different means of plotting one gets the same thing. In fact, in our hands the amount of nonspecific binding is not significantly changed with alteration of the temperature of the binding reaction.

E. Peck: I am not challenging the phenomenon, only the final numbers for K_d and B_{max}.

S. Cohen: Several years ago when Dr. Jost was here and gave a talk on the biogenesis of sexes, at that time I told him that I thanked him for adding a parameter to my understanding of biogenesis of sexes. My understanding of biogenesis of sexes began when I was aged four when I was taught that women came from the rib of a man. When I started going to school I learned that it had nothing to do with playing around with a rib but rather something to do with penile vaginal orientation. My faith in the bible was somewhat restored when endocrinologically it was discovered that the process of aromatization takes place and the woman comes from the man through the process of aromatization of testosterone to estradiol. Finally, Dr. Jost had just informed me that embryologically man develops only if there is androgen present so that normally it is the female to which something must be added to get a male. That left me in a confused state. I must admit that your talk tonight has done nothing to alleviate that confusion. But I have a question just the same. Namely, these hormones are very active apparently while the fetus is *in utero*. And then they stop suddenly for the prepubertal years. What causes that cessation. Why doesn't activity go right on? Do you think that it is due to the sudden removal of hCG with its LH activity?

J. D. Wilson: I presume those changes in testosterone production are due to changes in gonadotropin production and/or the sensitivity of the testis to gonadotropin.

M. M. Grumbach: Briefly, there is evidence in the primate, sheep, and guinea pig that the hypothalamic pituitary gonadotropin unit is functional in the fetus by midgestation if not earlier. In the human being, by about 1 week after birth, FSH and LH concentrations increase in the circulation in both male and female infants, sensitivity to LRF is at the pubertal level, and plasma testosterone in males and estrogens in females are elevated.

Within about 4 months, the sex steroid levels fall to close to prepubertal values and usually by 1 year or so gonadotropins and FSH and LH response evoked by exogenous LRF follows the pattern in prepubertal children. After about a decade of a low level of activity of the hypothalamic LRF–pituitary–gonadotropin apparatus, there is a reactivation of the frequency and amplitude of LRF episodic secretion and the reawakening of the pituitary gonadotropin–gonadal axis. The long quiescent prepubertal period of decreased LRF and gonadotropin secretion appears to be related to an intrinsic CNS inhibitory mechanism and increased sensitivity of the hypothalamic–pituitary unit to low level sex steroid negative feedback. It is during the long prepubertal period that erections are less common than in infancy or during the onset of puberty.

K. Sterling: I have a question relative to my understanding of the role of 5α-reductase and dihydrotestosterone later on in the later decades of male progression in the normal male. We have not only the bother of shaving, the cosmetic disfigurement of masculine senile alopecia, but also the serious incapacity of prostatic hypertrophy. I want to ask you first of all is that mainly due to dihydrotestosterone, rather than testosterone in the human male and is there current work on possibly blocking the enzyme 5α-reductase and preventing these awful phenomena which seem to be a penalty of being a normal male?

J. D. Wilson: The answer to both questions is yes, but it will probably not succeed in time to save either you or me from the knife. Several drug companies are working very intensively on the development of 5α-reductase inhibitors and inhibitors of dihydrotestosterone binding, and I presume that within a reasonable period of time, we will know whether or not the accumulation of dihydrotestosterone in the human prostate is in fact related to the pathogenesis of BPH and if so whether its correction will have therapeutic effects.

P. H. Saenger: Dr. Wilson, you showed very elegantly the *in vitro* methods for diagnosing 5α-reductase deficiency. As far as I recall, with the exception of Dr. Walsh's and your group's report on one patient who had normal or almost normal circulating dihydrotestosterone (DHT) levels, virtually all the other patients described had low DHT levels. I wonder then if careful evaluation of *in vivo* testosterone and dihydrotestosterone dynamics, particularly the response to hCG and also the urinary steroid analysis of 5α- and 5β-reduced testosterone metabolites will allow us to make a diagnosis of this enzymatic deficiency, particularly in those patients in whom preputial or clitoral skin is *not* available for fibroblast studies.

J. D. Wilson: I agree with you that they all have low dihydrotestosterone levels when they are measured. I'm convinced from Dr. Imperato-McGinley and Peterson's work that a combination of enzymatic techniques and measurements of ratios of urinary steroids and plasma steroids before and after hCG stimulation is sometimes necessary to substantiate the diagnosis. The more diagnostic parameters that are used, the more certain the diagnosis.

J. F. Crigler: I was interested in your comments about the early differentiation of enzymes in the fetal testes, especially the possible role of gonadotropins in the 3β-hydroxysteroid dehydrogenase and your final conclusion as I gathered it, was that the gonadotropins may have no effect there. We recently had the opportunity, as a matter of fact on two occasions, to see incompletely masculinized males with microphallus, chordee and hypospadias, and also anosmia. This had made me wonder if these individuals had a hypogonadotropic state resulting in less than total masculinization. I wondered whether you could enlarge somewhat upon the role of gonadotropins in the differentiation of enzyme systems during early embryogenesis.

J. D. Wilson: Well, that's very interesting. To my knowledge such case reports would be unusual. The vast majority of patients with hypogonadotropic hypogonadism have a normal male urethra. The usual prepubertal manifestation is the syndrome of microphallus. We have thought that perhaps the role of gonadotropins was to regulate the differential growth of the male external genitalia during the latter third of embryogenesis. The real question is whether the incidence of hypospadias in such patients is greater than the incidence of hypospadias in the population at large, that is, three or four per thousand.

H. J. Ringold: I might pose the following question. Perhaps there is no significant difference in the absolute biological or biochemical activity of testosterone and DHT as suggested in fact by many systems. Perhaps all the 5α-reductase does is to permit the organism a much greater pool of androgen and potential androgen. Instead of just testosterone and androstene dione in the absence of reductase, there is available with a functioning 5α-reductase 5α-DHT, the 5α-dione, the 3α-diol, the 3β-diol, and androsterone all of which are convertible to DHT.

J. D. Wilson: Well, that's analogous to a theory that I believed in for many years, that the net effect of dihydrotestosterone formation is to promote the availability of intracellular androgen. But direct evidence for this mechanism is hard to obtain. If you perform experiments in the cold in which you prevent dihydrotestosterone formation you do not change the intracellular to extracellular ratio of androgens.

L. E. Faber: You said earlier that you had sucrose gradient data relative to the size of the receptors in various genetic states. Could you elaborate on that; is the receptor for example larger or smaller in a genetic mutant?

J. D.Wilson: It depends on the situation and the circumstances of the centrifugation, etc. It is preliminary data and I really should not comment on it.

O. H. Pearson: I would like to come back to dihydrotestosterone versus testosterone in regard to male potency. Can you tell us which one is responsible for potency in the male. There is evidence that in hyperprolactinemic men, impotence occurs which is not corrected by administering testosterone. On the other hand, if one lowers the serum prolactin and then gets the testosterone back to normal, the potency is apparently restored. There has also been a report that hyperprolactinemia inhibits the conversion of testosterone to dihydrotestosterone and could be an inhibitor of 5α-reductase. Do you have any opinion about this effect of dihydrotestosterone versus testosterone on potency?

J. D. Wilson: No. It's an attractive idea, but in our hands we cannot consistently show an effect of prolactin on dihydrotestosterone formation, and it's possible to provide alternate explanations for any effects of prolactin on potency. In certain lower animals dihydrotestosterone is said not to restore normal male sexual behavior to the castrated animal whereas dihydrotestosterone plus permissive amounts of estradiol will. The castrated rhesus monkey given testosterone or dihydrotestosterone has normal male sexual behavior. I really think that there's a great deal to be learned about normal male sexual behavior. In the Norwegian studies 30% of castrated men who were normal before castration had normal male sexual drive that persisted up to about 5 years following castration. Thus, studies of potency in men are very complicated and have to be carefully controlled before one can draw conclusions.

L. Birnbaumer: What triggers the synthesis and secretion of testosterone by the embryo? Is it autonomous or is it under the control of LH?

J. D. Wilson: My own interpretation of our work and others is that during the latter part of gestation in the human, it is probably controlled by pituitary gonadotropin. What controls it during the first trimester is unresolved. It may be controlled by gonadotropin from the placenta or be independent of gonadotropin control.

Regulation and Function of the Primate Fetal Adrenal Gland and Gonad

ROBERT B. JAFFE, MARIA SERÓN-FERRÉ, KENT CRICKARD, DONALD KORITNIK, BRYAN F. MITCHELL, AND ILPO T. HUHTANIEMI

Reproductive Endocrinology Center, Department of Obstetrics, Gynecology and Reproductive Sciences, University of California San Francisco, San Francisco, California

Although the steroid-producing glands of the fetus, the adrenal gland and gonads, arise from proximate embryologic sites, their functions are markedly disparate.

Glucocorticoids secreted by the fetal adrenal gland play an important role in effecting homeostatic adjustments necessary for extrauterine life. These secretions affect the maturation of a variety of enzyme systems, including the liver, pancreas, gastrointestinal tract (Liggins, 1976) and adrenal medulla (Wurtman, 1966). In the lung, glucocorticoids induce the development of surfactant important in the prevention of hyaline membrane disease in human neonates. In addition, in certain species, the fetal adrenal gland is involved in the initiation of parturition (Liggins *et al.*, 1973).

In contrast, the gonads subserve different functions. In the male, the testis elaborates both testosterone, an essential stimulator of Wolffian ductal development (Jost *et al.*, 1973) and a Müllerian inhibiting factor (Blanchard and Josso, 1974) which prevents the development of the Müllerian ductal system. In addition, the conversion of testosterone to its 5α-reduced metabolite, dihydrotestosterone, occurs in the external genital structures (Siiteri and Wilson, 1974) and stimulates their development. The role of the secretions of the fetal ovary in female fetal development is unknown.

Our long-term goal is to study the role of the human and subhuman primate fetal and perinatal adrenal and gonad in these physiologic processes. As an intermediate step leading to this goal, we have sought greater understanding of the regulation and steroidogenic function of these glands. In this survey, attention will be focused primarily on work in which our laboratory has been engaged concerning the regulation and function of the human and subhuman primate fetal adrenal gland and gonads. Where possible, attempts have been made to integrate these findings into an understanding of human perinatal endocrine physiology.

ISBN 0-12-571137-9

I. The Fetal Adrenal Gland

A. MORPHOLOGY

The morphology of the human and rhesus monkey fetal adrenal glands is shown in Figs. 1 and 2. The gland grows rapidly in both species and, by the end of the first trimester in humans, has attained a size equal to or greater than that of the fetal kidneys. The human fetal adrenal gland grows rapidly between 10 and 20 weeks of gestation. The combined fetal adrenal glands weigh less than 100 mg at 10 weeks and increase to approximately 2 gm at 20 weeks (Jirasek, 1971). Further growth ensues, and by term the combined weight is 7 gm. A similar pattern of growth occurs in the rhesus monkey (Fig. 3). It is of interest that, in monkeys that deliver prematurely, adrenal gland weight for a given gestational age appears to be greater than in those that presumably would deliver spontaneously at term (Fig. 3).

The bulk of the fetal adrenal mass in both species is attributable to an inner, fetal zone which comprises approximately 80% of the volume of the gland. This zone is composed of large eosinophilic cells with pale staining nuclei (Figs. 1 and 2). Upon ultrastructural examination, these cells demonstrate the typical characteristics of steroid-secreting cells. The fetal zone is surrounded by the outer, definitive, or adult, zone which is composed of small basophilic cells that resemble those of the adult zona glomerulosa.

Most investigators have suggested that the fetal zone atrophies rapidly after birth. However, recent elegant studies by McNulty and colleagues at the Oregon Regional Primate Center (McNulty *et al.*, 1980) in the fetal rhesus monkey (Fig. 2) suggest that there may be a "remodeling" of the fetal zone into the zona fasciculata of the adult.

B. STEROID PRODUCTION AND REGULATION BY THE HUMAN FETAL ADRENAL *IN VITRO*

There is functional specialization of the fetal and definitive zones of the human fetal adrenal gland as demonstrated in superfusion studies (Serón-Ferré *et al.*, 1978a). In these studies the definitive zone was separated from the fetal zone by gently removing the capsule to which the definitive zone was attached. We found that the definitive zone produces primarily corticoids, the production of which can be stimulated by ACTH (Fig. 4a). In contrast, the fetal zone elaborates principally the placental estrogen precursor, dehydroepiandrosterone sulfate (DHAS), the production of which also can be stimulated by ACTH (Fig. 4b). Quantitatively,

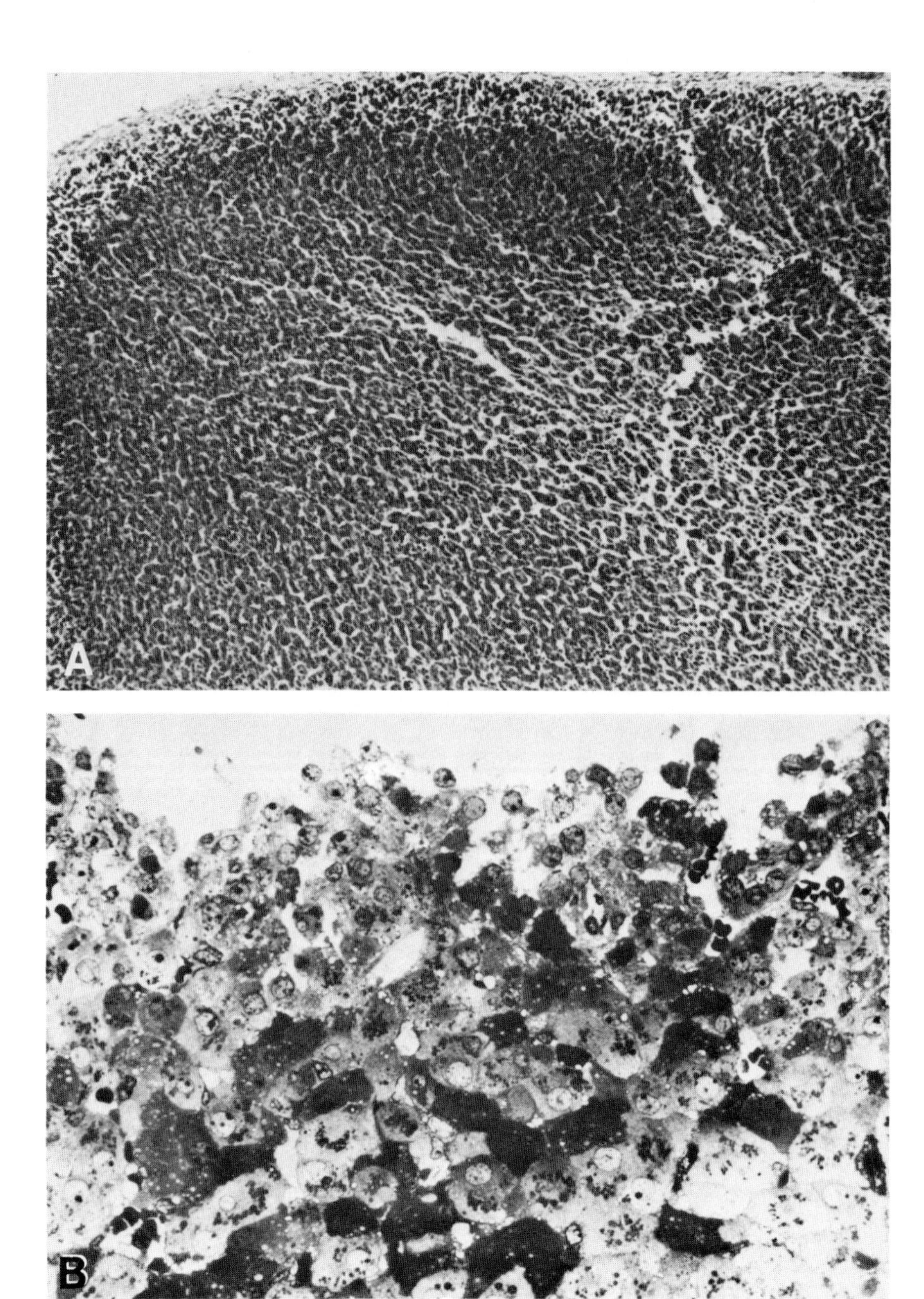

FIG. 1. (A) Histologic section of human fetal adrenal gland. Darker staining outer area is the definitive (adult) zone, and larger inner area is the fetal zone (H and E $\times 12.5$). (B) Higher power view of human fetal adrenal gland. Smaller cells at top are from the definitive zone and larger cells below are from the fetal zone (Toluidine blue, $\times 125$). From Yen and Jaffe (1978).

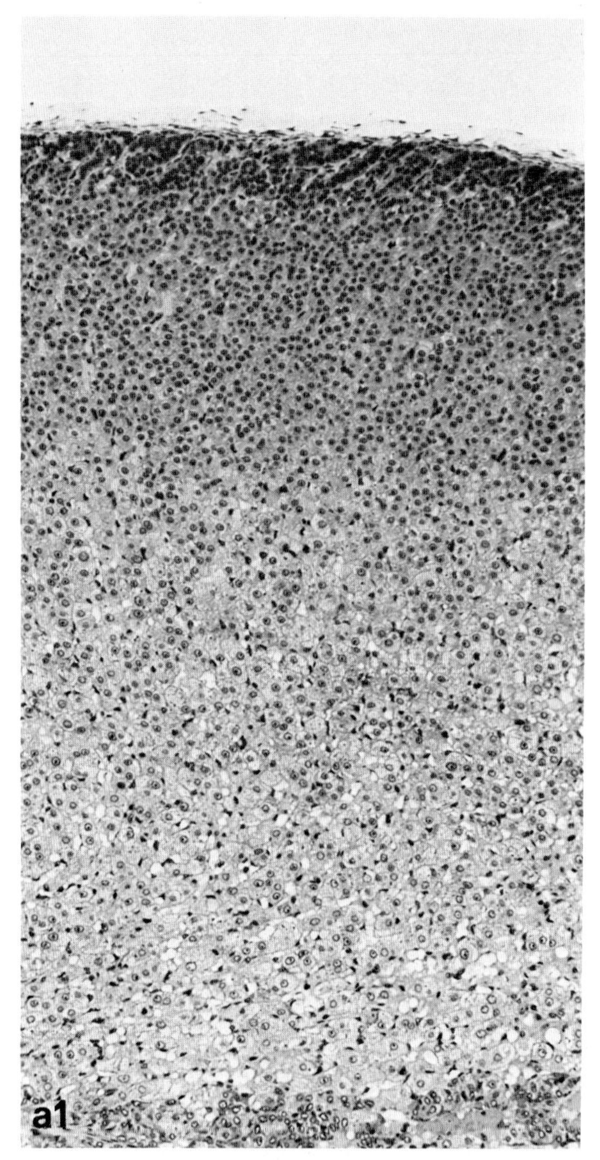

FIG. 2. (a) Full thickness of postnatal rhesus monkey adrenal cortex. Glycol methacrylate embedding, hematoxylin–methylene blue-basic fuchsin, ×100. (1) Age 1 day (169 days gestation). Condensation of outer fetal cortex, just beneath the glomerulosa. Inner fetal cortex unchanged from late gestation. (2) Age 20 days. Zone of condensation now about ⅓ in from the capsule. Fasciculata above, fetal cortex below. No necrosis or hemorrhage in fetal zone. (3) Age 90 days. Zone of condensation now about halfway. Lipid vacuolization of fasciculata. Fetal zone cells smaller, but not necrotic. (4) Age 469 days. Zone of condensation now about ¾ in from capsule. Remnant fetal zone persists between this zone and

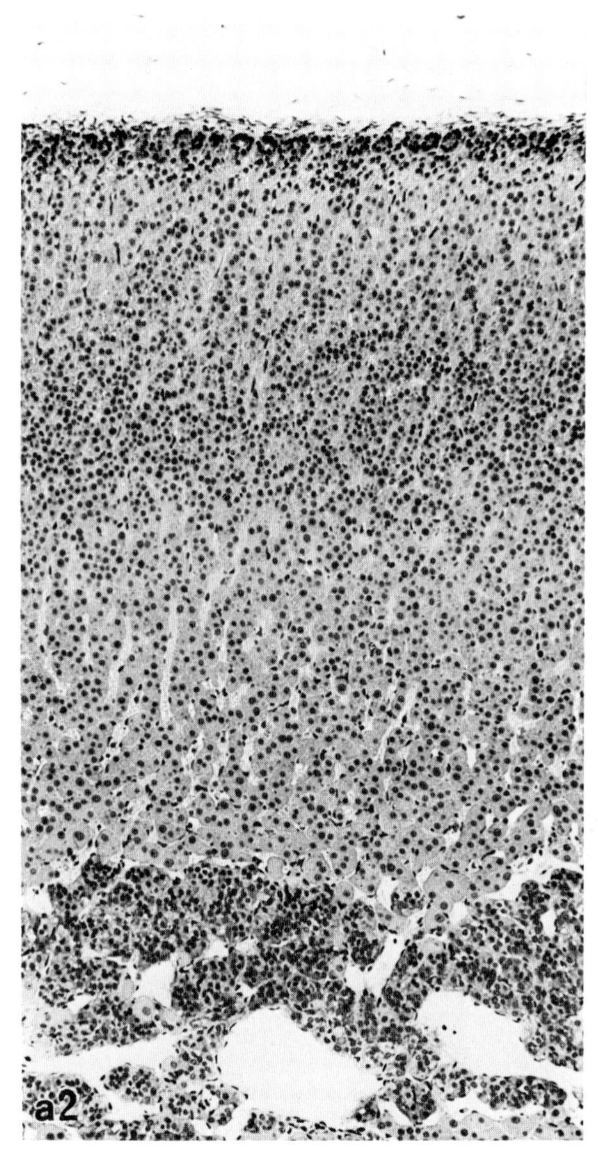

medulla. (b–e) Fetal zone immediately adjacent to medulla from same preparations as (a), ×530. (b) Age 1 day (169 days gestation). Large polygonal cells with large nuclei, abundant lacy cytoplasm. Wide sinusoids. (c) Age 20 days. Cells and nuclei smaller, cytoplasmic vacuolization diminished. Broad tortuous sinusoids. (d) Age 90 days. Similar to 20 days, although cells still smaller and loosely arranged in reticular framework. (e) Age 469 days. Cells with little cytoplasmic vacuolization now more densely packed. Sinusoids narrow and less tortuous. Courtesy of Dr. W. McNulty.

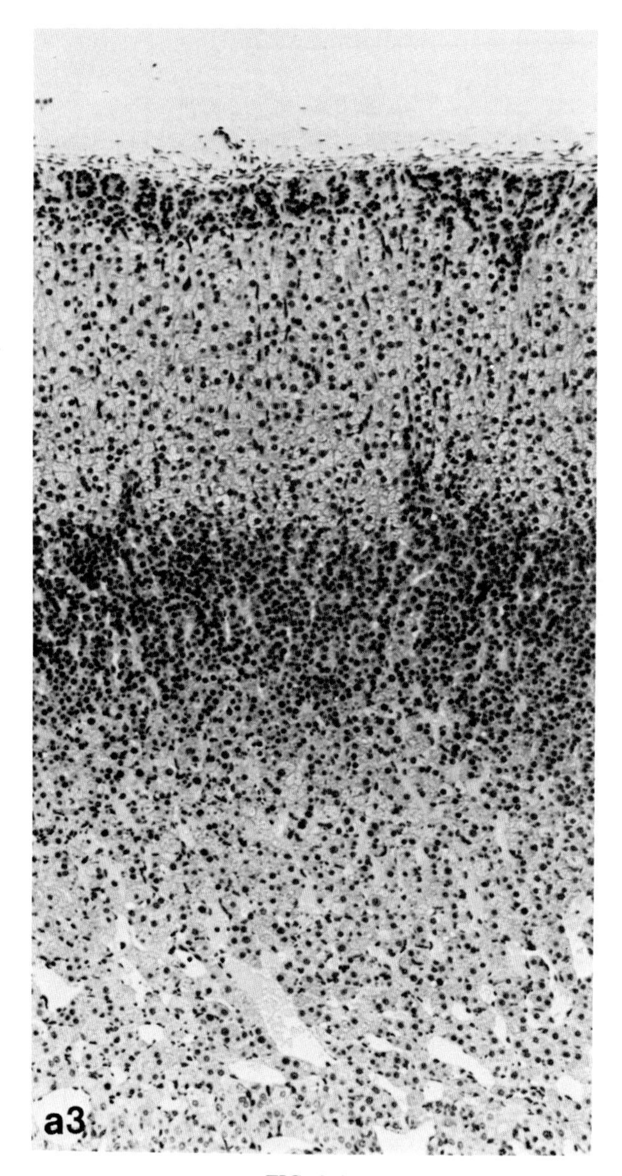

FIG. 2a3.

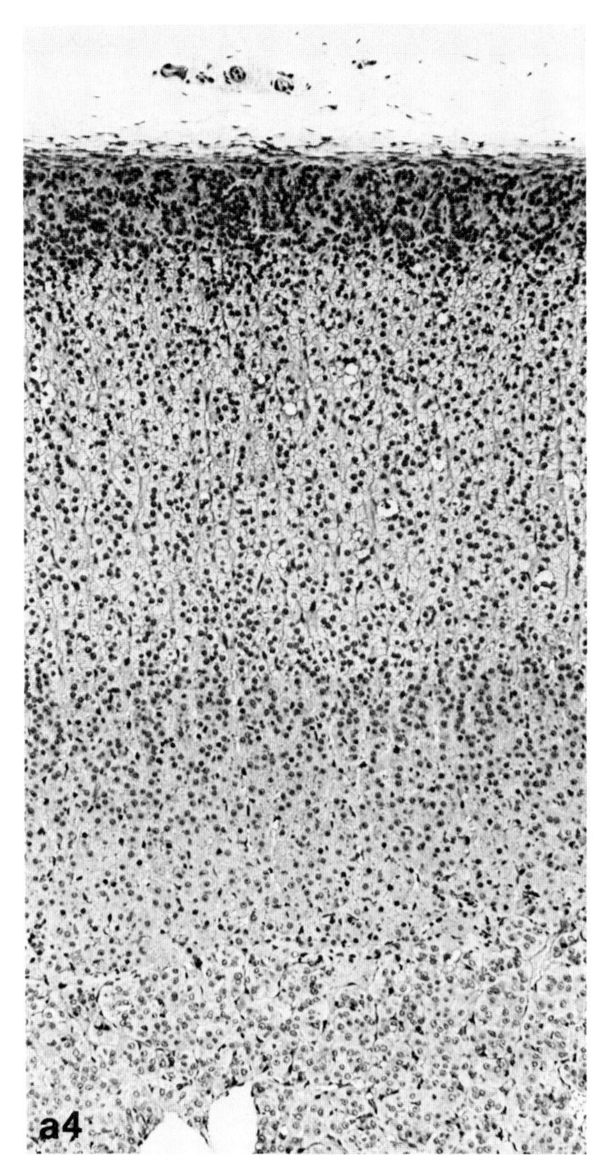

FIG. 2a4.

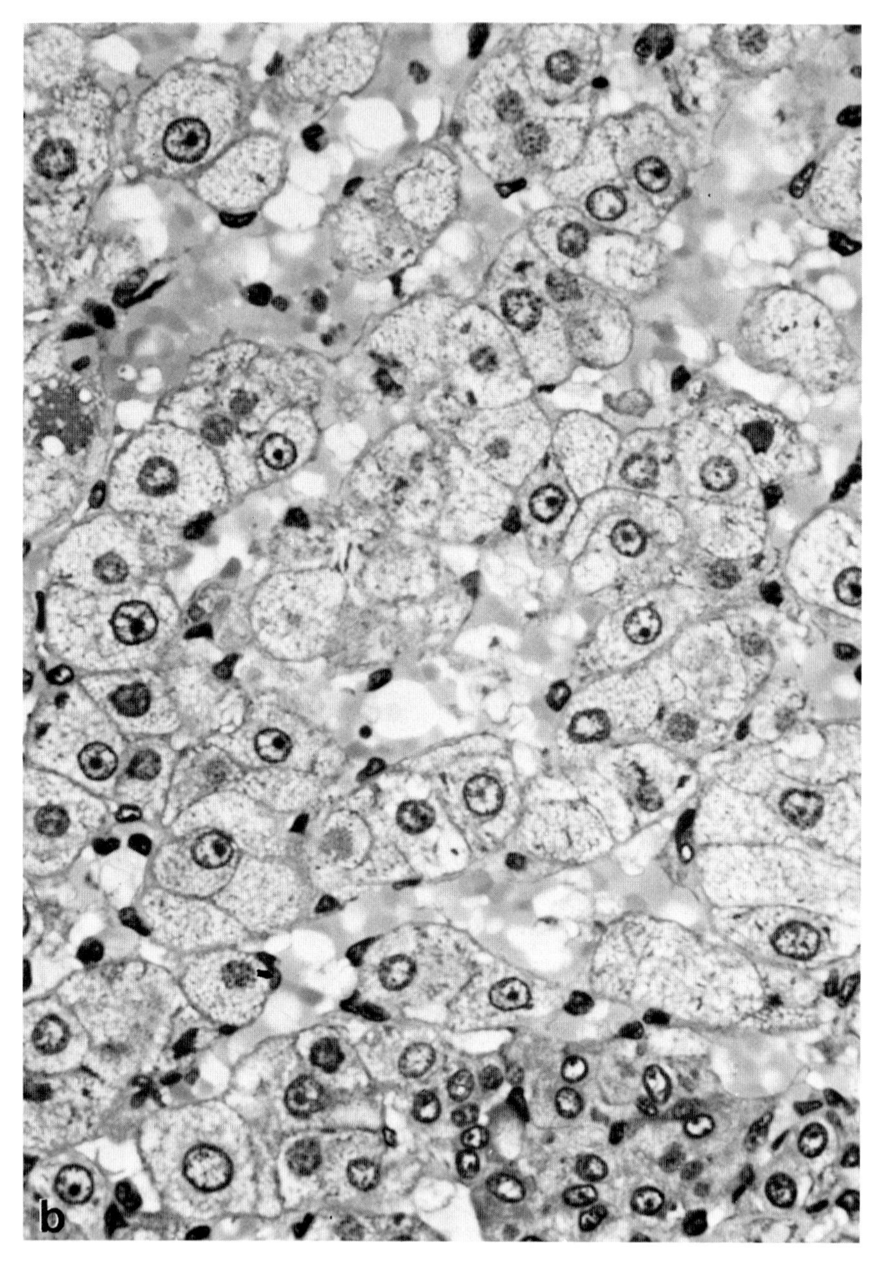

FIG. 2b.

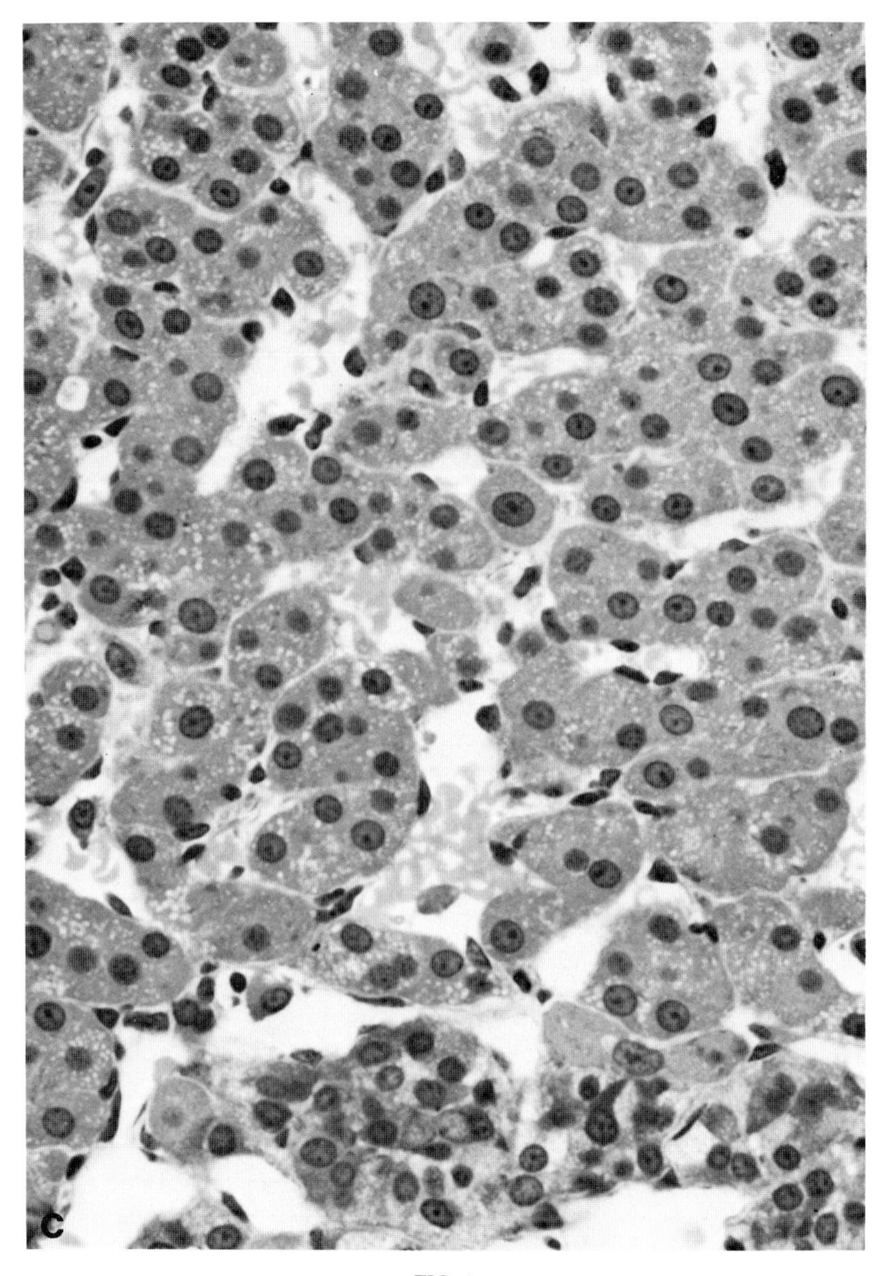

FIG. 2c.

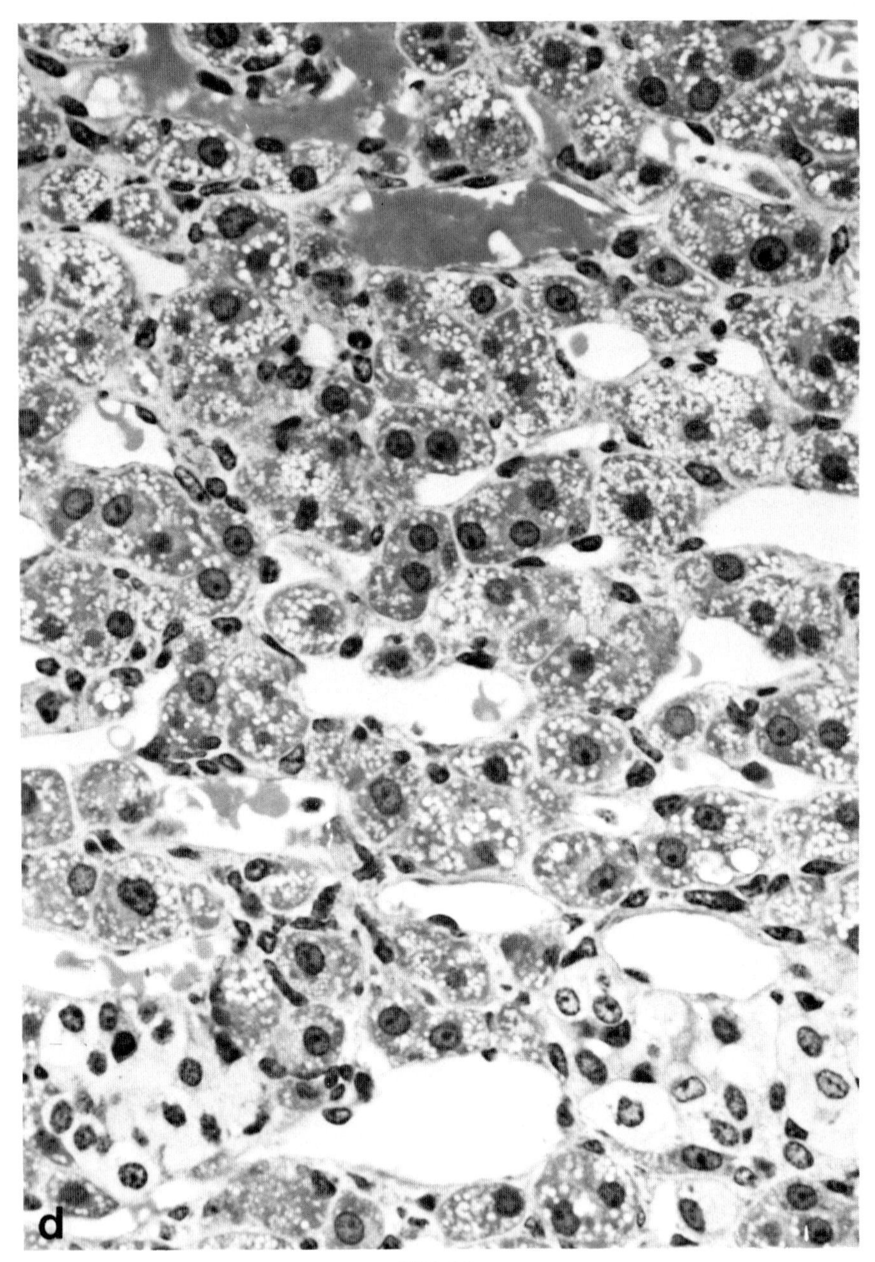

FIG. 2d.

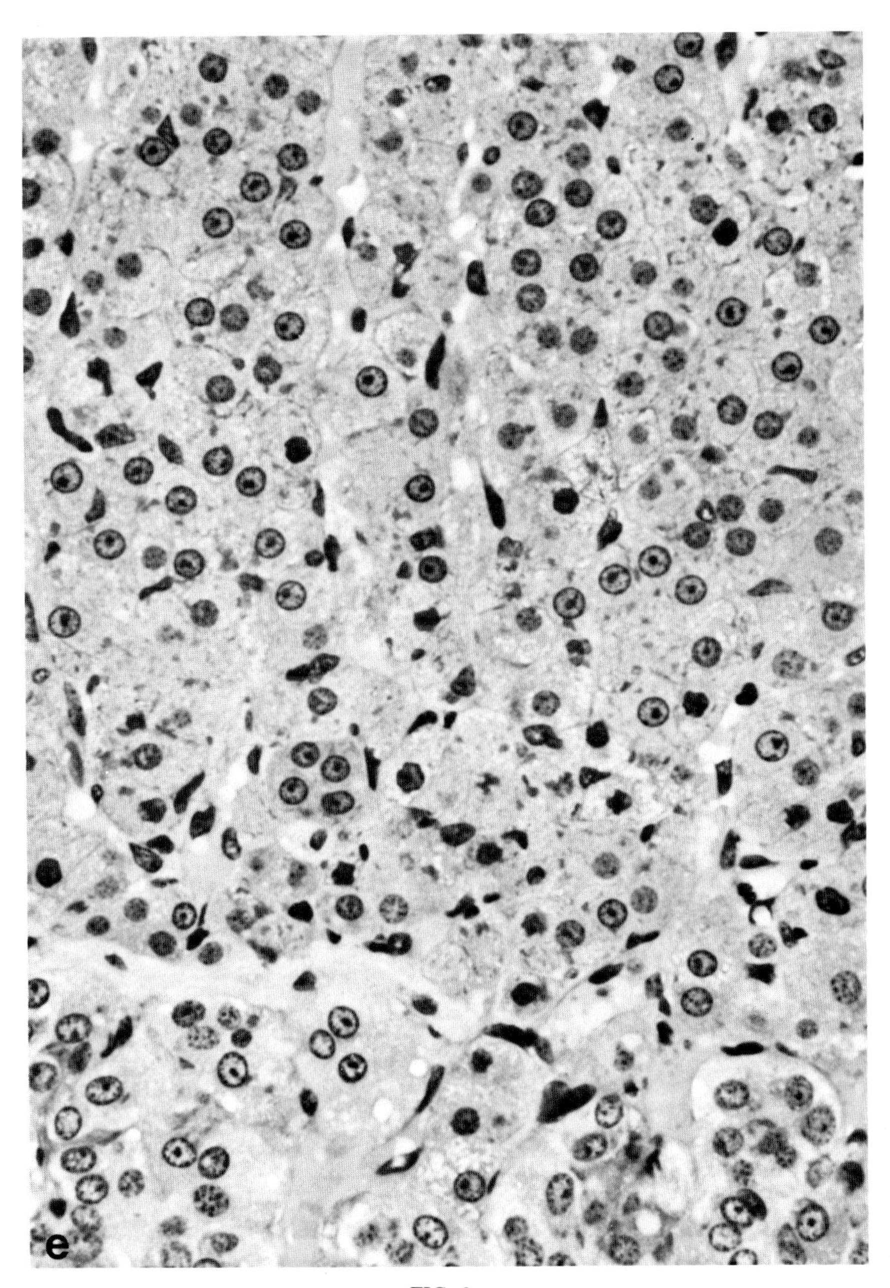

FIG. 2e.

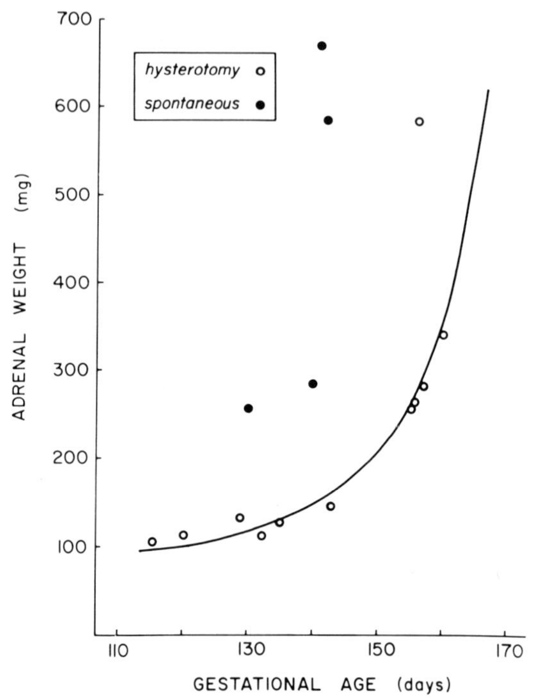

FIG. 3. Change in weight in rhesus monkey fetal adrenal gland with advancing gestational age. ○, Delivery by hysterotomy; ●, spontaneous delivery.

DHAS and cortisol are the two most prominent steroids produced by the fetal adrenal gland, with DHAS being the most abundant hormone present in the circulation.

In late gestation, the fetal zone of the human fetal adrenal gland is dependent on the presence of the fetal pituitary, as demonstrated indirectly by atrophy of the fetal zone in anencephalic and apituitary fetuses and atrophy of the adrenal and diminution of DHAS secretion after treatment with glucocorticoids (Easterling *et al.,* 1966). ACTH has been detected in the human fetal pituitary both by immunocytochemical (Baker and Jaffe, 1975) (Fig. 5) and biochemical (Siler-Khodr *et al.,* 1974) techniques by the tenth week of gestation. However, before midgestation, the obligatory nature of pituitary hormones for development and regulation of the fetal zone is not evident, since the gland develops normally up to 14 or 15 weeks in anencephalic fetuses. This suggests that extrapituitary, possibly placental, trophic factors also may regulate the fetal zone. Therefore, we superfused isolated fetal zones of adrenals from human fetuses from 12 to 17 weeks gestational age in the presence and absence of human

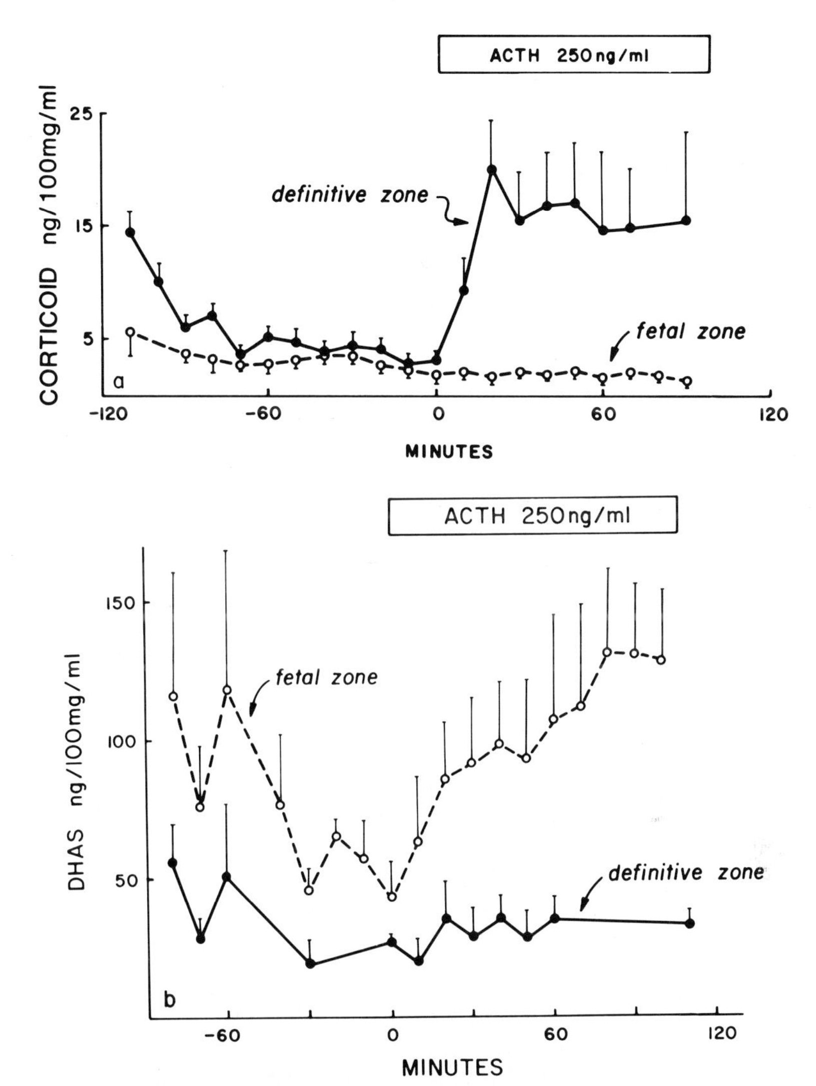

FIG. 4. (a) Corticoid secretion (mean ± SE) by minces of fetal and definitive zone of human fetal adrenal gland from seven fetuses. The data were normalized, considering time of addition of ACTH as time zero. Corticoid secretion by the definitive zone after ACTH treatment is significantly greater ($p < 0.05$) when compared to time zero at all time intervals after 10 minutes. (b) Dehydroepiandrosterone sulfate (DHAS) secretion (mean ± SE) by minces of fetal and definitive zones of the same glands shown in (a). DHAS secretion by the fetal zone was significantly ($p < 0.05$) higher at 30 and 50 minutes after addition of ACTH than at time zero. From Serón-Ferré *et al.* (1978a).

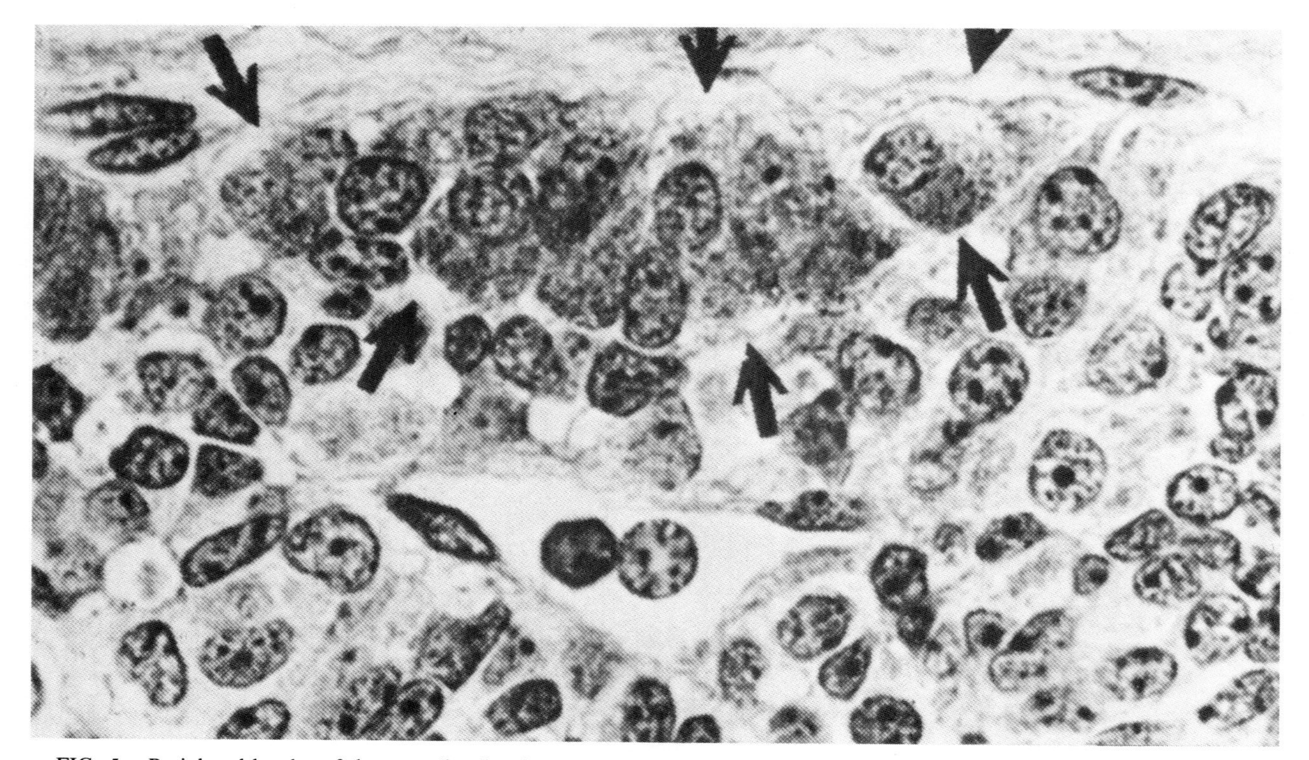

FIG. 5. Peripheral border of the pars distalis of an 11.5-week-old human fetus stained with the Masson procedure to show the basophils (arrows) which are the corticotrophs. ×600. From Baker and Jaffe (1975).

chorionic gonadotropin (hCG). A significant increase in DHAS production was observed in the presence of hCG (Serón-Ferré, *et al.*, 1978c) (Fig. 6). Since we found that ACTH also stimulates DHAS secretion, and as there is indirect evidence for a role of ACTH in the regulation of DHAS late in pregnancy, these observations suggest dual regulation by hCG and ACTH early in pregnancy and a possible transition to ACTH regulation of the fetal zone after the first trimester. If this thesis is correct, it would explain the observations by Bernirschke (Benirschke, 1956) and Gray and Abramovich (Gray and Abramovich, 1980) that the fetal zone of the anencephalic fetus is normal during the first trimester, when presumably hCG could stimulate this zone, but atrophies during the latter part of gestation when ACTH may subsume this role.

The data available provide strong evidence that ACTH plays a major role in stimulating steroid production by the fetal adrenal gland. However, it is likely that other substances (in addition to hCG), acting either synergistically or independently, influence both steroid production and growth of the fetal glands.

To study further the regulation of the human fetal adrenal and its response to trophic hormones, dispersed human fetal adrenal cells from the whole gland were studied in short-term incubations. Human fetal adrenals

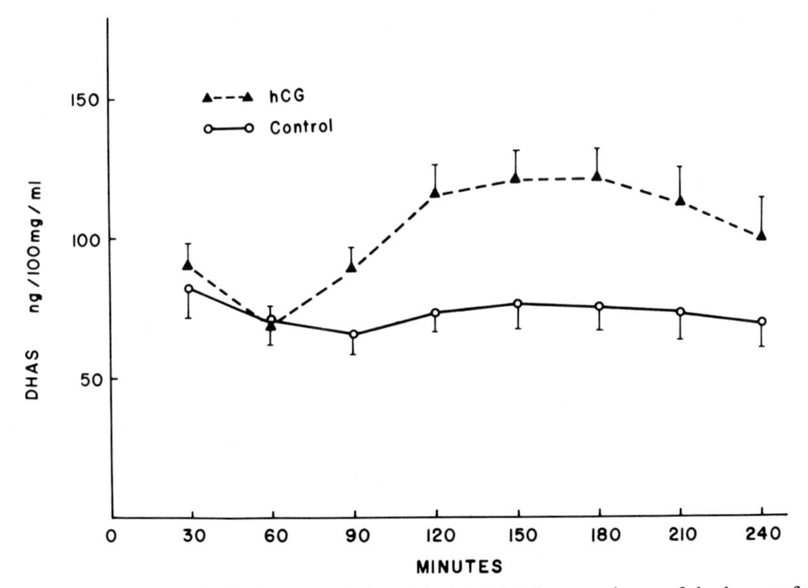

FIG. 6. DHAS levels during superfusion of isolated fetal zone minces of the human fetal adrenal gland in the presence and absence of 250 ng/ml hCG. Each point represents mean and SEM of the average DHAS concentration (nanograms/100 mg/ml) in samples of effluent collected every 10 minutes. From Serón-Ferré *et al.* (1978c).

from 13 to 20 weeks gestation were dissected from fetal tissues following dilatation and evacuation. During this period of gestation, DHAS, cortisol, and progesterone production is stimulated by ACTH (Crickard *et al.*, 1980). Maximum steroid production was noted with a 0.5 to 1.0 n*M* concentration of ACTH 1–39, which is within the reported physiologic range (Winters *et al.*, 1974). With supraphysiologic concentrations of ACTH, steroid production was noted to decrease from the maximally stimulated value, suggesting desensitization.

In studying the separated zones of the fetal adrenal gland to assess steroidogenesis in these short-term incubation studies, two technical considerations should be noted. First, the definitive zone tissue was obtained by gently removing the capsule of the gland to which the definitive zone is adherent as in the superfusion experiments. This procedure yielded a relatively pure preparation (95%) of definitive zone cells. The remainder consisted principally of fibroblasts. The fetal zone tissue remaining contained approximately 10% definitive zone cells adherent to its surface. To enrich the fetal zone cell preparations, the center portion of the fetal zone was biopsied with a needle, which yielded a population of fetal zone cells of comparable homogeneity to that of the definitive zone. The resultant fetal zone cells were then used for cell dispersion. Second, steroid production was measured using radioimmunoassay. For cortisol and progesterone, preparative chromatography was necessary because of cross-reactivity with other steroids. DHAS/DHA was measured directly by radioimmunoassay because of the large amount of DHAS/DHA relative to any other cross-reacting steroids.

DHAS production before and after ACTH 1–39 stimulation was determined for both zones of the human fetal adrenal gland. While the majority of DHAS production occurred in fetal zone cells, the definitive zone cells produced 5–10% of the DHAS per 100,000 cells. Cortisol production was limited to the definitive zone cells. It was found that fetal zone cells produced essentially no cortisol either during basal incubation or following ACTH 1–39 stimulation. It has been suggested that a deficiency or block of the 3β-hydroxysteroid dehydrogenase (3β-HSD) system in the fetal zone inhibits the formation of cortisol (Huhtaniemi, 1977). Preliminary data suggest that there also may be a block to 11β-hydroxylation; immunoassayable material in the fetal zone cells, which was detected with an antibody to cortisol, did not migrate with authentic [^{3}H]cortisol when cochromatography was employed (Fig. 7). When dispersed cells from the whole gland (containing both fetal and definitive zone cells) were incubated, cortisol was formed (Fig. 8). Preliminary data suggest that the second peak of corticoid-like material seen in Fig. 7 is 11-deoxycortisol. The same fetal zone cells also were placed in cell culture utilizing bovine

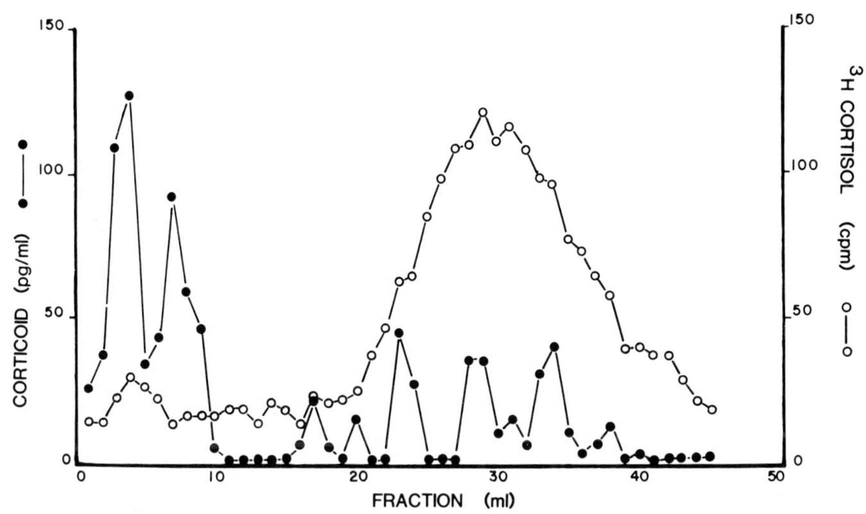

FIG. 7. Cochromatography elution patterns of immunoreactive (●---●) corticoids and radioactive (○---○) cortisol. Fetal zone cells were incubated for 2 hours at 37°C in the presence of ACTH 1–39. Media with [^{3}H]cortisol was chromatographed on Lipidex in hexane/chloroform (1 : 1, by vol). One milliliter fractions were collected for determining immunoreactive corticoids and radioactivity of [^{3}H]cortisol. Values less than 40 pg/ml were not significantly different than zero.

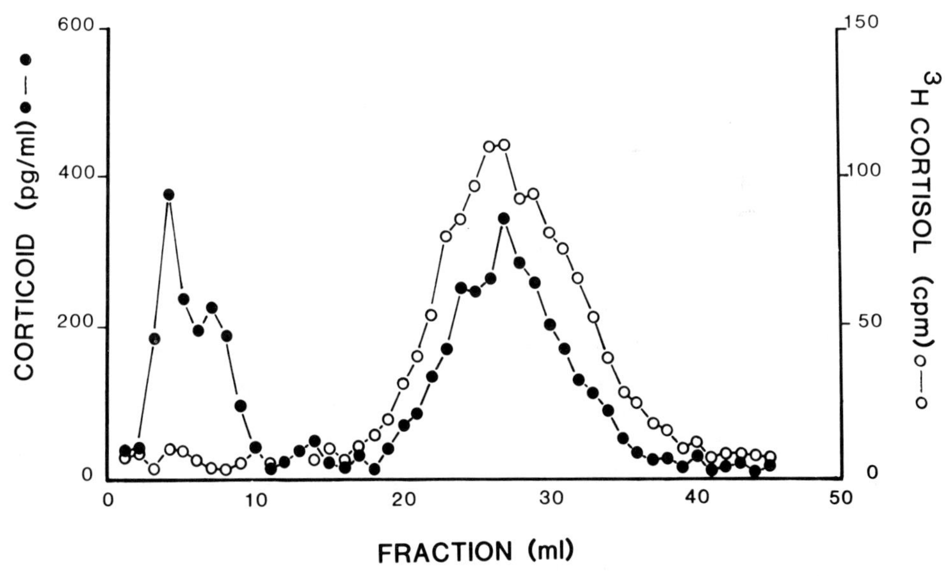

FIG. 8. Cortisol cochromatography from fetal adrenal cells. Dispersed cells from the whole fetal adrenal gland, containing both fetal and definitive zone cells, were incubated for 2 hours at 37°C in the presence of ACTH 1–39. Medium with [^{3}H]cortisol was chromatographed on Lipidex. One milliliter fractions were collected for immunoreactive (●---●) corticoids and radioisotopic (○---○) cortisol.

basement membrane as an extracellular substrate, as detailed subsequently. After 6 days in culture, the cells were stimulated with ACTH and the medium subjected to cochromatography. The peak corresponding to 11-deoxycortisol disappeared, with resultant cortisol formation. Taken collectively, these observations suggest the presence of a block in 11β-hydroxylation in the fetal zone. These findings were noted both under basal and ACTH-stimulated conditions. Thus, not only the 3β-HSD system may be impaired; there also may be a block of the 11β-hydroxylase enzyme in this zone. The physiologic significance of the distribution of these enzyme activities is not fully understood at present. In addition, the source and physiologic role of the corticoid(s), other than cortisol, asso-

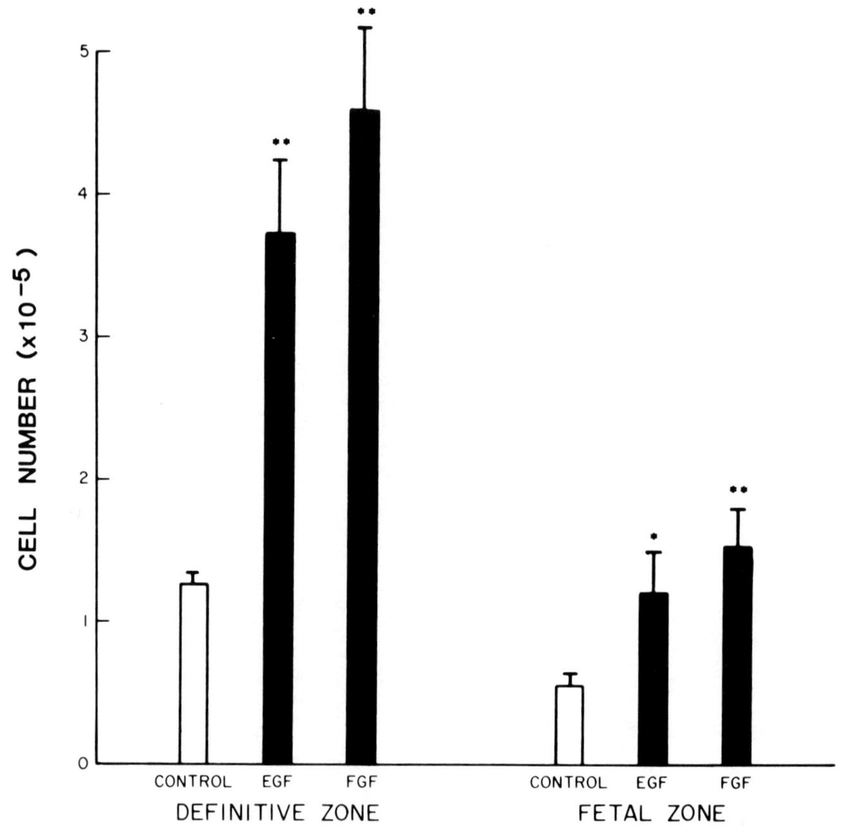

FIG. 9. Effect of FGF and EGF on the proliferation of fetal and definitive zone cells. Adrenal cells were plated at 10,000 cells/3.5 cm dish. They then were maintained in the presence of 10% fetal calf serum without or with EGF (20 ng/ml) or FGF (100 ng/ml). At day 9, cells were trypsinized and counted. The results are expressed as the mean ± SD of triplicate plates (*, $p < 0.01$; **, $p < 0.001$).

ciated with decreased 11β-hydroxylation in the fetal zone is not known. However, it is evident that cortisol production in the fetal zone is effectively blocked at least through 20 weeks gestation. The observation that cortisol is formed under cell culture conditions suggests the presence of a block of the enzyme rather than its deficiency.

C. HUMAN FETAL ADRENAL CELL PROLIFERATION

To further investigate the separated zones of the human fetal adrenal, efforts were directed toward developing a cell culture system that would serve as a useful model for studying factors influencing cell proliferation as well as steroidogenesis. Previous studies indicated a relatively rapid transformation of fetal zone cells into definitive zone-like cells in culture, which resulted in decreased DHAS production, evidence of corticoid production, and, in addition, decreased life-span unless specific mitogens were present in the medium (Simonian and Gill, 1980). While control of animal cell proliferation is poorly understood, a class of mitogenic polypeptides, termed growth factors, may play an important role in the process (Gospodarowicz and Moran, 1976). Such growth factors may mediate the effects of classical growth-promoting hormones (e.g., ACTH and growth hormone) since such hormones stimulate cell proliferation *in vivo* but not *in vitro* in most cases (Salmon and Daughaday, 1962).

The influence of epidermal growth factor (EGF) and fibroblast growth factor (FGF) on human fetal adrenal cell proliferation was compared. EGF, which was first isolated from submaxillary glands of adult mice (Cohen, 1962), is a potent mitogen for many cell types *in vitro,* including human diploid fibroblasts (Cohen and Carpenter, 1975). FGF has been purified from bovine pituitary and brain. It is a potent mitogen for a wide variety of mesoderm-derived cells (Gospodarowicz, 1975), including human adult and fetal adrenal cells (Gill *et al.,* 1978; Simonian and Gill, 1980). Separated definitive and fetal zone cells were prepared as mentioned previously and plated on plastic culture dishes at low density (10,000 cells) in Medium 199 supplemented with Earle's basic salt solution, 10% fetal calf serum, and antibiotics (gentamycin, penicillin, streptomycin, and fungizone). FGF (100 ng/ml) or EGF (20 ng/ml) was added every other day, and cells were counted after 9 days with a Coulter counter. Figure 9 represents the influence of EGF and FGF on cell proliferation; each point represents the mean of triplicate cultures. Both EGF and FGF are mitogenic for definitive and fetal zone cells. Fibroblasts accounted for less than 5% of the cells, based on criteria of steroidogenesis and lack of a retraction response to ACTH. Total DHAS and cortisol production over 9 days, as well as 8-hour ACTH 1–

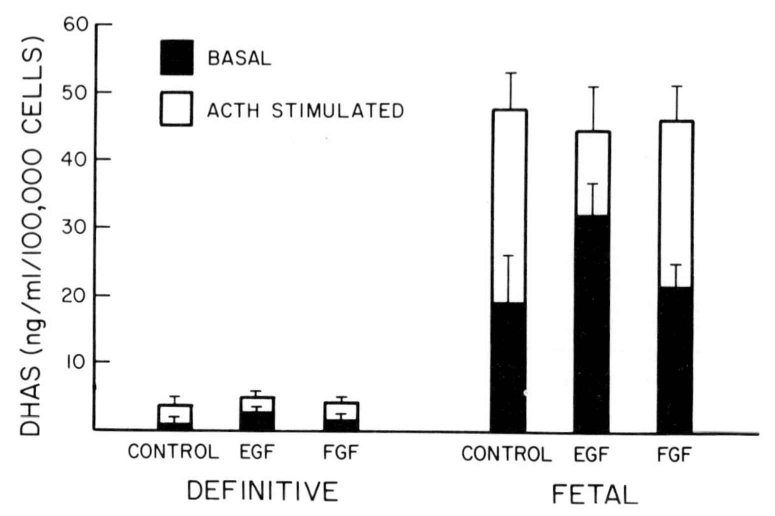

FIG. 10. Effect of EGF and FGF on ACTH-stimulated DHAS production. Separated fetal adrenal cells were incubated in the presence of 10% fetal calf serum without or with EGF or FGF for 9 days. After fresh medium containing 10% fetal calf serum was added, the fetal adrenal cells were incubated with (open bar) or without (closed bar) ACTH 1–39. After 8 hours, DHAS concentration was quantified. Error bars represent the mean ± SD for triplicate plates.

39-stimulated steroid production (after 9 days), were determined. The production rate of DHAS by fetal zone cells was approximately nine times that of the definitive zone cells over 9 days. Both zones were responsive to ACTH after 9 days in culture (Fig. 10). A slight, but significant, steroidogenic effect was noted with EGF. Total cortisol production over the 9 days was in the range of 1 to 2 ng per 100,000 cells for both zones. After changing the medium and stimulating with ACTH for 8 hours, additional, net cortisol production was in the picogram range. Thus, under primary cell culture conditions, EGF and FGF are mitogenic for human fetal adrenal cells, and the steroid responsiveness of these cells has been demonstrated. In addition, using ^{125}I-labeled EGF, we have demonstrated specific high-affinity receptors for EGF in both fetal zone and definitive zone cells.

For certain cell types, FGF induces the cells to form an extracellular matrix (Gospodarowicz *et al.*, 1979). Gospodarowicz *et al.* have emphasized the importance of the extracellular matrix in contributing to cell shape, growth, and function in cell culture (Gospodarowicz *et al.*, 1979). To evaluate the influence of the extracellular matrix, we grew human fetal adrenal cells on a matrix of basement membrane prepared from bovine corneal endothelial cells as described by Gospodarowicz and Ill (Gospodarowicz and Ill, 1980). Briefly, the corneal endothelial cells are plated at low density in the presence of DMEM, H-16 supplemented with 10% fetal calf serum, 5% calf serum, 5% Dextran T-40, and antibiotics (gentamycin and fungizone). FGF (100 ng/ml) is added every other day. After the cultures become confluent, the cells are solubilized with Triton X-100 in PBS and an intact extracellular matrix remains coating the dish. Bovine corneal endothelial cells were chosen because of their ability to form significant amounts of basement membrane under the influence of FGF (Gospodarowicz *et al.*, 1979).

Figure 11 demonstrates the proliferation of fetal and definitive zone cells cultured on basement membrane alone or on plastic substrate supplemented with EGF or FGF. The mitogenic effect of FGF, EGF, or basement membrane is dependent on the serum concentration in which the cells are maintained. Increasing the concentration of serum enhanced

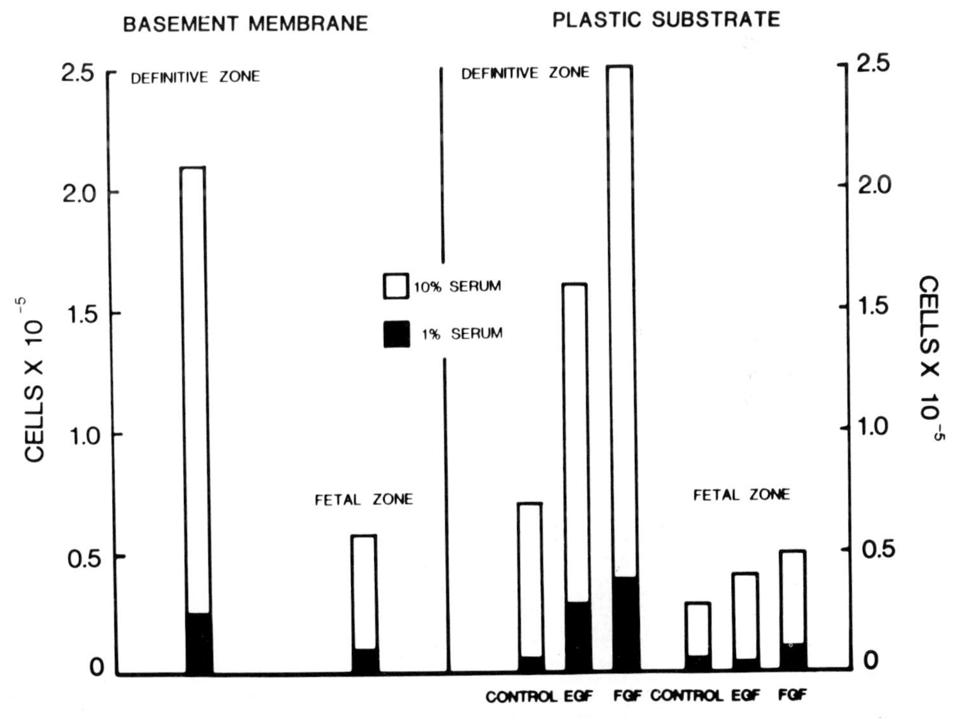

FIG. 11. Correlation between basement membrane, FGF, EGF, and serum concentration on culture growth. Separated fetal adrenal cells were plated at 6000 cells/3.5 cm plate coated with or without bovine basement membrane in the presence of 1% or 10% fetal calf serum. Fetal adrenal cells plated on plastic substrate were maintained with or without EGF or FGF. At day 9, the cells were trypsinized and counted. The results are expressed as the mean of duplicate plates.

the growth of cells maintained on basement membrane alone or on plastic substrate with FGF or EGF. With medium supplemented with 10% fetal calf serum, cell proliferation on basement membrane alone was similar to that obtained on plastic substrate in the presence of FGF. This would suggest that the extracellular collagen matrix is important in controlling cell growth of fetal adrenal cells. Of interest is the observation that fetal adrenal cells grown on basement membrane fail to demonstrate the retraction response to ACTH that is seen on plastic substrate. Preliminary results indicate that DHAS and corticoid production under primary cell culture conditions are similar between cells grown on basement membrane alone and plastic substrate supplemented with growth factors.

Factors controlling the proliferation of fetal adrenal cells *in vivo* are poorly understood. The observation that growth factors may play a role as mediators of cell proliferation is a recent finding. While most investigation concerning EGF has been directed toward animal studies, there is evidence that EGF may play a role in human cell growth. EGF has been isolated from human urine and amniotic fluid, primarily in the form of urogastrone (Hirata and Orth, 1979). EGF-like activity has been reported in human placental tissue, and recently EGF has been shown to stimulate hCG release from human choriocarcinoma cells in culture (Benveniste *et al.,* 1978). FGF has been reported to stimulate the growth of human umbilical vein endothelial cells. Thus, both EGF and FGF could play a role in embryogenesis by influencing cell and vascular proliferation. In addition, it is becoming clear that the extracellular matrix may have an important role in morphogenesis and differentiated cell function. Further studies with an extracellular matrix, such as bovine basement membrane, may serve as a useful model to investigate human fetal adrenal cell growth and function.

D. OTHER TROPHIC FACTORS REGULATING THE HUMAN FETAL ADRENAL GLAND

There is evidence that the human placenta synthesizes ACTH (Liotta *et al.,* 1977) and ACTH-related peptides, including β-endorphin (Houck *et al.,* 1980) and αMSH (Liotta *et al.,* 1977). The precise chemical identity of the immunoreactive ACTH-like material found in the human circulation has not been established. The possible existence of peptides in the fetal circulation related to ACTH, that could cross-react in an ACTH radioimmunoassay, has not been ruled out. CLIP, αMSH, β-endorphin, and ACTH have been found in the human fetal pituitary (Silman *et al.,* 1976); the proportion of ACTH relative to the other peptides increases with gestational age. The detection of these ACTH-related peptides has led to the suggestion that they may be trophic for the fetal adrenal gland at particular times in gestation. αMSH has been shown to stimulate corticosteroid secretion *in vitro* and *in vivo* in rodents (Rudman *et al.*, 1980). Moreover, in rodents, αMSH stimulates DNA synthesis by the fetal adrenal, while ACTH does not (Rudman *et al.*, 1980). In fact, ACTH inhibits DNA synthesis in the adult adrenal gland (Gill *et al.*, 1978). Human fetal adrenal cells in short-term incubation also increase corticoid and DHAS production in response to αMSH (Crickard *et al.*, 1980). In our dispersed human fetal adrenal cells in short-term incubation, αMSH was found to stimulate steroid production at a 1000-fold greater concentration than ACTH (Fig. 12), which suggests that αMSH is acting at an ACTH receptor site. Desacetyl αMSH, which stimulates steroidogenesis in the adrenals of some species, and hLH were not effective in stimulating steroid production in this preparation. A lack of effect of αMSH in the nanomolar range in organ culture of human fetal adrenal tissue has been reported (Branchaud *et al.*, 1978). CLIP also has been found ineffective in this system (Branchaud *et al.*, 1978). The physiologic importance of the fetal adrenal response to αMSH is not clear; the capacity of the fetal adrenal gland of most species, including the human, to respond to αMSH suggests maturational changes in the ACTH receptor during development since the adult adrenal gland does not respond to αMSH.

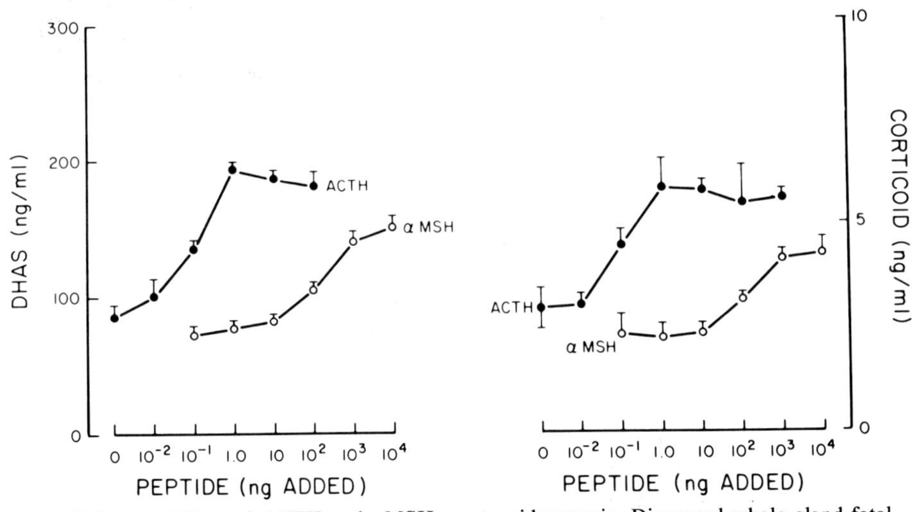

FIG. 12. Effect of ACTH and αMSH on steroidogenesis. Dispersed whole gland fetal adrenal cells were incubated in the absence or presence of increasing concentrations of ACTH 1–39 or αMSH for 2 hours at 37°C. DHAS and corticoid concentrations for each incubation (6,000,000 cells/0.6 ml) were quantified. Error bars represent the mean ± SD for triplicate incubations.

It has been suggested that other pituitary hormones also are adrenotropic in the human fetus, but the evidence for this is limited. The increase in prolactin during gestation parallels the pattern of fetal adrenal growth (Winters *et al.,* 1975). Prolactin has been reported to stimulate cortisol production in dispersed fetal adrenal cells (Glickman, *et al.,* 1979). However, the data are not conclusive. As indicated previously, hCG has the capacity to increase DHAS secretion *in vitro*. Since angiotensin is present in the fetal circulation in high concentration and is mitogenic as well as capable of stimulating steroidogenesis in the adult adrenal (Gill *et al.,* 1978), it is possible that it plays a trophic role, together with ACTH and other pituitary or placental peptides, e.g., FGF and EGF, in adrenal growth and regulation. Indeed, our preliminary data in the rhesus monkey *in vivo* suggest that angiotensin can increase circulating adrenal steroid levels.

E. STEROID PRODUCTION AND REGULATION IN THE RHESUS MONKEY FETAL ADRENAL *IN VITRO*

Our studies of the human fetal adrenal gland were limited to the period prior to midgestation for obvious reasons. As seen previously, the fetal adrenal gland of the rhesus monkey is similar morphologically to that of the human. There also are functional similarities in that the fetal zone secretes DHAS while cortisol is secreted primarily by the definitive zone in superfusion studies. In addition, as seen in Fig. 13 both respond to ACTH (Jaffe *et al.,* 1978). Therefore, we have chosen this animal as an

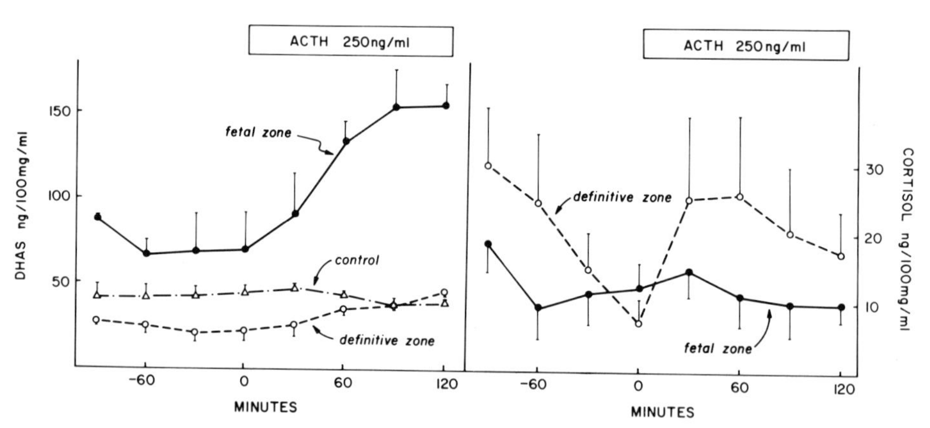

FIG. 13. DHAS and cortisol responses to ACTH in the separated fetal and definitive zones of the rhesus monkey fetal adrenal gland studied in a superfusion system. In the figure of DHAS data, a curve from fetal adrenal minced preparations to which no ACTH was added is shown for comparison. From Jaffe *et al.* (1978).

experimental model in which to investigate the regulation of the fetal adrenal gland in late gestation, the time when preparation for parturition and extrauterine life is occurring. Steroid biosynthesis in the rhesus monkey fetus is similar, in many respects, to the human, although important differences exist (e.g., the rhesus does not have appreciable 16-hydroxylating capacity in the adrenal or liver (Heinrichs and Colás, 1970; Gorwill *et al.,* 1971), and therefore placental aromatization to form estriol from 16-hydroxy-DHAS is limited. In addition, placental aromatization of DHA and DHAS is limited (Snyder *et al.,* 1971), which may explain why circulating levels of estrone and estradiol are much lower in the monkey than the human. We have studied the secretion of steroids by the fetal adrenal gland of the monkey, utilizing adrenal minces in a superfusion system, from 90 days of gestation to term (mean gestational length = 168 days). In this *in vitro* system, the monkey fetal adrenal gland secretes androstenedione, progesterone, aldosterone, and 11-deoxycorticosterone (DOC), corticosterone (B), 18 OH-DOC, and 18 OH-B (Fig. 14) in addition to cortisol and DHAS. We have found that the secretion of all of the mineralocorticoids, except aldosterone, is increased by ACTH. Aldosterone, which is present in high concentrations, can be stimulated when K^+ and ACTH are combined. Progesterone and DOC secretion decreases with gestational age while that of cortisol and aldosterone increases (Fig. 15). In addition, basal concentrations of androstenedione and the secretion of androstenedione in response to ACTH increase at the end of gestation. There also is an increase in cortisol secretion with advancing gestational age. We have speculated that the increasing concentrations of

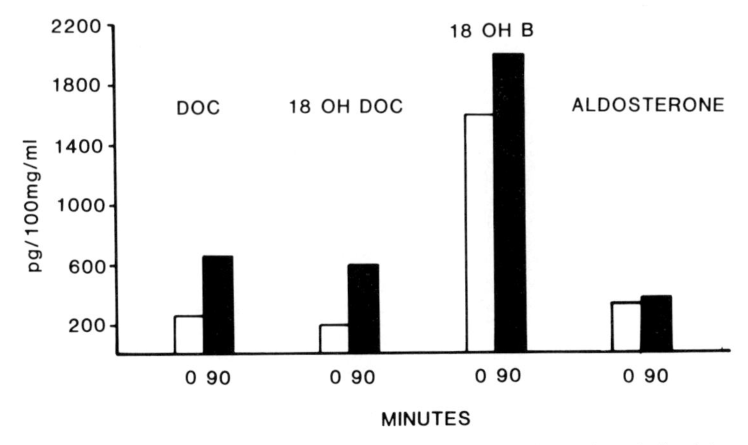

FIG. 14. Mineralocorticoid secretion by fetal rhesus monkey adrenal gland in superfusion. Response of DOC, 18 OH-DOC, 18 OH-B, and aldosterone to ACTH. Solid bar = 90 minutes after ACTH addition.

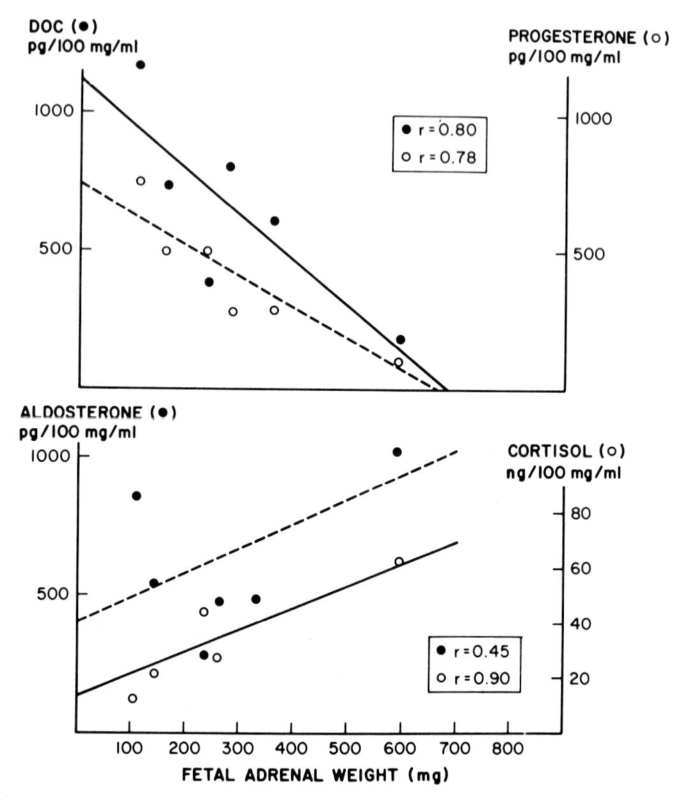

FIG. 15. Relationship of DOC, progesterone (upper panel), aldosterone, and cortisol (lower panel) to fetal adrenal weight in the fetal rhesus monkey.

androgens (which can function as estrogen precursors) and the increasing concentration of cortisol at the end of gestation provide a parallel situation to that in the sheep (Liggins *et al.,* 1973) in which increasing cortisol concentrations and an increasing estrogen to progesterone ratio lead to an increase in prostaglandin synthesis with the ensuant initiation of parturition.

Our *in vitro* data indicate that substantial amounts of DOC and aldosterone are secreted by the rhesus monkey fetal adrenal gland between 130 days and term (Serón-Ferré and Biglieri, 1980).

Taken together, these data indicate that the fetal adrenal gland of the rhesus monkey is a very active steroid-secreting organ. The decrease in progesterone and DOC with advancing gestation indicates a maturation of enzyme systems that are involved in the utilization of endogenous progesterone in the synthesis of cortisol, androstenedione, and aldosterone. The increases in cortisol and aldosterone production toward the end of gestation appear to presage the adult pattern of adrenal steroid production, perhaps in preparation for extrauterine life.

In the rhesus monkey fetal pituitary gland, as in the human, there is an increase in the proportion of ACTH to other ACTH-related peptides (αMSH, CLIP, β-endorphin) with advancing gestational age (Silman *et al.*, 1978). In our studies, αMSH stimulated cortisol *in vitro,* although to a lesser degree than ACTH. It also is less effective in the stimulation of DHAS and androstenedione and appears to have no effect on progesterone secretion by the monkey fetal adrenal *in vitro.*

F. *IN VIVO* STUDIES IN THE FETAL RHESUS MONKEY

To study endocrine regulation in the fetal rhesus monkey in a relatively physiologic manner, we have utilized the long-term catheterized rhesus monkey fetus shown schematically in Fig. 16. In this preparation, catheters are placed in the fetal carotid artery and jugular vein at the time of abdominal hysterotomy of the mother at 120 to 130 days of gestation (Serón-Ferré *et al.,* 1978b; Jaffe *et al.,* 1979). Electrodes for fetal electrocardiographic recording are implanted in the fetal thoracic skin, the fetus is returned to the uterus, and the arterial and venous catheters and fetal electrode, together with an amniotic fluid pressure transducer, are exteriorized either through the vagina or flank of the mother. Fetal status is monitored by fetal blood pH measurements, P_{O_2} and P_{CO_2} determinations, and electrocardiographic recordings. Judged by these criteria, the preparations studied were stable. All experiments were performed prior to evidence of alteration in fetal status or initiation of maternal labor. The mother was maintained, unanesthetized, in a primate chair. The longest that a preparation has been maintained is 23 days, and the mean is approximately 6 days. Although this species technically is more difficult to use than the sheep, in that there is a higher tendency to premature delivery, it has led to valuable information which may be more relevant to the situation obtaining in human pregnancy, given the morphologic and biochemical similarities between the fetal adrenal glands of the human and rhesus monkey to which reference was made previously.

In the rhesus monkey, ACTH is present in the fetal circulation in lower concentrations than has been reported for humans (Serón-Ferré *et al.,* 1978b). This either may indicate a species difference or that the human data also reflect the measurement of other ACTH-related peptides because of cross reaction with the antibody utilized for ACTH measurement. Treatment with high doses of dexamethasone suppresses 90% of the ACTH and cortisol in the fetal monkey circulation within 24 hours (Serón-Ferré *et al.,* 1978b). This suggests the integrity of the fetal

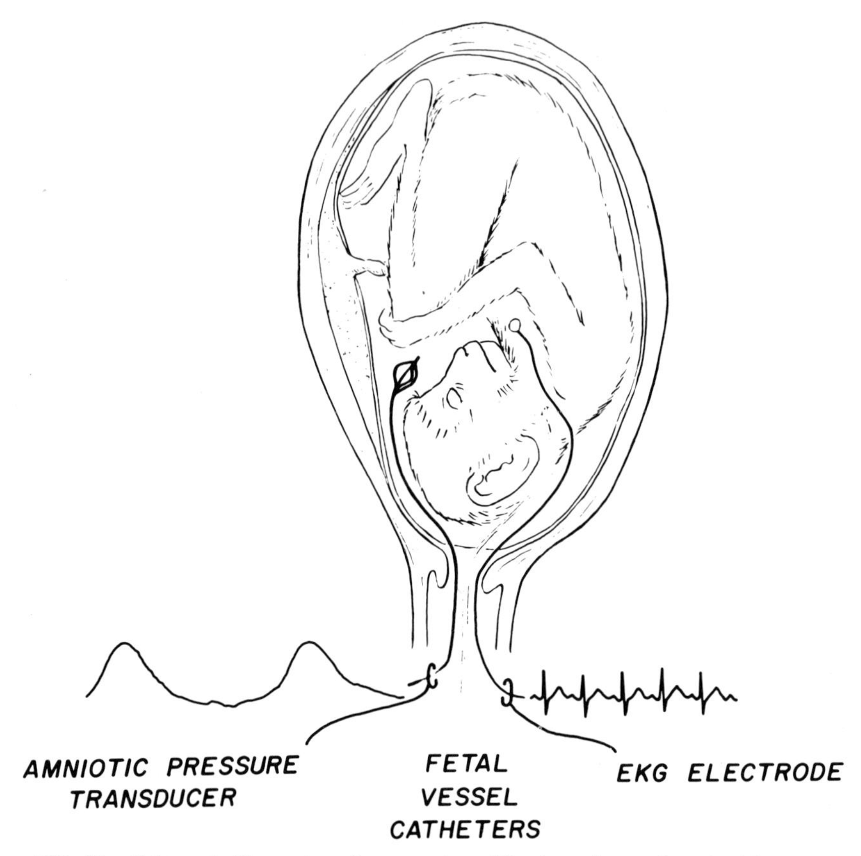

FIG. 16. Schematic illustration of preparation of fetal monkey catheterized *in utero*.

pituitary–adrenal axis. Values return to normal after cessation of dexamethasone administration. Treatment with supraphysiologic doses of ACTH as a bolus or infusion (Walsh *et al.*, 1979; Serón-Ferré and Jaffe, unpublished) restores cortisol levels to pretreatment values in the dexamethasone-treated fetus. Treatment of nonsuppressed fetuses with ACTH does not increase cortisol levels, suggesting a limitation of the ACTH-stimulated cortisol pathway, such as saturation of ACTH receptors *in utero*. αMSH also increases corticosteroids in dexamethasone-suppressed monkey fetuses, although the effect is of much lesser magnitude and more short-lived than the effects brought about by ACTH. Preliminary data suggest that angiotensin II, which *in vitro* also stimulates growth of the adult adrenal gland, can stimulate DHAS production by the rhesus monkey fetal adrenal *in vivo*.

1. Corticosteroid Dynamics in the Monkey Fetus

Particularly in pregnancy, measurement of circulating concentrations of a steroid in the fetus or mother may not reflect the dynamics of metabolism of that steroid. In addition, the study of cortisol secretion *in vivo* is complicated by the presence of other steroids in fetal plasma that can cross-react in most cortisol radioimmunoassays. Several authors have stressed the methodologic problems in measuring cortisol by radioimmunoassay in the fetal circulation of several species (Magyar *et al.*, 1979). Challis and colleagues reported a difference of 70% between chromatographed and nonchromatographed samples from the monkey fetus (Challis *et al.*, 1980). In our studies, using extracted plasma, there was 10% contamination using a radioimmunoassay utilizing an antibody against cortisol-3-hemisuccinyl-BSA.

Cortisol increases in the fetal circulation near term as seen in Fig. 17 (Jaffe *et al.*, 1978). Values rose from a mean of 76 ng/ml at 130–134 days to a mean of 135 ng/ml at 150–154 days. It should be recalled that the size of the fetal adrenal also increases markedly at this time (Fig. 3). As also can be seen in Fig. 17, mean cortisol levels were higher in fetal samples obtained during maternal labor.

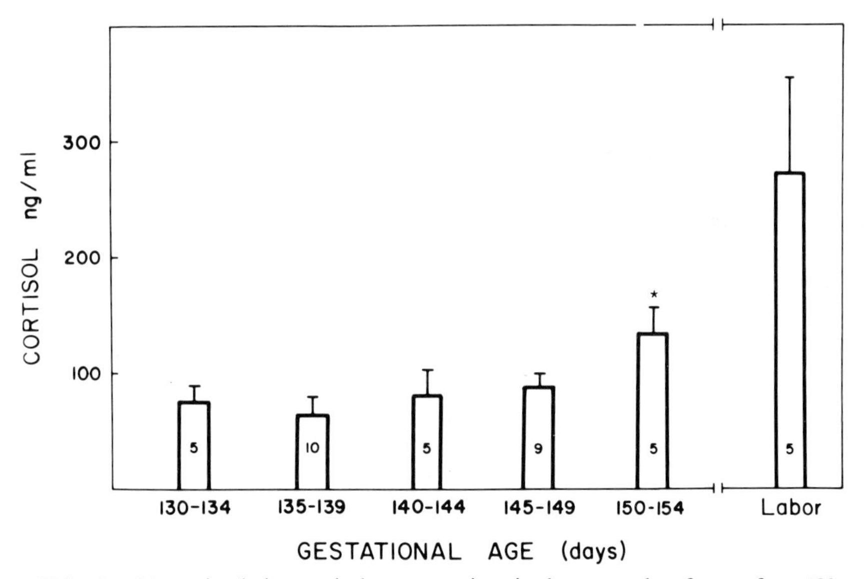

FIG. 17. Mean circulating cortisol concentrations in rhesus monkey fetuses from 130 to 154 days gestational age. Data were obtained from 20 fetuses with long-term catheterization *in utero*. A daily morning sample was obtained from each fetus. When a fetus was sampled over several consecutive days in a single time interval, the mean cortisol value for that fetus was used in calculating the group mean. From Jaffe *et al.* (1978).

The increase in fetal plasma cortisol during late gestation could be a result of a decrease in cortisol clearance by the fetus or an increase in any of the factors contributing to the cortisol production rate, i.e., an increase in fetal adrenal secretion, an increase in maternal–fetal transfer of cortisol, or an increase in conversion of cortisol prehormones, particularly cortisone, to cortisol in the fetus. An increase in fetal cortisol secretion rate would suggest fetal control of cortisol levels during this critical period. It also would suggest a parallel in the primate to the situation in species such as the sheep in which an increase in fetal cortisol secretion has been shown to be a trigger leading to the onset of labor (Liggins *et al.*, 1973).

Therefore, we measured the dynamics of cortisol handling in the long-term catherized monkey fetus. In the human fetoplacental unit, there is extensive ability to interconvert the active glucocorticoid, cortisol, and its biologically inactive metabolite, cortisone. The evidence suggests that maternal cortisol is oxidized extensively, via placental 11β-hydroxysteroid dehydrogenase, to cortisone during maternal–fetal transplacental passage. We used tracer techniques to study cortisol and cortisone production, clearance, interconversion, and placental transfer during late gestation (Mitchell *et al.*, 1980). There were two separate experimental protocols employed. In the first, a bolus injection of [^{3}H]cortisol was given to the fetus and results obtained compared with similar studies in infants and adults. This permitted determination of the metabolic clearance rate (MCR) and production rate (PR). The second set of experiments involved the constant infusion of [^{3}H]cortisol in the fetus and [^{14}C]cortisol into the mother. This permitted calculations of secretion rate (SR) and placental transfer, in addition to the MCR and PR.

We found that the factors that contribute to the regulation of circulating levels of cortisol include a high MCR and an efficient conversion of cortisol to cortisone (Mitchell *et al.*, 1981). The MCR of cortisol is very high in the fetus (23 liters/day or 86 liters/kg/day), significantly higher than in the mother or infant (11.9 and 27.1 liters/kg/day), respectively.

The increased MCR in the fetus occurs because of the rapid oxidation of cortisol to cortisone by the fetus and placenta and the transplacental passage of cortisol from fetus to mother. The PR of cortisol also is much higher in the fetus than in the mother. This fetal PR includes cortisol production from all sources, including adrenal secretion, placental transfer, and conversion of cortisone to cortisol. The conversion of cortisone to cortisol accounts for approximately 30% of the cortisol present in the fetal circulation.

There is significant transplacental passage of cortisol. Approximately 50% of fetal cortisol is of maternal origin. However, at 130 days, the fetus

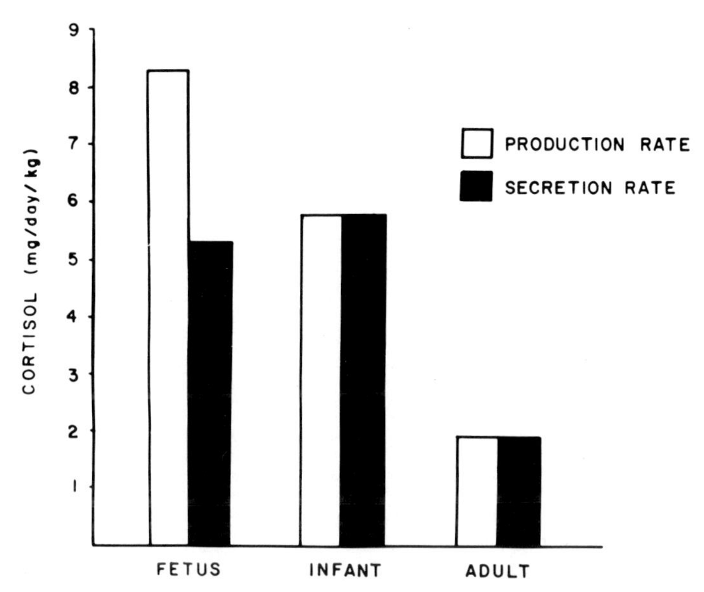

FIG. 18. Cortisol production rates and secretion rates in fetal, infant, and adult rhesus monkeys.

secretes as much cortisol per unit weight as the mother, indicating a very competent and active adrenal gland.

In Fig. 18, the cortisol production rates and secretion rates are compared in the fetus, neonate, and adult. The PR was calculated as the product of the MCR and mean cortisol concentration. MCR was calculated by analysis of the disappearance curve following a bolus injection of [^{3}H]cortisol. It should be recalled that the fetal PR includes placental transfer and conversion of cortisone to cortisol, in addition to adrenal secretion. From our studies, we determined that the fetal cortisol SR is approximately 65% of the total fetal cortisol PR. In the infant and adult, of course, the PR reflects only the SR and thus the secretion and production rates are about equal. Thus, in the fetus, the PR is higher than in the infant or adult. The SR is approximately the same in the fetus and the neonate, and both are higher than in the nonpregnant adult. The perinatal period may represent a time of maximal adrenal cortical activity.

The data from the second set of experiments (constant infusion) are presented in Table I. The results for MCR and PR for cortisone determined in these experiments are compared to those for cortisol. The data for cortisol–cortisone interconversion also were calculated and show that almost 80% of cortisol is converted to cortisone in the fetal circulation, and just less than 10% of cortisone is metabolized to cortisol. From these

TABLE I
Gluocorticoid Metabolism in the Rhesus Monkey Fetus

	Cortisol	Cortisone
MCR (liter/day/kg)	70.5 ± 8.7	138.8 ± 16.4
PR (mg/day/kg)	8.3 ± 1.6	26.1 ± 3.3
Conversion factor		
F → E (%)	79.5 ± 7.0	
E → F (%)		8.9 ± 1.2

data, we conclude that conversion of cortisol to cortisone in the fetus is another important factor resulting in the high fetal MCR of cortisol. We conclude also that the large circulating pool of fetal cortisone may be an important supply of prehormone for fetal cortisol and could account for 30% of the total cortisol PR in the fetus. Since we determined that 60% of cortisol in the fetus is transferred across the placenta and 80% is oxidized to cortisone, it is clear that cortisone itself must be transferred across the placenta. Thus, it also is possible that the interconversion of these two hormones is an important regulator of the amount of glucocorticoid crossing the placenta.

Figure 19 summarizes our studies of glucocorticoid metabolism in the monkey fetus. Fetal adrenal cortisol secretion of 5.3 mg/kg/day accounts for more than half of the circulating fetal cortisol at any particular time, as shown in the open part of the upper circle depicting cortisol. The remainder arises from placental transfer from the mother, appearing either directly as cortisol or as cortisone with subsequent reduction to cortisol. Fetal production of cortisone is much greater than for cortisol and, as shown in the closed portion of the lower circle depicting cortisone, more than 70% arises from the placental transfer of maternal cortisol or cortisone. Conversion of this large fetal pool of cortisone, involving the enzyme 11β-hydroxysteroid dehydrogenase, may contribute up to 30% of fetal cortisol production. The MCR of cortisol in the fetus is extremely rapid, with approximately 80% being rapidly oxidized to cortisone and 60% ultimately being transferred to the mother, either as cortisol or cortisone. To increase understanding of fetal glucocorticoid metabolism, further studies must address not only the factors controlling adrenal cortisol secretion but also the factors regulating placental transfer of cortisol and cortisone and the activity and direction of the 11β-hydroxysteroid dehydrogenase (11β-OH-SD) enzyme system. A mechanism of control of 11β-OH-SD has been proposed by Murphy (1980), who suggested that another steroid, secreted by the fetal adrenal gland, might regulate the extent of placental oxidation of cortisol. If this steroid inhibited oxidation,

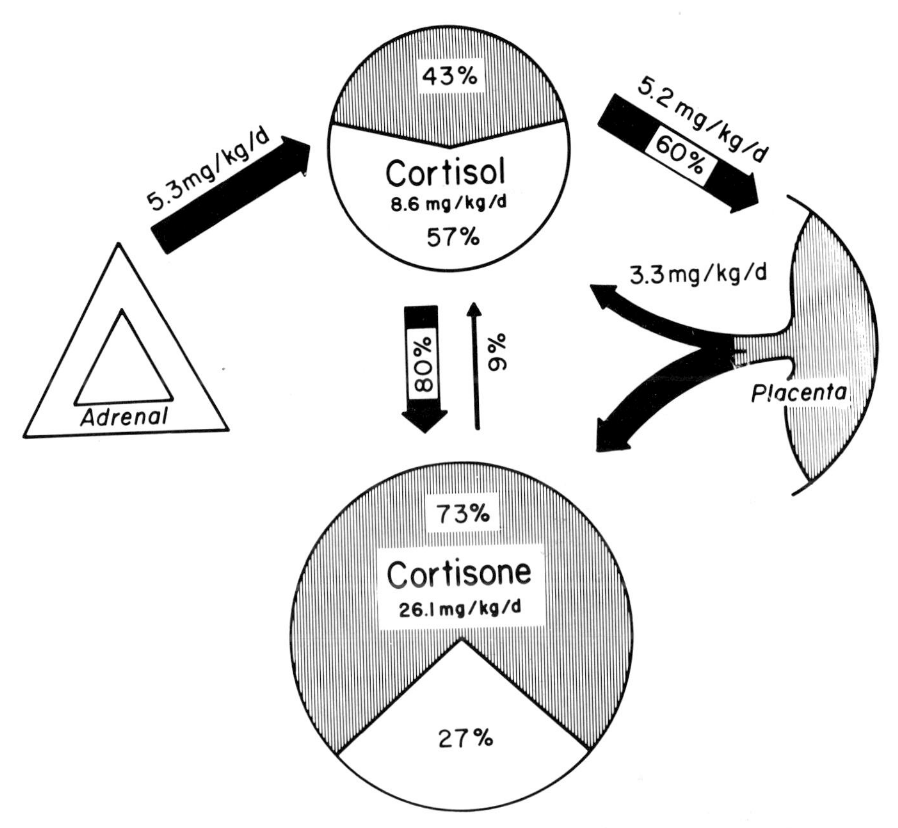

FIG. 19. Schematic illustration of glucocorticoid metabolism in the monkey fetus. See text for details.

and was secreted in greater amounts as term is approached (in concert with the increased fetal adrenal cortisol SR), it also would contribute to the maintenance of high cortisol levels at term. It also is possible that this steroid could help to maintain a relatively constant level of fetal cortisol throughout gestation in the face of marked fluctuations in maternal cortisol levels.

In addition to studying the intrauterine disposition of cortisol, we investigated further neonatal cortisol metabolism. We studied two groups of newborns during the first 12 hours of life with respect to basal and ACTH-stimulated cortisol levels. The first group was comprised of newborns delivered by hysterotomy at a mean gestational age of 152 days, prior to the onset of labor. The second group of animals was born following labor and vaginal delivery at a mean gestational age of 153 days. Figure 20 illustrates the basal cortisol levels in the two groups and their

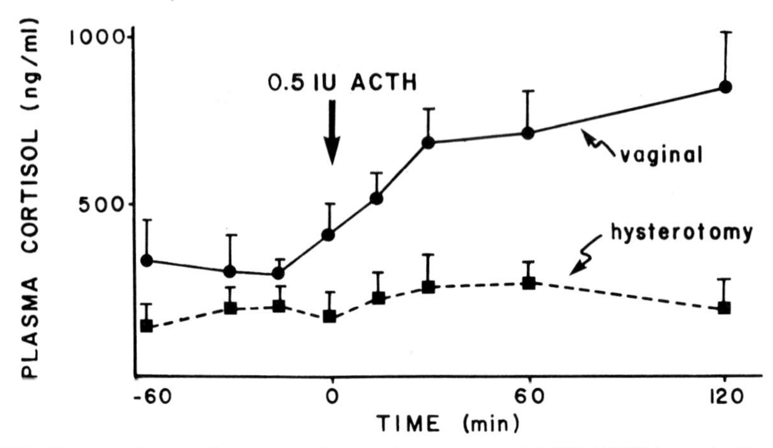

FIG. 20. Basal cortisol concentrations and response to 0.5 IU ACTH in vaginally delivered monkeys following spontaneous labor (●) and those delivered by hysterotomy prior to labor (■).

response to 0.5 IU ACTH. As can be seen, the basal cortisol is higher in the vaginally delivered group, and the response to ACTH is greater. The response to ACTH in the vaginally delivered group indicates a markedly increased capacity to respond to this trophic factor compared to the group delivered prior to the onset of labor. The data do not allow determination of whether this change in adrenal response occurred prior to or subsequent to the onset of labor. However, as indicated previously (Fig. 17), we have observed a significant increase in fetal plasma cortisol levels through late gestation, but prior to labor, in a different group of similarly catheterized fetuses studied longitudinally. Others have shown a similar late gestational increase in amniotic fluid cortisol in this species (Patrick *et al.*, 1976). These findings suggest that the increase in adrenal capacity begins before labor.

Mechanisms that regulate fetal cortisol *in utero* remain to be defined completely. The increase in cortisol after 150 days may be due to an increase in ACTH or other trophic hormones in the circulation, a change in sensitivity of the adrenal gland to trophic stimulation, adrenal maturation, increase in adrenal weight, changes in the metabolic clearance rate of cortisol, changes in glucocorticoid metabolism, and changes in the regulation of the 11β-OH-SD enzyme system leading to a decreased conversion of cortisol to cortisone. As with many other physiologic systems, it is highly likely that cortisol regulation is dependent upon more than one of these factors.

2. Dehydroepiandrosterone Sulfate in the Monkey Fetus and Infant

Concentrations of DHAS in the circulation of the fetal and infant rhesus monkey are depicted in Fig. 21. As can be seen, DHAS levels remain constant, approximately 200 ng/ml, until 150 days. At this time there is a sharp increase in DHAS concentrations, and levels up to 5 μg/ml are observed in cord blood at term. The levels of DHAS are much higher in the neonate than in the fetus and, in contrast to the human, remain high for 2 to 3 months after birth. Circadian variation of DHAS has been observed, with evening levels being 2-fold morning values (Challis *et al.*, 1980). We have found that suppression of ACTH by treatment with high doses of dexamethasone reduces plasma DHAS concentrations approximately 60% in 48 hours, while cortisol is suppressed 90% by this treatment. The partial suppression of DHAS by dexamethasone does not reflect a prolonged half-life of DHAS, since data from our laboratory indicate a half-life of approximately 3.3 hours while the persistence of 40% of DHAS at 48 hours requires a half-life of at least 20 hours.

The incomplete suppression of DHAS by dexamethasone is consonant with the findings of others (Challis *et al.*, 1975) of a partial suppression of androstenedione, estradiol, and estrone in the maternal circulation after long-term treatment with dexamethasone. The partial suppression of fetal DHAS with dexamethasone suggests that there may be another factor, in

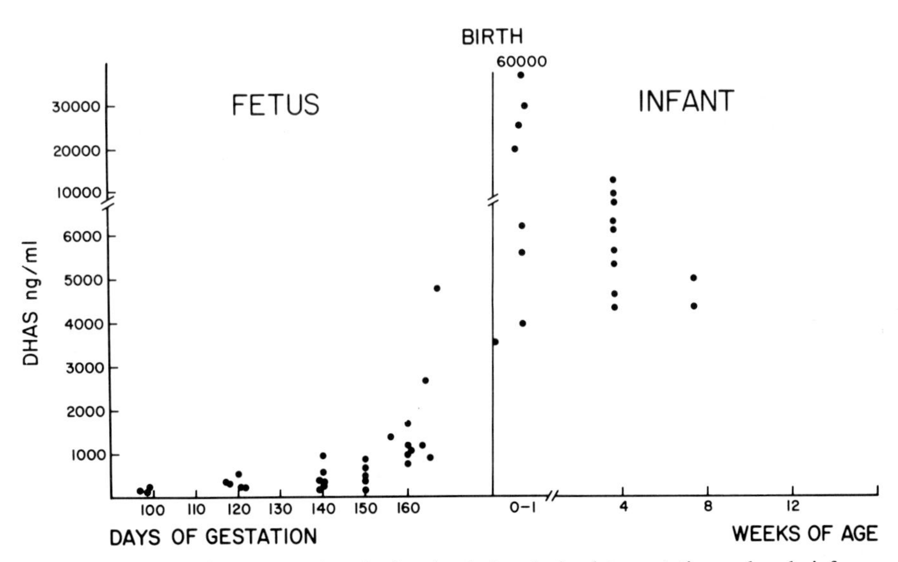

FIG. 21. DHAS concentrations in the circulation during late gestation and early infancy in rhesus monkeys.

addition to ACTH, that can stimulate DHAS secretion *in utero*. This is further suggested by the increase in the ratio of DHAS to cortisol which we have observed in the fetal circulation after 150 days (Fig. 22). An adrenal androgen-stimulating hormone, distinct from ACTH, has been proposed to explain the dissociation between adrenal androgen (DHAS) and cortisol secretion observed in humans at puberty, with anorexia nervosa, and following treatment with dexamethasone (Grumbach *et al.*, 1978; Parker and Odell, 1979). In the fetus, it is possible that this factor also could stimulate preferential growth of the fetal zone at the end of gestation.

Our recent, preliminary data suggest that, at least following birth in the monkey, DHAS may be capable of being stimulated by pituitary luteinizing hormone (LH). This would furnish the counterpart to our findings in the human fetus of DHAS stimulation by hCG. As seen in Figs. 21 and 23, DHAS concentrations in the newborn increase substantially above those found in the fetus. DHAS concentrations decreased by 3–6 months of age (Koritnik and Jaffe, 1980), probably reflecting fetal zone regression. [It is of interest that there is no elevation of DHAS in the pubertal monkey comparable to that seen during adrenarche in the human (Fig. 23).]

In 6-month-old males in which we implanted silastic estradiol-containing capsules, DHAS concentrations were decreased after implantation. The LH response to a bolus of gonadotropin-releasing hormone (GnRH) was absent in these estradiol-implanted monkeys. Although it is possible that the decreased concentrations of DHAS and the absence of a response of LH to GnRH were due to the normal decrease in responsive-

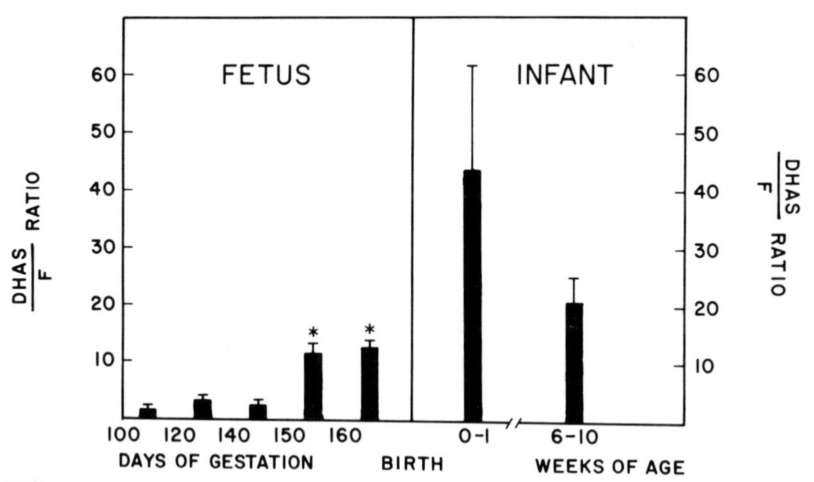

FIG. 22. Ratio of DHAS concentrations to cortisol concentrations during late gestation and early infancy in rhesus monkeys. Asterisks indicate significant differences ($p < 0.005$).

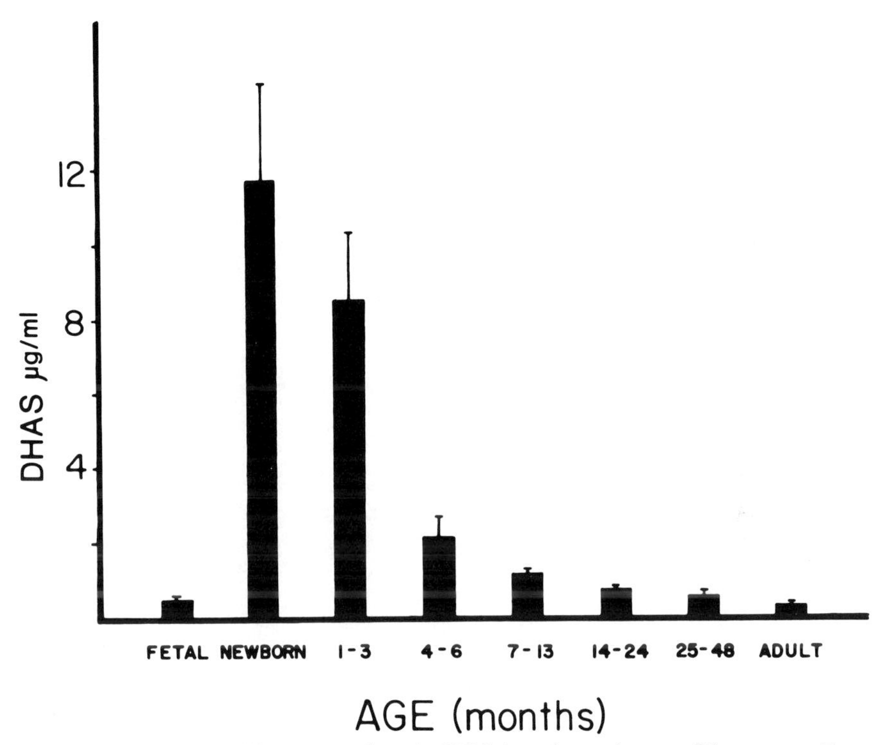

FIG. 23. Mean DHAS concentrations (± SEM) in male monkeys at different ages. From Koritnik and Jaffe (1980).

ness after 6 months of age, other animals not treated with estradiol continued to respond to the GnRH challenge during this period. This experiment suggested that LH suppression might influence the concentrations of DHAS. To evaluate this possibility, albeit indirectly, we assessed the response of DHAS to the administration of 10–20 μg/kg GnRH in male infant rhesus monkeys. As seen in Fig. 24, there was an increase in DHAS in newborn and 4- to 8-week-old infants. Data are presented as changes above or below basal concentrations. None of the older, 9- to 24-week-old infants responded consistently. However, because there were increases in cortisol in some of the infants during these tests, along with elevations in basal cortisol levels, there may have been a nonspecific adrenal response to the testing. Although the majority of infants tested were male, several female infants also had increased DHAS after GnRH administration. When basal concentrations of DHAS from 4- to 8-week-old male and female infants were compared, there was no significant difference.

Because of the possibility of a gonadal source of DHAS, 3-month-old rhesus males were castrated and the Leydig cells from their testes were

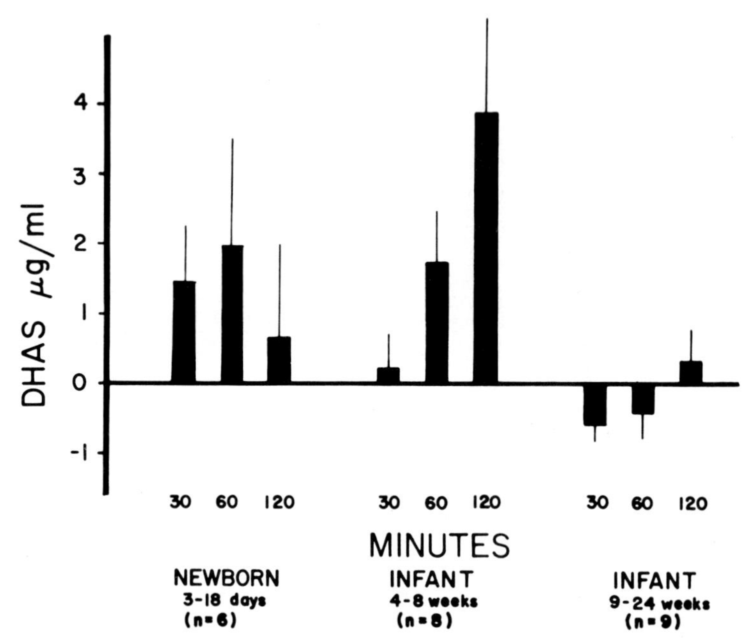

FIG. 24. Absolute increase or decrease in DHAS concentrations (± SEM) 30, 60, or 120 minutes after an iv bolus of GnRH (10–20 μg/kg) in infant monkeys.

dispersed with collagenase and incubated with monkey LH. The testosterone response of these cells during the 3-hour incubation occurred in a dose–response fashion. DHAS was not detectable at the concentrations tested and, although a response of unconjugated DHA was observed, it was at much lower levels than testosterone. The absence of a decrease in basal concentrations of DHAS after castration, coupled with the *in vitro* Leydig cell incubations, strongly suggests that the testes do not contribute substantially to the circulating DHAS concentrations in the rhesus monkey infant. The increases in bioassayable LH, measured in our *in vitro* Leydig cell assay (Huhtaniemi *et al.,* 1979), together with the continued transient increases of DHAS concentrations, suggest a stimulating influence of LH on DHAS concentrations in the rhesus monkey neonate. Current studies are directed toward the measurement of circulating DHAS concentrations following LH and hCG administration in intact and castrated infant rhesus monkeys.

II. Steroid Sulfate Metabolism in the Human Fetus

An interesting facet of human fetal life is the extensive sulfurylation of steroids that occurs in a variety of organs (Wengle, 1964). Sulfokinase activity is present in non-steroid-producing organs such as the lung as well as in endocrine glands. While the placenta has extensive sulfatase activity, that in the fetus is limited. We have performed a variety of studies of steroid sulfates in the human fetal adrenal and gonads.

We have demonstrated that the human fetal adrenal has the capacity to synthesize Δ^5-3β-hydroxysteroid sulfates *de novo* (Jaffe *et al.,* 1968), and that DHAS is the predominant neutral steroid sulfate formed by this route. However, cholesterol, derived from circulating low density lipoprotein (LDL), appears to be a major precursor of DHAS (Parker *et al.,* 1980). DHAS also can be formed in the human fetal adrenal gland by "direct conversion" of other steroid sulfates, without loss of the sulfate side chain (Peréz-Palacios *et al.,* 1968), i.e., via a pathway involving cholesterol sulfate → pregnenolone sulfate → 17 hydroxypregnenolone sulfate → DHAS. *In vitro,* the human fetal adrenal can metabolize DHAS further to 16α-hydroxydehydroepiandrostenone sulfate (Peréz-Palacios *et al.,* 1968), the precursor of placental estriol. The relative contribution to DHAS production of the direct sulfate pathway in the fetus *in vivo,* compared to formation via free (unconjugated) steroid intermediates, has not been ascertained. It is of interest that adult neoplastic tissue possesses the capacity for this direct steroid sulfate conversion, but not the normal adult adrenal. This suggests that the neoplastic tissue may revert to a fetal mode of metabolism.

In contrast to the *de novo* synthesis of steroid sulfates in the human fetal adrenal, we were unable to demonstrate steroid sulfate formation in the human fetal testis in a similar study, although the *de novo* synthesis of testosterone was shown (Serra *et al.,* 1970).

Since the adrenal and testes are of similar embryologic origin, a comparative study of the relative capacities of adrenals and testes from the same human fetuses to sulfurylate pregnenolone, dehydroepiandrosterone, and testosterone was undertaken (Jaffe and Payne, 1971). Sulfurylation of the Δ^5-3β-hydroxysteroids, pregnenolone and dehydroepiandrosterone, in the adrenal was markedly greater than in the testes (Fig. 25a and b). In addition, although there was extensive sulfurylation of testosterone in the adrenal, there was no sulfurylation of this potent androgen in the testes. These results suggest that the limited sulfokinase found in the fetal testes may be specific for 3β-hydroxysteroids. The data are consistent with the hypothesis that testosterone is kept in an active form in the testes and that free (unconjugated) testosterone is involved in genital development in the human male fetus.

With the exception of testosterone, pregnenolone sulfate is quantitatively the major steroid in the human adult testes (Ruokonen *et al.,* 1972). Steroid sulfates also are present in high concentrations in the circulation of

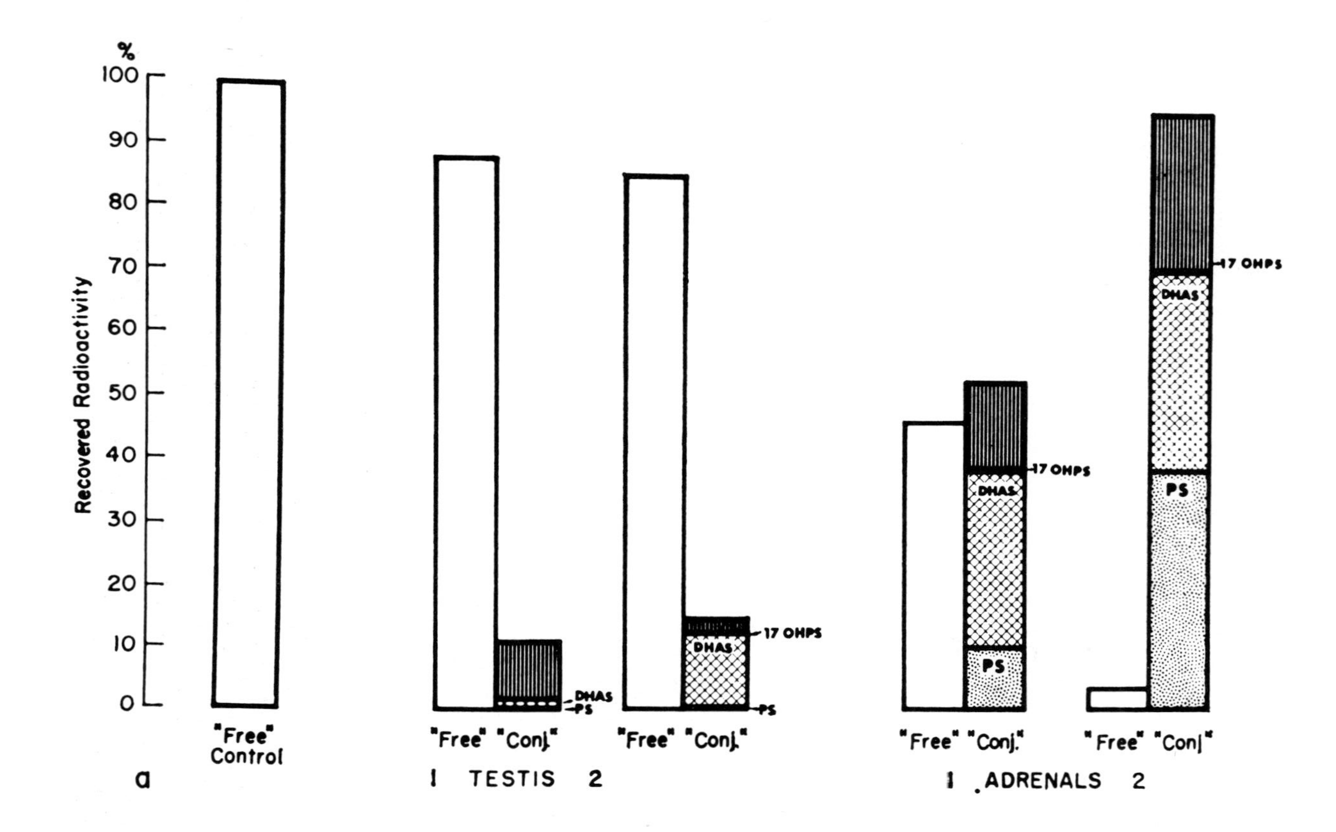
%
100
90
80
70
60
50
40
30
20
10
0
Recovered Radioactivity
a
"Free" Control
"Free" "Conj."
1 TESTIS 2
DHAS
PS
17 OHPS
1 ADRENALS 2

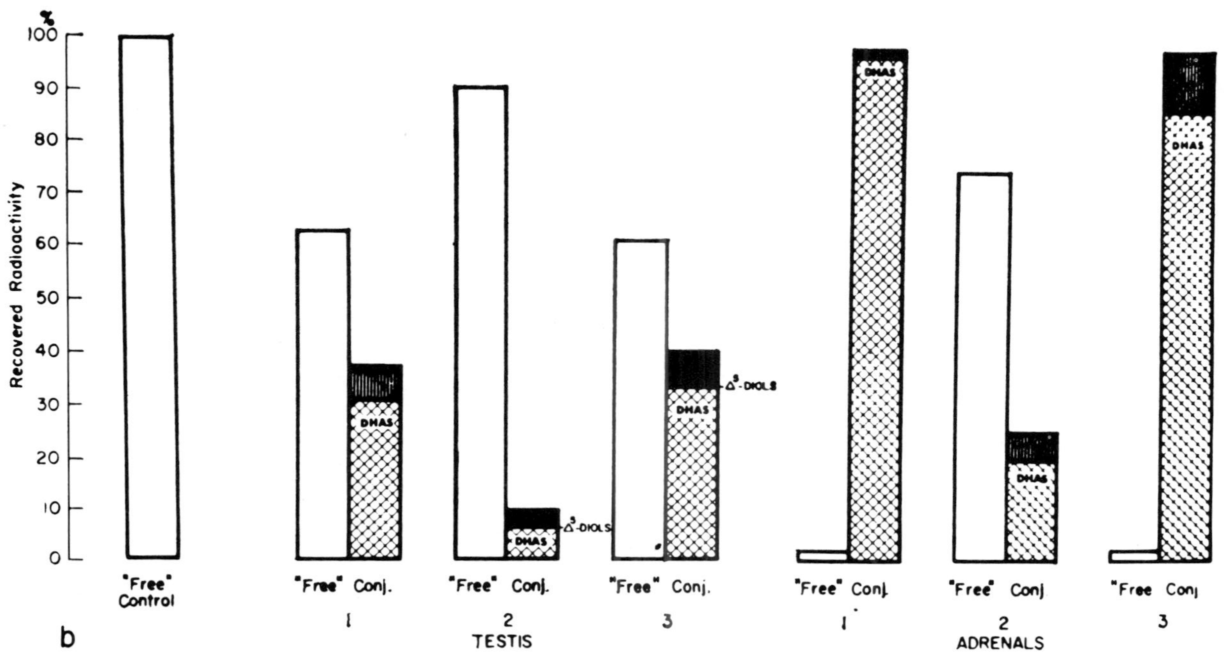

FIG. 25. (a) Comparative formation of sulfurylated steroids in human fetal testes and adrenals with pregnenolone as substrate. (b) Comparative formation of sulfurylated steroids in human fetal testes and adrenals with dehydroepiandrosterone as substrate. In all figures, vertical line shaded areas in "conj" column represent unidentified water-soluble material. From Jaffe and Payne (1971).

both male and female fetuses (Huhtaniemi and Vihko, 1970). Therefore, we studied the metabolism of pregnenolone sulfate, the preferred substrate for adult human testicular sulfatase (Payne, 1972), in human fetal testes and ovaries (Payne and Jaffe, 1975). In the testes, we compared androgen formation in the fetal testes with that in the neonatal, prepubertal, and adult testes.

In the testes, we found a correlation between the age of the subject and the amount of free (unconjugated) C_{19} steroids formed from pregnenolone sulfate by testicular homogenates (Payne and Jaffe, 1975). Testicular homogenates from three fetuses of gestational ages 107 to 152 days yielded the same amount of testosterone, 1.29–1.38 pmol/mg protein. Homogenates from a 3-week-old infant produced 0.22 pmol/mg protein. No testosterone was formed in the testicular homogenates from 2-month, 14-month, and 9-year-old subjects. Homogenates from adults 19, 23, and 52 years old synthesized 3.9, 1.6, and 0.9 pmol/mg protein, respectively. The capacity to convert pregnenolone sulfate to the C_{19} steroids, dehydroepiandrosterone, androstenedione, and testosterone, was greatest in testes from the youngest fetus and decreased reaching a minimum in the testes of the 9 year old. The changes observed in the capacity of testes from different stages of development to convert pregnenolone sulfate to testosterone correlate with previous reports on the histologic changes in the testes as well as plasma testosterone levels in male subjects during growth and development.

The capacity of the fetal testis to cleave pregnenolone sulfate is considerably greater than that found in the adrenal or liver from the same fetus. These findings are very similar to our studies in the fetal ovary (Payne and Jaffe, 1974) in which we demonstrated that fetal ovaries had a much greater capacity for pregnenolone sulfate cleavage than fetal adrenals or livers. The capacity for pregnenolone sulfate cleavage and further metabolism to C_{19} steroids is very similar in the male and female fetal gonad; the only difference observed between the fetal testes and ovary was the capacity for testosterone synthesis. Previously we had demonstrated the formation of testosterone from [^{14}C]acetate (Serra *et al.*, 1970). We (Lamont *et al.*, 1970; Payne and Jaffe, 1972) and others (Siiteri and Wilson, 1974) had demonstrated testosterone formation from pregnenolone, and Siiteri and Wilson (1974) had demonstrated its formation from progesterone. Our study thus identified another steroid, pregnenolone sulfate, which is present in high concentrations in the fetal circulation and which could serve, therefore, as a readily available precursor for testosterone synthesis in the fetal testes.

In the human fetal ovary, previous studies had suggested that this organ was incapable of metabolizing C_{21} steroids to C_{19} and C_{18} steroids (Bloch,

1964; Jungmann and Schweppe, 1968). We studied whether pregnenolone sulfate might serve as a precursor for free (unconjugated) steroids since, as noted above, steroid sulfates are present in high concentrations in the fetal circulation and may serve as precursors for active steroid hormones (Lamont *et al.*, 1970; Kawano *et al.*, 1973). We incubated fetal ovaries with [^{3}H]pregnenolone sulfate and studied the rate of cleavage and subsequent metabolism to other steroids (Payne and Jaffe, 1974). The rate of cleavage was three to seven times greater in ovaries than adrenals and liver from the same fetus. Pregnenolone, 17-hydroxypregnenolone, dehydroepiandrosterone, and androstenedione were identified as products in each incubation of fetal ovarian tissue. Although progesterone, testosterone, estradiol, and estrone were sought extensively, they were not found as products of pregnenolone sulfate metabolism. Gondos and Hobel reported that human fetal ovaries contain interstitial cells with characteristic features of steroid-secreting cells (Gondos and Hobel, 1973). Our observations on the capacity of human fetal ovaries to convert C_{21} to C_{19} steroids appear to be the biochemical counterpart of this morphologic observation.

Confirmation, *in vivo,* of the ability of the human fetus to extensively sulfoconjugate pregnenolone and to further metabolize pregnenolone sulfate to other steroid sulfates was furnished by a study in which [^{14}C]pregnenolone and [^{3}H]pregnenolone sulfate were perfused to the previable human fetus (Jaffe *et al.*, 1972). Double-labeled DHAS, 16α-hydroxypregnenolone sulfate, dihydropregnenolone sulfate, and pregnenolone sulfate were identified in several fetal tissues and double-labeled pregnenolone sulfate and DHAS were identified in the fetal adrenal. These results demonstrated that the human fetus is capable of effecting further metabolism of pregnenolone sulfate *in vivo* and releasing the conjugated conversion products into the fetal circulation.

Thus, steroid sulfates are prominent in intrauterine fetal life. The extent to which they serve as reservoirs for active steroid, in addition to furnishing precursors for placental estrogens, remains to be ascertained.

III. The Primate Fetal Gonad

The fetal testis of the male and ovary of the female are derived from the primitive undifferentiated gonad. While several functional roles have been ascribed to secretions of the fetal testis, the extent, if any, to which fetal ovarian secretions influence female development and homeostasis is unknown.

Testosterone from the fetal testis stimulates the development of the Wolffian ducts into the vas deferens, seminal vesicle, and epididymis. Conversion of testosterone to its 5α-reduced metabolite, dihydrotestosterone, in target tissues is responsible for development of the external genitalia (Siiteri and Wilson, 1974). (Another testicular secretory product, nonsteroidal in nature, is responsible for inhibition of Müllerian ductal development in the male.)

We have demonstrated *de novo* synthesis of testosterone in the human fetal testis (Serra *et al.*, 1970). The pattern of production of testosterone by the human fetal testes during early and midgestation parallels the concentration of human chorionic gonadotropin (hCG) found in the fetal circulation (Clements *et al.*, 1976; Reyes *et al.*, 1973). At this time, the concentration of luteinizing hormone (LH) is still low (Clements *et al.*, 1976; Grumbach and Kaplan, 1974). We have demonstrated specific hCG binding and testosterone production in testes of early human fetuses (Huhtaniemi *et al.*, 1977a). Our data indicate that the regulation of the fetal monkey testis is similar to that of the human. To study the primate hypothalamic–pituitary–gonadal axis in late gestation, we have utilized the long-term catheterized rhesus monkey fetus described in the previous section and illustrated schematically in Fig. 16. In addition, we have followed the regulation of the pituitary–gonadal axis in male and female rhesus monkeys from birth through puberty.

A. *IN VITRO* STUDIES IN THE FETAL TESTIS

To obtain *in vitro* confirmation of the effect of hCG on the fetal testis, human fetal tissue was obtained following prostaglandin-induced abortions of 14 to 20 weeks gestational age. Aliquots of minced testes were incubated in the presence of highly purified hCG, and portions of the medium were assayed for testosterone by radioimmunoassay at 1, 2, and 3 hours of incubation. Maximal stimulation was obtained with 5 and 50 ng/ml hCG (Fig. 26) which approximates the mean concentrations of 35 ng/ml observed in the fetal circulation at this time (Clements *et al.*, 1976). In addition, hCG was specifically bound to human fetal testicular tissue with an equilibrium association constant of $1 \times 10^{10}\ M^{-1}$ (Huhtaniemi *et al.*, 1977a). The monkey fetal testis was utilized to investigate the *in vitro* response to gonadotropins during the second half of gestation (Huhtaniemi *et al.*, 1977b). Since the monkey does produce chorionic gonadotropin, but not in detectable amounts after 40 days of gestation (Hodgen *et al.*, 1975), responses to hCG in the second half of gestation presumably reflect pituitary LH influences. The concentrations of hCG that achieved maximal stimulation in both species are comparable (Figs. 26 and 27). (Testosterone production in one of the control tissues is apparent. This tissue came from a fetus that had been stimulated *in utero* by

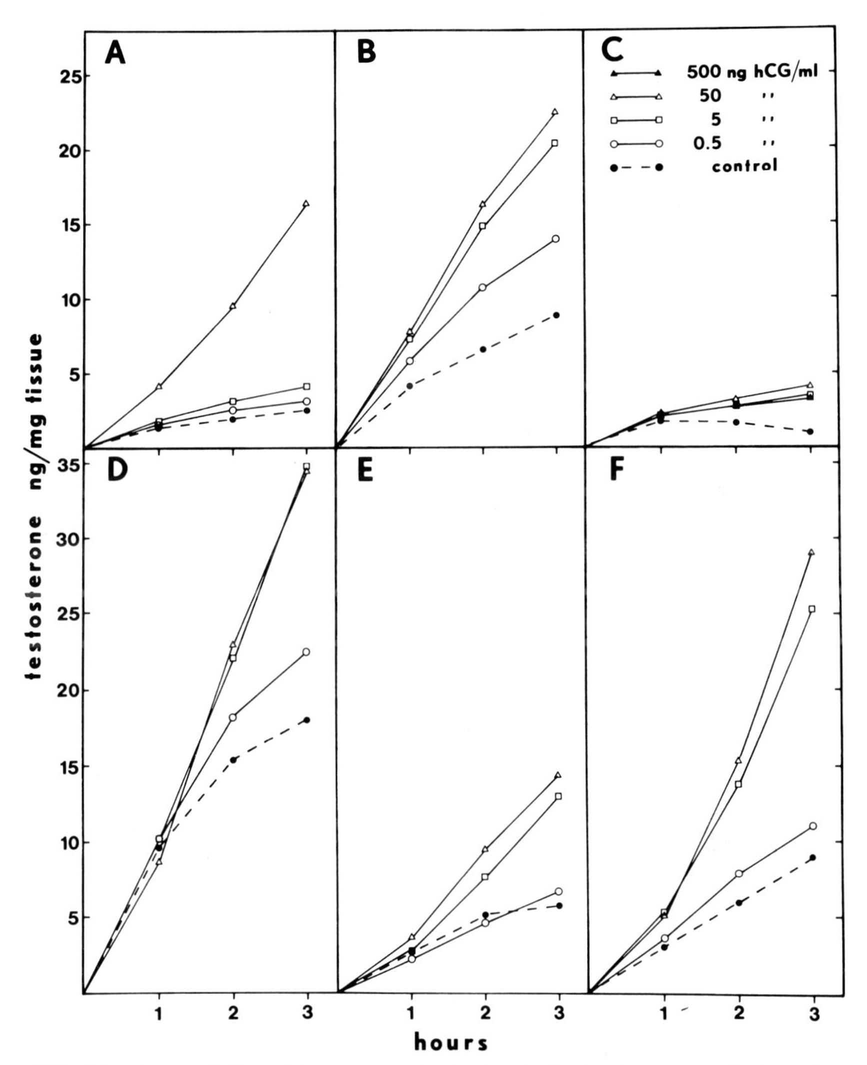

FIG. 26. Accumulation of testosterone in the incubation medium of testicular minces from 14–19 week human fetuses with and without hCG. Crown–rump lengths of the fetuses are: (A) 10.0 cm, (B) 10.5 cm, (C) 12.0 cm, (D) 13.0 cm, (E) 13.0 cm, and (F) 17.5 cm. Note higher hCG concentration (500 ng/ml) used in experiment C. From Huhtaniemi *et al.* (1977).

hCG administration and may reflect residual hCG from the prior experiment.) These studies demonstrate the capacity of the testes to respond to hCG *in vitro,* and suggest, but do not prove, that LH stimulates testosterone production.

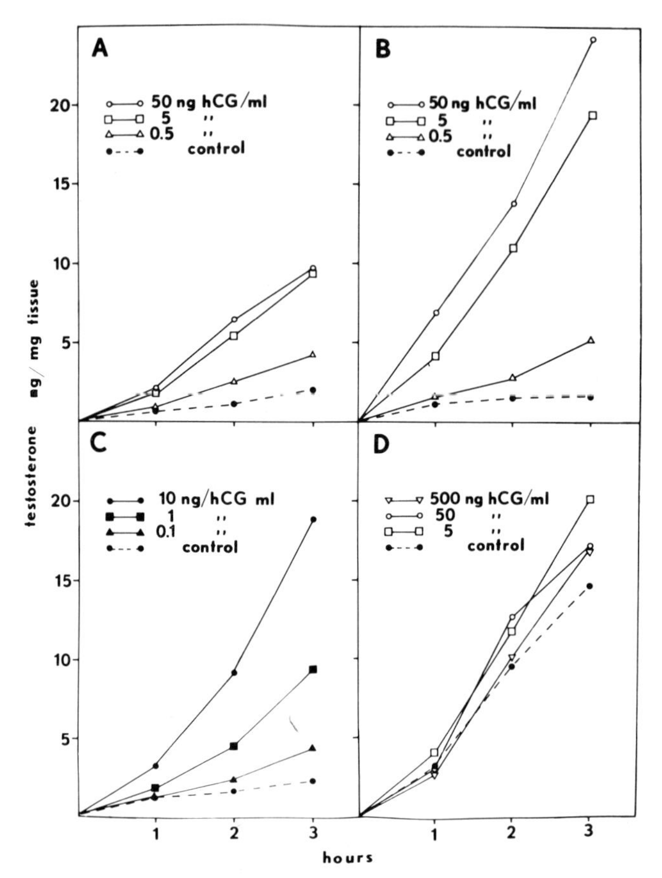

FIG. 27. Effect of different concentrations of hCG on testosterone production by monkey fetal testicular minces. A,B,C,D indicate four different monkey fetuses. In experiment D, the fetus had been infused *in utero* with 100 IU hCG 72 hours prior to the incubation. From Huhtaniemi *et al.* (1977).

B. SYNTHESIS OF hCG IN HUMAN FETAL TISSUES

Because of our interest in the role of hCG in the fetal gonad and adrenal, we quantified hCG in a variety of fetal tissues (Fig. 28) (Huhtaniemi *et al.*, 1978). We found that hCG content was high not only in the fetal testis, in which we had demonstrated specific hCG binding and testosterone stimulation, it also was high in other fetal tissues, including kidney, ovary, and thymus, as measured with a radioimmunoassay for the β subunit of hCG. Using a rat Leydig cell *in vitro* bioassay, we demonstrated that this hCG was biologically active.

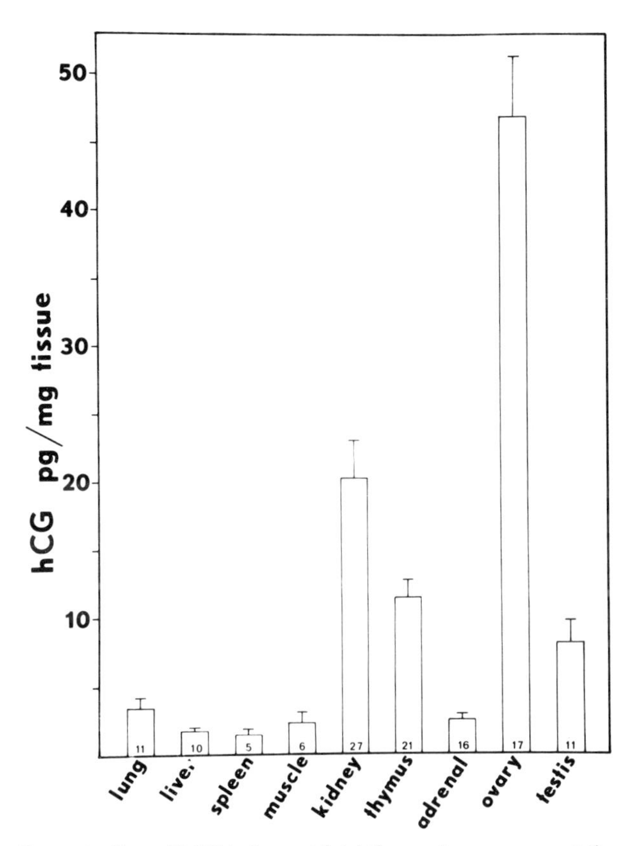

FIG. 28. Concentration of hCG in human fetal tissues (pg per mg wet tissue) measured with an hCG β-subunit RIA (mean ± SEM). The number of individual samples is indicated in the lower portion of each bar. The gestational ages of the fetuses varied between 12 and 20 weeks. From Huhtaniemi *et al.* (1978).

These observations led to an investigation of the source of the hCG in these fetal tissues. We speculated that hCG was being actively synthesized by these fetal tissues, rather than just being taken up from the fetal circulation. Therefore, human fetal kidney, liver, and lung were compared with placenta in a tissue explant system, studying incorporation of [^{35}S]methionine (Fig. 29). The tissue was obtained in the fresh state from 16- to 19-week-old fetuses following dilatation and evacuation. Technical considerations precluded study of the gonad or thymus. The tissue homogenates were immunoprecipitated with specific β-hCG antiserum. Figure 29 depicts the amount of labeled protein reactive with β-subunit antiserum, expressed per milligram protein. That these counts represent hCG has been demonstrated using SDS–polyacrylamide gel elec-

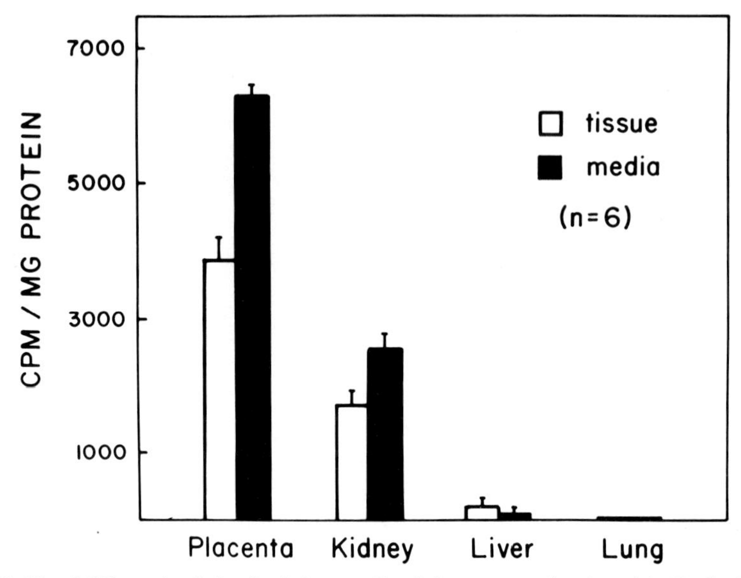

FIG. 29. hCG synthesis by fetal tissues. Fetal tissues were incubated in Krebs-Ringer bicarbonate buffer containing 200 mg% glucose and 30 μCi [^{35}S]methionine for 12 hours at 37°C under an atmosphere of 95% O_2–5% CO_2. Media and tissue were separated, the tissue homogenized, and both were centrifuged for 60 minutes at 105,000 g. Each was analyzed for the number of counts of [^{35}S]methionine incorporated into protein which was precipitated by specific antiserum prepared against the β-subunit of hCG. To compare experiments, the data have been normalized to the protein content of both medium and tissue homogenate as determined by Bradford dye-binding techniques.

trophoresis, on which virtually all labeled protein comigrates with the α- and β-subunits of highly purified hCG.

These data suggest that not only the placenta produces hCG, but the human fetal kidney actively synthesizes and secretes hCG as well. Very low levels were detected in the liver, and no synthesis could be demonstrated in the fetal lung. It is of interest that our recent studies of immunocytochemical localization of hCG suggest a degree of hCG tissue staining parallel to the extent of hCG synthesis, i.e., placenta > kidney > liver > lung. It is possible that the finding of chorionic gonadotropin in some adult human nontrophoblastic tumors represents an atavistic reversion to a fetal form of hormone synthesis.

C. *IN VIVO* STUDIES OF THE FETAL PITUITARY–TESTICULAR AXIS IN THE RHESUS MONKEY

The long-term catheterized fetal monkey preparation was used to investigate whether the fetal testis could be stimulated to produce testosterone

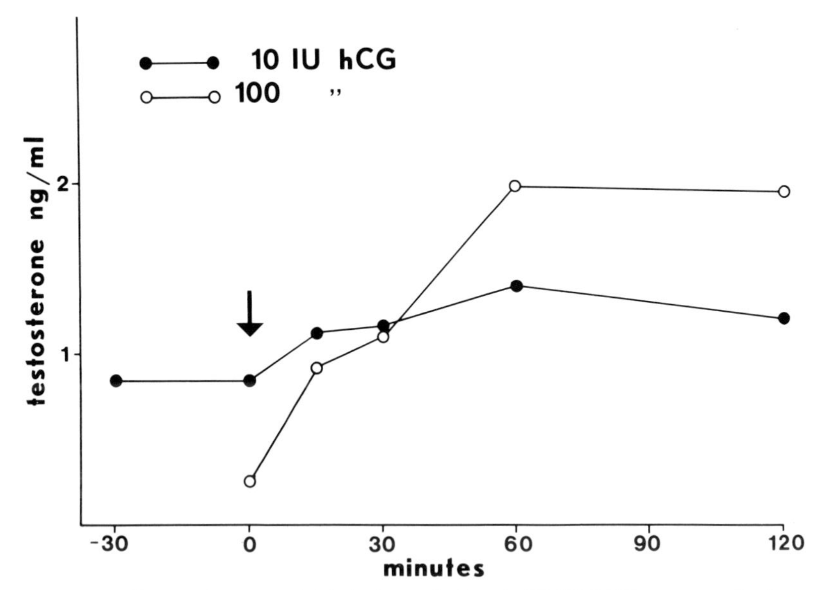

FIG. 30. Effect of intra-arterial infusions of 10 and 100 IU hCG on mean fetal serum testosterone levels *in utero*. The hCG was administered to two chronically catheterized male monkey fetuses (●,○). The arrows indicate the time of infusion. From Huhtaniemi *et al.* (1977).

in vivo (Huhtaniemi *et al.*, 1977b). Supraphysiologic concentrations (10 or 100 IU) or hCG were administered to the catheterized fetus (Fig. 30). As can be seen, both concentrations were capable of stimulating a rise in plasma testosterone.

Next, the integrity of the pituitary–gonadal axis in the perinatal period and infancy was assessed. Fetal and infant male monkeys were challenged with synthetic hypothalamic gonadotropin-releasing hormone (GnRH) between 130 days of gestation and 1 year after birth (Fig. 31) (Huhtaniemi *et al.*, 1979). LH and testosterone responses were measured. Intravenous administration of either 10 or 50 μg GnRH to catheterized fetuses *in utero* resulted in a mean LH increase of 857 ± 494% (SEM) and a mean testosterone increase of 69 ± 28% above basal levels. During the 4 days after delivery, 3–10 μg (10–20 μg/kg) GnRH stimulated similar rises in LH (592 ± 201%) and testosterone (93 ± 23%). From 18 to 89 days of age, a dose of 10–20 μg/kg resulted in a mean LH response of 862 ± 116% and the greatest testosterone response (371 ± 101%). After 3 months of age, LH and testosterone responses to the same dose of GnRH declined (174 ± 86 and 133 ± 37%, respectively, for ages 102–218 days; 16 ± 11 and 44 ± 30%, respectively, for ages 286–392 days). In other monkeys, subcutaneous injections of GnRH in slow release form (polyvinylpyrrolidone) (500

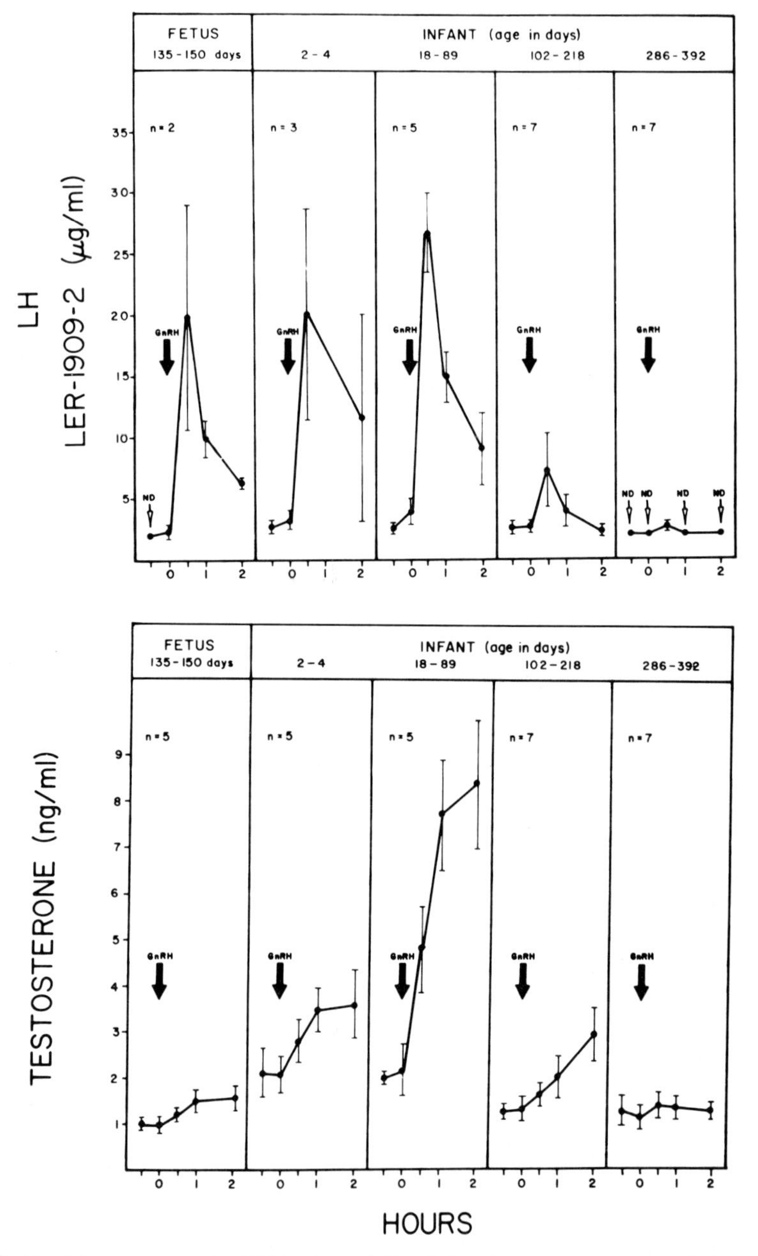

FIG. 31. Mean response (± SEM) of circulating LH and testosterone to a GnRH bolus in male fetal and infant monkeys. Bolus iv infusions of GnRH (10 or 50 μg in fetuses; 10–20 μg/kg in infants) were administered at times indicated by arrows. The pretest value represents a mean of the −30 and −15-minute measurement; *n*, number of different individuals tested in each age group. Undetectable levels of LH were assigned the value of 2 μg/ml. ND, Groups in which no individual had detectable levels. From Huhtaniemi *et al.* (1979).

μg every 2 weeks) produced high testosterone levels (6–10 ng/ml) until 65–80 days of age. No stimulation was seen from this time until approximately 2 years of age. Thus, in the perinatal period, the male monkey pituitary–gonadal axis reaches peak responsiveness to GnRH between 2 weeks and 3 months of age. Thereafter, the increased responsiveness declines regardless of whether or not the infant is exposed repetitively to GnRH. Whether repetitive pulsatile administration of GnRH would alter this responsiveness remains to be determined. It also seems unlikely that the production of high levels of testosterone decrease the responsiveness of the pituitary–testicular axis, since the repeated exposure to GnRH from 2 weeks of age, resulting in testosterone levels higher than those in controls, did not result in decreased responsiveness to GnRH earlier than 3 months of age.

Based on the data obtained in the fetal monkey, it seems possible that there is a switch in the regulation of the fetal testes such that chorionic

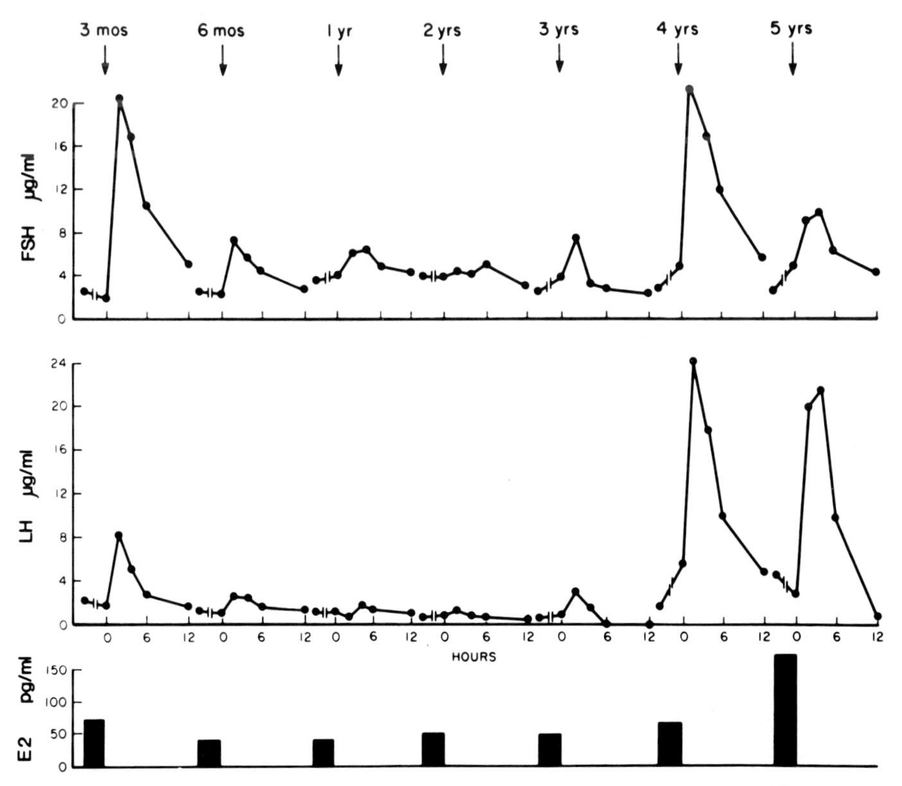

FIG. 32. Response of LH, FSH, and estradiol (E_2) after subcutaneous injection of GnRH (500 μg in 1.75 ml polyvinylpyrrolidone) in developing female rhesus monkeys. Blood was sampled at −24, 0, 2, 4, 6, and 12 hours in relation to the injection denoted by the arrow.

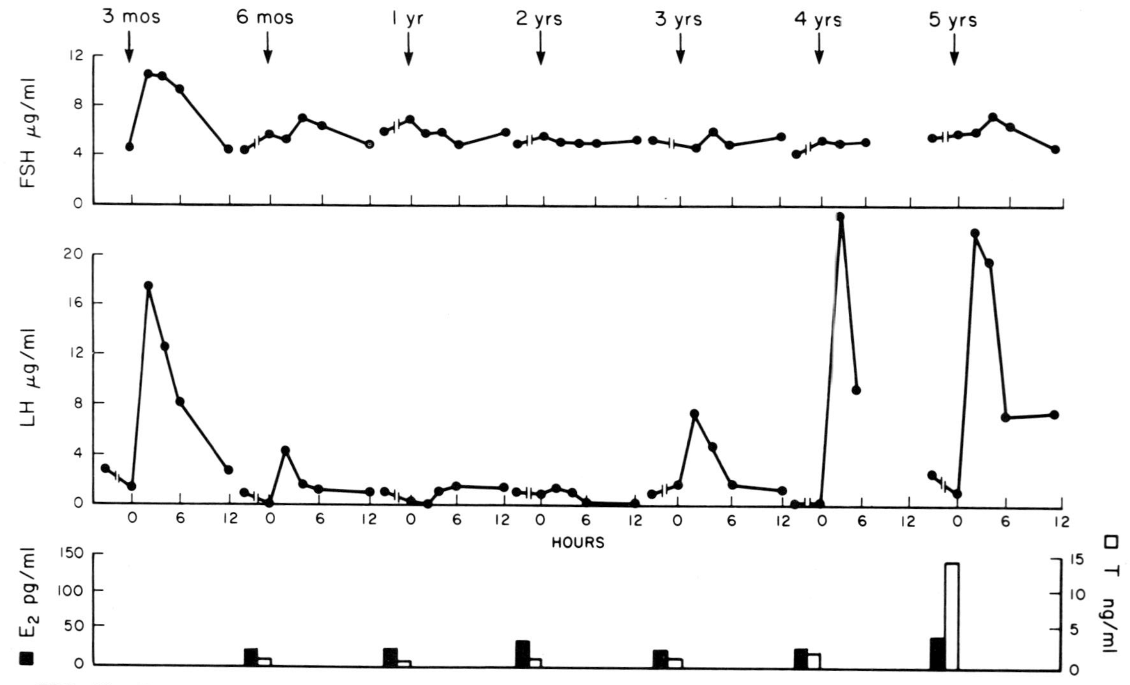

FIG. 33. Response of LH, FHS, estradiol (E_2), and testosterone (T) after subcutaneous injection of GnRH (500 μg in 1.75 ml polyvinylpyrrolidone) in developing male rhesus monkeys. See Fig. 34 for sampling protocol.

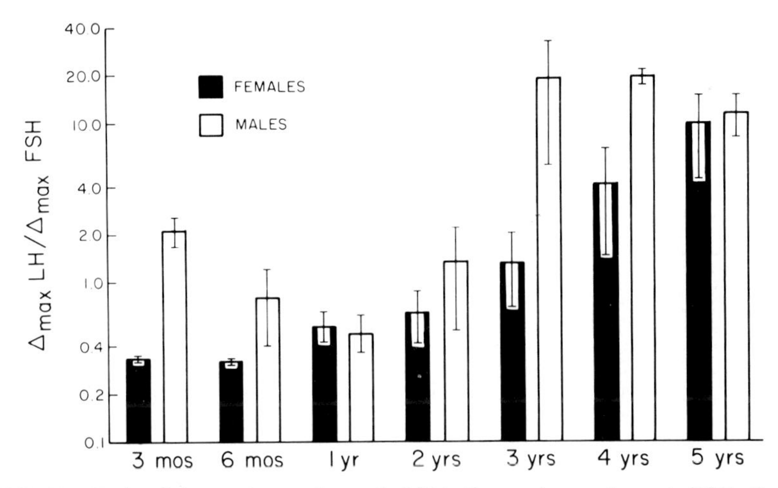

FIG. 34. Ratio of the maximum change in LH to the maximum change in FSH after the subcutaneous injection of 500 μg of GnRH in 1.75 ml of polyvinylpyrrolidone into rhesus monkeys during development. Maximum response occurred 2–6 hours after treatment.

gonadotropin regulates fetal testicular steroidogenesis in the first half of gestation, and that fetal pituitary LH assumes this role during the second half of gestation.

It has been suggested that a biologically inactive but immunologically detectable form of LH may be secreted by the prepubertal human pituitary (Forest *et al.*, 1976), and that this may explain the discrepancy in LH measurements in the prepubertal rhesus monkey detected when comparing a heterologous radioimmunoassay with the Leydig cell bioassay (Dufau *et al.*, 1977; Neill *et al.*, 1977). In our study (Huhtaniemi *et al.*, 1979), we used a Leydig cell bioassay which confirmed the biological activity of the LH response. A comparison of these bioassay data with radioimmunoassay data was precluded by the small amounts of serum available for assay.

The response of both LH and FSH to GnRH administered in subcutaneous injections of polyvinylpyrrolidone every 2 weeks through the first 5 years of life was compared in male and female monkeys (Figs. 32 and 33). Responsivity was increased in both sexes during the first 3 months of life. During this period, the Δ_{max} FSH significantly exceeded the Δ_{max} LH in the females, while the converse was true in the males (Fig. 34). Minimal to absent responses to the GnRH in polyvinylpyrrolidine were seen until approximately 2 to 3 years of age (Figs. 32 and 33), at which time the ratio of Δ_{max} FSH to Δ_{max} LH in the females was reversed from the ratio observed in infancy (Fig. 34), and the typical adult pattern was observed. These profiles of responsivity of LH and FSH from infancy to adulthood closely parallel the patterns seen in humans, and suggest that the rhesus monkey may serve as a useful model in which to study regulation of the pituitary–gonadal axis, as it also appears useful in the study of the perinatal pituitary–adrenal axis.

ACKNOWLEDGMENTS

The majority of the studies reported herein were supported by NIH Grant HD 08478. We are grateful for the invaluable contributions of many collaborators during these studies including E. Biglieri, P. Goldsmith, D. Gospodarowicz, C. Ill, C. Korenbrot, R. Kuhn, C. Lawrence, U. Lindholm, G. McGregor, S. Monroe, A. Payne, J. K. Ramachandran, P. K. Siiteri, W. Raymoure, and M. Yamamoto.

REFERENCES

Baker, B. L., and Jaffe, R. B. (1975). *Am. J. Anat.* **143,** 137.

Benirschke, K. (1956). *Obstet. Gynecol.* **8,** 412.

Benveniste, R., Speeg, K. V., Carpenter, G., Cohen, S., Linder, J., and Rabinowitz, D. (1978). *J. Clin. Endocrinol. Metab.* **46,** 169.

Blanchard, M., and Josso, N. (1974). *Pediatr. Res.* **8,** 968.

Bloch, E. (1964). *Endocrinology* **74,** 833.

Branchaud, C. T., Goodyer, C. G., St. G. Hall, C., Arato, J. S., Silman, R. E., and Giroud, C. J. P. (1978). *Steroids* **31,** 557.

Challis, J. R. G., Davies, I. J., Benirschke, K., Hendrickx, A. G., and Ryan, K. J. (1975). *Endocrinology* **96,** 185.

Challis, J. R. G., Socol, M., Murata, Y., Manning, F. A., and Martin, C. B. (1980). *Endocrinology* **106,** 1283.

Clements, J. A., Reyes, F. I., Winter, J. S. D., and Faiman, C. (1967). *J. Clin. Endocrinol. Metab.* **42,** 9.

Cohen, S. (1962). *J. Biol. Chem.* **237,** 1555.

Cohen, S., and Carpenter, G. (1975). *Proc. Natl. Acad. Sci. U.S.A.* **72,** 1317.

Crickard, K., Ramachandran, K. J., and Jaffe, R. B. (1980). *Soc. Gynecol. Invest.,* Abstr. No. 11.

Dufau, M. L., Hodgen, G. D., Goodman, A. L., and Katt, K. J. (1977). *Endocrinology* **100,** 1557.

Easterling, W. E., Jr., Simmer, H., Dignam, W. J., Frankland, M. V., and Naftolin, F. (1966). *Steroids* **8,** 151.

Forest, M. G., De Peritti, E., and Bertrand, J. (1976). *Clin. Endocrinol. (Oxford)* **5,** 551.

Gill, G. N., Hornsby, P. J., Ill, C. R., Simonian, M. H., and Weidman, R. E. (1978). *In* "The Endocrine Function of the Human Adrenal Cortex" (V. H. T. James, M. Serio, G. Guisti, and L. Martini, eds.), p. 207. Academic Press, New York.

Glickman, J. A., Carson, G. D., and Challis, J. R. G. (1979). *Endocrinology* **104,** 34.

Gondos, B., and Hobel, C. J. (1973). *Endocrinology* **93,** 736.

Gorwill, R. H., Snyder, D. L., Lindholm, U., and Jaffe, R. B. (1971). *Gen. Comp. Endocrinol.* **16,** 21.

Gospodarowicz, D. (1975). *J. Biol. Chem.* **250,** 2515.

Gospodarowicz, D., and Ill, C. (1980). *J. Clin. Invest.* **65,** 1351.

Gospodarowicz, D., and Moran, J. (1976). *Annu. Rev. Biochem.* **45,** 531.

Gospodarowicz, D., Brown, K. S., Birdwell, C. R., and Zetta, B. E. (1978). *J. Cell Biol.* **79,** 774.
Gospodarowicz, D., Vlodovsky, I., Greenburg, G., and Johnson, L. K. (1979). *In* "Hormones and Cell Culture" (G. H. Sato and R. Ross, eds.), p. 561. Cold Spring Harbor Laboratory, Cold Spring Harbor, New York.
Gray, E. S., and Abramovich, D. (1980). *Am. J. Obstet. Gynecol.* **137,** 491.
Grumbach, M. M., and Kaplan, S. E. (1974). *In* "Modern Perinatal Medicine" (L. Gluck, ed.), p. 247. Yearbook Medical Publ., Chicago, Illinois.
Grumbach, M. M., Richards, G. E., Conte, F. A., and Kaplan, S. L. (1978). *In* "The Endocrine Function of the Human Adrenal Cortex" (V. H. T. James, M. Serio, G. Guisti, and L. Martini, eds.), p. 583. Academic Press, New York.
Heinrichs, W. L., and Colás, A. E. (1970). *Gen. Comp. Endocrinol.* **14,** 149.
Hirata, Y., and Orth, D. N. (1979). *J. Clin. Endocrinol. Metab.* **48,** 4.
Hodgen, G. D., Niemann, W. H., and Tullner, W. W. (1975). *Endocrinology* **96,** 789.
Hornsby, P. J. (1980). *J. Biol. Chem.* **255,** 4020.
Houck, J. C., Kimball, C., Chang, C., Pedigo, N. W., and Yamamura, H. I. (1980). *Science* **207,** 78.
Huhtaniemi, I. (1977). *J. Steroid Biochem.* **8,** 491.
Huhtaniemi, I., and Vihko, R. (1970). *Steroids* **16,** 197.
Huhtaniemi, I. T., Korenbrot, C. C., and Jaffe, R. B. (1977a). *J. Clin. Endocrinol. Metab.* **44,** 963.
Huhtaniemi, I. T., Korenbrot, C. C., Serón-Ferré, M., Foster, D. B., Parer, J. T., and Jaffe, R. B. (1977b). *Endocrinology* **100,** 839.
Huhtaniemi, I. T., Korenbrot, C. C., and Jaffe, R. B. (1978). *J. Clin. Endocrinol. Metab.* **46,** 994.
Huhtaniemi, I. T., Koritnik, D. R., Korenbrot, C. C., Mennin, S., Foster, D. B., and Jaffe, R. B. (1979). *Endocrinology* **105,** 109.
Jaffe, R. B., and Payne, A. H. (1971). *J. Clin. Endocrinol. Metab.* **33,** 592.
Jaffe, R. B., Pérez-Palacios, G., Lamont, K. G., and Givner, M. L. (1968). *J. Clin. Endocrinol. Metab.* **28,** 1671.
Jaffe, R. B., Pérez-Palacios, G., and Diczfalusy, E. (1972). *J. Clin. Endocrinol. Metab.* **35,** 646.
Jaffe, R. B., Serón-Ferré, M., Parer, J. T., and Lawrence, C. C. (1978). *Am. J. Obstet. Gynecol.* **131,** 164.
Jaffe, R. B., Serón-Ferré, M., and Mitchell, B. F. (1979). *J. Steroid Biochem.* **11,** 549.
Jirasek, J. E. (1971). "Development of the Genital System and Male Pseudohermaphroditism," pp. 10–23. Johns Hopkins Press, Baltimore, Maryland.
Jost, A., Vigier, B., Prepin, J., and Perchellet, J. P. (1973). *Recent Prog. Horm. Res.* **29,** 1.
Jungmann, R. A., and Schweppe, J. S. (1968). *J. Clin. Endocrinol. Metab.* **28,** 1499.
Kawano, A. A., Payne, A. H., and Jaffe, R. B. (1973). *J. Clin. Endocrinol. Metab.* **37,** 441.
Koritnik, D., and Jaffe, R. B. (1980). *In* "Adrenal Androgens. Progress in Cancer Research and Therapy" (A. R. Gennazzani, V. H. H. Thijssen, and P. K. Siiteri, eds.). Raven, New York. (in press)
Lamont, K. G., Pérez-Palacios, G., and Jaffe, R. B. (1970). *Steroids* **16,** 127.
Liggins, G. C., Fairclough, R. J., Grieves, S. A., Kendall, J. Z., and Knox, B. S. (1973). *Recent Prog. Horm. Res.* **29,** 111.
Liggins, G. C. (1976). *Am. J. Obstet. Gynecol.* **126,** 931.
Liotta, A., Osothanondh, R., Ryan, K. J., and Krieger, D. T. (1977). *Endocrinology* **101,** 1552.
McNulty, W. P., Walsh, S. W., and Novy, M. J. (1981). Submitted.

Magyar, D. M., Elsner, C. W., Nathanielsz, P. W., Lowe, K. C., and Buster, J. E. (1979). *Annu. Meet. Soc. Gynecol. Invest., 26th* Abstr. No. 318.
Mitchell, B. F., Serón-Ferré, M., and Jaffe, R. B. (1980). *Endocrinology* (in press).
Mitchell, B. F., Serón-Ferré, M., Hess, D., and Jaffe, R. B. (1981). *Endocrinology* Submitted.
Murphy, B. E. P. (1980). *Endocrine Soc.* Abstr. No. 72.
Neill, J. D., Daily, R. H., Tsau, R. C., and Reichert, L. E., Jr. (1977). *Endocrinology* **100,** 856.
Parker, C. R., Jr., Simpson, E. R., Bilheimer, D. N., Leveno, K., Carr, B. R., and MacDonald, P. C. (1980). *Science* **208,** 512.
Parker, L. N., and Odell, W. D. (1979). *Am. J. Physiol.* **236,** 616.
Patrick, J. E., Challis, J. R. G., Johnson, P., Robinson, J. S., and Thorburn, G. D. (1976). *J. Endocrinol.* **68,** 161.
Payne, A. H. (1972). *Biochim. Biophys. Acta* **258,** 473.
Payne, A. H., and Jaffe, R. B. (1972). *Biochim. Biophys. Acta* **279,** 202.
Payne, A. H., and Jaffe, R. B. (1974). *J. Clin. Endocrinol. Metab.* **39,** 300.
Payne, A. H., and Jaffe, R. B. (1975). *J. Clin. Endocrinol. Metab.* **40,** 102.
Pérez-Palacios, G., Pérez, A. E., and Jaffe, R. B. (1968). *J. Clin. Endocrinol. Metab.* **28,** 19.
Reyes, F. I., Winter, J. S. D., and Faiman, C. (1973). *J. Clin. Endocrinol. Metab.* **37,** 74.
Rudman, D., Hollins, B. M., and Lewis, N. C. (1980). *J. Clin. Invest.* **65,** 822.
Ruokonen, A., Laatikainen, T., Laitinen, E. A., and Vikho, R. (1972). *Biochemistry* **11,** 1411.
Salmon, W. D., and Daughaday, W. H. (1962). *J. Biol. Chem.* **237,** 1555.
Serón-Ferré, M., and Biglieri, E. (1980). *Annu. Meet. Endocrine Soc.* Abstr. No. 70.
Serón-Ferré, M., Lawrence, C. C., Siiteri, P. K., and Jaffe, R. B. (1978a). *J. Clin. Endocrinol. Metab.* **47,** 603.
Serón-Ferré, M., Rose, J. C., Parer, J. T., Foster, D. B., and Jaffe, R. B. (1978b). *Endocrinology* **103,** 368.
Serón-Ferré, M., Lawrence, C. C., and Jaffe, R. B. (1978c). *J. Clin. Endocrinol. Metab.* **46,** 603.
Serra, G. B., Pérez-Palacios, G., and Jaffe, R. B. (1970). *J. Clin. Endocrinol. Metab.* **30,** 128.
Siiteri, P. K., and Wilson, J. D. (1974). *J. Clin. Endocrinol. Metab.* **38,** 113.
Siler-Khodr, T. M., Morganstern, L. L., and Greenwood, F. C. (1974). *J. Clin. Endocrinol. Metab.* **39,** 391.
Silman, R. E., Chard, T., Lowry, P. J., Smith, I., and Young, J. M. (1976). *Nature (London)* **260,** 716.
Silman, R. E., Holland, D., Chard, T., Lowry, P. J., Hope, J., Robinson, J. S., and Thorburn, G. D. (1978). *Nature (London)* **276,** 526.
Simonian, T. H., and Gill, G. N. (1980). *Annu. Meet. Endocrine Soc.* Abstr. No. 69.
Snyder, D. L., Goebelsmann, U., Jaffe, R. B., and Kirton, K. T. (1971). *Endocrinology* **88,** 274.
Walsh, S. W., Norman, R. L., and Novy, M. (1979). *Endocrinology* **104,** 1805.
Wengle, B. (1964). *Acta Soc. Med. Ups.* **69,** 105.
Winters, A. J., Colston, C., MacDonald, P. C., and Porter, J. C. (1975). *J. Clin. Endocrinol. Metab.* **41,** 626.
Wurtman, R. J. (1966). *Endocrinology* **79,** 608.
Yen, S. S. C., and Jaffe, R. B. (1978). "Reproductive Endocrinology," p. 531. Saunders, Philadelphia, Pennsylvania.

DISCUSSION

B. E. P. Murphy: All of our studies have been done in the human. For ethical reasons we have to rely largely on studies of concentration, many of these in autopsy tissue. While this is not ideal, nevertheless, our studies do parallel those of Dr. Jaffe's and his colleagues closely.

Figure A summarizes our studies of cortisol levels in the human fetus at birth (B. E. P. Murphy, M. Sebenick, and M. D. Pakhell, *J. Steroid Biochem.* **12,** 37, 1980). The letter C indicates that the data were obtained at Caesarean section. Since the means of obtaining the material was essentially similar in early gestation between 10 and 20 weeks and later at 33 weeks and at 38 weeks, I think it is quite clear that the cortisol level in the human fetus, as in the monkey fetus, does rise before labor commences. At the time of labor there is a further rise and just what causes this is not entirely clear yet. The results of our studies of the 11-hydroxysteroid dehydrogenase (B. E. P. Murphy, *J. Steroid Biochem.* **11,** 509, 1979) are also in accord with those of Dr. Jaffe, who concluded that degradation of cortisol is very rapid in the fetus and then it decreases markedly at the time of birth; our studies suggest it is resumed after birth. The observation that it seems to be blocked at the time of birth led us to investigate the reason for this; we have found that there is a novel steroid in the fetal tissues at the time of birth which appears to decrease the rate of degradation by competing for sites

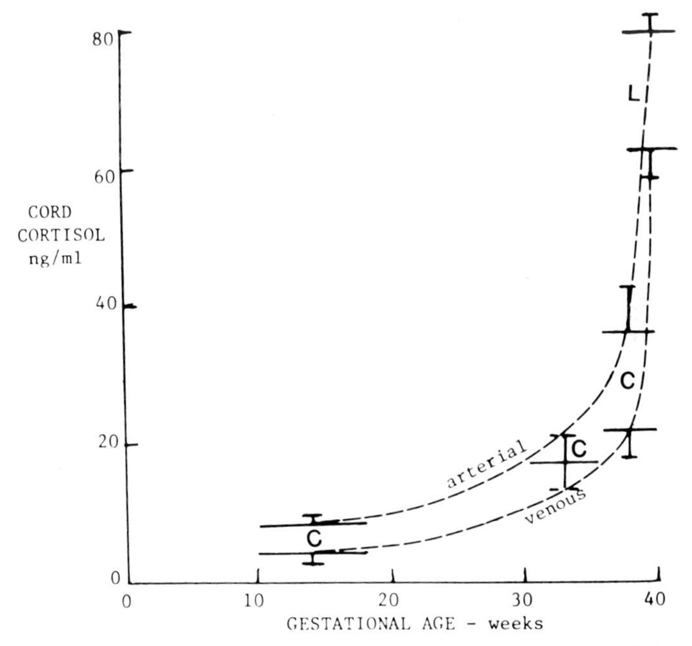

FIG. A. Cord cortisol levels in relation to gestational age. The width of the bars spans the limits of the ages of the infants whose samples were used to calculate the mean value. Standard errors are indicated. Arterial levels show upper SE limits; venous levels show lower SE limits. The value at 33 weeks was mixed arterial and venous serum. The number of patients studied in each group was 10, 5, 6, and 45 for 14, 33, 38, and 40 weeks, respectively. C, Delivery by Caesarean section; L, normal vaginal delivery of spontaneous onset. From Murphy *et al.* (1980).

on the enzyme 11β-hydroxysteroid dehydrogenase. We have shown that the concentration of this steroid is about 100 times higher in the fetal zone of the fetal adrenals of infants at the time of birth. In Fig. B we compared the serum concentrations of cord blood obtained at various types of delivery. We measured this material by assaying total 11β-hydroxysteroids in cortisol equivalents and then subtracting the cortisol concentrations. Definitive identification has been hindered by the instability of this compound which is referred to here as nonglucocorticoid 11-hydroxysteroids. In mid-pregnancy and at term Caesarean section without labor the levels are very low. We are particularly interested in premature labor and at spontaneous vaginal delivery of 33 weeks gestation we find very high levels of this inhibitory steroid, higher than those after induced labor and comparable to those of spontaneous vaginal deliveries at term (B. E. P. Murphy, *Am. J. Obstet. Gynecol.*, in press). We therefore wonder if this material rather than cortisol is related to the onset of labor, via a mechanism we postulated at the recent Endocrine Society meeting. I have two questions for Dr. Jaffe; one is that in doing our studies of the 11-hydroxy dehydrogenase activity, we found that the membranes starting at about 20 weeks gestation, and unlike other fetal tissues, convert cortisone to cortisol. Barry Smith has also confirmed this finding and we've also found the same thing in the uterus. I wonder if he's looked at this in monkeys. Second, we have found that cortisol sulfate appears to be a good indicator of the amount of cortisol that is being produced in the fetal adrenal and I wonder if he has looked at cortisol sulfate in the monkeys.

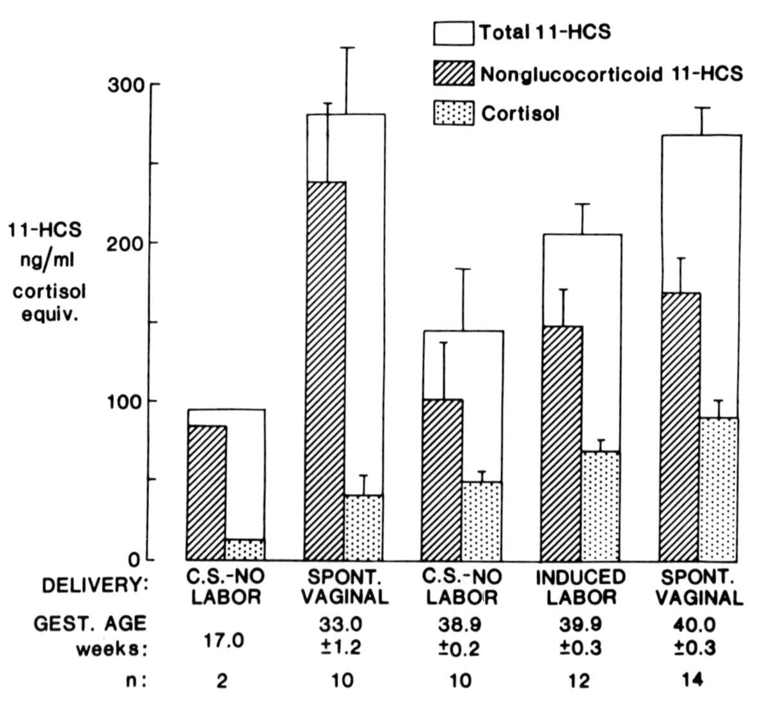

FIG. B. 11β-Hydroxycorticosteroids (11-HCS) in umbilical cord serum at delivery, expressed in cortisol equivalents. C.S., Caesarean section; Spont., spontaneous; Gest., gestational. *n*, Number of sera in each group. Standard errors are indicated.

R. Jaffe: I agree with Dr. Murphy. The regulation of 11β-hydroxysteroid dehydrogenase may be a key factor in understanding late gestational events in regard to corticoid concentrations. Factors regulating the 11β-hydroxysteroid dehydrogenase in the placenta at term play a very important role in determining the amount of cortisol in the fetal compartment. In regard to your second question although we have studied a large number of steroid sulfates in pregnancy, these have not been corticoid sulfates. We are aware of your work on cortisol sulfate. I think this is very important, but we have not studied that particular compound as yet.

V. Cortes-Gallegos: Actually the data I brought with me is unrelated to the adrenal neonatal period. We have analyzed gonadotropins and steroid in 6-year-olds up to 15.9.

G. J. Pepe: As you are aware, we have been doing work in my laboratory measuring cortisol–cortisone dynamics in fetal–maternal circulation in the baboon. Consistent with what you have shown today, we have previously shown that the interconversion of cortisol–cortisone by the fetus favors cortisone formation. The reverse reaction occurs minimally. In addition, we have also shown that the fetal metabolic clearance rate of cortisol changes late in gestation, due, in part, to a decrease in fetal serum cortisol binding globulin levels which occurs concomitantly. As a result of these and additional adrenal enzymatic changes, fetal adrenal cortisol secretion as well as fetal plasma cortisol levels increase markedly late in primate pregnancy, information consistent with what you have presented today.

Recently, in collaboration with Dr. Eugene Albrecht, our efforts have been directed to an examination of the trans-uteroplacental interconversion of cortisol–cortisone at mid (100 days) and late (175 days, term = 184 days) baboon gestation. To determine these transfer constants, we constantly infuse [^{3}H]cortisol and [^{14}C]cortisone via a maternal antecubital vein. After isotopic steady-state is achieved, blood samples are taken from a maternal saphenous vein, uterine vein, and the umbilical vein; ^{3}H/^{14}C steroids are isolated and transfer constants calculated. In maternal saphenous vein, at both mid and late gestation, $F \rightleftharpoons E$ interconversion favors cortisol formation. In contrast, when we examine values in the umbilical vein, we note that in late gestation, $F \rightarrow E$ averages 62% and $E \rightarrow F$ 20%. Thus, in placenta, cortisone formation is favored, a finding consistent with the high levels of placental 11β-steroid dehydrogenase to which you alluded. Hence, near term, the primary corticoid reaching the fetus is cortisone. What we feel is most interesting, however, is that when we analyze umbilical serum at mid-gestation, we see the reverse. Thus, the conversion of cortisol to cortisone is only 14% while the conversion of cortisone to cortisol averages 55%. We assume, therefore, that at mid-gestation, the fetus is receiving primarily cortisol from the mother. Although the levels of cortisol in fetal plasma are lower than those measured late in gestation, we assume that they are sufficient to suppress the production of pituitary hormones capable of stimulating fetal adrenal steroidogenesis. In this regard, hCG may then be able to act on adrenal fetal zone tissue to enhance dehydroepiandrosterone production as you've indicated. However, at some time during gestation, the pattern of placental corticoid metabolism changes. As a consequence, the fetus becomes exposed to more cortisone, or conversely, we could say it becomes exposed to less cortisol. We predict, therefore, that as a result of placental metabolism, fetal F levels drop temporarily. The pituitary, recognizing this purported decline in fetal cortisol, responds and fetal adrenal cortisol secretion is stimulated. We do not know what is regulating placental corticoid metabolism, although work in our laboratories is underway to elucidate the regulatory factors. We would like to emphasize that the placenta, in addition to the factors you have discussed, must also be regarded a bit more in depth since we feel that placental metabolism of cortisol may determine when and what the fetal adrenal will eventually do steroidogenically late in gestation.

R. Jaffe: I think that's a very interesting observation, Dr. Pepe and I suspect that as one ascends the phylogenetic series there will be changes in the time that the regulation of the interconversion of cortisol and cortisone occurs.

If I recall when I visited Dr. Pepe at the NIH some time ago, when he was there, they had done some very interesting studies suggesting that the length of time that chorionic gonadotropin was present in primate circulation also varied as one went along the series of primates, and I wonder if he could comment on that. It was an intriguing observation that I haven't seen followed up.

G. J. Pepe: We haven't done too much more work with chorionic gonadotropin but we have started to look at the effects of prolactin and growth hormone on adrenal activity in the baboon neonate.

R. Jewelewicz: Human placental lactogen or somatomammotropin is one of the hormones with the highest concentration in maternal blood during pregnancy; you haven't mentioned anything about the effect of HPL on the fetal adrenal or on the fetal testes?

R. B. Jaffe: We haven't studied human chorionic somatomammotropin either in the adrenal or the testes. I'm aware that there are receptors for chorionic somatomammotropin in the adrenals of certain species. We have tried to ascertain whether prolactin may play a role in regulation of the fetal adrenal as has been suggested by the Dallas group. As you know, prolactin concentrations both in the human as shown by Winters and his colleagues in Dallas, and in the monkey as Dr. Serón-Ferré and we have shown, increase in a parallel fashion to the increasing volume of the adrenal gland. Those correlations between prolactin and adrenal weight are much better than the correlations between ACTH and adrenal weight. To date, we have been unable to detect stimulation of steroidogenesis by prolactin, but we have not studied human chorionic somatomammotropin.

R. Jewelewicz: Betamethasone is used extensively and clinically to enhance fetal maturity in cases of imminent premature labor and the question is for how long and how much is the fetal adrenal suppressed by pharmacological doses of betamethasone?

R. B. Jaffe: We haven't studied betamethasone specifically. With our dexamethasone suppression in the fetal monkey, within 48 hours after discontinuance of dexamethasone, both ACTH and cortisol, as measured by radioimmunoassay, were back to presuppression levels. Dr. Grumbach and his colleagues have data on betamethasone so perhaps he can comment.

M. Grumbach: Philip Ballard, G. C. Liggins, and our group studied the effect of betamethasone given to pregnant women in premature labor to prevent the respiratory distress syndrome on the concentration of plasma cortisol, dehydroepiandrosterone, and growth hormone in their preterm offspring. Maximum suppression of cortisol and dehydroepiandrosterone levels was noted between 24 and 48 hours after the last dose of betamethasone had been given to the mother; the steroid concentrations rose to control values by 6–7 days after the last dose. Plasma growth hormone but not prolactin also was suppressed and returned to control or higher levels by 40 hours after the last dose of betamethasone.

R. B. Jaffe: That raises a very interesting point, one in which I know Dr. Grumbach is very interested. As I mentioned earlier, we saw approximately 90% suppression of both ACTH and cortisol with the administration of dexamethasone. However, the dehydroepiandrosterone sulfate is only suppressed about 60%. In addition, as pregnancy proceeds the ratio of dehydroepiandrosterone sulfate to cortisol increases markedly, both in basal states and following ACTH stimulation. This suggests, as both Dr. Odell and Dr. Grumbach have suggested, that there may be a substance in the fetus, distinct from ACTH, which has the capacity to stimulate the androgen, dehydroepiandrosterone sulfate; this also may play a role in the regulation of the fetal zone, and its disappearance may contribute to fetal zone atrophy. We don't have any specific data concerning that substance, although we, as many others, have been looking for it.

R. E. Miller: Would you comment on the doses of ACTH you use in your perifused preparation. I am particularly interested in how the doses you use relate to the concentrations of ACTH found in the human fetus throughout gestation.

R. B. Jaffe: In the human fetus, in the superfusion studies, we used 250 ng/ml, which is supraphysiologic. In cell dispersions in which we compared ACTH with αMSH, we used ACTH concentrations from 0.01 to 1000 ng/ml and we could demonstrate maximum ACTH activity around 1 ng/ml. That was a 1–39 ACTH. These studies were performed in collaboration with Dr. Ramachandran.

M. New: I just wanted to call attention to you and to Dr. Murphy of three families we've studied with a genetic defect of 11β-hydroxydehydrogenase deficiency. As far as I can tell, the patients were affected *in utero* (although we evaluated the youngest one at three) and the patients were delivered after a perfectly normal labor.

R. B. Jaffe: I think this is the major unanswered question. In human pregnancy we don't know the extent to which adrenal cortical increased activity at the time of birth is the trigger for parturition. We don't know whether it may be a fail-safe mechanism or whether it plays a predominant role. There are several factors which suggest that it may not be the only mechanism; for example, anencephalic pregnancies also go into labor, even though they don't go into labor at as precise a time. There are other indications that adrenal cortical activity is not the only factor initiating parturition in the primate.

T. Fujii: Which tissues could be the source of EGF or FGF during fetal development?

R. B. Jaffe: The question, as I understood it is: What are the sources of EGF and FGF in the fetus: In the adult rodent EGF is produced among other tissues by the submaxillary gland. We have been purifying FGF from bovine brain in the adult. While the sources of EGF and FGF in the fetus remain to be ascertained, EGF has been identified in amniotic fluid in the form of urogastrone. The placenta may produce an EGF-like substance.

H. L. Bradlow: It has been well established that there is episodic secretion of cortisol in the adult monkey. Did you mean to imply by your statement on the constancy of cortisol levels in the fetal monkey that there is no episodic or circadian pattern to cortisol levels in the fetal state and that F $\rightleftharpoons$ E interconversion smooths out the cortisol level?

R. B. Jaffe: That's a very good question and I'm not sure of the answer. We have been able to demonstrate diurnal variation in cortisol in the fetal monkey but other investigators have not. Episodicity of dihydrosulfate has been demonstrated both by Dr. Patrick and Challis and by their co-workers and by us and we're very aware that the time to do these studies and the possible rhythms in corticoid secretion need to be taken into account.

G. B. Cutler: I have a question about the relationship between the androgen secretion by the fetal adrenal and the adult adrenal after adrenarche. In the human, after the fetal zone regresses, there is a latent period in which histologically there is the zona fasciculata and hormonally there is very little androgen secretion. This latent period separates two homologous periods—the fetal period in which there is a fetal zone and DHA secretion and the postadrenarchal period in which there is a reticular zone and DHA secretion. When we looked at the rhesus monkey several years ago we found, similar to your findings, that DHA sulfate levels do decrease markedly after birth but that DHA and androstenedione levels don't fall. These adrenal androgens maintain the same levels from the perinatal period through adulthood, so that it looked as if, notwithstanding the fall in the DHA sulfate, there was not the sort of latent period that is seen in the human, since the DHA and androstenedione levels remain high. I wondered if there is a histologic correlate of this: does the rhesus fetal zone persist, or is there evidence that the fetal zone of the rhesus atrophies and is replaced by a reticular zone comparable to man?

R. B. Jaffe: These figures, which were kindly loaned to me by Dr. McNulty, I believe are very elegant—they appear in the article. They are from Dr. McNulty's work at the Oregon

Primate Center. What he has demonstrated is that the fetal zone in the rhesus monkey does not atrophy but rather is remodeled into the zone fasiculata during the first year of life. Further, the fetal zone does not appear to disappear as rapidly in the monkey as it's been alleged to disappear in the human; that is why we think the dehydroepiandrosterone sulfate levels persist for longer periods in the monkey. We haven't quantified androstenediol during the first year of life.

G. B. Cutler: Is there a well-defined reticular zone in the adult rhesus monkey?

R. B. Jaffe: I don't know. I can't answer that. I don't know the reticular zone of the adult. Presumably androgens are coming from the reticular zone but in the monkey I haven't looked at that.

S. L. Cohen: In none of the adrenal sections you showed did I see any medulla; is there no medulla in the fetus and if not, when does it first appear?

R. B. Jaffe: There is indeed a medulla, and it is first recognized at about 11–12 weeks. Some of the classic work on this has been done by Dr. Wurtman. As you probably recall, he was able to demonstrate that corticosteroids secreted by the cortex may play a role in the maturation of the enzyme necessary for the conversion of norepinephrine to epinephrine; it may therefore be no coincidence that the adrenal cortex surrounds the medulla. On the first figure that I showed, I did indicate that corticosteroids elaborated by the adrenal play a role in the maturation of the fetal adrenal medulla.

B. F. Rice: In your data on the monkey you show testosterone rising quite a bit in the superfusion studies; do you think there's a difference in monkey testes and human testes in later gestation?

R. B. Jaffe: As I indicated, the production of testosterone is greatest in early gestation, probably in both species. We've looked at testosterone formation in the human fetus only in early gestation and in the monkey in late gestation, so I can't give any relative comparison throughout gestation. There are several possible sources of the testosterone both in early and late gestation. We both have demonstrated synthesis of testosterone by the fetal testis. Early in gestation, at the time indicated by Dr. Wilson, *de novo* synthesis seems to be a major pathway. Dr. Payne and I have demonstrated that pregnenolone sulfate, which quantitatively is one of the major steroids in the fetal circulation, can serve as a substrate both for testosterone in the ovary.

M. M. Grumbach: The human and sheep fetus show striking similarities in the pattern of change in the concentration of fetal pituitary FSH and LH in the circulation and pituitary gland. The studies in sheep were carried out in chronically catheterized stable fetuses. The plasma concentration of fetal pituitary gonadotropins was high in midgestation and fell to low values late in the last trimester. There was good correlation in the sheep fetus between the plasma gonadotropin level and the peak rise in LH and FSH following the intravenous administration of LRF to the fetus from 84 days to term (147 days). In the human fetus, the plasma concentration of testosterone decreases to levels in the female range by about 24 weeks of gestation. Several explanations for this fall in testosterone concentration have been suggested including the lower concentration of hCG than during the first trimester and the reduced output of fetal pituitary LH, as well as the effect of high estrogen and prolactin levels on the biosynthesis of testosterone. A significant body of evidence supports the view that in the primate, chorionic gonadotropin and not fetal pituitary gonadotropin is the major extratesticular regulator of testosterone secretion by the fetal testis during the critical period of sex differentiation.

W. D. Odell: Dr. Jaffe, you have stated that fetal tissues synthesize hCG and you postulate trophoblastic neoplasms in the adult regain this fetal characteristic. We would offer a different interpretation. We have previously reported (Odell *et al.*, 1977, Yoshimoto *et al.*, 1977, 1979, Moorish *et al.*, 1980) that virtually every adult human tissue contains extractable hCG and synthesizes this material. This normal tissue hCG, in contrast to placental hCG, does not bind to Con A, has a markedly altered carbohydrate content, and a smaller molecular weight. This fetal tissue and normal adult tissue have this property in common. We have postulated the carcinomas and trophoblastic neoplasms also synthesize this protein, but in contrast to normal tissues glycosylate the material, prolonging its survival in biological fluid to permit reaching higher concentrations and biological potency.

I have one question. For the EGF and FGF data, you presented only single dose data. What are the dose–response and potency characteristics of EGF and FGF on adrenal cell replication? Does ACTH stimulate cell replication in your studies?

R. B. Jaffe: Those were all at least triplicate or quadruplicate determinations. Those were the means shown on the figure.

W. D. Odell: You did show dose–response data and so I'd like to ask the relative potency of EGF and FGF and whether ACTH had any effect on the replication.

R. B. Jaffe: We have done dose–response curves. The dose that is maximal for EGF seems to be around 1 ng/ml (range studied was 0.1–50 ng/ml). The maximal response for FGF was noted at 100 ng/ml (range studied was 1–500 ng/ml).

W. D. Odell: Does ACTH affect the cell level?

R. B. Jaffe: We don't know that yet.

I. Rothchild: To come back to the primary question of what regulates the time of parturition and the role of the adrenal gland in it: we may be losing sight of the fact that the final common pathway must be through prostaglandin switch-on in the uterus and the relationship of this to effects of progesterone, which is obviously the hormone of pregnancy because it can keep the fetus in the uterus. To add to the mystery of how it does this, there are at least two species in which the relationship is puzzling. One is the bandicoot, a marsupial, which delivers its babies at the peak of its progesterone secretion; the other is the armadillo, a eutherian, which does the same thing. Of course people do this also, but at the end of a long slow rise in progesterone.

R. B. Jaffe: Certainly, prostaglandin synthesis is important in the initiation of parturition, and the question is what controls that synthesis?

S. W. Spaulding: Is anything known about the effect of dopamine on the fetal adrenal?

R. B. Jaffe: We have not studied the effects of dopamine on the adrenal. The juxtaposition of the medulla and the cortex raises very interesting questions about the interaction between catecholamines, including dopamine, and corticosteroids.

C. Eil: Inasmuch as CBG levels of corticosteroid binding globulin increases in the mother during gestation, can you say how much of the cortisol levels in the fetus is due to free or bound cortisol?

R. B. Jaffe: I can't give you absolute levels, there seems to be a decrease in binding globulin in the fetal circulation at the very end of gestation.

C. Eil: Perhaps it relates to the amount of cortisol that is present after dexamethasone suppression.

R. B. Jaffe: It could. It could also depend upon the amount of estrogen present which may govern the amount of binding globulin.

RECENT PROGRESS IN HORMONE RESEARCH, VOL. 37

An Update of Congenital Adrenal Hyperplasia[1]

MARIA I. NEW,* BO DUPONT,† SONGJA PANG,* MARILYN POLLACK,†
AND LENORE S. LEVINE*

*Division of Pediatric Endocrinology, Department of Pediatrics, The New York Hospital-Cornell Medical Center, New York, New York, and †Tissue Typing Laboratory, Sloan-Kettering Institute for Cancer Research, New York, New York

"You never step in the same river twice" (Heracleitus).

I. Introduction

Congenital adrenal hyperplasia is a family of disorders of adrenal steroidogenesis resulting from an inherited deficiency of one of several enzymes necessary for normal steroid synthesis.

The earliest documented description of congenital adrenal hyperplasia (CAH) was by De Crecchio in 1865 (De Crecchio, 1865). This Neapolitan anatomist described a cadaver having a penis with first degree hypospadias but no externally palpable gonads. Dissection revealed a vagina, uterus, fallopian tubes, ovaries, and markedly enlarged adrenals. It is interesting that the subject, Giuseppe Marzo, suffered a confusion of sex assignment, being declared a female at birth and a male 4 years later (Bongiovanni and Root, 1963). He conducted himself as a male sexually and socially. This remarkable description, written more than 100 years ago, could easily apply to some present-day cases.

Since the original description of this case, there have been many investigators who have unraveled the pathophysiology of the inborn errors of steroidogenesis. In 1967 Dr. Bongiovanni *et al.* (1967) presented at this conference an exhaustive review of the known enzyme defects. In 1975, a symposium was held honoring Lawson Wilkins at the twenty-fifth anniversary of the treatment of congenital adrenal hyperplasia (Lee *et al.*, 1977). At this symposium, Bartter (1977) presented a masterful review of

[1] This investigation was supported in part by USPHS, NIH Grant awards HD 00072, HD 5895 from the NICHHD; CA-22507, CA-08748, CA-19267 from the NCI; AICA 16093 from the NIAID; and a grant (RR 47) from the General Clinical Research Centers Program of the Division of Research Resources, NIH and a Clinical Research Grant (6-274) from the National Foundation March of Dimes.

ISBN 0-12-571137-9

the historical events leading to the current understanding of the disorder.

The purpose of this article is to describe the recent advances in congenital adrenal hyperplasia. These advances have come from the interdisciplinary collaboration of embryologists, teratologists, enzymologists, immunogeneticists, population geneticists, steroid endocrinologists, and gender psychologists. We are grateful to have been part of this immensely educational endeavor.

II. Steroidogenesis and Enzymatic Conversions of Adrenal Steroid Hormones

A. STEROIDOGENESIS

A simplified scheme of adrenal steroidogenesis is depicted in Fig. 1. Each hydroxylation step is indicated and the newly added hydroxyl group is circled. The adrenal synthesizes three main classes of hormones: mineralocorticoids, glucocorticoids, and sex steroids. The action of ACTH on the adrenals is to increase the conversion of cholesterol to pregnenolone.

A detailed discussion of steroidogenesis is omitted here since it has been extensively reviewed in other texts (Bongiovanni, 1978; Bongiovanni and Root, 1963; Bongiovanni *et al.*, 1967; Root *et al.*, 1971; Finkelstein and Shaefer, 1979). For the purpose of understanding the clinical manifestations of congenital adrenal hyperplasia, reference to the simplified scheme in Fig. 1 will suffice.

1. Mineralocorticoids

Pregnenolone, a Δ^5-steroid, is converted to a biologically active Δ^4-steroid, progesterone, by the enzymes 3β-hydroxysteroid dehydrogenase (3β-HSD) and isomerase. The progesterone is then hydroxylated at the ^{21}C position to form deoxycorticosterone (DOC), an active salt-retaining hormone. When DOC is hydroxylated at the ^{11}C position, corticosterone (B) is formed, which is a weak mineralocorticoid. Corticosterone, however, is the precursor of aldosterone, the most potent salt-retaining hormone (Gaunt, 1971). Synthesis of aldosterone, a unique hormone because of the aldehyde group at ^{18}C, occurs in the zona glomerulosa of the adrenal cortex, while synthesis of other adrenal corticosteroids occurs in the zona fasciculata and the zona reticularis. Discussion below indicates that regulation of the zona glomerulosa differs from that of the others. The synthesis of aldosterone from corticosterone has not been entirely elucidated.

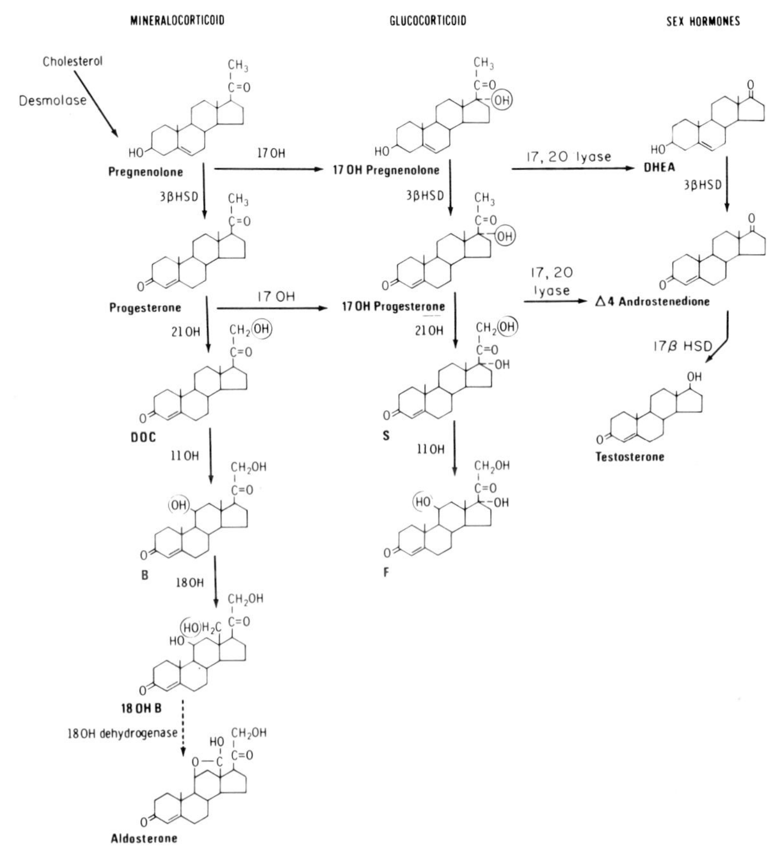

FIG. 1. Simplified scheme for adrenal steroidogenesis. Each hydroxylation step is indicated and the newly added hydroxyl group is circled. From New and Levine (1973).

2. *Glucocorticoids*

Glucocorticoid synthesis requires hydroxylation at the ^{17}C position. Thus, pregnenolone and progesterone yield 17-hydroxypregnenolone and 17-hydroxyprogesterone (17-OHP), respectively, when acted upon by the 17-hydroxylase enzyme. 17-Hydroxypregnenolone, a Δ^5-steroid, is converted to 17-hydroxyprogesterone, a Δ^4-steroid, by enzymatic steps similar to those that convert pregnenolone to progesterone. When 17-hydroxyprogesterone undergoes 21-hydroxylation, 11-deoxycortisol (S) is formed, and this is further hydroxylated at ^{11}C to form cortisol (F), the most potent glucocorticoid in man. Thus, it can be seen from Fig. 1 that parallel hydroxylation steps at ^{21}C and ^{11}C of progesterone and 17-hydroxyprogesterone result in corticosterone and cortisol, respectively.

3. Sex Hormones

The main ^{19}C steroid secreted by the adrenal cortex is dehydroepiandrosterone (DHEA). It results from the side-chain cleavage of the ^{21}C steroid, 17-OH pregnenolone, by the action of a desmolase enzyme. DHEA, a Δ^5-steroid with little androgenic activity, is converted to Δ^4-androstenedione, a moderately active androgen, by the 3β-HSD and isomerase enzymes. When Δ^4-androstenedione is reduced at the ^{17}C position, testosterone, man's most potent adrenal androgen, is formed.

B. MECHANISM OF ADRENAL STEROID REGULATION

The hypothalamic–pituitary–adrenal feedback is mediated through the circulating level of plasma cortisol. The central nervous system controls the secretion of ACTH, its diurnal variation, and its increase in stress via corticotropin-releasing factor (Ganong, 1963; Guillemin and Schally, 1963). Any condition which decreases cortisol secretion will result in increased ACTH secretion. In those forms of congenital adrenal hyperplasia in which an enzyme deficiency causes impaired cortisol synthesis, there is excessive ACTH secretion and hyperplasia of the adrenal cortex (Fig. 2).

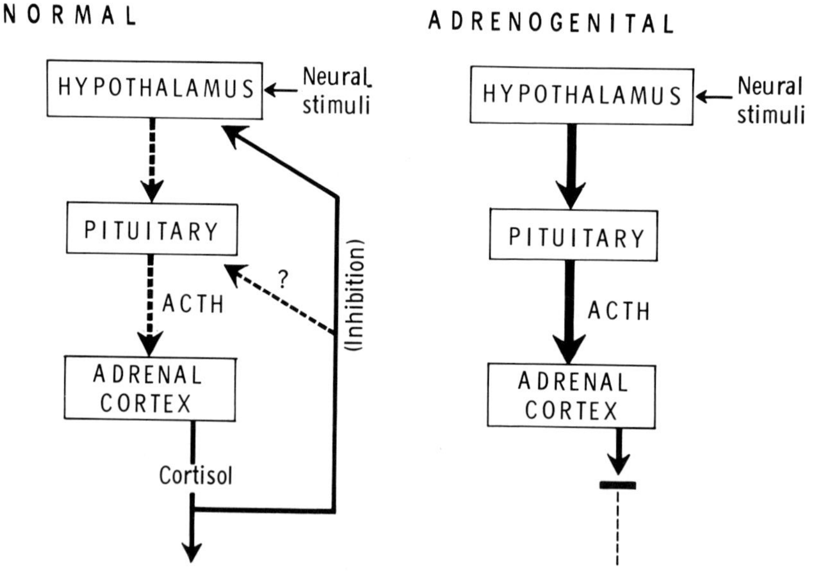

FIG. 2. The regulation of cortisol secretion in normal subjects and in patients with congenital adrenal hyperplasia. From New and Levine (1973).

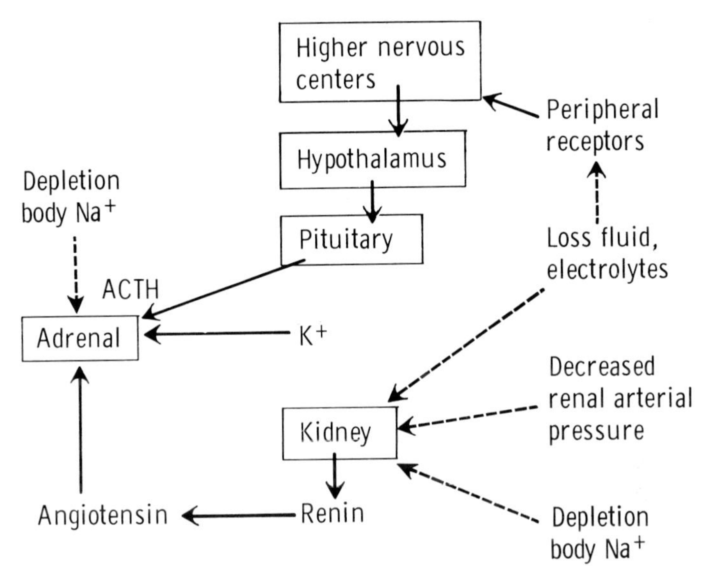

FIG. 3. Regulation of aldosterone secretion. From New and Peterson (1966).

Aldosterone secretion is primarily regulated via the renin–angiotensin system, which is responsive to the state of electrolyte balance (Fig. 3). Aldosterone secretion is also stimulated directly by the serum potassium concentration. The juxtaglomerular apparatus produces renin. The enzyme renin reacts with an α_2-globulin known as renin substrate to release angiotensin I. The substrate is thought to arise from the liver. Angiotensin I is converted to angiotensin II by a converting enzyme. Angiotensin II is a potent stimulator of aldosterone secretion. Although this scheme is generally accepted, there are many aspects of aldosterone regulation which still remain unexplained (Laragh, 1971; Mueller, 1971). With respect to regulation and secretion, the zona glomerulosa and the zona fasciculata behave as two separate glands. Thus, ACTH stimulates secretion of cortisol, corticosterone, and androgens by the zona fasciculata, while angiotensin stimulates aldosterone secretion by the zona glomerulosa.

III. Fetal Sexual Development

In order to understand the pathophysiology of CAH, it is necessary to discuss normal sexual differentiation briefly.

According to the hypothesis developed by Jost (1966) and discussed by Federman (1968), normal differentiation of male genitalia is dependent on two functions of the fetal testis:

1. Secretion of the fetal androgen, perhaps testosterone, to cause stimulation of Wolffian ducts, posterior migration of the labioscrotal folds such that the male phallus lies anterior to the scrotum, elongation of the genital tubercle, and midline fusion of the genital folds and swellings to form the penis and scrotal sacs. Complete differentiation demands that the urethra open at the tip of the penis. In the male, the source of androgen is the fetal testis, but any source of androgen can cause masculinization of external genitalia, e.g., adrenal androgen during the first trimester of pregnancy.
2. Secretion of a nonsteroidal substance (Josso, 1972) which inhibits Müllerian development such that normal males are born without a uterus.

Failure to secrete sufficient androgen results in various degrees of male pseudohermaphroditism. Failure to secrete Müllerian inhibiting factor in the presence of normal androgen secretion results in the rare condition known as "persistent oviduct syndrome" or "hernia uteri inguinale" (Federman, 1968; Hanley, 1953; Kozzol, 1942; Nilson, 1939). In this condition, male external genitalia are normal but there is some preservation of Müllerian remnants internally, generally surprising the surgeon who is operating on an inguinal hernia.

Since the fetal ovary secretes neither testosterone nor the inhibiting factor necessary to inhibit Müllerian structures, the normal female is born without male differentiation of external genitalia, i.e., with female external genitalia, and without Müllerian repression, i.e., with a uterus and fallopian tubes. This is shown schematically in Fig. 4.

Thus, in the above scheme, the ovary does not play a determining role in sex differentiation.

Female fetuses exposed to high levels of androgen consequent to CAH (discussed below) or androgen-producing tumor in the mother (Bretnall, 1945), or due to administration of androgens to the mother, manifest virilization of the external genitalia (Federman, 1968) but normal internal genitalia (Wilkins, 1960; Wilkins *et al.,* 1958; Grumbach *et al.,* 1959).

IV. Enzyme Defects in Congenital Adrenal Hyperplasia

The following enzymatic deficiencies of steroidogenesis have been described:

21-hydroxylase
- simple virilizing
- salt wasting

[references after 1975 indicated by (a); references prior to 1975, see Lee *et al.,* 1977]

11β-hydroxylase [references indicated by (b)]
3β-hydroxysteroid dehydrogenase (3β-HSD) [references indicated by (c)]
17α-hydroxylase [references indicated by (d)]
cholesterol desmolase [references indicated by (e)]
18-hydroxylase [references indicated by (f)]
18-dehydrogenase of 18-hydroxycorticosterone (methyloxidase Type II) [references indicated by (g)]
17β-hydroxysteroid dehydrogenase (17β-HSD) [references indicated by (h)]

A summary of the clinical and biochemical features of these disorders is shown in Table I. It should be noted that sexual ambiguity is not a feature of the 18-hydroxylase and the 18-dehydrogenase of 18-hydroxycorticosterone (methyloxidase Type II) since these defects do not involve the ^{19}C pathway. The 17β-hydroxysteroid dehydrogenase defect may occur only in the gonad (Virdis *et al.*, 1978). Since the enzyme activity is normally low in the adrenal, exclusion of an adrenal defect is difficult. It is included in Table I for completeness. Only in those defects associated with cortisol deficiency is there adrenal hyperplasia, *vide supra*.

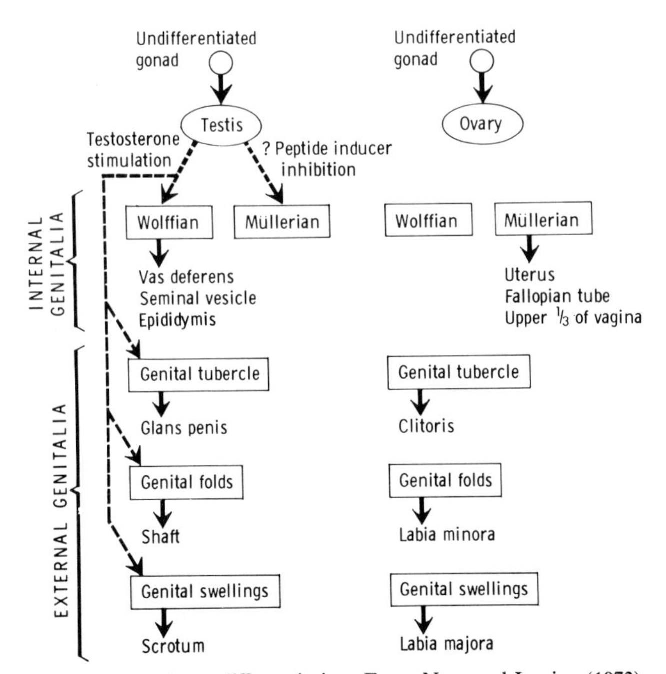

FIG. 4. Fetal sex differentiation. From New and Levine (1973).

TABLE I

Clinical and Laboratory Features of Various Forms of Adrenal Disorders of Steroidogenesis

Clinical features						Laboratory findings								
Newborn with sexual ambiguity						Urinary excretion				Circulating hormones				
Female	Male	Salt wasting	Hypertension	Postnatal virilization	Enzyme deficiency	17-KS	17-OH	P'triol	Aldo	17-OHP	Δ^4	DHEA	Testosterone	Renin
					21-Hydroxylase									
+	0	0	0	+	Not salt wasting	↑↑	N or ↓	↑↑	N	↑↑	↑↑	N or ↑ (DHEA/Δ^4 ↓)	↑	N or ↑
+	0	+	0	+	Salt wasting	↑↑	↓	↑↑	↓	↑↑	↑↑	N or ↑	↑	↑↑
+	0	0	+	+	11β-Hydroxylase	↑↑	↑↑[a]	↑	↓	↑	↑↑	↑	↑	↓↓
+	+	+	0	0	3β-HSD[b]	↑[c]	↓↓	↑	↓	N or ↑	N or ↑	↑↑↑	↓ or N	↑
0	+	0	+	0	17α-Hydroxylase	↓↓	↓↓	↓↓	↓	↓	↓	↓	↓	↓
0	+	+	0	0	Cholesterol desmolase	↓↓	↓↓	↓↓	↓↓	↓	↓	↓	↓	↑
0	0	+	0	0	18-Hydroxylase	N	N	N	↓↓	N	N	N	N	↑
0	0	+	0	0	18-Dehydrogenase of 18-hydroxycorticosterone (Methyloxidase Type II)	N	↑[d]	N	↓↓	N	N	N	N	↑
?	+	—	—	+[e]	17β-Hydroxysteroid dehydrogenase[f]	N↑	N	N	N	N	↑↑	N or ↑	N or ↓ (Δ^4/T↑↑)	N[g]

[a] Mostly THS.
[b] The values presented apply to the infant and very young child.
[c] Mostly Δ^5-17 ketosteroids.
[d] Largely 18-hydroxy THA, which gives a Porter–Silber reaction.
[e] Only in males at puberty.
[f] This defect may occur only in the gonad.
[g] N, normal.

V. Recent Advances in 21-Hydroxylase and 11β-Hydroxylase Deficiencies

A. THE ADRENAL FASCICULATA AND GLOMERULOSA AS TWO SEPARATE GLANDS

1. 11β-Hydroxylase Deficiency

It was proposed in 1970 (New and Seaman, 1970) that the adrenal fasciculata and glomerulosa functioned as two separate glands. According to this concept, steroidogenesis of the fasciculata is regulated by ACTH while that of the glomerulosa is regulated by the renin–angiotensin system. It was further proposed that the genetic defect of 11β-hydroxylation may be present only in the fasciculata and not in the glomerulosa. This was supported by subsequent reports (Gregory and Gardner, 1976; Zachmann *et al.*, 1971; Sizonenko *et al.*, 1972a; Tan *et al.*, 1978) and was confirmed by recent extensive studies in four patients with 11β-hydroxylase deficiency (Levine *et al.*, 1980b). This recent report also suggested that the 11β- and 18-hydroxylase of the adrenal fasciculata are functionally related and may involve the same enzyme protein and catalytic site as proposed by Ulick (1976a). In this study of four patients with 11β-hydroxylase deficiency, the fasciculata and glomerulosa were separately stimulated by ACTH and renin. Results in one patient are illustrated in Fig. 5. In the untreated state, when renin was suppressed, ACTH stimulation resulted in a further increase of the markedly elevated 11-deoxy steroids [deoxycorticosterone (DOC), tetrahydrodeoxycorticosterone (THDOC)] while the 11-hydroxylated steroids [aldosterone (aldo) and 18-hydroxycorticosterone (18-OHB)] did not rise. In contrast, when the ACTH was suppressed by dexamethasone, and renin was stimulated by low salt diet, the 11-hydroxylated steroids increased normally. These results indicated that the renin-stimulable zone (glomerulosa) was not defective in 11β-hydroxylation. Further the failure of 18-OHDOC to rise in concert with DOC suggested that there was an 18-hydroxylase defect as well as an 11β-hydroxylase defect in the ACTH-stimulable zone (fasciculata). The normal rise in 18-OHB with renin stimulation indicated that the 18-hydroxylase as well as the 11β-hydroxylase enzyme was not defective in the glomerulosa.

The serum androgen concentrations in these patients showed a predominance of Δ^4, similar to the pattern observed in patients with 21-hydroxylase deficiency (Korth-Schutz *et al.*, 1976).

Although a number of studies have demonstrated inhibition of 11β- and 18-hydroxylation functions by androgens (Molteni *et al.*, 1970; McCall *et al.*, 1978), it is unlikely that the elevated androgens are the major cause of

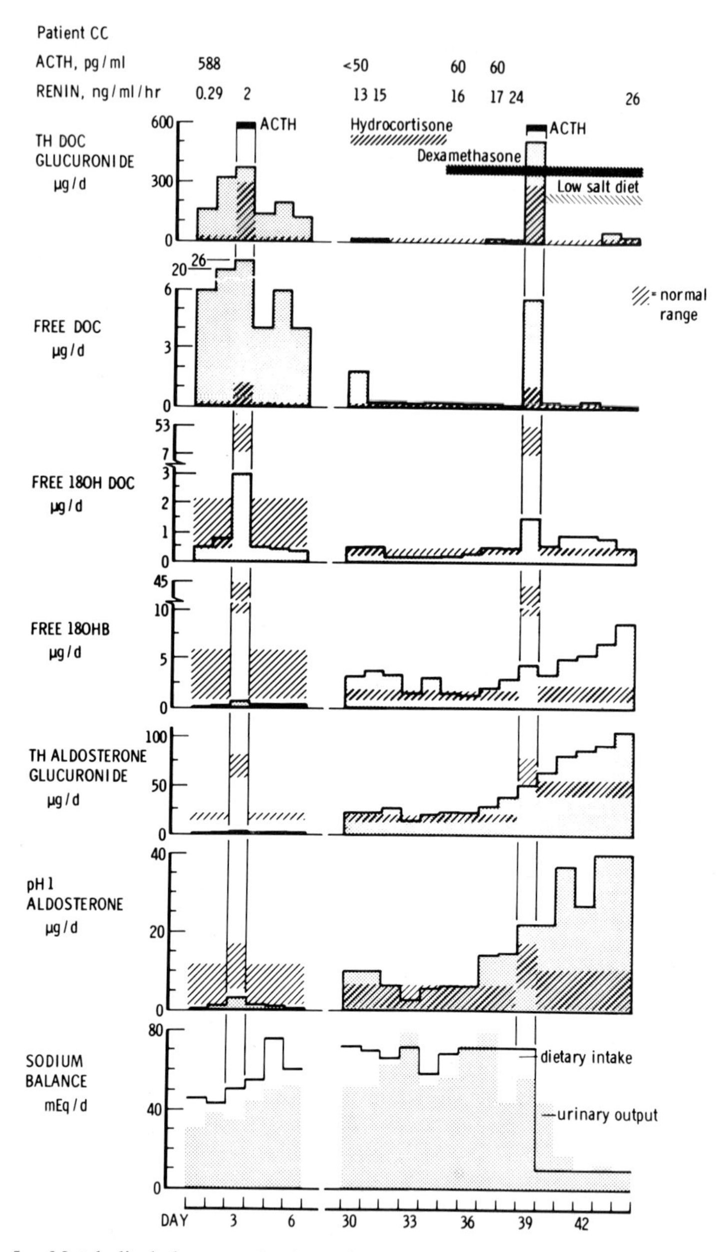

FIG. 5. Metabolic balance and urinary hormone excretion in a prepubertal boy with 11β-hydroxylase deficiency during baseline, ACTH, dexamethasone, and dexamethasone and low salt periods. □, Patient's response; ▨, normal control response. From Levine *et al.* (1980b).

the defective enzyme function. In these patients persistent 11β- and 18-hydroxylation deficiencies were demonstrated when the adrenal androgens were well suppressed and ACTH was readministered; an excessive rise in DOC and an inadequate rise in 18-hydroxydeoxycorticosterone (18-OHDOC) again occurred. In addition, in patients with simple virilizing CAH due to 21-hydroxylase deficiency, aldosterone secretion, which requires 11β-hydroxylation and 18-hydroxylation, is normal despite extremely high levels of Δ^4 (New and Seaman, 1970).

On the basis of the remarkable parallelism of 11β- and 18-hydroxylation functions of the fasciculata zone, Ulick (1976a) has proposed that both activities may reside in the same enzyme protein. Though it may seem surprising that one enzyme may catalyze hydroxylation at more than one position, Ulick pointed out that there is precedence for this in microbial steroid hydroxylases. In patients with a genetic defect in 11β-hydroxylation, the presence of both an 11β- and 18-hydroxylation defect in the fasciculata provides strong evidence for the parallelism of these two enzymatic functions in humans.

2. 21-Hydroxylase Deficiency

Additional evidence supporting the concept that the adrenal fasciculata and glomerulosa function as two separate glands has been gained from the recent study of patients with 21-hydroxylase deficiency.

In CAH due to 21-hydroxylase deficiency, two different clinical syndromes are recognized: the simple virilizing and the salt-wasting forms. In both forms, there is defective 21-hydroxylation of the 17-hydroxy steroids leading to elevation of 17-hydroxyprogesterone (17-OHP) and diminished production of cortisol (Bongiovanni and Eberlein, 1958). The nature of the 21-hydroxylase enzyme defect in the 17-deoxy pathway in both the salt-wasting and simple virilizing forms of CAH remains controversial, though it is widely accepted that aldosterone synthesis is more deficient in salt wasters than in simple virilizers. The hypotheses proposed to explain the different syndromes are based either on a "one-enzyme" or a "two-enzyme" defect. However, neither *in vivo* (Blizzard *et al.*, 1959; Bryan *et al.*, 1965; Degenhart *et al.*, 1965; Kowarski *et al.*, 1965, New *et al.*, 1966; Bartter *et al.*, 1968; Simopoulos *et al.*, 1971; Rösler *et al.*, 1977c; Horner *et al.*, 1965; Degenhart *et al.*, 1965; Kowarski *et al.*, 1965, New *et al.*, 1966; Nelson and Bryan, 1975; Mackler *et al.*, 1971; Bryan *et al.*, 1974; Orta-Flores *et al.*, 1976) studies have been conclusive and results compatible with both theories have been reported.

The "one-enzyme" theory attributes the differences between salt wasting and simple virilizing CAH to a different degree of enzymatic deficiency, the most severe deficiency leading to salt wasting (Bongionvanni and Eberlein, 1958; Blizzard *et al.*, 1959; Kowarski *et al.*, 1965; Rösler *et al.*, 1977c). The "two enzyme" theory postulates that the simple virilizers have an enzymatic deficiency in the 17-hydroxy pathway, whereas the salt wasters have a deficiency in both the 17-hydroxy and 17-deoxy pathway of adrenal steroidogenesis. This theory is supported by normal or elevated aldosterone secretion or excretion in simple virilizers in contrast to the impaired aldosterone production in salt wasters (Bryan *et al.*, 1965; Degenhart *et al.*, 1965; New *et al.*, 1966; Bartter *et al.*, 1968; Simopoulos *et al.*, 1971).

Recent studies from our laboratory have suggested a new hypothesis to explain the differences in salt wasting and simple virilizing adrenal hyperplasia. This hypothesis states: (a) in both simple virilizers and salt wasters, there is a fasciculata defect of 21-hydroxylation in both the 17-deoxy and 17-hydroxy pathways, and (b) in the salt waster there is a defect in 21-hydroxylation in the glomerulosa as well, while in the simple virilizer, the glomerulosa is spared this defect. This hypothesis is schematically presented in Fig. 6. A sample of the data supporting this hypothesis is presented in Figs. 7 and 8.

The failure of serum levels and urinary metabolites of F, DOC, and B to respond normally to the stimulation of ACTH in both the simple virilizer and the salt waster indicated a 21-hydroxylase defect for both the 17-hydroxy and 17-deoxy pathway in the ACTH-responsive zona fasciculata (Fig. 7). The 21-hydroxylase deficiency in the zona fasciculata appeared to be more severe in the salt wasters than in the simple virilizers since the response to ACTH demonstrated a greater deficiency in the products of 21-hydroxylation in the salt wasters.

The findings in the 17-hydroxy pathway agree with previous reports which have shown elevated 17-OHP (Bongiovanni and Eberlein, 1958; Lippe *et al.*, 1974), and diminished cortisol synthesis (Bongiovanni and Eberlein, 1958; Franks, 1974), particularly in response to ACTH (Beitins *et al.*, 1972).

Fewer data are available on steroids in the 17-deoxy pathway of the zona fasciculata. West *et al.* (1979) recently reported normal or elevated baseline progesterone and corticosterone values in simple virilizers as well as in salt wasters, and concluded from these data that the 21-hydroxylation of the 17-deoxy pathway is unaffected in this disorder. Our data also showed normal baseline levels of corticosterone for both salt wasters and simple virilizers. However, progesterone as has been reported earlier (Strott *et al.*, 1969; Simopoulos *et al.*, 1971) was extremely elevated in both forms of CAH indicating defective 21-hydroxylation. During stimulation with ACTH the impaired 21-hydroxylation of the 17-deoxy pathway was even more apparent, since progesterone levels rose

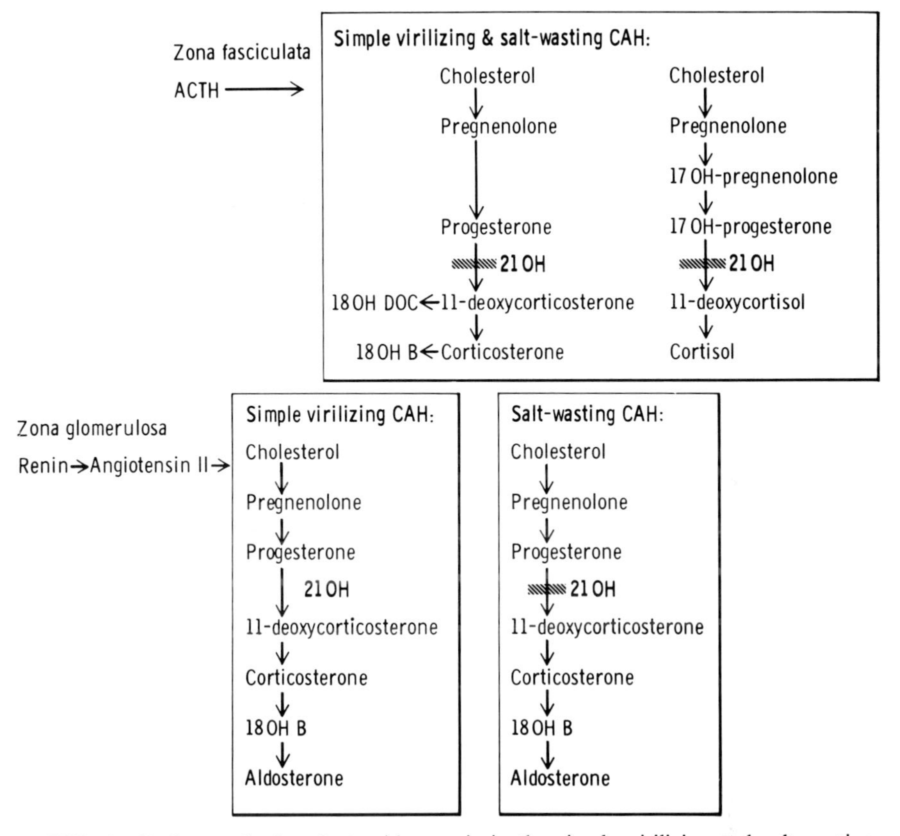

FIG. 6. Pathway of adrenal steroidogenesis in the simple virilizing and salt-wasting forms of congenital adrenal hyperplasia.

markedly while the DOC and B responses were minimal. Similarly, in secretion rate studies of two simple virilizers, New and Seaman (1970) reported normal baseline secretion rates of corticosterone but no increase during ACTH stimulation.

Elevated baseline DOC levels, particularly in patients with the simple virilizing form, have been reported earlier (New *et al.*, 1966; Mantero *et al.*, 1975) and were variably explained by inhibition of 11-hydroxylation due to excessive androgens (Sharma *et al.*, 1963) or an intraadrenal event caused by ACTH (Schambelan *et al.*, 1980). Similar to the findings in corticosterone, however, the impaired DOC and 18-OHDOC response to ACTH demonstrated the defective 21-hydroxylation in the 17-deoxy pathway.

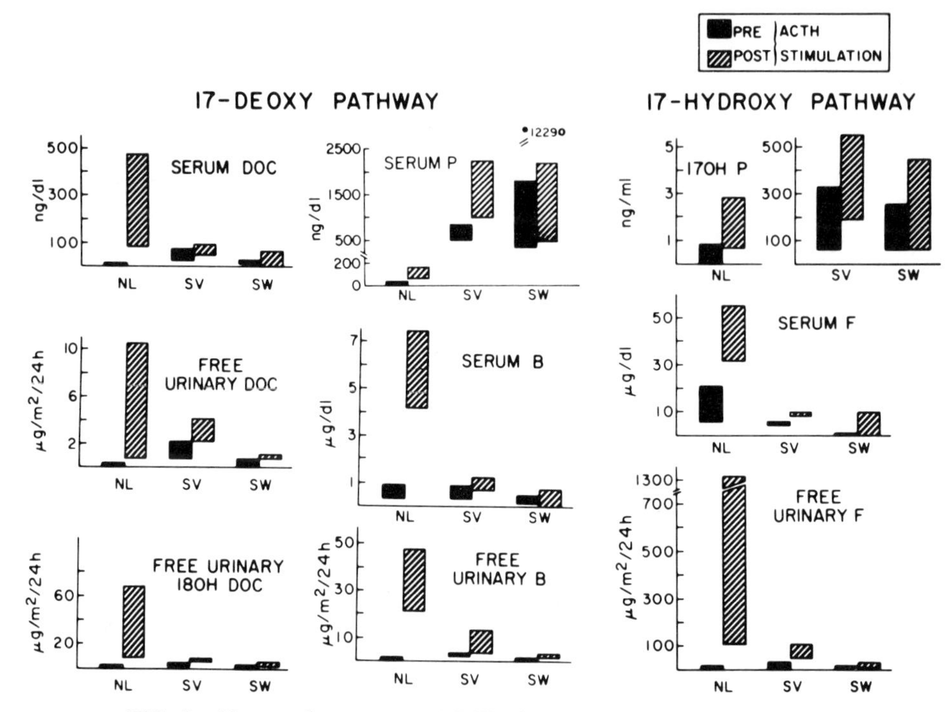

FIG. 7. Hormonal response to ACTH stimulzation of the zona fasciculata.

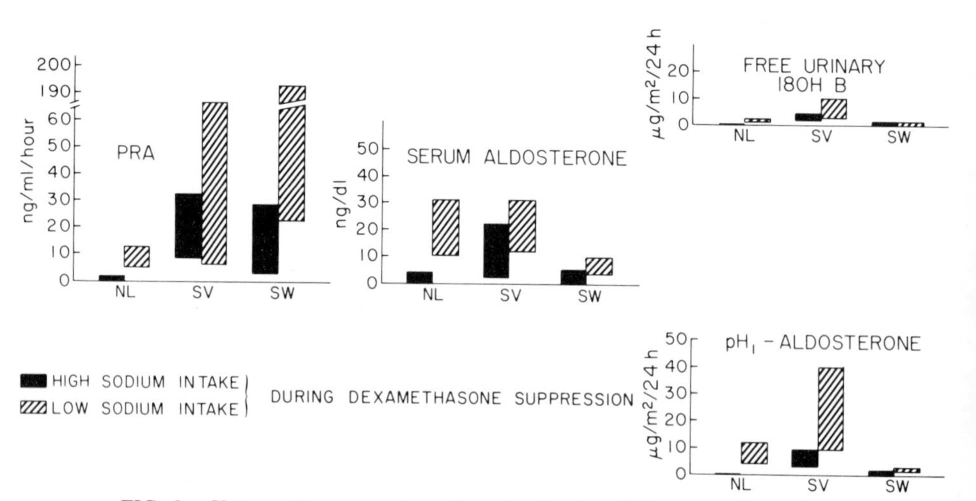

FIG. 8. Hormonal response to sodium deprivation of the zona glomerulosa.

The difference between the two groups of CAH patients in 21-hydroxylase function in the glomerulosa was demonstrated by their response to elevations in plasma renin activity (PRA) (Fig. 8). Thus, the elevated serum and urinary aldosterone, and urinary 18-OHB levels in response to elevated PRA in the baseline state, and further elevation with sodium restriction, indicated that 21-hydroxylation in the zona glomerulosa of the simple virilizers was not defective. In contrast, despite elevated PRA, the zona glomerulosa of the salt wasters failed to respond with an adequate rise in aldosterone and 18-OHB, indicating defective 21-hydroxylation.

Normal (Degenhart *et al.*, 1965; New *et al.*, 1966) or elevated (Kowarski *et al.*, 1965; Loras *et al.*, 1970; Dahl *et al.*, 1972) secretion rates of aldosterone in simple virilizers and low secretion rates of aldosterone in salt wasters (Degenhart *et al.*, 1965; Kowarski *et al.*, 1965; Loras *et al.*, 1970) have been reported. According to this new hypothesis the salt wasting in congenital adrenal hyperplasia is due to an aldosterone synthesis defect of the glomerulosa. Since the glomerulosa is spared the 21-hydroxylase defect in simple virilizing adrenal hyperplasia, aldosterone secretion is not impaired and there are no salt-wasting symptoms.

The increased aldosterone secretion and excretion in simple virilizers is in response to increased PRA. The basis for the high PRA in simple virilizers was not evident since these patients were capable of conserving sodium to the same degree as the normal controls. High PRA resulting in aldosterone elevation has been reported by several investigators despite an absence of salt wasting in simple virilizers (Bartter, 1977; Strickland and Kotchen, 1972; Goddard *et al.*, 1968; Simopoulos *et al.*, 1971; Edwin *et al.*, 1979). It has been suggested that the oversecretion of aldosterone is a compensatory response to natriuretic hormones secreted by the adrenals in these patients (Klein, 1960; Prader *et al.*, 1955). The existence of such hormones, however, has not been proven.

In an autopsy report of six salt wasters who died during a salt-wasting crisis, no glomerulosa zone was detected in the hyperplastic adrenal cortex, while in three simple virilizers who died from intercurrent disease, the zona glomerulosa was markedly hypertrophic (Osterwalder, 1971). Both forms of CAH showed a marked increase in the juxtaglomerular cell count. These findings correlate well with the increased PRA and elevated aldosterone found in simple virilizers and increased PRA and decreased aldosterone found in salt wasters.

In the recent report of Kuhnle *et al.* (1980, 1981) both normal subjects and simple virilizers, but not salt wasters, demonstrated a rise in serum and urinary aldosterone and 18-OHB when the zona glomerulosa was stimulated with a low sodium intake while the zona fasciculata was suppressed by dexamethasone. This again supports the absence of a 21-hydroxylase deficiency in the zona glomerulosa of the simple virilizer and shows that in both the normal subjects and in the simple virilizers, the zona glomerulosa can increase aldosterone in response to renin stimulation independent of precursor hormones of the zona fasciculata.

In summary, the new data have shown that in CAH, there is a 21-hydroxylation defect in the zona fasciculata of simple virilizers and salt wasters whereas the zona glomerulosa is defective in salt wasters and not in simple virilizers (Fig. 6). The data suggest that there is one enzyme involved in the 21-hydroxylation of the 17-hydroxy and 17-deoxy pathways of adrenal steroidogenesis in the zona fasciculata. The finding of an enzymatic deficiency only in the zona fasciculata, sparing the zona glomerulosa, has been reported in CAH due to 11-hydroxylase deficiency (Sizonenko *et al.,* 1972a; Levine *et al.,* 1980b).

These findings presented herein provide further evidence that the zona fasciculata and the zona glomerulosa can function as separate glands under different regulation (New and Seaman, 1970). These findings further suggest the possibility of separate genetic loci for the regulation of the 21-hydroxylase activity in the zona fasciculata and the zona glomerulosa. However, one genetic locus seems to regulate the 21-hydroxylase enzyme activity in both the 17-hydroxy and 17-deoxy pathways of the zona fasciculata.

B. GENETICS

Several surveys have established that the 21-hydroxylase deficiency is transmitted as an autosomal recessive trait (Prader, 1958a; Wilkins, 1962; Childs *et al.,* 1956). Males and females are equally at risk (Baulieu *et al.,* 1967). With few exceptions (Rosenbloom and Smith, 1966b), the severity of the 21-hydroxylase deficiency, which parallels the degree of salt wasting is consistent within one family.

In Europe and the United States recent estimates of the incidence of CAH due to 21-hydroxylase deficiency have been between 1 : 5000 and 1 : 15,000. In Alaska the incidence in Yupiks is unusually high while the low incidence reported in Maryland may be due to inadequate case ascertainment (Table II).

The gene frequency is estimated as approximately 1 in 100 and the carrier frequency as approximately 1 in 50 (Müller *et al.,* 1979). The salt-wasting variety occurs in about 30 to 80% of patients with 21-hydroxylase deficiency (Cohen, 1969; Rimoin and Schimke, 1971). A very high incidence of the salt-wasting variant has been found among Yupik Eskimos in Alaska (Hirschfeld and Fleshman, 1969).

TABLE II
Estimated Incidence of CAH (21-Hydroxylase Deficiency)

Reference	Population	Patient/live births
Childs *et al.* (1956)	Maryland, United States	1:67,000
Prader (1958a)	Zurich, Switzerland	1:5,041
Hubble (1966)	Birmingham, England	1:7,255
Rosenbloom and Smith (1966a)	Wisconsin, United States	1:15,000
Hirshfeld and	Alaska, United States	1:700[a]
Fleshman (1969)	Yupik Eskimo, United States	1:245
Qazi and Thompson (1972)	Toronto, Canada	1:13,000[a]
Mauthe *et al.* (1977)	Munich, Germany	1:9,831
Muller *et al.* (1979)	Tirol, Austria	1:8,991
Werder *et al.* (1980)	All of Switzerland	1:15,472

[a] Incidence was corrected for both variants of salt waster and non-salt waster.

The 11β-hydroxylase deficiency is also transmitted as an autosomal recessive trait, but is rarer than the 21-hydroxylase deficiency.

C. STUDIES OF HLA LINKAGE TO CONGENITAL ADRENAL HYPERPLASIA

The genes for HLA (human leukocyte antigens), cell surface antigens important in transplantation, are located on the sixth chromosome. The HLA complex consists of at least four genetic loci which code for the antigens HLA-A, HLA-B, HLA-C, and HLA-D/DR. Each of the loci is polymorphic and multiple alleles have been demonstrated for each locus (see Table III). In addition to the HLA loci several other loci have been mapped on the sixth chromosome in close linkage with HLA (Fig. 9).

Each individual inherits one sixth chromosome from his father and one from his mother. The HLA genes are codominantly expressed and the gene products of the HLA-A, -B, -C, and -D/DR loci from both parents are expressed on the cell surface of all nucleated cells.

An example of an HLA geneotype of an individual is written as follows:

$$\frac{\text{A3, Bw47(w4), Cw6, DRw7}}{\text{A28, Bw35(w6), Cw4, DRw5}}$$

in which one haplotype [the set of A3, Bw47(w4), CW6, DRw7] is inherited from one parent, while the other haplotype [A28, Bw35(w6), Cw4, DRw5] is inherited from the other parent.

The genotype is determined by serologic reaction with specific antibodies, usually using lymphocytes in the complement dependent microcytotoxicity test.

TABLE III

W.H.O.-Recognized HLA Specificities—1980[a,b]

HLA-A	HLA-B			HLA-C	HLA-D	HLA-DR
A1	B5	Bw44(12)		Cw1	Dw1	DR1
A2	B7	Bw45(12)		Cw2	Dw2	DR2
A3	B8	Bw46		Cw3	Dw3	DR3
A9	B12	Bw47		Cw4	Dw4	DR4
A10	B13	Bw48		Cw5	Dw5	DR5
A11	B14	Bw49(w21)		Cw6	Dw6	DRw6
Aw19	B15	Bw50(w21)		Cw7	Dw7	DR7
Aw23(9)	Bw16	Bw51(5)		Cw8	Dw8	DRw8
Aw24(9)	B17	Bw52(5)			Dw9	DRw9
A25(10)	B18	Bw53			Dw10	DRw10
A26(10)	Bw21	Bw54(w22)			Dw11	
A28	Bw22	Bw55(w22)	[22.1]		Dw12	
A29	B27	Bw56(w22)	[22.2]			
Aw30	Bw35	Bw57(17)	[17.1]			
Aw31	B37	Bw58(17)	[17.2]			
Aw32	Bw38(w16)	Bw59	[8.2]			
Aw33	Bw39(w16)	Bw60(40)	[40.1]			
Aw34(10)	B40	Bw61(40)	[40.2]			
Aw36	Bw41	Bw62(15)	[15.1]			
Aw43	Bw42	Bw63(15)	[15.2]			
	Bw4					
	Bw6					

[a] From World Health Organization (1980).

[b] Broad specificities are listed in parentheses after narrow specificities; previously used designations for the new HLA-B specificities are indicated in brackets.

1. Studies of HLA Linkage to Congenital Adrenal Hyperplasia due to 21-Hydroxylase Deficiency

a. Genetic Linkage to HLA. In 1977, close genetic linkage between HLA and CAH due to 21-hydroxylase deficiency was first described (Dupont *et al.*, 1977). In this initial study, HLA genotyping of parents and children in six families with more than one child affected with CAH due to 21-hydroxylase deficiency was performed.

In five of these families, all of the affected offspring were identical and different from their unaffected sibs (Table IV).

Subsequently, studies of 34 unrelated families with a total of 48 patients were reported from New York and Zurich (Levine *et al.*, 1978). The findings of this study are exemplified by the two typical pedigrees shown in Fig. 10. As can be observed in Fig. 10A, the three affected sibs are HLA identical. In Fig. 10B, the unaffected sibs are all HLA different from their affected sister. Both HLA haplotypes of the patient are therefore pre-

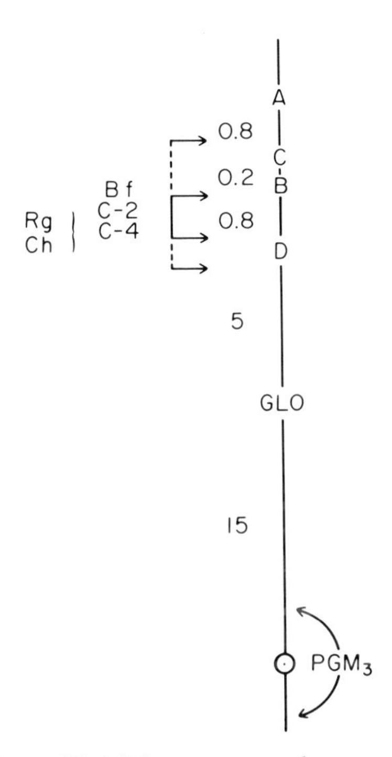

FIG. 9. HLA-linkage group on chromosome 6.

sumed to be linked to the gene for 21-hydroxylase deficiency. Thus any member of the family who shares one HLA haplotype with the patient should also carry the gene for the enzyme defect.

In Fig. 10B, the corresponding HLA haplotype presumed to carry the genetic enzyme defect is represented by an asterisk.

Thus each parent has transmitted one HLA haplotype carrying the gene for 21-hydroxylase deficiency to the patient. The brother and the sister having one haplotype linked to the gene for CAH are presumed heterozygotes, as is each parent who transmitted that haplotype. The sib sharing neither haplotype with the patient is presumed not to carry the gene for the 21-hydroxylase deficiency.

The formal demonstration of close genetic linkage between the 21-hydroxylase deficiency gene and HLA was made by the Lod Score analysis (see below). This established that the gene for 21-hydroxylase deficiency was located very close to the HLA-B locus (Dupont *et al.*, 1977; Levine *et al.*, 1978; Grosse-Wilde *et al.*, 1979).

Thus the HLA genotype is a marker for the CAH genotype. These studies again demonstrated that the gene for CAH due to 21-hydroxylase

TABLE IV

HLA Genotyping of Six Families with Siblings Affected with CAH[a]

Family	Parents[b]	HLA haplotype	Affected children	HLA haplotype	Unaffected children	HLA haplotypes
1	F A3;Bw35(w6);Cw4 A3;B7	a/b	Child 1 A3;Bw35(w6)Cw4 Aw24(9);B15(w6);Cw3	a/c		
	M Aw24(9);B15(w6);Cw3 A1;Bw35(w4);Cw4	c/d	Child 2 A3;Bw35(w6);Cw4 Aw24(9);B15(w6);Cw3	a/c		
2	F A3;B7(w6);Cw3 A11;B40	a/b	Child 1 A3;B7(w6);Cw3 Aw24(9);B15	a/c		
	M Aw24(9);B15 A3;B7(w6);Cw3	c/d	Child 2 A3;B7(w6);Cw3 Aw24(9);B15			
3	F A2;B-;Cw3 Aw31;B40(w6)	a/b	Child 1 A2;B-;Cw3 A28;B12(w4)	a/c		
	M A28;B12(w4) A1;Bw37	c/d	Child 2 A2;B-;Cw3 A28;B12(w4)	a/c		
4	F Aw24(9);Bw35;Cw4 A29;B12(w4)	a/b	Child 1 Aw24(9);Bw35;Cw4 A1;B8(w6)	a/c	Child 2 Aw24(9);Bw35;Cw4 A3;B7(w6)	a/d
	M A1;B8(w6) A3;B7(w6)	c/d	Child 3 Aw24(9);Bw35;Cw4 A1;B8(w6)	a/c		
5	F A26(10);B5(w4);Cw3 A28;B-	a/b	Child 1 A26(10);B5(w4);Cw3 A-;B14	a/c	Child 3 A28;B- A11;B5(w4)	b/d
	M A-;B14 A11;B5(w4)	c/d	Child 2 A26(10);B5(w4);Cw3 A-;B14	a/c		
			Child 4 A26(10);B5(w4);Cw3 A-;B14	a/c		
6	F A11;Bw22;Cw1 A11;Bw35(w6);Cw4	a/b	Child 2 A11;Bw22;Cw1 Aw33;B14(w6)	a/c	Child 1 A11;Bw35(w6);Cw4 A28;B12(w4)	b/d
	M Aw33;B14(w6) A28;B12(w4)	c/d	Child 3[c] A11;Bw22;Cw1 A28;B14(w6)	a/cxd		

[a] From Dupont *et al.* (1977).
[b] M, Mother; F, father.
[c] Child with HLA-A/B recombination.

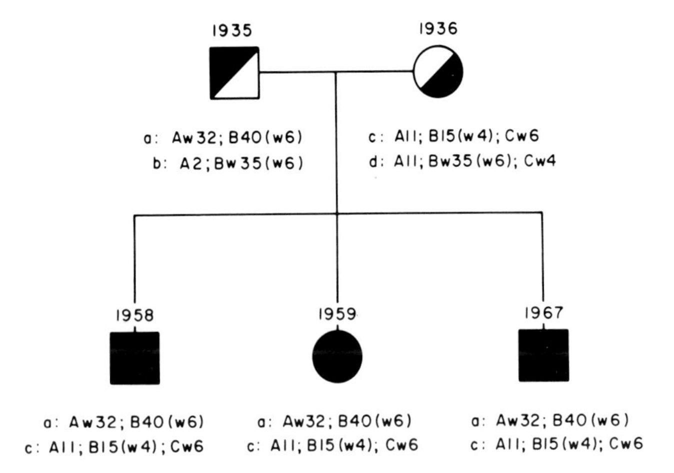

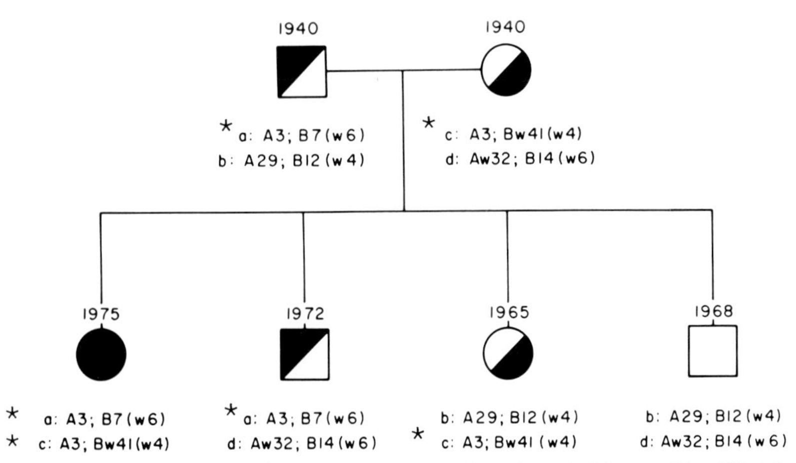

FIG. 10. Pedigrees for two families with 21-hydroxylase deficiency. The HLA haplotypes for the HLA-A, HLA-B, and HLA-C alleles are given in each family. The paternal haplotypes are labeled a and b, and the maternal haplotypes c and d. The parents are obligate heterozygous carriers for the 21-hydroxylase deficiency gene (denoted by the half-black symbols). The affected children are denoted by black symbols. In A, three affected siblings are HLA genotypically identical. In B, one affected child is HLA genotypically different from the three unaffected siblings. One sibling who carries the parental a and d haplotypes is presumed to be a heterozygous carrier for 21-hydroxylase deficiency because he shares the a haplotype with the patient. Another sibling has the parental b and c haplotypes and shares the c haplotype with the patient, and should be a carrier of the 21-hydroxylase deficiency gene. The child with the b and d haplotypes should be normal for the gene. From Levine *et al.* (1978).

deficiency is located very close to the HLA locus on the sixth chromosome.

b. Fine Gene Mapping. i. Separation from HLA-A locus. The 21-hydroxylase deficiency gene has been mapped within the HLA complex. The gene has been separated from the HLA-A locus by genetic recombination in several families.

In the first report by Dupont *et al.* (1977), one patient had inherited a maternal HLA-A/B recombinant haplotype and the disease gene segregated with the HLA-B. Additional studies with HLA genotyping of families with 21-hydroxylase deficiency have separated the gene from the HLA-A locus and have confirmed the close genetic linkage between the HLA-B locus and 21-hydroxylase deficiency (Levine *et al.*, 1978; Murtaza *et al.*, 1978; Price *et al.*, 1978; Weitkamp *et al.*, 1978; Zappacosta *et al.*, 1978; Grosse-Wilde *et al.*, 1979).

ii. Separation from the glyoxalase I (GLO) marker. More detailed genetic mapping of the 21-hydroxylase deficiency gene within the HLA genetic linkage group has been provided from the study of the polymorphic genetic traits Bf (Alper *et al.*, 1972) and glyoxalase I (Koempf *et al.*, 1975). The data shown in Table V are informative for segregation of glyoxalase I since the father is homozygous (2/2) for the glyoxalase I marker and the mother is heterozygous (1/2) for this genetic marker. The three children are HLA genotypically identical (a/c) and all are affected with CAH. If no genetic recombination had occurred in this family between the glyoxalase I locus and the 21-hydroxylase deficiency gene, the

TABLE V
HLA-Glyoxalase (GLO) Recombinant in Family Zurich 7[a,b]

Family member	HLA genotype	Bf	GLO	HLA-Bf-GLO
Father	a/b	SS	2-2	a-S-2/b-S-2
Mother	c/d	FF	1-2	c-F-1/d-F-2
Child 1[c]	a/c	SF	2-2	a-S-2/c-F-2[d]
Child 2[c]	a/c	SF	2-1	a-S-2/c-F-1
Child 3[c]	a/c	SF	2-1	a-S-2/c-F-1

[a] From Levine *et al.* (1978).

[b] The paternal HLA haplotypes are labeled a and b, and the maternal haplotypes are labeled c and d. The children are all HLA genotypically identical (a/c). The family is informative for GLO (the mother is GLO 1-2 and the father is GLO 2-2). Child 1 has a maternal recombinant haplotype (HLA : GLO), which separates the 21-hydroxylase deficiency gene from the GLO locus.

[c] Patients with congenital adrenal hyperplasia.

[d] HLA-B : Bf, GLO, or Bf : GLO recombinant.

three siblings would also be identical for the glyoxalase I marker. Child 2 and Child 3 are glyoxalase I (2/1), but Child 1 is glyoxalase I (2/2), and therefore must carry a maternal recombinant haplotype for this GLO I. It could not be determined whether the glyoxalase I recombination in Child 1 is between HLA and Bf (HLA : Bf, glyoxalase I); or between Bf and glyoxalase I (HLA, Bf: glyoxalase I). However, since all three children were affected with congenital adrenal hyperplasia but Child 1 had a glyoxalase I variant different from that of Child 2 and Child 3, it was concluded that the 21-hydroxylase deficiency trait could be separated from the glyoxalase I locus.

International studies of the genetic linkage between HLA and CAH and fine mapping of the gene for CAH due to 21-hydroxylase have been reported. These studies from 25 laboratories were recently summarized in the report from the Eighth International Histocompatibility Workshop (Dupont *et al.*, 1980).

Table VI summarizes the data on families which were informative for genetic mapping of the 21-hydroxylase deficiency gene within the HLA linkage group. Seven families were informative for mapping the 21-hydroxylase deficiency gene in relation to the HLA-A locus because of HLA-A : B or HLA-C : B recombinations. The 21-hydroxylase deficiency gene segregated in each of these families with the HLA-B locus.

Fourteen families were informative for mapping of 21-hydroxylase deficiency in relation to HLA-D/DR and GLO. In 13 of these families, the 21-hydroxylase deficiency gene segregated with HLA. One family reported by Klouda *et al.* (1980) demonstrated that the 21-hydroxylase deficiency gene could be separated from the HLA-D/DR locus and therefore must be located between HLA-DR and the GLO locus. One additional family reported by Betuel *et al.* (1980) contained two HLA-A, B, C, D/DR identical siblings of which only one had 21-hydroxylase deficiency. These two families would therefore place the 21-hydroxylase deficiency gene outside HLA-D/DR between DR and GLO. Pucholt *et al.* (1979) have, however, reported on one family with an HLA-B : D/DR recombination. The 21-hydroxylase deficiency gene segregated in this family with the HLA-B locus and could clearly be separated from the HLA-D/DR locus.

The international studies of congenital adrenal hyperplasia due to 21-hydroxylase deficiency have thus established that the 21-hydroxylase deficiency gene is very closely linked to HLA.

The study of Levine *et al.* (1978) established that both the salt wasting and non-salt wasting forms of 21-hydroxylase deficiency are in very close genetic linkage with HLA-B and that the gene for the 21-hydroxylase enzyme of the mineralocorticoid pathway and the glucocorticoid pathway is located close to the locus for the HLA-B determinants.

TABLE VI
21-Hydroxylase Deficiency: HLA Recombinants

Recombination	21-OH-def Gene	Reference
HLA A:B	Segregate with HLA-B	Dupont *et al.* (1977) Levine *et al.* (1978)
A:B	Segregate with HLA-B	Gelsthorpe *et al.* (1980)[a]
A:B	Segregate with HLA-B	Couillin *et al.* (1980)[a]
A:C	Segregate with HLA-C	Price *et al.* (1978)
A:Bf or A:B	Segregate with Bf or HLA-B	Weitkamp *et al.* (1978)
C:B	Segregate with HLA-B	Kastelan *et al.* (1980)[a]
C:B	Segregate with HLA-B	Betuel *et al.* (1980)[a]
B:D/DR	Segregate with HLA-B	Pucholt *et al.* (1979)
DR:GLO	Segregate with DR in two families	Levine *et al.* (1978)
DR:GLO	Segregate with DR	Couillin *et al.* (1980)[a]
DR:GLO	Segregate with DR in two families	Manderville *et al.* (1980)[a]
DR:GLO	Segregate with DR in four families	Kastelan *et al.* (1980)[a]
DR:GLO	Segregate with DR	Mayer *et al.* (1980)[a]
DR:GLO	Segregate with GLO	Klouda *et al.* (1980)
DR:GLO	Segregate with DR in three families	Hansen *et al.* (1980)[a]
HLA A,B,C,DR/D id. siblings discordant for 21-OH-def	21-OH-def outside HLA-D	Betuel *et al.* (1980)[a]

[a] Denotes families reported only as part of the Eighth International Histocompatibility Workshop (Dupont *et al.*, 1980).

iii. Lod Score. The statistical method for the assessment of linkage is based on the logarithm of the odds (Lod Score) of a given sequence of genetic events occurring if the loci are linked as compared to its occurring if the loci are not linked. Linkage is considered to be established if a Lod Score exceeds 3. The closer together the two linked genes are, the less likely they will be separated by recombination (or crossing over). The recombination frequency is a direct index of the distance between the genes. The frequency of recombination is expressed as the recombination fraction (θ). When the peak Lod Score occurs at θ equal to zero, i.e., no recombination between the genes, this indicates that two genes are located very close together. Thus the Lod Score is a measure of linkage while the recombination frequency is a measure of distance between two linked genes.

The Workshop's results of the Lod Score analysis for linkage between HLA and 21-hydroxylase deficiency are shown in Table VII. The linkage analysis was performed on data from 19 families with two or more affected children. A peak Lod Score of 15.65 was found for the recombinant fraction $\theta = 0.00$ for linkage between HLA and 21-hydroxylase deficiency. Eleven of these families were also informative for linkage analysis for 21-hydroxylase deficiency and Bf. A peak Lod Score of 1.76 for $\theta = 0.00$ was found for the linkage between this genetic marker and 21-hydroxylase deficiency (Table VII). Eleven families were informative for linkage analysis for 21-hydroxylase deficiency and GLO. A negative Lod Score of -2.05 was obtained for $\theta = 0.00$ and the peak Lod Score of 1.26 for $\theta = 0.07$ was found for linkage between 21-hydroxylase deficiency and GLO (Table VII). These data confirm that the 21-hydroxylase deficiency gene is very close to the HLA-B locus on the sixth chromosome.

The Lod Score analysis for 131 families with 21-hydroxylase deficiency are summarized in Table VIII. This table contains data from the previously reported studies from New York, Zurich, and Munich (Levine *et al.*, 1978; Grosse-Wilde *et al.*, 1979), and three additional laboratories. The data consistently demonstrate a peak Lod Score for the recombinant fraction $\theta = 0.00$ for genetic linkage between HLA and 21-hydroxylase deficiency.

In addition, the Lod Score analysis demonstrates that the gene must be very close to the HLA-B locus. The additional typing for Bf and GLO demonstrate that 21-hydroxylase deficiency follows Bf and is located 5–10

TABLE VII

LOD Scores for Linkage between 21-OH Deficiency and HLA, Bf, and GLO[a]

Recombination fraction θ	LOD Scores between 21-OH and		
	HLA	Bf	GLO
0.10	11.36	1.32	1.23
0.09	11.79	1.36	1.24
0.08	12.22	1.41	1.25
0.07	12.65	1.45	1.26
0.06	13.08	1.50	1.24
0.05	13.51	1.54	1.21
0.04	13.94	1.59	1.15
0.03	14.37	1.63	1.05
0.02	14.80	1.68	0.88
0.01	15.23	1.72	0.56
0.0	15.65	1.76	−2.05

[a] From Dupont *et al.* (1980).

TABLE VIII

21-Hydroxylase Deficiency and HLA LOD Score Analysis (131 Families)

Reference	Origin	Recombinant fraction θ										Number of families
		0.00	0.01	0.02	0.03	0.04	0.05	0.10	0.20	0.30	0.40	
Levine *et al.* (1978)	New York Zurich	9.5	9.3	9.1	9.0	8.9	8.4	7.5	4.7	2.6	0.95	34
Grosse-Wilde *et al.* (1979)	Munich	3.4	—	—	—	—	2.9	2.5	1.7	0.8	0.14	17
Manderville *et al.*[a]	Glasgow	5.0	4.9	4.8	4.6	4.5	4.3	3.7	2.4	1.2	0.38	17
Gelsthorpe *et al.*[a]	Sheffield	8.5	8.3	8.0	7.8	7.7	7.4	6.1	3.9	1.8	0.62	20
Couillin *et al.*[a]	Paris	18.7	18.2	17.6	17.1	16.6	16.1	—	—	—	—	43

[a] Results appear only in the Eighth International Histocompatibility Workshop (Dupont *et al.*, 1980).

cM from the GLO locus. The fine mapping of the 21-hydroxylase deficiency gene within HLA demonstrates that it is located close to the HLA-B and the HLA-D/DR locus and clearly can be separated from the HLA-A locus and from the GLO locus. The position of the 21-hydroxylase deficiency gene relative to HLA-B and HLA-DR is inconsistent. The family studied by Klouda *et al.* (1980) and the family studied by Betuel *et al.* (1980) indicate that the 21-hydroxyase deficiency gene is located outside HLA-DR. The family studied by Pucholt *et al.* (1979) demonstrates, however, that the gene is located between HLA-B and HLA-DR. If one assumes that none of these three recombinant HLA haplotypes have undergone double recombination, it must be concluded that the genetic control of 21-hydroxylase activity in the adrenal gland is controlled by two closely linked genes, of which one is located between HLA-B and HLA-DR, and the other is located between HLA-DR and GLO.

The loci mapped on chromosome no. 6 within the HLA linkage group are shown in Fig. 11. The 21-hydroxylase deficiency gene is located between the HLA-A locus and the centromere but further away from the centromere than the glyoxalase I locus. The gene is thus mapped within 3–4 cM.

c. HLA Genotyping and Hormonal Studies in Clinical Practice and in Genetic Counselling. Prior to the discovery of the HLA linkage to the 21-hydroxylase deficiency gene, attempts were made to test for hormonal heterozygosity using the obligate heterozygote parents of children with CAH. A mild deficiency of 21-hydroxylase was demonstrated in parents by hormonal measurements by several investigators (Bongiovanni, 1953; Lee and Gareis, 1975; Cleveland *et al.,* 1972; Bergada *et al.,* 1965; Hall *et al.,* 1970; Qazi *et al.,* 1971; Gutai *et al.,* 1977; Homoki *et al.,* 1977; Knorr *et al.,* 1977; Kerensky *et al.,* 1977; Roux *et al.,* 1977). However, similar studies in sibs of patients with CAH have been difficult to interpret because of the inability to ascertain which sibs are carriers of the gene and which are genetically unaffected. With the demonstration of linkage between the genes for HLA and 21-hydroxylase deficiency, HLA genotyping made it possible to predict which sibs were carriers and which sibs could be assumed to be genetically unaffected. The method for utilizing HLA genotyping in this prediction is shown in Fig. 10. The validity of the prediction of heterozygosity by HLA genotyping is supported by hormonal studies.

Thus in family studies, the response of 17-OHP to ACTH stimulation was higher in family members who were predicted to be heterozygotes than in family members predicted to be genetically unaffected by HLA genotyping (Fig. 12). No other hormonal measurement was useful in dis-

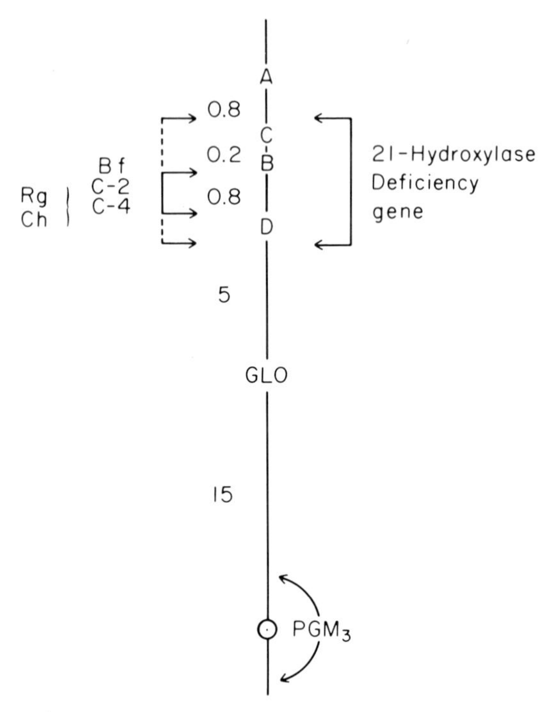

FIG. 11. HLA linkage group on chromosome 6. The recombinant fractions for the known linkages between A : C, C : B, B : D, B : GLO, and GLO : PGM_3 are shown. The position of the genes for factor B (Bf), complement C-2 and complement C-4 and Rodgers (Rg) and Chido (Ch) blood groups is also indicated. The 21-hydroxylase deficiency gene can be mapped between HLA-A and glyoxalase I (GLO). The most likely position of the 21-hydroxylase deficiency gene is very close to HLA-B. From Levine *et al.* (1978).

criminating heterozygotes from normals (Lorenzen *et al.,* 1979, 1980). Other investigators observed similar correlations between HLA genotyping and hormonal measurements (Grosse-Wilde *et al.,* 1978, 1979; Sobel *et al.,* 1980).

The hormonal test distinguished the unaffected person from heterozygotes with moderate reliability in the prepubertal child and in the adult male, while in the adult female the response is overlapping. Thus, for an adult male in the general population who is not a family member of a patient with CAH, it is possible to predict heterozygosity by a 6-hour ACTH stimulation test. In the adult female, such predictions may not be possible if the response is in the overlapping range. Grosse-Wilde *et al.* (1979) recently reported that administering dexamethasone to women before a 60-minute ACTH (Cortrosyn) stimulation test resulted in complete segregation of heterozygote adult females from controls. Lejeune-Lenain

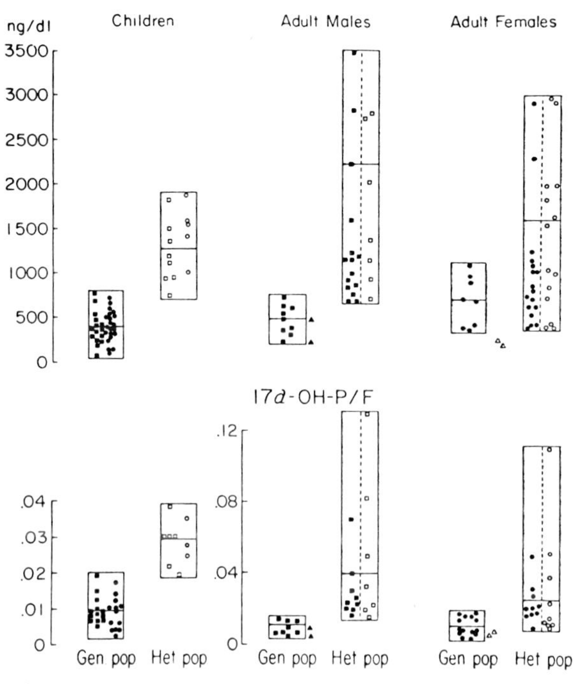

FIG. 12. Stimulated 17-OHP level and the stimulated 17-OHP to F ratio in prepubertal and early pubertal children, postpubertal males, and postmenarchal females. Gen. pop., general population (■, male, ●, female, ▲, homozygous normal brother of a patient with CAH, based on HLA typing, △, homozygous normal sister, based on HLA typing). Het. pop., heterozygous population (■, father, ●, mother, □, heterozygous brothers or heterozygous male family members, based on HLA typing; ○, heterozygous sisters or heterozygous female family members, based on HLA typing). The bar represents the range; the heavy horizontal line represents the mean. From Lorenzen *et al.* (1980).

et al. (1980) also recommended pretreatment with dexamethasone for heterozygote detection.

In an autosomal recessive disorder the Mendelian ratio of affected: heterozygote : unaffected among sibs is expected to be 1 : 2 : 1. By HLA genotyping of sibs of affected patients the following distribution was found:

affected sibs (HLA-B identical to the index case and hormonally proven)	= 26
heterozygotes	= 89
unaffected (HLA normal)	= 37

Seventy-eight families with classical adrenal hyperplasia due to 21 hydroxylase deficiency were studied for segregation ratio between affected and unaffected siblings.

Thirty-six families had two children, 24 had 3 children, 8 had 4 children, 5 had 5 children, 2 had 6 children, and 3 families had 8, 9, and 13 children each.

The segregation ratio was calculated by the single selection method and the assumption that the disease behaves as a simple autosomal recessive disorder. The significance level was calculated by the formula

$$X = \frac{(\text{Observed affected} - \text{Expected affected})^2}{\text{Variance}}$$

$$= \frac{(105 - 119.25)^2}{30.9375} = 6.5636$$

$$0.01 < p < 0.025$$

This demonstrates a significant under representation of affected children in these families.

There were however 8 additional infant males in these families, who died during the first few months of life from symptoms indicating possible salt-wasting crises. If these 8 children are included in the analysis as affected children the X analysis gives:

$$X = \frac{(114 - 122.25)^2}{32.4375} = 2.0983$$

$$0.10 < p < 0.20$$

which is not a significant deviation from expectations.

d. Cryptic 21-Hydroxylase Deficiency. We have recently described a new and cryptic form of steroid 21-hydroxylase deficiency in family members of patients with classical CAH. In the course of HLA genotyping and hormonal testing of families, we encountered a conflict between the HLA and hormonal predictions of CAH genotype in the sister of an index case who was predicted by HLA genotyping to be unaffected (Lorenzen *et al.*, 1979) (Fig. 13). ACTH tests indicated that her stimulated 17-OHP level was within the heterozygote range (Fig. 14). This conflict between the HLA prediction and the hormonal findings was resolved when it was discovered that the father was an asymptomatic patient with mild 21-hydroxylase deficiency. Thus the genotype of the pedigree was revised to indicate that both the father's haplotypes were linked to a 21-hydroxylase deficiency gene (Fig. 13). One was transmitted to the index case and the other to the unaffected sib who responded appropriately to hormonal testing as a heterozygote. It was surprising to find that the father was a patient

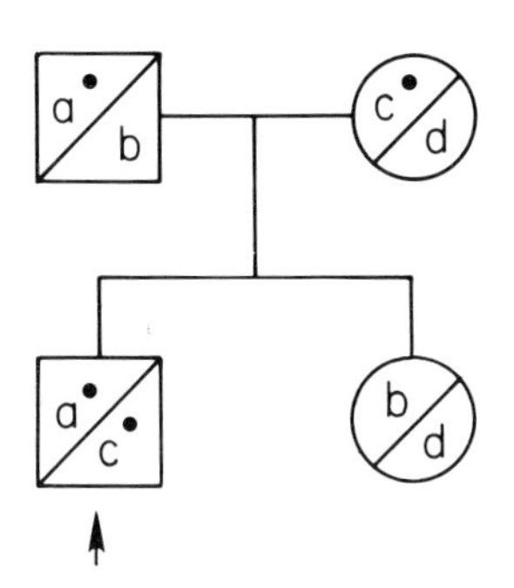

Posthormonal studies

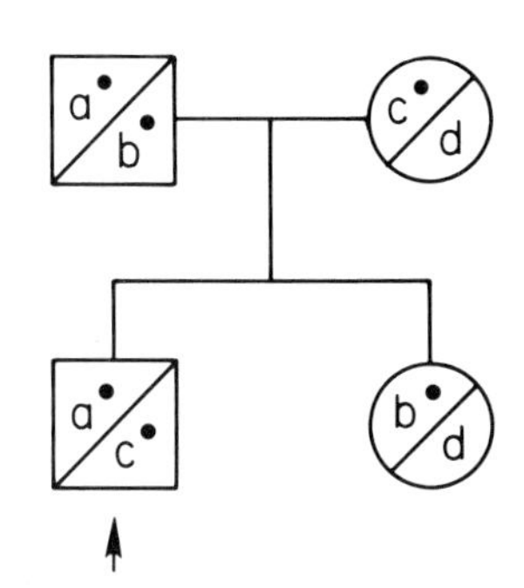

FIG. 13. Revision of interpretation of CAH genotyping before and after hormonal studies which revealed the father to be a patient with 21-hydroxylase deficiency. a,b,c, and d represent HLA haplotypes. a● and c● represent the HLA haplotypes linked with gene for CAH in the affected child (arrow). Hormonal studies revealed the father to be affected and thus the b haplotype was also linked with the gene for CAH. This resulted in reassignment of the sister as a heterozygote (b●/d). From Lorenzen *et al.* (1979).

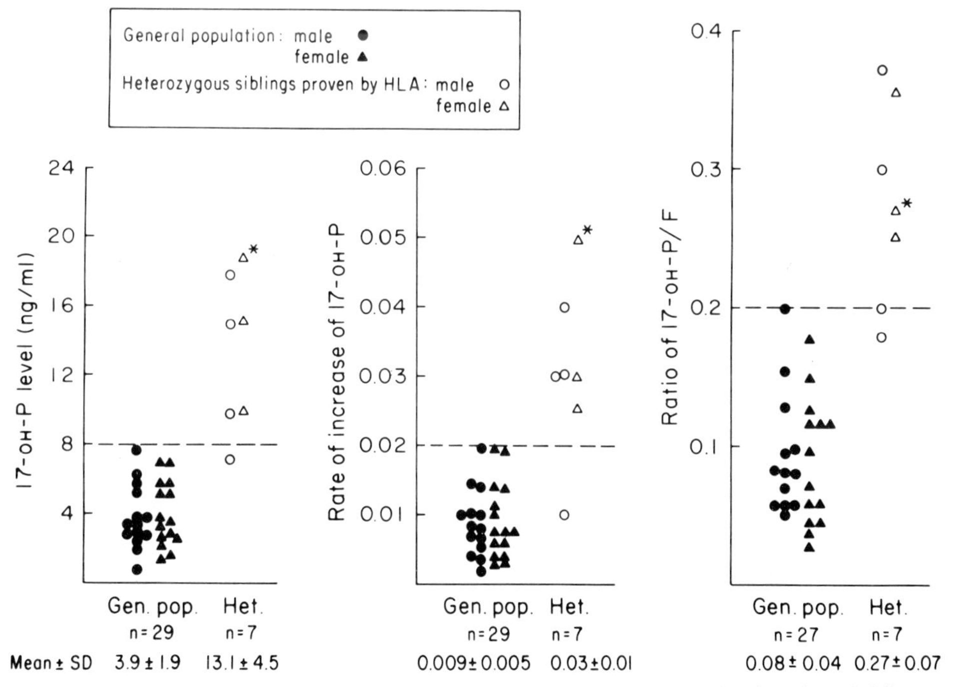

FIG. 14. Hormonal response to ACTH stimulation in prepubertal and early pubertal children (Tanner I–III). Gen. pop., general population; Het., assumed to be heterozygous for CAH according to HLA-geneotyping; ---, upper range in general population; Δ*, offspring of a probably affected father and heterozygous mother for CAH. From Lorenzen *et al.* (1979).

with 21-hydroxylase deficiency without the hallmarks commonly accompanying this disorder. We have now studied 120 families and have found 8 pedigrees in which family members of an index case have a mild but asymptomatic 21-hydroxylase deficiency which we have called cryptic 21-hydroxylase deficiency. Within each generation the family members with cryptic 21-hydroxylase deficiency were HLA identical (Figs. 15 and 16). Each shared one HLA haplotype with the index case with classical congenital adrenal hyperplasia and would have been predicted before hormonal testing to be heterozygote carriers. These family members are genetic compounds, having 21-hydroxylase deficiency as a result of two recessive gene defects: a severe 21-hydroxylase gene defect present in the index case, and a mild 21-hydroxylase gene defect. Thus, the CAH genotype in the family members with cryptic 21-hydroxylase deficiency was $21\text{-OH}^{CAH}/21\text{-OH}^{CRYPTIC}$.

Lod Score analysis for linkage between the cryptic 21-hydroxylase trait and HLA gave a combined Lod Score for males and females for $\theta = 0.00$ of 3.409. Close genetic linkage between HLA and $21\text{-OH}^{CRYPTIC}$ was thus established (Levine *et al.,* 1980c).

These family members have no signs or symptoms suggestive of 21-hydroxylase deficiency: they are not virilized at birth, do not show signs of progressive virilization after birth, have undergone normal puberty, and are fertile. Although physical examination does not distinguish these family members from normal, their biochemical profile indicates that they have mild 21-hydroxylase deficiency. The disorder in these family members was only uncovered in the course of HLA genotyping and hormonal studies in families of patients with classical congenital adrenal hyperplasia. The biochemical profile in these patients is best described by a nomogram relating the baseline and ACTH stimulable levels of 17-OHP, Δ^4-androstenedione (Δ^4), dehydroepiandrosterone (DHEA), the ratio of DHEA/Δ^4, and testosterone. Figure 17 demonstrates that patients with classical CAH ($21\text{-OH}^{CAH}/21\text{-OH}^{CAH}$), cryptic 21-hydroxylase ($21\text{-OH}^{CAH}/21\text{-OH}^{CRYPTIC}$), and heterozygotes for these disorders ($21\text{-OH}^{CAH}/21\text{-OH}^{NORMAL}$ or $21\text{-OH}^{CRYPTIC}/21\text{-OH}^{NORMAL}$) aggregate into groups which are easily distinguished.

The groups are distributed on a regression line in the following descending order: classical adrenal hyperplasia, cryptic 21-hydroxylase deficiency, heterozygotes for the classical and cryptic 21-hydroxylase deficiency, and subjects genetically unaffected (by HLA). The general population which was not HLA genotyped is at the lower end, but some fall in the heterozygote group suggesting that they may be carrying the gene for 21-hydroxylase deficiency. A similar distribution of groups along a regression line is observed for Δ^4 and testosterone in females (Figs. 18 and 19).

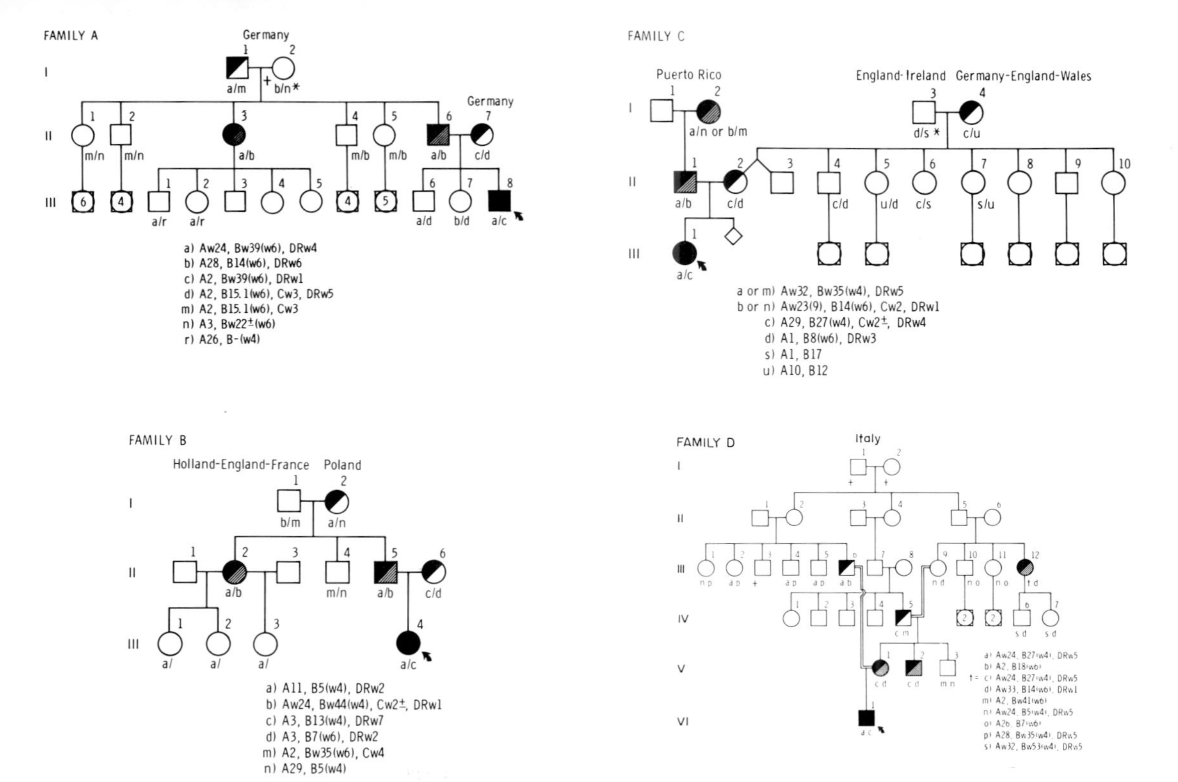

FIG. 15. Pedigrees of families A–D. The HLA haplotypes for HLA-A, HLA-B, HLA-C, and HLA-DR are indicated for each family member tested. The index case with CAH is assigned the haplotypes a/c. Asterisk indicates haplotypes deduced from offspring. Half solid symbols indicate obligate heterozygous carriers of the severe deficiency gene for CAH. Half solid–half striped symbols indicate family members with cryptic 21-hydroxylase deficiency, having both a severe and a mild deficiency gene. Circle within a square indicates offspring, number if known. From Levine *et al.* (1980c).

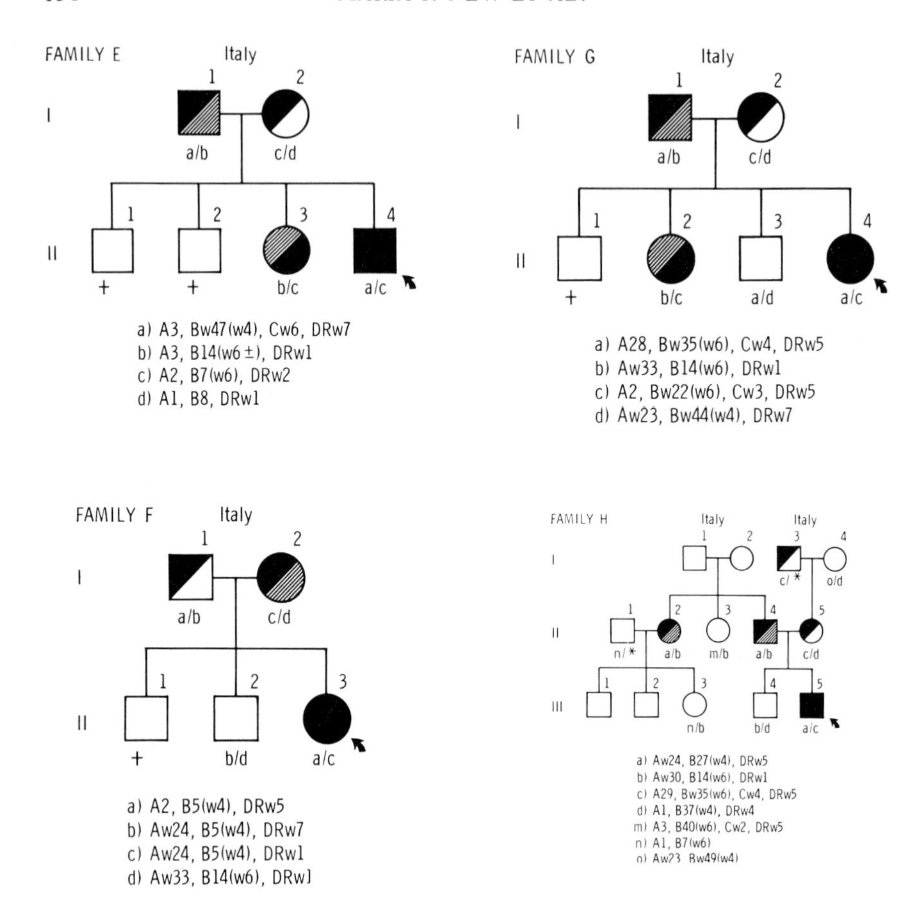

FIG. 16. Pedigrees of families E–H. See Fig. 15 for symbols. From Levine *et al.* (1980c).

Although the DHEA values (Fig. 20) do not aggregate in groups, the ratio of DHEA/Δ^4 aggregates in reverse order from that of 17-OHP (Fig. 21). The mean testosterone level in males with classical CAH was lower than that of heterozygotes (Fig. 22).

These nomograms provide a sensitive and powerful tool by which to assign the 21-hydroxylase deficiency genotype, i.e., patients whose hormonal values fall on the regression line within a defined group are assigned to that group. It should be noted that the heterozygotes for cryptic 21-hydroxylase deficiency (21-OH^{CRYPTIC}/21-OH^{NORMAL}) fall in the same range as the heterozygotes for classical 21-hydroxylase deficiency (21-OH^{CAH}/21-OH^{NORMAL}). This finding confirms our postulate that patients with cryptic 21-hydroxylase deficiency are genetic compounds (21-OH^{CAH}/21-OH^{CRYPTIC}) and excludes the suggestion that they are unusually manifest-

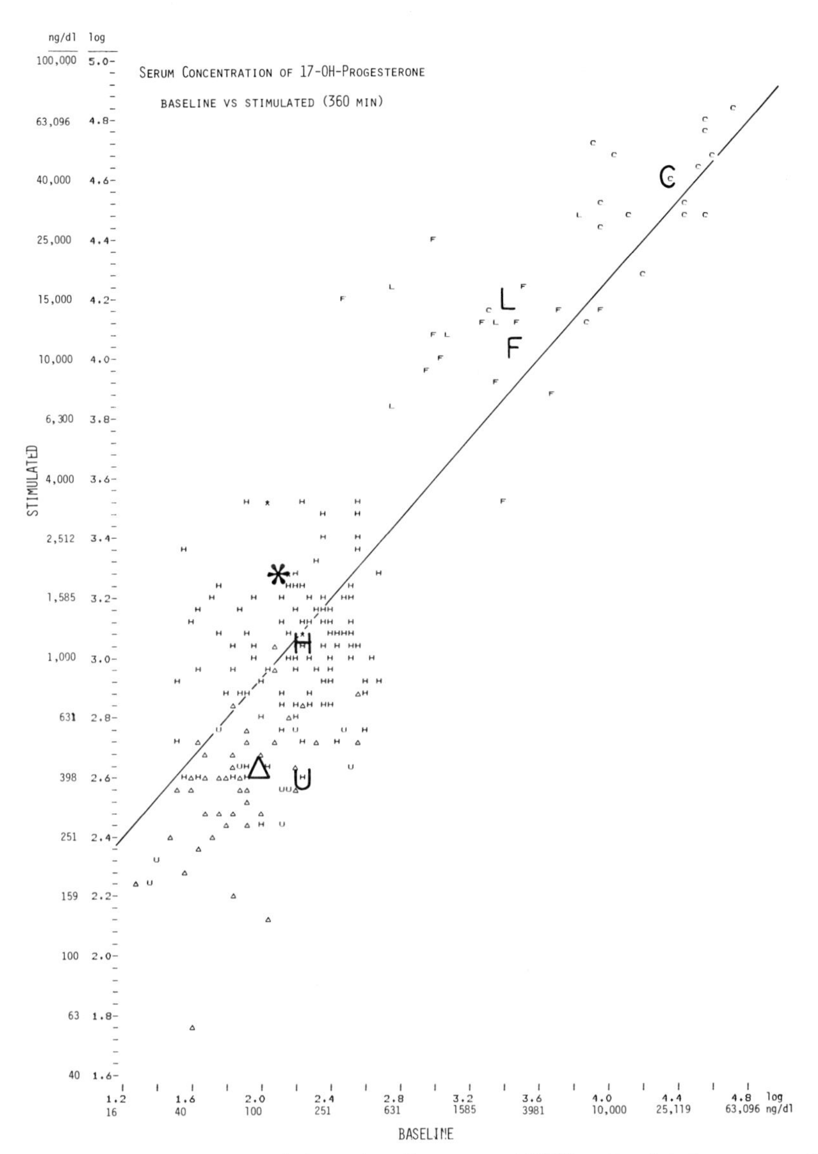

FIG. 17. Nomogram relating baseline to ACTH stimulated serum 17-hydroxyprogesterone concentration. Values for the $\log_{10}$ and the antilog are indicated. The mean for each group is indicated by a large symbol. C, classical CAH patients off treatment; F, cryptic 21-hydroxylase deficiency patients; *, heterozygotes for cryptic 21-hydroxylase deficiency; H, heterozygotes for classical CAH; U, family members predicted by HLA genotyping to be genetically unaffected; Δ, general population; L, patients with late onset 21-hydroxylase deficiency. The values for each group aggregate in descending order along the regression line. Note that the heterozygotes for the cryptic 21-hydroxylase defect are in the same range as the heterozygotes for the classical 21-hydroxylase defect.

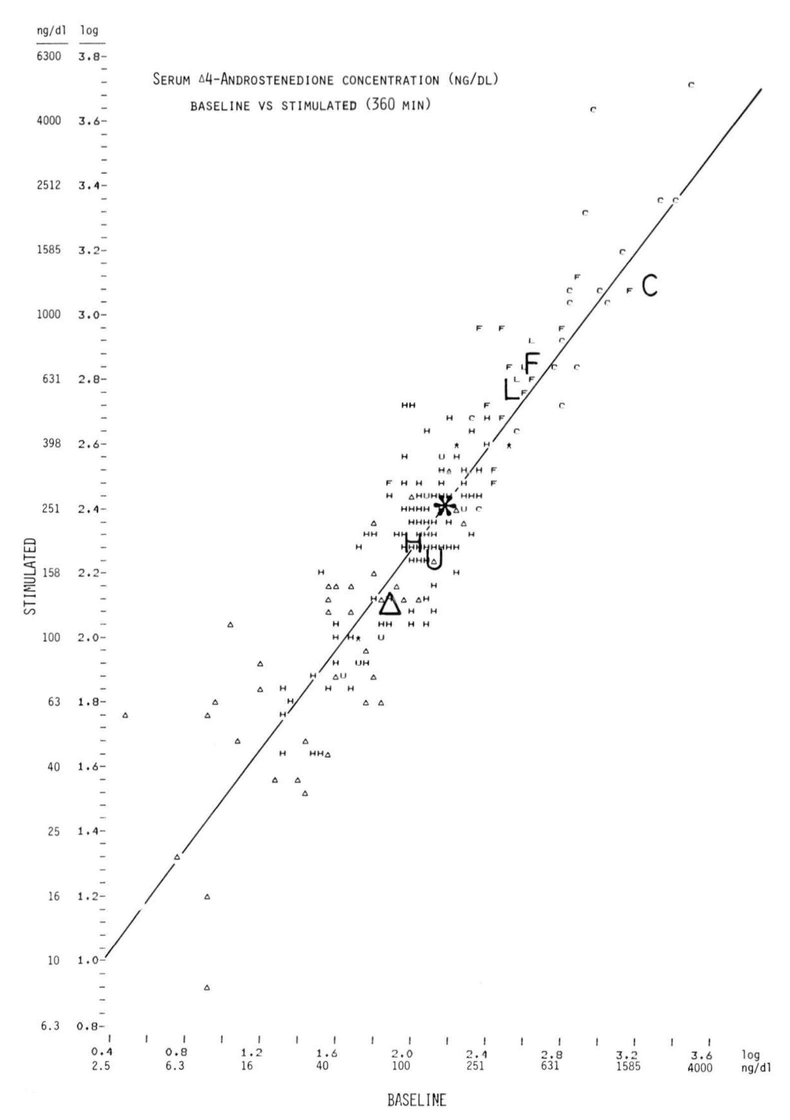

FIG. 18. Nomogram relating baseline to the ACTH stimulated serum Δ^4 androstenedione concentration. Values for the $\log_{10}$ and the antilog are indicated. The mean for each group is indicated by a large symbol. C, classical CAH patients off treatment; F, cryptic 21-hydroxylase deficiency patients; *, heterozygotes for cryptic 21-hydroxylase deficiency; H, heterozygotes for classical CAH; U, family members predicted by HLA genotyping to be genetically unaffected; Δ, general population; L, patients with late onset 21-hydroxylase deficiency. The values for each group aggregate in descending order along the regression line. Note that the values for the asymptomatic patients with cryptic 21-hydroxylase deficiency are in the same range as the symptomatic virilized females with late onset 21-hydroxylase deficiency.

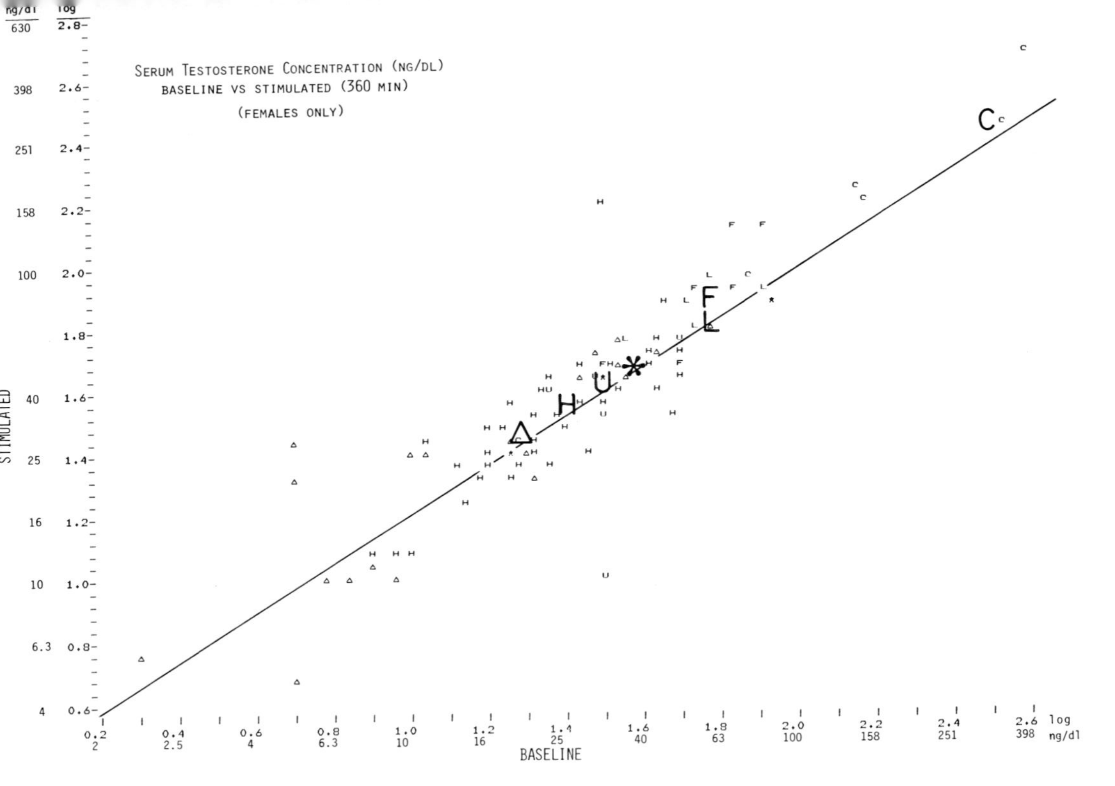

FIG. 19. Nomogram relating baseline to ACTH stimulated serum testosterone concentration in females. Values for the $\log_{10}$ and the antilog are indicated. The mean for each group is indicated by a large symbol. C, classical CAH patients off treatment; F, cryptic 21-hydroxylase deficiency patients; *, heterozygotes for cryptic 21-hydroxylase deficiency; H, heterozygotes for classical CAH; U, family members predicted by HLA genotyping to be genetically unaffected; Δ, general population; L, patients with late onset 21-hydroxylase deficiency. The values for each group aggregate in descending order along the regression line. Note that the values for the asymptomatic females with cryptic 21-hydroxylase deficiency are in the same range as the symptomatic virilized females with late onset 21-hydroxylase deficiency.

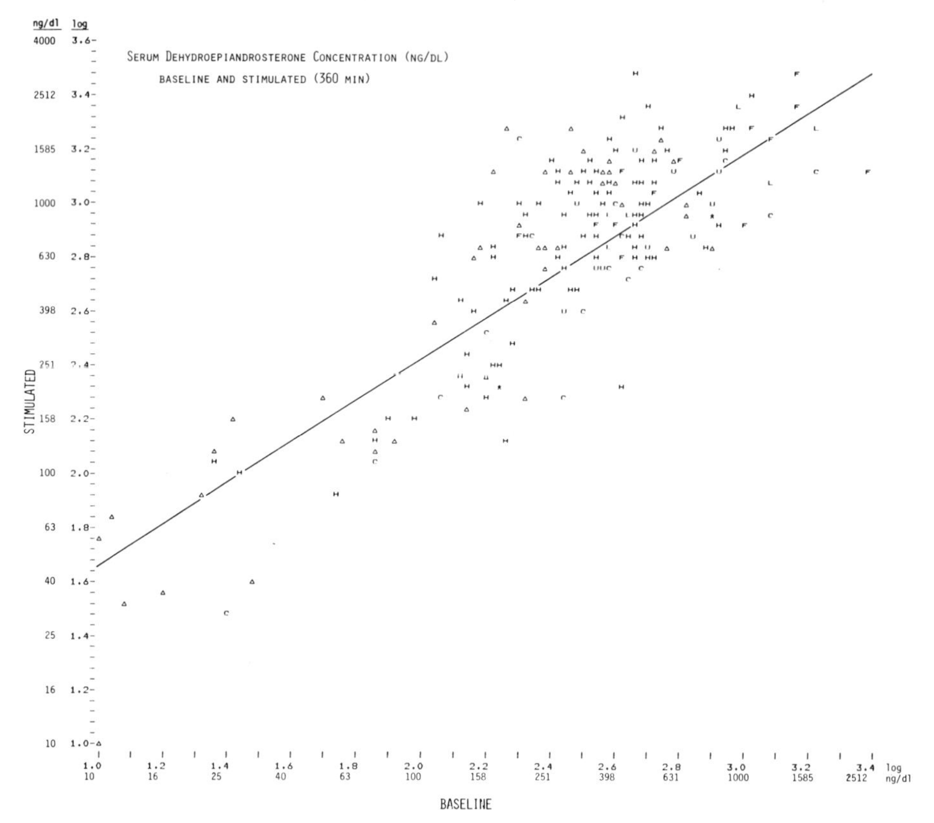

FIG. 20. Nomogram relating baseline to ACTH stimulated serum dehydroepiandrosterone concentration. Values for the $\log_{10}$ and the antilog are indicated. Note that the serum dehydroepiandrosterone concentration does not aggregate according to group. See Fig. 19 for symbols.

ing heterozygotes for the classical gene ($21\text{-OH}^{CAH}/21\text{-OH}^{NORMAL}$) (Zachmann and Prader, 1978, 1979). Based on these nomograms, the genotype for 21-hydroxylase deficiency in the members of families A-H (Figs. 15 and 16) can now be refined (Figs. 23 and 24). In Figs. 23 and 24, the family members who are heterozygous for the cryptic 21-hydroxylase deficiency and the classical 21-hydroxylase deficiency are shown.

e. Late Onset Adrenal Hyperplasia (21-Hydroxylase Deficiency). Virilization and menstrual disturbances presenting in later childhood or early adulthood and associated with endocrinological features consistent with congenital adrenal hyperplasia due to 21-hydroxylase deficiency are a puzzling syndrome to which the term late onset or "acquired" adrenal hyperplasia (AAH) is applied (Newmark *et al.*, 1977).

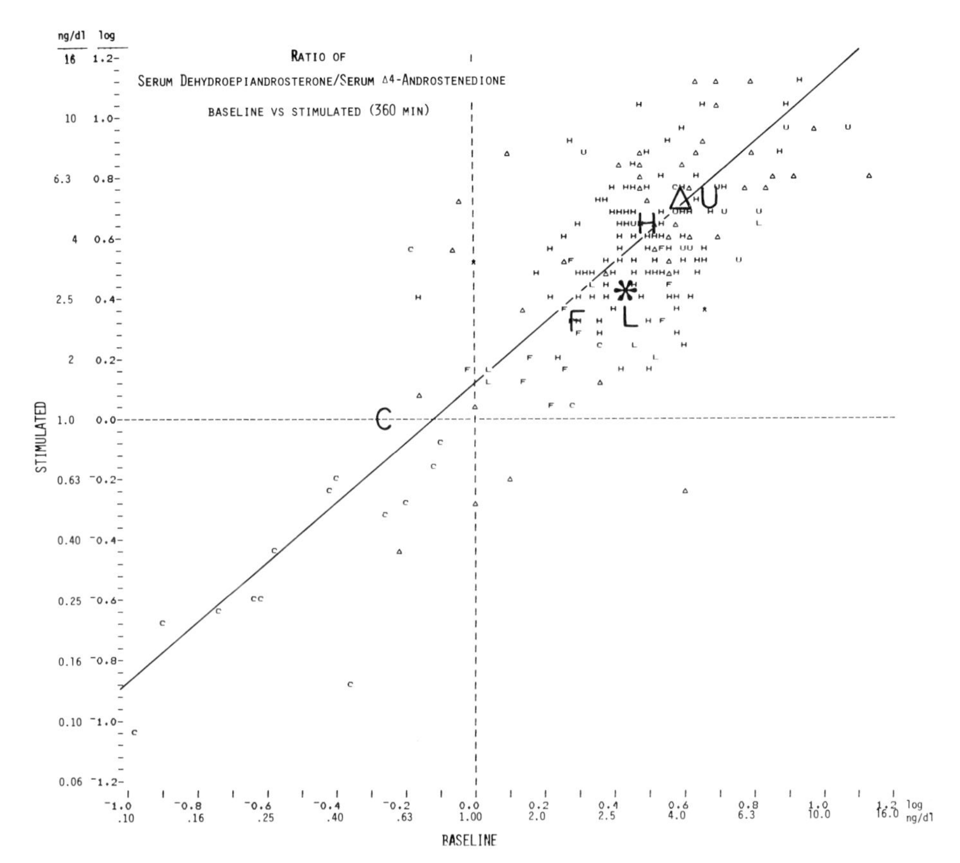

FIG. 21. Nomogram relating baseline to ACTH stimulated ratio of serum dehydroepiandrosterone/Δ^4 androstenedione concentrations. Values for the $\log_{10}$ and the antilog are indicated. The mean for each group is indicated by a large symbol. C, classical CAH patients off treatment; F, cryptic 21-hydroxylase deficiency patients; *, heterozygotes for cryptic 21-hydroxylase deficiency; H, heterozygotes for classical CAH; U, family members predicted by HLA genotyping to be genetically unaffected; Δ, general population; L, patients with late onset 21-hydroxylase deficiency. The values for each group aggregate in descending order along the regression line. Note that the ratio of DHEA/Δ^4 is lower in patients with congenital adrenal hyperplasia and that this group is easily distinguished from other groups by the ratio.

The late presentation of a biochemical enzyme defect has raised the question as to whether this is the same inherited disorder as CAH with delayed presentation or is an "acquired" disorder distinct from CAH.

Our first study of the possible genetic linkage between late onset 21-hydroxylase deficiency and HLA indicated that the late form was not linked (New *et al.,* 1979). This was based on the fact that there were two

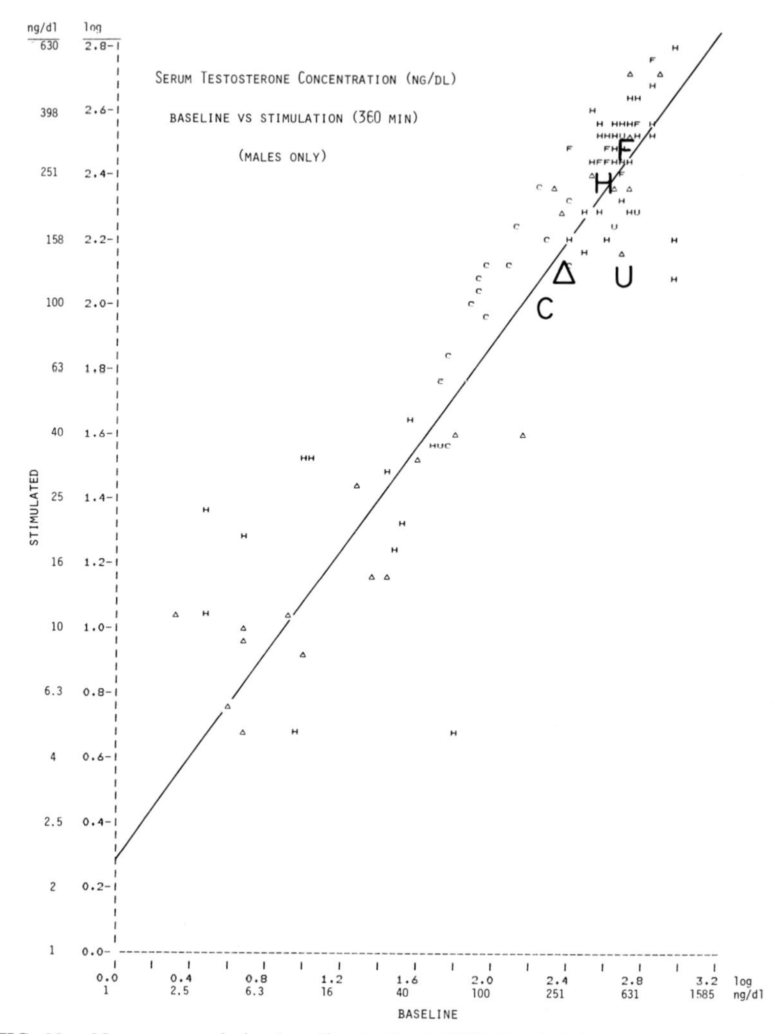

FIG. 22. Nomogram relating baseline to the ACTH stimulated serum testosterone concentration in males. Values for the $\log_{10}$ and the antilog are indicated. The mean for each group is indicated by a large symbol. C, classical CAH patients off treatment; F, cryptic 21-hydroxylase deficiency patients; *, heterozygotes for cryptic 21-hydroxylase deficiency; H, heterozygotes for classical CAH; U, family members predicted by HLA genotyping to be genetically unaffected; Δ, general population; L, patients with late onset 21-hydroxylase deficiency. Note that in males the serum testosterone does not distinguish the groups as well as in females.

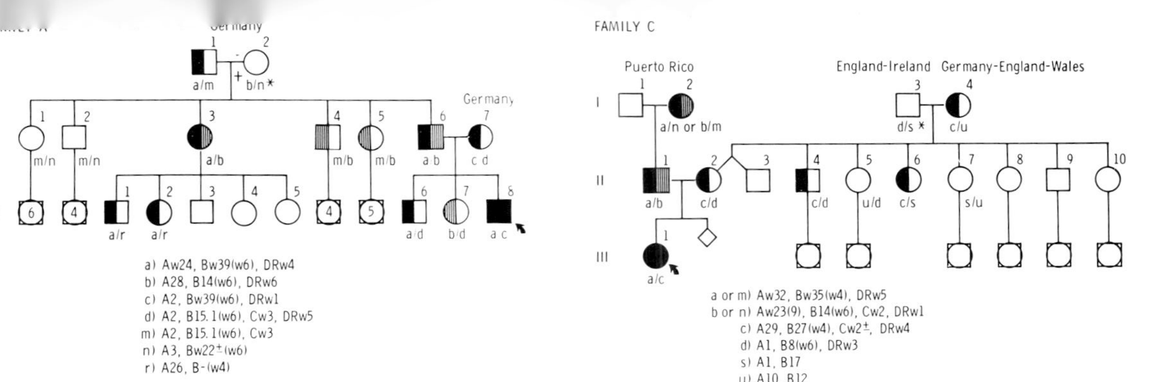

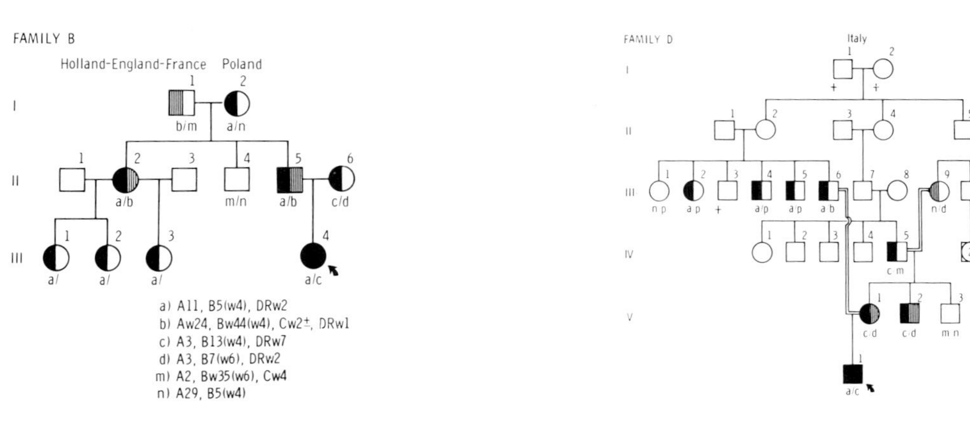

FIG. 23. Pedigrees of families A–D. The HLA haplotypes for HLA-A, HLA-B, HLA-C, and HLA-DR are indicated for each family member tested. The index case with CAH is assigned the haplotypes a/c. Asterisk indicates haplotypes deduced from offspring. Half solid–half open symbols indicate heterozygous carriers of the severe deficiency gene for CAH. Half solid–half striped symbols indicate family members with cryptic 21-hydroxylase deficiency, having both a severe and a mild deficiency gene. Half striped–half open symbols indicate heterozygous carriers of the cryptic 21-hydroxylase deficiency gene. Circle within a square indicates offspring, number if known.

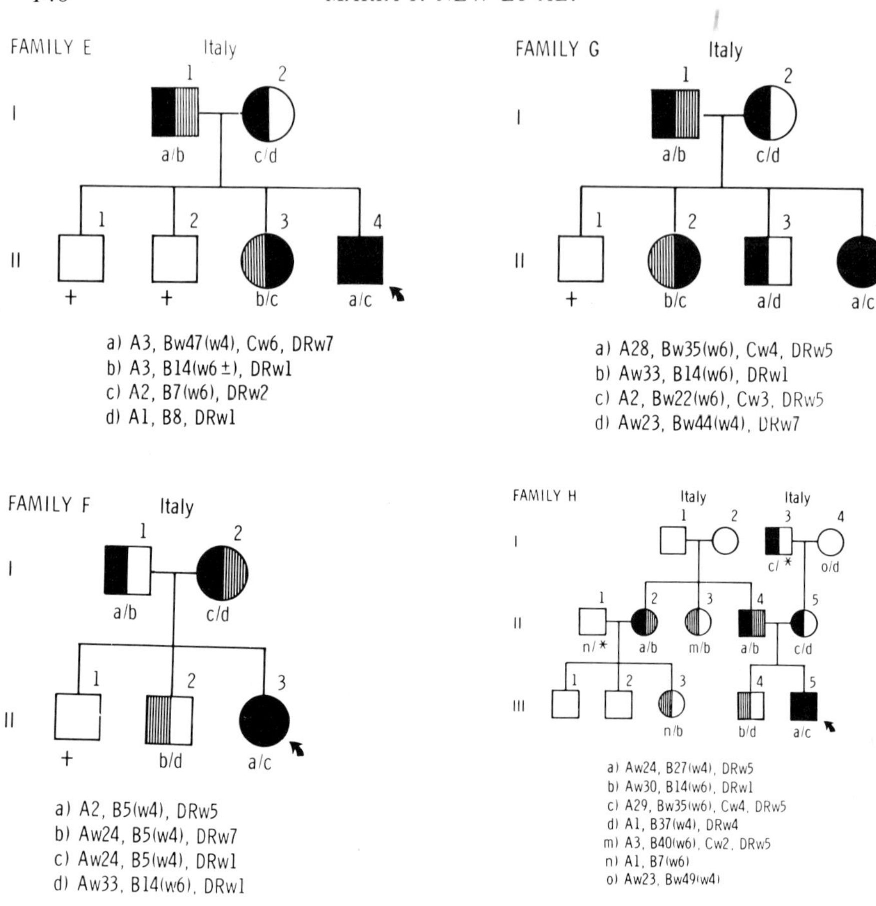

FIG. 24. Pedigrees of families E–H. See Fig. 23 for symbols.

sibs who were HLA identical (but GLO different), only one of whom gave hormonal evidence of 21-hydroxylase deficiency. Further, the father who should have been an obligate heterozygote, if this were an autosomal recessive disorder, demonstrated a 17-OHP response to ACTH within the normal range of the reference population and lower than that of the adult males heterozygous for classical congenital adrenal hyperplasia. The non-linkage was supported by the report of Morillo and Gardner (1979). However, as our reference population was expanded, we observed several heterozygotes for 21-hydroxylase deficiency whose 17-OHP response was similar to the father of our patient with late onset 21-hydroxylase deficiency. Thus, the father's response is now compatible with heterozygosity. Subsequently, reports from other laboratories as well as ours have suggested that late onset 21-hydroxylase deficiency may be linked to HLA (Blankstein *et al.*, 1980; Laron *et al.*, 1980).

Relevant to the question of linkage to HLA of late onset adrenal hyperplasia is the report in the Eighth International Histocompatibility Workshop, of 2 families in which the gene for 21-hydroxylase deficiency was placed outside the HLA-D/DR locus and between DR and GLO (Dupont *et al.*, 1980). In view of these reports, the HLA/GLO recombination in our family with late onset adrenal hyperplasia may explain the divergence of the hormonal findings in the two HLA-A, B, C and D/DR genotypically identical but GLO different sibs, only one of whom had evidence for late onset adrenal hyperplasia. Further studies are required to prove genetic linkage to HLA and to clarify the genetic transmission of late onset adrenal hyperplasia.

An interesting biological paradox which remains to be elucidated is the absence of clinical signs in patients with cryptic 21-hydroxylase deficiency in contrast to the severe virilization noted in patients with late onset 21-hydroxylase deficiency ("acquired adrenal hyperplasia") who demonstrate similar biochemical abnormalities (Figs. 17–22). Thus, in the group with late onset 21-hydroxylase deficiency, the excessive androgen levels produce a biologic effect while in the other, no effect is observed, hence the term "cryptic" 21-hydroxylase deficiency. Patients with late onset 21-hydroxylase deficiency are detected because of symptoms and are not family members of patients with classical CAH, whereas the cryptic 21-hydroxylase deficiency has been detected as a result of CAH family studies.

f. Genetic Linkage Disequilibrium. An important consideration is the distinction between linkage which we have described between HLA-B and the CAH gene, and genetic linkage disequilibrium which is the occurrence of alleles of two closely linked loci together at a higher frequency than would be expected. In CAH and cryptic 21-hydroxylase deficiency both linkage and genetic linkage disequilibrium have been demonstrated.

Our initial studies (Levine *et al.*, 1978) suggested a lack of association between the 21-hydroxylase deficiency gene and a specific HLA-A, HLA-B, or HLA-C antigen. However, other studies suggested that the gene for congenital adrenal hyperplasia is in genetic disequilibrium with HLA-Bw47 (Klouda *et al.*, 1978; Price *et al.*, 1978; Pucholt *et al.*, 1978) with HLA-B5 (Grosse-Wilde *et al.*, 1978) and with HLA-B35 (Zappacosta *et al.*, 1978).

At the Eighth International Histocompatibility Workshop, the data indicating that genetic linkage disequilibrium is present in 21-hydroxylase deficiency were summarized. The most significant association for 21-hydroxylase deficiency was found for Bw47, where the combined Relative

Risk is 15.4. Slight increases were also found for Bw51, Bw53, Bw60, and DR7. In reviewing the Bw47 positive haplotypes in patients with 21-hydroxylase deficiency, it is found that this antigen very frequently occurs on one particular haplotype: A3, Cw6, Bw47, BfF, DR7. While the gene frequency for Bw47 in different Caucasian populations is always very low (<0.005), it is remarkable to find that Bw47 has been identified in Caucasian patients with CAH due to 21-hydroxylase deficiency in most of the geographical areas where HLA typing in this disease has been performed. The highest antigen frequency for Bw47 among the patients was found in Sheffield, England (up to 50%). The frequency of Bw47 varies in most other areas from 6 to 15%. Bw47 has so far been identified in patients with CAH due to 21-hydroxylase deficiency in the United Kingdom (Sheffield, Manchester, Glasgow, Birmingham); France (Lyon, Strasbourg, Rennes, Paris); Germany (Tübingen, Munich); Denmark (Copenhagen); Italy (Bologna, Milan); Yugoslavia (Zagreb); United States (New York, Seattle); Canada (Winnepeg).

Bw47 was not identified among the 12 Japanese patients studied at that Workshop, but HLA-A 11 is particularly increased among the Japanese patients with this disease.

It was also demonstrated that A1, B8, and DRw3 are consistently decreased among Caucasian patients with 21-hydroxylase deficiency. This finding is in agreement with previously reported studies (Klouda *et al.*, 1978; Levine *et al.*, 1978; Grosse-Wilde *et al.*, 1979; Pollack *et al.*, 1979b).

Genetic linkage disequilibrium between HLA-B14, DR1, and late onset adrenal hyperplasia has also been demonstrated (Laron *et al.*, 1980). This finding is supported by the report of Blankstein *et al.* (1980) who found HLA-B14 on one haplotype in two sisters with late onset adrenal hyperplasia. These two sisters were HLA identical and different from their two unaffected sisters.

Nonrandom gametic association with B14 and DR1 has also been found in cryptic 21-hydroxylase deficiency (Dupont *et al.*, 1980).

g. Allelic Variants. In 1973, McKusick listed congenital adrenal hyperplasia due to 21-hydroxylase deficiency among the disorders in which the phenotypic diversity might be attributed to allelic series (McKusick, 1973).

McKusick noted that genetic compounds were an additional source of phenotypic diversity. Although the phenotypic variants of salt wasting and simple virilizing congenital adrenal hyperplasia have long been recognized, the new phenotypic variant of cryptic 21-hydroxylase deficiency has only recently been described (Levine *et al.*, 1980c).

We propose that there are allelic variants at the 21-hydroxylase locus which produce different degrees of 21-hydroxylase deficiency resulting in the phenotypic diversity of classical, cryptic, and late onset 21-

hydroxylase deficiency. Further, we suggest that the cryptic form of 21-hydroxylase deficiency represents a genetic compound of the classical (or more severe 21-hydroxylase deficiency) and the less severe cryptic 21-hydroxylase deficiency. This postulate awaits proof by complementation studies. Ultimate proof may be obtained by sequencing the gene by recombinant DNA techniques and demonstrating the site of genetic mutation for each allelic variant.

One may anticipate that a similar degree of genetic heterogeneity is likely to be found in the other inherited enzyme defects of steroidogenesis. Thus the phenotypic variability already recognized in 11β-hydroxylase and 17β-hydroxysteroid dehydrogenase deficiency may be other examples of genetic heterogeneity.

2. *Studies of HLA Linkage to Congenital Adrenal Hyperplasia due to 11β-Hydroxylase Deficiency*

Congenital adrenal hyperplasia due to 11β-hydroxylase deficiency is much less common than the 21-hydroxylase deficiency type, and preliminary studies have suggested that the 11β-hydroxylase deficiency allele is not linked to HLA. However, the disease occurs much more frequently in some geographical areas than others, and prior to the Eighth International Histocompatibility Workshop, only two patient families in Denmark and nine North African Jewish patient families had been studied for linkage to HLA (Brautbar *et al.*, 1979; Glenthøj *et al.*, 1979). Since 11β-hydroxylase deficiency might result from disease alleles at a different genetic locus in different populations, several new families from different geographic and ethnic backgrounds were studied at the Workshop in order to determine whether or not absence of HLA linkage could be established.

Twelve additional families with 11β-hydroxylase deficiency were studied and demonstrated that this disease does not have any HLA antigen associations.

Genetic linkage for the gene for 11β-hydroxylase deficiency and HLA can now be excluded for recombinant fractions from 0.00 to 0.20. Hormonal studies of families of patients with 11β-hydroxylase deficiency have not proven useful in the detection of heterozygosity (Pang *et al.*, 1980a).

D. PRENATAL DIAGNOSIS OF CONGENITAL ADRENAL HYPERPLASIA

1. *21-Hydroxylase Deficiency*

Since the report by Jeffcoate and his associates (1965) of the prenatal diagnosis of CAH by elevated concentrations of 17-ketosteroids and pregnanetriol in the amniotic fluid of the affected fetus, several investigators have attempted the prenatal diagnosis by measurement of various hormones (New and Levine, 1973).

More recently, elevated levels of 17-OHP in the amniotic fluid of fetuses affected with CAH due to 21-hydroxylase deficiency have been reported (Hughes and Laurence, 1979; Milunsky and Tulchinsky, 1977; Frasier *et al.*, 1975; Nagamani *et al.*, 1978). In addition, Δ^4-androstenedione concentrations of amniotic fluid have also been reported to be elevated when the fetus is affected (Pang *et al.*, 1980b) (Fig. 25). HLA genotyping of amniotic cells has provided an additional method for prenatal diagnosis of CAH in a pregnancy at risk and has made possible the prediction of a heterozygous fetus (Pollack *et al.*, 1979a). When HLA genotyping of amniotic cells reveals that the fetus is HLA identical to the affected sib, then the fetus is predicted to be affected (Fig. 26). This should always be corroborated by hormonal measurement of 17-OHP and Δ^4-androstenedione in amniotic fluid. Caution must be exercised in interpreting results if multiple births are expected or if there is antigen sharing in the parents (Pollack *et al.*, 1979b).

2. 11β-Hydroxylase Deficiency

Recently, levels of 11-deoxycortisol and tetrahydrocortisol (THS) in amniotic fluid and THS in maternal urine have been found to be increased in pregnancies with fetuses affected with 11β-hydroxylase deficiency (Rösler *et al.*, 1979; Schumert *et al.*, 1980) suggesting that prenatal diagnosis of this disorder by hormonal measurements is feasible. Since this disorder is not linked to HLA, HLA typing of amniotic cells is not helpful (Glenthøj *et al.*, 1979).

E. RECENT ADVANCES IN TREATMENT OF 21-HYDROXYLASE DEFICIENCY

Since 1949, when Wilkins (Lee *et al.*, 1977) and Bartter (Bartter, 1977) discovered the efficacy of cortisone therapy in congenital adrenal hyperplasia, glucocorticoid therapy has been the keystone of treatment. Although salt-retaining steroids in addition to glucocorticoids have been used in the treatment of the salt-wasting form of the disorder, it has not been customary to treat non-salt-wasting patients with salt-retaining steroids, although it was recognized that plasma renin activity was elevated in the non-salt wasting form as well as the salt wasting form (Dillon, 1975; Bartter, 1977; Goddard *et al.*, 1968; Strickland and Kotchen, 1972).

In 1977, Rösler *et al.* (1977c) proposed that addition of salt-retaining hormone to glucocorticoid therapy in patients with elevated plasma renin activity improved the hormonal control of the disease. Rösler showed that

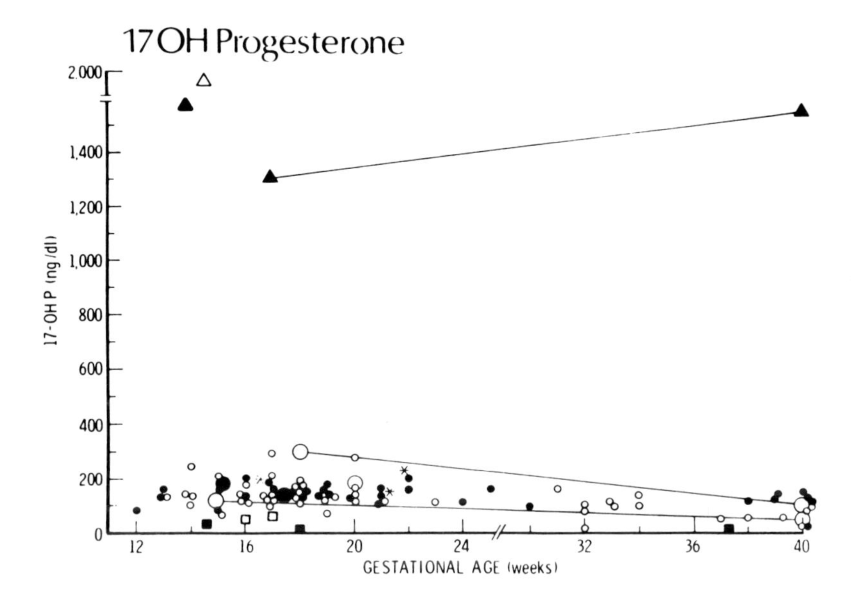

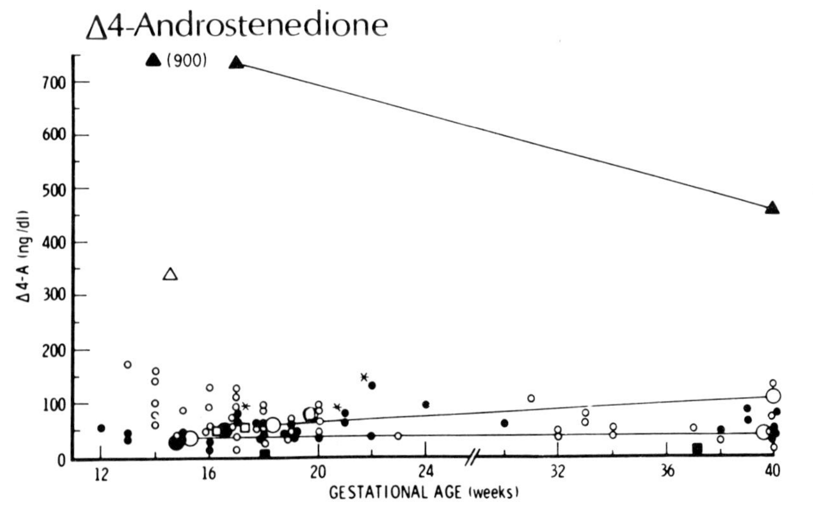

FIG. 25. 17-Hydroxyprogesterone (17-OHP) and androstenedione (Δ^4) concentrations in amniotic fluid samples of normal, CAH, and anencephalic fetuses from gestational age 12 weeks to term. The lines between two values indicate specimens from the same fetuses. Asterisk indicates amniotic fluid contaminated with blood. CAH, male △, female ▲; control, male ○, female ●; anencephalic, male □, female ■; "normal" at risk for CAH, male ◯, female ⬤. From Pang *et al.* (1980b).

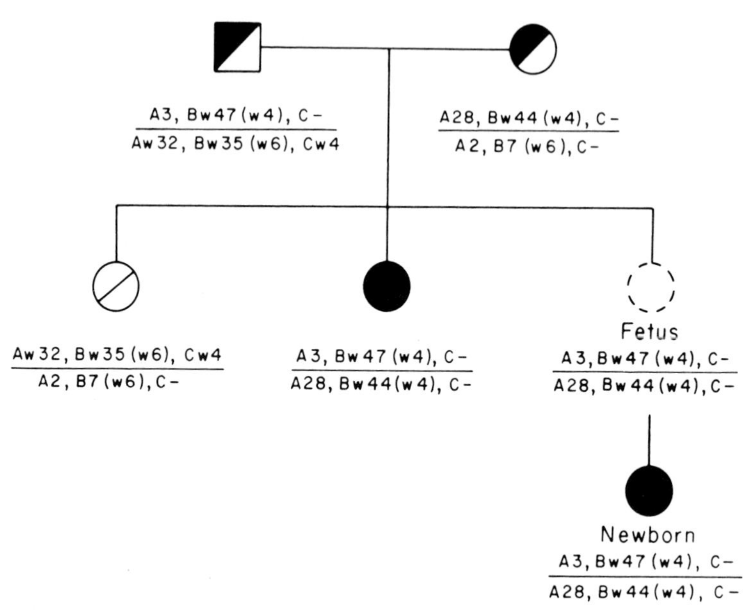

FIG. 26. HLA genotypes of parents, children, and amniotic cells in family M. Shading indicates 21-OH deficiency genes in linkage with particular parental HLA haplotypes. From Pollack *et al.* (1979a).

the plasma renin activity was closely correlated to the ACTH level (Fig. 27). Thus, when plasma renin activity was normalized by the addition of 9α-fludrohydrocortisone administration (9 FF) the ACTH level fell and excessive androgen stimulation by ACTH decreased (Fig. 28). The addition of salt-retaining steroids to the therapeutic regimen often made possible a decrease in the glucocorticoid dose. Normalization of PRA also resulted in improved statural growth (Gunczler *et al.*, 1979; New *et al.*, 1980b) (Fig. 29).

In the past, urinary 17-ketosteroids and pregnanetriol excretion have been the biochemical monitors of hormonal control. Since the advent of radioimmunoassay, it has been possible to establish normal serum androgen concentrations for children of various ages (Gandy and Peterson, 1968; Rosenfield and Eberlein, 1969; Ito and Horton, 1970; Winter and Faiman, 1972; Hopper and Yen, 1975; Korth-Schutz and New, 1975; Migeon *et al.*, 1957; Frasier *et al.*, 1969; Rosenfield *et al.*, 1971; Wieland *et al.*, 1971; August *et al.*, 1972; Boon *et al.*, 1972; Forest *et al.*, 1973; Knorr *et al.*, 1974a; Lee *et al.*, 1974; Forest and Cathaird, 1975; Gupta *et al.*, 1972,

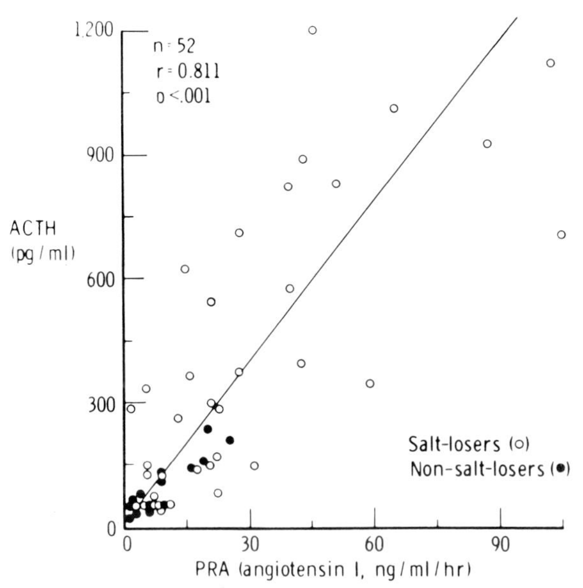

FIG. 27. Correlation between ACTH and plasma renin activity (PRA) levels in patients with CAH treated with constant replacement doses of glucocorticoids equivalent to 25 mg/m²/day of hydrocortisone. Patients were studied during different states of sodium balance. From Rösler *et al.* (1977c).

1975; Korth-Schutz *et al.*, 1976; Winter *et al.*, 1976). Recent studies have indicated that the serum 17-OHP and Δ^4 levels provide a sensitive index of biochemical control. The serum testosterone is useful in females and prepubertal males but not in newborn and pubertal males (Solomon and Schoen, 1975; Youssefnejadian and David, 1975; Hughes and Winter, 1976, 1978; Rivarola *et al.*, 1967; Strott *et al.*, 1969; Lippe *et al.*, 1974; West *et al.*, 1973; Cook *et al.*, 1976; Gupta *et al.*, 1977; Rapaport and Limal, 1977; Korth-Schutz *et al.*, 1978; Pang *et al.*, 1979).

The combined laboratory determinations of plasma renin activity, 17-OHP and serum androgens, and the clinical assessment of growth and pubertal status must all be considered in adjusting the dose of glucocorticoid and salt-retaining steroid. In our clinic, we employ hydrocortisone and 9α-fludrohydrocortisone as treatment modalities. This approach to therapy has recently been confirmed by Winter (1980). Measurement of plasma renin activity can be used to monitor efficacy of treatment not only in 21-hydroxylase deficiency but also in the other salt-losing forms of CAH (cholesterol desmolase, 3β-HSD). It is also useful as a therapeutic index in those forms of CAH with mineralocorticoid excess and suppressed plasma renin activity (11β-hydroxylase and 17α-hydroxylase). In

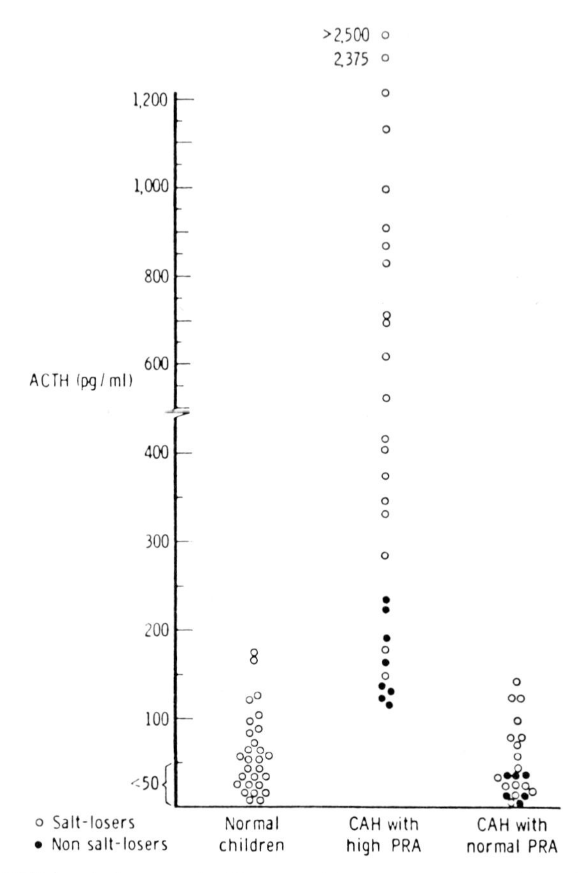

FIG. 28. ACTH levels in normal children and in seven patients with CAH treated with constant replacement doses of glucocorticoids equivalent to 25 mg/m²/day of hydrocortisone. Samples were drawn between 0800 and 0900 hours. Levels of plasma renin activity (PRA) were high during the *ad lib.*, normal, and low sodium diets. Normal PRA levels were achieved by sodium repletion with a high sodium diet and/or additional 9α-fludrohydrocortisone. From Rösler *et al.* (1977c).

the former, the plasma renin activity is elevated in poor control whereas in the latter it is suppressed (Fig. 30).

VI. Future Population Studies

In 1977 neonatal screening for CAH became possible by the development of a microfilter paper method for measuring 17-OHP (Pang *et al.*, 1977). This method utilizes a heel stick for obtaining a capillary blood specimen to spot on filter paper which is then analyzed for 17-OHP by

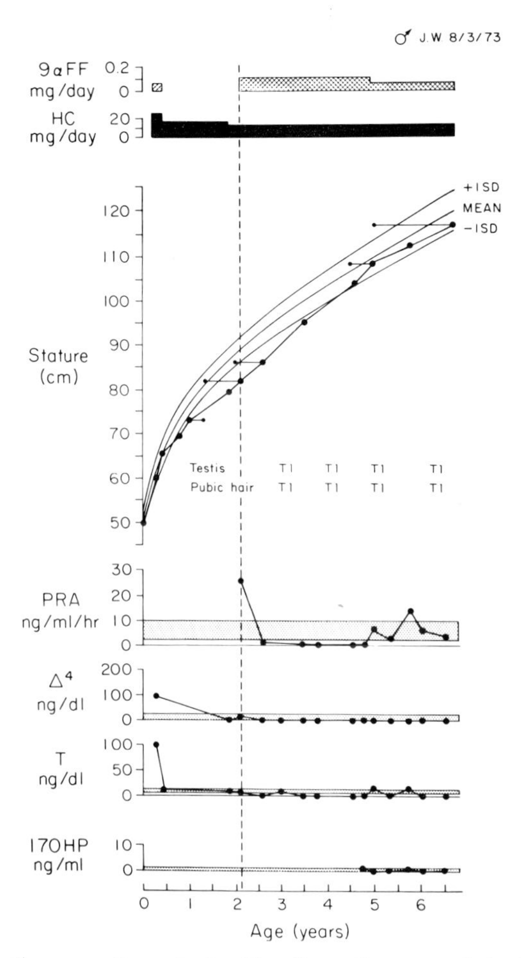

FIG. 29. Growth curve of a patient with salt wasting congenital adrenal hyperplasia before and after therapeutic control of plasma renin activity. Note that with renin suppression, hydrocortisone dose could be lowered, growth improved, and androgen suppression was maintained despite the decrease in hydrocortisone dose.

radioimmunoassay. Typical results are shown in Fig. 31. The hormone is stable on filter paper and the filter paper specimens can be sent to an appropriate laboratory by surface mail. The reliability and feasibility of this method have recently been proven by screening all infants born in Alaska in 1 year. A similar approach to screening for hypothyroidism and phenylketonuria has been successful and is mandated in most states. Based on the population surveys which indicate that the incidence of 21-hydroxylase deficiency is 1 : 15,000 before screening (an incidence

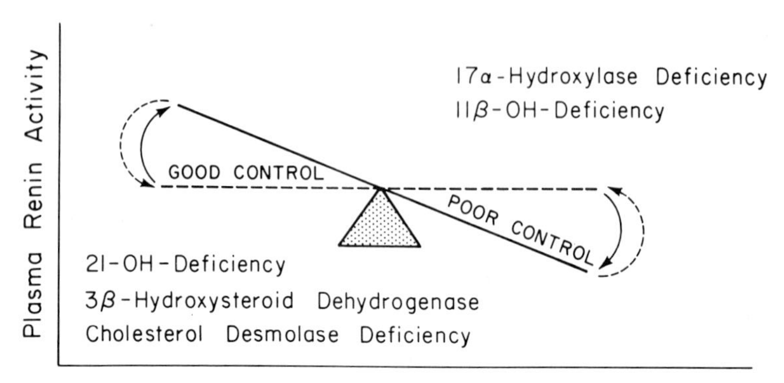

FIG. 30. The pivotal role of monitoring plasma renin activity in therapy of various forms of congenital adrenal hyperplasia. In poor control, renin is elevated in 21-hydroxylase deficiency, 3β-hydroxysteroid deficiency, and cholesterol desmolase deficiency and decreases with proper mineralocorticoid treatment. In contrast in 17α-hydroxylase deficiency and 11β-hydroxylase deficiency, renin is suppressed in poor control and rises with proper treatment.

equal to that of phenylketonuria after screening) we and others have proposed that the newborn population be screened for 21-hydroxylase deficiency (Werder *et al.,* 1980). We predict that such screening will demonstrate a higher incidence of the disease, as has occurred with screening of other disorders.

It should also be possible to screen the general population for classical and cryptic 21-hydroxylase deficiency by microfilter paper assay of 17-OHP. Both these disorders have gone unrecognized in the families and the general population (Price *et al.,* 1978; Lorenzen *et al.,* 1979; Levine *et al.,* 1980c).

In the course of studying 700 subjects selected from family members of patients with CAH and the general population, we have found members of the general population who appear to be carriers of the gene for 21-hydroxylase deficiency (Fig. 32); thus it can be seen that those members of the general population whose stimulated values of 17-OHP exceeded 700 ng/dl are possible heterozygotes. These findings have been observed by others (Cleveland *et al.,* 1962; Gutai *et al.,* 1977; Child *et al.,* 1979). It can also be appreciated from the histogram (Fig. 32) that those members of the general population whose stimulated level is in the range of those family members predicted by HLA genotyping to be unaffected are also likely to be unaffected. Expansion of this histogram by testing of additional members of families and the general population will establish the limits of this hormonal test in discriminating heterozygotes from normals. The augmentation of the group of HLA proven normals will be of particular value.

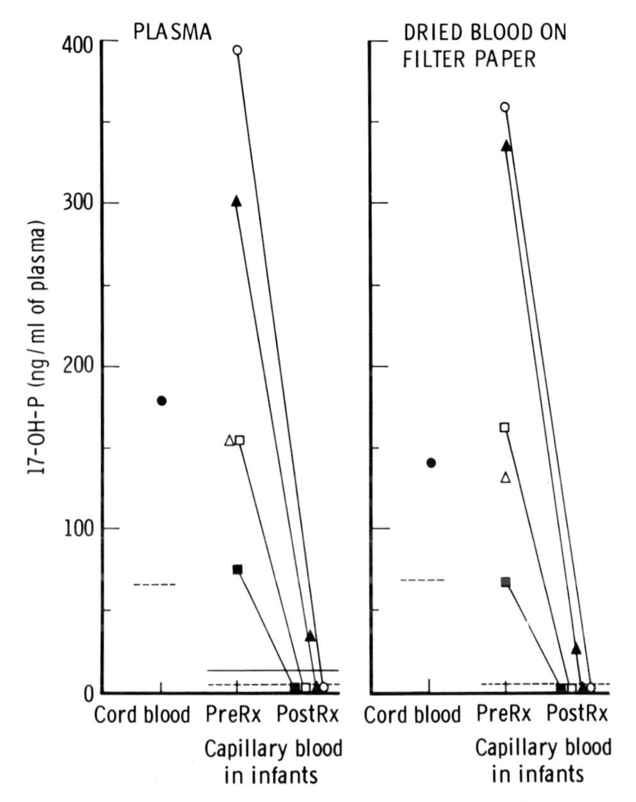

FIG. 31. 17α-OH-progesterone concentrations in cord and capillary blood samples in infants with CAH. Ages of infants at diagnosis were as follows: ●, cord blood; △, 2 days; □, 4 days; ■, 7 days; ▲, 2 weeks; ○, 4 weeks. Samples on treatment were taken from 5 days to 1 month after treatment was begun. The dashed line indicates upper limit of normal infants. The solid line indicates upper limit of pooled plasma in sick infants. Plasma samples were pippetted quantiatively and assayed. Cord blood samples were also quantitatively pipetted onto filter paper. Capillary samples were directly applied to filter paper without quantitation and a 3-mm disc was punched out for analysis. From Pang *et al.* (1977).

VII. Summary

Disorders of steroidogenesis transmitted by an autosomal recessive gene have been investigated by hormonal and immunogenetic techniques.

Genetic linkage between the genes for HLA and steroid 21-hydroxylase has been demonstrated by family studies indicating that the gene for 21-hydroxylase is on the sixth chromosome close to the HLA-B locus. Various phenotypic forms of 21-hydroxylase deficiency have been described which may represent allelic variants at the 21-hydroxylase locus. Genetic linkage disequilibrium between HLA-Bw47 and the more severe 21-

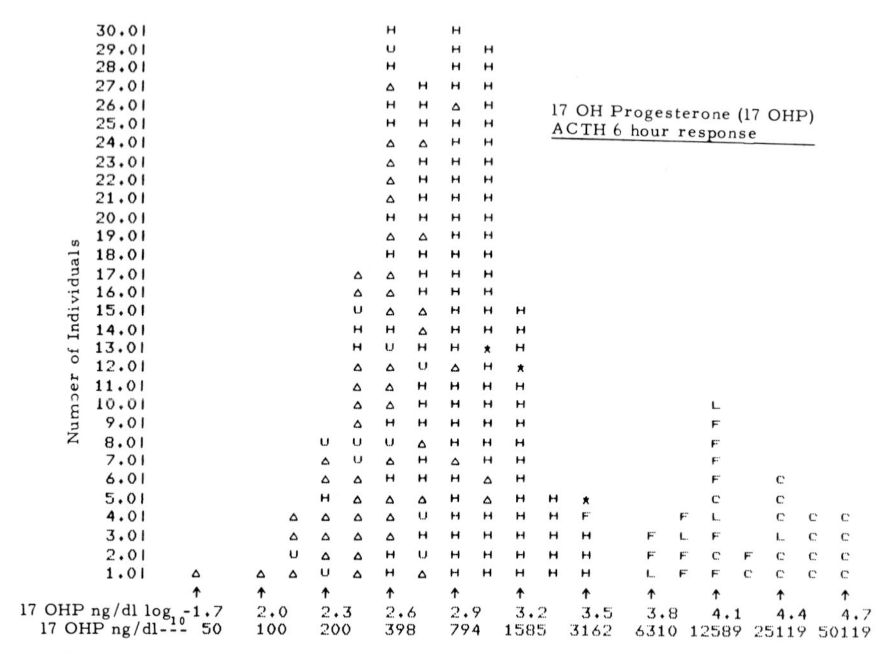

FIG. 32. The histogram describes a selected population of family members who were tested. It does not describe a distribution in a random population. The population tested is easily separated into four groups based on the ACTH stimulated 17-OH progesterone level. The highest responders are patients with congenital adrenal hyperplasia, the next are patients with cryptic or late onset 21-hydrosylase deficiency. Lower responses are observed in the heterozygotes for classical or cryptic 21-hydroxylase deficiency while the lowest response is in the group of subjects who are HLA normal or the general population in whom the HLA genotype is unknown. Those members of the general population whose response is in the heterozygote range may be carriers of a 21-hydroxylase gene defect. See Fig. 22 for symbols.

hydroxylase deficiency has been demonstrated. The cryptic and late onset 21-hydroxylase defects appear to be in nonrandom gametic association with HLA-B14 and DR1. Hormonal tests have confirmed the prediction of heterozygosity by HLA genotyping.

There is no genetic linkage between HLA and 11β-hydroxylase deficiency and neither HLA genotyping nor hormonal studies are useful in detecting heterozygosity for this disorder.

Prenatal diagnosis of the 21-hydroxylase deficiency by combined hormonal testing and HLA genotyping is possible, whereas only hormonal studies are useful in prenatal diagnosis of 11β-hydroxylase deficiency.

Further hormonal and immunogenetic studies should prove helpful in elucidating the biological basis for the variable expression of these disorders of adrenal steroidogenesis.

ACKNOWLEDGMENTS

The authors wish to acknowledge the untiring efforts of Vita Amendolagine for the preparation of this manuscript, of Kevin Grumbach for the literature research, and of Alan Lerner for the data management. We also wish to acknowledge our technicians and the past and present members of the Division of Pediatric Endocrinology (indicated by an asterisk) who collaborated in the development and execution of these studies. This work represents an international collaboration between New York, Hershey, Zurich, Bologna, Milano, Padua, Parma, Ancona, Cagliari, Verona, Zagreb, and Tel Aviv. The work of various investigators in these cities made possible the family studies reported. Finally, we wish to thank the families who participated in this study and without whose cooperation this work could not have been done. Collaborators: F. Barboni, E. Bartolotta, A. Becca, E. Cacciari, A. Cassio, G. Chiumello, A. Cicognani, *M. Dumic, L. Gargantini, G. Giovannelli, *P. Gunczler, *B. Kohn, *S. Korth-Schutz, *U. Kuhnle, H. Kulin, Z. Laron, E. Leiberman, *F. Lorenzen, F. Mantero, C. Migliori, S. Moses, *M. Novogroder, *S. Oberfield, C. Pintor, A. Prader, *R. Rapaport, G. Rondanini, *A. Rosler, J. Sack, *P. Saenger, S. Salardi, C. Scaroni, *N. Sonino, L. Tato, *R. Virdis, M. Zachmann, *G. Zanconato.

REFERENCES

(h) Akesode, F. A., Meyer, W. J., III, and Migeon, C. J. (1977). *Clin. Endocrinol.* **7,** 443.

Alper, C. A., Boenisch, T., and Watson, L. (1972). *J. Exp. Med.* **135,** 68.

(e) Alvarez, M. N., Cloutier, M. D., and Hayles, A. B. (1973). *Pediatr. Res.* **7,** 325.

August, G. P., Grumbach, M. M., and Kaplan, S. (1972). *J. Clin. Endocrinol. Metab.* **34,** 319.

(a) Bacon, G. E., and Kelch, R. P. (1979). *J. Endocrinol. Invest.* **2,** 93.

(a) Bacon, G. E., Spencer, M. L., and Kelch, R. P. (1977). *Clin. Endocrinol. (Oxford)* **6,** 113.

(a) Bailey, C. C., Komrower, G. M., and Palmer, M. (1978). *Arch. Dis. Child.* **53,** 132.

(a) Bakhratova, T. P., Bogdanova, E. A., and Kotliarskaia, E. I. (1977). *Sov. Med.* **6,** 87.

(a) Ballard, J. (1978). *South. Med. J.* **71,** 966.

Bartter, F. C. (1977). *In* "Congenital Adrenal Hyperplasia" (P. A. Lee, L. P. Plotnick, A. A. Kowarski, and C. J. Migeon, eds.), pp. 9–18. Univ. Park Press, Baltimore, Maryland.

Bartter, F. C., Henkin, R. I., and Bryan, G. T. (1968). *J. Clin. Invest.* **47,** 1742.

Bauleiu, E. E., Peillow, F., and Migeon, C. J. (1967). *In* "The Adrenal Cortex" (A. B. Eisenstein, ed.), pp. 553–638. Little, Brown, Boston, Massachusetts.

(a) Beazley, J. M., Sells, R. A., Hipkin, L. J., Diver, M. J., Wade, A. P., and Davis, J. C. (1978). *Br. J. Obstet. Gynaecol.* **85,** 965.

Beitins, I. Z., Bayard, F., Kowarski, A., and Migeon, C. J. (1972). *J. Clin. Endocrinol. Metab.* **35,** 595.

(a) Benso, L., Campagnoli, C., Fessia, L., Galante, A. M., and Perno, M. (1976a). *Minerva Pediatr.* **28,** 1659.

(a) Benso, L., Campagnoli, C., Giacchino, M., and Perona, M. (1976b). *Minerva Pediatr.* **28,** 538.

Bergada, C., Rivarola, M. A., and Cullen, M. (1965). *Excerpta Medica (Amsterdam)*, Int. Congr. Ser. No. 99, E. 130.

(b) Bergman, P., Sjögren, B., and Kakansson, B. (1962). *Acta Endocrinol. (Copenhagen)* **40,** 555.

(e) Bernheim, P. (1962). *Acta Endocrinol.* **41,** 48.

Betuel, H., Fauchet, R., Gebuhrer, L., Freidel, C., and Bouhallier, O. (1980). *Int. Histocompat. Workshop 8th, Newslett.* **20,** 89.

(d) Biglieri, E. G., and Mantero, F. (1973). *In* "Research on Steroids" (M. Finkelstein, P. Jungblut, A. Klopper, and C. Conti, eds.), pp. 385–399. Soc. Edit. Univ., Rome.

(d) Biglieri, E. G., Herron, M. A., and Brust, N. (1966). *J. Clin. Invest.* **45,** 1946.

(a) Blankstein, J., Faiman, C., Reyes, F. I., Schroeder, M. L., and Winter, J. S. D. (1980). *Am. J. Med.* **68,** 441.

Blizzard, R. M., Liddle, G. W., Migeon, C. J., and Wilkins, L. (1959). *J. Clin. Invest.* **38,** 1442.

(b) Blunck, W. (1958). *Acta Endocrinol.* (*Copenhagen*) (*Suppl.*) **59,** 134.

(b) Blunck, W., and Bierich, J. R. (1968). *Acta Paediatr. Scand.* **57,** 157.

Bongiovanni, A. M. (1953). *Bull. Johns Hopkins Hosp.* **92,** 244.

(c) Bongiovanni, A. M. (1961). *J. Clin. Endocrinol. Metab.* **21,** 860.

(c) Bongiovanni, A. M. (1962). *J. Clin. Invest.* **41,** 2086.

Bongiovanni, A. M. (1978). *In* "The Endocrine Function of the Human Adrenal Cortex" (V. H. T. James, M. Serio, G. Giusti, and L. Martini, eds.), pp. 265–270. Academic Press, New York.

(c) Bongiovanni, A. M. (1979). *In* "Genetic Mechanisms of Sexual Development" (H. L. Vallet and I. H. Porter, eds.), pp. 189–196. Academic Press, New York.

Bongiovanni, A. M., and Eberlein, W. R. (1958). *Pediatrics* **21,** 661.

Bongiovanni, A. M., and Root, A. W. (1963). *N. Engl. J. Med.* **268,** 1283.

Bongiovanni, A. M., Eberlein, W. R., Goldman, A. S., and New, M. I. (1967). *Recent Prog. Horm. Res.* **23,** 375.

(c) Bongiovanni, A. M., Eberlein, W. R., and Moshang, T. (1971). *J. Clin. Invest.* **50,** 2751.

Boon, D. A., Keenan, R. E., Slaunwhite, W. R., Jr., and Aceto, T. (1972). *Pediatr. Res.* **6,** 111.

(b) Brautbar, C., Rösler, A., Landau, H., Cohen, I., Nelken, D., Cohen, T., Levine, L. S., and New, M. I. (1979). *N. Engl. J. Med.* **300,** 205.

(b) Brautbar, N. N., and Ben-David, M. M. (1977). *Arch. Intern. Med.* **137,** 1608.

Bretnall, C. (1945). *J. Obstet. Gynaecol. Br. Emp.* **52,** 235.

(b) Bricaire, H., Aubert, P., and Laudat, P. (1966). *Prensa Med. Argent.* **53,** 226.

(d) Bricaire, H., Luton, J. P., Laudat, P., Legrand, J. C., Turpin, G., Corvol, P., and Lemmer, M. (1972). *J. Clin. Endocrinol. Metab.* **35,** 67.

Bryan, G. T., Kliman, B., and Bartter, F. C. (1965). *J. Clin. Invest.* **44,** 957.

Bryan, G. T., Lewis, A. M., Harkins, J. B., Micheletti, S. F., and Boyd, G. S. (1974). *Steroids* **23,** 185.

(a) Cacciari, E., Cicognani, A., Pirazzoli, P., Tassoni, P., Salardi, S., Bernardi, F., Zappula, F., and Iaboli, A. (1976a). *Minerva. Pediatr.* **28,** 1991.

(a) Cacciari, E., Cicognani, A., Pirazzoli, P., Tassoni, P., Zappulla, F., Salardi, S., Bernardi, F., Mazzanti, L., and Vianelli, P. (1976b). *J. Clin. Endocrinol. Metab.* **43,** 1146.

(e) Camacho, A. M., Kowarski, A., Migeon, C. J., and Brough, A. J. (1968). *J. Clin. Endocrinol. Metab.* **28,** 153.

(a) Cavallo, A., Corn, C., Bryan, G. T., and Meyer, W. J., III (1979). *J. Pediatr.* **95,** 33.

(b) Chaptal, J., Jean, R., Cristol, P., and Bonnet, H. (1959). *Ann. Endocrinol.* (*Paris*) **20,** 323.

Child, D. F., Bullock, D. E., Hilliier, V. F., and Anderson, D. C. (1979). *Clin. Endocrinol.* (*Oxford*) **11,** 383.

Childs, B., Grumbach, M. M., and Van Wyk, J. J. (1956). *J. Clin. Invest.* **35,** 213.

Cleveland, W. W., Nikezic, M., and Migeon, C. J. (1962). *J. Clin. Endocrinol. Metab.* **22,** 281.

Cohen, J. M. (1969). *Pediatrics* **44,** 621.

(g) Cohen, T., Theodor, R., and Rösler, A. (1977). *Clin. Genet.* **11,** 25.

(a) Colabucci, F., and Marietti, G. (1976). *Minerva Pediatr.* **28,** 1406.
(a) Colabucci, F., Marietti, G., and Tortorolo, G. (1976). *Minerva Pediatr.* **28,** 2095.
(a) Connors, M. H., and Sheikholislam, B. M. (1976). *West. J. Med.* **124,** 335.
(h) Conte, F. A., Reiter, E., Grumbach, M. M., Siiteri, P., and Kaplan, S. L. (1976). *Clin. Res.* **24,** 166A.
Cook, D. M., Kendall, J. W., Allen, J. P., and Lagerquist, L. G. (1976). *Clin. Endocrinol.* **5,** 303.
Dahl, V., Rivarola, M. A., and Bergada, C. (1972). *J. Clin. Endocrinol. Metab.* **34,** 661.
(e) David, M. (1970). *Pediatrie* **25,** 348.
(g) David, R., Golan, S., and Drucker, W. (1968). *Pediatrics* **41,** 403.
(g) David, R., Asnis, M., and Drucker, W. (1972). *J. Clin. Endocrinol. Metab.* **35,** 604.
De Crecchio, L. (1865). *Morgagni* **7,** 1951.
(a) De Filippo, P., Tomasi, L., and Cirillo, B. (1978). *Pediatria (Naples)* **86,** 77.
(d) De Lange, W. E., Weeke, A., Artz, W., Jansen, W., and Doorenbos, H. (1973). *Acta Med. Scand.* **193,** 565.
(d) De Lange, W. E., Lappöhn, R. E., Sluiter, W. J., and Doorenbos, H. (1977). *Dtsch. Med. Wochenschr.* **102,** 1024.
(e) Degenhart, H. J. (1971). *Acta Pediatr. Scand.* **60,** 611.
Degenhart, H. J., Visser, K. H. A., Wilmink, R., and Croughs, W. (1965). *Acta Endocrinol. (Copenhagen)* **48,** 587.
(f) Degenhart, H. J., Frankena, L., Visser, H. K. A., Cost, W. S., and Van Seters, A. P. (1966). *Acta Physiol. Pharmacol. Neerl.* **14,** 1.
(e) Degenhart, H. J., Visser, H. K. A., Boor, H., and O'Doherty, N. J. (1972). *Acta Endocrinol.* **71,** 512.
(a) Delsner, G., Kraiem, Z., Lunenfeld, B., Akstein, E., Goldman, B., and Serr, D. M. (1978). *Monogr. Hum. Genet.* **10,** 178.
Dillon, M. J. (1975). *Arch. Dis. Child.* **50,** 330.
(b) Di Matteo, J., Sabaut, D., Delvaux, J. C., and Sellier, P. (1972). *Coeur Med. Interne* **11,** 187.
(a) Doneva, V., Sadikario, A., Zdraveva, M., Vlaski, J., and Grozdanov, L. J. (1976). *God. Zb. Med. Fak. Skopje.* **22,** 569.
(e) Drabos, E. (1974). *Morphol. Igazsagugyi Orv. Sz.* **14,** 305.
(a) Drobnjak, P., Funduk-Kurjak, B., Puharic, I., and Mayer, V. (1976). *Jugosl. Ginekol. Opstet.* **16,** 121.
Dupont, B., Oberfield, S. E., Smithwick, E. M., Lee, T. D., and Levine, L. S. (1977). *Lancet* **2,** 1309.
Dupont, B., Pollack, M. S., Levine, L. S., O'Neill, G. J., Hawkins, B., and New, M. I. (1980). *In* "Histocompatibility Testing 1980" (P. I. Terasaki, ed.), pp. 693–706. UCLA Tissue Typing Laboratory, Los Angeles.
(b) Eberlein, W. R., and Bongiovanni, A. M. (1955). *J. Clin. Endocrinol. Metab.* **15,** 1531.
(b) Eberlein, W. R., and Bongiovanni, A. M. (1956). *J. Biol. Chem.* **223,** 85.
(a) Edwin, C., Lanes, R., Migeon, C. J., Lee, P. A., Plotnick, L. P., and Kowarski, A. A. (1979). *J. Pediatr.* **95,** 534.
Federman, D. D. (1968). "Abnormal Sexual Development." Saunders, Philadelphia, Pennsylvania.
(a) Ferrante, L. (1976a). *Minerva Pediatr.* **28,** 1403.
(a) Ferrante, L. (1976b). *Minerva Pediatr.* **28,** 1443.
(a) Fiet, J., Phaam-Huu-Trung, M. T., Dreux, C., and Girard, F. (1979). *C.R. Soc. Biol. (Paris)* **173,** 504.

Finkelstein, M., and Shaefer, J. M. (1979). *Physiol. Rev.* **59,** 353.
Forest, M. G., and Cathiard, A. M. (1975). *J. Clin. Endocrinol. Metab.* **41,** 977.
Forest, M. G., Cathiard, A. M., and Bertrand, J. A. (1973). *J. Clin. Endocrinol. Metab.* **36,** 1132.
(e) Fox, R. R., and Crary, D. D. (1978). *J. Hered.* **69,** 251.
Franks, R. C. (1974). *J. Clin. Endocrinol. Metab.* **39,** 1009.
Frasier, S. D., Gafford, F., and Horton, R. (1969). *J. Clin. Endocrinol. Metab.* **29,** 1404.
(b) Frasier, S. D., Horton, R., and Ulstrom, R. A. (1969). *Pediatrics* **44,** 201.
Frasier, S. D., Thorneycroft, I. H., Weill, B. A., and Horton, R. (1975). *J. Pediatr.* **86,** 310.
(b) Fukushima, D. K., Finkelstein, J. W., Yoshida, K., Boyar, R. M., and Hellman, L. (1975). *J. Clin. Endocrinol. Metab.* **40,** 1.
(a) Fukushima, D. K., Nishina, T., Wu, R. H., Hellman, L., and Finkelstein, J. W. (1979). *Clin. Endocrinol.* (*Oxford*) **10,** 367.
(b) Gabrilove, J. L., Sharma, D. C., and Dorfman, R. I. (1965). *N. Engl. J. Med.* **272,** 1189.
(a) Gandullia, E., De Langlade, F., and Marchese, N. (1976). *Minerva Pediatr.* **28,** 1437.
Gandy, H. M., and Peterson, R. E. (1968). *J. Clin. Endocrinol. Metab.* **28,** 949.
(b) Gandy, H. M., Keutmann, E. H., and Izzo, A. J. (1960). *J. Clin. Invest.* **39,** 364.
Ganong, W. F. (1963). *In* "Advances in Neuroendocrinology" (A. V. Nalbandov, ed.), pp. 92–149. Univ. of Illinois Press, Urbana.
Gaunt, R. (1971). *In* "The Human Adrenal Cortex" (N. P. Christy, ed.), pp. 273–302. Harper, New York.
(a) Geefhuysen, J., Hall, D. M., and Wolfsdurf, J. (1976). *S. Afr. Med.* **50,** 851.
(c) Gendrel, D., Chaussain, J. L., Roger, M., and Job, J. C. (1979). *Arch. Fr. Pediatr.* **36,** 647.
(a) Ghali, I., David, M., and David, L. (1977). *Clin. Endocrinol.* (*Oxford*) **6,** 425.
(a) Gillet, P., David, M., Sassard, J., Bertrand, J., Jeune, M., and Francois, R. (1977). *Arch. Fr. Pediatr.* (*Suppl.*) **34,** 139.
(h) Givens, J. R., Wiser, W. L., Summitt, R. L., Kerber, I. J., Andersen, R. N., Pittaway, D. E., and Fish, S. A. (1974). *N. Engl. J. Med.* **291,** 938.
(b) Glenthøj, A., Nielsen, M. D., Starrup, J., and Svejgaard, A. (1979). *Tissue Antigens* **14,** 181.
(b) Glenthøj, A., Damjaer Nielsen, M., and Starrup, J. (1980). *Acta Endocrinol.* **93,** 94.
(c) Gobel, P. (1967a). *Endokrinologie* **52,** 22.
(c) Gobel, P. (1967b). *Endokrinologie* **52,** 168.
Godard, C., Riondel, A. M., Veyrat, R., Megevand, A., and Muller, A. F. (1968). *Pediatrics* **41,** 883.
(h) Goebelsmann, U., Horton, R., Mestman, J. H., Arce, J. J., Nagat, Y., Nakamura, R. M., Thorneycroft, I. H., and Mishell, D. R. (1973). *J. Clin. Endocrinol. Metab.* **36,** 867.
(h) Goebelsmann, U., Hall, T. D., Paul, W. L., and Stanczyk, F. Z. (1975). *J. Clin. Endocrinol. Metab.* **41,** 1136.
(a) Golden, M. P., Lippe, B. M., Kaplan, S. A., Lavin, N., and Slavin, J. (1978). *Pediatrics* **61,** 67.
(e) Goldman, A. S. (1970). *Endocrinology* **86,** 1245.
(d) Goldman, A. S., Bongiovanni, A. M., Yakowac, W. C., and Prader, A. (1964). *J. Clin. Endocrinol. Metab.* **24,** 894.
(d) Goldsmith, O., Solomon, D. H., and Horton, R. (1967). *N. Engl. J. Med.* **277,** 673.
(a) Gourmelan, M., Phaam-Huu-Trung, M. T., Breton, M. G., and Girard, F. (1979). *Acta Endocrinol.* (*Copenhagen*) **90,** 481.
(a) Grant, D. B., Dillon, M. J., Atherden, S. M., and Levinsky, R. J. (1977). *Eur. J. Pediatr.* **126,** 86.

(b) Green, O. C., Migeon, C. J., and Wilkins, L. (1960). *J. Clin. Endocrinol. Metab.* **20,** 929.
(b) Gregory, T., and Gardner, L. I. (1976). *J. Clin. Endocrinol. Metab.* **43,** 769.
Grosse-Wilde, H. J., Weil, J., Scholz, A. E., Bidlingmaier, F., and Knorr, D. (1978). *Pediatr. Res.* **12,** 1088.
Grosse-Wilde, H., Weil, J., Albert, E., Scholz, S., Bidlingmaier, F., Sippel, W. G., and Knorr, D. (1979). *Immunogenetics* **8,** 41.
Grumbach, M. M., Ducharme, J. R., and Moloshok, R. E. (1959). *J. Clin. Endocrinol. Metab.* **19,** 1369.
Guillemin, R., and Schally, A. V. (1963). *In* "Advances in Neuroendocrinology" (A. V. Nalbandov, ed.), p. 314. Univ. of Illinois Press, Urbana.
Gunczler, P., Levine, L. S., Rösler, A., Oberfield, S., and New, M. I. (1979). *Pan Am. Congr. Androl., 1st, Venezuela* Abstracts and Presentations.
Gupta, D., McCafferty, E., and Rager, K. (1972). *Steroids* **19,** 411.
Gupta, D., Attanasio, A., and Raaf, S. (1975). *J. Clin. Endocrinol. Metab.* **40,** 636.
Gupta, D., Rager, K., Klemm, W., and Attanasio, A. (1977). *In* "Congenital Adrenal Hyperplasia" (P. A. Lee, L. P. Plotnick, A. A. Kowarski, and C. J. Migeon, eds.), pp. 283–300. Univ. Park Press, Baltimore, Maryland.
Gutai, J. P., Kowarski, A. A., and Migeon, C. J. (1977). *J. Pediatr.* **90,** 924.
Hall, R., Smith, P. A., Harkness, R. A., and Smart, G. A. (1970). *Proc. R. Soc. Med.* (*Biol.*) **63,** 1040.
(a) Halperin, G., and Maschler, I. (1979). *Steroids* **33,** 33.
(b) Halperin, G., Muller, A., and Finkelstein, M. (1973). *Steroids* **22,** 581.
(a) Hamilton, W. (1976). *Clin. Chim. Acta* **73,** 135.
(c) Hamilton, W., and Brush, M. G. (1964). *Arch. Dis. Child.* **39,** 66.
(g) Hamilton, W., McCandless, A. E., Ireland, J. T., and Gray, C. E. (1976). *Arch. Dis. Child.* **51,** 576.
(a) Hammans, W., and Caniels, B. (1976). *Geburtschilfe Frauenheilkd.* **36,** 941.
(d) Hammerstein, J., Zielske, F., Distler, A., and Wolff, H. P. (1973). *Acta Endocrinol.* (*Copenhagen*) (*Suppl.*) **173,** 76.
(a) Handwerger, S., and Silverstein, J. H. (1977). *Urol. Clin. N. Am.* **4,** 193.
Hanley, H. G. (1953). *Br. J. Surg.* **41,** 216.
(a) Hansen, J. W., and Loriaux, D. L. (1976). *Pediatrics* **57,** 942.
(h) Harkness, R. A., Thistlethwaite, D., Darling, J. A. B., Skakkeback, N. E., and Corker, C. S. (1975). *J. Endocrinol.* **67,** 16.
(d) Heremans, G. F. P., Moolenaar, A. J., and Van Geldren, H. H. (1976). *Arch. Dis. Child.* **51,** 721.
(e) Hierro, F. R., Orus, A., Corretger, J. M., Ballestra, F., and Cruz, M. (1979). *An. Esp. Pediatr.* **12,** 229.
(a) Hirano, T., and Seeler, R. A. (1978). *J. Pediatr.* **93,** 326.
Hirschfeld, A. G., and Fleshman, J. K. (1969). *J. Pediatr.* **75,** 492.
(g) Hochberg, R. B., McDonald, P. D., Feldman, M., and Lieberman, S. (1974). *J. Biol. Chem.* **249,** 1277.
(a) Hofman, W., and Kluge, R. (1977). *Z. Urol. Nephrol.* **70,** 295.
(b) Holcombe, J. H., Keenan, B. S., Nichols, B. L., Kirkland, R. T., and Clayton, G. W. (1980). *Pediatrics* **65,** 777.
(d) Holland, O. B., Child, J. M., and Braunstein, H. (1980). *J. Clin. Invest.* **65,** 347.
(a) Holsboer, F., and Knorr, D. (1977). *J. Steroid Biochem.* **8,** 1197.
Holzer, H., Spona, J., Swoboda, W., Parth, K., and Zimprich, H. (1976). *Paediatr. Paedol.* **11,** 129.
Homoki, J., Fazekas, A. T. A., and Teller, W. M. (1977). *In* "Congenital Adrenal

Hyperplasia'' (P. A. Lee, L. P. Plotnick, A. A. Kowarski, and C. J. Migeon, eds.), pp. 479–485. Univ. Park Press, Baltimore, Maryland.

Hopper, B. R., and Yen, S. S. C. (1975). *J. Clin. Endocrinol. Metab.* **40,** 458.

(a) Horner, J. M., Hintz, R. L., and Leutscher, J. A. (1979). *J. Clin. Endocrinol. Metab.* **48,** 776.

(b) Hrnciar, J., Izacovic, V., and Starka, L. (1972). *Cas. Lek. Cesk.* **111,** 459.

Hubble, D. (1966). *In* ''Basic Concepts of Inborn Errors and Defects of Steroid Biosynthesis. Proceedings of the Third Symposium of the Society for the Study of Inborn Errors of Metabolism'' (K. S. Holt and D. N. Raine, eds.), pp. 68. Livingstone, Edinburgh.

Hughes, I. A., and Laurence, K. M. (1979). *Lancet* **2,** 7.

(a) Hughes, I. A., and Winter, J. S. D. (1976). *J. Pediatr.* **88,** 766.

(a) Hughes, I. A., and Winter, J. S. D. (1977). *Can. Med. Assoc. J.* **117,** 363.

(a) Hughes, I. A., and Winter, J. S. D. (1978). *J. Clin. Endocrinol. Metab.* **46,** 98.

(a) Hughes, I. A., Williams, D. H., and Birch, A. D. (1977). *Lancet* **1,** 487.

(a) Hughes, I. A., Wilton, A., Lole, C. A., and Gray, D. P. (1979). *Arch. Dis. Child.* **54,** 350.

(a) Huseman, C. A., Varma, M. M., Blizzard, R. M., and Johanson, A. (1977). *J. Pediatr.* **90,** 538.

(b) Imai, M., Igarashi, Y., and Sokabe, H. (1968). *Pediatrics* **41,** 897.

(h) Imperato-McGinley, J., Peterson, R. E., Stoller, R., and Goodwin, W. E. (1979). *J. Clin. Endocrinol. Metab.* **49,** 391.

(d) Ito, S. (1977). *Jpn. J. Hum. Genet.* **21,** 247.

Ito, T., and Horton, R. (1970). *J. Clin. Endocrinol. Metab.* **31,** 362.

(e) Iwamasa, T., Tokumitsu, S., Sunagawa, H., Nagayoshi, C., and Ooara, H. (1973). *Kumamoto Med. J.* **26,** 47.

(c) Jänne, O., Perheentupa, J., and Vihko, R. (1970). *J. Clin. Endocrinol. Metab.* **531,** 162.

(a) Jarz Ebowska, H., Renkielski, J., Komarnicka, R., and Konefka, H. (1976). *Ginekol. Pol.* **47,** 763.

(f) Jean, R., Legrand, J. C., Meylan, F., Rieu, D., and Astruc, J. (1969). *Arch. Fr. Pediatr.* **26,** 769.

Jeffcoate, T. N. A., Fliegners, J. R. H., Russell, S. H., Davis, J. C., and Wade, A. P. (1965). *Lancet* **2,** 553.

Josso, N. (1972). *J. Clin. Endocrinol. Metab.* **34,** 265.

Jost, A. (1966). *Excerpta Med. Int. Congr. Ser.* **132,** 74.

(a) Kadair, R. G., Block, M. B., Katz, F. H., and Hofeldt, F. D. (1977). *Am. J. Med.* **62,** 278.

Kahnt, F. W., and Neher, R. (1972). *Acta Endocrinol.* (*Copenhagen*) **70,** 315.

(g) Katznelson, D., Sack, J., Kraiem, Z., and Lunenfeld, B. (1979). *Horm. Res.* **11,** 22.

(a) Keenan, B. S., Holcombe, J. H., Kirkland, R. T., Potts, V. E., and Clayton, G. W. (1979a). *J. Clin. Endocrinol. Metab.* **48,** 1979.

(a) Keenan, B. S., McNeel, R., Barrett, G. N., Holcombe, J. H., Kirkland, R. T., and Clayton, G. W. (1979b). *J. Lab. Clin. Med.* **94,** 799.

(c) Kenny, F. M., Reynolds, J. W., and Green, O. C. (1971). *Pediatrics* **48,** 756.

(d) Kershnar, A. K., Borut, D., Kogut, M. D., Biglieri, E. G., and Schambelan, M. (1976). *J. Pediatr.* **89,** 395.

(e) Kirkland, R. T., Kirkland, J. L., Johnson, C., Horning, M., Librick, L., and Clayton, G. W. (1973). *J. Clin. Endocrinol. Metab.* **36,** 488.

(a) Kirkland, R. T., Keenan, B. S., Holcombe, J. H., Kirkland, J. L., and Clayton, G. W. (1979). *N. Engl. J. Med.* **300,** 988.

Klein, R. (1960). *J. Pediatr.* **57,** 452.

(a) Klingensmith, G. J., Wenta, A. C., Meyer, W. J., and Migeon, C. J. (1976). *J. Clin. Endocrinol. Metab.* **43,** 933.

(a) Klingensmith, G. J., Garcia, S. C., Jones, H. W., Migeon, C. J., and Blizzard, R. M. (1977). *J. Pediatr.* **90,** 996.

Klouda, P. T., Harris, R., and Price, D. A. (1978). *Lancet* **2,** 1046.

Klouda, P. T., Harris, R., and Price, D. A. (1980). *J. Med. Genet.* **17,** 337.

(b) Knorr, D., and Bidlingmaier, F. (1974). *Helv. Paediatr. Acta (Suppl.)* **34,** 119.

(h) Knorr, D., Bidlingmaier, F., and Engelhardt, D. (1973). *Acta Endocrinol. (Copenhagen) (Suppl.)* **173,** 37.

Knorr, D., Bidlingmaier, F., Butenandt, O., Fendel, H., and Ehrtwehle, R. (1974a). *Acta Endocrinol. (Copenhagen)* **75,** 181.

(h) Knorr, D., Bidlingmaier, R., Butenandt, O., and Engelhardt, D. (1974b). *Klin. Wochenschr.* **52,** 537.

Knorr, D., Bidlingmaier, F., Butenandt, O., Schnakenburg, K. B., and Wagner, W. (1977). *In* "Congenital Adrenal Hyperplasia" (P. A. Lee, L. P. Plotnick, A. A. Kowarski, and C. J. Migeon, eds.), pp. 495–500. Univ. Park Press, Baltimore, Maryland.

Koempf, J., Bissbort, S., and Gussman, S. (1975). *Humangenetik* **27,** 141.

(a) Koepp, P. (1976). *J. Pediatr.* **89,** 338.

(c) Kogut, M. D. (1965). *Am. J. Dis. Child.* **110,** 562.

(e) Koizumi, S., Kyoya, S., Miyawaki, T. M., Kidani, H., and Funabashi, T. (1977). *Clin. Chim. Acta* **77,** 301.

Korth-Schutz, S., and New, M. I. (1975). *Ann. Meet. Lawson Wilkins Pediatr. Endocrine Soc., April 1975, Denver Program and Abstracts.*

Korth-Schutz, S., Levine, L. S., and New, M. I. (1976). *J. Clin. Endocrinol. Metab.* **42,** 117.

(a) Korth-Schutz, S., Virdis, R., Saenger, P., Chow, D. M., Levine, L. S., and New, M. I. (1978). *J. Clin. Endocrinol. Metab.* **46,** 452.

(a) Koshimizu, T. (1979). *Clin. Endocrinol. (Oxford)* **10,** 515.

Kowarski, A., Finkelstein, J. W., Spaulding, J. S., Holman, G. H., and Migeon, C. J. (1965). *J. Clin. Invest.* **44,** 1505.

Kozoll, D. D. (1942). *Arch. Surg.* **45,** 578.

Krensky, A. M., Bongiovanni, A. M., Marion, J., Parks, J., and Tenore, A. (1977). *J. Pediatr.* **90,** 930.

(b) Kreutzmann, D., Vines, R. H., Hensley, W. J., and Silink, M. (1979). *Aust. Paediatr. J.* **15,** 36.

Kuhnle, U., Chow, D., Levine, L. S., and New, M. I. (1980). *Pediatr. Res.* **14,** 480.

Kuhnle, U., Chow, D., Pang, S., Levine, L. S., and New, M. I. (1981). *J. Clin. Endocrinol. Metab.* **52,** 534.

(c) Laatikainen, T., Perheentupa, J., Vihko, R., Makino, I., and Sjövall, J. (1972). *J. Steroid Biochem.* **3,** 715.

(a) Lahoud, H. J., Luttrell, B. M., and Steinbeck, A. W. (1976). *Steroids* **27,** 211.

Laragh, J. H. (1971). *In* "The Human Adrenal Cortex" (N. P. Christy, ed.), pp. 483–507. Harper, New York.

Laron, Z., Pollack, M. S., Zamir, R., Roitman, A., Dickerman, Z., Levine, L. S., Lorenzen, F., O'Neill, G. J., Pang, S., New, M. I., and Dupont, B. (1980). *Hum. Immunol.* **1,** 55.

Lee, P. A., and Gareis, F. J. (1975). *J. Clin. Endocrinol. Metab.* **41,** 415.

Lee, P. A., Jaffe, R. B., and Midgely, A. R., Jr. (1974). *J. Clin. Endocrinol. Metab.* **36,** 664.

(a) Lee, P. A., Plotnick, L. P., Kowarski, A. A., and Migeon, C. J. (1977). "Congenital Adrenal Hyperplasia." Univ. Park Press, Baltimore, Maryland.

(a) Leichter, S. B., and Jacobs, L. S. (1976). *J. Clin. Endocrinol. Metab.* **42,** 575.
Lejeune-Lenain, C., Cantraine, F., Dufrasnes, M., Prevot, F., Wolter, R., and Franckson, J. R. M. (1980). *Clin. Endocrinol.* **12,** 525.
Levine, L. S., Zachmann, M., New, M. I., Prader, A., Pollack, M. S., O'Neill, G. J., Yang, S. Y., Oberfield, S. E., and Dupont, B. (1978). *N. Engl. J. Med.* **299,** 911.
(h) Levine, L. S., Lieber, E., Pang, S., and New, M. I. (1980a). *Pediatr. Res.* **14,** 480.
(b) Levine, L. S., Rauh, W., Gottesdiener, K., Chow, D., Gunczler, P., Rapaport, R., Pang, S., Schneider, B., and New, M. I. (1980b). *J. Clin. Endocrinol. Metab.* **50,** 258.
Levine, L. S., Dupont, B., Lorenzen, F., Pang, S., Pollack, M., Oberfield, S., Kohn, B., Lerner, A., Cacciari, E., Mantero, F., Chiumello, G., Rodanini, G. F., Giovannelli, G., Virdis, R., Bartolotta, E., Migliori, C., Pintor, C., Tato, L., Barboni, F., and New, M. I. (1980c). *J. Clin. Endocrinol. Metab.* **51,** 1316.
(b) Lim, N. Y., Mimica, N., and Dingman, J. F. (1970). *J. Clin. Endocrinol. Metab.* **29,** 1564.
(a) Limal, J. M., Rappaport, R., and Bayard, F. (1977). *J. Clin. Endocrinol. Metab.* **45,** 500.
(d) Linquette, M., Dupont, A., Racadot, A., Lefebvre, J., May, J. P., and Cappoen, J. P. (1971). *Ann. Endocrinol. (Paris)* **32,** 574.
Lippe, B. M., La Franchi, S. H., Lavin, N., Parlow, A., Coyotupa, J., and Kaplan, S. A. (1974). *J. Pediatr.* **85,** 782.
(a) Loeuille, G. A. (1978). *Lille Med.* **23,** 354.
(a) Lombardi, G., Faggiano, M., Lupoli, G., and Minozzi, M. (1976). *Minerva Pediatr.* **28,** 1450.
Lombardi, G., Oliver, C. H., Lupoli, G., and Minozzi, M. (1977). *Acta Endocrinol. (Copenhagen)* **85,** 118.
Loras, B., Haour, F., and Bertrand, J. (1970). *Pediatr. Res.* **4,** 145.
(b) Loras, B., Dazord, A., Roux, H., and Bertrand, J. (1971). *Rev. Eur. Etud. Clin. Biol.* **16,** 6.
Lorenzen, F., Pang, S., New, M. I., Dupont, B., Pollack, M., Chow, D., and Levine, L. S. (1979). *Pediatr. Res.* **13,** 1356.
Lorenzen, F., Pang, S., New, M. I., Pollack, M., Oberfield, S. E., Dupont, B., Chow, D., and Levine, L. S. (1980). *J. Clin. Endocrinol. Metab.* **50,** 572.
(e) Luttrell, B., Hochberg, R. B., Dixon, W. R., McDonald, P. D., and Lieberman, S. (1972). *J. Biol. Chem.* **247,** 1462.
McCall, A. L., Stern, J., Dale, S. I., and Melby, J. C. (1978). *Endocrinology* **103,** 1.
(a) McKenna, T. J., Jennings, A. S., Liddle, G. W., and Burr, I. M. (1976). *J. Clin. Endocrinol. Metab.* **42,** 918.
McKusik, V. A. (1973). *Am. J. Hum. Genet.* **25,** 446.
Mackler, B., Haynes, B., Tattoni, D. S., Tippit, D. F., and Kelley, V. C. (1971). *Arch. Biochem. Biophys.* **145,** 194.
(b) Maclaren, N. K., Migeon, C. J., and Raiti, S. (1975). *J. Pediatr.* **86,** 579.
(d) Madan, K., and Schoemaker, J. (1980). *Hum. Genet.* **53,** 291.
(b) Madsen, P. O. (1963). *J. Urol.* **90,** 466.
(c) Magrini, U., Bertoli, G., and Mazzola, R. (1969). *Pathol. Eur.* **4,** 30.
(d) Mallin, S. R. (1969). *Ann. Intern. Med.* **70,** 69
(d) Mantero, F., Busnardo, B., Riondel, A., Veyrat, R., and Austoni, M. (1971). *Schweiz. Med. Wochenschr.* **101,** 38.
Mantero, F., Armaniani, D., Opocher, G., Gion, M., Sonino, N., Massarotto, P., Rudolfi, P., and Boscaro, M. (1975). *In* "Atti del secondo convegno sui metodi radioimmunoligci in endocrinologia," p. 201. Serono Symposium, Milano, 19-21 Maggio.
(a) Marwoto, S. A. (1976). *Paediatr. Indones.* **16,** 9.

(b) Maschler, I., Weidenfeld, J., Muller, A., Slavin, S., Shaefer, J., Chowers, I., and Finkelstein, M. (1977). *Acta Endocrinol. (Copenhagen)* **85,** 832.

(a) Massolo, F., Galli, V., Tamborino, G., Laudizi, L., Capella, L., and Carani, C. (1976). *Minerva Pediatr.* **28,** 1454.

(a) Mauthe, I., and Lapse Knorr, D. (1977). *Klin. Paediatr.* **189,** 172.

(g) Méndez Aparicio, M. (1975). *An. Esp. Pediatr.* **8,** 435.

(a) Menghi, P. (1976). *Minerva Pediatr.* **28,** 1396.

(a) Meyer, W. J., III, Diller, E. C., Bartter, F. C., and Halberg, F. (1976). *J. Clin. Endocrinol. Metab.* **43,** 1122.

(a) Migeon, C. J. (1977). *Hosp. Pract.* **12,** 75.

Migeon, C. J., Keller, A. R., Laurence, B., and Shepard, T. H. II (1957). *J. Clin. Endocrinol. Metab.* **17,** 1051.

(g) Milla, P. J., Trompeter, R., Dillon, M. J., Robbins, D., and Shakleton, C. (1977). *Arch. Dis. Child.* **52,** 580.

(d) Mills, I. H., Wilson, R. J., Tait, A. D., and Cooper, H. R. (1967). *J. Clin. Endocrinol. Metab.* **38,** XIX–XX.

Milunsky, A., and Tulchinsky, D. (1977). *Pediatrics* **59,** 768.

(a) Mininberg, D. T., Levine, L. S., and New, M. I. (1979). *Invest. Urol.* **17,** 169.

(a) Montalto, J., Davies, H. E., and Connelly, J. F. (1977). *Aust. Paediatr. J.* **13,** 12.

Molteni, A., Skelton, F. R., and Brownie, A. C. (1970). *Lab. Invest.* **23,** 429.

(e) Moragas, A., and Ballabriga, A. (1969). *Helv. Paediatr. Acta* **24,** 226.

Morillo, E., and Gardner, L. I. (1979). *Lancet* **2,** 202.

Mueller, J. (1971). "Regulation of Aldosterone Biosynthesis." Springer-Verlag, Berlin and New York.

(a) Müller, W., Prader, A., Kofler, J., Glatzl, J., and Geir, W. (1979). *Paediatr. Paedol.* **14,** 151.

Murtaza, L. M., Hughes, I. A., Sibert, S. R., and Balfour, I. C. (1978). *Lancet* **2,** 524.

Nagamani, M., McDonough, P. G., Ellegood, J. O., and Mahesh, V. B. (1978). *Am. J. Obstet. Gynecol.* **130,** 791.

(d) Narasimhulu, S., Cooper, D. Y., and Rosenthal, O. (1965). *Life Sci.* **4,** 2101.

(a) Natoli, G., and Schwarzenbuerg, T. L. (1976). *Minerva Pediatr.* **28,** 1418.

Nelson, E. B., and Bryan, G. T. (1975). *J. Clin. Metab.* **41,** 7.

(d) New, M. I. (1970). *J. Clin. Invest.* **49,** 1930.

New, M. I., and Levine, L. S. (1973). *In* "Advances in Human Genetics" (H. Harris and K. K. Hirschhorn, eds.), pp. 251–326. Plenum, New York.

New, M. I., and Peterson, R. E. (1966). *Pediatr. Clin. No. Am.* **13,** 43.

(b) New, M. I., and Seaman, M. P. (1970). *J. Clin. Endocrinol. Metab.* **30,** 361.

New, M. I., Miller, B., and Peterson, R. E. (1966). *J. Clin. Invest.* **45,** 412.

(a) New, M. I., Lorenzen, F., Pang, S., Gunczler, P., Dupont, B., Pollack, M., and Levine, L. S. (1979). *J. Clin. Endocrinol. Metab.* **48,** 356.

New, M. I., Dupont, B., and Levine, L. S. (1980a). *In* "HLA in Endocrine and Metabolic Disorders" (M. Farid, ed.). Academic Press, New York (in press).

New, M. I., Gunczler, P., Rösler, A., Oberfield, S., and Levine, L. S. (1980b). *Int. Congr. Pediatr. 16th, Sept. 8–13, Barcelona Abstracts and Presentations.*

Newmark, S., Dluhy, R., Williams, G., Pochi, P., and Rose, L. (1977). *Am. J. Obstet. Gynecol.* **127,** 594.

Nilson, O. (1939). *Acta Chir. Scand.* **83,** 231.

(a) Nozaki, Y., Kato, S., Shimizu, S., Amamiya, N., and Asayama, K. (1979). *Horumon To Rinsho* **27,** 1038.

(e) O'Doherty, N. J. (1964). *Guy's Hosp. Rep.* **113,** 368.
(a) Oetliker, O. H., and Zurbrugg, R. P. (1978). *J. Clin. Endocrinol. Metab.* **46,** 543.
Orta-Flores, Z., Cantu, J. M., and Dominguez, O. V. (1976). *J. Steroid Biochem.* **7,** 761.
Osterwalder, H. (1971). *Schweiz, Med. Wochenschr.* **101,** 1298.
(a) Pang, S., Hotchkiss, J., Drash, A. L., Levine, L. S., and New, M. I. (1977). *J. Clin. Endocrinol. Metab.* **45,** 1003.
(a) Pang, S., Levine, L. S., Chow, D. M., and New, M. I. (1978). *Pediatr. Res.* **12,** 417.
(a) Pang, S., Levine, L. S., Chow, D., Faiman, C., and New, M. I. (1979). *Clin. Endocrinol. (Oxford)* **11,** 575.
Pang, S., Levine, L. S., Lorenzen, F., Chow, D., Pollack, M. S., Dupont, B., and New, M. I. (1980a). *J. Clin. Endocrinol. Metab.* **50,** 586.
Pang, S., Levine, L. S., Cederqvist, L. L., Fuentes, M., Riccardi, V. M., Holcombe, J. H., Nitowsky, H. M., Sachs, G., Anderson, C. E., Duchon, M. A., Owens, R., Merkatz, I., and New, M. I. (1980b). *J. Clin. Endocrinol. Metab.* **51,** 223.
(c) Parks, G. A., Bermudez, J. A., Anast, C. S., Bongiovanni, A. M., and New, M. I. (1971). *J. Clin. Endocrinol. Metab.* **33,** 269.
(a) Parth, K., Zimprich, H., Swoboda, W., Brunel, R., and Bohrn, E. (1978). *Acta Endocrinol. (Copenhagen)* **87,** 148.
(h) Peretti, E., Saez, J., and Bertrand, J. (1970). *Excerpta Med. Int. Congr. Ser.* **210,** 205.
(a) Pertzelan, A., Laron, Z., Adler-Bier, M., Prager-Lewin, R., and Kaufman, H. (1978). *Arch. Dis. Child.* **53,** 305.
(a) Petersen, K. E., and Christensen, T. (1979). *Acta Paediatr. Scand.* **68,** 205.
(a) Pham-Huu-Trung, M. T., Raux, M. C., Gourmelan, M., Baron, M. C., and Girard, F. (1976). *Acta Endocrinol.* **82,** 572.
(h) Pittaway, D. E., Andersen, R. N., and Givens, J. R. (1976). *J. Clin. Endocrinol. Metab.* **43,** 457.
Pollack, M. S., Levine, L. S. Pang, S., Owens, R. P., Nitowsky, H. M., Maurer, D., New, M. I., Duchon, M., Merkatz, I. R., Sachs, G., and Dupont, B. (1979a). *Lancet* **1,** 1107.
Pollack, M. S., Levine, L. S., Zachmann, M., Prader, A., New, M. I., Oberfield, S. E., and Dupont, B. (1979b). *Transplant Proc.* **IX,** 1315.
Prader, A. (1958a). *Helv. Paediatr. Acta* **13,** 426.
Prader, A. (1958b). *Helv. Paediatr. Acta* **14,** 426.
(e) Prader, A., and Anders, G. J. (1962). *Helv. Paediatr. Acta* **17,** 285.
(e) Prader, A., and Gurtner, H. P. (1955). *Helv. Paediatr. Acta* **10,** 397.
(e) Prader, A., and Siebermann, R. E. (1957). *Helv. Paediatr. Acta* **12,** 509.
Prader, A., Spahr, A., and Neher, R. (1955). *Schweiz. Med. Wochenschr.* **85,** 45.
(a) Pribuda, B. A., and Min'kovich, L. D. (1976). *Arkh. Patol.* **38,** 89.
Price, D. A., Klouda, P. T., and Harris, R. (1978). *Lancet* **1,** 930.
Pucholt, V., Fitzsimmons, J. S., Gelsthorpe, K., Pratt, R. F., and Doughty, R. W. (1978). *Lancet* **2,** 1046.
Pucholt, V., Fitzsimmons, J. S., Reynolds, M. A., and Gelsthorpe, K. (1979). *Pediatr. Res.* **13,** 1186.
Qazi, Q. H., and Thompson, M. W. (1972). *Arch. Dis. Child.* **47,** 302.
Qazi, Q. H., Hill, J. G., and Thompson, M. W. (1971). *J. Clin. Endocrinol. Metab.* **33,** 23.
(a) Raiti, S., Maclaren, N. K., and Akesode, F. A. (1978). *Pediatr. Res.* **12,** 87.
Rappaport, R., and Limal, J.-M. (1977). *In* "Congenital Adrenal Hyperplasia" (P. A. Lee, L. P. Plotnick, A. A. Kowarski, and C. J. Migeon, eds.), pp. 263–272. Univ. Park Press, Baltimore, Maryland.

(a) Rappaport, R., and Prevot, C. (1977). *J. Pediatr.* **90,** 963.
(g) Rappaport, R., Dray, F., Legrand, J. C., and Royer, P. (1968). *Pediatr. Res.* **2,** 456.
(a) Rass, I. T., Kuznetsova, E. S., and Zhukovskii, W. A. (1979). *Pediatria* **9,** 26.
(g) Ravussin, J.-J., De Martinville, B., Lauras, B., Chatelain, P., and Freycon, F. (1977). *Pediatrie* **32,** 781.
(g) Reiter, E. O., and Teree, T. M. (1979). *Pediatr. Res.* **13,** 384.
(b) Reynolds, J. W., and Ulstrom, R. A. (1963). *J. Clin. Endocrinol. Metab.* **23,** 191.
(b) Riddick, D. H., and Hammond, C. H. (1975). *Obstet. Gynecol.* **45,** 15.
(e) Rimoin, D. L., and Schimke, R. N. (1971). "Genetic Disorders of the Endocrine Glands." Mosby, St. Louis, Missouri.
(b) Riondel, A. M., Veyrat, R., Sizonenko, P., and Paunier, L. (1972). *Schweiz. Med. Wochenschr.* **102,** 1282.
Rivarola, M. A., Saez, J. M., and Migeon, C. J. (1967). *J. Clin. Endocrinol. Metab.* **27,** 624.
Root, A. W., Bongiovanni, A. M., and Eberlein, W. R. (1971). *In* "The Human Adrenal Cortex" (N. P. Christy, ed.), pp. 427–474. Harper, New York.
Rosenbloom, A. L., and Smith, D. W. (1966a). *Lancet* **1,** 660.
Rosenbloom, A. L., and Smith, D. W. (1966b). *Pediatrics* **38,** 215.
Rosenfeld, R. S., Hellman, L., Roffwarg, H., Weitzman, E. D., Fukushima, D. K., and Gallagher, T. F. (1971). *J. Clin. Endocrinol. Metab.* **3,** 87.
Rosenfield, R. L., and Eberlein, W. R. (1969). *J. Pediatr.* **74,** 932.
(c) Rosenfield, R. L., Niepomnisze, A., Kenny, F. M., and Genel, M. (1974). *J. Clin. Endocrinol. Metab.* **39,** 370.
(a) Rosenwaks, Z., Lee, P. A., Jones, G. S., Migeon, C. J., and Wentz, A. C. (1979). *J. Clin. Endocrinol. Metab.* **49,** 335.
(g) Rösler, A., Theodor, R., Gazit, E., Boichis, H., and Rabinowitz, D. (1973). *Lancet* **1,** 959.
(g) Rösler, A., Theodor, R., Boichis, H., Rabinowitz, D., and Ulick, S. (1974). *Annu. Meet. 56th, Endocrine Soc., Atlanta* Abstract No. 63, A-87.
(g) Rösler, A., Rabinowitz, D., Theodor, R., Ramirez, L. C., and Ulick, S. (1977a). *J. Clin. Endocrinol. Metab.* **44,** 279.
(g) Rösler, A., Theodor, R., Boichis, H., Gerty, R., Ulick, S., Alagem, M., Tabachnik, E., Cohen, B., and Rabinowitz, D. (1977b). *J. Clin. Endocrinol. Metab.* **44,** 292.
(a) Rösler, A., Levine, L. S., Schneider, B., Novogroder, M., and New, M. I. (1977c). *J. Clin. Endocrinol. Metab.* **45,** 500.
(b) Rösler, A., Leiberman, E., Rosenmann, A., Ben-Uzilio, R., and Weidemfeld, J. (1979). *J. Clin. Endocrinol. Metab.* **49,** 546.
(a) Ross, G., Jr., Schneider, R. E., Thompson, I. A., Anast, C. S., and Montie, J. E. (1976). *J. Urol.* **115,** 462.
Roux, H., Loras, B., and Forest, M. G. (1977). *In* "Congential Adrenal Hyperplasia" (P. A. Lee, L. P. Plotnick, A. A. Kowarski, and C. J. Migeon, eds.), pp. 487–493. Univ. Park Press, Baltimore, Maryland.
(d) Rovner, D. R., Conn, J. W., Cohen, E. L., Berlinger, F. G., and Kem, D. C. (1968). *J. Lab. Clin. Med.* **72,** 1009.
(d) Rovner, D. R., Conn, J. W., Cohen, E. L., Berlinger, F. G., Kem, D. C., and Gordon, D. L. (1979). *Acta Endocrinol* **90,** 490.
(g) Royer, P., Lestradet, H., de Menibus, C. H., and Vermeil, G. (1961). *Ann. Pediatr. (Paris)* **8,** 133.
(g) Russell, A., Levin, B., Sinclair, L., and Oberholzer, V. G. (1963). *Arch. Dis. Child.* **38,** 313.

(h) Saez, J. M., De Peretti, E., Morea, A. M., David, M., and Bertrand, J. (1971a). *J. Clin. Endocrinol. Metab.* **32,** 604.
(h) Saez, J. M., Frederich, E., De Peretti, E., and Bertrand, J. (1971b). *Birth Defects* **VII,** 150.
(h) Saez, J. M., Morera, A. M., and De Peretti, E. (1972). *J. Clin. Endocrinol. Metab.* **34,** 598.
(a) Saito, N., Niwa, T., Nakaguchi, M., Nonoda, A., and Yoshida, H. (1977). *Horumon To Rinsho* **25,** 981.
(b) Schaison, G., and Gilbert-Dreyfus, G. (1974). *Ann. Med. Interne (Paris)* **125,** 163.
(h) Schaison, G., and Gilbert-Dreyfus, G. (1975). *Ann. Endocrinol.* **36,** 99.
(h) Schaison, G., and Sitruk, L. R. (1976). *Horm. Metab. Res.* **8,** 307.
Schambelan, M., Rost, G. R., Sebastian, A., and Biglieri, E. G. (1980). *Int. Congr. Endocrinol. 6th, Melbourne, February Abstracts and Program,* p. 241.
(h) Schneider, G., and Bardin, C. W. (1970). *Endocrinology* **87,** 864.
(c) Schneider, G., Genel, M., Bongiovanni, A. M., Goldman, A. S., and Rosenfield, R. L. (1975). *J. Clin. Invest.* **55,** 681.
(d) Schoemaker, J., Madan, K., Puyenbroek, J., and Stolk, J. (1980). *Clin. Genet.* (in press).
Schumert, Z., Rosenmann, A., Landau, H., and Rösler, A. (1980). *Clin. Endocrinol. (Oxford)* **12,** 257.
(a) Shackleton, C. H. L. (1976). *Clin. Chim. Acta* **67,** 287.
(g) Shackleton, C. H. L., Honour, J. S., Dillon, M., and Milla, P. (1976). *Acta Endocrinol. (Copenhagen)* **81,** 762.
Sharma, D. C., Forchielli, E., and Dorfmann, R. J. (1963). *J. Biol. Chem.* **238,** 572.
(b) Shepard, T. H., and Clausen, S. W. (1951). *Pediatrics* **8,** 805.
(a) Shimozawa, K., Tomita, M., Nakagawa, S., Saito, Y., and Sakurada, N. (1979). *Horumon To Rinsho* **27,** 1048.
(b) Shul'ga, I. U. D., and Bil'chenko, O. S. (1976). *Klin. Med.* **54,** 118.
Simopoulos, A. P., Marshall, J. R., Delea, C. S., and Bartter, F. C. (1971). *J. Clin. Endocrinol. Metab.* **32,** 438.
(b) Sizonenko, P.-C., Riondel, A.-M., Kohlberg, I. J., and Paunier, L. (1972a). *J. Clin. Endocrinol. Metab.* **35,** 281.
(b) Sizonenko, P.-C., Schindler, A.-M., Kohlberg, I. J., and Paunier, L. (1972b). *Acta Endocrinol. (Copenhagen)* **7,** 539.
(b) Smolik, R., Lange, A., Kasza, S., and Czarnowska, J. (1969). *Pol. Arch. Med. Wewn.* **41,** 937.
Sobel, D. O., Gutai, J. P., Jones, J. C., Wagener, D. K., and Smith, W. (1980). *Lancet* **1,** 47.
(b) Solomon, I. L., and Schoen, E. J. (1975). *J. Clin. Endocrinol. Metab.* **40,** 355.
(a) Solyom, J., Hammond, G. L., and Vihko, R. (1979). *Clin. Chim. Acta* **92,** 117.
Strickland, A. L., and Kotchen, T. A. (1972). *J. Pediatr.* **81,** 962.
Strott, C. A., Yoshimi, T., and Lipsett, M. B. (1969). *J. Clin. Invest.* **48,** 930.
(a) Suwa, S. (1979). *Nippon Rinsho* **37,** 380.
(a) Tan, S. Y., Donabedian, R., Genel, M., and Mulrow, P. J. (1977). *J. Lab. Clin. Med.* **89,** 735.
(b) Tan, S. Y., Noth, R. H., and Mulrow, P. J. (1978). *J. Am. Med. Assoc.* **240,** 123.
(e) Tanae, A., Matsuura, M., and Hibi, I. (1976). *Clin. Endocrinol. (Tokyo)* **24,** 775.
(a) Taylor, N. F., Curnow, D. H., and Shackleton, C. H. (1978). *Clin. Chim. Acta* **85,** 219.
(a) Thomsett, M. J. (1978). *Aust. Pediatr. J.* **14,** 16.
(b) Toaff, M. E., Toaff, R., and Chayen, R. (1975). *Am. J. Obstet. Gynecol.* **121,** 202.
(e) Tohuhiro, E., and Suwa, S. (1978). *Horumon To Rinsho* **26,** 1197.

(h) Tourniaire, J., Laubie, B., Saez, J., Leung, T. K., Perrin, J., Dutrieux, N., and Guinet, P. (1973). *Ann. Endocrinol. (Paris)* **34,** 461.
(d) Tourniaire, J., Audi-Parera, L., Loras, B., Blum, J., Castelnovo, P., and Forest, M. G. (1976). *Clin. Endocrinol.* **5,** 53.
(e) Tsutsui, Y., Hirabayashi, N., and Ito, G. (1970). *Acta Pathol. Jpn.* **20,** 227.
(g) Ulick, S. (1972). *Proc. Int. Congr. Endocrinol. 4th, Washington Excerpta Med. Int. Congr. Ser.* No. 273, p. 761.
(b) Ulick, S. (1976a). *Am. J. Cardiol.* **38,** 814.
(g) Ulick, S. (1976b). *J. Clin. Endocrinol. Metab.* **43,** 92.
(g) Ulick, S., Gautier, E., Vetter, K. K., Markello, J. R., Yaffe, S., and Lowe, C. U. (1964). *J. Clin. Endocrinol. Metab.* **24,** 669.
(a) Urban, M. D., Lee, P. A., and Migeon, C. J. (1978). *N. Engl. J. Med.* **299,** 1392.
(a) Valeri, O. M., Natoli, G., and Schwarzenberg, T. L. (1976). *Minerva Pediatr.* **28,** 1384.
(b) Van Deijk, W. A., Blom, P. S., and Vd Vijver, J. C. (1979). *Neth. J. Med.* **22,** 191.
(g) Veldhuis, J. D., Kulin, H. E., Santen, R. J., Wilson, T. E., and Melby, J. C. (1980). *N. Engl. J. Med.* **303,** 117.
(a) Villee, D. B., and Crigler, J. F., Jr. (1976). *Clin. Perinatol.* **3,** 211.
Virdis, R., Saenger, P., Senior, B., and New, M. I. (1978). *Acta Endocrinol.* **87,** 212.
Visser, H. K. A. (1970). *Proc. R. Soc. Med.* **63,** 1037.
(a) Visser, H. K. A. (1978). *Ned. Tijdschr. Geneeskd.* **122,** 1406.
(f) Visser, H. K. A., and Cost, W. S. (1964). *Acta Endocrinol. (Copenhagen)* **47,** 589.
Volkova, T. N., Lukina, L. I., and Varvantseva, M. P. (1977). *Vopr. Okhr. Materin. Det.* **22,** 38.
(a) Von Petrykowski, W., and Kreuzer, H. B. (1976). *Monatsschr. Kinderheilkd.* **124,** 391.
(a) Von Schnakenburg, K. (1977). *Med. Welt* **28,** 1415.
(a) Von Schnakenburg, K., Bidlingmaier, F., and Knorr, D. (1977). *Monatsschr. Kinderheilkd.* **125,** 579.
(a) Wajchenberg, B. L., Achando, S. S., Okada, H., Shimizu, T., White, A., Lima, S. S., Pieroni, R. R., and Leme, C. E. (1979). *J. Clin. Endocrinol. Metab.* **49,** 46.
(d) Waldhausl, W., Herkner, K., Nowotny, P., and Bratusch-Marrain, P. (1978). *J. Clin. Endocrinol. Metab.* **46,** 236.
(a) Walker, R. F., and Fahmy, D. R. (1978). *J. Endocrinol.* **79,** 64P.
Walker, R. F., Read, G. F., Hughes, I. A., and Fahmy, R. D. (1979). *Clin. Chem.* **25,** 542.
Weitkamp, L. R., Bryson, M., and Bacon, G. E. (1978). *Lancet* **1,** 931.
(a) Wentz, A. C., Garcia, S. C., Klingensmith, G. J., Migeon, C. J., and Jones, G. S. (1976). *J. Clin. Endocrinol. Metab.* **42,** 239.
Werder, E. A., Siebenmann, R. E., Knorr-Murset, G., Zimmermann, A., Sizonenko, P. C., Theintz, P., Girard, J., Zachmann, M., and Prader, A. (1980). *Helv. Paediatr. Acta* **35,** 5.
West, C. D., Stanchfield, J. B., Atcheson, J. B., Rallison, M. L., and Tyler, F. H. (1973). *Clin. Res.* **21,** 190.
(a) West, C. D., Atcheson, J. B., Stanchfield, J. B., Rallison, M. L., Chavre, V. J., and Tyler, F. H. (1979). *J. Steroid Biochem.* **11,** 1413.
Wieland, R. G., Chen, J. C., Zorn, E. M., and Hallberg, M. C. (1971). *J. Pediatr.* **79,** 999.
Wilkins, L. (1960). *J. Am. Med. Assoc.* **172,** 1028.
Wilkins, L. (1962). *Arch. Dis. Child.* **37,** 231.
(b) Wilkins, L., Lewis, R. A., Klein, R., Gardner, L. I., Crigler, J. F., Rosemberg, E., and Migeon, C. J. (1951). *J. Clin. Endocrinol. Metab.* **11,** 1.
(b) Wilkins, L., Crigler, J. F., Silverman, S. H., Gardner, L. I., and Migeon, C. J. (1952a). *J. Clin. Endocrinol. Metab.* **12,** 277.

(b) Wilkins, L., Crigler, J. F., Silverman, S. H., Gardner, L. I., and Migeon, C. J. (1952b). *J. Clin. Endocrinol. Metab.* **12,** 1015.
Wilkins, L., Jones, H. W., Jr., Holman, G., and Stempfel, R. S., Jr. (1958). *J. Clin Endocrinol. Metab.* **18,** 559.
(a) Winter, J. S. D. (1980). *J. Pediatr.* **97,** 81.
Winter, J. S. D., and Faiman, C. (1972). *Pediatr. Res.* **6,** 126.
Winter, J. S. D., Hughes, I. A., Reyes, F. I., and Faiman, C. (1976). *J. Clin. Endocrinol. Metab.* **42,** 679.
(a) Wolff, P. B., Wilbois, R. P., Weldon, V. V., and Haymond, M. W. (1977). *J. Pediatr.* **91,** 951.
(a) Wong, E. T., Brown, D. R., Ulstrom, R. A., and Steffes, M. W. (1979). *J. Clin. Endocrinol. Metab.* **49,** 335.
World Health Organization (1980). *Tissue Antigens* **16,** 113.
Youssefnejadian, E., and David, R. (1975). *Clin. Endocrinol.* **4,** 451.
(b) Zachmann, M., and Prader, A. (1975). *J. Pediatr.* **87,** 839.
Zachmann, M., and Prader, A. (1978). *Acta Endocrinol.* **87,** 557.
Zachmann, M., and Prader, A. (1979). *Acta Endocrinol.* **92,** 542.
(b) Zachmann, M., Völlmin, J. A., New, M. I., Curtuis, H.-C., and Prader, A. (1971). *J. Clin. Endocrinol. Metab.* **33,** 501.
(c) Zachmann, M., Forest, M. G., and De Peretti, E. (1979). *Horm. Res.* **11,** 292.
(b) Zadik, Z., Pertzelan, A., Kaufman, H., Levin, S., and Laron, Z. (1979). *Helv. Pediatr. Acta* **34,** 185.
Zappacosta, S., De Felice, M., Minozzi, M., Lombardi, G., Valentino, R., and Vancote, G. (1978). *Lancet* **2,** 524.
(h) Zürbrugg, R. (1974). *Helv. Paediatr. Acta (Suppl.)* **34,** 63.

DISCUSSION

J. E. Rall: From your concept of two separate adrenocorticals I infer that you mean two genes. In this regard, I wonder if you have checked the enzymology to see whether there are differences in, for example, the affinity constants for the different substrates on the V_{maxes} which might tell you that there were different mutations in a single gene. Alternatively through linkage analysis you might find that there really are two genes which segregate differently. Have you done either of those?

M. I. New: It is impossible to do enzymology because the 21-hydroxylase enzyme has not been purified. Your second question is a very interesting question and I would ask Dr. Dupont to respond after I make this statement. The clinical experience of the pediatrician in general is that the salt wasters and the simple virilizers breed true in a family. We are looking for the family in which there is a salt waster and non-salt waster to see if a recombination has occurred. Dr. Dupont might have a comment on that.

B. Dupont: In the studies in the Eighth International Histocompatibility Workshop in 1980, in which about 25 laboratories worldwide participated in studies of 21-hydroxylase deficiency more than 400 families with 21-hydroxylase deficiency were studied and that provided enormous amounts of data and the possibility of identifying rare genetic recombinations within HLA or within the HLA linkage group, i.e., between HLA and the gene for glyoxylase I, which is located 5 centimorgans distal to the HLA-D locus. In these studies a couple of very interesting recombinants were identified. These recombinants are very informative for the fine mapping of 21-hydroxylase locus. There is one study from Sheffield in England where Dr. Pucholt has demonstrated that two siblings who were both affected with the disease were different for the HLA-D/DR locus on one HLA haplotype. This means that they would be identical for the ACB segment of HLA but different for HLA-D/DR because of a genetic recombination and that would place the gene for 21-hydroxylase deficiency between the HLA-B and the HLA-D/DR locus. There are two additional families studied: one from Lyon, France and one from Manchester, England and they both demonstrate two HLA-A,C,B, D/DR identical siblings of which only one is affected with 21-hydroxylase deficiency in each sibship. These two studies would thus place the 21-OH-def gene outside HLA between HLA-D/DR and GLO-I. If these 3 family studies are correct, it means that there are two genes for 21-hydroxylase with one gene between the HLA-B locus and the HLA-D locus and there is one gene outside the HLA-D locus closer to the GLO-I locus. These families have been very well studied and I do not think that there is any reasonable doubt about the findings, which would imply the presence of two genes for 21-OH. I think the problem with this finding is that we cannot really explain why we do not see isolated salt wasting alone without virilization.

One of the ways to answer the question of two or more HLA linked genes involved in 21-hydroxylase deficiency will be to perform genetic marker studies in families to patients where two siblings have different disease manifestations, i.e., one being classical salt waster and one being simple virilized. So far, none of the families we have studied have provided such an opportunity.

F. C. Bartter: As you know, we agree with you that the zona glomerulosa is "a different gland" from the zona fasciculata. Specifically, the 21-hydroxylase for the glomerulosa probably has different substrate specificity, i.e., progesterone, from that in the fasciculata, i.e., 17-hydroxyprogesterone. Some previously published results (*JCI* **47,** 1742, 1968) (Fig. A) illustrate this: aldosterone is used as an index of glomerulosa function. With 4 days of sodium deprivation, six patients with sodium-losing adrenogenital syndrome resulting from 21-hydroxylase deficiency (solid dots) could increase urinary aldosterone little or not at all. The increase in six normal controls is shown (dotted lines, open circles) and the rise, enormous in the older subjects, in seven patients with the non-sodium-losing form is shown (triangles).

I would like to ask you and Dr. Dupont to enlarge on his statement that recombination had led him to believe that there are two separate loci for the 21-hydroxylase defect in the HLA region on chromosome 6. Can he rule out the possibility that one of these is for 21-hydroxylation in the zona glomerulosa and the other for 21-hydroxylation in the fasciculata—a finding which might suggest that there was a genetic mechanism for the "true breeding" of salt losers as opposed to non-salt losers? Alternatively, with your enormous and beautiful family study, can you rigorously rule out such a possiblity?

Finally, in view of the convincing evidence that the two "pathways" do not occur in the same cell, I would like to offer a schema (Fig. B) which would allow you to eliminate the necessity for labeling pathways as "mineralocorticoid" and "glucocorticoid" in your Fig. 1.

M. I. New: Dr. Dupont has indicated that there were two recombinants suggesting there was a gene inside the HLA-D locus and one outside the HLA-D locus. The problem is that we're at the phenotypic level of this disorder. We can study the expression of the HLA genotype. We can study the hormonal expression of the defect, but we have no idea where the genetic defect is in terms of molecular biology. We do not know whether all these children suffer exactly the same gene mutation, whether the mutation is in the same place in all the patients, and whether the salt waster and simple virilizer are more different than two simple virilizing patients. I think that these questions are probably going to have to be resolved by recombinant DNA techniques.

P. K. Donahoe: Have you considered carrying prenatal diagnosis one step further to prenatal treatment?

M. I. New: I'm glad you asked that. You see amniocentesis is safely done only after the labioscrotal folds are fused. Thus prenatal diagnosis cannot prevent urogenital sinus forma-

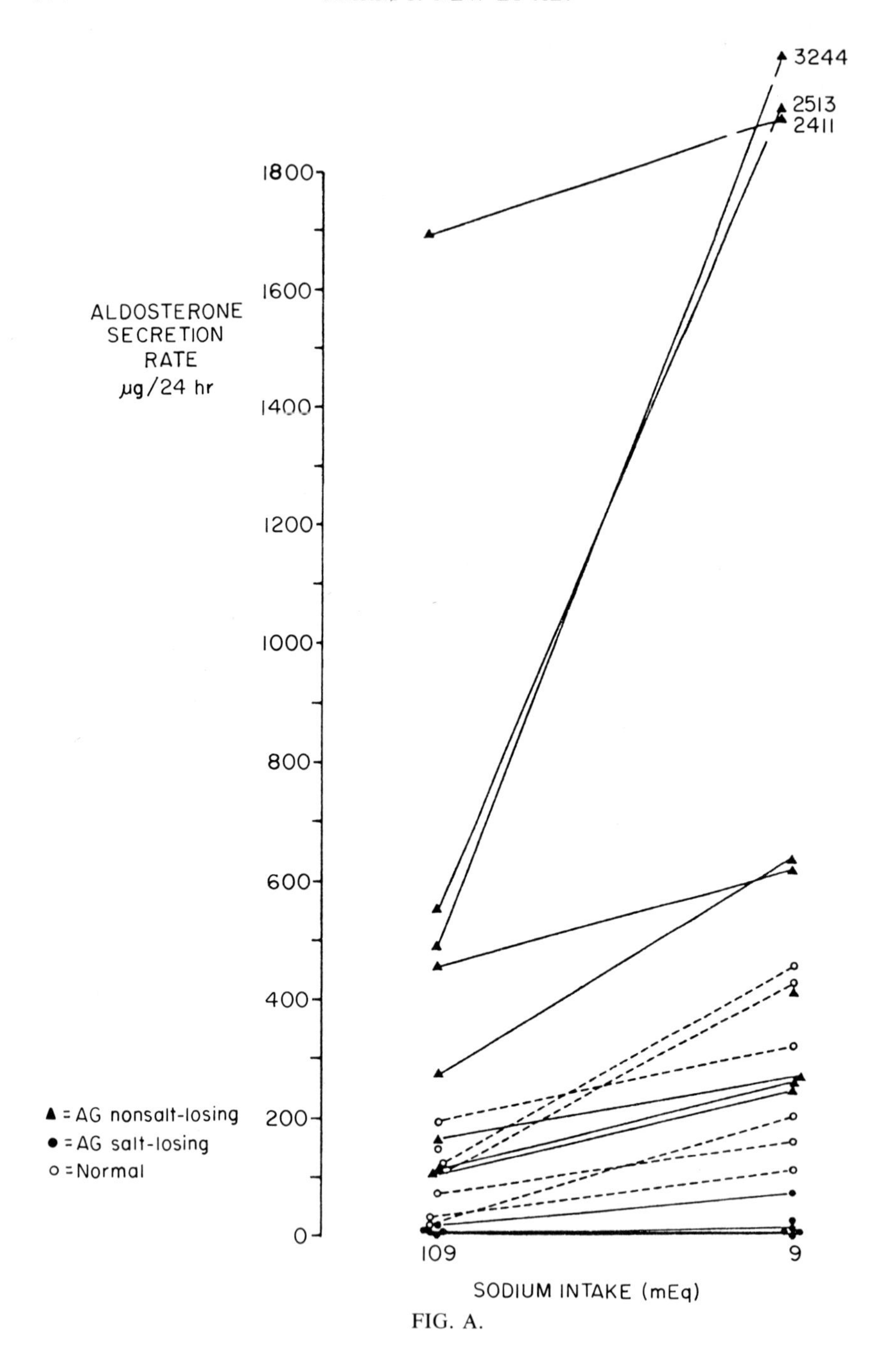
3244
2513
2411
ALDOSTERONE SECRETION RATE µg/24 hr
1800
1600
1400
1200
1000
800
600
400
200
0
▲ = AG nonsalt-losing
● = AG salt-losing
○ = Normal
109
9
SODIUM INTAKE (mEq)

FIG. A.

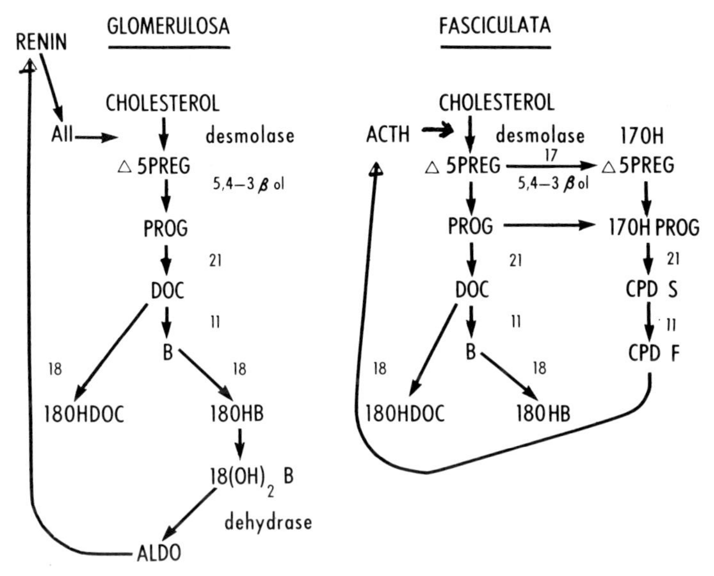

FIG. B.

tion. I might take this moment to say two things that I didn't have time to say previously: It might be very important to really know more about the incidence of this disease. In a recent survey at Zurich, Professor Prader indicated that the incidence in Zurich where the case ascertainment is excellent is one in five thousand. The incidence of disease in the Tyrol was one in five thousand. Dr. Pang in my laboratory has done the first screening survey of the disorder and has screened 18,000 newborns from Alaska by a microfilter paper test that she has devised. The incidence in Caucasian Alaska was one in 3000. The incidence of disease always increases with screening. Phenylketonuria went from one in 26,000 to one in 16,000 after screening. I would predict that this disease may turn out to be the second commonest genetic recessive disorder after cystic fibrosis, and therefore it would urge us not only to do prenatal diagnosis but perhaps to consider mounting screening programs.

G. B. Cutler: I may have missed some of the evidence but, in view of the fact that the late onset and the cryptic patient seemed to have virtually identical hormonal parameters, I wondered why you were so certain that they were separate genes, rather than that some other factor modified the phenotypic expression of the same gene.

M. I. New: You're right. I have no reason for saying that they are separate genes. The classical gene is in genetic linkage disequilibrium with a different HLA-B allele from the cryptic gene, while it appears that the cryptic and late onset gene are both in genetic linkage disequilibrium with HLA-B14.

B. Dupont: As Dr. New pointed out, the HLA system is a highly polymorphic genetic system with a large number of alleles at each of the HLA-A,B,C and D/DR loci. This fact provides a unique opportunity for identifying if any particular determinant of the HLA system is specifically increased among patients with a given disease. The term "association" is often used when a particular gene or gene product is identified with a higher frequency among patients with the disease than the frequency of the same allele in the normal control population. Such a finding does not imply that the gene involved in the disease and the marker gene necessarily are located on the same chromosome. A number of different diseases of multifactorial nature have been found to be associated with HLA determinants. The insulin dependent diabetes mellitus is for example associated primarily with DR3 and DR4 and Graves' disease is associated with DR3.

One of the conspicuous characteristics of the HLA gene complex is the tremendous degree of nonrandom gametic associations, i.e., genetic linkage disequilibrium which is found for alleles of the different HLA loci. When the genetic linkage was found for the gene for 21-hydroxylase deficiency and HLA, it was natural to investigate if this particular allele of the 21-hydroxylase locus (21-OH) would demonstrate genetic linkage disequilibrium to any HLA determinant and if any particular HLA haplotype was found to be particularly frequent among the patients with classical, congenital 21-hydroxylase deficiency. Such studies have demonstrated that HLA-B5;B40 and Bw47 are increased among patients with this disease and that B8 and DR3 are significantly decreased in frequency among the patients. But it should be noted, that a great variety of different HLA haplotypes and most of the HLA-B determinants have been identified in patients with this disease. The associations with Bw47 are very interesting, since this antigen occurs only with a frequency of 2–3 per 1000 random Caucasian individuals while it occurs with a frequency of 5–25% among Caucasian patients with 21-hydroxylase deficiency. The Bw47 positive haplotypes will frequently be A3;Cw6;Bw47;BfF;DR7. It may very well be that the Bw47 antigen identified in the normal population in most instances will be linked to the 21-OH-def gene and that such individuals in fact are heterozygous carriers of the disease gene. It should however be noted that so far, no difference in the HLA antigen frequency has been observed between salt wasters and simple virilizers. This may, however, reflect that the patient samples are still too small from any single center to allow for such an analysis. It should be noted that the Bw47 antigen is absent in patients from Iceland and in the Japanese patients studied so far.

I think that the large number of HLA-B alleles which have been identified in the patients with this disease indicate that the 21-hydroxylase deficiency mutation is either very old or that several independent mutations resulting in the same defect have occurred.

Another interesting aspect of genetic linkage disequilibrium and the 21-hydroxylase deficiency syndromes is that the allele for the cryptic deficiency of the 21-OH locus is very strongly associated with HLA-B14 and DR1. So far, the cryptic gene has not been identified on a Bw47 positive haplotype. This also indicates that the cryptic allele is genetically different from the classical deficiency allele and probably has arisen as a result of a different mutation. The HLA association for the cryptic allele is very strong. So far the HLA-B14 and/or DR 1 has been identified on 90% of the haplotypes with the $21\text{-OH}^{\text{CRYPTIC}}$ allele.

B. E. P. Murphy: Our recent studies of cortisol–cortisone interconversion in neonates suggested that the identity of the infant liver is poor with respect to converting the cortisone to cortisol. Since this is what we depend on in treatment it would seem to me that it would be much better to treat these people with cortisol rather than cortisone although I understand that at least as many people use cortisone. I wonder, just to complete your update, if you would mention current treatment and monitoring.

M. I. New: The treatment of congenital adrenal hyperplasia of the 21-hydroxylase deficiency type has changed significantly as well as the others with respect really to one factor. We were used to, when I was trained, to watch growth, the signs of virilization, and the urinary ketosteroids, and really that was pretty good. Now instead of monitoring only 17-ketosteroids in terms of hormones we monitor the serum 17-hydroxyprogesterone and the serum androgens and we have shown that the Δ^4 and the testosterone in the female are very useful androgens to monitor while only the Δ^4 is useful in the male. Dehydrepiandrosterone is not useful. But the new thing is this. We have discovered that many patients, both virilizers and salt wasters have hyperreninemia. This hyperreninemia, through a mechanism that isn't clear, stimulates ACTH and the increased ACTH then stimulates androgens and you get poor control. Thus we have found that if we monitor the renin as carefully as we monitor the 17-hydroxyprogesterone, and that means administering a salt-retaining hormone like 9α-fludrohydrocortisone to normalized renin, we can treat the children with lower doses of glucocorticoid such as hydrocortisone and growth improves and, as a matter of fact, I am going to present that in Barcelona because we now have seven children that we have followed for 4 years of such treatment and we can show without a doubt that it is in the postrenin monitoring era, we have improved growth and lower doses of hydrocortisone.

B. Rice: You have done a very beautiful job of outlining what appears to be very clearly a genetic problem in a series of families in girls or boys that have this cryptic or late onset congenital adrenal hyperplasia. Is the entity that you have described as late onset adrenal hyperplasia fairly common, or are we confusing it in these patients with what we had labeled as polycystic ovary disease.

M. I. New: I don't know how frequent late onset 21-hydroxylase deficiency is. Those patients with late onset 21-hydroxylase deficiency had genetic defects which may also be linked to HLA as was the cryptic. We went about asking our colleagues for patients who had the syndrome of late onset virilization and we have come up with very few. I don't know how frequent it is and I do not know whether the patient that you would classify as Stein Leventhal or polycystic ovary syndrome may in fact fall into several categories among which one might be an HLA linked genetic variety of late onset 21-hydroxylase deficiency. I would never recommend giving dexamethosone to children for two reasons. One, it is very difficult to govern the dose and the last thing we want to do is make them cushioned and arrest their growth. The second is that dexamethosone unlike hydrocortisone has very low salt-retaining properties and does not enter the mineralocorticoid receptor. I feel that the treatment with hydrocortisone is safer because it has both salt retaining and glucocorticoid properties and one can regulate the dose carefully.

M. M. Grumbach: In studies carried out with my colleague, Dr. Styne, dexamethasone had about 80× the ACTH-suppressing activity of cortisol and 96× that of cortisone acetate orally in children with virilizing congenital adrenal hyperplasia. Because of its potent inhibiting effect on growth and the difficulty in dispensing dexamethasone in an appropriate dose within a narrow safe range, we avoid its use in affected infants and children. However, once patients have achieved their final height, it is a useful and safe form of therapy, especially in adolescent girls and women who are inadequately controlled with cortisol or less potent glucocorticoid analogs.

P. Saenger: Having had the unique opportunity of having been trained by Dr. New, one's interest in this disorder about which we heard so many exciting new facts continues. Dr. New showed us a considerable overlap in diagnosing particularly the postpubertal female heterozygotes with an ACTH stimulation test and measuring their 17-hydroxyprogesterone response. Presumably this overlap is due to the ovarian contribution of 17-hydroxyprogesterone (Fig. C). An alternate approach would be to measure not only 17-hydroxyprogesterone, but also the 11-hydroxylated product of 17-hydroxyprogesterone, 21-deoxycortisol. The steroid enzyme 11-hydroxylase is limited according to our current knowledge, to the adrenal; 11-hydroxylation does not occur in the ovary. 21-Deoxycortisol would be a more uniquely adrenal metabolite and would not be altered so much by the ovarian contribution. We measured 21-deoxycortisol in serum using an antibody provided kindly by Dr. Fukushima at our institution (Fig. D). Preliminary data show that postpubertal male and female controls don't show a great difference in their peak 21-deoxycortisol response after 6 hours of ACTH infusion. So far, two HLA proven heterozygotes for 21-

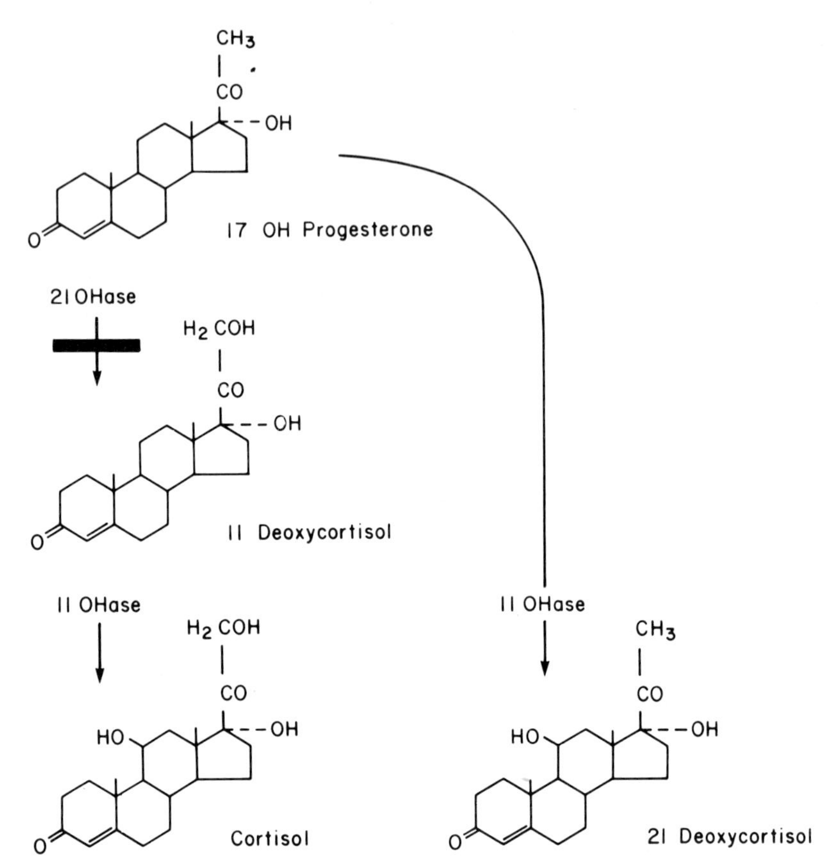

FIG. C. Metabolism of 17-OH progesterone to 21-deoxycortisol.

hydroxylase deficiency and the mother of one patient were outside of the range defined by normal controls. Measurement of 21-deoxycortisol may be another promising approach in diagnosing heterozygotes in this disorder.

M. I. New: I think it's very important to add this hormone, but our experience has been that as we've expanded the heterozygote population, those that we thought were below the heterozygote range have suddenly come within the heterozygote range. It might be very useful to plot your data the same way that we did for the other hormones, that is, the baseline versus the stimulated level.

C. Monder: The number of 21-hydroxylase remains a subject for study. It's obvious that we don't know how many there are in humans and many other species. The rabbit might prove to be an instructive model since it has now been demonstrated that there are indeed at least two 21-hydroxylases in the rabbit. One is expressed in the adrenal gland, and the other is in the liver. They differ in a number of properties. One of the more striking differences between them is the susceptibility of the adrenal enzyme to carbon monoxide and the apparent lack of susceptibility of the liver enzyme to carbon monoxide. Dr. Senciall and

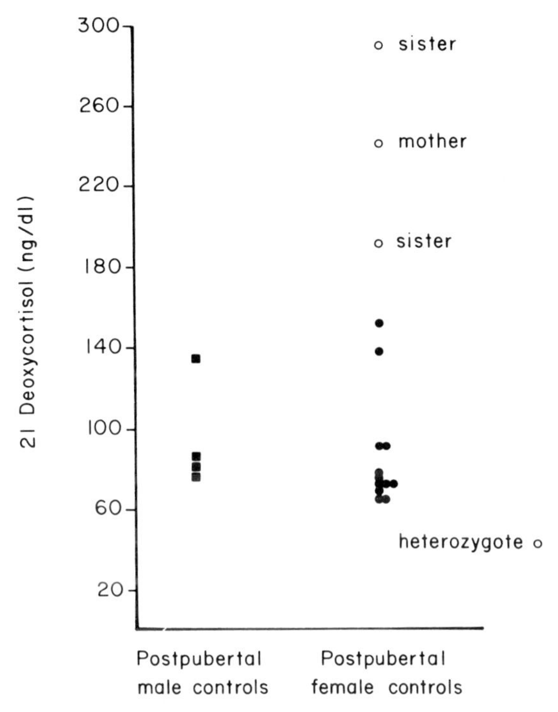

FIG. D. 21-Deoxycortisol levels (ng/dl) in postpubertal male and female controls compared to obligate heterozygote (mother) and two postpubertal sisters heterozygote for 21-hydroxylase deficiency (based on HLA testing). ACTH (40 units of Acthar) was administered iv for 6 hours. 21-Deoxycortisol was determined by radioimmunoassay as previously described (D. K. Fukushima *et al., Clin Endocrinol.* **10**, 367, 1979).

co-workers [A. C. Dey and I. R. Senciall (1978) *J. Steroid Biochem.* **9**, 1099] have come to the conclusion that the liver enzyme is not P450 dependent.

F. C. Bartter: Do you not now believe, as I think you once did, that the plasma renin is elevated in the non-salt-losing patients with the 21-hydroxylase deficiency because their secretion of progesterone and 17-hydroxyprogesterone is very high, and that these two steroids are inducing sodium loss by direct renal effect? A second question: I understood that you stated that renin stimulates ACTH secretion. I am not aware of any evidence for this.

M. I. New: There is some evidence that angiotensin II stimulates ACTH. Are 17-hydroxyprogesterone and progesterone salt wasting hormones? I have not been convinced by the data indicating they are naturetic hormones.

I. Mowszowicz: I would like to make one comment and ask one question to Dr. New. The comment is about the difference between hirsute patients with either the late onset of congenital adrenal disease (CAH) or polycystic ovary disease. They both have high plasma testosterone and androstenedione levels, and a high urinary 3α-androstanediol excretion. However patients with the ovarian disease have a high rate of *in vitro* conversion of testosterone to 5α-reduced metabolites [F. Kuttenn, I. Mowszowicz, G. Schaison, and P. Mauvais-Jarvis (1977). *J. Endocrinol.* **75**, 83] while in patients with the adrenal disease, *in vitro* 5α-reductase activity in pubic skin is within the normal range [P. Bouchard, F. Kuttenn, I. Mowszowica, G. Schaison, M.-C. Raux-Eurin, and P. Mauvais-Jarvis (1980). *Acta Endocrinol. (Copenhagen)*, in press]. It therefore appears that in patients with the ovarian disease hirsutism results from both hyperproduction and hyperutilization of androgens, whereas in patients with the late onset form of CAH, it results only from androgen hyperproduction without increased utilization by the skin.

My question relates to the late onset form of CAH. Dr. New, did you find some of these patients in the same families where you find the classical form of CAH, and do you have a way to predict which patients, heterozygous for 21-hydroxylase deficiency, will develop hirsutism at puberty?

M. I. New: In the families that we have personally examined in New York who have late onset disease, none have been members of patients with a classical patient, however, Dr. Laron in Israel has a family in which he believes that there is both a classical and a late onset patient. The cryptic patients are found only through the classical case. Hirsute women present frequently but very few of those patients demonstrate 21-hydroxylase deficiency by hormonal testing. A number of patients referred to the physician because of hirsutism and polycystic ovaries may indeed be late onset cases, but the bulk of patients with polycystic ovary disease probably do not have 21-hydroxylase deficiency. Dr. Bartter, do you think 17-hydroxyprogesterone is a naturetic hormone?

F. C. Bartter: I do indeed believe that progesterone and 17-hydroxyprogesterone are natriuretic hormones. Doctor Jack George studied this point directly some years ago (*JCEM* **25**, 621, 1965); we found the evidence that both of these steroids are natriuretic *in vivo* quite convincing. We treated Addisonian patients receiving a constant, small amount of sodium-retaining steroids with progesterone or 17-hydroxyprogesterone, and found that both of them could induce sodium loss and negative sodium balance.

M. New: May I just tell you of a brief experiment we did in which we took a simple virilizer who had high 17-hydroxy P and high aldo levels pretreatment. We treated him only with non-α-fludrohydrocortisone, lowered his renin, and lowered his aldo, yet we couldn't demonstrate salt wasting as a result of his continued elevation of 17-hydroxyprogesterone.

M. M. Grumbach: This is a controversial issue, and the discussion is reminiscent of the lively and illuminating comments following Dr. Bongiovanni's paper at the 1966 Laurentian Hormone Conference. Dr. New, have you studied the differential effect of ACTH on 18-OHB and 18-OH DOC secretion by measuring plasma concentrations in the salt-losing and simple virilizing forms of 21-hydroxylase deficiency? Dr. E. Biglieri and our group are using this approach in estimating the relative deficiency of 21-hydroxylation in the 17-hydroxy- and 17-deoxy pathways.

M. I. New: We've actually studied it. In the salt waster both 18-hydroxy B and aldosterone synthesis is impaired. In the simple virilizer neither is impaired. In the salt waster and the simple virilizer 18-hydroxy DOC is impaired because DOC synthesis is impaired.

I. Rothchild: Did you leave the question unexplained of why the cryptic does not have symptoms?

M. I. New: Absolutely, we don't know.

I. Rothchild: One would expect then that since the diagnosis is made on the basis of a response to an increase in ACTH, every time these kids got a cold, had had to take an exam, she would start secreting lots of testosterone. It reminds me of the figure that Charlie Lloyd used to show of a girl reading a Dear Jane letter and growing a beard at the same time. Stress provokes an increased ACTH secretion and that's exactly what you're doing with your test. I imagine that a stress response would last a good deal longer than the 6 hours of your test, and you've shown clearly that there's an increased secretion not only of 17-hydroxyprogesterone but of testosterone as well. Why don't they become virilized?

M. New: I don't know and I think that's the challenge for the future.

Some time ago, Dr. Soffer wrote a paper about the pleomorphic expression of the 11β-hydroxylase defect which he found in some patients after pregnancy, and after puberty, and that some of them indeed did not present as the classical patient with ambiguous genitalia. I wonder whether again in that enzyme defect, we're not seeing the same allelic variants that we're seeing in 21-hydroxylase deficiency.

W. F. Crowley: Just to follow up on that, Dr. New, would you comment about the different diagnostic ACTH stimulation tests which have been used to unearth the defect?

M. I. New: I can't answer your question now. We're in the process of double testing a number of extremely cooperative families. Soon I shall be able to tell you whether the short test, the cortrosyn test, is as discriminating as the 6-hour test which is the test with which we have the greatest experience.

W. F. Crowley: What about the time course of your 6-hour test? Is there any evidence of a plateau before 6 hours or are the responses still rising at its termination?

M. I. New: We have not done a dose–response curve.

R. B. Jaffe: In about 80% or more of women who have polycystic ovarian syndrome, the concentrations of luteinizing hormone and the ratio between LH and FSH is increased. I wonder whether either you or Dr. Gordon Cutler have quantified LH in this group of patients, the hirsute patients with late onset adrenocortical abnormalities. We have data suggesting that LH may play a stimulatory role in the fetal and neonatal production of dehydroepiandrosterone sulfate. It would be very interesting to see whether LH is increased in these patients.

M. I. New: I can answer exactly only for the patients with the cryptic disorder, in those patients who were clinically asymptomatic even though they're menstruating normally.

H. G. M. Raj: I would like to share some of my experience in treating women with hirsutism [S. G. Raj, I. E. Thompson, M. J. Berger, and M. L. Taymor (1977). *Am. J. Obstet. Gynecol.* **49,** 552]. The most common cause of hirsutism is due to polycystic ovary syndrome of ovarian origin, also known as Stein Leventhal syndrome. In a small percentage of women hirsutism is due to an adrenal disorder such as postpubertal adrenal hyperplasia. Although the clinical symptoms are the same in these two groups of patients, there are a number of differences in their endocrinology. Women with Stein Leventhal syndrome usually have elevated serum LH levels. The ovaries are polycystic and enlarged. Twenty-four-hour urinary pregnanetriol and tetrahydrodeoxycorticosteroid (compound "S") levels after 24-hour ACTH stimulation are within normal limits. Ovulation can be induced easily by administering clomiphene citrate (Clomid) or human gonadotropins [S. G. Raj, E. H. Grimes, M. J. Berger, and M. L. Taymor (1977). *Fertil. Steril.* **28,** 1280]. Hirsute women with postpubertal adrenal hyperplasia have normal LH levels and normal sized ovaries. The 24-hour urinary pregnanetriol and/or compound S levels after 24-hour ACTH stimulation are elevated. Good response to treatment is noticed after treatment with prednisone.

C. A. Winkel: I would like to make some comments regarding the issue of different forms of 21-hydroxylase deficiency. Recently, in collaboration with Dr. MacDonald in Dallas, we reported finding fairly high levels of 21-hyroxylase activity both in adult and in fetal kidney tissues. Whether or not renal steroid 21-hydroxylase plays a role in various forms of 21-hydroxylase deficiency, I don't think is yet known. I think questions must be raised concerning the physiologic significance of renal 21-hydroxylase activity and whether or not there is a dichotomy in the presence of this enzyme in the kidneys of patients who have the salt-losing or non-salt-losing forms of 21-hydroxylase deficiency.

M. I. New: I think it would be very interesting to know whether the patients with cryptic 21-hydroxylase deficiency have different 21-hydroxylase activity in the kidney.

C. A. Winkel: As of yet we haven't had the opportunity to study kidney tissues obtained from patients with either non-salt-losing forms or salt-losing forms of 21-hydroxylase deficiency.

The Regulation of the Mammalian Corpus Luteum[1]

I. ROTHCHILD

Department of Reproductive Biology, Case Western Reserve University School of Medicine, Cleveland, Ohio

I. Introduction

A. LH DEPENDENCY IN THE RAT

During roughly the last 10 years my colleagues and I have worked on an aspect of corpus luteum (CL) activity in the rat that we called LH dependency. The term arose as the result of studies that began to appear from about the mid-1960s, suggesting or demonstrating that LH, as well as prolactin, played a part in the luteotrophic process (Alloiteau and Bouhours, 1965; Kiracoffe *et al.*, 1969; Loewit *et al.*, 1969; Raj and Moudgal, 1970; Chang *et al.*, 1971; Lawrence *et al.*, 1971; Moudgal *et al.*, 1972; Maneckjee *et al.*, 1973; Yoshinaga *et al.*, 1972). Raj and Moudgal (1970) showed that the need for LH was a crucial one between days 8 and 12 of pregnancy and Morishige, Pepe, and I showed that this need appeared quite suddenly between days 7 and 8 of pregnancy (Morishige and Rothchild, 1974), but that it also appeared in pseudopregnant rats of various types, usually about a day later (Rothchild *et al.*, 1974). LH thus seemed to be as important a luteotrophin in the rat as prolactin, and since it was also becoming clear at this time that LH probably was an even more widespread luteotrophin among the species than prolactin, its luteotrophic effect in the rat raised the question of how the rat's CL was related to those of other species.

Our own studies of the characteristics of LH dependency in the rat eventually led us to the inescapable conclusion that it was a developmental phenomenon of all luteal phase conditions in which the CL were exposed to LH. LH, in other words, induced the dependency on LH. We also found that the progestational uterus advanced, and that prolactin delayed the time of appearance of LH dependency; the uterus was not essential for its development, however, nor could prolactin delay its ap-

[1] This article is dedicated to the memory of my dear friend and colleague Jean-Jacques Alloiteau (d. 1968).

ISBN 0-12-571137-9

pearance indefinitely (Lam and Rothchild, 1977; Nanes *et al.*, 1980; Garris and Rothchild, 1980; Nanes and Rothchild, 1981; Garris *et al.*, 1981).

Many nagging questions accompanied our effort to define the characteristics of LH dependency. Why was LH suddenly needed when prolactin had been sufficient until then? Why was prolactin still needed after LH had become essential? Why did LH dependency shorten the CL's life span? How did the uterus promote LH dependency without being essential? Why was LH essential for the development of LH dependency? But the most nagging questions of all were: What did LH dependency mean? Could it help us understand the nature of the CL in general? Could LH dependency in the rat be an important clue to our understanding of CL physiology, because the rat's CL was an exception to, or an example of, the general nature of a CL?

The search for an answer to these questions finally led to the realization that one must *start* with a concept of the general nature of the CL in order to answer them. The definition of this general nature is the primary object of this article. It was not easy to achieve, because the CL is probably the wierdest endocrine gland in the body.

B. THE PECULIARITIES OF THE CL

The CL is really an ovarian follicle in which the rapid regression that is otherwise the fate of all postovulatory follicles is temporarily arrested. In the mammalian CL progesterone secretion goes hand in hand with this postponement of regression. It is fairly certain that reptilian CL also secrete progesterone (Yaron, 1972; Browning, 1973; Callard and Lance, 1977; Lance and Callard, 1979; Cuellar, 1979; Callard and Ho, 1980). The CL of the other vertebrates probably also do so (Browning, 1973).

The mammalian CL is formed during the period around ovulation by a transformation ("luteinization") of the cells lining the cavity of the follicle (Harrison, 1962; Rothchild, 1965; Greenwald and Rothchild, 1968; Mossman and Duke, 1973). Luteinization affects the granulosa cells in all species, but in some, a similar or related process may also affect the theca interna cells, although the latter are never more than a small proportion of the CL (Mossman and Duke, 1973). Luteinization involves an enormous enlargement of the cell with a great increase in the nucleus–cytoplasm ratio and the formation of a very distinct cell wall, the development of an extensive capillary network enmeshing all the cells, marked proliferation of the endoplasmic reticulum, and its tranformation from a predominantly rough to a predominantly smooth type, and of the mitochondria from a small round or rod shape type with lamelliform cristae into larger and more varied shapes with tubular and villiform cristae, and an increase in complexity of the Golgi apparatus (Christensen and Gillim, 1969; Enders, 1973; Koering, 1974; Crisp *et al.*, 1970; Paavola, 1977). The CL's activity differs most from that of the follicle in how much rather than in what kinds of steroid it makes. The principal change is a striking increase in progesterone secretion, accompanied by a variable, but severe fall or even loss (among different species) of the capacity for estrogen and androgen secretion (Dorrington, 1977; Savard, 1973). The ability to make androgens and estrogens is probably directly related to the extent to which theca cells take part in the composition of the CL. A fall in the production of prostaglandins (PGs), which the ovary and especially the preovulatory follicle makes in large amounts (Channing and Tsafriri, 1977; Behrman, 1979; Shemesh, 1979; Chasalow and Pharris, 1972; Espey, 1980; Plunkett *et al.*, 1975; Goldberg and Ramwell, 1975; Lindner *et al.*, 1977; Poyser, 1978), also accompanies the formation of the CL.

Since the CL secretes progesterone and since progesterone is necessary for the establishment and maintenance of pregnancy in mammals (Heap *et al.*, 1973; Amoroso and Perry, 1977), the physiologic connection between mammalian viviparity and the CL is easy to understand. But the CL apparently also occurs in all reptilian species (Miller, 1948), among which, however, only some, and these only among the squamates (snakes and lizards) are viviparous (Packard *et al.*, 1977; Yaron, 1972). The connection between the CL and viviparity in reptiles, therefore, is not as obvious as it is in mammals, although the fact that the CL may control the time of oviposition in the oviparous forms (Cuellar, 1979; Klick and Mahmoud, 1977; Roth *et al.*, 1973) suggests that its general effect in reptiles is to retain the egg in the oviduct (Callard and Ho, 1980; Cuellar, 1979). Among the fish and amphibian species which form CL the relation of the CL to viviparity is even more obscure than it is in the reptiles (Browning, 1973; Hisaw and Hisaw, 1959), although a connection with viviparity is again implied by the fact that the birds, all of which are oviparous, do not form CL.

In spite of the universal connection between CL activity and viviparity among the mammals, the relation of the period of CL activity to that of pregnancy varies enormously. CL activity in some species, with only minor exceptions, may last as long in the nonpregnant female as in the pregnant one, and as long as pregnancy itself, yet this duration can be as little as about 2 weeks as in many marsupials (Sharman, 1970, 1976; Tyndale-Biscoe, 1973) or about 2 months, as in many carnivores (Eckstein and Zuckerman, 1956; Asdell, 1964) or even as much as 10 months, as in the roe deer (Hoffmann *et al.*, 1978). Among marsupials pregnancy ends before or with the regression of the CL; in no case does pregnancy prolong the period of CL activity (Tyndale-Biscoe, 1973, 1979; Sharman, 1970, 1976), nor is pregnancy itself, considered from the time of attachment of the embryo to the uterine wall until parturition, longer than about 2 weeks. This rule applies even to the bandicoots, which have a CL with an active life span of at least 6–8 weeks (Hughes, 1962; Gemmell, 1981) so that in them parturition occurs when progesterone secretion is at its *peak* (Gemmell, 1981). Among many eutherian species, however, the duration of pregnancy also varies greatly (e.g., 16 days in hamsters, and 280 days in the human) (Amoroso and Finn, 1962; Amoroso and Perry, 1977; Asdell, 1964) but in these species pregnancy itself prolongs the section of progesterone by the CL (Sauer, 1979; Heap *et al.,* 1973; Jöchle, 1969; Hilliard, 1973; Greenwald and Rothchild, 1968; Amoroso and Perry, 1977). In some cases the prolongation is for only a part of the duration of pregnancy, as in the horse (Amoroso and Perry, 1977), and in others, for the full duration of pregnancy, as in the human (Guraya, 1972; LeMaire *et al.,* 1968; Maqueo and Goldzieher, 1966; Weiss *et al.,* 1977), or the rat (Hilliard, 1973; Greenwald and Rothchild, 1968) (Fig. 15).

The mammalian CL seems to belong to the same class of endocrine glands to which the adrenal cortex and the thyroid belong; that is, the ability of the CL to secrete progesterone depends in general on trophic hormones of the pituitary. Yet among the marsupials—with the probable exception of the bandicoots—the CL is probably completely independent of such control, and among the eutherian mammals there are some species in which the CL, during at least the first part of its life cycle, is also independent of the pituitary but becomes dependent on it later, and others, in which the CL seems to always depend on the pituitary for growth and secretion (p. 194).

The CL differs from the other pituitary-dependent endocrine glands in other ways. In contrast to the adrenal cortex and the thyroid, for example, in which the trophic hormones are ACTH and TSH, respectively, for *all* species, in the case of the CL there is no such thing as a single trophic pituitary (or other) hormone for all species. In some it may be LH, in others prolactin, in still others, combinations of prolactin and LH or FSH (Rothchild, 1965, 1966; Greenwald and Rothchild, 1968; Hilliard, 1973; Niswender *et al.,* 1972; Hansel *et al.,* 1973; Knobil, 1973). Even in the same species, as exemplified by LH dependency in the rat, the CL may secrete progesterone in response to prolactin during the first week of its life, but only in response to *both* prolactin and LH during its second week (Morishige and Rothchild, 1974; Rothchild *et al.,* 1974). In the rabbit, estrogens secreted by neighboring follicles are the essential stimulus (Keyes and Nalbandov, 1967; Spies *et al.,* 1967b, 1968a,b; Rothchild 1965; Fuller and Hansel, 1971); although in some other species like the cow (Hansel, 1975) or the human (p. 210) estrogens prevent the CL from secreting progesterone. Even more striking is the contrast between this diversity of regulation of the CL's activity and the relative uniformity of the way the follicle, from which it comes, is regulated; there are probably only minor exceptions to the generalization that the follicle's growth to maturity, its ability to ovulate, and its secretion of estrogens depend crucially on the combined effects of FSH and LH and very probably the estrogens themselves, throughout the vertebrate series (Licht *et al.*, 1977; Lance and Callard, 1979).

The CL differs from the other pituitary-dependent endocrine glands in yet another important way. The general level of activity of the adrenal and thyroid, for example, is determined mainly by a negative feedback control system. Such a control system is not typical of the CL. In fact, in some animals, as for example the rat, there is a positive feedback relationship between progesterone and prolactin secretion (Alloiteau and Vignal, 1958; Rothchild, 1960; Rothchild and Schubert, 1963; Everett, 1963; Rothchild and Schwartz, 1965; de Greef and Zeilmaker, 1976, 1978, 1979; van der Schoot *et al.*, 1978; Freeman and Sterman, 1978; Murakami *et al.*, 1979, 1980; Gilman *et al.*, 1980; Damassa *et al.*, 1980; Takahashi *et al.*, 1980). Furthermore the response of the adrenal cortex or thyroid to their respective trophic hormones does not change significantly with time; the trophins thus can maintain them at a constant level of activity. In the case of the CL, on the other hand, the response changes with time, so that, in spite of the presence of the trophic hormone, progesterone secretion inevitably regresses and stops. In the intact individual the negative feedback control of the adrenal cortex and thyroid allows the activity of these glands to oscillate around a given mean level. The CL's activity on the other hand is essentially nonoscillatory; that is, it is a single cycle or ephemeral system.

Its ephemerality is its most distinguishing and important characteristic but in this too there is variety in how it is expressed. The life span of all CL consists of three parts. For example, the pattern of progesterone secretion is made up of *a rising phase, a plateau phase,* and *a regression phase* (Fig. 1). Growth tends to accompany the rising and plateau phases closely in all species, but regression in size may lag behind regression of progesterone secretion in some (Bonnin-Lafargue *et al.*, 1972) or accompany it in others (Rothchild, 1965; Mossman and Duke, 1973; Harrison and Weir, 1977). Growth itself may be the result of only cellular hypertrophy in some species, of cellular hyperplasia in others, and of both hypertrophy and hyperplasia in still others (Mossman and Duke, 1973). The whole cycle in the nonpregnant animal can be as short as 3 days, as in rats (Uchida *et al.*, 1969, 1970b; Butcher *et al.*, 1974; Smith *et al.*, 1975; van der Schoot and de Greef, 1976; Nequin *et al.*, 1979) and mice (Michael, 1976), or as much as 10 months as in the roe deer (Hoffmann *et al.*, 1978). The rising and plateau phases together can occupy as little as 2 days, as in rats, are usually over 5 to 10 days in most polyestrous species,

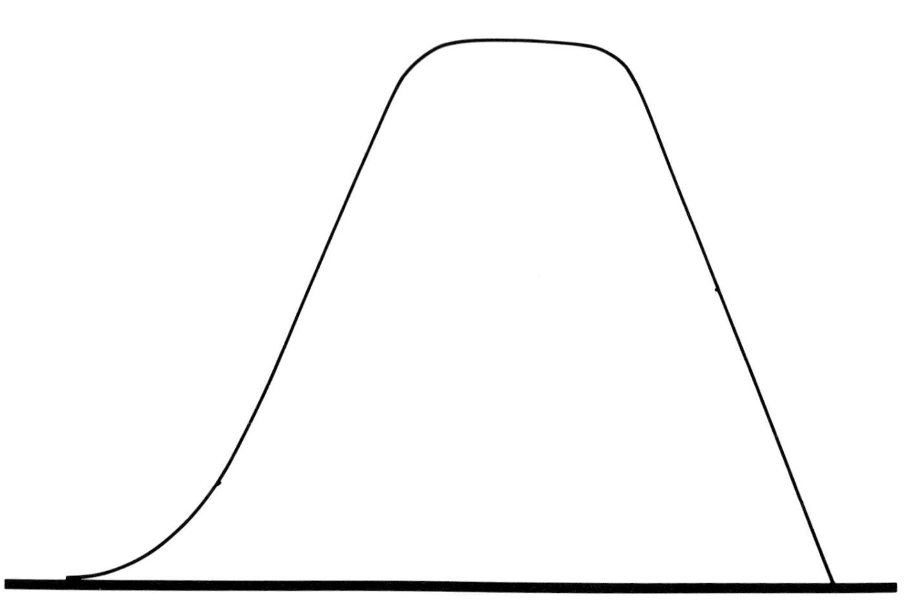

FIG. 1. An idealized CL life cycle. The curve describes the general pattern of change with time (abscissa), in size and progesterone secretion (ordinate), of all mammalian, and probably all vertebrate CL. The rising and regression phases are always easily visible, but a plateau phase may at times or in some species be nonexistent or very brief (see also Fig. 2).

or from about 10 days to 3 weeks in monestrous eutherian carnivores, as, e.g., ferrets (Blatchley and Donovan, 1972; Heap and Hammond, 1974), dogs (Christie *et al.,* 1971; Jones *et al.,* 1973a; Smith and MacDonald, 1974; Concannon *et al.,* 1975; Gräf, 1978), wolves (Seal *et al.,* 1979), cats (Shille and Stabenfeldt, 1979; Verhage *et al.,* 1976), skunks (Mead and Swannock, 1978), minks (Møller, 1973a; Papke *et al.,* 1980), and foxes (Møller, 1973b), but can be 6 months long as in the roe deer (Hoffmann *et al.,* 1978). The regression phase can also vary considerably. Even if we disregard species like the rat, regression occurs in about 3–4 days in sheep (Moore *et al.,* 1969; Stabenfeldt *et al.,* 1969; Pant *et al.,* 1978). Variations between these extremes are easy to find. Among the eutheria all the polyestrous species have only short-lived CL, that is, CL with a life cycle of about 2 weeks duration, while the monestrous species have only long-lived CL, that is, CL with a life cycle of between about 5 weeks and 2 months or more. The roe deer may be a minor exception to this rule since it has the longest lived CL known, yet this CL comes from the *second* ovulation of its breeding season (Hoffmann *et al.,* 1978). Almost all marsupials are monestrous but their "short-lived" CL have a more variable life span than the eutherian CL; the bandicoots are also polyestrous but their CL secrete progesterone in a pattern remarkably like that of the long-lived CL of the monestrous eutherian carnivores (Gemmell, 1981) (Fig. 2).[2]

In some species even the basic pattern of the CL's life cycle has been modified by the appearance of a quiescent period before the rising phase begins. This can be associated either with an effect of season, as, for example, in the european badger (Canivenc and Bonnin-Lafargue, 1973), the western spotted skunk (Mead and Eik-Nes, 1969), the short-tailed stoat (Gulahusein and Thawley, 1974), or with lactation as well as season, as in the tammar wallaby (Hearn, 1973). This modification illustrates the general inverse relation between activity and life span, i.e., these CL may live for almost a year in the quiescent state, but for only about 2 weeks (wallaby) or months (eutherian species), once the rising phase begins. Although the roe deer, and apparently also the armadillo (Peppler and Stone, 1980), are exceptions in having CL that are active throughout a very long luteal phase, the general association reminds one of a similar one between the growth rate of ovarian follicles and the interval to atresia.

There is also an enormous variability in the rate at which the CL secretes progesterone and this seems to have little to do with taxonomic divisions. If we look at circulating levels of progesterone, for example, among rodents, the peak level in the guinea pig's cycle is only about 3 ng/ml (Blatchley *et al.*, 1976; Challis *et al.*, 1971) but is over 50 ng/ml in pseudopregnant rats (Bartosik and Szarowski, 1973; Pepe and Rothchild, 1974). Among some primates, as, e.g., the human (Cargille *et al.*, 1969; Neill *et al.*, 1967), baboon (Stevens *et al.*, 1970), chimpanzee (Graham *et al.*, 1972; Reyes *et al.*, 1975), or monkey (Atkinson *et al.*, 1975; Wilks, 1977), the level is between 5 and 15 ng/ml but is over 60 ng/ml in capuchin monkeys (Nagle *et al.*, 1979) and over 250 ng/ml in the squirrel monkey (Wolf *et al.*, 1977). Many other examples of such differences could be cited.

Prostaglandins (PGs) are probably an essential part of what causes the CL to die (p. 208) but even here there is variability. In some species (the sheep is the most completely documented example) uterine PGs are unquestionably the most important single factor that determines when the CL dies (Horton and Poyser, 1976). In a great many others, however, the uterus has only a minor say (e.g., rabbits, rats) or none at all (e.g., primates, marsupials, monestrous breeders) in determining how long the CL lives (see below: p. 244) in spite of the fact that in these species the uterus

[2] The monotreme CL is probably the same type as the marsupial CL, but too little is known about it (Hill and Gatenby, 1926; Eckstein and Zuckerman, 1956; Hughes and Carrick, 1978) to justify putting it into either the marsupial or eutherian category or into one of its own.

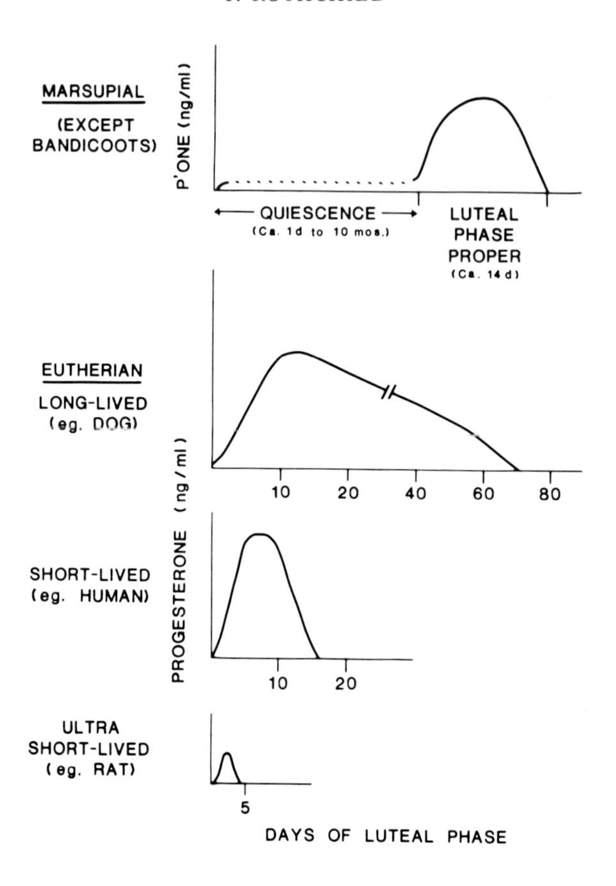

FIG. 2. The types of mammalian CL. (Activity is represented in terms of the pattern of progesterone concentration in the peripheral circulation.) *Marsupial* CL, with the exception of the bandicoots (Peramelidae) (Gemmell, 1981), have short-lived CL although in some species a quiescent phase may precede the luteal phase proper. Neither pregnancy, the uterus, nor the type of ovulation cycle affects the duration of the luteal phase proper. The three main varieties of *eutherian* CL differ in how they are affected by pregnancy etc. *Long-lived CL* are typical of monestrous breeders, and the duration of their activity is not affected by pregnancy or the uterus. *Short-lived CL* are typical of all polyestrous breeders and the duration of their activity is always increased by pregnancy. *Ultra-short-lived CL* are typical of a group of polyestrous rodents (possibly also some insectivores). The duration of their activity is increased by sterile mating and still further by pregnancy (see also Fig. 15). The peak of activity of the ultra-short-lived CL, in relation to that of other types of CL, can actually be much greater than shown here.

probably makes as much of the same kinds of PG that the sheep uterus does (Horton and Poyser, 1976; Thorburn and Challis, 1979; Abel and Baird, 1980).

C. A COMMON SYSTEM OF REGULATION OF ALL MAMMALIAN CL?

The one thread of uniformity throughout this pattern of diversity is the CL's emphemerality. It is its most important characteristic precisely because it is universal, and if there is a basic, common system of regulation of all mammalian CL, the clue to its nature must be in what causes ephemerality. Three characteristics of the CL are important expressions of this ephemerality: *autonomy of progesterone secretion,* which appears to a variable extent among the mammalian species; *responsiveness to the luteolytic effect of PGs,* which does not seem to be but probably is a universal characteristic; and *the ability to make PGs,* which is probably also a universal characteristic. It is reasonable to assume that autonomy of progesterone secretion appears among the mammalian species to only an occasional extent because it is a sign of an older, once universal attribute of all CL, remnants of which persist today to varying degrees among the species; this variability is in no way different in principle from, for example, the extent to which hair, a specific mammalian characteristic, appears among the mammals. One may also assume that the luteolytic action of PGs and the CL's ability to make them represent universal and probably even more primitive attributes, not only of all CL, but of all vertebrate ovarian follicles, particularly during the period that follows ovulation.

When these characteristics of the CL were put together with the evidence that progesterone has effects which tend in general to postpone the CL's ability to make and release PGs, the idea emerged that the CL was an ephemeral gland because the basic system that regulates its activity consisted of two mutually opposing processes, each of which was regulated by positive feedback. In the rest of this article, I will first describe the evidence and ideas that led to this concept. I will then try to trace the path of evoluation that gave rise to the great diversity in CL activity and its regulation. Finally, as an example of the usefullness of the theory, I will try to show the origin of the rat's (and similar mammals') peculiarly ultra-short-lived CL and its relation to LH dependency. Before beginning, definitions of a few terms that I will use throughout the article may be useful.

D. DEFINITIONS

1. Luteotrophic Process

In all its forms (e.g., luteotrophism, luteotrophin, etc.) this means the quality of promoting progesterone secretion (production and/or release) by the CL. It should be kept apart from whatever term we will eventually use to describe the stimulation of progesterone secretion in nonluteal tissues, such as the follicular granulosa cells. A luteotrophic effect can be one that raises the rate of progesterone secretion, or one that maintains an existing rate, or even (as I will show) one that only reduces the rate of regression of progesterone secretion. The term does not include or imply the promoting of other activities in the CL such as estrogen production, for example, unless such activities specifically promote or stimulate progesterone secretion. The growth of the CL is not in itself evidence of a luteotrophic effect, but it is often (and justifiably) assumed to be so because a growing CL is almost always also secreting progesterone.

It may be convenient to think of two kinds of luteotrophic effects: permissive and stimulatory. A *permissive* effect is one which facilitates the CL's production of progesterone but does not itself determine how the process works or at what rate, even though it may be essential for such production. For example, an agent which facilitates the passage of cholesterol through the mitochondrial membrane might act as a permissive luteotrophin. Although this is not necessarily the way prolactin acts, many of its luteotrophic attributes suggest that prolactin is primarily a permissive luteotrophin.

A *stimulatory* luteotrophin is one which raises the rate of production and/or release of progesterone, usually in direct proportion to dose over a wide range of doses. It may or may not affect the basic process through which progesterone is made, and it may not maintain the increased rate of secretion which it induced, and it is also immaterial whether it induces the effect itself, or through another agent. Many of the effects of LH suggest that it is primarily a stimulatory luteotrophin.

2. *The Luteolytic Process*

The term in all its forms (e.g., luteolysis, luteolysin, etc.) means the exact opposite of luteotrophic, that is: the quality of stopping the secretion of progesterone by the CL. Luteolysis is sometimes described as functional or structural, but this helps only to describe what I mentioned above as the difference between the regression of progesterone secretion and of size. There should also be no distinction made between slow and rapid regression, as evidence of luteolysis, since both are variants of the same process.

3. *Antiluteolytic Effect*

It is sometimes convenient to use this term to describe a luteotrophic action which occurs primarily or exclusively by inhibiting a luteolytic one. It can be useful because under the right conditions it may imply the presence of an autonomous luteotrophic process.

4. Luteal Phase and Related Terms

This term means the period of progesterone secretion by the CL during the rising, plateau, and regression phases of the CL's life span (Figs. 1 and 2). It thus excludes periods of quiescence mentioned above, which I will refer to, where necessary, as "quiesence." Long, drawn-out regression in size of the CL, after progesterone secretion has stopped, is also not included within the term "luteal phase." Some authors use the term for the endometrial changes induced by progesterone; I will not use it in this way. To some extent I will use the terms "long luteal phase," "short luteal phase," and "ultra-short luteal phase" interchangeably with "long-lived," "short-lived," and "ultra short-lived" CL, but the reasons for this will be self-evident.

5. Dating System for the CL Life Cycle

Day 1 is the day of ovulation and, therefore, the first day of the CL's life cycle. I will use this system in all references to the age of the CL regardless of whatever system particular authors may have used.

6. Polyestrous and Monestrous

These terms refer to patterns of ovulation cycles (Fig. 7). Monestrous cycles are those that occur only at long intervals, such as 6 months to a year. In a true monestrous ovulation cycle there is at least a month or two of anestrus between the end of the postovulatory period of one ovulation cycle, and the beginning of the preovulatory part of the next one. Polyestrous cycles are those that occur at frequent intervals with no anestrus between ovulations, and with each ovulation usually not much more than 2.5 to 5 weeks apart; in rats, mice, hamsters, voles, gerbils, however, the cycles can be as little as 4 or 5 days long. In both monestrous and polyestrous cycles, ovulation itself can be either monovular (ovulation of a single follicle) or polyovular (ovulation of several follicles).

7. Eutheria, Metatheria, Prototheria, Pantotheria, Therapsida, Synapsida, Cotylosaura

Eutheria include all mammals except the metatheria and prototheria. *Metatheria* are the marsupials. *Prototheria* are a group of mammals, all of which are now extinct except for two genera of monotremes (egg-laying mammals) (Walker, 1968). The *pantotheria* were early therian mammals (200 million to 70 million years before present) which gave rise to several groups of now extinct mammals, as well as to the metatheria and eutheria. *Therapsids* were mammal-like reptiles from some of which the pantotheres and prototheres descended. The *synapsids*—which include the therapsids and other groups of mammal-like reptiles—were one of several lines of reptile descendants of the stem reptiles (*cotylosaurs*) about 300 million years before present (Romer, 1966; Crompton and Jenkins, 1979).

II. The Basic System of Regulation of the Mammalian CL

The three characteristics I will discuss here—autonomy of progesterone secretion, responsiveness to the luteolytic effect of PGs, and the ability of the CL to make PGs—do not at first glance appear to be universal properties of mammalian CL. The purpose of this discussion, however, is to summarize the evidence for their existence and to show that if certain assumptions are made, the lack of universality does not remain as important as it might at first appear to be.

A. AUTONOMY OF PROGESTERONE SECRETION

The central issue in the search for a common luteotrophic process is not whether all mammalian CL depend on LH, or on prolactin, or on estrogens, or on any other extrinsic luteotrophin, or on combinations of any of these. The central issue is whether progesterone secretion is essentially autonomous. This is so because none of the extrinsic luteotrophins can satisfy the absolute requirement for commonality, which is that it must be necessary, not only in all species, but at all times during the life of the CL.

The idea of autonomy, in the sense that the CL can function independently of pituitary or other extrinsic controls is not new. Hisaw and Hisaw (1959) suggested that autonomy might account for the behavior of the CL among nonmammalian vertebrates. Yaron (1972) also suspected that the CL of viviparous reptiles may function independently of the pituitary. Armstrong *et al.* (1970) theorized that the rat CL could make progesterone from cholesterol autonomously, since prolactin, which is essential for prolonged progesterone secretion by the rat's CL (Rothchild, 1965; Greenwald and Rothchild, 1968; Hilliard, 1973) seemed to have only the effect of preventing the reduction of progesterone to 20α-pregn-4-en-3-one (20α-OHP) (Wiest *et al.*, 1968; Armstrong *et al.*, 1969, 1970; Lamprecht *et al.*, 1969). Raj and Moudgal (1970) tried to explain the secretion of progesterone by the rat's CL, after day 12 of pregnancy, on the basis of what was essentially an autonomous process, and my colleagues and I did indeed find a limited capacity for autonomous progesterone secretion in the rat's CL between days 12 and 15 of pregnancy (Rothchild *et al.*, 1973; Rothchild, 1973). Brinkley *et al.* (1964b) and Cook and Nalbandov (1968) had suggested that the initial stimulus of ovulation was all that was necessary for the CL of the pig, or of marsupials, respectively, to function for about 2 weeks. Knobil (1973) implied that the monkey CL functioned by itself during the luteal phase of the ovulation cycle, aided only by the "permissive" action of LH.

1. *Evidence for Autonomy*

Evidence for autonomy comes from several sources. The main ones are from effects of hypophysectomy and related procedures, and from the behavior of granulosa cells in tissue culture. Some of the other sources have to do with the response of the CL to treatment with a particular luteotrophin, but this is not inconsistent with the concept of autonomy, since autonomy should not be seen as an absolute quality. In the examples I will describe we should keep in mind that we are looking at differences among species in *how long* the CL secretes progesterone autonomously, not whether it can or cannot. As a general rule we can even say that no CL secretes progesterone autonomously for longer than about 2 weeks; beyond this time, it depends on either a permissive or stimulatory luteotrophin or a combination of both, to continue to secrete progesterone.

a. Effects of Hypophysectomy. CL of the sheep (Denamur *et al.*, 1973; Kann and Denamur, 1974), the pig (Anderson *et al.*, 1967; du Mesnil du Buission, 1966), and the guinea pig (Perry and Rowlands, 1962; Heap *et al.*, 1967; Illingworth *et al.*, 1973) can grow and both by direct and indirect (Rothchild, 1965, p. 275) evidence, secrete progesterone for almost the full duration of a normal luteal phase (about 2 weeks) in the absence of the pituitary.

The CL of the tammar wallaby (*Macropus eugenii*), a marsupial, has a long quiescent period associated with both lactation and season (Tyndale-Biscoe, 1973; Tyndale-Biscoe *et al.*, 1974). Hypophysectomy during the quiescent period activates the CL almost exactly as does the change in season, or as does stopping lactation in the intact animal (Hearn, 1973, 1974).

The growth of the CL and its rate of progesterone secretion in the rabbit, hypophysectomized immediately after ovulation, are no different from that of intact rabbits during the first few days after ovulation (Yuh, 1980). This fits with other evidence that the rabbit CL does not depend on estrogens until it is about 4 or 5 days old (Miller and Keyes, 1975) and with the fact that LHAS treatment induces luteolysis in rabbits only when the CL are older than 3 days, an effect specifically preventable by estrogen treatment (Spies and Quadri, 1967).

CL induced in hypophysectomized women by treatment with FSH and LH will function for about 3 or 4 days, without any further treatment after the LH dose that induced ovulation and for the full length of a luteal phase (about 2 weeks) if ovulation was induced with hCG (Vande Wiele *et al.*,

1970); although the half life of hCG is much greater than that of LH, this probably does not alone account for the longer period of CL activity than with LH induction.

Hypophysectomy induces luteolysis in the dog, but the rate of regression of progesterone secretion after hypophysectomy on day 10 of the luteal phase is very much slower than after hypophysectomy on day 34 or later (Concannon, 1980). In the western spotted skunk the histologic signs of CL activity during the quiescent period of delayed implantation are not affected by hypophysectomy, and the operation induces only a very slow decline in the peripheral serum progesterone levels although it prevents the increase that normally accompanies implantation (Mead, 1975). There seems to be a similar lack of effect of hypophysectomy on CL histology in the short-tailed weasel (Matson, 1969, cited by Mead, 1975).

In the rat's estrous cycle the rising, plateau, and regression phases of a CL life cycle occupy only 3 days (Uchida *et al.*, 1970b; Butcher *et al.*, 1974; Smith *et al.*, 1975; van der Schoot and de Greef, 1976). Removal of the pituitary just after ovulation has no effect on the CL's pattern of progesterone secretion (Uchida *et al.*, 1969, 1970b; Smith *et al.*, 1975). Acker and Alloiteau (1968) also found biological evidence for such activity and suggested that it was due to autonomy of progesterone secretion. Uchida *et al.* (1969) came to the same conclusion.

Another group of findings related to those of hypophysectomy comes from treatment with inhibitors of a presumed essential luteotrophin. For example, progesterone treatment of pigs during the luteal phase of the ovulation cycle doesn't interfere with CL function (Sammelwitz *et al.*, 1961), but similar treatment of pigs with active CL older than about 15 days, as for example, during early pregnancy, causes luteolysis (Brinkley *et al.*, 1964a). The effects of treatment with a specific antiserum to LH (LHAS), which neutralizes the biological activity of LH in the circulation (Spies *et al.*, 1967a) or with methallibure, an inhibitor of gonadotrophin secretion (Schafer *et al.*, 1973), has essentially the same results. In the sheep LH and prolactin are needed to maintain activity of CL that are older than about 2 weeks (Denamur *et al.*, 1973; Kann and Denamur, 1974) but treatment with 2-Br-α-ergocryptine, which inhibits the pituitary's secretion of prolactin, during the middle of the luteal phase of the ovulation cycle has no apparent effect on its activity (Niswender 1974; Niswender *et al.*, 1976; Kann and Denamur, 1974), and treatment with LHAS reduces progesterone levels in the peripheral circulation by only about 50% (Niswender *et al.*, 1976). In the cow, LH is assumed to be an important, if not exclusive luteotrophin during the ovulation cycle (Hansel and Seifert, 1967; Hansel *et al.*, 1973), but treatment with LHAS does not shorten the duration of the luteal phase (Hoffmann *et al.*, 1974) or reduce the concentration of progesterone in the CL (Snook *et al.*, 1969).

Treatment with 2-Br-α-ergocryptine also has no effect on the short period of progesterone secretion during the first day of diestrus of the rat's estrous cycle (Döhler and Wuttke, 1974), although secretion of progesterone beyond this time is prevented by the absence of prolactin (Rothchild, 1965; Greenwald and Rothchild, 1968; Hilliard, 1973; Smith *et al.*, 1975; Day *et al.*, 1980b). Another possible indication of autonomy in rat CL is the finding that young CL remain responsive to prolactin, after hypophysectomy, for a much longer time (Malven, 1969; Acker and Alloiteau, 1968) than do older CL (Rothchild, 1965), and in either the intact or hypophysectomized rat the CL of diestrus do not respond to prolactin with an increase in progesterone secretion, until they are at least 48 hours old (Day *et al.*, 1980). In the ferret (Donovan, 1963; Murphy, 1979) as in the mink (Papke *et al.*, 1980) prolactin is almost certainly an important luteotrophin, but treatment of ferrets with 2-Br-α-ergocryptine during the first 10 days after ovulation has no noticeable effect on the growth or activity of the CL (Blatchley and Donovan, 1974). The bandicoot CL is probably also responsive to prolactin, but treatment with 2-Br-α-ergocryptine early in the luteal phase does not affect the CL (R. T. Gemmell, personal communication).

b. Granulosa Cells in Tissue Culture. In every species in which granulosa cells have been removed from the follicle before luteinization began, and maintained in tissue culture, the cells have luteinized and secreted progesterone spontaneously, that is, in the absence of added specific hormones (Table I). In spite of great differences in amounts and duration of such progesterone production the pattern of progesterone production was similar in general to that of intact CL *in vivo*. Accompanying ultrastructural (Crisp and Channing, 1972) and intracellular enzyme changes (Fischer and Kahn, 1972) fit very well with these signs of autonomous progesterone secretion.

In the monkey also, cells from mid-luteal phase CL maintained *in vitro* secreted progesterone, although in decreasing amounts, for at least 4 days in the absence of added hormones (Gulyas *et al.*, 1979; Gulyas and Hodgen, 1981). Rice *et al.* (1976) made a similar finding with human CL cells maintained in tissue culture; human CL maintained in organ culture, also continued to make progesterone for several days without added hormones (Sadler *et al.*, 1980).

This and the evidence summarized in Table I are especially important because several of the species listed have CL which do not seem to be able to secrete progesterone *in vivo* after hypophysectomy. The *in vitro*

TABLE I

Species in Which Follicle Granulosa Cells (GC), Maintained in Tissue Culture, Have Luteinized Spontaneously and Secreted Progesterone for at Least Several Days in the Absence of Extrinsic Luteotrophins[a]

Species	Source of GCs and related information	Reference
Rat	Preov. foll. of PMSG-treated immat.	Bernard (1975)
	Preov. foll. of PMSG-LH treated immat.	Crisp (1977); Centola (1979)
Hamster	Preov. foll. 1.5–2 hours after spontaneous LH surge	Makris and Ryan (1975)
Rabbit	Normal preov. foll.	Erickson *et al.* (1974); Erickson and Ryan (1975); Nicosia (1972)
	Preov. foll. of PMSG-treated immat.	Shirley and Stephenson (1973)
Sheep	Preov. foll. of cyclic sheep	Moor (1977)
Pig	Sl.h.: various sizes, incl, large preov.	Channing (1970); Channing and Crisp (1972); van Thiel *et al.* (1971); Stouffer *et al.* (1976); Henderson and McNatty (1977); Goldenberg *et al.* (1972)
	Large, med., sm. foll. from known stages o.c.	Channing *et al.* (1980)
Horse	Sl.h.: various sizes	Channing (1970); Channing and Crisp (1972)
Cow	Individual foll. of various size Sl.h. large foll.	Korenman *et al.* (1973) Henderson and McNatty (1977)
Human	Late foll.ph. large foll. at lap.	Henderson and McNatty (1977); NcNatty *et al.* (1974)
	"Active" and "inactive" foll. at lap.	McNatty and Sawers (1975); McNatty *et al.* (1975);
	Various size foll. from ov. wedge at lap.	Channing (1970); Channing and Crisp (1972)
Monkey	Various sizes, incl. preov. foll.	Channing (1970); Channing and Crisp (1972); Gould *et al.* (1977)

[a] Abbreviations: foll., follicle(s); foll.ph., follicular phase of ovulation cycle; immat., immature animals; incl., including; lap., laparotomy; med., medium (size follicle); preov., preovulatory; o.c., ovulation cycle; ov., ovary; ovarian; sl.h., slaughter house material; sm., small (follicle).

evidence thus implies a potential capacity for autonomy which is unable to be expressed under the conditions accompanying hypophysectomy.

c. Other Evidence. In the Introduction I touched on another kind of indirect but important evidence, not so much for autonomy per se, but for the possibility that the rate of progesterone secretion is determined by intrinsic rather than extrinsic factors. This is the general lack of direct relation between the pattern of progesterone secretion and that of the luteotrophin on which the secretion of progesterone is assumed to depend. Two very good examples are the following. In the monkey, LH is believed to be the essential luteotrophin, but there is no relation between the progesterone and the LH levels in the circulation in either the intact monkey (Karsch *et al.,* 1973), or in the median-edminence lesioned or stalk-sectioned monkey in which a constant low level of LH secretion was achieved through the pulsatile infusion of a fixed dose of GnRH (Knobil, 1980). In the rabbit estrogen is the essential luteotrophin (Greenwald and Rothchild, 1968; Hilliard, 1973) and there is a similar lack of relation between progesterone secretion in the hypophysectomized rabbit and the constant level of estrogen in the circulation, achieved through an estrogen containing Silastic implant (Bill *et al.,* 1980). Other examples are summarized in Table II. Additional evidence for this is the relative ineffectiveness of a presumed luteotrophin to stimulate progesterone secretion in the young CL of the sheep (Weiss *et al.,* 1978), cow (Schomberg *et al.,* 1967), pig (Channing *et al.,* 1980), human (Sadler *et al.,* 1980), monkey (Nutting *et al.,* 1980), and rabbit (Miller and Keyes, 1975).

Another manifestation of autonomy may be that CL formed either naturally or in response to hormone treatment during the life cycle of an existing set of CL tend to grow and regress independently of the original set. Some examples of this were mentioned in Rothchild (1965, p. 299), and have also been reported for the pig (Caldwell *et al.,* 1969), Uganda kob (Morrison, 1971), rat (Nakamura and Ichikawa, 1978; Takahashi *et al.,* 1979), rabbit (Scott and Rennie, 1970), and the brush-tailed possum (Pilton and Sharman, 1962).

During the last few years a group of findings imply that if CL *in vitro* are supplied with substrate (cholesterol) in the form of lipoproteins they cannot only increase the amount of progesterone made in response to a given dose of luteotrophin (Azhar *et al.,* 1980), but do not even need the "luteotrophin" to increase their progesterone production (Sadler *et al.,* 1980; Schreiber and Nakamura, 1980; Schuler *et al.,* 1980a,b). There is also a direct relation between progesterone and lipoprotein lipase activity in the cow's CL (Shemesh *et al.,* 1976). Adrenal cortical cells, however, require ACTH to respond to lipoproteins to an equivalent extent (Brown *et al.,* 1979). It is interesting, in this connection, that adrenal cortical mitochondria do not make corticosteroids *in vitro* except in response to ACTH, and that this response can be increased by lipoproteins, although the latter have no effect by themselves (Farese and Sabir, 1980; Carr *et al.,* 1980). CL mitochondria, however, can make progesterone *in vitro* even in the absence of luteotrophins or lipoproteins (Dimino and Campbell, 1976; Dimino, 1977).

TABLE II

Absence of a Direct Relation between the Pattern of Progesterone Secretion[a] during the Ovulation Cycle, and That of a Known, Suspected, or Possible Extrinsic Luteotrophin

Species	Pattern of "luteotrophin"[b] secretion	Reference
Human	LH: low and constant, or slightly inverse to progesterone	Neill *et al.* (1967); Cargille *et al.* (1969)
Monkey (intact)	LH: low and constant, or slightly decreasing	Kirton *et al.* (1970); Karsch *et al.* (1973); Monroe *et al.* (1970); Resko *et al.* (1974); Wilks (1977); Goodman *et al.* (1977); Hodgen *et al.* (1976)
Monkey (with denervated pituitary[c,d])	LH: low and constant	Knobil (1974, 1980)
Chimpanzee	LH: as in human	Reyes (1975)
Baboon	LH: as in human	Stevens *et al.* (1970)
Sheep	LH: low and constant	Niswender (1974); Pant *et al.* (1977); Salamonson *et al.* (1973); Scaramuzzi *et al.* (1970)
	FSH? slightly parallels progesterone	Pant *et al.* (1977); Salamonson *et al.* (1973)
	PRL: mostly constant, but increases as progesterone decreases	Niswender (1974, 1976)
Pig	LH: generally low and constant or slightly inverse to progesterone	Niswender *et al.* (1970); Parvizi *et al.* (1976); Ginther *et al.* (1972)
	PRL: peaks during regression phase of progesterone	Dusza and Krzymowska (1979)
Horse	LH: generally inverse to progesterone	Nett *et al.* (1976); Evans and Irvine (1975)
	FSH: broad peak in early luteal phase	Evans and Irvine (1975)
Cow	LH: low and constant	Henricks *et al.* (1970); Snook *et al.* (1971)
Dog	PRL: increases as progesterone decreases	Gräf (1978)
Rat[e]	PRL: 2 daily surges but of average constant value	Smith and Neill (1976); Freeman *et al.* (1974); de Greef and Zeilmaker (1978)
	Low and constant in *in vitro* medium of luteinized granulosa cells	Crisp (1977)
	LH (after day 8): low and constant, with tendency to rise toward end of luteal phase	Morishige *et al.* (1973); Welschen *et al.* (1975); Linkie and Niswender (1972)
Rabbit[f]	Estrogen: low and constant	Hilliard *et al.* (1973); Challis *et al.* (1973); Bill *et al.* (1980)

(*Continued*)

TABLE II (*Continued*)

Species	Pattern of "luteotrophin"[b] secretion	Reference
Rabbit[g]	Estrogen (per Silastic implant): low and constant	Bill *et al.* (1980)
Guinea pig	LH: generally inverse to progesterone low and constant	Blatchley *et al.* (1976); Croix and Franchimont (1976)
	FSH: low and constant	Blatchley *et al.* (1976); Croix and Franchimont (1976)

[a] Progesterone secretion is assumed to parallel the level of progesterone in the peripheral circulation; it is expressed in *all* cases as a typical rise, plateau, and fall (see Fig. 2).
[b] During the luteal phase only.
[c] FSH pattern is generally like that of LH (e.g., Resko *et al.*, 1974).
[d] Denervation was by median eminence lesion, or stalk secretion. The animals were treated by pulsatile infusion of a constant average daily dose of GnRH.
[e] Pseudopregnant.
[f] Pregnant.
[g] Hypophysectomized immediately after ovulation.

Besides the ability of the tammar wallaby's CL to function independently of pituitary stimulation, several other characteristics of CL physiology among marsupials (with the exception of the bandicoots, which I will consider below in relation to the evolution of the eutherian CL) are indirect but provocative evidence for autonomy. Although the length of the luteal phase can vary among the species from about 12 days (in most) to as much as 5 weeks (in the large kangaroos) (Sharman, 1970; Tyndale-Biscoe, 1973; Tyndale-Biscoe *et al.*, 1974; Tyndale-Biscoe and Hawkins, 1977) the longer luteal phases probably all include a quiescent phase before the true rapid increase typical of a rising phase begins. This can be seen in the difference in progesterone levels between the brushtailed possum, which lacks a quiescent phase (Thorburn *et al.*, 1971), and the tammar (Lemon, 1972) and quokka (Cake *et al.*, 1980) which have one; the very slow increase in the size of the CL during the first few weeks of the luteal phase in the large kangaroos (Tyndale-Biscoe, 1973) probably is only a variant of this pattern. In other words, no true long-lived CL, of the type seen among eutherian monestrous breeders seems to occur among the marsupials (excepting the bandicoots), although at least one genus (*Antechinus*) is known to be a monestrous breeder (Lee *et al.*, 1977). This is significant in comparison with the eutheria, because among the latter, no polyestrous breeder has a luteal phase longer than 2.5 weeks, and no monestrous breeder has a luteal phase shorter than about 5 weeks, and this difference seems to depend, among other things, on the *responsiveness* of the eutherian CL to extrinsic controls (p. 235).

Pregnancy also does not affect the length of the luteal phase in any marsupial species so far examined (Sharman, 1970, 1976; Tyndale-Biscoe, 1973, 1979; Cake *et al.*, 1980), although it is becoming more and more clear that the marsupial conceptus is not endocrinologically inactive, as was once thought to be the case. It has a specific growth stimulating effect on the uterus (Renfree, 1977) and evidence for *in vitro* production of progesterone by the placenta, for example, has been found in the quokka (Bradshaw *et al.*, 1975) and the tammar (Renfree, 1977).

The marsupial CL's life span is also unaffected by hysterectomy, whether the animal is pregnant or not (Sharman, 1970, 1976; Tyndale-Biscoe, 1973, 1979; Tyndale-Biscoe and Hawkins, 1977). Thus the lack of influence of pregnancy, the uterus, or the type of ovulation cycle on the life span of the marsupial CL implies that it is largely insensitive to extrinsic controls, and, therefore, is regulated primarily by intrinsic ones. It would not be surprising to find that the monotreme CL was similarly regulated.

2. *The Implications of Autonomy*

The first question raised by these manifestations of autonomy among representatives of at least five eutherian orders (ungulates, rodents, lagomorphs, carnivores, primates) and probably among most marsupials is: if autonomy of progesterone secretion is presumed to be a universal characteristic of the mammalian CL, why is it not present to the same extent among all mammalian species? The answer is that differences in the capacity to secrete progesterone autonomously could have arisen as the result of the selection process; I will discuss this later (p. 243). The other question raised by the possibility of autonomy is: what might be the stimulus to progesterone secretion within the CL? This will be considered now.

The Role of Progesterone in the Regulation of Progesterone Secretion. A rather assorted collection of findings, in addition to those described in a previous paper (Rothchild, 1965, p. 274), fit with or suggest the possibility that progesterone may have a stimulatory effect on its own secretion. One was already mentioned: the lack of relation between the pattern of progesterone secretion and that of its known or assumed luteotrophin (Table II). Even more significant is that the progesterone concentration within the CL is directly related to the rate of progesterone secretion (as reflected in changes in the level of progesterone in the peripheral circulation) (Table III). The rising phase is in part, of course, the result of growth of the CL, but if it was due entirely to growth the progesterone concentration within the CL would not increase as progesterone secretion increases. This conclusion fits with the general relationship between the pattern of growth and that of progesterone secretion. In the sheep, for example, the CL is fully grown by about day 6 after ovulation (Stabenfeldt *et al.*, 1969) while progesterone secretion continues to increase to between days 9 and 11

TABLE III

The Direct Relation between Changes in Progesterone (P) Secretion and Changes in the Intraluteal Concentration of Progesterone (P/CL) [a]

Species	Remarks	Reference
Pig	P/CL changes in o.c. and experimental conditions parallel changes in CL size and P secretion	Anderson *et al.* (1967); Rathmacher and Anderson (1968); Rombauts *et al.* (1965); Restall (1964)
	P/CL and P in ov. vein directly related in o.c., pregnancy, after hysterectomy	Masuda *et al.* (1967)
Sheep	P/CL directly related to changes in CL size and/or P secretion in o.c.	Deane *et al.* (1966); Caffrey *et al.* (1979b)
Cow	Direct relation between growth and/or P secretion during o.c.	Shemesh *et al.* (1976); Hafs and Armstrong (1968); Kristofferson (1960)
	P/CL decreases slowly with duration of extended luteal ph. in hysterectomized cows	Brunner *et al.* (1969)
Monkey	P/CL decreases after day 6 luteal ph.	Butler *et al.* (1975)
Human	P/CL fell with P secretion after norgesterol treatment	Mukherjee *et al.* (1972)
Guinea pig	P/CL directly related to CL size and P secretion during o.c.	Heap *et al.* (1967)
Rabbit	P/CL directly related to P secretion throughout pseudopregnancy	Horrell *et al.* (1972)
Cuis	P/CL directly related to P secretion in o.c. and pregnancy	Tam (1973)
Tammar wallaby	P/CL parallels CL growth and P secretion during luteal ph.	Renfree *et al.* (1979) (P/CL); Lemon (1972) (P)
Rat	P/CL directly related to P secretion throughout pregnancy	Wiest *et al.* (1968); Wiest (1970)
	In pseudopregnancy also	Rothchild (unpublished)
	In pseudopregnancy on day 8, in connection with several experimental conditions	Terranova (1980)
Hamster	Direct relation P/CL and P secretion in o.c. and experimental conditions in pseudopregnancy	Terranova *et al.* (1978); Terranova and Greenwald (1978)
Garter snake	P/CL directly related to P secretion throughout gestation	Highfill and Mead (1975)

[a] Abbreviations as in Table I. Progesterone secretion is assumed to parallel changes in peripheral circulation levels of progesterone. Not all the references contain information about P secretion itself, but the latter information is available from many other sources. For references to same subject before 1965, see Rothchild (1965, p. 272).

(Pant *et al.*, 1977; Plotka and Erb, 1967; Stabenfeldt *et al.*, 1969; Thorburn and Mattner, 1971). The rate of conversion of pregnenolone to progesterone by the horse CL *in vitro* (Evans *et al.*, 1975) also increases with the increase in progesterone secretion, as does acetate incorporation into progesterone by the rabbit CL *in vitro* (Suzuki *et al.*, 1977). Progesterone secretion increases during the rising phase, in other words, not just because the amount of producing tissue increases, but because each unit of tissue increases its rate of progesterone production. This direct relationship between the intraluteal progesterone concentration and the rate of progesterone secretion is such a dramatic contrast to the lack of relation between progesterone secretion and that of its presumed extrinsic stimulus (Table II) that it points to the possiblity that an intrinsic stimulus increases the rate of autonomous progesterone secretion, a conclusion which is almost self-evident from the typical S-shaped pattern of the curve of progesterone secretion during the rising phase.

The following findings suggest that this stimulus may indeed be progesterone itself. The CL makes progesterone from free cholesterol through the action of the cholesterol side chain cleavage enzyme (Chol SCC) and the 3β-hydroxysteroid dehydrogenase (3β-OHSDH) and Δ^{4-5}-isomerase enzymes. Esterified cholesterol must first be hydrolyzed before it can be converted to progesterone, and one of the actions of progesterone is to activate cholesterol esterases (Caffrey *et al.*, 1979b; Dorrington, 1977). Progesterone also depresses the activity of the cholesterol ester synthetases in human cancer cells, but only in the presence of low density lipoproteins (LDL) (Gal and Simpson, 1980). The general inverse relation between intraluteal cholesterol concentration and progesterone secretion (Rothchild, 1965; Spies *et al.*, 1968a; Guraya, 1975) is also consistent with a stimulating effect of progesterone on the conversion of cholesterol.

In the rat the neutralization of circulating LH by LHAS treatment between days 8 and 12 of pregnancy results in luteolysis and abortion (Raj and Moudgal, 1970; Morishige and Rothchild, 1974), accompanied by a marked increase in the production of 20α-OHP by the CL. This is reflected in increased activity of the enzyme 20α-hydroxysteroid dehydrogenase (20α-OHSDH) (Loewit and Zambelis, 1979). Treating the rats with progesterone, after the injection of LHAS prevented the increase in 20α-OHSDH, even when the pregnant uterus was removed (Loewit and Zambelis, 1979); this suggests that the progesterone may have affected the CL directly.

The lack of an inhibiting effect of large doses of progesterone on the CL during the first 2 weeks of its life span in rats (Rothchild, 1965), sheep (Woody *et al.*, 1967; Thwaites and Edey, 1970), and pigs (Spies *et al.*, 1967a) is one expression of the absence of negative feedback control of its activity (Rothchild, 1965). Progesterone treatment around day 35 of pregnancy also has no effect on the cow's CL (Menge and Verville, 1969); treatment of pregnant rats at a dose calculated to be 5 times the estimated daily production rate also had no effect on the rat's CL (Bartholameusz and Bruce, 1976). In the guinea pig also progesterone treatment did not affect the CL (Bland and Donovan, 1970). Related to these findings is the direct relationship between the number of CL and the level of progesterone in the circulation in the rat (de Greef and Zeilmaker, 1974; Elbaum *et al.*, 1975; Nuti and Meyer, 1975) and cow (Lemon and Saumande, 1972) (in the latter different numbers of CL were induced by gonadotrophin treatment). The absence of negative feedback control does not of course prove that progesterone facilitates its own secretion, but it is consistent with such a possibility. The presence of a negative feedback control of estrogen secretion by the ovary, in fact, hindered the recognition of the fact that estrogens can also stimulate their own production within the follicle. Perhaps the findings of Uchida *et al.* (1970a, 1972) that treatment of proestrous rats with progesterone raised the rate of progesterone secretion by the preovulatory follicle, without affecting the level of LH secretion, is another indication that progesterone may potentiate its own secretion.

Alloiteau's (1957) suggestive finding of a direct trophic effect of progesterone on the rat's CL (Rothchild, 1965, p. 275) is supported not only by those of Loewit and Zambelis (1979) mentioned above, but by others. Ahmad (1971) treated pregnant rats with a combination of progesterone and estrogen only until day 12, after hypophysectomy on day 8, and found that this allowed pregnancy to continue to term. Raj *et al.* (1979) found a similar result after treating pregnant rats with LHAS on day 8, together with dydrogesterone from day 8 to 12. Dydrogesterone is a synthetic progestogen that does not have the luteolytic effect typical of many other synthetics (Raj *et al.*, 1979; see below also), and, at this time in pregnancy, LHAS by itself always induces luteolysis and abortion. The significance of these findings comes from the fact that the CL are needed to maintain pregnancy after day 12, that placental hormones alone are needed to maintain CL activity after day 12, but that only the *combined* effect of the pregnant uterus and LH will maintain the CL between days 8 and 12 (Morishige and Rothchild, 1974). Since the CL remained alive in the absence of the pituitary in the one experiment, and in the absence of LH in the other, the findings suggest that progesterone and dydrogesterone had a direct trophic action on the CL. The finding of Pal *et al.* (1976) that progesterone treatment not only prevented the aborting action of PMSG treatment in the rat, but also the luteolysis that caused the abortion, suggests a similar conclusion.

In guinea pigs injected with a luteolytic dose of PGs, progesterone secretion fell very soon after treatment but pregnenolone production fell much more slowly (Dwyer and Church, 1979). If the primary effect of PGs was on the biosynthesis of cholesterol or pregnenolone, one would expect pregnenolone production to fall at least as quickly, or even sooner than that of progesterone. This finding suggests, therefore, that the guinea pig CL could not maintain its production of pregnenolone in the absence of progesterone.

The idea that progesterone may facilitate its own secretion seems to disagree with some findings. For example, active immunization of rabbits against progesterone markedly increased the progesterone level in the circulation (French, 1977; Surve *et al.*, 1976), but since the binding of progesterone to an immune globulin undoubtedly prolonged its stay in the circulation without prolonging its biological activity at all [the treatment had no effect, for example, on the length of the luteal phase (Surve *et al.*, 1976)], this finding probably has no significance for the effect of progesterone on its own secretion.

Although a limited period of progesterone treatment does not affect CL activity, a prolonged one may. The effect, however, can almost always be identified as the result of an action of progesterone outside the CL. For example, Rothchild and Schwartz (1965) found that after 4 weeks of progesterone treatment of intact rats, the CL had markedly regressed. The progesterone treatment did not reduce pituitary LH concentration, but when the same progesterone treatment was combined with estrogen treatment, pituitary LH concentration was reduced and the CL did not regress. In the sheep, prolonged progesterone treatment has no inhibiting effect on the CL in the absence of the uterus (Woody and Ginther, 1968).

Treatment of women with synthetic progestins during the luteal phase of the cycle slightly but definitely shortens its duration and reduces the peak progesterone level in the circulation (Johannsson, 1971; Mukherjee *et al.*, 1972). The effect may be a direct one since in *in vitro* experiments Schreiber *et al.* (1981) found that the synthetics prevented FSH and androgen from stimulating progesterone production in rat follicular granulosa cells. In cows, however, such treatment increased the progesterone concentration in the CL (Johnson and Erb, 1962). In any case, the synthetics may not act as progesterone does and in fact their ability to bind to the same receptor that binds progesterone (Schreiber *et al.*, 1981) may explain their inhibiting effect if they do not act on the CL as progesterone does. Dydrogesterone, as I have already mentioned, not only does not inhibit progesterone secretion, but may enhance it (Raj *et al.*, 1979).

In both the sheep (Caffrey *et al.*, 1979a) and the human (Shinada *et al.*, 1978) progesterone inhibits the conversion of pregnenolone to progesterone by CL *in vitro*. It also inhibits this step in progesterone biosynthesis in human placental tissue *in vitro* (Saure *et al.*, 1977). Serum in the medium prevents this effect on the sheep's CL, presumably because it contains a progesterone-binding protein, and only the free progesterone had this effect. Progesterone (Cook *et al.*, 1968) or pregnenolone (Haksar *et al.*, 1967) may also inhibit one or more of the biosynthetic steps from acetate to cholesterol and progesterone by CL *in vitro*. However, regardless of whatever differences there may have been between the effective concentration of progesterone under these conditions and the ones that would be expected in the CL or placenta *in vivo*, and regardless also of the intrinsic interest of such findings, the fact is that the CL and the placenta keep making progesterone in large amounts *in vivo* in spite of intraluteal concentrations which in the *in vitro* conditions prevented progesterone production.

The findings suggesting the idea that progesterone, by whatever means, promotes its own secretion do not prove that it does so, but that they exist at all in an ephemeral organ like the CL must be more than just a coincidence. The instability of the graafian follicle, i.e., the overwhelming tendency for most of them to become atretic, is almost certainly also an expression of the self-stimulating quality of follicular estrogen production (Rothchild, 1965, p. 275) and the dependency of follicle growth on the stimulating effects of estrogen (e.g., Richards, 1979). Ephemerality means that the essence of the system that controls the CL's ability to make progesterone is instability; i.e., it lacks intrinsic mechanisms that allow it to maintain a constant level of activity, and what, indeed, could be more essentially unstable than a positive feedback system of regulation? Everything about the pattern of progesterone secretion during a typical luteal phase fits with such an intrepretation and justifies the idea that progesterone is probably the intrinsic factor which facilitates the CL's production of progesterone. To a significant extent, the CL's ability to maintain progesterone secretion may depend on the presence within the CL of progesterone at some concentration above a critically *low* one. Having said this, I can add that progesterone has precisely two qualities that one would expect to find in a universal luteotrophin that has defied identification for a long time. One is that is has always been right under our noses and therefore invisible. The other is that all CL will be exposed to it.

The dependency of progesterone secretion on itself, while it is an important element contributing to the CL's limited life span, does not by itself guarantee a limited life span, for if nothing ever disturbed it, the system could continue to work indefinitely. The inevitability of regression of the CL, therefore, must be the result of another process, with the effects of progesterone on it, and the self-dependency of progesterone secretion, operating to determine *when* this process brings the life of the CL to an end. In the following discussion I will summarize the evidence that it is the CL's production of PGs which is ultimately responsible for its ephemerality.

B. PROSTAGLANDINS IN RELATION TO THE BASIC SYSTEM OF REGULATION OF THE CL

1. *The Luteolytic Action of PGs*

The most thorough body of evidence that $PGF_{2\alpha}$ is the natural cause of luteolysis comes from studies of the sheep (Horton and Poyser, 1976; Goldberg and Ramwell, 1975; McCracken *et al.*, 1972; Ginther, 1974; Hansel, 1975; Ramwell *et al.*, 1977). That PGs are an important element in luteolysis in other species, however, although based on a less extensive body of evidence, is an inescapable conclusion, since they induce luteolysis in rats, mice, rabbits, guinea pigs, hamsters, cows, pigs, horses (Horton and Poyser, 1976; Goldberg and Ramwell, 1975; Pharriss and Shaw, 1974; Ramwell *et al.*, 1977), cats (Nachreiner and Marple, 1974; Shille and Stabenfeldt, 1979), dogs (Concannon and Hansel, 1977; Vickery and McRae, 1980), and the swamp buffalo (Kamonpatna *et al.*, 1979). They almost certainly do so also in primates (discussed below).

The PGs as a group are perhaps ideal candidates for the final common agent of luteolysis. Although no one knows exactly *how* they stop progesterone secretion, hardly anyone denies that they do, and their ability to labilize lysosomal membranes (Schwarz *et al.*, 1977; Liggins, 1979; Thorburn and Challis, 1979) allows one to see how easily their action could also lead to structural regression of the CL. Arachidonic acid, their obligate precursor (Lands, 1979; Bergstrom *et al.*, 1968; Hinman, 1972; Pong and Levine, 1977; Ramwell *et al.*, 1977), is universally distributed throughout tissues as one of the most frequently found fatty acid in the phospholipids and as a less frequent but important fatty acid in the cholesterol esters (Sabine, 1977; Vogt, 1978; Kuehl, 1974). The enzymes that free arachidonic acid from the phospholipids or cholesterol esters are also in rich supply in the CL and neither the cycloxygenases, which convert arachidonic acid to the endoperoxides (PGG_2 or PGH_2) in the presence of molecular oxygen (Lands, 1979), nor the enzymes which transform PGH_2 into PGs of the E or F series (Lands, 1979; Bergstrom *et al.*, 1968; Hinman, 1972) are limiting factors in PG synthesis. Furthermore, the effect of PGs themselves on the liberation of the acyl hydrolyases from lyosomal membranes, for example, but also from other intracellular membranes, sets up ideal conditions for a self-propagating process of PG formation

(Hinman, 1972; Kuehl, 1974; Nathanielsz, 1978; Pong and Levine, 1977; Schwarz *et al.*, 1977; Lands, 1979; Thorburn and Challis, 1979).

In spite of their ability to cause luteolysis in the species mentioned above and the general inverse relation between signs of PG production and progesterone secretion in most of this group of mammals (see Table V), the main reason for hesitating at all to look on them in the role of a final common agent of luteolysis is that their luteolytic effect among the primates is not as easy to see as it is among the other mammals. This is because of the inconsistency with which attempts to induce luteolysis by PG treatment have met with success. Failures are well-recognized (Goldberg and Ramwell, 1975; Horton and Poyser, 1976; Ramwell *et al.*, 1977; Swanston *et al.*, 1977) and continue to be reported (e.g., Gould *et al.*, 1977; Kajonoja *et al.*, 1978; Rao, 1979).

Negative findings, however, do not mean as much as positive ones. One reason is that, although PGs can act as hormones in the classical sense, in some mammals, under some conditions, PGs have their typical effects at the site of their production (Lands, 1979) and their half-life in the circulation is extremely short (Bergstrom *et al.*, 1968; Hinman, 1972; Lands, 1979). I am going to develop the point in this section that *intraluteal* PGs are probably the final common agent of luteolysis in all mammals, and that they have remained the *sole* source of PGs among some (or all?) of the primates; while among some of the other species, uterine PGs became incorporated into the process that switches on the intraluteal ones. There may be reasons peculiar to primates, therefore, for the failure of *in vivo* administered PGs or even PG synthesis inhibitors to affect the CL consistently. The negative findings in primates should be judged not only in comparison with whatever direct evidence there is for success, but also in relation to the connection between PGs and luteolysis as a whole. This includes at least the following: the luteolytic action of estrogens in monkeys and humans; the effect of estrogens on the release of PGs; the possibility of synergism between estrogens and PGs in inducing luteolysis; the inverse relationship between progesterone and PG production by the CL; and the influence of age of the CL and of its vasculature on the responsiveness to PGs.

There is suggestive evidence for *in vivo* luteolytic effects of $PGF_{2\alpha}$ treatment in women (Lehmann *et al.*, 1972; Arata and Chatterton, 1974; Korda *et al.*, 1975) and monkeys (Kirton *et al.*, 1970; Kirton and Koering, 1973; Spilman *et al.*, 1977) and somewhat more definite evidence from treatment with analogs of $PGF_{2\alpha}$ in monkeys (Russell, 1975; Spilman *et al.*, 1977; McCracken *et al.*, 1979; Wilks, 1979). In *in vitro* experiments with human or monkey CL or luteinized granulosa cells in tissue culture,

$PGF_{2\alpha}$ or its analogs (McNatty *et al.*, 1975; Henderson, 1976), or PGE_2 (Salazar and Archer, 1974) unquestionably induces luteolysis.

Hoffmann's (1960) suggestion that estrogens can cause luteolysis in women has been confirmed in women (Board *et al.*, 1973; Johannsson, 1973; Lehman *et al.*, 1975; Williams *et al.*, 1979), monkeys (Karsch *et al.*, 1973; Butler *et al.*, 1975; Karsch and Sutton, 1976; Stouffer *et al.*, 1977; Auletta *et al.*, 1978; Balmacida *et al.*, 1980), and baboons (Westfahl and Kling, 1981). The effect is quite clearly directly on the CL (Karsch and Sutton, 1976; Stouffer *et al.*, 1977; Williams, 1979), and probably through an effect on PGs. Auletta *et al.* (1978) found that an increase in intraluteal PG concentration accompanied the luteolytic action of estrogen treatment in monkeys and that indomethacin treatment prevented both the luteolytic action of the estrogen and the increase in PG concentration. The finding that neither $PGF_{2\alpha}$ nor estradiol treatment alone induced luteolysis in monkeys, while the combined treatment did (Shaikh, 1972) is probably related to the findings of Auletta *et al.* Another is that estrogen treatment of monkeys during the first 7 days of the luteal phase induced a suggestive increase in the intraluteal PGF/PGE concentration ratio and eventually an earlier luteolysis than in the controls (Balmacida *et al.*, 1980). In sheep estrogens may facilitate (although they are probably not essential for) the luteolytic effect of $PGF_{2\alpha}$ (Hansel, 1975). A similar or related kind of interaction may be a necessary part of the way PGs and estrogens control luteolysis in the primate CL.

Another way through which estrogens may be involved in PG-induced luteolysis is by initiating an increase in the release of intraluteal PGs. They have a similar effect, especially after a priming one by progesterone, in the endometrium, where this is an important part of the chain of events that leads eventually to parturition in most if not all mammals (p. 214).

In rats, rabbits, guinea pigs, pigs, and cows, an inverse relationship has been described between some measure of progesterone secretion and one of PG production within the CL. This varies in clarity among these species, but it is at least suggestive in all of them. It occurs between the concentration of progesterone and of $PGF_{2\alpha}$ in the guinea pig ovary (Sharma *et al.*, 1976) during the luteal phase of the ovulation cycle, between the progesterone and PG concentrations in the ovarian vein of pseudopregnant rats (Hall and Robinson, 1978), between the rates of progesterone and PG production by luteinized rabbit granulosa cells in tissue culture (Challis *et al.*, 1974), between the progesterone and PG concentrations, and their rates of production *in vitro,* in pig CL (Patek and Watson, 1976), and in the cow's CL between the $PGF_{2\alpha}$ concentration and the rate of progesterone production *in vitro* (Lukeszewska and Hansel, 1979).

A similar inverse relationship in the human and monkey CL seems to exist. Although Swanston *et al.* (1977) found that the PG concentration in the human CL did not rise during the late luteal phase, Downie *et al.* (1974) found that the concentration of PGEs and PGFs increased during the late luteal phase, the PGEs increasing more than the PGFs. Challis *et al.* (1976) found that the production of PGFs and PGEs similarly increased. This does not argue against a role of PGs in luteolysis in primates, although some PGEs can stimulate progesterone production by human CL *in vitro* (Channing, 1972; Henderson, 1976; Gould *et al.*, 1977) and they can even prevent the luteolytic effect of $PGF_{2\alpha}$ in the human (McNatty *et al.*, 1975) and the sheep (Henderson *et al.*, 1977). However, $PGF_{2\alpha}$ will sometimes stimulate progesterone production under *in vitro* conditions even in CL of some species (e.g., cow) (Hixon and Hansel, 1979) in which it readily induces luteolysis *in vivo* (Pharriss and Shaw, 1974; Goldberg and Ramwell, 1975). Furthermore, PGEs are not always luteotrophic (e.g., Weems *et al.*, 1979) and a very important determinant of how they act could be the enzyme PGE_2-9-keto reductase, which converts PGE_2 to $PGF_{2\alpha}$. Its presence in human, pig, and rat CL (Watson *et al.*, 1979) may be a clue to the eventual solution of many of the peculiarities of the PG–CL relationship among mammals.

Henderson and McNatty (1977) found that the binding of PGFs to human CL cells was inversely related to their progesterone production. Shutt *et al.* (1975) first described a suggestive and later a more definite inverse relationship (1976) between progesterone and PG concentrations in the human CL; they also showed that the intraluteal PGF concentration did not increase in early pregnancy (Shutt *et al.*, 1976), a finding consistent with the continued and somewhat increased rate of progesterone secretion by the CL of early pregnancy (Johansson, 1969; Mishell *et al.*, 1973).

The $PGF_{2\alpha}$ levels in ovarian vein blood during the first trimester of pregnancy in women were also found to be less than during the ovulation cycle; in contrast to the latter condition, in which the $PGF_{2\alpha}$ level is higher in the blood draining the CL-bearing ovary than in that from the other ovary, there was no difference in the blood PG level between the two ovaries in pregnancy (Aksel *et al.*, 1978). The same authors also found that in one patient with a persistent CL, there was less $PGF_{2\alpha}$ in the blood draining her CL-bearing ovary than in that from the other ovary, and that the levels from both ovaries were below those found in normal women during the ovulation cycle. The intraluteal PGF/PGE concentration ratio and production rates of each PG increased during the late luteal phase in monkeys (Balmecida *et al.*, 1979), and the levels of PGF and of progesterone in monkey ovarian vein blood were inversely related to each other during the luteal phase of the ovulation cycle (Fernandez *et al.*, 1980).

During the rising phase of the CL life cycle, the CL do not respond to the luteolytic effect of PGs, while older ones do (Table IV). This phenom-

TABLE IV

Evidence That Young CL Are Less Sensitive to the Luteolytic Effect of PGs Than Are Older CL

Species	Earliest time in luteal phase at which response to PG appears[a]	Reference
Cow	After day 4–5 and before day 9	Donaldson *et al.* (1965)[b]; Harms *et al.* (1969)[b]; Rowson *et al.* (1972); Auletta *et al.* (1972)[b]; Henricks *et al.* (1974); Henderson and McNatty (1977)
Sheep	After day 3, 4, or 5	Hawk and Bolt (1970)[c]; Hearnshaw *et al.* (1973); Mellin and Busch (1976); Acritopolous and Haresign (1980)
Horse	After day 4 or 5	Allen and Rowson (1973); Neely *et al.* (1975)
Pig	Late in luteal ph., i.e., about day 10	Hallford *et al.* (1975); Lindloff *et al.* (1976); Moeljono *et al.* (1976); Watson and Maule Walker (1977); Krzymowski *et al.* (1978)
Human	Young CL less responsive than older; after day 5 of luteal ph[d]	Turksoy and Safaii (1975); Henderson and McNatty (1977); Hamberger *et al.* (1980)*
Rabbit	CL of mid-pregnancy much more responsive to $PGF_{2\alpha}$ than are younger CL	Koering and Kirton (1973)
Rat	After day 3, before day 7	Lamprecht *et al.* (1975)*; Mercier-Parot and Tuchmann-Duplessis (1976); Khan *et al.* (1979)*; Hamberger *et al.* (1980)*
Cat	After day 11	Shille and Stabenfeldt (1979)
	Not in *early* luteal ph. (?)	Wildt *et al.* (1979)
Dog	After day 8	Concannon and Hansel (1977)
	After day 20	Vickery and McRae (1980)
Ferret	After day 30 (?)	Heap *et al.* (1977)

[a] In some studies (e.g., Khan *et al.*, 1979) there was a clear relationship between the luteolytic effect of PGs and their ability to prevent adenyl cyclase stimulation by LH, or to increase 20α-OHSDH activity. Such information has also been used here to show a lack of effect of PG on young CL. These are marked by an asterisk.

[b] In relation to luteolytic effect of oxytocin, which probably acts through uterine PGs (Horton and Poyser, 1976).

[c] In relation to effect of estrogen, the luteolytic effect of which is probably through uterine PGs (Horton and Poyser, 1976; Thorburn and Challis, 1979).

[d] In the monkey, the luteolytic effect of estrogens, which is probably a PG-mediated effect, is much greater in older than younger CL (Stouffer *et al.*, 1977).

enon has not gone unnoticed (Henderson and McNatty, 1975), but Table IV makes it very obvious that the age of the CL must be considered in testing the responsivity of a given species' CL to the luteolytic effect of a PG. It's very difficult to know exactly how much this relationship accounts for the reported failures of PG treatment to induce luteolysis in primates, but that it could account for at least some is certain, and it is also possible that it could account for all. The pig's CL, for example, does not become sensitive to the luteolytic effect of administered PGs until late in the luteal phase (Table IV), and it is much easier to determine the exact age of the CL in pigs than it is in women or monkeys. One indication of the importance of age is that 9-day-old human CL were much more sensitive to the luteolytic effect of PGs *in vitro* than were 7-day-old CL (Nutting *et al.*, 1980).

The inconsistency of the primate CL's response to PGs may be due not only to inaccuracy in determining how old the CL was at the time of testing, but perhaps also to a difference from other species in the vasculature of the CL. It is at least worth remarking that in all the species in which PGs readily induce luteolysis the CL receives a significant part of the luteolysis-inducing PGs from the uterus. This could mean that these CL are adapted to receive *extrinsic* PGs in a way which does not exist in the primates, in which *intraluteal* PGs may be solely responsible for the changes leading to regression. Hamberger *et al.* (1980) have shown that the ability of PGs to inhibit hCG-induced stimulation of adenyl cyclase in human CL *in vitro* is absent in young CL, and appears only in late luteal phase ones; the relation of the PG effect to age, thus, is exactly the same as that shown in Table IV between age and the luteolytic response to PGs. What is even more interesting is that they also showed that the appearance of responsiveness to PGs in the older CL was associated with the appearance of norepinephrine in their blood vessels, and that the addition of β-adrenergic blocking agents to the *in vitro* medium blocked the inhibiting effect of PGs on hCG stimulation of adenyl cyclase.

In the monestrous species, as in primates, the uterus has no influence on how long the CL function (p. 236). If the cat and the dog are typical of these species, the luteolytic response to PGs also appears in them only relatively late in the luteal phase (Concannon and Hansel, 1977; Shille and Stabenfeldt, 1979; Vickery and McRae, 1980). In the ferret PG treatment on day 30 or earlier of pregnancy did not induce abortion (Heap *et al.*, 1977), but I know of no studies of the effect of PG treatment on progesterone secretion later in the luteal phase.

2. Production of PGs by the CL

A few studies show directly that the CL can make PGs. In addition several others show that the CL contains PGs. Since PG metabolism is very rapid (Bergstrom *et al.*, 1968; Hinman, 1972; Lands, 1979) it is likely that their presence in the CL means that they were made there. This should not be surprising since the follicle makes PGs very well (p. 185).

In addition to the evidence mentioned above for the inverse relationship between PG and progesterone productions by the CL, several related findings indicate that the CL can make PGs. The human CL contains large amounts of PGs (Henderson and McNatty, 1975) and makes them *in vitro* (Henderson and McNatty, 1975); their metabolites also appear in the blood draining the human (Aksel *et al.*, 1977, 1978) and monkey ovary (Fernandez *et al.*, 1980). The cow's CL makes PGs from arachidonic acid (Hansel, 1975; Shemesh and Hansel, 1975b,c) but it can also make PGs without added precursors, although in somewhat smaller amounts (Shemesh and Hansel, 1975c). The luteolytic synergism between estrogens and PGs, as for example, in the sheep (Hansel, 1975; Hixon *et al.*, 1975) or cow (Gengenbach *et al.*, 1977), most likely depends on intraluteal PG production, since the sheep's CL can also make PGs *in vitro* (Rexroad and Guthrie, 1979). Guthrie *et al.* (1978, 1979), like Watson and his co-workers, have shown that the pig CL makes PGs *in vitro*. The rat's CL contains PGs and can make them *in vitro* (Demers *et al.*, 1973; Strauss and Stambaugh, 1974), and indomethacin prevents PMSG-induced luteolysis in hysterectomized rats (Basu and Chatterton, 1978). Luteinized rabbit granulosa cells in tissue culture (Erickson *et al.*, 1977) and rabbit CL *in vitro* (Wilks *et al.*, 1972) also make PGs; this ability probably explains the readiness with which arachidonic acid treatment induces luteolysis in the rabbit (Hoffman, 1974; Carlson and Gole, 1978).

3. *The Effect of Progesterone on the Production and/or Effect of Luteolytic PGs*

Even in species (e.g., sheep, pig) in which the effect of *uterine* PGs on the CL is the most important single factor that determines when luteolysis begins, the CL's ability to make progesterone seems to be inversely related to its ability to make PGs (Patek and Watson, 1976). Although such a relationship could be the result of only the luteolytic effect of PGs, it is also possible that it is an expression of the inhibiting effect of progesterone on PG production. Although there is almost no information about the influence of progesterone on intraluteal PG production, the fairly large amount of information about its effect on endometrial and related PG production suggests that progesterone probably suppresses the CL's ability to make PGs.

The pregnancy- and, particularly, the parturition-related information on this point is especially clear. From the analyses and summaries of findings made in recent years (Liggins, 1973, 1979; Goldberg and Ramwell, 1975;

Karin and Hillier, 1975; Currie and Thorburn, 1977; Csapo, 1977; Flower, 1977; Heap *et al.*, 1977; Schwarz *et al.*, 1977; Nathanielsz, 1978; Thorburn and Challis, 1979), two main points become very clear: progesterone increases the tissue's potential ability to make PGs and, at the same time, it suppresses their actual production and/or relase, and reduces their effect. The suppressing effect is not well understood, but may depend in part on stabilizing various intracellular membranes (Liggins, 1979) within which are stored both the arachidonic acid-rich phospholipids and the phospholipases which hydrolyze them from the parent compounds. The potentiating effect may include, among other things,the building up of stores of arachidonic acid-rich phospholipids (Thorburn and Challis, 1979), the formation of lysosomes (Henzl *et al.*, 1972), the richest source of phospholipases, and increasing cathepsin D synthesis and storage in the lysosomes (Elangovan and Moulton, 1980). How the changes in progesterone, estrogens, and intrauterine PG production eventually lead to parturition need not concern us here, except to say that, almost beyond question, the final common pathway is through a switch-on of an increase of intrauterine PG production, arising in part from the removal or bypassing of the inhibiting effect of progesterone, and in part from the self-propagating quality of PG production and the ability of PGs to reduce progesterone secretion, and to stimulate myometrial activity (Currie and Thorburn, 1977; Csapo, 1977; Flower, 1977; Schwarz *et al.*, 1977; Nathanielsz, 1978; Lands, 1979; Liggins, 1979; Thorburn and Challis, 1979, 1980).

In general, progesterone seems to have a similar influence on endometrial PGs during the ovulation cycle. The same kind of inverse relationship we have already seen between intraluteal progesterone and PG production exists between progesterone secretion during the ovulation cycle and various measures of endometrial PG activity (Table V). More direct evidence is that, although progesterone may under some conditions of prolonged treatment be associated with an increase in uterine PG production (e.g., sheep: Louis *et al.*, 1978), in general it suppresses uterine PG production but sets up conditions which allow estrogen to stimulate PG production and release (*human:* Abel and Baird, 1980; Kelly and Abel, 1980; *monkey:* Demers *et al.*, 1974; *rat:* Castracane and Jordan, 1975; Kelly and Abel, 1980; *mouse:* Saksena and Lau, 1973; *sheep:* Caldwell *et al.*, 1972; Wilson *et al.*, 1972; Murdoch *et al.*, 1978; *guinea pig:* Blatchley and Poyser, 1974) (see also Horton and Poyser, 1976).

In a few conditions, however, the inverse relationship between progesterone secretion by the CL and PG production by the uterus either does not hold or cannot be readily seen. In the sheep, for example, progesterone secretion during early pregnancy remains at a level equivalent to

TABLE V

The General Inverse Relation between the Progesterone Level in the Circulation and PG Production by and/or Release from the Uterus[a]

Species	Activities compared	Reference
Guinea pig	PGs/ut.ov.vein increase after day 11, o.c. as P/ut.ov.vein falls	Earthy *et al.* (1975)
	Inverse relationship P secretion and PG/circ. on day 12–15 of o.c.	Blatchley *et al.* (1975)
	PGs/uterus increase toward end luteal ph.	Poyser (1972)
	PG production by uterus does not increase in early preg. as P stays high	Maule Walker and Poyser (1973); Blatchley *et al.* (1975)
Rat	PG/uterus and in ut.ov.vein increase toward end of psp.	Weems *et al.* (1975); Castracane and Shaikh (1976); Weems (1979)
Sheep	PGs/uterus increase toward end of luteal ph.	Wilson *et al.* (1972b)
	PGF/ut.vein increases at end luteal ph.	Several authors (see Horton and Poyser, 1976)
	Cyclooxygenase/uterus maximum by day 14 of o.c.	Huslig *et al.* (1979); Smith *et al.* (1980)
Cow	Surges of PG release into ut.vein begin as P falls in late luteal ph.	Kindahl *et al.* (1980)
	Arachidonic acid/endometrium increases with fall in progesterone at end luteal ph.	Hansel *et al.* (1975)
	PG/uterus and ut.vein as for arachidonic acid	Shemesh and Hansel (1975a)
Pig	Spikes of PG release into ut.vein as P falls in late luteal ph.	Gleeson *et al.* (1974)
	PGF/circ. increase after day 12	Moeljono *et al.* (1977)
	Luteolytic effect endometrial extracts *in vitro* at max. at end luteal ph.	Watson and Maule Walker (1977)
	Endometrial production PGs *in vitro* increase from mid- to late luteal ph.	Patek and Watson (1976)
Horse	PGs/ut.vein increase to max. by middle of CL regression ph.	Douglas and Ginther (1976)
	Inverse relation P and PG metabolites/circ. throughout o.c.	Neely *et al.* (1979)
Monkey	PG/ut. fluid increases to max. by day 20–25 o.c.	Demers *et al.* (1974)
Human	Inverse relation P and PG metabolites/circ. during luteal ph.	Koullapis and Collins (1980)
	Activity of 15-OHPGDH/endometrium parallels P secretion pattern	Casey *et al.* (1980)
	PGs/endometrium increase at end luteal ph.	Downie *et al.* (1974); Singh *et al.* (1975)
	PGF/endometrium decreases in early pregnancy as P stays high	Willman and Collins (1976)

[a] Abbreviations as in Table I, plus these: max., maximum; P/ut.ov.vein, level of progesterone in the utero-ovarian vein; PG/circ., level of PG in the peripheral circulation; PG/uterus, level of PG in the uterus; preg., pregnancy; psp., pseudopregnancy; ut., uterine.

the peak reached during the ovulation cycle (Bassett *et al.*, 1969; Stabenfeldt *et al.*, 1970; Thorburn and Mattner, 1971), but the concentration of PGF in the uterine vein (Pexton *et al.*, 1975; Lewis *et al.*, 1978; Ellinwood *et al.*, 1979) and the apparent rate of PG production by the endometrium (Lewis *et al.*, 1977; Ellinwood *et al.*, 1979) are as high during this time as during the ovulation cycle. A similar situation exists in the cow (Lukaszewska and Hansel, 1979). The pulses of PGF released into the uterine vein, however, which typically occur at the end of the luteal phase of the ovulation cycle in sheep, do not occur at the equivalent time in early pregnancy (Peterson *et al.*, 1976; Niswender, 1981). In the rat also the process through which decidual tissue (DT) formation prevents the luteolytic action of the uterus (Bradbury *et al.*, 1950; Rothchild, 1965, p. 283; Anderson *et al.*, 1969) does not involve a decrease in uterine PGF production (Anteby *et al.*, 1975; Weems *et al.*, 1975; Weems, 1979; Castracane and Shaikh, 1976).

Although the reduced luteolytic action of the uterus under these conditions in rat and sheep may be connected with an increased production of PGEs (Anteby *et al.*, 1975; Castracane and Shaikh, 1976; Ellinwood *et al.*, 1979), some of which can prevent the luteolytic effect of $PGF_{2\alpha}$ (Henderson *et al.*, 1977; Weems *et al.*, 1979), the reason why the continued secretion of progesterone at a high level does not suppress the production of uterine PGFs is not easy to see. It may be that only a *rising* rate of progesterone secretion, i.e., *not* a constant one, can stop or reverse an already started increase in PG production.

4. *The Self-Stimulating Quality of PG Production*

Although inhibitory control over intracellular PG production exists as, for example, cyclooxygenases can catalyze their own destruction (Lands, 1979), most if not all tissues contain the elements needed for the self-stimulation of PG production. This positive feedback quality of PG production has been remarked on in most reviews dealing either with the control of PG biosynthesis or related topics (Hinman, 1972; Pong and Levine, 1977; Ramwell *et al.*, 1977; Lands, 1979; Thorburn and Challis, 1979). Among other things, the ubiquity of arachidonic acid esters and of acyl hydrolases within various kinds of cell membrane, the facts that cyclooxygenases are rarely a limiting factor in PG biosynthesis, and that molecular oxygen has to be almost nonexistant for there to be too little to maintain PG biosynthesis, and that PG metabolizing enzymes are more easily suppressed than are those that stimulate PG biosynthesis (Blackwell *et al.*, 1975) are the most obvious reasons for it. The autocatalytic aspects of PG production are also due to the ability of PGs to labilize cellular membranes (Vogt, 1978; Buhr *et al.*, 1979) and thus free the enzymes and substrates needed for PG biosynthesis (Morita *et al.*, 1979; Murota *et al.*, 1978).

These processes can occur in the CL. PGE treatment of the rat CL *in vitro* increased their production of $PGF_{2\alpha}$ (Demers *et al.*, 1973). A similar effect of colprostenol (a synthetic PGF analog) occurs in pig (Guthrie *et al.*, 1979) and sheep CL (Rexroad and Guthrie, 1979). The description by Salazar *et al.*, (1976) of the EM changes that occur in rat CL in response to a single treatment with colprostenol implies that the treatment increased the production of intraluteal PGs. The fact that phospholipase A_2 concentrations reach a peak in the cow's CL just before regression begins (Shemesh *et al.*, 1976) and that lysosomal membrane fragility is at its peak at this time (Dingle *et al.*, 1968) are further indications that an initiating stimulus may be all that is necessary to set PG synthesis in motion. For example, although LH can stimulate intraluteal PG production (p. 240), the increase in PG production and decrease in progesterone secretion started by arachidonic acid treatment in the cow's CL (Hansel *et al.*, 1973; Hansel, 1975) can proceed without any change in the level of LH in the circulation (Shemesh and Hansel, 1975b). I have already mentioned that the same authors showed that even without added arachidonic acid the cow's CL can make PGs *in vitro*.

Another factor peculiar to the CL that probably contributes to the self-propagation of PG production is that progesterone stimulates the activity of the 15-hydroxy PG dehydrogenase (15-OHPGDH) (Flower, 1977; Liggins, 1979), the most important of the enzymes that metabolize PGs and reduce their biological activity (Hinman, 1972; Lands, 1979). Thus, the fall in progesterone concentration induced by intraluteal PGs would itself increase the concentration of biologically active PGs. Essentially the same interrelationship between progesterone and PGs is an important part of events leading to parturition.

C. A THEORY OF THE BASIC AND COMMON ELEMENTS OF REGULATION OF ALL MAMMALIAN CL

The unique attribute of all vertebrate CL is ephemerality. The ability to secrete progesterone and the connection to viviparity are not unique, since other tissues can secrete progesterone and a one-to-one relationship between the CL and viviparity is true only of the mammalian species. The connection between CL activity and viviparity in its many forms, however, is related to the cause of the CL's ephemerality, as I will try to show.

No explanation of the CL's ephemerality can depend crucially on how an extrinsic luteotrophin acts or on how an extrinsic luteolysin acts, or on how widespread a dependency on either of such extrinsic controlling agents may be among the species, because ephemerality is common to *all* species' CL, and the dependency on either an extrinsic luteotrophin or luteolysin is not. Earlier explanations for one or another aspect of the CL's ephemerality (whether they were expressed as such or not), as for example, those of Caldwell *et al.* (1972), McCracken *et al.* (1972), Henderson and McNatty (1975), Kuehl (1974), and my own (Rothchild, 1960), although they grasped part of the relationship of the CL's ephemerality to the instability of the system that regulated CL activity, failed to see how important it was to differentiate between intrinsic and extrinsic controls in the construction of a theory that could apply to *all* species. In a word: since the CL can go through its life cycle in the absence of extrinsic controls in at least *some* species, and in others, under at least some conditions, the cause of its ephemerality, which is to say, the basic and common elements of regulation that determine the CL's ability to secrete progesterone, and that bring this secretion and with it the life of the CL as a whole to an end, *must lie within the CL itself,* in *all* species. But *what* the intrinsic causes are must also be common to all CL, and therefore, they cannot depend crucially on such things as estrogens, androgen, relaxin, inhibin, etc., since these are not common to all CL at all times.

I pointed out above that an essential quality of regulation of an ephemeral system like the CL must be instability, i.e., the absence of controls that maintain constancy. Ideal conditions for ephemerality, therefore, would be a positive feedback regulation of progesterone production and either ubiquity of factors that could interfere with progesterone production, or the potentiation, by progesterone, of processes that could reduce progesterone production (Rothchild, 1964, 1965; McCracken *et al.,* 1972). Autonomy of progesterone secretion, the possibility that progesterone stimulates its own secretion, the luteolytic effect of PGs, the production of PGs by the CL, the self-stimulating quality of PG production, and the way progesterone affects PG production, are all qualities of the CL that admirably satisfy the requirements for a regulating system that could account for ephemerality. The summary of information about each of these does not establish beyond any question that they are attributes of CL physiology. There is enough evidence for each of them, however, to confirm in me the belief that they are more than a collection of unrelated attributes of the CL, but rather indications of what the basic system of regulation of the CL actually consists of. I will theorize, therefore, that the system is put together according to the following five postulates.

1. *Progesterone production is an intrinsic property of the luteinized granulosa cell.* This means that the production of progesterone by the

CL is essentially autonomous, in the same sense that production of prolactin by the pituitary lactotroph is autonomous. The follicular granulosa cells probably develop this property as they mature but their ability to express it is inhibited by the intrafollicular environment. Removal from this environment or the change in the environment induced by LH removes this inhibition and allow the intrinsic ability to be expressed. Progesterone secretion, although essentially autonomous, can be influenced by extrinsic luteotrophins, and under certain conditions, even become dependent on such extrinsic controls.

2. *Progesterone is the primary stimulus to its own secretion.* How it does this is unknown and for the moment, at least, immaterial. The importance of the postulate is that it helps to explain at least one aspect of ephemerality, since all systems regulated by positive feedback are ephemeral. The system can work to maintain progesterone secretion permanently, therefore, only as long as it is undisturbed, but since it is self-dependent, *any* disturbance that causes progesterone secretion to fall must eventually induce a further fall and the eventual disintegration of the system as a whole.

3. *The CL makes PGs, but progesterone suppresses their production.* The action of progesterone as previously described (p. 214) is to set up the conditions for an eventual high rate of PG production, at the same time that it suppresses their actual production, and/or increases their inactivation. The suppressing effect is strongest during the rising phase of the CL's life cycle; it becomes weaker during the plateau phase, and it progressively diminishes to the point of complete disappearance during the regression phase.

4. *PG production is a self-stimulating intrinsic property of the CL, and PGs inhibit progesterone secretion.* This and the first three postulates imply that the essence of the CL is that it is a postovulatory vertebrate follicle whose regression has been temporarily arrested by its ability to make progesterone. The ultimate cause of its regression comes from its ability to make PGs, and the effects of PGs on progesterone secretion and the integrity of the CL cell. The CL cannot secrete progesterone permanently because this secretion is self-dependent and because progesterone builds up the potential for PG production. PGs, by contrast, regardless of how they suppress progesterone secretion, do so without potentiating future progesterone secretion. Once PGs begin to reduce progesterone secretion, therefore, the CL's potential ablity to secrete progesterone is also reduced. The self-stimulating quality of PG production and the inhibiting effect of PGs on progesterone secretion thus eventually become meshed with the progesterone secretion process in a way which leads to inevitable and irreversible regression of progesterone secretion.

5. *An increase in the intraluteal concentration of progesterone above a critical level initiates the regression phase of the CL life cycle.* Since the intraluteal concentration of progesterone rises as the rate of progesterone secretion rises, it is obvious that the CL would eventually consist of nothing but progesterone if the process continued indefinitely. Some event, therefore, initiated by an increase in the intraluteal progesterone concentration above a critical level must act to decrease the rate at which progesterone secretion rises. Once this begins, it sets in motion the processes that eventually lead to regression, because it will tend to reduce both the suppressing effect of progesterone on PG production and the stimulating effect of progesterone on its own production. The plateau phase is the first symptom of these changes, and, therefore, of regression and it is the most critical period of the CL life cycle. Extrinsic factors, such as pituitary and placental hormones, estrogens, uterine PGs, may affect the system as a whole by acting either to raise the rate of progesterone secretion or of PG production, or by interfering with the effect of progesterone on PG production or vice versa, or by inhibiting the production of either progesterone or PGs. They begin to have their major effects during the early part of the plateau phase.

Summary of the Theory

The CL is ephemeral because of a Yin/Yang type of interaction between the process that stimulates progesterone secretion and the one that stimulates PG production. Each process is self-propagating and tends to suppress the other. Progesterone, however, potentiates the CL's ability to make PGs while PGs only reduce the CL's ability to make progesterone. The CL begins its life cycle with a high potential ability for progesterone secretion, and therefore for suppressing PG production. As progesterone secretion rises so does the intraluteal progesterone concentration, and when the latter rises above a critical level, it initiates the CL's eventual regression by reducing the suppressing effect of progesterone on PG production. Once the balance swings toward PG production regression becomes inevitable (Figs. 3 and 4).

D. OBJECTIONS OR ALTERNATIVES TO THE THEORY

Can the ephemerality of the CL be explained solely on the basis of a self-destruct system due to an inhibiting effect of progesterone on its own secretion? For example, since the concentration of progesterone within the CL rises as the rate of secretion of progesterone rises, the critical intracellular concentration could be said to be the only factor required to shut off progesterone secretion, possibly by inhibiting the activity of 3β-

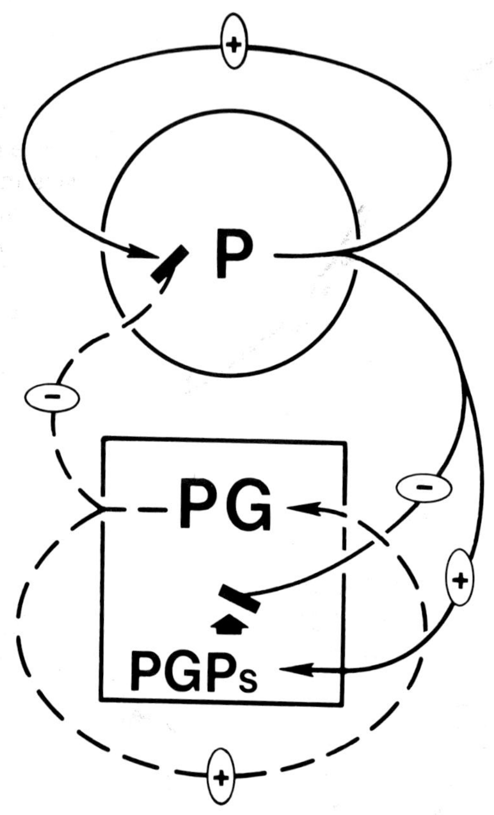

FIG. 3. A schematic representation of the essence of the intrinsic factors that regulate CL activity. P, Progesterone secretion; PG, prostaglandin production; PGPs, prostaglandin precursors; ⊕, stimulation; ⊖, inhibition. The diagram represents the concept that the CL's two basic activities, secretion of progesterone and production of PGs, are each self-stimulating (i.e., regulated by positive feedback) and are mutually inhibitory. Progesterone, however, increases the CL's potential ability to produce PGs (e.g., by stimulating the storage of PG precursors), as it suppresses their production (e.g., by preventing the use of PG precursors for PG synthesis), while the effect of PGs on progesterone secretion is purely inhibitory (see also Fig. 4).

OHSDH (p. 206). If this was so, why is it necessary to invoke a PG effect as the cause of regression?

If the only effect of a critically high intraluteal progesterone concentration was to reduce the rate of progesterone secretion, the system would tend to work like an oscillating, self-correcting one (perhaps the way pituitary lactotrophs secrete prolactin when removed from the inhibiting effect of the CNS) because the reduction in progesterone secretion would also reduce the intralutal progesterone concentration below the critical

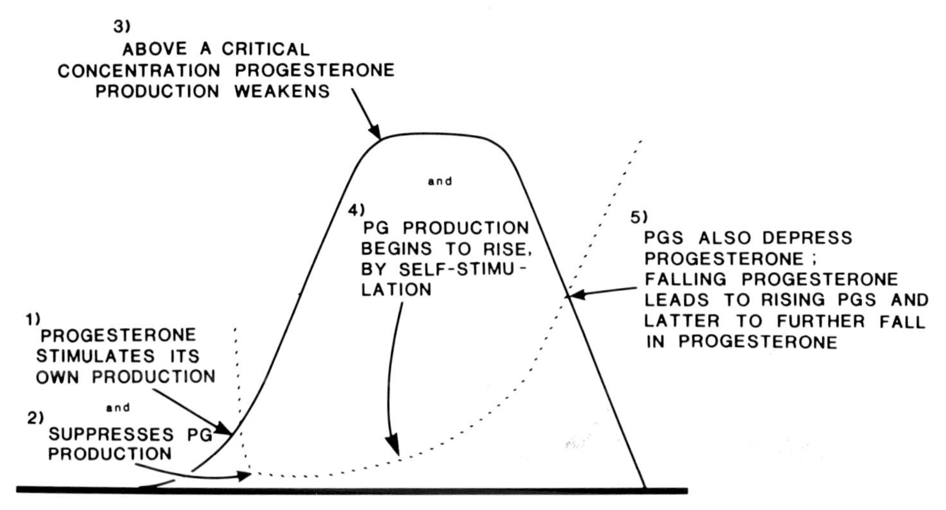

FIG. 4. A CL life cycle expressed in terms of how progesterone secretion and PG production are related to one another. Solid line, progesterone secretion; broken line, PG production (1 and 2) The *rising phase* reflects the self-stimulating quality of progesterone secretion; during this period, progesterone strongly suppresses PG production. (3 and 4) The *plateau phase* reflects the change in the rate of increase in progesterone secretion that arises from the effects of a critically high intraluteal concentration of progesterone. Exactly what this effect is is unknown, but it is postulated to reduce progesterone secretion and switch on an increase in production of PGs. (5) The *regression phase* is the result of the steadily increasing production of PGs, and their suppression of progesterone secretion. Once PG production begins to increase, regression is inevitable because of the self-stimulating quality of its production, and because, as progesterone secretion falls, it reduces the stimulus to its own secretion, and the suppression of PG production (see text, p. 219).

level, and so remove its inhibiting effect. The importance of self-stimulation as a cause of ephemerality is not just that the system disintegrates as soon as *any* reduction in the product occurs. The reduction must gather a certain momentum before disintegration becomes inevitable. The ability of PGs to reduce progesterone secretion means that with each such oscillation, the amount of progesterone produced during each upswing would be slightly less than that produced during the previous one. This is why the ability to make PGs and the way they affect progesterone production fit so much better with the facts of the CL's life cycle than would only the possible inhibiting effect of a critically high progesterone concentration on progesterone secretion.

One may also question the necessity to include the self-stimulating quality of progesterone secretion as one of the important causes of ephemerality in a theory which postulates that PGs are what cause the inevitable regression of the CL. The answer to this has two parts. The first is that progesterone secretion could theoretically continue indefinitely, if it was not disturbed (as, e.g., in the experiment of Korenman *et al.*, 1973). The other is that, while PGs are the inevitable cause of death of the CL, the ability to secrete progesterone determines *when* that event occurs, because progesterone can suppress the production and/or release of PGs. The dependency of progesterone secretion on progesterone, thus ensures that this suppression will not be permanent.

III. The Evolution of Diversity in the Regulation of the Mammalian CL

Even if one granted that there is some truth in this concept of how the CL in general is regulated, the connection between it and how the CL of, for example, a platypus, kangaroo, sheep, dog, woman, rat, or rabbit might be regulated is certainly not self-evident. I believe the connection is in the evolution of responsiveness of the CL to factors that first modified the plateau phase of the CL's life cycle and then the other phases as well. These factors, therefore, could then either prolong, or even as in the case of the rat, shorten the duration of the CL's life span. The first and most important of such factors were probably pituitary hormones, and the CL's ability to respond to them made it possible for the later evolution of responsiveness to other factors, such as placental hormones, ovarian estrogens, and uterine PGs, which could modify the basic system of regulation. A good part of what I will now describe has to include speculations based on what we know about the CL of present day species, but how else can one describe the evolution of things that leave no fossil records?

A. THE METATHERIAN–EUTHERIAN DICHOTOMY

The essential difference between marsupial and eutherian viviparity is in its duration. In no known marsupial species is pregnancy longer than 35 days (Tyndale-Biscoe *et al.*, 1974) and it is only during roughly the last week or two of this time that the embryo attaches to the uterine wall and develops rapidly (Hughes, 1974; Lyne and Hollis, 1977). It is born, therefore, as an embryo and it completes its development, which may occupy many months, during lactation (Sharman, 1970, 1976; Tyndale-Biscoe, 1973). Among the eutherians, however, intrauterine gestation is in all known species long enough for the embryo to progress far beyond where even the most advanced marsupial young is at birth (Parker, 1977); even though many species of eutheria give birth to altricial young. The formation of these two main branches of mammalian descendants from a common ancestor is often referred to as the metatherian–eutherian dichotomy, and it is usually explained as arising from a difference between them in the kind of placenta the embryo formed (e.g., Lillegraven, 1979). It is more probable that the difference between them in their placentas, which is profound, arose first from a difference in the kind of CL they had, and in the responsiveness of their uteri to progesterone. The first change was probably the appearance of responsiveness to the luteotrophic action of prolactin in one of the descendants of the common ancestor.

The modern marsupial CL, as I have indicated above, seems to be almost or completely autonomous (except in the bandicoots), and is probably in a direct line of descent from the CL of the stem reptiles (the cotylosaurs) which first appeared about 300,000,000 years ago (Romer, 1966). These early reptiles, like their modern reptilian and avian descendants, probably made megalecithal eggs. Whether they laid these about a day or so after ovulation, as birds do (Fraps, 1954), or retained them in the oviduct for at least a week before laying them as an entire clutch as modern reptiles do (Callard and Lance, 1977; Cuellar, 1979) may never be known. However, the fact that the postovulatory follicle in birds is not luteinized (Jones, 1978) while in all modern reptiles it forms a true CL (Miller, 1948) suggests that when the CL first appeared in the stem reptiles or in their immediate descendants, its activity was associated with the retention of the egg in the oviduct.

It may make it easier to grasp the significance of this change by comparing the activity of the bird's postovulatory follicle with that of the reptile CL, in relation to the passage of the egg through the reproductive tract. In the chicken the secretion of progesterone by the postovulatory follicle falls off so rapidly that by 1 to 2 days after ovulation, it is less than 1/30 the amount secreted before ovulation (Dick *et al.,* 1978) (Fig. 5). In contrast, beginning about 10 hours after ovulation, it produces PGFs at a steadily rising rate until at least the time of the next ovulation (Day and Nalbandov, 1977) (Fig. 5), which occurs as a rule within each clutch about 24+ hours after ovulation (Fraps, 1954). The avian postovulatory follicle determines when the egg is laid, since if it is removed (Rothchild and Fraps, 1944; Rothchild, 1946; Tanaka and Nakada, 1974) or its blood supply cut off (Wood-Gush and Gilbert, 1964) or its granulosa cells removed or destroyed (Gilbert *et al.,* 1978) oviposition is delayed for about 1 to 5 days. Oviposition can also be delayed in intact birds by indomethacin treatment (Hertelendy, 1973; Hertelendy and Biellier, 1978b) and it can be induced in those whose postovulatory follicle has been removed, by treatment with PGs (Hertelendy and Biellier, 1978a) or oxytocin, the effect of which can be prevented by indomethacin (Hertelendy, 1973). The changes in PG levels in the circulation fit with those in the postovulatory follicle and with the time of oviposition (Hertelendy and Biellier, 1978a,b).

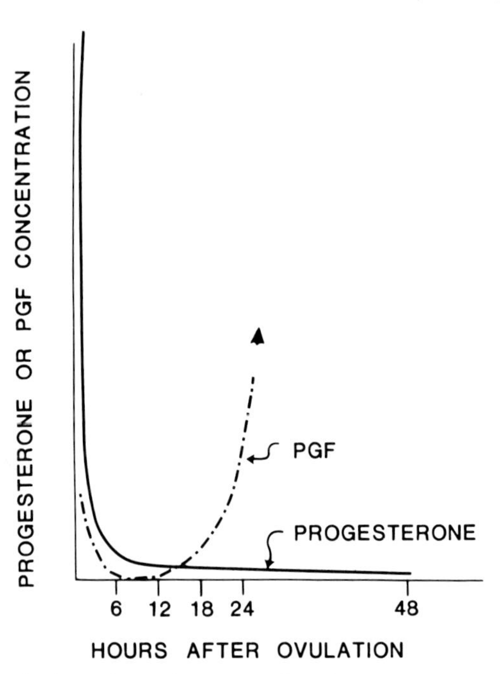

FIG. 5. The qualitative relation between PG and progesterone production in a non-luteinized postovulatory follicle (POF). The progesterone pattern is adapted from the findings of Dick *et al.* (1978), and the PG pattern from the findings of Day and Nalbandov (1977), for the domestic hen. The point of the relationship is that in the absence of luteinization—which is an expression of the prolongation of progesterone secretion by the POF—PG production begins very soon after ovulation and is probably responsible for the rapid regression of the POF, as well as for the relatively short stay of the egg in the reproductive tract (see text, p. 225).

These findings, taken together with the more prolonged stay of the egg in the reptile's than in the bird's oviduct (Cueller, 1979), are arguments in favor of the idea that luteinization, when it first appeared in the stem reptiles' postovulatory follicle, postponed its production of PGs. The fact that removal of the bird's postovulatory follicle delays but does not prevent oviposition suggests that the follicular PGs switch on the intrauterine PGs, and that, in the absence of the former, the latter switch themselves on, but at a slower rate. The increase in the postovulatory follicle's PGs does not depend on pituitary hormones, as Day and Nalbandov (1977) implied, since oviposition occurs on time in the vast majority of birds, in the absence of the pituitary (Rothchild, 1946). The switch-on of intrauterine PGs is probably also an autonomous process, although a slower one. Luteinization, therefore, by indirectly postponing the production of intraoviductal PGs, also postponed the expulsion of the egg from the reproductive tract. I suggest that this is how viviparity among reptiles and mammals began, and is the mechanism behind the idea of Amoroso (1955) and of Hisaw (1959) that the first effect of the CL, which led toward viviparity, was to retain the egg in the reproductive tract. If so, I think the first effect of progesterone may not have been directly on the reproductive tract itself but on the production of ovarian PGs. I would also suggest that vertebrate follicles may have been making PGs long before they started making steroids, and that the PGs acted primarily as the agents of follicular rupture, postovulatory regression of the follicle, and the rapid passage of the eggs through the reproductive tract to the outside world.

The basic system of regulation of the stem reptile's CL was probably essentially what I have described above, and it probably also remained unchanged in any important detail, through the line of descent from the stem reptiles, until the metatherian–eutherian dichotomy of about 100,000,000 years ago.

The stem reptiles threw off several lines of descendants. Among them, one led to the modern birds, another led to the modern reptiles, and a third to the mammal-like reptilian ancestors (therapsids) of early mammals (Romer, 1966; Crompton and Jenkins, 1979) (Fig. 6). The therapsids presumably remained oviparous, with a long interval between ovulation and oviposition. The prototheria are generally assumed to have arisen from them and they eventually progressed to an ovoviviparous form of reproduction, which we still see today in their only surviving descendants, the monotremes (Hill and Gatenby, 1926; Hughes and Carrick, 1978). It was formerly believed that the eutherian line came off directly from a similar therapsied ancestor, but a more likely course of descent (Hopson and Crompton, 1969; Hopson, 1973; Lillegraven, 1975, 1979; Marshall, 1979) is from a primitive mammalian ancestor (pantothere) which progressed from the ovoviviparity of the therapsids and prototheria to a kind of limited viviparity not essentially different in its basic characteristic from what we see today in marsupials like the American oppossum. These early mammals probably had a CL still regulated entirely by intrinsic processes; it could secrete progesterone and/or postpone its production of PGs only long enough to allow for the initial stages of embryonic development in the uterus, the rest of development taking place during lactation. It was a slightly more advanced form of viviparity than the ovoviviparity practiced by the monotremes, and one which the modern marsupials modified to only a minor degree.

The modern marsupials became fixed on this method of reproduction, in spite of the fact that there are at least two groups among them with CL that are responsive, apparently, to two quite different effects of prolactin; one of

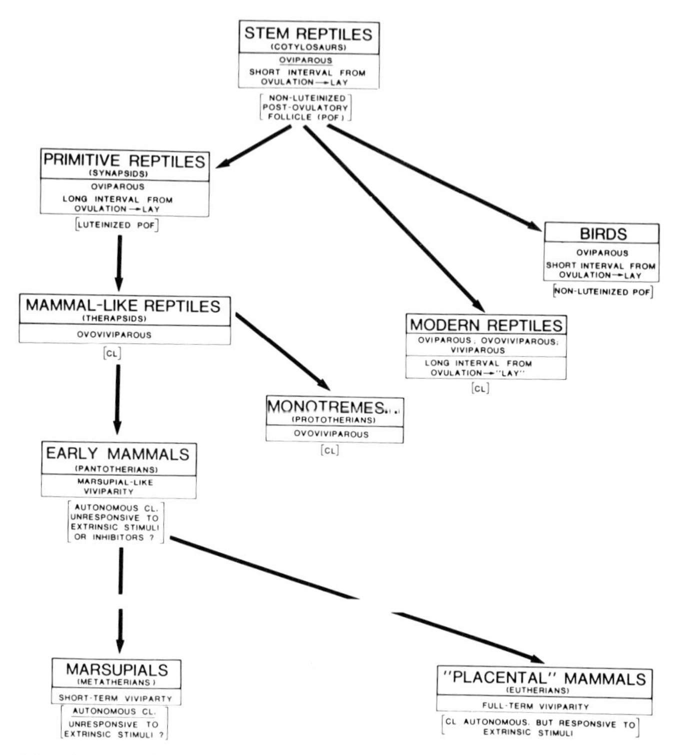

FIG. 6. The descent of the mammalian CL. The stem reptiles (cotylosaurs) arose about 300 million years ago. Among their many descendants are the three lines shown here, in the perspective of the postovulatory phase of reproduction. The birds either never evolved a CL, or else lost it; their postovulatory follicle (POF) regresses very quickly, and the egg passes through the oviduct within a day or two after ovulation. The modern reptiles, and presumably also the primitive reptiles (synapsids) which led to the mammals, evolved a CL from the POF; even in those with an oviparous form of reproduction, the egg was retained in the oviduct until all the eggs of a clutch had been ovulated, i.e., for about 2 weeks. Among the modern reptiles ovoviviparity and true viviparity also evolved, and are related to more prolonged periods of CL activity. The CL in the descendants of the synapsids remained presumably an essentially intrinsically controlled organ until about 100 million years ago, and postovulatory reproduction changed only to the extent that oviparity progressed to ovoviviparity (still seen today in the monotremes) and in the pantotheres, to the limited form of viviparity similar to that of modern marsupials. The evolution of the CL of the "placental" (eutherian) mammals began about 100 million years ago, with the appearance of responsiveness to pituitary luteotrophin hormones (see text, p. 230, and Fig. 8).

these effects actually prolongs the life span of the CL well beyond the limits of the typical short luteal phase of most marsupials (see below). This implies that the failure of marsupials to evolve a eutherian type of viviparity (i.e., an intrauterine gestation long enough for most of embryogenesis) was the result of more than just the very short life span of their CL or a failure to evolve CL responsive to extrinsic factors. Although the short-lived CL appears to be, and may indeed be the major reason for the short gestation among the polyprotodont marsupials (e.g., the American oppossum, the brush-tailed possum, etc.; see Tyndale-Biscoe and Hawkins, 1977) it cannot be the only reason, because the bandicoots, which are also polyprotodonts, also have a gestation of only 12 days, in spite of having long-lived CL (Hughes, 1962; Gemmel, 1981); the long luteal phase (about 6 weeks) is probably because the CL have become responsive to the luteotrophic effects of prolactin. The representative of the other type of responsiveness is the tammar wallaby (a macropodid; the latter include the kangaroos, and are part of the second major division of the marsupials, the diprotodonts). In the tammar, the CL have evolved responsiveness to the "luteostatic" effect of prolactin, one which probably accounts for the long period of CL quiescence during lactation and anestrus (Hearn, 1973, 1974; Tyndale-Biscoe and Hawkins, 1977; Tyndale-Biscoe, 1979). Thus although the CL of most marsupials probably remained unresponsive to extrinsic controls, it did not remain so in all, and one may wonder, therefore, what it was about the marsupials that fixed them on a short gestation and a long lactation as a way of reproducing.

These facts and the one that removal of the CL does not interrupt pregnancy once the embryo has attached itself to the uterine wall (Tyndale-Biscoe, 1973; Renfree, 1974, 1977; Sharman, 1976; Tyndale-Biscoe and Hawkins, 1977; Young and Renfree, 1979) imply that the primary function of the progesterone secreted by the CL in marsupials is not its pregnancy-*maintaining* action on the uterus, but its PG-suppressing action on the ovary. The marsupial CL may function mainly as it did in the first oviparous reptiles, as a device that delayed the production of ovarian PGs and so delayed the switch-on of oviductal and uterine PGs, and thus allowed the embryo to be retained in the uterus long enough for the embryo itself to take over the control of its further stay there (Renfree and Tyndale-Biscoe, 1973). To come back to the point I started with: the essential difference between marsupial and eutherian viviparity is in the duration of intrauterine gestation; regardless of whether the marsupial embryo controls its intrauterine stay through the secretion of progesterone by its placenta (Bradshaw *et al.*, 1975) or by other means, one of the essential changes that prolonged intrauterine gestation in the eutheria was the evolution of responsiveness of the uterus to the progesterone secreted by the CL, which reached the uterus through the circulation.

It would be logical to expect, from a familiarity with eutherian viviparity, that a prolonged luteal phase would not only be a necessary, but a sufficient, condition for the transition from marsupial to eutherian viviparity. The peculiarity of the bandicoot's CL and its relation to pregnancy, in comparison with the general relation between the CL and pregnancy in marsupials, tell us very clearly that this transition was the result of more than *just* the prolongation of the luteal phase. The change that accompanied the prolongation of CL activity and that made the transition possible must have been one that prolonged the stay of the embryo in the uterus, i.e., a change in the responsiveness of the *uterus* to progesterone.

The bandicoot seems to have crossed the metatherian–eutherian line with the change that prolonged its CL's life span, but retained the marsupial form of viviparity, because its uterus has not undergone the change that would make it respond to progesterone. The relation between the CL and pregnancy in the bandicoot tempts me to suggest the heretical idea that the first eutherian descended from a bandicoot-like *marsupial* ancestor, rather than from a pantothere ancestor common to both marsupials and eutherians, as is generally believed (Romer, 1966; Lillegraven *et al.*, 1979). Regardless of its parentage, however, the ancestor of the eutherian mammals must very probably have been the first of the primitive mammals to evolve *both* a long-lived CL and a uterus that could respond to progesterone in a way that prolonged the embryo's stay within it. By prolonging the duration of gestation these changes made the further steps toward eutherian viviparity possible, since they provided conditions for the evolution of trophoblast far beyond where it could go among the marsupials (see Taylor and Padykula, 1978; and Lillegraven, 1979), and this in turn made the enormously diverse forms of eutherian viviparity possible.[3] The very first step, in any case, was the prolongation of the CL's life span, and I believe it occurred as it probably did in the bandicoot, by the appearance of responsiveness to the luteotrophic effects of prolactin.

B. THE EVOLUTION OF THE EUTHERIAN CL

1. The Pivotal Role of Prolactin

There are several intuitive reasons for speculating that responsiveness to prolactin's luteotrophic action was the *first* change that led to the evolution of the eutherian CL. Its luteotrophic effects prolong rather than raise the rate of progesterone secretion. Since the pantotheres depended on lactation to complete embryogenesis, prolactin secretion must have begun to rise soon after ovulation, and have reached a fairly high level by about the time of the plateau phase of the CL's life cycle, so it would have been more readily available than, for example, a hormone like LH, which

[3] Regardless of whether eutherian viviparity had no or a great selective advantage over metatherian viviparity (see Lillegraven, 1975, 1979, Parker, 1977, and Kirsch, 1977, for examples of arguments pro and con) the fact is that it did evolve, through its own momentum, I suspect, if indeed it had no selective advantage over the metatherian type.

would be secreted only at basal levels between each ovulation. Prolactin is also an extremely versatile hormone (Nicoll and Bern, 1972; Nicoll, 1980) with effects throughout the vertebrates that seem to be more related to postovulatory than to preovulatory aspects of reproduction (Riddle, 1963).

It has luteotrophic effects which, as has been noted earlier (Rothchild, 1966; Short, 1967), are more widely distributed than only among the species with ultra-short-lived CL. It is an essential luteotrophin not only in the latter, but probably also for the prolonged luteal phase of monestrous breeders. It also has luteotrophic effects in several polyestrous breeders with short-lived CL (Table VI). In most or all of the latter it is not an essential luteotrophin, but the absence of essentiality is probably a late stage in the evolution of the polyestrous eutherian CL (p. 246) and in at least one of these species, the sheep, the need for it during the period of early pregnancy has persisted (Denamur *et al.*, 1973; Kann and Denamur, 1974).

One of the peculiar things about the luteotrophic action of prolactin is that in the rat, in which it is an essential luteotrophin, it has very little dose-related effect *in vitro* (Crisp, 1977; Wu and Wiest, 1978; Shiota and Wiest, 1979), while in the goat (Mohini *et al.*, 1980) and pig (Hammond *et al.*, 1980) in which it is not apparently essential [except possibly in mid to late pregnancy in the pig (du Mesnil du Buisson, 1973)], there is clear evidence of a dose-related stimulatory effect over a wide range of doses *in vitro*. Crisp (1977), for example, found that in luteinized rat granulosa cells in tissue culture, 0.10 μg of prolactin increased progesterone production more than did 0.01 μg, but 1.0 μg was no more effective than 0.10 μg. Wu and Wiest (1978) and Shiota and Wiest (1979) studied perifused rat CL cells and found that the major effect of prolactin was to preserve the cell's ability to produce progesterone at a low rate and to respond to the stimulating effect of LH on progesterone production. In human luteinized granulosa cells in tissue culture prolactin even had a dose-related inhibiting effect on progesterone production (McNatty *et al.*, 1974), although neutralization of the prolactin in the tissue culture medium reduced progesterone production (Table VI). In spite of the dose-related effect on pig and goat CL *in vitro*, prolactin has, in general, no effect at all on progesterone secretion by CL *in vitro* under conditions in which LH would have a clear dose-related stimulatory effect (Rothchild, 1966).

In vivo also one may see only a slight (Everett, 1944; Lam and Rothchild, 1977) or no (Yoshinaga *et al.*, 1967) indication of a dose-related effect on progesterone secretion; its action seems to be primarily all-or-none although there may be a dose-related effect on the duration of progesterone secretion (Malven *et al.*, 1967; Macdonald *et al.*, 1971).

TABLE VI
Various Direct and Indirect Indications of the Luteotrophic Action of Prolactin in Species Other Than the Rat

Species	Type of effect or relation to CL function	Reference
Mink	PRL induces active phase of P secretion; 2-Br-α-ergocryptine prevents appearance of active ph.	Papke *et al.* (1980)
Ferret	Stalk section does not interrupt luteal ph.	Donovan (1963)
	PRL treatment maintains P secretion after hypophysectomy	Murphy (1979)
Bandicoot	Only marsupial known with CL that secretes progesterone during lactation	Gemmell (1981)
Cow	Stalk section does not prevent maintenance of CL	Henricks *et al.* (1969)
	CL in whole organ perfusion increased progesterone production in presence of PRL	Bartosik *et al.* (1967)
Sheep	Stalk section compatible with maintenance of CL, in hysterectomized sheep, beyond normal luteal ph.; hypophysectomy is not	Denamur *et al.* (1973); Kann and Denamur (1974)
	PRL plus LH (neither alone) maintain CL after hypophysectomy and hysterectomy	Kann and Denamur (1974)
	PRL decreased luteolytic effect PGF	Chamley *et al.* (1973)
	LH alone did not maintain CL after complete hypophysectomy, and only in presence of PRL after incomplete hypophysectomy	Schroff *et al.* (1971)
	PRL increased progesterone release after hypophysectomy in mid luteal ph.	Hixon and Clegg (1969)
Pig	Stalk section on day 70 of luteal ph. of hysterectomized pigs did not prevent maintenance of CL; PRL treatment after hypophysectomy on day 70 maintained CL × 10 days	du Mesnil du Buisson (1966, 1973)
	PRL increased P production by GC luteinized in tissue culture	Hammond *et al.* (1980)
	Pituitary autotransplanted to kidney may have maintained CL longer than after hypophysectomy	Kraeling (1970)
Goat	PRL increased P production by CL cells *in vitro*	Mohini *et al.* (1980)
Rabbit	PRL in presence of estrogen or FSH increased P production	Spies *et al.* (1968b); Hilliard *et al.* (1968)
Human[a]	2-Br-α-ergocryptine decreased P levels in cyclic women	Schulz *et al.* (1976, 1978)
	Antiserum to PRL decreased P production by luteinized GC in tissue culture	McNatty *et al.* (1974)

(*Continued*)

TABLE VI (*Continued*)

Species	Type of effect or relation to CL function	Reference
Monkey	P/circ. higher in lactating than nonlactating postpartum monkeys	Weiss *et al.* (1973)
	Evidence for 1′ trophic effect summarized	Walsh *et al.* (1977)
	Bromocryptine + estrogen treatment induced luteolysis in cyclic monkeys	Castracane and Shaikh (1980)
	PRL treatment of postpartum monkeys increased P/circ.	Maneckjee *et al.* (1977)
	TRH treatment during luteal ph. increased P/circ.	Hagino and Kayama (1979)
Guinea pig	CL grow and secrete P after stalk section; PRL maintains CL growth after hypophysectomy	Illingworth and Perry (1971)
Dog	Treatment with 2-Br-α-ergocryptine in mid- to late luteal ph. depressed P secretion	Conconnon (see discussion)

[a] The human CL's response to prolactin is peculiar, because other evidence indicates that exposure to high levels of prolactin may depress progesterone secretion.

A variety of other CL-related effects of prolactin (Table VII), taken together with these, suggest that it is a *permissive* luteotrophin; that is, it permits the CL to secrete progesterone at a rate determined either by its intrinsic ability, or by whatever extrinsic luteotrophin it may have become sensitive to. This permissive action [which is implied in my earlier characterization of its effect as one that depresses the "activity of the enzymes that convert progesterone to androgens and estrogens" (Rothchild, 1965, p. 283), as well as in Lindner's (1979) description of it as an "inhibitory" hormone, and of Armstrong's (1969) and Raj and Moudgal's (1970) view of its principal action as that of depressing the activity of 20α-OHSDH] may include protection of the CL against the luteolytic action of PGs (Table VII), or reduction in intraluteal PG production directly (a theoretical possibility) or through the maintenance of an optimal intraluteal progesterone concentration (Table VII). Blunting of PG induced luteolysis, however, may not be the only way its permissive (or other?) effects work. For example, we have recently found that indomethacin treatment does not prevent 2-Br-α-ergocryptine-induced luteolysis in hysterectomized pseudopregnant rats (Sanchez-Criado and Rothchild, 1981). This implies that (in the rat, at least) one of the steps in the biosynthetic pathway may have become completely dependent on prolactin, and will not proceed in its absence, even when PG synthesis is inhibited.

The idea that part of the luteotrophic effect of prolactin may be due to an ability to suppress PG production may seem to disagree with evidence that prolactin stimulates PG production in the mammary gland (Rillema,

TABLE VII

Some Effects of Prolactin Which May Help to Explain its Luteotrophic Effect

Description of the effect	Reference
Prevents reduction of progesterone to 20-αOHP (rat)	Armstrong *et al.* (1969); Hashimoto and Wiest (1969); Lamprecht *et al.* (1969)
Prevents 5α-reduction of progesterone (rat)	Armstrong *et al.* (1975); Dorrington (1977); Lahav *et al.* (1977a)
Prevents 17α-hydroxylation of progesterone (rat)	D. C. Johnson (personal communication)
Increases synthesis of cholesterol (rat)	Everett (1947); Armstrong *et al.* (1969); Hashimoto and Wiest (1969); Behrman *et al.* (1971)
Prevents cholesterol accumulation (rat)	Everett (1947); Behrman *et al.* (1971); Guraya (1975)
Prevents cholesterol accumulation (rabbit)	Hilliard *et al.* (1968); Spies *et al.* (1968b)
Permits LH to increase progesterone production by CL *in vitro* (rat)	Armstrong *et al.* (1969)
Prevents $PGF_{2\alpha}$-induced luteolysis, increase in 20α-OHSDH, and loss of LH receptors (rat)	Strauss and Stambaugh (1974); Lamprecht *et al.* (1975); Grinwich *et al.* (1976); Behrman *et al.* (1978)
Reduces but does not prevent luteolytic effect $PGF_{2\alpha}$ in sheep	Chamley *et al.* (1973); Sasser *et al.* (1977)
Inhibits PMSG-, hCG-, or FSH-induced increase in PGF production by follicular GCs (rat)	Knazek *et al.* (1980)
Prevents PG-induced abortion in early pregnancy (rat)	Chatterjee (1973, 1976); Saksena and Lau (1978)
Prevents luteolytic effect of PMSG treatment (rat)	Hixon and Armstrong (1974)
Prevents luteolytic effect of LH (hamster)	Choudhary and Greenwald (1968)
Prevents luteolytic effect of LH (rat)	Krey and Everett (1973); Krey *et al.* (1973); Day and Birnbaumer (1980)
Prevents release of cathepsin D but increases amount bound to lysosome membranes (rat)[a]	Lahav *et al.* (1977b)
Prevents estrogen-induced luteolysis (rat)	Gibori and Keyes (1980)
Prevents estrogen production by luteinized GC in tissue culture (rat)	Crisp (1977)

[a] Effect may be mediated by progesterone.

1980) and possibly the mesentery (Horrobin, 1978). Even if such findings are confirmed, the fact that PGs induce luteolysis in rats, in which prolactin is very clearly an essential luteotrophin, the basic question is: what prevents prolactin from stimulating PG production in the *CL*? I can offer only the speculation that it is the very high concentration of progesterone in the CL that does this, and that probably also transforms the effect of prolactin on PG production into an inhibiting one either on production or effect or both. The fact that prolactin *has* a luteolytic effect in the rat, but only on CL that cannot secrete progesterone (Desclin, 1949; Malven, 1969; Wuttke and Meites, 1971; Grandison and Meites, 1972; Lam and Rothchild, 1973) tends to support this supposition. If this is so, the action of prolactin on intraluteal PGs also differs from that of LH, because the latter can stimulate PG production in CL that are actively secreting progesterone (p. 240).

The First Eutherian CL Was a Long-Lived CL. Regardless of exactly how prolactin acts on the CL, it seems in general to protect the CL's ability to make progesterone, and thus slows down the rate of regression of progesterone secretion. When responsiveness to this action first appeared, therefore, it provided the progesterone that would be needed for a long intrauterine gestation. The accompanying change that made such a long gestation possible—uterine responsiveness to this progesterone—probably evolved very slowly, with the resulting increases in gestation length taking place in small steps; the tantalizing finding of a fossil *eutherian* with a pelvic girdle that seems to have articulated with marsupial epipubic bones (Kielan-Jaworowska, 1975) would support this interpretation. As intrauterine gestation increased in duration, it in turn provided conditions that facilitated the evolution of the trophoblast. But this could not have happened, as I have tried to show in the preceding discussion, without the prolongation of progesterone secretion, and the acquisition by the uterus of responsiveness to progesterone. The third change (possibly part of the latter one) that made a prolonged intrauterine gestation possible was one that protected the embryo against immunologic rejection by the mother. Evidence and arguments for the importance of trophoblast in this change are impressive (Lillegraven, 1975, 1979; Amoroso and Perry, 1975; Amoroso, 1979; Heap *et al.*, 1979; Beer and Billingham, 1979); I add only the essential point that the changes in progesterone secretion and in uterine responsiveness to progesterone must have occurred first and so must have set up the conditions that made the evolution of the highly developed trophoblastic placenta possible. The possible immunosuppressive effects of progesterone (e.g., Siiteri *et al.*, 1977; Beer and Billingham, 1979; Kincl and Ciacco, 1980), the ability of progesterone to also suppress PGs, the role of PGs in inflammation (Espey, 1980), and the connection between immunologic rejection and inflammation (Beer and Billingham, 1976) suggest that perhaps one of progesterone's effects on the uterus served as a bridge toward the evolution of the trophoblastic placenta.

If indeed the first change in what was until then a completely autonomous CL was responsiveness to prolactin, the first eutherians would have tended to evolve long-lived CL. As long as these CL remained otherwise autonomous, which, in this case, means unresponsive to any of the effects of LH, their life span would have been determined primarily by how efficiently prolactin reduced the rate of regression. If the changes had begun in species that were already monestrous breeders, they would have tended to remain as such; if they began in polyestrous breeders, the lengthened luteal phase might have tended to transform them into monestrous breeders, but the potential for polyestrous breeding could have been retained, and may have been one of the factors that eventually led to the return to polyestry (see next section). In either case, the effect of prolactin would have led eventually to the evolution of a CL that secreted progesterone long enough for the embryo to complete the major part of its development within the uterus. In this evolution toward the pattern of viviparity among present day monestrous eutheria, I am assuming that if the trophoblast evolved into a hormone-secreting tissue, its hormones did not determine how long the CL secreted progesterone, and even if they raised its rate of secretion, as seems to be true, for example of the dog (Concannon *et al.*, 1977; Smith and MacDonald, 1974), the elevated levels were not essential for the maintenance of pregnancy (Concannon, 1980).

The evolution of the monestrous breeder's long-lived CL was probably facilitated by the relation of their CL to LH secretion, and to the uterus. During the course of evolution these CL probably eventually became responsive to other hormones as well as to prolactin; the most important of these was LH since it has both luteolytic and luteotrophic effects (p. 238). However, monestrous ovulation cycles are almost certainly associated with a relative deficiency of gonadotrophin secretion during the postovulatory period (e.g., Seal *et al.*, 1979) (Fig. 7), so these CL would not have been exposed, presumably, to enough LH to have shortened their life span. The dog's long luteal phase, for example, can be shortened considerably by treatment that raises the level of LH in the circulation (Jones *et al.*, 1973b). In a seasonal polyestrous breeder, as, e.g., the sheep, by contrast, the basal level of gonadotrophins in the circulation remains as high during the "anestrus" as during the breeding season (Yuthasastrakosol *et al.*, 1975; Walton *et al.*, 1977; Karsch *et al.*, 1980), and the CL formed at the last ovulation of each season, therefore, are still short-lived CL.

Various kinds of evidence indicate that the uterus does not have the luteolytic effect among the monestrous eutheria that it has in several of the polyestrous eutherian species. For example, in the dog and cat there is no connection between the uterine vein and ovarian artery of the kind the sheep has (Del Campo and Ginther, 1974) and hysterectomy of the dog, if anything, may shorten the luteal phase (Hadley, 1975). Hysterectomy has no effect on the histology and size of the CL during the luteal phase of the ferret (Deansley and Parkes, 1933; Deansley, 1967) or the European badger (Canivenc *et al.*, 1962), and it does not change the duration or pattern of progesterone secretion in the western spotted skunk

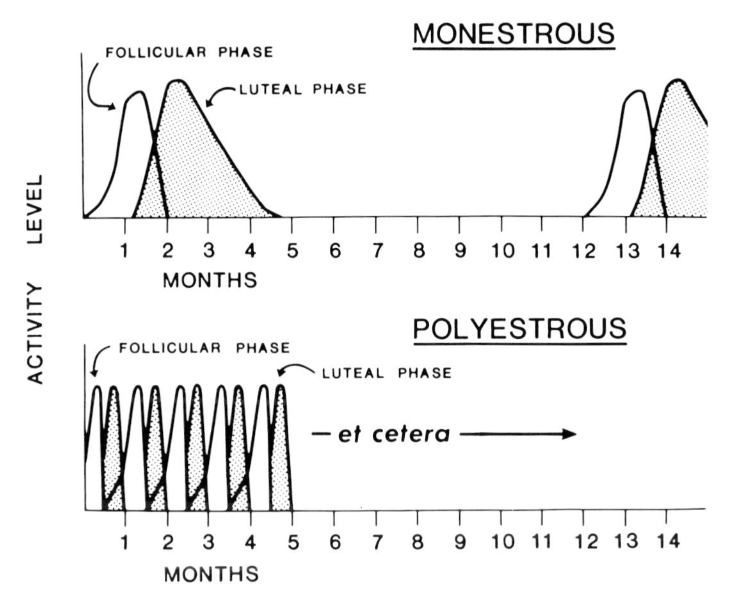

FIG. 7. Comparison of monestrous and polyestrous ovulation cycles among eutherian mammals. A major difference between the two types of ovulation cycles is in CNS control of the basal level of secretion of the gonadotrophins. Among monestrous breeders in general, seasonal and/or hereditary factors are responsible for a relatively long interval (6 months to over a year) between each period of increase in gonadotrophin secretion that leads to ovulation, and the anestrus between each ovulation is almost certainly due to a very low basal level of gonadotrophin secretion. Among polyestrous breeders, the basal level of gonadotrophin secretion remains at a higher level than in the monestrous breeders throughout the year or during the breeding season, and frequent surges (i.e., at intervals of about 2–4 weeks as a rule) of gonadotrophin secretion lead to frequent ovulations. Since LH has a luteolytic as well as a luteotrophic effect, one of the reasons for the difference between monestrous and polyestrous breeders in the length of the luteal phase is postulated to be the relative absence of LH in the monestrous breeders after each ovulation.

(Mead and Swannock, 1978). The lack of any difference in the duration of the luteal phase between the pregnant and nonpregnant dog (Smith and MacDonald, 1974; Concannon *et al.*, 1975), wolf (Seal *et al.*, 1979), mink (Canivenc *et al.*, 1966; Møller, 1973a), ferret (Carlson and Rust, 1969; Heap and Hammond, 1974; Blatchley and Donovan, 1976), roe deer (Hoffmann *et al.*, 1978), and only a small one between pregnancy and pseudopregnancy in the cat (Verhage *et al.*, 1976) also suggest that the uterus does not affect the duration of progesterone secretion in monestrous breeders. Their failure to evolve a luteolytically active uterus thus also contributed to the evolution of the long-lived CL.

Thus, the capacity for autonomous progesterone secretion, protected by the action of prolactin, the reduction of the luteolytic potential of LH, and the absence of a luteolytic uterus combined to produce a luteal phase long enough for most of intrauterine embryogenesis, and there was no selection pressure among the monestrous breeders, therefore, to evolve an endocrine placenta, or to become dependent on it for the maintenance of progesterone secretion during pregnancy. As in the marsupial, but for quite different reasons, the duration of pregnancy thus remained essentially the same as that of the luteal phase itself (Fig. 8).

2. *Polyestrous Breeding and the Evolution of the Short-Lived CL*

a. The Pivotal Role of LH. Species with short-lived CL and polyestrous breeding may have arisen directly from the polyestrous pantotheres but were more likely to have arisen from the early monestrous eutheria. The trophoblast-bearing placenta, as it slowly evolved among the latter species, almost certainly also evolved the ability to secrete hormones with luteotrophic and/or antiluteolytic properties. If this occurred among species with a tendency toward polyestrous ovulation cycles, and if they also evolved a CL which could respond to the effects of LH, the combination of these three things might have made it possible for them to return to polyestrous breeding and still retain a eutherian form of viviparity. The reasons for this are in the following discussion.

The essence of the difference between monestrous and polyestrous ovulation cycles is in the CNS control of gonadotrophin secretion. Polyestrous ovulation cycles are the result of a CNS control that induces a higher basal rate of LH and FSH secretion throughout the year than occurs in species with monestrous ovulation cycles. In the latter, the basal level of gonadotrophin secretion becomes very low soon after ovulation, and does not rise again to the equivalent of the polyestrous breeders' basal level until the next breeding period (Fig. 7). The cyclic character of gonadotrophin secretion among polyestrous breeders follows from interactions between the ovaries, pituitary, and CNS (see Karsch *et al.*, 1979, 1980, for example). The general importance of polyestry for CL function, therefore, is this: if the CL can respond to LH, its luteolytic effect (Table VIII) and the relatively high basal level of its secretion would tend to shorten the duration of the luteal phase. LH's luteolytic effect, I suspect, is probably much older in phylogeny than its luteotrophic effect. Its *primary* role in vertebrate reproduction may have been the stimulation of intrafollicular PG production, and among the reptiles and mammals it also released inhibition over the granulosa cells' ability to make progesterone. The former effect thus caused ovulation itself, and the latter the formation of the CL. It is also able to stimulate PG production in luteinized granulosa cells, however (Table VIII), and because of this, it became an important cause of luteolysis and therefore an important element in the evolution of

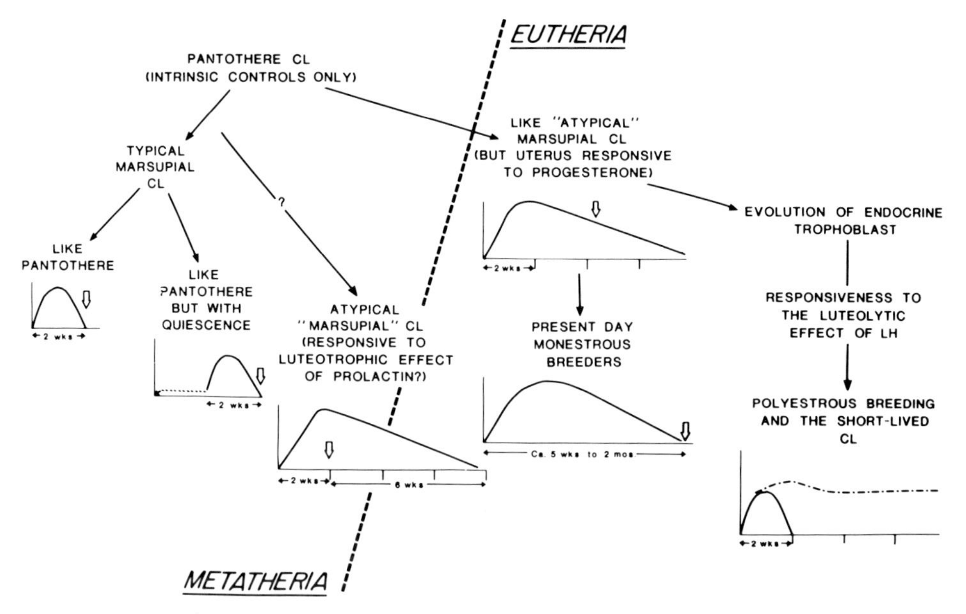

FIG. 8. The evolution of the mammalian CL in relation to the pattern of viviparity. The information in this figure continues from where Fig. 6 left off, and is intended to make the transition from metatherian (marsupial) to eutherian viviparity and CL regulation more understandable. The broken line represents the dichotomy between marsupial and eutherian viviparity. Luteal phase patterns are shown by the curves with time on the abscissa and progestereone secretion on the ordinate. The open arrows represent the time of parturition. The fine lines ending in arrows represent probable lines of descent and/or progression of change. Among the marsupials, intrauterine gestation remained very short, probably not much different from that in the pantothere ancestor; the young are always born in an extremely altrical (immature) state, even among the bandicoots (third curve from the top on the metatherian side), which have long-lived CL (Gemmell, 1981). The exact path of evolution of the bandicoot CL is unknown. The first eutherian CL (upper curve to right of the broken line) is presumed to have been like the bandicoots, and may have arisen from a pantothere ancestor (as shown), or from a bandicoot-like marsupial ancestor (not shown). Its longer life span is believed to have been the result of responsiveness to the luteotrophic effect of prolactin. As the uterus evolved responsiveness to the effect of the prolonged secretion of progesterone, the time of parturition was postponed and the duration of embryonic development increased; this led eventually to the pattern of viviparity seen in modern monestrous breeders. This progression also gave rise to the fully developed trophoblastic placenta, and with it, both the protection of the embryo against immune rejection by the mother, and the secretion of placental luteotrophic/antiluteolytic hormones. With the evolution of the endocrine placenta, therefore, polyestrous breeding, which was otherwise incompatible with a prolonged intrauterine gestation (because of the shortness of the luteal phase) became possible, since the placental hormones were secreted into the maternal bloodstream after implantation; their action on the CL prevented regression and prolonged the secretion of progesterone (lowermost curve on the right). Because of the prolonging effect of prolactin on CL activity, the return to the short luteal phase of the polyestrous ovulation cycle is believed to have occurred through the evolution of responsiveness to the luteolytic effect of LH. The appearance of responsiveness to the luteotrophic effect of LH also helped to make the short-lived CL compatible with eutherian viviparity; eventually this effect of LH predominated over the CL's capacity for autonomous progesterone secretion.

TABLE VIII

Evidence Suggesting or Showing the Luteolytic Effect of LH (or Related Hormones, such as PMSG, hCG)[a]

Species	Remarks	Reference
Stimulation of intraluteal PG production		
Rat	LH increased PGF production by CL in organ culture	Demers *et al.* (1973)
	PMSG-induced luteolysis *in vivo* inhibited by indomethacin	Basu and Chatterton (1978)
Rabbit	LH doubled PGF production by luteinized GC in tissue culture	Erickson *et al.* (1977)
Pig	LH increased PGF production by CL *in vitro*	Guthrie *et al.* (1979)
Cow	LH increased PGF production *in vitro* by late luteal ph. CL	Shemesh and Hansel (1975c)
Rat, others	LH frees arachidonic acid from cholesterol esters by activating cholesterol esterases	Kuehl (1974)
Desensitization and related effects		
Rabbit	LH (or hCG) on day 9 psp. causes luteolysis	Spies *et al.* (1967b); Kelly and Stormshak (1969); Flint *et al.* (1974); Hunzicker-Dunn and Birnbaumer (1976)
Rat	LH (or hCG) after day 6 causes luteolysis in PMSG-hCG treated immat.	Catt *et al.* (1979)
Other effects		
Monkey	In presence of LH, PGs had only a luteolytic effect on luteinized GC in tissue culture	Channing (1972)
Rat	LH treatment of hypophysectomized pituitary transplanted or PRL-injected rat reduced duration of P secretion	Rothchild (1965); Macdonald *et al.* (1970)
	LH treatment [like PGF (Lamprecht *et al.*, 1975)] increased 20α-OHSDH activity in CL	Hashimoto and Wiest (1969); Rodway and Kuhn (1975)
	LH decreased 3β-OHSDH activity in CL	Lawrence *et al.* (1978)
Sheep	LH treatment on day 12 o.c. increased estrogen production[b]	Baird *et al.* (1976)
Hamster	LH causes rapid luteolysis of o.c. CL	Choudhary and Greenwald (1968)
Dog	Inverse relation between plasma LH levels and duration of P secretion	Jones *et al.* (1973b)
Rabbit	Estrogens prolong CL activity after hypophysectomy but not in intacts; LH prevents prolonging effect of estrogens in hypophysectomized rabbits	Spies *et al.* (1968a)

[a] See also Rothchild (1965, p. 277).

[b] Estrogens are luteolytic in sheep during late luteal phase (Horton and Poyser, 1976; Kann and Denamur, 1974).

eutherian polyestry and the short-lived CL. The selective advantage of the luteolytic effect of LH was that in cycles in which ovulation was not followed by conception, it helped to keep the luteal phase short, and since progesterone inhibits ovulation (Rothchild, 1965), this kept the interval to the next ovulation no loner than the length of such a luteal phase plus whatever time was needed for the completion of follicular growth.

This speculation does not mean that the luteolytic action of LH in modern polyestrous eutheria is the *only* factor responsible for initiating regression of the CL. During the course of evolution, other factors, in addition to or in place of LH, became incorporated into the luteolytic component of the basis for polyestrous breeding among some of the modern eutheria, but I think that in the *early* eutheria, prolactin had blunted the effectiveness of the intrinsic process, and responsiveness to the luteolytic effect of LH, therefore, was probably the change that had the greatest chance of succeeding as a counterbalance to its effect; it thus served as the first step in the evolution of other luteolytic mechanisms.

Polyestrous breeding, because it was inseparable from the short-lived CL, was also incompatible with eutherian viviparity except under the condition that the embryo's trophoblast hormones could prevent at least the luteolytic effect of LH and thus delay the onset of regression of the CL. My speculations to this point suggest that the sequence of evolutionary changes that allowed this to happen was as follows. The responsiveness of the pantothere CL to prolactin led to the evolution of the long-lived CL. This, among other things, made the evolution of the trophoblast placenta possible, and eventually, also, the evolution of luteotrophic/antiluteolytic hormone secretion by the trophoblast. When responsiveness to the luteolytic effect of LH then appeared in the CL of these eutheria, it made *both* the return to polyestry and eutherian viviparity possible, because the secretion of hormones by the trophoblast had evolved *before* responsiveness of the CL to the luteolytic effect of LH.

Successful reproduction in the early polyestrous eutheria thus came to depend crucially on the hormones secreted by the trophoblast, but the efficacy of these hormones must obviously also have hinged on the CL's ability to remain responsive to them until they were secreted into the bloodstream. This interval would have been determined by the time it took for the zygote to reach the uterus and implant there, and, in general, it could not have been much less than 1 week from ovulation; more than this would probably have been required for the amount of trophoblast hormone in the circulation to reach a level of dependable effectiveness. The early polyestrous eutheria, therefore, must have also possessed mechanisms that could prolong the plateau phase of the CL's life cycle at least enough for the CL to remain responsive to the trophoblast hormones when these finally reached it.

The blunting action of prolactin on both the luteolytic effect of LH and the intrinsic luteolytic process must have been one of these mechanisms; it was probably not until much later, as other control systems evolved, that the CL of some species lost their original dependency on it. Another change which eventually became a prominent element of the luteotrophic process among the polyestrous eutheria, occurred, I suspect, around the time these changes were taking place. This was the appearance of responsiveness to the *luteotrophic* effect of LH.[4]

The many ways by which LH facilitates progesterone secretion by the CL (see Rothchild, 1965; Armstrong, 1968; Savard, 1973; Dorrington, 1977; Channing and Tsafriri, 1977; Birnbaumer *et al.*, 1979, for reviews) make it fairly clear that LH acts quite differently from prolactin. Even though it seems to act permissively in some conditions (Table II), its action *in vitro* on the CL of so many species is so clearly dose-related, while that of prolactin, as already noted, is not, that it is best characterized, as far as its general luteotrophic effects are concerned, as a *stimulatory* luteotrophin. It probably works simply by raising the rate of progesterone production (see, e.g., Armstrong, 1968), while prolactin, by contrast, presumably has no direct effect on the rate, but simply protects the process of production from interference, and so allows it to continue. Neither, according to the theory, changes the basic nature of the process itself.

The two effects, in fact, probably account for most of the examples of synergism between prolaction and LH shown in Table VI. The action of LH is not synonymous or even compatible with a prolonged luteotrophic effect, but even a short one, if it increased the rate of progesterone secretion, would be valuable in postponing the onset of regression, because of the suppressing effect of progesterone on intraluteal PG production. This effect, therefore, helped to ensure survival of the CL during the interval before the trophoblast hormones reached it.

Thus, the first polyestrous eutheria started out with a CL, which, in addition to the intrinsic controls inherited from the pantothere ancestor, had become responsive to three things that could affect those controls: prolactin's protective action on, and the stimulating effect of LH on the rate of progesterone secretion; and the facilitating action of LH on intra-

[4] It is worth noting at this point, that, if the dog and ferret are typical, the long-lived CL of monestrous breeders never became crucially dependent on LH as a luteotrophin, although the CL may respond to it (Concannon, 1980); in the dog, treatment with LHAS even late in the luteal phase does not stop progesterone secretion (P. W. Concannon, personal communication), and in the ferret, prolactin alone will maintain the CL after hypophysectomy (Murphy, 1979) (see also the discussion of the relation between the need for LH and the luteolytic effect of LH, in the rat, p. 256).

luteal PG production. Combined, these effects resulted in a luteal phase of about 2 weeks, long enough for the zygote to reach the uterus, implant, and secrete its hormones into the mother's bloodstream, yet short enough for the animal to enjoy the selective advantage of polyestrous breeding.

Through a long evolutionary digression,[5] the polyestrous eutheria thus ended up with a CL which had a life span, determined by the balance between intrinsic and extrinsic controls, not much different from that of their pantothere ancestors or marsupial cousins, whose CL had a life span determined almost entirely by intrinsic controls. The digression, however, had permitted the evolution of the endocrine placenta. The short luteal phase, therefore, no longer put a limit, as it did in the marsupials, on the ways in which intrauterine viviparity could be practiced.

Responsiveness to the luteotrophic effect of LH, I would guess, was probably of the greatest importance in the balance between the forces promoting progesterone secretion and those promoting PG production within the CL, and eutherian viviparity among polyestrous breeders owed a significant part of its success as a way of reproduction to this effect. It thus became fixed in the genome of the polyestrous eutheria. LH seems to have the characteristics of a universal luteotrophin, not because it really is one, but because we have been more aware of sheep, pigs, cows, guinea pigs, people, than we have been of kangaroos and brush-tailed possums, or of minks, skunks, ferrets, dogs, and other such mammals, in which it is probably not an essential luteotrophin.

b. How the CL of Modern Polyestrous Eutheria Came to Differ in the Extrinsic Factors That Regulate Their Activity. Most of these differences probably arose as the result of the spreading apart of certain traits, once common to all, through the process of selection. The most important of these probably were: the relation between the critical intraluteal progesterone concentration and the switch-on of the increase in intraluteal PG production; the responsivity to the luteolytic effect of LH; and the balance between autonomous progesterone secretion and a dependency on the luteotrophic actions of LH and prolactin. Selection could have led, eventually, to species which differed enough from each other in each of

[5] It is, of course, theoretically possible that the short-lived CL of the polyestrous eutheria could have arisen directly from the pantothere CL. However, since the latter was presumably entirely autonomous to start with, such a transition could have been associated with eutherian viviparity only if it occurred simultaneously with the appearance of responsiveness of the CL to pituitary and trophoblastic luteotrophins, of hormone secretion by the trophoblast, of the ability of trophoblast to protect the embryo against immune rejection by the mother, and of responsiveness of the uterus to the progesterone secreted by the CL. It is more *probable*, therefore, that these changes occurred sequentially, as I have suggested above, than simultaneously.

these traits to account for most if not all of the diversity we see today in the regulation of the CL. For example, at one extreme might be species like the rat, in which responsivity to the luteolytic effect of LH increased so far above the norm, while the level at which the intraluteal progesterone concentration switched on the increase in PG production decreased so far below the norm, that these changes become responsible for the evolution of the ultra-short luteal phase (discussed in detail in the next section).

At the other extreme, selection could have led to species with CL so insensitive to the luteolytic effect of LH that the switch-on of intraluteal PG production would again have come to depend entirely on the intrinsic controlling factors, as in their pantothere ancestors. In these species, however, prolactin was now presumably also controlling progesterone secretion, and its action would have reduced the effectiveness of the intrinsic controls, and so would have prolonged the regression phase of the CL life cycle. Such species (perhaps the roe deer is an example) might, therefore, have returned to a long luteal phase, similar to that of the monestrous breeders. Most, however, probably remained polyestrous because of the evolution of a connection between the venous drainage of the uterus and the arterial circulation to the ovary (Ginther, 1974). In these species, the uterine PGs acted in place of LH as the agent that switched on intraluteal PG production or may even have supplanted the latter, in the process that kept the CL short-lived. The view that species evolved intraluteal PG production as a compensatory trait, arising from the lack of such a uterus-related mechanism of luteolysis induction, is probably the exact opposite of what actually happened, an interpretation already hinted at by Patek and Watson (1976).

Among all the eutheria, at least two, possibly three things, in addition to the intrinsic controls themselves (as in the theory), seem to have evolved, that lead to the switch-on of intraluteal PGs, and that affect the rate of the regression phase. These were LH, the uterine PGs, and possibly estrogens (either intraluteal or follicular). Examples of the relative importance of the intrinsic controls, LH, and the uterine PGs can be seen by comparing their effects in the rat, and by comparing the rat with the guinea pig and the dog (Figs. 9 and 10). In the dog, intrinsic controls alone seem to be responsible for the switch-on of luteal PGs but since the CL's secretion of progesterone is maintained by an extrinsic luteotrophic stimulus (probably prolactin), regression is a slow, long drawn-out process (Figs. 9 and 10A). In the guinea pig (as a representative of species like the sheep, pig, cow) the action of the uterine PGs, either alone or with the switched-on intrinsic PGs, induces the rapid rate of regression typical of the short-lived CL (Fig. 9); in their absence, as after hysterectomy, the rate of regression

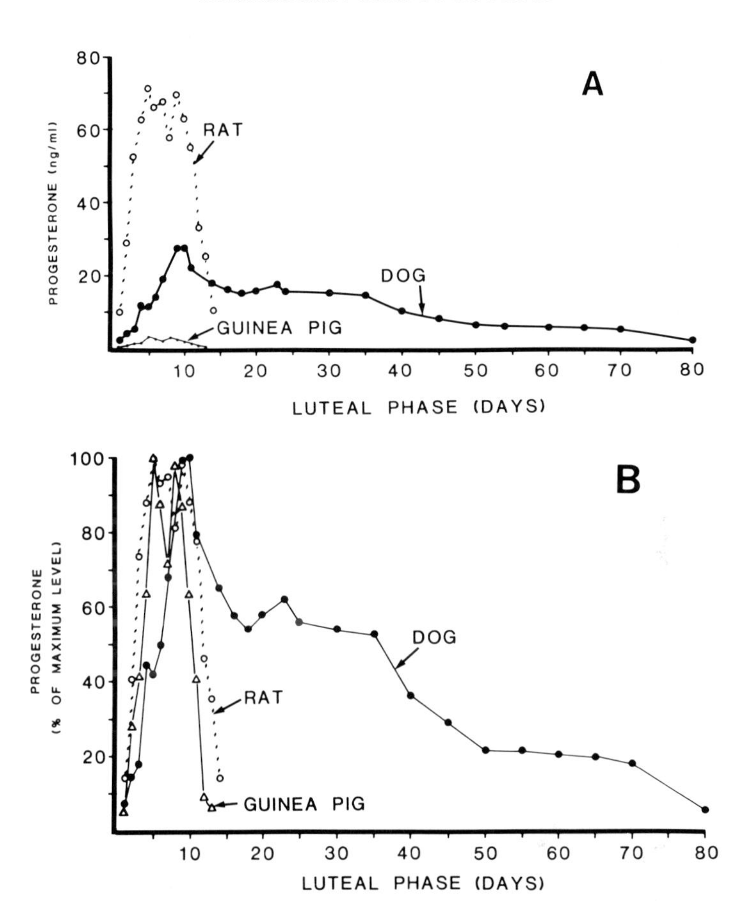

FIG. 9. A comparison of the pattern of progesterone secretion in three mammals. (A) The short luteal phase of the guinea pig and of the pseudopregnant rat, and the long luteal phase of the nonpregnant dog, are compared, in terms of actual levels of progesterone in peripheral serum or plasma. (B) The same values are expressed as the percentage of the maximum value. (Rat data are from Pepe and Rothchild, 1974; guinea pig data are from Blatchley *et al.*, 1976; dog data are from Smith and MacDonald, 1974.)

would be determined only by the intrinsic process, and, as in the dog, therefore, regression is a very slow, long drawn-out process (Fig. 10A). In the rat, LH, the uterine PGs, and the intrinsic controls seem to be involved (Figs. 9 and 10B). In the human, estrogens and intrinsic controls may have come to have the same importance that LH, the uterine PGs, and the intrinsic controls have in the rat.

In the evolution of changes in the balance between the capacity for autonomous progesterone secretion and a dependency on the luteotrophic

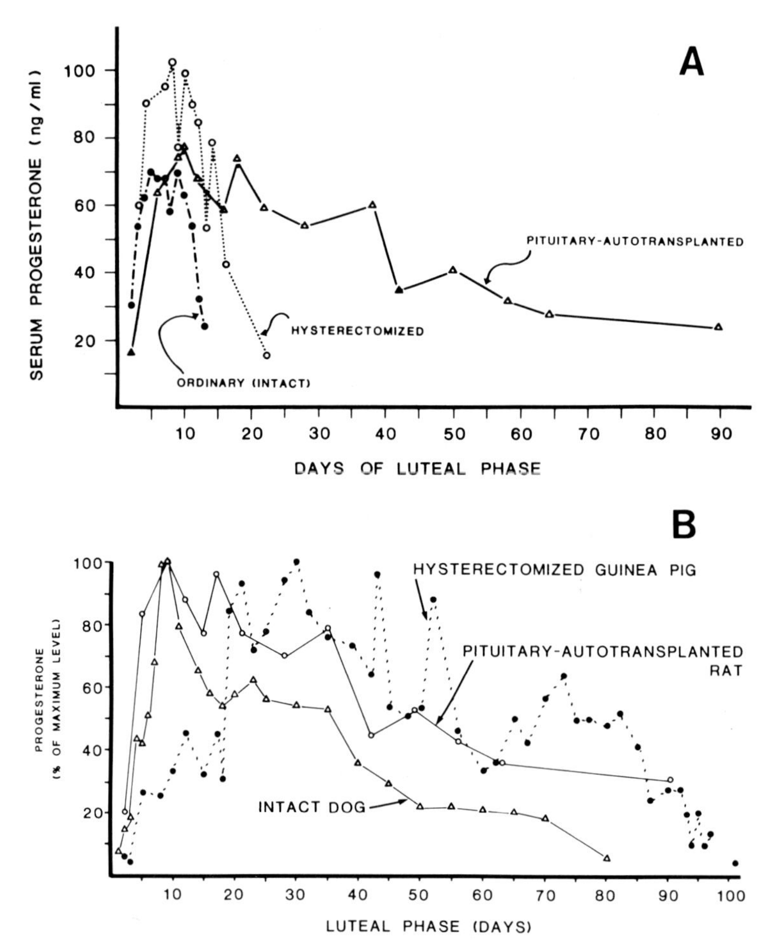

FIG. 10. The factors affecting the duration of the CL's life span in the nonpregnant animal. (A) The ordinary (intact) pseudopregnant rat, compared with the hysterectomized pseudopregnant rat, and with the hypophysectomized pituitary-autotransplanted rat. (B) The hysterectomized guinea pig compared with the pituitary-autotransplanted rat and the intact dog (continuation of Fig. 9, with the values expressed as percentage of maximum). The two figures illustrate the principle that regression is inevitable because of the action of intrinsically produced PGs, but that the rate of regression can depend on how rapidly the CL produces PGs, and on the presence of an extrinsic source of PGs. In the intact rat (A), three sources of PGs affect the CL: those produced intrinsically, those produced in response to LH, and those produced in the uterus. Regression is thus rapid. In the hysterectomized rat the rate of regression is reduced because the uterine PGs are absent. In the pituitary-autotransplanted rat almost no LH is secreted, and the uterus, subjected only to the action of progesterone, produces almost no PGs; thus regression is very slow under the influence of only the intrinsically produced PGs. In the intact dog (B), neither the uterus nor LH seems to be involved in the regression of the CL, and a similar slow regression occurs. In the hysterectomized guinea pig (B), the absence of the uterine PGs presumably also leaves only the intrinsically produced PGs as the cause of regression. Hysterectomized guinea pig data from Horton and Poyser (1976); pituitary-autotransplanted rat data from Ochiai *et al.* (1981).

effects of prolactin and LH, at least one general trend seems to be discernible. This is a reduction in autonomy, and an increase in dependency on LH; this change seems also to have been accompanied by a reduction in or loss of dependency on the luteotrophic effect of prolactin.

Among some species, as, e.g., the pig or sheep, the capacity for autonomous progesterone secretion has remained almost as high as the CL's maximum capacity for progesterone secretion, and one sees little difference in the pattern of progesterone secretion, therefore, between an intact animal and one hypophysectomized shortly after ovulation. In others, as, e.g., the human, the capacity for autonomous progesterone secretion probably accounts for only a very small fraction of the CL's maximum capacity for progesterone secretion, but the latter can be realized through the luteotrophic action of LH. In the rat (discussed in detail in the next section) the capacity for autonomous progesterone secretion may be intermediate between these extremes, but can be expressed only through the permissive effects of prolactin; maximum capacity for progesterone secretion differs from the capacity for autonomous secretion only after about day 9 of the luteal phase, and so depends on the luteotrophic effects of LH to be realized after this time.

C. THE BASIC PRINCIPLE UNDERLYING DIVERSITY OF CL REGULATION

This is probably no different from that underlying diversity in the control of many other physiological processes. For example, the maintenance of a constant body temperature among warm-blooded vertebrates came about through a primary change in the hypothalamus which allowed it to recognize deviations from a given core temperature and to correct them by whatever means were available. The fact that all species do not use the same body processes in this regulation does not confuse us at all, because we recognize that the basic and common element in the regulation of body temperature is the organization of the hypothalamus and not the particular body process through which body heat is lost, conserved, or increased. An exactly parallel situation in the case of the CL, i.e., the use of either prolactin, or LH, or estrogens, or no extrinsic control at all, in the stimulation of progesterone secretion, by different species, confuses us because we have not understood what the basic controlling system was. The basic principle behind the diversity in CL regulation is the evolution of processes that could work through the basic system in a way that was compatible with mammalian viviparity, and particularly, eutherian viviparity. The theory describing this basic system may come close to what it actually is, and may help, perhaps, to reduce some of the confusion in our understanding of the CL. Although not *all* of the peculiarities of the CL described in the Introduction are immediately understandable with the help of this theory, one example of its usefulness is the interpretation of the ultra-short luteal phase and its peculiar relation to the development of LH dependency. This is discussed in the next section.

IV. The Ultra-Short-Lived CL and LH Dependency

The ultra-short-lived CL is the third variety of eutherian CL (Fig. 2). Its characteristics have been most thoroughly documented in the rat; I will refer to its main features and the peculiarities of its dependency on LH, using the rat as the type example. From work done on the need for LH as well as for prolactin in the hamster and mouse (Greenwald and Rothchild, 1968; Munshi *et al.,* 1973; Ford and Yoshinaga 1975d; Mukku and Moudgal, 1975; Terranova and Greenwald, 1978, 1979a,b) and on the need for prolactin in the vole (Breed and Clarke, 1970; Milligan, 1975; Charlton *et al.,* 1978) and gerbil (Rich, 1968), it is clear that the rat is fairly representative of the group.

The ovulation cycle is 4 or 5 days long; if the day of ovulation is taken as day 1, the CL is fully organized (although not yet fully grown) by day 2 (Long and Evans, 1922; Mossman and Duke, 1973; Terranova *et al.,* 1980) and the peak of progesterone secretion occurs during the night between days 2 and 3 of a 4-day cycle (Uchida *et al.,* 1970b; Butcher *et al.,* 1974; Hiroyoshi and Suzuki, 1974; Smith *et al.,* 1975; van der Schoot and de Greef, 1976; de Greef and van der Schoot, 1979; Nequin *et al.,* 1979). Between day 3 and day 4 (proestrous of a 4-day cycle) the CL stops secreting progesterone and begins a slow regression in size.

Prolactin transforms this CL into one equivalent to the short-lived CL of the other polyestrous eutheria (Rothchild, 1965; Greenwald and Rothchild, 1968; Hilliard, 1973) but responsiveness to this effect does not appear until the morning of day 3 (Döhler and Wuttke, 1974; Smith *et al.,* 1975; Day *et al.,* 1980); the CL then remain dependent on prolactin to the end of the luteal phase ("pseudopregnancy"). Not enough prolactin is secreted during the interval between ovulations to have this effect, but copulation, or an equivalent stimulus (Long and Evans, 1922), induces a large enough increase in its secretion, which occurs in the form of two large daily surges (see Table II, under "rat") to transform the CL into the short-lived type.

When the CL are 8 or 9 days old, LH dependency becomes as important as the dependency on prolactin; the need for LH persists to the end of the luteal phase in pseudopregnant rats but only until day 12 in pregnant ones (Raj and Moudgal, 1970; Morishige and Rothchild, 1974; Akaka *et al.,* 1977). The peculiar appearance of LH dependency only after the first week of the CL's life cycle may be an integral part of what accounts for the ultra-short life of the CL itself. To show this connection I will first enlarge on the main characteristics of LH dependency, so far only briefly described in the Introduction. Since a good part of the information comes from work done in our own laboratory, a description of methods and related material would be in order.

A. METHODS

The induction of luteolysis by a single injection of 0.5 ml of a horse antiserum to beef LH (LHAS) was taken as evidence for LH dependency. The antiserum is specific for LH and the dose is more than enough to neutralize the available LH in the circulation (Morishige and Rothchild, 1974). If this treatment did not induce luteolysis, we assumed that the CL were not dependent on LH. The primary indication of luteolysis was a fall in the rate of progesterone secretion [determined by the change in the peripheral serum level, since the latter reflects the change in secretion rate (Pepe and Rothchild, 1973)] within 72 hours of the LHAS injection (Fig. 11) to one too low to prevent ovulation or to maintain pregnancy or

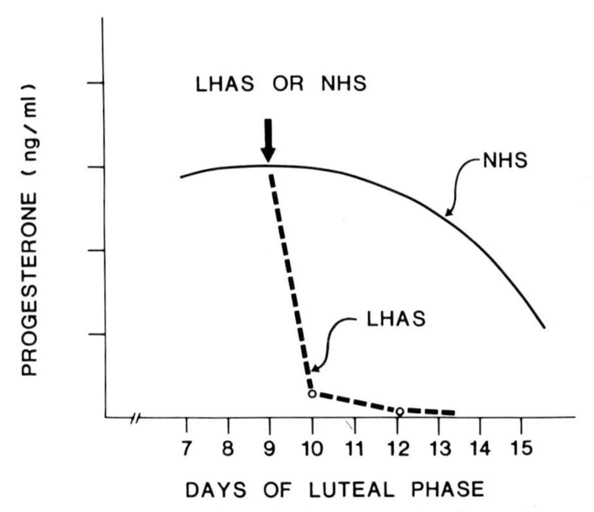

FIG. 11. The test for LH dependency in the rat. On the chosen day (e.g., day 9 in the figure), the rat is injected with either an antiserum to LH (LHAS) or with normal horse serum (NHS), and the serum progesterone level is determined from samples collected just before the injection, and 24 and 72 hours afterward. If the progesterone level falls, as shown, and is accompanied by a shortening of the vaginal diestrus, abortion, or regression of decidual tissue in the uterus (depending, of course, on the kind of rat the test is done on), the CL are judged to be LH-dependent. If the progesterone level in response to the LHAS injection is not different from that of the rats that received NHS, and if no change occurs in the length of the vaginal diestrus, etc., the CL are judged to be LH-independent.

decidual tissue (DT) growth in the uterus (Morishige and Rothchild, 1974; Rothchild *et al.*, 1974).

We also used the transplanted rat pituitary's ability to secrete prolactin (Everett, 1956; Meites *et al.*, 1972) to study prolactin's effect on LH dependency. The peripheral serum level of prolactin in a rat bearing a single pituitary transplant beneath the kidney capsule was about the same as the peak level of the two daily surges secreted by the *in situ* pituitary of the pregnant or pseudopregnant rat (Lam and Rothchild, 1977), and was fairly constant throughout the day (de Greef and Zeilmaker, 1978). In a rat bearing a pituitary transplant, therefore, the level of prolactin secretion was higher than in a pregnant or pseudopregnant rat secreting prolactin only by its *in situ* pituitary (Garris and Rothchild, 1980; Nanes *et al.*, 1980). The amount of prolactin secreted was also almost directly proportional to the number of pituitaries transplanted (Lam and Rothchild, 1977).

The role of LH in the induction of LH dependency was studied in two general ways. One was by the effects of hypophysectomy and pituitary auto- or homotransplantation. This reduces the secretion of LH markedly (e.g., see Lam and Rothchild, 1977) at the same time that it increases the secretion of prolactin. The other was by treating rats daily with LHAS for various periods of time, starting at different times in the CL's life cycle (Lam and Rothchild, 1977; Nanes and Rothchild, 1981). The effects of treatment with LH in the pituitary transplanted rat also helped to define some aspects of the action of LH.

Since almost all the information about LH dependency comes from experiments done on pseudopregnant or pregnant rats, the following background material may also be helpful. An *ordinary* pseudopregnancy lasts for about 13 days, and pregnancy for 23 days. Hysterectomy at any time on or before day 10 of pseudopregnancy prolongs pseudopregnancy to a mean duration of about 20 days; DT induction by scratching the uterus on day 5 has the same effect (Rothchild, 1965, p. 283). The pseudopregnancy of lactation also lasts for about 3 weeks, if the litter is a large one, but for about 16 days if the litter is less than 3 pups (Rothchild, 1960). Pregnancy in lactating rats lasts longer than in nonlactating rats, by an interval (about 1 week) equivalent to the delay in implantation induced by lactation (e.g., Yogev and Terkel, 1978).

B. THE MAIN CHARACTERISTICS OF LH DEPENDENCY

LH dependency probably develops primarily because of an effect of LH exerted directly on the CL (Lam and Rothchild, 1977; Nanes and Rothchild, 1981). As a result of this effect, LH dependency appears by the morning of day 8 in pregnant rats (Morishige and Rothchild, 1974) and by the next day in pseudopregnant ones (Rothchild *et al.,* 1974; Garris *et al.,* 1980). In the presence of the inducing action of LH from day 1 onward, an excess secretion of prolactin (e.g., by one or more pituitary transplants) can postpone LH dependency (Lam and Rothchild, 1977; Garris and Rothchild, 1980) but not to beyond day 12 (Nanes *et al.,* 1980), and the progestational uterus (Garris and Rothchild, 1980), especially if it contains implanting blastocysts (Morishige and Rothchild,1974), can advance the time of appearance of LH dependency, but not to before day 8 (Fig. 12). If the inducing action of LH is delayed, LH dependency is delayed (Veomett and Daniel, 1971, 1975a,b,c; Rothchild *et al.,* 1974; Ford and Yoshinaga, 1975a,b; Lam and Rothchild, 1977; Nanes and Rothchild, 1981), and if it is permanently prevented, LH dependency is also prevented (Lam and Rothchild, 1977; Ochiai *et al.,* 1981). The inducing action of LH on LH dependency is over a threshold effect by day 5; i.e., the CL will become LH-dependent by day 9 even if they are no longer exposed to LH after day 5, if they have been exposed to LH until day 5 (Lam and Rothchild, 1977; Nanes and Rothchild, 1981).

The time of appearance of LH dependency corresponds closely to the transition from the plateau to the regression phase of the CL's life cycle. This is obvious in the case of ordinary pseudopregnant rats, in which regression clearly begins about day 9 (Pepe and Rothchild, 1974); it is less

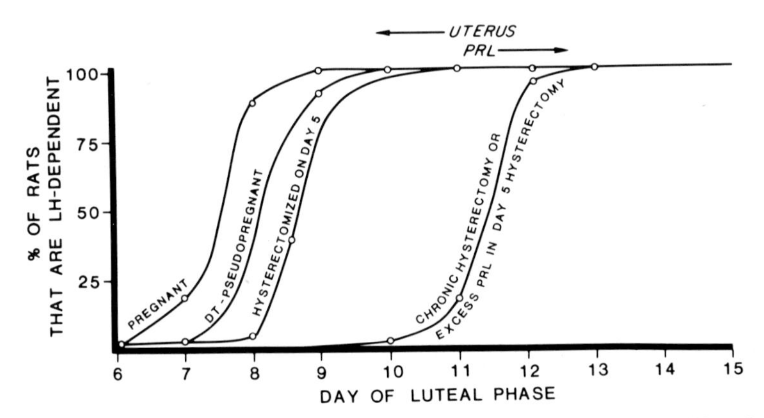

FIG. 12. The pattern of appearance of LH dependency in various types of luteal phase conditions in the rat. The values are the incidence of rats with LH-dependent CL, in relation to the days of the luteal phase. Among pregnant rats, all will have LH-dependent CL by days 8 to 9. DT-bearing pseudopregnant rats will all have LH-dependent CL by days 9 to 10, and rats hysterectomized on day 5 will all become LH-dependent about a day later. Hysterectomy before day 5, or treatment with an excess of prolactin, postpones the appearance of LH dependency to about day 12. The figure illustrates the principle that the uterus and prolactin do not affect the intensity of the need for LH but only *when* the full intensity is reached (Nanes *et al.,* 1980).

clear in the case of DT-bearing or hysterectomized rats because their regression phase lasts longer than in ordinary pseudopregnant rats (Pepe and Rothchild, 1974; de Greef *et al.*, 1976) and the transition from plateau to regression is less easy to see. LH dependency appears in pregnant rats' CL when regression *would* have started if they were not pregnant; the hormonal influence of the placenta prevents regression but does not prevent LH dependency until after day 12 (Raj and Moudgal, 1970; Morishige and Rothchild, 1974).

The mutually opposing actions of the progestational uterus and prolactin on LH dependency (Lam and Rothchild, 1977) are related to one another quantitatively (Garris and Rothchild, 1980). In the absence of an excess of prolactin, the advancing action of the uterus on LH dependency is over a threshold effect by day 5, and in the presence of an excess of prolactin, by day 8 (Garris and Rothchild, 1980) (Fig. 13). DT, or the change in the uterus associated with the DT-inducing stimulus (e.g., needle scratch of the endometrium), advances the time of appearance of LH dependency more than does the progestational uterus of the ordinary pseudopregnant rat (Rothchild *et al.*, 1974); this is a specific effect of DT,

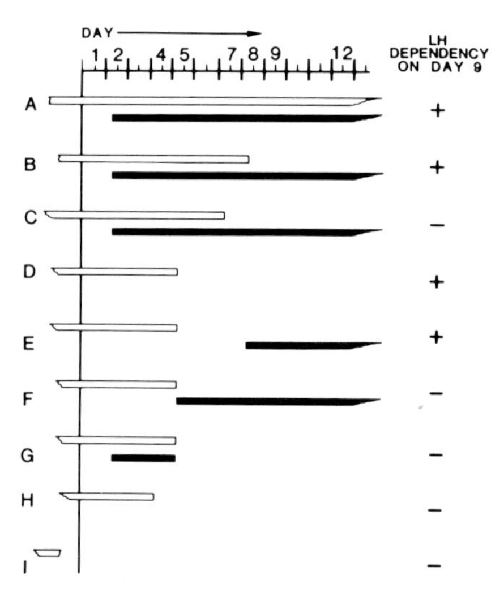

FIG. 13. The effects of prolactin and the uterus on the appearance of LH dependency by day 9 of pseudopregnancy in the rat. Solid bar: an excess of prolactin, secreted by a single pituitary homotransplant; open bar: the presence of the uterus. The figure illustrates the principle that the action of the uterus which leads to the appearance of LH dependency by day 9 is over a threshold effect earlier in the absence (D) than in the presence of an excess of prolactin (A, B, C). It also illustrates the principle that the earlier the uterus is removed, the less prolactin is needed to have a delaying effect on LH dependency (D–I). The figure is another way of looking at the same principles illustrated in Fig. 12 (from Garris and Rothchild, 1980).

and it includes a shortening of the delay in appearance of LH dependency caused by preventing the inducing effect of LH early in the CL's life cycle (Nanes and Rothchild, 1981). The actions of the uterus and prolactin do not affect the intensity of the need for LH, but only when the full intensity of this need appears (Nanes *et al.*, 1980) (Fig. 12). The action of the uterus does not seem to be essential for the appearance of LH dependency (Ford and Yoshinaga, 1975c; Garris and Rothchild, 1980; Nanes *et al.*, 1980), if the inducing effect of LH is present.

The life span of LH dependent CL is considerably shorter than that of CL which are not LH dependent (Lam and Rothchild, 1977; Takahashi *et al.*, 1978; Ochiai *et al.*, 1981), probably because of the process that induces LH dependency, rather than LH dependency itself. In spite of the crucial need for the luteotrophic action of LH, the CL cannot secrete progesterone in response to LH in the absence of prolactin or an equivalent hormone (e.g., placental hormone(s) secreted between the time of implantation and day 12) (Morishige and Rothchild, 1974). The luteotrophic effect of LH may be at least partially substituted for, during the period of LH dependency, by estrogens, either as such (Gibori *et al.*, 1977b; Gibori and Richards, 1978; Garris *et al.*, 1981), or in the form of androgens that can be converted to estrogens within the CL (Gibori *et al.*, 1978). In pseudopregnant rats the effective amount of estrogen is much less early than late in the period of LH dependency and is also much less in the absence than in the presence of the progestational uterus (Garris *et al.*, 1981).

The amount of LH bound to CL cell membranes and the affinity of LH for these membranes is the same in LH -dependent and LH-independent CL (Garris *et al.*, 1980). The signs of LH dependency, that can be brought out by treatment with LHAS, will also appear if LH secretion is prevented by hypophysectomy (Alloiteau and Bouhours, 1965; Ahmad *et al.*, 1969; Gibori and Richards, 1978), by treatment of intact rats with an antiserum to GnRH (Nishi *et al.*, 1976), or if LH secretion is reduced by increasing the intensity of the suckling stimulus [which depresses LH secretion (Hammons *et al.*, 1973; Ford and Melampy, 1973)] in lactating pregnant rats (Veomett and Daniel 1971, 1975a,b,c; Ford and Yoshinaga, 1975a,b).

C. THE RELATION BETWEEN LH DEPENDENCY AND THE ULTRA-SHORT-LIVED CL

1. The Physiology of the Ultra-Short Luteal Phase

I have previously summarized (p. 233) many of the peculiarities of prolactin's luteotrophic effect and suggested that it is best characterized as a permissive luteotrophin, its action being one that protects the CL's ability to secrete progesterone. This implies that the ultra-short-lived CL relies on prolactin, not to initiate progesterone secretion, but to maintain its ability to secrete progesterone autonomously. This in turn implies that there is an important difference between these CL and the short-lived CL of other polyestrous eutheria, as, e.g., the monkey's or the human's, which seem to depend on LH from very early on in their life cycle. Because LH acts luteotrophically by raising the rate of progesterone secretion (p. 242), the need for LH in species with short-lived CL means that the CL have lost most of their capacity for autonomous secretion of progesterone, and have come to depend on LH to secrete enough of it to satisfy the needs of reproduction. The absence of any need for the luteotrophic effect of LH in the rat during the first 8 days of the CL's life cycle, therefore, implies that, during this period at least, the CL can secrete enough progesterone autonomously for the needs of reproduction, as long as this ability is protected by prolactin. The luteal phase of these CL is ultra-short in the absence of prolactin, in other words, not because the CL cannot secrete progesterone for a long time, but because something keeps them from doing so, and their peculiar need for prolactin arises from its ability to reduce the effect of this interfering process.[6]

I think the interfering process has two parts: the ultra-short-lived CL is hypersensitive to the luteolytic effect of LH; and, it switches on PG production in response to an abnormally low critical intraluteal progesterone concentration. These changes probably evolved as intensifications of the normal traits that were part of the inheritance of the early polyestrous eutherian CL. The species survived as successful reproducers through whatever accident it was that coupled these changes with the one that suppressed prolactin secretion throughout the ovulation cycle, except after copulation [or during proestrus (Butcher *et al.*, 1974), when the CL can no longer secrete progesterone (Krey and Everett, 1973; Krey *et al.*, 1973)]. The whole complex of changes led to a highly efficient form of viviparous reproduction, among other reasons, because the ultra-short-life of the CL meant that, in the absence of a chance to copulate, only 4 or 5 days were lost, instead of about 2 weeks, before another chance for conception presented itself.

Whether the luteolytic effect of LH and the switch-on of intraluteal PGs through the critical intraluteal progesterone concentration are any different from those of the short-lived eutherian CL, except in sensitivity to these factors, is unknown. It is also unknown (as I hinted above, p. 233) whether prolactin acts on the CL to do more than suppress PG production

[6] There is a tantalizing implication of a similar idea about how prolactin acts in the rat, in an abstract by Chatterton and Greep (1965).

or the response to PGs. In any case, a few findings fit with this interpretation of the physiologic basis for the ultra-short-lived CL, even if they do not establish its validity.

When rat granulosa cells luteinize spontaneously in tissue culture, the duration of their progesterone secretion, in the absence of prolactin or other hormones added to the medium (even though the amount secreted is not very impressive), is about 4 to 6 days, instead of the 2 to 3 days of the estrous cycle *in vivo* (Crisp, 1977). If the 4-day cyclic rat is given a single injection of LHAS before the day 2 peak of progesterone secretion, this secretion, which presumably comes from the CL (de Greef and van der Schoot, 1979), continues for about another 24 hours (Sánchez-Criado and Rothchild, 1981). Although this resembles the effect of *LH* treatment on day 2 (Alloiteau and Acker, 1969; Buffler and Roser, 1971, 1974; Roser and Buffler, 1972; Boehm *et al.*, 1980) it is not the same, since the latter effect is almost certainly the result of partial luteinization of follicles (Chateau, 1969; Chateau and Aron, 1970; Buffler and Roser, 1972). Indomethacin treatment during the same part of the estrous cycle also tends to prolong progesterone secretion by about a day (Sánchez-Criado and Rothchild, 1981).

The explanation for the physiologic basis of the ultra-short-lived CL may make clear a hitherto unexplained finding of Ferin *et al.* (1969); after a single injection of an antiserum to estradiol into cyclic rats on day 2, about 50% of the rats went into a diestrus that lasted as long as an ordinary pseudopregnancy. The luteolytic effect of LH could be exerted through its role in stimulating estrogen production, since estrogens can stimulate PG release (p. 210). The inhibition of the estrogen effect by the antiserum, thus might have allowed progesterone secretion to continue long enough for it to initiate the surges of prolactin secretion, since progesterone has this effect in the rat (Alloiteau and Vignal, 1958; Everett, 1963; Rothchild and Schubert, 1963; Murakami *et al.*, 1980; see also p. 187). It is very interesting that in both Everett's (1963) study and that of Ferin *et al.* (1969), the maintenance of the long diestrus depended on isolating the rats and not taking daily vaginal smears.

The explanation also fits with prolactin's ability to prevent the luteolytic effect of the preovulatory surge of LH secretion (see Krey and Everett, 1973; Krey *et al.*, 1973; and Day and Birnbaumer, 1980, in Table VII). It also may help to clarify the finding that LH-stimulable adenyl cyclase activity in the rat's CL parallels the pattern of progesterone secretion during the ovulation cycle (Birnbaumer *et al.*, 1979), and accompanies the rise in progesterone secretion that occurs in response to prolactin during the transition to pseudopregnancy (Day *et al.*, 1980), even though the need for the *luteotrophic* action of LH will not appear until about a week later. If the luteolytic effect of LH, like its luteotrophic one, works through the adenyl cyclase-cAMP system, the ability of LH to stimulate adenyl cyclase activity at this time in the life cycle of the CL is probably an expression of its *luteolytic,* not its luteotrophic effect.

2. *The Physiologic Basis of LH Dependency*

a. The Essentiality of LH. The critical question in defining the cause of LH dependency is: *What* action of LH induces the dependency ln LH? If my explanation of the basis for the ultra-short-lived CL is correct, it becomes immediately obvious that it must be the luteolytic effect of LH which induces the latter crucial need for its luteotrophic effect. I think this comes about in the following way.

The luteolytic effect of LH probably works in all of the polyestrous eutheria by facilitating luteal PG production. In these CL, the intrinsic capacity to produce PGs has not been lost, but has come to depend on extrinsic factors such as LH and/or the uterine PGs. Essentially the same relationship between extrinsic and intrinsic control of luteal PG production probably exists in the species with ultra-short-lived CL as in the other polyestrous eutheria, except that the *normal* level of sensitivity to the effect of LH and the *normal* threshold of response to the critical intraluteal progesterone concentration depend crucially on prolactin. PG production thus begins as the luteal phase of pseudopregnancy or pregnancy begins, but at a very slow rate.

I will also suggest that, thus protected by prolactin, the rat CL's capacity for autonomous progesterone secretion is the same as its maximum capacity for progesterone secretion during all of the rising phase. LH, therefore, has no luteotrophic effect during this period because the CL are already secreting at maximum capacity; depriving the CL of LH also has no effect, since progesterone secretion is autonomous. Because of the self-stimulating quality of PG production and because progesterone potentiates this production as it suppresses it, an increase in intraluteal PG concentration is inevitable, although the rate of increase, especially during the rising phase, is slow. This is probably because progesterone suppresses PG production best only when the CL secretes it at maximum capacity.

Because PG production does increase, however, and because of the effect of the critical intraluteal progesterone concentration, a point will eventually be reached at which the PG concentration is just high enough to induce a slight decrease in the CL's capacity for autonomous progesterone secretion. At this point the plateau phase begins. It progresses because of the interplay between progesterone secretion and PG production, as described in the theory, and as it does so, the gap between the

CL's maximum capacity for progesterone secretion and its capacity for autonomous progesterone secretion widens asymptotically. The regression phase is about to begin when this gap has reached a critical value (Fig. 14).

Since LH is postulated to act luteotrophically by raising the rate of progesterone secretion, the CL probably responds to this effect as soon as the gap between maximum capacity and capacity for autonomous progesterone secretion appears, but because the gap is very small at first, the effect of LH is not noticeable until the gap has reached a critical size. At this point the CL's response to LH is a large one. It is also an essential one, for without it the CL will undergo immediate luteolysis, because the capacity for autonomous progesterone secretion has now fallen too far

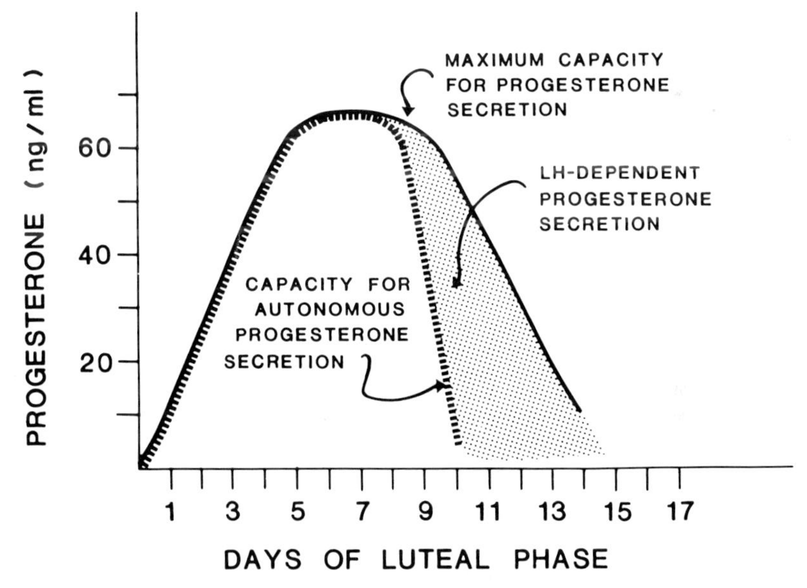

FIG. 14. A schematic representation of the hypothetical cause of LH dependency in the rat. During the rising phase, the lack of difference between the CL's capacity for autonomous progesterone secretion and its maximum capacity for progesterone secretion explains why neither LH treatment nor LH withdrawal affects progesterone secretion. Because LH is presumed to facilitate PG production by the CL, the PGs eventually lead to a fall in the capacity for autonomous progesterone secretion and, therefore, to a gap between this capacity and the CL's maximum capacity for progesterone secretion. When the gap reaches a critical value, the need for LH becomes very easy to see, since its ability to raise the rate of progesterone secretion restores progesterone secretion to the CL's maximum capacity, and in its absence, progesterone secretion falls precipitously. The luteolytic effect of LH thus induces the need for its luteotrophic effect. The latter, however, does not prevent regression, since this comes from the already switched-on PG production, but it slows down the rate of regression.

below the maximum capacity, for progesterone secretion to maintain itself. Progesterone secretion would stop almost immediately, therefore, if LH was not available to maintain it at the CL's maximum capacity (Fig. 14). The CL thus appears to have suddenly become crucially dependent on LH.

The ability to respond to the luteotrophic effect of LH, however, does not prevent the CL from regressing, but it reduces the rate of regression. The response to LH reduces this rate least of all in the ordinary pseudopregnant rat, because it is opposed by the effects of both the uterine and luteal PGs. It reduces regression more effectively in hysterectomized or DT-bearing pseudopregnant rats, because it is opposed only by the effect of the luteal PGs. In the pregnant rat, regression is even halted by the response to LH, because the response is supported by the placental hormones, and the uterine PGs do not oppose it.

Regression occurs in spite of the effect of LH, presumably, because the CL's maximum capacity for progesterone secretion has been under constant attrition from the effect of PGs, and at the point where LH dependency appears, PG production itself has progressed to where its continued increase cannot be prevented, but can only be kept from becomming a rapid increase by the combined effects of progesterone, and of prolactin. The PGs thus progressively reduce the CL's maximum capacity for progesterone secretion, until this secretion stops altogether. Preliminary findings in our laboratory fit with this, since the luteolytic effect of LHAS treatment of hysterectomized pseudopregnant rats, on day 10, can be prevented by indomethacin treatment (Sánchez-Criado and Rothchild, 1981).

Some of the other aspects of the effects of LH, in relation to LH dependency, become clearer with the help of this explanation. Thus, in the virtual absence of LH, as in the rat hypophysectomized and pituitary transplanted on day 2, the luteolytic effect of LH is also absent, and the need for its luteotrophic effect never appears (Lam and Rothchild, 1977; Macdonald, 1978; Ochiai *et al.*, 1981). If LH secretion is reduced, as in lactation (Ford and Melampy, 1973; Hammons *et al.*, 1973), or postponed, as in rats treated with LHAS daily from days 2 to 5 (Lam and Rothchild, 1977; Nanes and Rothchild, 1981) or longer (Lam and Rothchild, 1977), the dependency on LH also appears later than it would otherwise. Similarly, the shorter life span of LH-dependent than LH-independent CL can be seen to be the result of the differences between them, most probably in the rate of PG production rather than in the need for LH. Luteal PG production probably goes on in the LH-independent CL also, but at such a slow rate that the CL's capacity for progesterone secretion never falls below its maximum capacity, and the regression phase, therefore, is greatly prolonged (Fig. 10).

It is also probable that when rat CL, which *in vivo* do not respond to LH and do not stop secreting progesterone when deprived of LH, are placed *in vitro,* the *in vitro* conditions themselves induce a difference between their maximum and their actual capacity for progesterone production; LH, therefore, by raising progesterone secretion to the cell's maximum capacity, now appears to have a dose-related luteotrophic effect (e.g., Shiota and Wiest, 1979; Rodway and Rothchild, 1977; Strauss and Flickinger, 1977).

This explanation for the role of LH in LH dependency, incidentally, also helps to resolve the puzzle of why LH treatment, in spite of its luteolytic effect in hypophysectomized, pituitary transplanted, or equivalent rats (Rothchild, 1965; Macdonald *et al.,* 1970; Takahashi *et al.,* 1978; Ochiai *et al.,* 1981), cannot shorten the duration of the luteal phase to less than that of an ordinary pseudopregnancy. It is because the balance between the CL's capacities for progesterone secretion and for PG production is such that the change from high progesterone/low PG to high PG/low progesterone, which leads to regression, never takes less than this amount of time, even in the presence of an optimal amount of LH. This, in turn, is because LH has two effects. Treatment with a luteolytic PG like $PGF_{2\alpha}$, however, by throwing the balance toward high PG/low progesterone after the plateau phase has begun, *can* shorten the duration of the luteal phase (Behrman, 1979). LH treatment may prevent this effect of PGs (Behrman, 1979) possibly in the same way that estrogens (Gibori *et al.,* 1977b, 1978), even in very small amounts (Garris *et al.,* 1981), prevent the luteolytic effect of LHAS, i.e., by causing a temporary increase in progesterone secretion, which in turn prevents a full scale switch-on of intraluteal PG production.

b. The Delaying Effect of Prolactin. According to this explanation, the balance between the processes promoting progesterone secretion and those promoting PG production will determine when LH dependency appears. Prolactin's effects array it on the side of progesterone secretion and against PG production, and this tends to postpone the appearance of LH dependency. This delaying effect is probably the reason for the continued need for prolactin after LH dependency appears, since it is only the combined effects of prolactin and the progesterone secretion stimulated by LH that hold the increase in PG production to a moderate one.

The action of prolactin, however, must be such that in the presence of the inducing effect of LH and even in the absence of the uterus, which works with this effect of LH (see next subsection), it can put off the change in PG production that leads to LH dependency only until about day 12 (Fig. 12). In the absence of the inducing effect of LH, on the other hand, and probably in cooperation with the suppressing effect of progesterone itself on PG production, prolactin can postpone LH dependency indefinitely and thus greatly prolong the CL's ability to secrete progesterone. This, presumably, describes the conditions of the hypophysectomized, pituitary transplanted rat (Fig. 10).

c. The Advancing Effect of the Uterus. The effect of the uterus in the events leading to LH dependency seems to be part of those which (like that of LH) promote luteal PG production, but this effect is different from that on the CL's life span. The latter is without question the result of the production and delivery to the CL of luteolytic PGs (Horton and Poyser, 1976), and these, together with those produced by the CL itself, determine the rate of regression of the CL, for example, in the ordinary pseudopregnant rat. There are at least two reasons to postulate that its effect of advancing the appearance of LH dependency is different from this. One is that the effect on LH dependency is over a threshold by day 5 (Garris and Rothchild, 1980) (Fig. 13), while the life-shortening effect can be prevented by hysterectomy even as late as day 10 (Silbiger and Rothchild, 1963; Melampy *et al.*, 1964). The other is that both the DT-bearing uterus and the uterus of early pregnancy advance the appearance of LH dependency at least as much as (or even more than) the ordinary pseudopregnant rat's uterus (Morishige and Rothchild, 1974; Rothchild *et al.*, 1974; Nanes and Rothchild, 1981), yet they prolong the CL's life span as much as does hysterectomy (Rothchild, 1965, p. 283).

The uterus hastens LH dependency, therefore, through the action of a different substance from that which shortens the CL's life span (Nanes and Rothchild, 1981). The hypothetical substance, like LH, may facilitate the production of intraluteal PGs, and thus oppose prolactin's delaying effect. Some of its characteristics have an uncanny resemblance to those of LH, and it is interesting that both Morishige, in a pilot study (see Rothchild *et al.*, 1974) and de Greef *et al.* (1976) in a definitive one, found significantly lower peripheral serum levels of LH in chronically hysterectomized than in ordinary pseudopregnant rats. In the presence of LH, the uterine substance is not essential for the induction of LH dependency, since chronically hysterectomized rats do become LH dependent by day 12–15 (Ford and Yoshinaga, 1975c; Nanes *et al.*, 1980), but whether it would induce LH dependency in the absence of LH has never been tested definitively. It seems at least to cooperate with LH, in inducing LH dependency, and both this effect of LH and that of the uterus are over a threshold effect by day 5.

The uterine substance must also be made by the DT-bearing uterus, which differs from that of the ordinary pseudopregnant rat's uterus only after day 5 [the day on which an endometrial scratch or other stimulus most effectively induces DT formation (De Feo, 1967)], and until day 8, only in the extent of the small amount of DT which has formed by then (De Feo, 1967). By day 8, the ordinary pseudopregnant rat's uterus is over a threshold effect for preventing the delaying effect of prolactin on LH dependency (Garris and Rothchild, 1980). There is thus little or no essential difference between the DT-bearing uterus and the ordinary progestational uterus in their action of advancing the appearance of LH dependency, and the slightly greater effectiveness of DT may be due perhaps only to an enhanced release of the uterine substance at the time of endometrial scratching. Why the implanting blastocyst also advances the appearance of LH dependency, however, remains a mystery.

By contrast, there is a very big difference between the ordinary pseudopregnant rat's uterus and the DT-bearing uterus in their contribution to the pool of PGs which determines how rapidly progesterone secretion falls during the regression phase. Whatever the exact cause for it the DT-bearing uterus lacks the ability—which the ordinary pseudopregnant rat's uterus has—to contribute to this pool. As a result, the regression phase of the CL's life cycle, in rats bearing DT, is like that of a hysterectomized rat (see, e.g., Pepe and Rothchild, 1974).

3. Pregnancy and LH Dependency

Pregnancy and its effect on the CL is a subject altogether too large to be included in this article except to say that the prolongation of progesterone secretion in the rat, for example, by pregnancy (Fig. 15) is typical of the evolution of the CL–trophoblast relationship among the polyestrous eutheria. Even the change in LH dependency in the rat's CL caused by pregnancy is a subject in itself, and I will not do more at this point, therefore, than mention some of the more important and interesting of its aspects.

There is only suggestive evidence (Haour *et al.*, 1976; Blank *et al.*, 1979) that the rat placenta secretes a chorionic gonadotrophin (rCG) (i.e., a hormone homologous with hCG), in addition to the placental luteotrophin (rPL) (Kelly *et al.*, 1976). There is good evidence that estrogens stimulate progesterone secretion after day 12 of pregnancy (Takayama and Greenwald, 1973; Gibori *et al.*, 1977a, 1978; Kato *et al.*, 1979; Ochiai and Rothchild, 1980; Rodway *et al.*, 1981), but estrogens are apparently not essential, since progesterone secretion can be maintained at the level reached by day 12, until at least day 20, by treatment with only the serum of day 12 pregnant rats, after hypophysectomy and hysterectomy on day 12 (Gibori *et al.*, 1977a). We have also found only equivocal evidences so

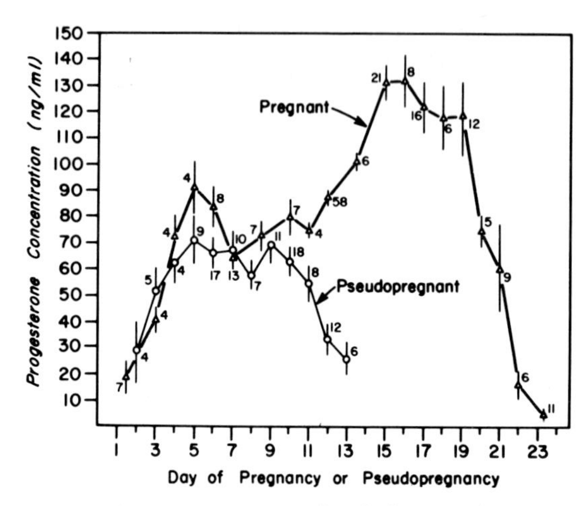

FIG. 15. The pattern of progesterone secretion during pseudopregnancy and pregnancy in the rat. The rat has an ultra-short-lived CL, whose life span is increased ("pseudopregnant" curve) to that of a short-lived CL (Fig. 2) by the prolactin secreted in response to sterile mating or an equivalent stimulus, such as mechanical stimulation of the cervix. The prolongation of progesterone secretion by pregnancy in the rat is an example of the fact that pregnancy has this effect in all polyestrous eutheria (from Pepe and Rothchild, 1974).

far that antiestrogen treatment during the period after day 12 interferes with progesterone secretion (Rodway and Rothchild, unpublished findings).

Although the evidence is still far too sketchy to be certain that any interpretation of the loss of LH dependency after day 12 is correct, the most likely one may be that the placental hormones change the progesterone/PG relations within the CL in such a way that support of progesterone secretion through a mechanism like the luteotrophic action of LH may not be necessary for at least the first several days after day 12; if it is necessary beyond that point, it is through a hormone other than LH itself. The pattern of progesterone secretion after day 12 (Fig. 15), the fact that the CL secrete progesterone autonomously for about 3 days after day 12 (Rothchild, 1973; Rothchild *et al.,* 1973), and that neither prolactin (Rodway *et al.,* 1981) nor rPL (in the form of day 12 pregnancy serum) (Gibori *et al.,* 1977a) will raise the rate of this secretion form the basis for this interpretation. In fact, it is almost strikingly obvious, from a comparison of the progesterone curves for pregnancy and ordinary pseudopregnancy (Fig. 15), that the hormonal conditions of pregnancy have induced a new life cycle in the CL, almost identical in pattern to that of pseudopregnancy, but superimposed on the pseudopregnancy cycle at the point where regression would have begun. On a time scale about 20 times longer than in rat pregnancy, the same thing seems to happen in the roe deer

(Fig. 16). The placental hormones, thus, not only prevent the CL from regressing, but in some way reactivate the capacity for autonomous progesterone secretion to such an extent that by day 12, the CL are no longer LH dependent, and they can even secrete progesterone in the absence of both pituitary and placentas for 3 days (Rothchild *et al.*, 1973).

How this comes about and why estrogens at this point assume the importance they have in inducing the rise in progesterone that occurs between days 12 and 15 will have to be the subject of another article.

V. Summary

The CL is a peculiar endocrine gland, characterized by a bewildering diversity of patterns of progesterone secretion, of regulation of this secretion, and, even among the mammals, in the relationship between CL activity and viviparity. Its unique and universal characteristic, however, is ephemerality, which is expressed in a typical nonoscillating pattern of

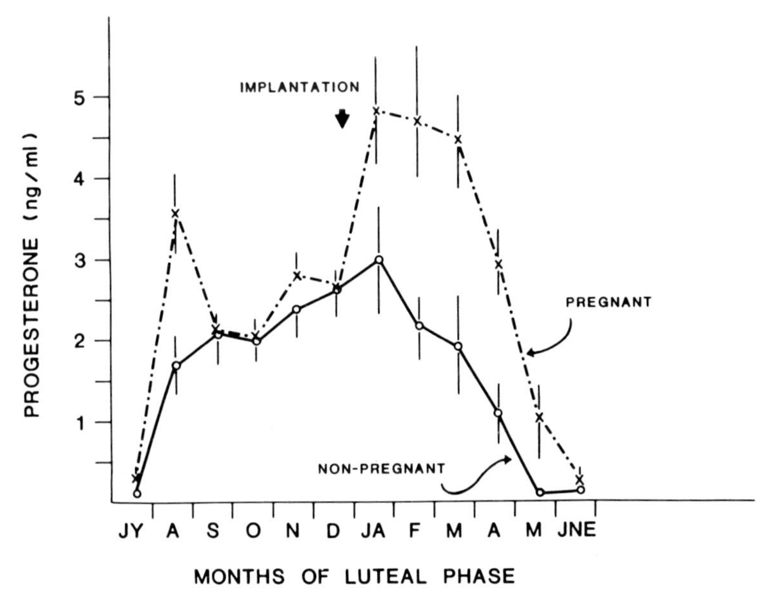

FIG. 16. The difference in pattern of the luteal phase between the pregnant and nonpregnant roe deer, a monestrous breeder. (Adapted from data of Hoffman *et al.*, 1978.) The difference is not in duration of the luteal phase, but in the amount of progesterone secreted after implantation, and is almost exactly like that between the pseudopregnant and pregnant rat, in which the whole cycle of pregnancy occupies a period of only about 3 weeks (Fig. 15). The armadillo (Peppler and Stone, 1980) and the prairie dog (Foreman, 1962), which are also monestrous breeders, probably also have long-lived CL with a duration of activity little different from that during pregnancy.

progesterone secretion and change in size, in which a rising phase, a plateau phase, and a regression phase are easy to see. A group of characteristics of the mammalian CL—although they do not seem to be universal ones—appear to be crucial clues to the cause of this ephemerality. These are: the ability of the CL of several species to secrete progesterone autonomously, i.e., in the absence of any known extrinsic stimulus; the luteolytic effect of prostaglandins (PGs); the ability of the CL to make PGs; the self-stimulating quality of PG production; and, the ability of progesterone to suppress PG production, and at the same time to stimulate the potential for PG production. The implications of autonomy are that progesterone itself may be the primary stimulus of its own secretion, a possibility for which suggestive evidence can be found.

From a consideration of how these characteristics are related to one another, I have theorized that ephemerality arises from the nature of the basic and common system of regulation of all CL; this system can be described by the following five postulates:

1. The CL secretes progesterone autonomously.
2. Progesterone is the primary stimulus of its own secretion.
3. The CL also makes PGs, but progesterone suppresses their production, at the same time that it increases the CL's potential ability to make them.
4. The luteal PGs are also made autonomously, are self-stimulating, and they prevent progesterone secretion without increasing the CL's potential for progesterone secretion.
5. As progesterone secretion rises, so does the intraluteal progesterone concentration; when this reaches a critical level, it reduces the rate of further increase in progesterone secretion and switches on an increase in PG production. The self-stimulating quality of progesterone secretion and PG production and their mutually opposing effects lead inevitably to regression of progesterone secretion and eventual disappearance of the CL.

The essence of the CL's ephemerality is thus that both progesterone secretion and PG production are regulated by positive feedback and are mutually opposing. Extrinsic factors that stimulate (luteotrophins) or inhibit (luteolysins) progesterone secretion presumably have their effects by acting on each of these intrinsic processes.

The pathway to diversity in the regulation of the CL (as well as in its other attributes) began with the evolution of the CL itself. The principal effect of luteinization of the postovulatory follicle (POF), when it first occurred in the primitive reptile ancestors of modern reptiles and mammals, is postulated to have been the postponement of the POF's production of PGs. This postponed the production of PGs in the female reproductive tract and thus also the expulsion of the egg. From this *first* step, through a series of intermediate stages, such as the ovoviviparity of the monotremes, until the limited form of viviparity of the modern marsupials, the principal effect of the progesterone secreted by the CL probably remained essentially unchanged; the intrinsic regulating system of the CL probably also remained essentially unaffected by outside factors.

The eutherian CL evolved because of the appearance within it of responsiveness to extrinsic factors. The first of these must have been the pituitary hormones, and later ones included placental hormones, estrogens, uterine PGs, etc. I have speculated that the eutherian CL and eutherian viviparity evolved according to the following sequence.

The first change was responsiveness to the luteotrophic effects of prolactin, which are postulated to work mainly through depression of either or both the effects or production of intraluteal PGs. Prolactin, therefore, increased the duration of progesterone secretion well beyond the approximately 2-week period of the marsupial and earlier CL. Among modern marsupials, the bandicoot's CL has apparently evolved to this stage. The second change was responsiveness of the uterus to the gestation-prolonging effect of the CL's progesterone. The bandicoots have not yet evolved to this stage, their young still being born only 12 days after ovulation, in spite of a prolonged secretion of progesterone. The first eutherians were probably monestrous breeders, in which prolongation of progesterone secretion through the effect of prolactin, and of intrauterine gestation through the effect of progesterone, provided the *minimum* conditions for the transition from the marsupial to the eutherian form of viviparity. Eventually this led to the pattern of viviparity seen in modern eutherian monestrous breeders, in which the luteal phase in the absence of pregnancy is as long as it is during pregnancy (e.g., in the dog, about 2 months).

Another change probably occurred almost simultaneously. This was the evolution of the trophoblastic placenta, which, together with the effects of progesterone on the uterus, helped to prolong intrauterine gestation by protecting the embryo from immune rejection by the mother. During the course of its evolution, the trophoblast acquired the ability to secrete hormones with luteotrophic/antiluteolytic properties. Although these may have affected the amount of progesterone secreted by the monestrous breeders' CL, they did not affect the duration of CL activity, and were probably not essential for the maintenance of pregnancy. Their appearance, however, made it possible for polyestrous breeding to be compatible with eutherian viviparity.

The next change was the appearance of responsiveness to the *luteolytic* effect of LH. This effect, probably a facilitation of intraluteal PG production, together with an increase in the basal rate of secretion of LH and FSH, made polyestrous ovulation cycles possible, since it shortened the life span of the CL to about 2 weeks, and thus also the interval to the next ovulation. Polyestrous cycles were not compatible with eutherian viviparity, however, until they appeared in the descendants of the monestrous breeders in which an endocrine placenta had already evolved. The latter prevented the luteolytic effect of LH and thus prolonged the CL's life span enough to make eutherian viviparity possible.

Such CL were already presumably responsive to the luteotrophic action of prolactin, and this helped preserve their responsiveness to the placental hormones until these were secreted into the blood stream. The next or almost simultaneous change was the appearance of responsiveness to the *luteotrophic* effect of LH, one believed to act by raising the rate of progesterone secretion. This also helped to preserve CL activity and responsiveness to the placental hormones, and eventually became a major element in the luteotrophic process of most, if not all, polyestrous eutheria.

The first polyestrous eutheria were thus species with CL responsive to the luteotrophic effect of LH and prolactin, and to the luteolytic effect of LH, and with a placenta which secreted hormones that prevented the latter. The later paths of evolution of CL regulation involved changes primarily in these three attributes, and in the balance between them and the CL's capacity for autonomous progesterone secretion; changes in the factors contributing to the intraluteal control of PG production, and in the source of PGs responsible for the CL's regression also occurred. Examples of these are described.

One example of the usefulness of the theory is in the interpretation of the rat's ultra-short luteal phase of the estrous cycle, and its relation to the rat's peculiar need for the luteotrophic effects of both prolactin and LH. The ultra-short luteal phase is postulated to be the result of evolution of a supernormal sensitivity to the luteolytic effect of LH and of a subnormal threshold for the switch-on of an increase in intraluteal PG production. Both changes limit the life of the CL to less than about 3 days, but prolactin, by reducing both effects, allows the CL to express its capacity for autonomous progesterone secretion. This is enough to maintain progesterone secretion for at least 8 or 9 days after ovulation.

The luteolytic effect of LH causes the development of the crucial need for the luteotrophic effect of LH; this need appears by day 8 or 9. Although the luteolytic action of LH is reduced by prolactin, it is not altogether prevented, and it leads eventually to a gap between the CL's capacity for autonomous progesterone secretion and its maximum capacity for progesterone secretion. By raising the rate of progesterone secretion, LH thus maintains the CL's maximum capacity, but it does not prevent regression. This occurs because of the cumulative effect of the PGs, which eventually reduce the maximum capacity for progesterone secretion to zero.

Thus, *the essence of a CL,* in a word, is that it is a vertebrate postovulatory follicle whose inevitable regression, itself the result of its intrinsic ability to make PGs, is postponed by its ability to make progesterone. The duration of this postponement is determined primarily by the duration of progesterone secretion.

ACKNOWLEDGMENTS

I thank my colleagues, Drs. Peter van Rees, Erik Noach, and Eylard van Hall, and the medical faculty of the University of Leiden for recommending me, and the Ministry of Education and Science and former Queen Juliana, for approving the recommendation, for an appointment as a Boerhaave Professor in the Department of Pharmacology of the University of Leiden for the academic year 1977–1978. This appointment gave me the ideal atmosphere and opportunity for the major effort of conceiving and preparing the background material for this article.

The work done in our laboratory has been supported by Ford Foundation Training Grants 670-135, NIH-NICHD Contract 70-2310, NIH-NICHD Research Grant HD-07640, and NIH-NICHD Training Grants HD-00024 and HD-07120. I am indebted to Dr. Wm. Hansel for the liberal supplies of LHAS, and to Drs. Gordon Niswender, Jimmy Neill, and Leo Reichert, and to the Program Officer of the Hormone Distribution Program of the NIH, for keeping my colleagues and me supplied with the materials needed for the RIA of progesterone, gonadotrophins, and prolactin.

To my colleagues Walter Morishige, Gerald Pepe, Daniel Castracane, Geula Gibori, Richard Rodway, Jeffrey Akaka, Paul Lam, Mark Nanes, Hiroshi Kato, Kazunori Ochiai, José Sánchez-Criado, and David Garris, who have worked with me in the effort to solve some of the mysteries of CL function in the rat, I here give my unlimited thanks for their interest, enthusiasm, hard work, and endless arguments.

For permission to reproduce already published findings I want to thank the editors and publishers of *Endocrinology,* for the rat and dog data of Figs. 9 and 10, and for all of Figs. 13 and 15; of *Biology of Reproduction,* for the chicken data of Fig. 5, the guinea pig data of Fig. 9, and the roe deer data of Fig. 16; of the *Journal of Reproduction and Fertility,* for the chicken data of Fig. 5; and of *Physiological Reviews,* for the hysterectomized guinea pig data of Fig. 10B.

I also want to acknowledge my indebtedness to colleagues too numerous to mention by name, for listening to and criticizing the ideas which form the substance of this paper. And finally, to my secretary Ms. Rosa Garnett, my thanks once more for her patience and skill in preparing this manuscript.

REFERENCES

Abel, M. H., and Baird, D. T. (1980). *Endocrinology* **106,** 1599.
Acker, G., and Alloiteau, J.-J. (1968). *C. R. Soc. Biol.* **162,** 29.
Acritopoulou, S., and Haresign, W. (1980). *J. Reprod. Fertil.* **58,** 219.

Ahmad, N. (1971). *Biol. Reprod.* **4,** 106.
Ahmad, N., Lyons, W. R., and Papkoff, H. (1969). *Anat. Rec.* **164,** 291.
Akaka, J., O'Laughlin-Phillips, E. Antczak, E., and Rothchild, I. (1977). *Endocrinology* 100, 1334.
Aksel, S., Schomberg, D. W., and Hammond C. B. (1977). *Obstet. Gynecol.* **50,** 333.
Aksel, S., Schomberg, D. W., and Hammond, C. B. (1978). *Obstet. Gynecol.* **52,** 421.
Allen, W. R., and Rowson, L. E. A. (1973). *J. Reprod. Fertil.* **33,** 539.
Alloiteau, J.-J. (1957). *C. R. Soc. Biol.* **151,** 2009.
Alloiteau, J.-J., and Acker, G. (1969). *C. R. Acad. Sci. (Paris) Ser. D* **268,** 826.
Alloiteau, J.-J., and Bouhours, J. (1965). *C. R. Acad. Sci. (Paris)* **261,** 4230.
Alloiteau, J.-J., and Vignal, A. (1958). *C. R. Acad. Sci. (Paris)* **246,** 2804.
Amoroso, E. C. (1955). *Br. Med. Bull.* **11,** 117.
Amoroso, E. C. (1979). Discussion of Beer and Billingham (1979).
Amoroso, E. C., and Finn, C. A. (1962). *In* "The Ovary" (Lord Zuckerman, ed.), 1st Ed. p. 451. Academic Press, New York.
Amoroso, E. C., and Perry, J. S. (1975). *Phil. Trans. R. Soc.* **B271,** 343.
Amoroso, E. C., and Perry, J. S. (1977). *In* "The Ovary" (Lord Zuckerman and B. J. Weir, eds.), 2nd Ed., Vol. 2, p. 316. Academic Press, New York.
Anderson, L. L., Dyck, G. W., Mori, H., Henricks, D. M., and Melampy R. M. (1967). *Am. J. Physiol.* **212,** 1188.
Anderson, L. L., Bland, K. P., and Melampy, R. M. (1969). *Recent Prog. Horm. Res.* **25,** 57.
Anteby, S. O., Bauminger, S., Zor, U., and Lindner, H. R. (1975). *Prostaglandins* **10,** 991.
Arata, W. S. M., and Chatterton, R. T. (1974). *Am. J. Obstet. Gynecol.* **120,** 954.
Armstrong, D. T. (1968). *Recent Prog. Horm. Res.* **24,** 255.
Armstrong, D. T., Miller, L. S., and Knudsen, K. A. (1969). *Endocrinology* **85,** 393.
Armstrong, D. T., Knudsen, K. A., and Miller, L. S. (1970). *Endocrinology* **86,** 634.
Armstrong, D. T., Kraemer, M. A., and Hixon, J. E. (1975). *Biol. Reprod.* **12,** 599.
Asdell, S. A. (1964). "Patterns of Mammalian Reproduction," 2nd Ed. Cornell Univ. Press, Ithaca, New York.
Atkinson, L. E., Hotchkiss, J., Fritz, G. R., Surve, A. H., Neill, J. D., and Knobil, E. (1975). *Biol. Reprod.* **12,** 335.
Auletta, F. J., Currie, G. N., and Black, D. L. (1972). *Acta Endocrinol.* **69,** 241.
Auletta, F. J., Agins, H., and Scommegna, A. (1978). *Endocrinology* **103,** 1183.
Azhar, S., Menon, M., and Menon, K. M. J. (1980). *Annu. Meet. Endocrine Soc.* **62,** Abstr. No. 542, p. 210.
Baird, D. T., Swanston, I., and Scaramuzzi, R. J. (1976). *Endocrinology* **98,** 1490.
Balmacida, J., Asch, R. H., Valenzuela, G., Eddy, C. A., and Pauerstein, C. J. (1979). *Fertil. Steril.* **31,** 214.
Balmacida, V. P., Valenzuela, G., Eddy, C. A., and Asch, R. H. (1980). *Int. J. Obstet. Gynecol.* (in press).
Bartholomeusz, R. K., and Bruce, N. W. (1976). *Biol. Reprod.* **15,** 84.
Bartosik, D., and Szarowski, D. H. (1973). *Endocrinology* **92,** 949.
Bartosik, D., Romanoff, E. B., Watson, D. J., and Scricco, E. (1967). *Endocrinology* **81,** 186.
Bassett, J. M., Oxborrow, T. J., Smith, I. D., and Thorburn, G. D. (1969). *J. Endocrinol.* **45,** 449.
Basu, R., and Chatterton, R. T. (1978). *Fertil. Steril.* **29,** 640.
Beer, A. E., and Billingham, R. E. (1976). "The Immunobiology of Mammalian Reproduction." Prentice-Hall, New York.
Beer, A. E., and Billingham, R. (1979). *Ciba Found. Symp.* No. 64, p. 293.
Behrman, H. R. (1979), *Annu. Rev. Physiol.* **41,** 685.

Behrman, H. R., MacDonald, G. J., and Greep, R. O. (1971). *Lipids* **6,** 791.
Behrman, H. R., Grinwich, D. L., Hichens, M., and MacDonald, G. J. (1978). *Endocrinology* **103,** 349.
Bergstrom, S., Carlson, L. A., and Weeks, J. R. (1968). *Pharmacol. Rev.* **20,** 1.
Bernard, J. (1975). *J. Reprod. Fertil.* **43,** 453.
Bill, C. H., III, Godsby, J. E., and Keyes, P. L. (1980). *Annu. Meet. Soc. Study Reprod.* **13,** Abstr. No. 87.
Birnbaumer, L., Day, S. L., Hunzicker-Dunn, M., and Abramowitz, J. (1979). *In* "Ontogeny of Receptors and Reproductive Hormones" (T. H. Hamilton, J. H. Clark, and W. A. Sadler, eds.), p. 173. Raven, New York.
Blackwell, G. J., Flower, R. J., Parsons, M. F., and Vane, J. R. (1975). *Br. J. Pharmacol.* **53,** 467P.
Bland, K. P., and Donovan, B. T. (1970). *J. Endocrinol.* **47,** 225.
Blank, M. S., Dufau, M. L., and Friesen, H. G. (1979). *Life Sci.* **25,** 1023.
Blatchley, F. R., and Donovan, B. T. (1972). *J. Reprod. Fertil.* **31,** 331.
Blatchley, F. R., and Donovan, B. T. (1974). *J. Endocrinol.* **60,** 91.
Blatchley, F. R., and Donovan, B. T. (1976). *J. Reprod. Fertil.* **46,** 455.
Blatchley, F. R., and Poyser, N. L. (1974). *J. Reprod. Fertil.* **40,** 205.
Blatchley, F. R., Maule Walker, F. M., and Poyser, N. L. (1975). *J. Endocrinol.* **67,** 225.
Blatchley, F. R., Donovan, B. T., and Ter Haar, M. B. (1976). *Biol. Reprod.* **15,** 29.
Board, J. A., Bhatnagar, A. S., and Bush, C. W. (1973). *Fertil. Steril.* **24,** 95.
Boehm, N., Hassani, M., Kerdelhue, B., and Aron, C. (1980). *Biol. Reprod.* **22,** 466.
Bonnin-Lafargue, M., Canivenc, R., and Lajus-Boue, M. (1972). *C. R. Acad. Sci. (Paris) Ser. D* **274,** 85.
Bradbury, J. T., Brown, W. E., and Gray, L. A. (1950). *Recent Prog. Horm. Res.* **5,** 151.
Bradshaw, S. D., McDonald, I. R., Hähnel, R., and Heller, H. (1975). *J. Endocrinol.* **65,** 451.
Breed, W. G., and Clarke, J. R. (1970). *J. Reprod. Fertil.* **23,** 447.
Brinkley, H. J., Norton, H. W., and Nalbandov, A. V. (1964a). *Endocrinology* **74,** 9.
Brinkley, H. J., Norton, H. W., and Nalbandov, A. V. (1964b). *Endocrinology* **74,** 14.
Brown, M. S., Kovanen, P. T., and Goldstein, J. L. (1979). *Recent Prog. Horm. Res.* **35,** 215.
Browning, H. C. (1973). *Biol. Reprod.* **8,** 128.
Brunner, M. A., Donaldson, L. E., and Hansel, W. (1969). *J. Dairy Sci.* **52,** 1849.
Buffler, G., and Roser, S. (1971). *C. R. Soc. Biol.* **165,** 1440.
Buffler, G., and Roser, S. (1972). *J. Interdiscipl. Cycle Res.* **3,** 209.
Buffler, G., and Roser, S. (1974). *Acta Endocrinol.* **75,** 569.
Buhr, M. M., Carlson, J. C., and Thompson, J. E. (1979). *Endocrinology* **105,** 1330.
Butcher, R. L., Collins, W. E., Fugo, N. W., (1974). *Endocrinology* **94,** 1704.
Butler, W. R., Hotchkiss, J., and Knovil, E. (1975). *Endocrinology* **96,** 1509.
Caffrey, J. L., Nett, T. M., Abel, J. H., Jr., and Niswender, G. D. (1979a). *Biol. Reprod.* **20,** 279.
Caffrey, J. L., Fletcher, P. W., Diekman, M. A., O'Callaghan, P. L., and Niswender, G. D. (1979b). *Biol. Reprod.* **21,** 601.
Cake, M. H., Owen, F. S., and Bradshaw, S. D. (1980). *J. Endocrinol.* **84,** 153.
Caldwell, B. V., Moor, R. M., Wilmut, I., Polge, C., and Rowson, L. E. A. (1969). *J. Reprod. Fertil.* **18,** 107.
Caldwell, B. V., Tillson, S. A., Brock, W. A., and Speroff, L. (1972). *Prostaglandins* **1,** 217.
Callard, I. P., and Ho, S. M. (1980). *Prog. Reprod. Biol.* **5,** 5.
Callard, I. P., and Lance, V. (1977). *In* "Reproduction and Evolution" (J. H. Calaby and C. H. Tyndale-Biscoe, eds.), p. 199. Australian Academy of Science.

Canivenc, R., and Bonnin-Laffargue, M. (1973). *In* "Le Corps Jaune" (R. Denamur and A. Netter, eds.), p. 135. Masson, Paris.
Canivenc, R., Bonnin-Laffargue, M., and Relexans, M-C. (1962). *C. R. Soc. Biol.* **156,** 1372.
Canivenc, R., Bonnin-Laffargue, M., and Lajus, M. (1966). *C. R. Soc. Biol.* **160,** 2285.
Cargille, C. M., Ross, G. T., and Yoshimi, T., (1969). *J. Clin. Endocrinol. Metab.* **29,** 12.
Carlson, I. H., and Rust, C. C. (1969). *Endocrinology* **85,** 623.
Carlson, J. C., and Gole, J. W. D. (1978). *J. Reprod. Fertil.* **53,** 381.
Carr, B. R., Parker, C. R., Jr., Milewich, L., Porter, J. C., MacDonald, P. C., and Simpson, E. R. (1980). *Endocrinology* **106,** 1854.
Casey, M. L., Hemsell, D. L., MacDonald, P. C., and Johnston, J. M. (1980). *Prostaglandins* **19,** 115.
Castracane, V. D., and Jordan, V. C. (1975). *Biol. Reprod.* **13,** 587.
Castracane, V. D., and Shaikh, A. A. (1976). *J. Reprod. Fertil.* **46,** 101.
Castracane, V. D., and Shaikh, A. A. (1980). *J. Clin. Endocrinol. Metab.* **51,** 1311.
Catt, K. J., Harwood, J. P., Richert, N. D., Conn, P. M., Conti, M., and Dufau, M. L. (1979). *Adv. Exp. Med. Biol.* **112,** 647.
Centola, G. M. (1979). *Adv. Exp. Med. Biol.* **112,** 225.
Challis, J. R. G. (1980). *Int. Rev. Physiol.* **22,** 278.
Challis, J. R. G., Heap, R. B., and Illingworth, D. V. (1971). *J. Endocrinol.* **51,** 333.
Challis, J. R. G., Davies, I. J., and Ryan, K. J. (1973). *Endocrinology* **93,** 971.
Challis, J. R. G., Erickson, G. F., and Ryan, K. J. (1974). *Prostaglandins* **7,** 183.
Challis, J. R. G., Calder, A. A., Dilley, S., Forster, C. S., Hillier, K., Hunter, D. J. S., Mackenzie, I. Z., and Thorburn, G. D. (1976). *J. Endocrinol.* **68,** 401.
Chamley, W. A., Cerini, J. C., and Goding, J. R. (1973). *Prostaglandins* **4,** 711.
Chang, C. C., Badawy, S., and Laurence, K. A. (1971). *Fertil. Steril.* **22,** 663.
Channing, C. P. (1970). *Recent Prog. Horm. Res.* **26,** 589.
Channing, C. P. (1972). *Prostaglandins* **2,** 331.
Channing, C. P., and Crisp, T. M. (1972). *Gen. Comp. Endocrinol. Suppl* **3,** 617.
Channing, C. P., and Tsafriri, A. (1977). *Metabolism* **26,** 413.
Channing, C. P., Brinkley, H. J., and Young, E. P. (1980). *Endocrinology* **106,** 317.
Charlton, H. M., Milligan, S. R., and Versi, E. (1978). *J. Reprod. Fertil.* **52,** 283.
Chasalow, F. I., and Pharris, B. B. (1972). *Prostaglandins* **1,** 107.
Chateau, D. (1969). *C. R. Acad. Sci. (Paris) Ser. D* **269,** 788.
Chateau, D., and Aron, C. (1970). *Bull. Assoc. Anat.* **147,** 172.
Chatterjee, A. (1973). *Prostaglandins* **4,** 915.
Chatterjee, A. (1976). *Prostaglandins* **12,** 525.
Chatterton, R. T., and Greep, R. O. (1965). *Fed. Proc. Fed. Am. Soc. Exp. Biol.* **24,** 384.
Choudhary, J. B., and Greenwald, G. S. (1968). *Endocrinology* **83,** 129.
Christensen, A. K., and Gillim, S. W. (1969). *In* "The Gonads" (K. W. McKerns, ed.), p. 415. Appleton, New York.
Christie, D. W., Bell, E. T., Horth, C. E., and Palmer, R. F. (1971). *Acta Endocrinol.* **68,** 543.
Concannon, P. (1980). *J. Reprod. Fertil.* **58,** 407.
Concannon, P. W., and Hansel, W. (1977). *Prostaglandins* **13,** 533.
Concannon, P. W., Hansel, W., and Visek, W. J. (1975). *Biol. Reprod.* **13,** 112.
Concannon, P. W., Powers, M. E., Holder, W., and Hansel, W. (1977). *Biol. Reprod.* **16,** 517.
Cook, B., and Nalbandov, A. V. (1968). *J. Reprod. Fertil.* **15,** 267.
Cook, B., Niswender, G. D., Sutterlin, N. S., Norton, H. W., and Nalbandov, A. V. (1968). *Steroids* **11,** 321.
Crisp, T. M. (1977). *Endocrinology* **101,** 1286.
Crisp, T. M., and Channing, C. P. (1972). *Biol. Reprod.* **7,** 55.

Crisp, T. M., Dessouky, D. A., and Denys, F. R., (1970). *Am. J. Anat.* **127,** 37.
Croix, D., and Franchimont, P. (1975). *Neuroendocrinology* **19,** 1.
Crompton, A. W., and Jenkins, F. A., Jr. (1979). *In* "Mesozoic Mammals: The First Two-Thirds of Mammalian History" (J. A. Lillegraven, Z. Kielan-Jaworowska, and W. A. Clemens, eds.), p. 59. Univ. of California Press, Berkeley.
Csapo, A. I. (1977). *Ciba Found. Symp.* No. 47, p. 159.
Cuellar, H. S. (1979). *Gen. Compar. Endocrinol.* **39,** 150.
Currie, W. B., and Thorburn, G. D. (1977). *Ciba Found. Symp.* No. 47, p. 49.
Damassa, D. A., Gilman, D. P., Lu, K. H., Judd, H. L., and Sawyer, C. H. (1980). *Biol. Reprod.* **22,** 571.
Day, S. L., and Birnbaumer, L. (1980). *Endocrinology* **106,** 382.
Day, S. L., and Nalbandov, A. V. (1977). *Biol. Reprod.* **16,** 486.
Day, S. L., Kirchick, H. J., and Birnbaumer, L. (1980). *Endocrinology* **106,** 1265.
Deane, H. W., Hay, M. F., and Moor, R. M. (1966). *Acta Endocrinol.* **51,** 245.
Deanesly, R. (1967). *J. Reprod. Fertil.* **13,** 183.
Deanesly, R., and Parkes, A. S. (1933). *J. Physiol.* **78,** 80.
De Feo, V. J. (1967). *In* "Cellular Biology of the Uterus" (R. M. Wynn, ed.), p. 191. Plenum, New York.
de Greef, W. J., and van der Schoot, P. (1979). *J. Endocrinol.* **83,** 205.
de Greef, W. J., and Zeilmaker, G. H. (1974). *Endocrinology* **95,** 565.
de Greef, W. J., and Zeilmaker, G. H. (1976). *Endocrinology* **98,** 305.
de Greef, W. J., and Zeilmaker, G. H. (1978). *Endocrinology* **102,** 1190.
de Greef, W. J., and Zeilmaker, G. H. (1979). *Endocrinology* **105,** 195.
de Greef, W. J., Dullaart, J., and Zeilmaker, G. H. (1976). *Endocrinology* **98,** 1228.
Del Campo, C. H., and Ginther, O. J. (1974). *Am. J. Vet. Res.* **35,** 397.
Demers, L. M., Behrman, H. R., and Greep, R. O. (1973). *Adv. Biosci.* **9,** 701.
Demers, L. M., Yoshinaga, K., and Greep, R. O. (1974). *Prostaglandins* **5,** 513.
Denamur, R., Martinet, J., and Short, R. V. (1973). *J. Reprod. Fertil.* **32,** 207.
Desclin, L. (1949). *Ann. Endocrinol. (Paris)* **10,** 1.
Dick, H. R., Culbert, J., Wells, J. W., Gilbert, A. B., and Davidson, M. F. (1978). *J. Reprod. Fertil.* **53,** 103.
Dimino, M. J. (1977). *Endocrinology* **101,** 1844.
Dimino, M. J., and Campbell, M. D. (1976). *Proc. Soc. Exp. Biol. Med.* **152,** 54.
Dingle, J. T., Hay, M. F., and Moor, R. M. (1968). *J. Endocrinol.* **40,** 325.
Döhler, K. D., and Wuttke, W. (1974). *Endocrinology* **94,** 1003.
Donaldson, L. E., Hansel, W., and van Vleck, L. D. (1965). *J. Dairy Sci.* **48,** 331.
Donovan, B. T. (1963). *J. Endocrinol.* **27,** 201.
Dorrington, J. H. (1977). *In* "The Ovary" (Lord Zuckerman and B. J. Weir, eds.), 2nd Ed., Vol. 3, p. 359. Academic Press, New York.
Douglas, R. H., and Ginther, O. J. (1976). *Prostaglandins* **11,** 251.
Downie, J., Poyser, N. L., and Wunderlich, M. (1974). *J. Physiol. (London)* **236,** 465.
du Mesnil du Buisson, F. (1966). *J. Reprod. Fertil.* **12,** 413.
du Mesnil du Buisson, F. (1973). *In* "Le Corps Jaune" (R. Denamur and A. Netter, eds.), p. 225. Masson, Paris.
Dusza, L., and Krzymowska, H. (1979). *J. Reprod. Fertil.* **57,** 511.
Dwyer, R. J., and Church, R. B. (1979). *J. Reprod. Fertil.* **56,** 81.
Earthy, M., Bishop, C., and Flack, J. D. (1975). *J. Endocrinol.* **64,** 11P.
Eckstein, P., and Zuckerman, S. (1956). *In* "Marshall's Physiology of Reproduction" (A. S. Parkes, ed.), 3rd Ed., Vol. 1, Part 1, p. 226. Longmans, Green, New York.
Elangovan, S., and Moulton, B. C. (1980). *Annu. Meet. Endocrine Soc.* **62,** Abst. No. 626, p. 231.

Elbaum, D. J., Bender, E. M., Brown, J. M., and Keyes, P. L. (1975). *Biol. Reprod.* **13,** 541.
Ellinwood, W. E., Nett, T. M., and Niswender, G. D. (1979). *Biol. Reprod.* **21,** 845.
Enders, A. C. (1973). *Biol. Reprod.* **8,** 158.
Erickson, G. F., and Ryan, K. J. (1975). *Endocrinology* **97,** 108.
Erickson, G. F., Challis, J. R. G., and Ryan, K. J. (1974). *Dev. Biol.* **40,** 208.
Erickson, G. F., Challis, J. R. G., and Ryan, K. J. (1977). *J. Reprod. Fertil.* **49,** 133.
Espey, L. L. (1980). *Biol. Reprod.* **22,** 73.
Evans, J. W., Faria, D. A., Hughes, J. P., Stabenfeldt, G. H., and Cupps, P. T. (1975). *J. Reprod. Fertil. Suppl.* **23,** 177.
Evans, M. J., and Irvine, C. H. G. (1975). *J. Reprod. Fertil. Suppl.* **23,** 193.
Everett, J. W. (1944). *Endocrinology* **35,** 507.
Everett, J. W. (1947). *Endocrinology* **41,** 364.
Everett, J. W. (1956). *Endocrinology* **58,** 786.
Everett, J. W. (1963). *Nature* (*London*) **198,** 695.
Farese, R. V., and Sabir, A. M. (1980). *Endocrinology* **106,** 1869.
Ferin, M., Tempone, A., Zimmering, P. E., and Vande Wiele, R. L. (1969). *Endocrinology* **85,** 1070.
Fernandez, E. O., Ghidoni, J., Asch, R. H., and Pauerstein, C. P. (1980). *Annu. Meet. Soc. Gynecol. Invest.*
Fischer, T. V., and Kahn, R. H. (1972). *In Vitro* **7,** 201.
Flint, A. P. F., Grinwich, D. L., Kennedy, T. G., and Armstrong, D. T. (1974). *Endocrinology* **94,** 509.
Flower, R. J. (1977). *Ciba Found. Symp.* No. 47, p. 297.
Ford, J. J., and Melampy, R. M. (1973). *Endocrinology* **93,** 540.
Ford, J. J., and Yoshinaga, K. (1975a). *Endocrinology* **96,** 329.
Ford, J. J., and Yoshinaga, K. (1975b). *Endocrinology* **96,** 335.
Ford, J. J., and Yoshinaga, K. (1975c). *Biol. Reprod.* **13,** 353.
Ford, J. J., and Yoshinaga, K. (1975d). *Proc. Soc. Exp. Biol. Med.* **150,** 425.
Foreman, D. (1962). *Anat. Rec.* **142,** 391.
Fraps, R. M. (1954). *Proc. Natl. Acad. Sci. U.S.A.* **40,** 348.
Freeman, M. E., and Sterman, J. R. (1978). *Endocrinology* **102,** 1915.
Freeman, M. E., Smith, M. S., Nazian, S. J., and Neill, J. D. (1974). *Endocrinology* **94,** 875.
French L. R. (1977). *Biol. Reprod.* **16,** 363.
Fuller, G. B., and Hansel, W. (1971). *Proc. Soc. Exp. Biol. Med.* **137,** 539.
Gal, D., and Simpson, E. R. (1980). *Annu. Meet. Soc. Gynecol. Invest.*
Garris, D. R., and Rothchild, I. (1980). *Endocrinology* **107,** 1112.
Garris, D. R., Nanes, M. S., Seguin, C., Kelly, P. A., and Rothchild, I. (1980). *Endocrinology* **107,** 486.
Garris, D. R., Rodway, R. G., and Gibori, G. (1981). In preparation.
Gemmell, R. T. (1981). *Gen. Compar. Endocrinol.* (in press).
Gengenbach, D. R., Hixon, J. E., and Hansel, W. (1977). *Biol. Reprod.* **16,** 571.
Gibori, G., and Keyes, P. L. (1980). *Endocrinology* **106,** 1584.
Gibori, G., and Richards, J. S. (1978). *Endocrinology* **102,** 767.
Gibori, G., Antczak, E., and Rothchild, I. (1977a). *Endocrinology* **100,** 1483.
Gibori, G., Rodway, R., and Rothchild, I. (1977b). *Endocrinology* **101,** 1683.
Gibori, G., Keyes, P. L., and Richards, J. S. (1978). *Endocrinology* **103,** 162.
Gilbert, A. B., Davidson, M. F., and Wells, J. W. (1978). *J. Reprod. Fertil.* **52,** 227.
Gilman, D. P., Lu, K. H., Judd, H. L., and Whitmoyer, D. I. (1980). *Fed. Proc. Fed. Am. Soc. Exp. Biol.* **39,** 585.
Ginther, O. J. (1974). *J. Anim. Sci.* **39,** 550.
Ginther, O. J., Guthrie, H. D., Henricks, D. M., and Handlin, D. L. (1972). *Endocrinology* **91,** 675.

Gleeson, A. R., Thorburn, G. D., and Cox, R. I. (1974). *Prostaglandins* **5,** 521.
Goldberg, V. J., and Ramwell, P. W. (1975). *Physiol. Rev.* **55,** 325.
Goldenberg, R. L., Bridson, W. E., and Kohler, P. O. (1972). *Biochem. Biophys. Res. Commun.* **48,** 101.
Goodman, A. L., Descalzi, C. D., Johnson, D. K., and Hodgen, G. D. (1977). *Proc. Soc. Exp. Biol. Med.* **155,** 479.
Gould, K. G., Graham, C. E., and Collins, D. C. (1977). *J. Reprod. Fertil.* **50,** 341.
Gräf, K.-J. (1978). *J. Reprod. Fertil.* **52,** 9.
Graham, C. E., Collins, D. C., Robinson, H., and Preedy, J. R. K. (1972). *Endocrinology* **91,** 13.
Grandison, L., and Meites, J. (1972). *Proc. Soc. Exp. Biol. Med.* **140,** 323.
Greenwald, G. S., and Rothchild, I. (1968). *J. Anim. Sci.* **27,** Suppl. 1, 139.
Grinwich, D. L., Hichens, M., and Behrman, H. R. (1976). *Biol. Reprod.* **14,** 212.
Gulamhusein, A. P., and Thawley, A. R. (1974). *J. Reprod. Fertil.* **36,** 405.
Gulyas, B. J., and Hodgen, G. D. (1981). *In* "Dynamics of Ovarian Function" (N. B. Schwartz and M. Hunzicker-Dunn, eds.). Raven Press, New York (in press).
Gulyas, B. J., Stouffer, R. L., and Hodgen, G. D. (1979). *Biol. Reprod.* **20,** 779.
Guraya, S. S. (1972). *Acta Endocrinol.* **69,** 107.
Guraya, S. S. (1975). *J. Reprod. Fertil.* **42,** 59.
Guthrie, H. D., Rexroad, C. E., Jr., and Bolt, D. J. (1978). *Prostaglandins* **16,** 433.
Guthrie, H. D., Rexroad, C. E., Jr., and Bolt, D. J. (1979). *Adv. Exp. Med. Biol.* **112,** 627.
Hadley, J. C. (1975). *J. Reprod. Fertil.* **45,** 389.
Hafs, H. D., and Armstrong, D. T. (1968). *J. Anim. Sci.* **27,** 134.
Hagino, N., and Koyama, T. (1979). *Horm. Metab. Res.* **11,** 358.
Haksar, A., Romanoff, E. B., Hagino, N., and Pincus, G. (1967). *Steroids* **9,** 405.
Hall, A. K., and Robinson, J. (1978). *Prostaglandins* **15,** 1013.
Hallford, D. M., Wettemann, R. P., Turman, E. J., and Omtvedt, I. T. (1975). *J. Anim. Sci.* **41,** 1786.
Hamberger, L., Dennefors, B., Hamberger, B., Janson, P. O., Nilsson, L., Sjögren, A., and Wiqvist, N. (1980). *Adv. Prostagl. Thrombox. Res.* **8,** 1365.
Hammond, J. M., Veldhuis, J. D., and Klasse, P. (1980). *Annu. Meet. Endocrine Soc.* **62,** Abstr. No. 360, p. 164.
Hammons, J.-A., Velasco, M. E., and Rothchild, I. (1973). *Endocrinology* **92,** 206.
Hansel, W. (1975). *Ann. Biol. Anim. Bioch. Biophys.* **15,** 147.
Hansel, W., and Seifart, K. H. (1967). *J. Dairy Sci.* **50,** 1948.
Hansel, W., Concannon, P. W., and Lukaszewska, J. H. (1973). *Biol. Reprod.* **8,** 222.
Hansel, W., Shemesh, M., Hixon, J., and Lukaszewska, J. (1975). *Biol. Reprod.* **13,** 30.
Haour, F., Tell, G., and Sanchez, P. (1976). *C. R. Acad. Sci. (Paris)* Ser. D **282,** 1183.
Harms, P. G., Niswender, G. D., and Malven, P. V., (1969). *Biol. Reprod.* **1,** 228.
Harrison, R. J. (1962). *In* "The Ovary" (S. Zuckerman, ed.), 1st Ed., p. 143. Academic Press, New York.
Harrison, R. J., and Weir, B. J. (1977). *In* "The Ovary" (Lord Zuckerman and B. J. Weir, eds.), 2nd Ed., Vol. 1, p. 113. Academic Press, New York.
Hashimoto, I., and Wiest, W. G. (1969). *Endocrinology* **84,** 886.
Hawk, H. W., and Bolt, D. J. (1970). *Biol. Reprod.* **2,** 275.
Heap, R. B., and Hammond, J. Jr., (1974). *J. Reprod. Fertil.* **39,** 149.
Heap, R. B., Perry, J. S., and Rowlands, I. W. (1967). *J. Reprod. Fertil.* **13,** 537.
Heap, R. B., Perry, J. S., and Challis, J. R. (1973). *In* "Handbook of Physiology" (R. O. Greep and E. B. Astwood, eds.), Section 7: Endocrinology, Vol. II, Part 2, p. 217. American Physiological Society, Washington, D.C.
Heap, R. B., Galil, A. K., Harrison, F. A., Jenkin, G., and Perry, J. S. (1977). *Ciba Found. Symp.* No. 47, p. 127.

Heap, R. B., Flint, A. P., and Gadsby, J. E. (1979). *Br. Med. Bull.* **35,** 129.
Hearn, J. P. (1973). *Nature (London)* 241, 207.
Hearn, J. P. (1974). *J. Reprod. Fertil.* **39,** 235.
Hearnshaw, H., Restall, B. J., and Gleeson, A. R. (1973). *J. Reprod. Fertil.* **32,** 322.
Henderson, K. M. (1976). *J. Endocrinol.* **71,** 259.
Henderson, K. M., and McNatty, K. P. (1975). *Prostaglandins* **9,** 779.
Henderson, K. M., and McNatty, K. P. (1977). *J. Endocrinol.* **73,** 71.
Henderson, K. M., Scaramuzzi, R. J., and Baird, D. T. (1977). *J. Endocrinol.* **72,** 379.
Henricks, D. M., Oxenreider, S. L., and Anderson, L. L. (1969). *Am. J. Physiol.* **216,** 1213.
Henricks, D. M., Dickey, J. F., and Niswender, G. D. (1970). *Biol. Reprod.* **2,** 346.
Henricks, D. M., Long, J. T., Hill, J. R., and Dickey, J. F. (1974). *J. Reprod. Fertil.* **41,** 113.
Henzl, M. R., Smith, R. E., Boost, G., and Tyler, E. T. (1972). *J. Clin. Endocrinol. Metab.* **34,** 860.
Hertelendy, F. (1973). *Life Sci.* **13,** 1581.
Hertelendy, F., and Biellier, H. V. (1978a). *Biol. Reprod.* **18,** 204.
Hertelendy, F., and Biellier, H. V. (1978b). *J. Reprod. Fertil.* **53,** 71.
Highfill, D. R., and Mead, R. A. (1975). *Gen. Comp. Endocrinol.* **27,** 389.
Hill, J. P., and Gatenby, J. W. B. (1926). *Proc. Zool. Soc. London* **47,** 715.
Hilliard, J. (1973). *Biol. Reprod.* **8,** 203.
Hilliard, J., Spies, H. G., Lucas, L., and Sawyer, C. H. (1968). *Endocrinology* **82,** 122.
Hilliard, J., Scaramuzzi, R. J., Penardi, R., and Sawyer, C. H. (1973). *Endocrinology* **93,** 1235.
Hinman, J. W. (1972). *Annu. Rev. Biochem.* **41,** 161.
Hiroyoshi, H., and Suzuki, Y. (1974). *Endocrinol. Jpn.* **21,** 69.
Hisaw, F. L. (1959). *In* "Comparative Endocrinology" (A. Gorbman, ed.), p. 533. Wiley, New York.
Hisaw, F. L., Jr., and Hisaw, F. L. (1959). *Anat. Rec.* **135,** 269.
Hixon, J. E., and Armstrong, D. T. (1974). *Biol. Reprod.* **10,** 111.
Hixon, J. E., and Clegg, M. T. (1969). *Endocrinology* **84,** 828.
Hixon, J. E., and Hansel, W. (1979). *Adv. Exp. Med. Biol.* **112,** 613.
Hixon, J. E., Gengenbach, D. R., and Hansel, W. (1975). *Biol. Reprod.* **13,** 126.
Hodgen, G. D., Wilks, J. W., Vaitukaitis, J. L., Chen, H.-C., Papkoff, H., and Ross, G. T. (1976). *Endocrinology* **99,** 137.
Hoffman, F. R. (1960). *Geburtshilfe Frauenheilk.* **20,** 1153.
Hoffman, L. H. (1974). *J. Reprod. Fertil.* **36,** 401.
Hoffmann, B., Schams, D., Bopp, R., Enders, M. L., Giménez, T., and Karg, H. (1974). *J. Reprod. Fertil.* **40,** 77.
Hoffmann, B., Barth, D., and Karg, H. (1978). *Biol. Reprod.* **19,** 931.
Hopson, J. A. (1973). *Am. Nat.* **107,** 446.
Hopson, J. A., and Crompton, A. W. (1969). *In* "Evolutionary Biology" (T. Dobzhansky, M. K. Hecht, and W. C. Steere, eds.), Vol. 3, p. 15. Appleton, New York.
Horrell, E., Major, P. W., Kolpatrick, R., and Smith, B. (1972). *J. Endocrinol.* **55,** 89.
Horrobin, D. F. (1978). "Prostaglandins." Eden Press, Montreal.
Horton, E. W., and Poyser, N. L. (1976). *Physiol. Rev.* **56,** 595.
Hughes, R. L. (1962). *Nature (London)* **194,** 890.
Hughes, R. L. (1974). *J. Reprod. Fertil.* **39,** 173.
Hughes, R. L., and Carrick, F. N. (1978). *Aust. Zool.* **20,** 233.
Hunzicker-Dunn, M., and Birnbaumer, L. (1976). *Endocrinology* **99,** 211.
Huslig, R. L., Fogwell, R. L., and Smith, W. L. (1979). *Biol. Reprod.* **21,** 589.
Illingworth, D. V., and Perry, J. S. (1971). *J. Endocrinol.* **50,** 625.

Illingworth, D. V., Perry, J. S., Ackland, N., and Burton, A. M. (1973). *J. Endocrinol.* **59,** 163.

Jöchle, W. (1969). *In* "Handbuch der experimentellen Pharmokologie" (O. Eichler, A. Farah, H. Herken, and A. D. Welch, eds.), Vol. 22/2, p. 606. Springer-Verlag, Berlin and New York.

Johansson, E. D. B. (1969). *Acta Endocrinol.* **61,** 607.

Johansson, E. D. B. (1971). *Acta Endocrinol.* **68,** 779.

Johansson, E. D. B. (1973). *Contraception* **8,** 27.

Johnson, K. R., and Erb, R. E. (1962). *J. Dairy Sci.* **45,** 633.

Jones, G. E., Boyns, A. R., Cameron, E. H. D., Bell, E. T., Christie, D. W., and Parkes, M. F. (1973a). *J. Endocrinol.* **57,** 331.

Jones, G. E., Boyns, A. R., Bell, E. T., Christie, D. W., and Parkes, M. F. (1973b) *Acta Endocrinol.* **72,** 573.

Jones, R. E. (1978). *In* "The Vertebrate Ovary" (R. E. Jones, ed.), p. 731. Plenum, New York.

Kajanoja, P., Ranta, T., and Seppälä, M. (1978). *Prostaglandins* **16,** 327.

Kamonpatana, M., Kunawongkrit, A., Bodhipaksha, P., and Luvira, Y. (1979). *J. Reprod. Fertil.* **56,** 445.

Kann, G., and Denamur, R. (1974). *J. Reprod. Fertil.* **39,** 473.

Karim, S. M. M., and Hillier, K. (1975). *In* "Prostaglandins and Reproduction" (S. M. M. Karim, ed.), p. 23. Univ. Park Press, Baltimore, Maryland.

Karsch, F. J., and Sutton, G. P. (1976). *Endocrinology* **98,** 553.

Karsch, F. J., Krey, L. C., Weick, R. F., Dierschke, D. J., and Knobil, E. (1973). *Endocrinology* **92,** 1148.

Karsch, F. J., Foster, D. L., Legan, S. J., Ryan, K. D., and Peter, G. K. (1979). *Endocrinology* **105,** 421.

Karsch, F. J., Goodman, R. L., and Legan, S. J. (1980). *J. Reprod. Fertil.* **58,** 521.

Kato, H., Morishige, W. K., and Rothchild, I. (1979). *Endocrinology* **105,** 846.

Kelley, H. E., and Stormshak, F. (1969). *J. Reprod. Fertil.* **20,** 171.

Kelly, P. A., Tushima, T., Shiu, R. P. C., and Friesen, H. G. (1976). *Endocrinology* **99,** 765.

Kelly, R. W., and Abel, M. H. (1980). *Adv. Prostagl. Thrombox. Res.* **8,** 1369.

Keyes, P. L., and Nalbandov, A. V. (1967). *Endocrinology* **80,** 938.

Khan, M. I., Rosberg, S., Lahav, M., Lamprecht, S. A., Selstam, G., Herlitz, H., and Ahren, K. (1979). *Biol. Reprod.* **21,** 1175.

Kielan-Jaworowska, Z. (1975). *Nature (London)* **252,** 698.

Kincl, F. A., and Ciaccio, L. A. (1980). *Endocrinol. Exp.* **14,** 27.

Kindahl, H., Edqvist, L., and Lindell, J. (1980). *Adv. Prostagl. Thrombox. Res.* **8,** 1351.

Kiracofe, G. H., Singh, A. R., and Nghiem, N. D. (1969). *J. Reprod. Fertil.* **20,** 473.

Kirsch, J. A. W. (1977). *Evolution* **31,** 898.

Kirton, K. T., and Koering, M. J. (1973). *Fertil. Steril.* **24,** 926.

Kirton, K. T., Niswender, G. D., Midgley, A. R., Jr., Jaffe, R. B., and Forbes, A. D. (1970). *J. Clin. Endocrinol. Metab.* **30,** 105.

Klicka, J., and Mahmoud, I. Y. (1977). *Gen. Comp. Endocrinol.* **31,** 407.

Knazek, R. A., Christy, R. J., Watson, K. C., Liu, S. C., van Gorde, P. N., Connelly, K. M., and Lim, M. F. (1980). *Annu. Meet. Endocrine Soc.* **62,** Abstr. No. 709, p. 252.

Knobil, E. (1973). *Biol. Reprod.* **8,** 246.

Knobil, E. (1974). *Recent Prog. Horm. Res.* **30,** 1.

Knobil, E. (1980). *Recent Prog. Horm. Res.* **36,** 53.

Koering, M. J. (1974). *In* "Reproductive Biology of the Primate" (W. P. Luckett, ed.), p. 38. Karger, Basel.

Koering, M. J., and Kirton, K. T. (1973). *Biol. Reprod.* **9,** 226.

Korda, A. R., Shutt, D. A., Smith, I. D., Shearman, R. P., and Lyneham, R. C. (1975). *Prostaglandins* **9,** 443.

Korenman, S. G., Loh, P. M., Beceiro, J., Sherman, B. M., and Granner, D. K. (1973). *Endocrinology* **93,** 1423.

Koullapis, E. N., and Collins, W. P. (1980). *Acta Endocrinol.* **93,** 123.

Kraeling, R. R. (1970). Ph.D. Thesis, Iowa State University, Ames, Iowa.

Krey, L. C., and Everett, J. W. (1973). *Endocrinology* **93,** 377.

Krey, L. C., Tyre, L., and Everett, J. W. (1973). *Endocrinology* **93,** 385.

Kristoffersen, J. (1960). *Acta Endocrinol.* **33,** 417.

Krzymowski, T., Kotwica, J., Okrasa, S., Doboszynska, T., and Ziecika, A. (1978). *J. Reprod. Fertil.* **54,** 21.

Kuehl, F. A. Jr. (1974). *Prostaglandins* **5,** 325.

Lahav, M., Lamprecht, S. A., Amsterdam, A., and Lindner, H. R. (1977a). *Mol. Cell. Endocrinol.* **6,** 293.

Lahav, M., Meidan, R., Amsterdam, A., Gebauer, H., and Lindner, H. R. (1977b). *J. Endocrinol.* **75,** 317.

Lam, P. C. O., and Rothchild, I. (1973). *J. Endocrinol.* **56,** 609.

Lam, P. C. O., and Rothchild, I. (1977). *Endocrinology* **101,** 1503.

Lamprecht, S. A., Lindner, H. R., and Strauss, J. F. III (1969). *Biochim. Biophys. Acta* **187,** 133.

Lamprecht, S. A., Herlitz, H. V., and Ahrén, K. E. B. (1975). *Mol. Cell. Endocrinol.* **3,** 273.

Lance, V., and Callard, I. D. (1979). *In* "The Vertebrate Ovary" (R. E. Jones, ed.), p. 361. Plenum, New York.

Lands, W. E. M. (1979). *Annu. Rev. Physiol.* **41,** 633.

Laurence, K. A., Chang, C. C., Hassouna, H., Badawy, S., and Loewit, K. (1971/1972). *Gynecol. Invest.* **2,** 57.

Lawrence, I. E., Jr., Burden, H. N., and Louis, T. M. (1978). *J. Reprod. Fertil.* **53,** 131.

Lee, A. K., Bradley, J., and Braithwaite, R. W. (1977). *In* "The Biology of Marsupials" (B. Stonehouse and D. Gilmore, eds.), p. 209. Univ. Park Press, Baltimore.

Lehmann, F., Just-Nastansky, I., Behrendt, B., Czygan, P.-J., and Bettendorf, G. (1975). *Acta Endocrinol.* **79,** 329.

LeMaire, W. J., Rice, B. F., and Savard, K. (1968). *J. Clin. Endocrinol. Metab.* **28,** 1249.

Lemon, M. (1972). *J. Endocrinol.* **55,** 63.

Lemon, M., and Saumande, J. (1972). *J. Reprod. Fertil.* **31,** 501.

Lewis, G. S., Wilson, L., Jr., Wilks, J. W., Pexton, J. E., Fogwell, R. L., Ford, S. P., Butcher, R. L., Thayne, W. V., and Inskeep, E. K. (1977). *J. Anim. Sci.* **45,** 320.

Lewis, G. S., Jenkins, P. E., Fogwell, R. L., and Inskeep, E. K. (1978). *J. Anim. Sci.* **47,** 1314.

Licht, P., Papkoff, H., Farmer, S. W., Muller, C. H., Tsui, H. W., and Crews, D. (1977). *Recent Prog. Horm. Res.* **33,** 169.

Liggins, G. C. (1973). *In* "Endocrine Factors in Labour" (A. Klopper and J. Gardener, eds.), p. 119. Cambridge Univ. Press, London and New York.

Liggins, G. C. (1979). *Br. Med. Bull.* **35,** 145.

Lillegraven, J. A. (1975). *Evolution* **29,** 707.

Lillegraven, J. A. (1979). *In* "Mesozoic Mammals: The First Two Thirds of Mammalian History" (J. A. Lillegraven, Z. Kielan-Jaworowska, and W. A. Clemens, eds.), p. 259. Univ. of California Press, Berkeley.

Lillegraven, J. A., Kielan-Jaworowska, Z., and Clemens, W. A., eds. (1979). "The Mesozoic Mammals: The First Two Thirds of Mammalian History." Univ. of California Press, Berkeley.

Lindloff, G., Holtz, W., Elsaesser, F., Kreikenbaum, K., and Smidt, D. (1976). *Biol. Reprod.* **15,** 303.

Lindner, H. R. (1979). Discussion of Tyndale-Biscoe (1979).

Lindner, H. R., Amsterdam, A., Salomon, Y., Tsafriri, A., Nimrod, A., Lamprecht, S. A., Zor, U., and Koch, Y. (1977). *J. Reprod. Fertil.* **51,** 215.

Linkie, D. M., and Niswender, G. D. (1972). *Endocrinology* **90,** 632.

Loewit, K., and Zambelis, N. (1979). *Acta Endocrinol.* **90,** 176.

Loewit, K., Badawy, S., and Laurence, K. (1969). *Endocrinology* **84,** 244.

Long, J. A., and Evans, H. M. (1922). *Memoirs Univ. Calif. Publ. Zool.* **6,** 1.

Louis, T. M., Parry, D. M., Robinson, J. S., Thorburn, G. D., and Challis, J. R. G. (1978). *J. Endocrinol.* **73,** 427.

Lukaszewska, J., and Hansel, W. (1979). *Adv. Exp. Med. Biol.* **112,** 511.

Lyne, A. G., and Hollis, D. E. (1977). *In* "Reproduction and Evolution" (J. H. Calaby and C. H. Tyndale-Biscoe, eds.), p. 293. Australian Academy of Science.

Macdonald, G. J. (1978). *Proc. Soc. Exp. Biol. Med.* **159,** 441.

Macdonald, G. J., Tashjian, A. H., Jr., and Greep, R. O. (1970). *Biol. Reprod.* **2,** 202.

Macdonald, G. J., Yoshinaga, K., and Greep, R. O. (1971). *Proc. Soc. Exp. Biol. Med.* **136,** 687.

McCracken, J. A., Carlson, J. C., Glew, M. E., Goding, J. R., Baird, D. T., Green, K., and Sammuelsson, B. (1972). *Nature (London) New Biol.* **238,** 129.

McCracken, J. A., Einer-Jensen, J., and Fried, J. (1979). *Adv. Exp. Med. Biol.* **112,** 577.

McNatty, K. P., and Sawers, R. S. (1975). *J. Endocrinol.* **66,** 391.

McNatty, K. P., Sawers, R. S., and McNeilly, A. S. (1974). *Nature (London)* **250,** 653.

McNatty, K. P., Henderson, K. M., and Sawers, R. S. (1975). *J. Endocrinol.* **67,** 231.

Makris, A., and Ryan, K. J. (1975). *Endocrinology* **96,** 694.

Malven, P. V. (1969). *Endocrinology* **84,** 1224.

Malven, P. V., Hansel, W., and Sawyer, C. H. (1967). *J. Reprod. Fertil.* **13,** 205.

Maneckjee, R., Raj, H. G. M., and Moudgal, N. R. (1973). *Biol. Reprod.* **8,** 43.

Maneckjee, R., Moudgal, R. N., and Banavar, S. R., (1977). *Fertil. Steril.* **28,** 986.

Maqueo, M., and Goldzieher, J. W. (1966). *Fertil. Steril.* **17,** 676.

Marshall, L. G. (1979). *Zool. J. Linnean Soc.* **66,** 369.

Masuda, H., Anderson, L. L., Henricks, D. M., and Melampy, R. M. (1967). *Endocrinology* **80,** 240.

Maule Walker, F. M., and Poyser, N. L. (1973). *Acta Endocrinol. Suppl.* **179,** 312.

Mead, R. A. (1975). *Biol. Reprod.* **12,** 526.

Mead, R. A., and Eik-Nes, K. B. (1969). *J. Reprod. Fertil.* Suppl. No. 6, 397.

Mead, R. A., and Swannack, A. (1978). *Biol. Reprod.* **18,** 379.

Meites, J., Lu, K. H., Wuttke, W., Welsch, C. W., Nagasawa, H., and Quadri, S. K. (1972). *Recent Prog. Horm. Res.* **28,** 471.

Melampy, R. M., Anderson, L. L., and Kragt, C. L. (1964). *Endocrinology* **74,** 501.

Mellin, T. N., and Busch, R. D. (1976). *Prostaglandins* **12,** 303.

Menge, A. C., and Verville, R. (1969). *J. Anim. Sci.* **28,** 253.

Mercier-Parot, L., and Tuchmann-Duplessis, H. (1976). *C. R. Acad. Sci. (Paris) Ser. D* **283,** 353.

Michael, S. D. (1976). *Proc. Soc. Exp. Biol. Med.* **153,** 254.

Miller, J. B., and Keyes, P. L. (1975). *Endocrinology* **97,** 83.

Miller, M. R. (1948). *Univ. Calif. Publ. Zool.* **47,** 197.

Milligan, S. R. (1975). *J. Reprod. Fertil.* **42,** 35.

Mishell, D. R., Jr., Thorneycroft, I. H., Nagata, Y., Murata, T., and Nakamura, R. M. (1973). *Am. J. Obstet. Gynecol.* **117,** 631.

Moeljono, M. P. E., Bazer, F. W., and Thatcher, W. W. (1976). *Prostaglandins* **11,** 737.

Moeljono, M. P. E., Thatcher, W., Bazer, F. W., Frank, M., Owens, L. J., and Wilcox, C. J. (1977). *Prostaglandins* **14,** 543.
Mohini, P., Raj, B. J., and Chapekar, T. N. (1980). *J. Endocrinol.* **84,** 311.
Møller, O. M. (1973a). *J. Endocrinol.* **56,** 121.
Møller, O. M. (1973b). *J. Endocrinol.* **59,** 429.
Monroe, S. E., Atkinson, L. E., and Knobil, E. (1970). *Endocrinology* **87,** 453.
Moor, R. M. (1977). *J. Endocrinol.* **73,** 143.
Moore, N. W., Barrett, S., Brown, J. B., Schindler, I., Smith, M. A., and Smyth, B. (1969). *J. Endocrinol.* **44,** 55.
Morishige, W. K., and Rothchild, I. (1974). *Endocrinology* **95,** 260.
Morishige, W. K., Pepe, G. J., and Rothchild, I. (1973). *Endocrinology* **92,** 1527.
Morita, I., Nakayama, Y., Murota, S., (1979). *Prostaglandins* **18,** 507.
Morrison, J. A. (1971). *J. Reprod. Fertil.* **26,** 297.
Mossman, H. W., and Duke, K. L. (1973). "Comparative Morphology of the Mammalian Ovary." Univ. of Wisconsin Press, Madison.
Moudgal, N. R., Behrman, H. R., and Greep, R. O. (1972). *J. Endocrinol.* **52,** 413.
Mukherjee, T. K., Wright, S. W., Davidson, N. J. H., and Fotherby, K. (1972). *J. Obstet. Gynecol. Brit. Commonw.* **79,** 175.
Mukku, V., and Moudgal, N. R. (1975). *Endocrinology* **97,** 1455.
Munshi, S. R., Purandare, T. V., and Rao, S. S. (1973). *J. Endocrinol.* **58,** 123.
Murakami, N., Takahashi, M., and Suzuki, Y. (1979). *Biol. Reprod.* **21,** 263.
Murakami, N., Takahashi, M., and Suzuki, Y. (1980). *Biol. Reprod.* **22,** 253.
Murdoch, W. J., Lewis, G. S., Inskeep, E. K., and Tillson, S. A. (1978). *Am. J. Obstet. Gynecol.* **132,** 81.
Murota, S., Yokoi, T., and Mori, Y. (1978). *Prostaglandins* **15,** 697.
Murphy, B. D. (1979). *Biol. Reprod.* **21,** 517.
Nachreiner, R. F., and Marple, D. N. (1974). *Prostaglandins* **7,** 303.
Nagle, C. A., Denari, J., Quiroga, S., Riarte, A., Merlo, A., Germino, N. I., Gómez-Argana, F., and Rosner, J. M. (1979). *Biol. Reprod.* **21,** 979.
Nakamura, Y., and Ichiakawa, S. (1978). *Biol. Reprod.* **19,** 1014.
Nanes, M. S., Garris, D. R., and Rothchild, I. (1980). *Proc. Soc. Exp. Biol. Med.* **164,** 299.
Nanes, M. S., and Rothchild, I. (1981). In preparation.
Nathanielsz, P. W. (1978). *Annu. Rev. Physiol.* **40,** 411.
Neely, D. P., Hughes, J. P., Stabenfeldt, G. H., and Evans, J. W. (1975). *J. Reprod. Fertil. Suppl.* **23,** 235.
Neely, D. P., Kindahl, H., Stabenfeldt, G. H., Edqvist, L.-E., and Hughes, J. P. (1979). *J. Reprod. Fertil. Suppl.* **27,** 181.
Neill, J. D., Johansson, E. D. B., Datta, J. K., and Knobil, E. (1967). *J. Clin. Endocrinol. Metab.* **27,** 1167.
Nequin, L. G., Alvarez, J., and Schwartz, N. B. (1979). *Biol. Reprod.* **20,** 659.
Nett, T. M., Pickett, B. W., Seidel, G. E., Jr., and Voss, J. L. (1976). *Biol. Reprod.* **14,** 412.
Nicoll, C. S. (1980). *Fed. Proc. Fed. Am. Soc. Exp. Biol.* **39,** 2563.
Nicoll, C. S., and Bern, H. A. (1972). *In* "Lactogenic Hormones" (G. E. W. Wolstenholme and J. Knight, eds.), p. 299. Churchill, London.
Nicosia, S. V. (1972). *Fertil. Steril.* **23,** 791.
Nishi, N., Arimura, A., de la Cruz, K. G., and Schally, A. V. (1976). *Endocrinology* **98,** 1024.
Niswender, G. D. (1974). *Endocrinology* **94,** 612.
Niswender, G. D. (1981). *In* "Dynamics of Ovarian Function" (N. B. Schwartz and M. Hunzicker-Dunn, eds.). Raven Press, New York (in press).
Niswender, G. D., Reichert, L. E., Jr., and Zimmerman, D. R. (1970). *Endocrinology* **87,** 576.

Niswender, G. D., Menon, K. M. J., and Jaffe, R. B. (1972). *Fertil. Steril.* **23,** 432.
Niswender, G. D., Reimers, T. J., Diekman, M. A., and Nett, T. M. (1976). *Biol. Reprod.* **14,** 64.
Nuti, K. M., and Meyer, R. K. (1975). *Biol. Reprod.* **13,** 415.
Nutting, E. F., Metcalf, L., and Calhoun, D. W. (1980). *Fed. Proc. Fed. Am. Soc. Exp. Biol.* **39,** 984.
Ochiai, I., and Rothchild, I. (1980). *Annu. Meet. Endocrine Soc.* **62,** Abstr. No. 365, p. 166.
Ochiai, K., Nanes, M. S., and Rothchild, I. (1981). In Preparation.
Paavola, L. G. (1977). *Am. J. Anat.* **150,** 565.
Packard, G. C., Tracy, C. R., and Roth, J. J. (1977). *Biol. Rev.* **52,** 71.
Pal, A. K., Gupta, T., and Chatterjee, A. (1976). *Acta Endocrinol.* **83,** 506.
Pant, H. C., Hopkinson, C. R. N., and Fitzpatrick, R. J. (1977). *J. Endocrinol.* **73,** 247.
Papke, R. L., Concannon, P. W., Travis, H. F., and Hansel, W. (1980). *J. Anim. Sci.* **50,** 1102.
Parker, P. (1977). *In* "The Biology of Marsupials" (B. Stonehouse and D. Gilmore, eds.), p. 273. Univ. Park Press, Baltimore.
Parvizi, N., Elsaesser, F., Smidt, D., and Ellendorff, F. (1976). *J. Endocrinol.* **69,** 193.
Patek, C. E., and Watson, J. (1976). *Prostaglandins* **12,** 97.
Pepe, G. J., and Rothchild, I. (1973). *Endocrinology* **93,** 1200.
Pepe, G. J., and Rothchild, I. (1974). *Endocrinology* **95,** 275.
Peppler, R. D., and Stone, S. C. (1980). *Lab. Anim. Sci.* **30,** 188.
Perry, J. S., and Rowlands, I. W. (1962). *J. Endocrinol.* **25,** v.
Peterson, A. J., Tervit, H. R., Fairclough, R. J., Havik, P. G., and Smith, J. F. (1976). *Prostaglandins* **12,** 551.
Pexton, J. E., Weems, C. W., and Inskeep, E. K. (1975). *J. Anim. Sci.* **41,** 154.
Pharriss, B. B., and Shaw, J. E. (1974). *Annu. Rev. Physiol.* **36,** 391.
Pilton, P. E., and Sharman, G. B. (1962). *J. Endocrinol.* **25,** 119.
Plotka, E. D., and Erb, R. E. (1967). *J. Anim. Sci.* **26,** 1363.
Plunkett, E. R., Moon, Y. S., Zamecnik, J., and Armstrong, D. T. (1975). *Am. J. Obstet. Gynecol.* **123,** 391.
Pong, S., and Levine, L. (1977). *In* "The Prostaglandins" (P. W. Ramwell, ed.), Vol. 3, p. 41. Plenum, New York.
Poyser, N. L. (1972). *J. Endocrinol.* **54,** 147.
Poyser, N. L. (1978). *Biochem. Soc. Trans.* **6,** 718.
Raj, H. G. M., and Moudgal, N. G. (1970). *Endocrinology* **86,** 874.
Raj, H. G. M., Talbert, L. M., and Easterling, W. E. (1979). *Adv. Exp. Med. Biol.* **112,** 535.
Ramwell, P. W., Leovey, E. M. K., and Sintetos, A. L. (1977). *Biol. Reprod.* **16,** 70.
Rao, B. (1979). *Prostaglandins* **18,** 93.
Rathmacher, P. P., and Anderson, L. L. (1968). *Am. J. Physiol.* **214,** 1014.
Renfree, M. B. (1974). *J. Reprod. Fertil.* **39,** 127.
Renfree, M. B. (1977). *In* "Reproduction and Evolution" (J. H. Calaby and C. H. Tyndale-Biscoe, eds.), p. 325. Australian Academy of Science.
Renfree, M. B., and Tyndale-Biscoe, C. H. (1973). *Dev. Biol.* **32,** 28.
Renfree, M. B., Green, S. W., and Young, I. R. (1979). *J. Reprod. Fertil.* **57,** 131.
Resko, J. A., Norman, R. L., Niswender, G. D., and Spies, H. G. (1974). *Endocrinology* **94,** 128.
Reştall, B. J. (1964). *Aust. J. Exp. Agric.* **4,** 274.
Rexroad, C. E., Jr., and Guthrie, H. D. (1979). *Adv. Exp. Med. Biol.* **112,** 639.
Reyes, F. I., Winter, J. S. D., Faiman, C., and Hobson, W. C. (1975). *Endocrinology* **96,** 1447.
Rice, B. F., Harkin, G., Dhurandhar, N., MacPhee, A. A., and Sternberg, W. H. (1976). *Clin. Res.* **24,** 44A.

Rich, S. T. (1968). *Lab. Anim. Sci.* **18,** 235.
Richards, J. S. (1979). *Recent Prog. Horm. Res.* **35,** 368.
Riddle, O. (1963). *J. Natl. Cancer Inst.* **31,** 1039.
Rillema, J. A. (1980). *Fed. Proc. Fed. Am. Soc. Exp. Biol.* **39,** 2593.
Rodway, R. G., and Kuhn, N. J. (1975). *Biochem. J.* **152,** 445.
Rodway, R. G., and Rothchild, I. (1977). *Fed. Proc. Fed. Am. Soc. Exp. Biol.* **36,** 312.
Rodway, R. G., Garris, D. R., and Gibori, G. (1981). In preparation.
Rombauts, P., Popin, F., and Terqui, M., (1965). *C. R. Acad. Sci.* **261,** 2753.
Romers, A. S. (1966). "Vertebrate Paleontology," 3rd Ed. Univ. of Chicago Press, Chicago, Illinois.
Roser, S., and Buffer, G. (1972). *C. R. Acad. Sci. (Paris) Ser. D* **274,** 1708.
Roth, J. J., Jones, R. E., and Gerrard, A. M. (1973). *Gen. Comp. Endocrinol.* **21,** 569.
Rothchild, I. (1946). *Endocrinology* **39,** 82.
Rothchild, I. (1960). *Endocrinology* **67,** 9.
Rothchild, I. (1964). *Proc. Int. Congr. Endocrinology, 2nd London* p. 686.
Rothchild, I. (1965). *Vitam. Horm.* **23,** 209.
Rothchild, I. (1966). *J. Reprod. Fertil. Suppl.* **1,** 49.
Rothchild, I. (1973). *In* "Regulation of Mammalian Reproduction" (S. J. Segal, R. Crozier, P. Crofman, and P. G. Condliffe, eds.), p. 419. Thomas, Springfield, Illinois.
Rothchild, I., and Fraps, R. M. (1944). *Proc. Soc. Exp. Biol. Med.* **56,** 79.
Rothchild, I., and Schubert, R. (1963). *Endocrinology* **72,** 969.
Rothchild, I., and Schwartz, N. B. (1965). *Acta Endocrinol.* **49,** 120.
Rothchild, I., Billiar, R. B., Kline, I. T., and Pepe, G. (1973). *J. Endocrinol.* **57,** 63.
Rothchild, I., Pepe, G. J., and Morishige, W. K. (1974). *Endocrinology* **95,** 280.
Rowson, L. E. A., Tervit, R., and Brand, A. (1972). *J. Reprod. Fertil.* **29,** 145.
Russell, W. (1975). *Prostaglandins* **10,** 163.
Sabine, J. R. (1977). "Cholesterol." Dekker, New York.
Sadler, R. K., Rochelle, D. B., Capp, B. R., MacDonald, S., MacDonald, P. C., Winkel, C. A., and Simpson, E. R. (1980). *Annu. Meet. Soc. Gynecol. Invest.*
Saksena, S. K., and Lau, I. F. (1973). *Prostaglandins* **3,** 317.
Saksena, S. K., and Lau, I. F. (1978). *Prostagl. Med.* **1,** 201.
Salamonsen, L. A., Jonas, H. A., Burger, H. G., Buckmaster, J. M., Chamley, W. A., Cumming, I. A., Findlay, J. K., and Goding, J. R. (1973). *Endocrinology* **93,** 610.
Salazar, H., and Archer, D. F. (1974). *Int. J. Obstet. Gynaecol. Reprod. Biol.* **4,** (Suppl), S19.
Salazar, H., Furr, B. J. A., Smith, G. K., Bently, M., and Gonzalez-Angulo, A. (1976). *Biol. Reprod.* **14,** 458.
Sammelwitz, P. H., Aldred, J. P., and Nalbandov, A. V. (1961). *J. Reprod. Fertil.* **2,** 387.
Sanchez-Criado, J., and Rothchild, I. (1981). In preparation.
Sasser, R. G., Niswender, G. D., and Nett, T. M. (1977). *Prostaglandins* **13,** 1201.
Sauer, M. J. (1979). *J. Reprod. Fertil.* **56,** 725.
Saure, A., Teräväinen, T., and Karjalainen, O. (1977). *J. Reprod. Fertil.* **51,** 369.
Savard, K. (1973). *Biol. Reprod.* **8,** 183.
Scaramuzzi, R. J., Caldwell, B. V., and Moor, R. M. (1970). *Biol. Reprod.* **3,** 110.
Schafer, J. H., Christenson, R. K., Teague, H. S., and Grifo, A. P., Jr. (1973). *J. Anim. Sci.* **36,** 722.
Schomberg, D. W., Coudert, S. P., and Short, R. V. (1967). *J. Reprod. Fertil.* **14,** 277.
Schreiber, J. R., and Nakamura, K. (1980). *Annu. Meet. Endocrine Soc.* **62,** Abstr. No. 162, p. 115.
Schreiber, J. R., Nakamura, K., and Erickson, G. F. (1981). *In* "Dynamics of Ovarian Function" (N. B. Schwartz and M. Hunzicker-Dunn, eds.). Raven Press, New York (in press).

Schroff, C., Klindt, J. M., Kaltenbach, C. C., Graber, J. W., and Niswender, G. D. (1971). *J. Anim. Sci.* **33,** 268.
Schuler, L. A., Christie, M. H., Langeberg, K., and Strauss, J. F. III. (1980a). *Annu. Meet. Endocrine Soc.* **62,** Abstr. No. 161, p. 115.
Schuler, L. A., Strauss, J. F., III, and Gwynn, J. T. (1980b). *Annu. Meet. Soc. Study Reprod.* **13,** Abst. No. 81.
Schulz, K-D., Geiger, W., Del Pozo, E., Lose, K. H., Künzig, H. J., and Lancranjan, I. (1976). *Arch. Gynäkol.* **221,** 93.
Schulz, K.-D., Geiger, W., Del Pozo, E., and Künzig, H. J. (1978). *Am. J. Obstet. Gynecol.* **132,** 561.
Schwarz, B. E., Milewich, L., Gant, N. F., Porter, J. C., Johnston, J. M., and MacDonald, P. C. (1977). *Ann. N.Y. Acad. Sci.* **286,** 304.
Scott, R. S., and Rennie, P. I. C. (1970). *J. Reprod. Fertil.* **23,** 415.
Seal, U. S., Plotka, E. D., Packard, J. M., and Mech, L. D. (1979). *Biol. Reprod.* **21,** 1057.
Shaikh, A. A. (1972). *Prostaglandins* **2,** 227.
Sharma, S. C., Wilson, C. M. M., and Pugh, D. M. (1976). *Prostaglandins* **11,** 555.
Sharman, G. B. (1970). *Science* **167,** 1221.
Sharman, G. B. (1976). *In* "Reproduction in Mammals" (C. A. Austin and R. V. Short, eds.), Book 6, p. 32. Cambridge Univ. Press, London and New York.
Shemesh, M. (1979). *J. Endocrinol.* **82,** 27.
Shemesh, M., and Hansel, W. (1975a). *Proc. Soc. Exp. Biol. Med.* **148,** 123.
Shemesh, M., and Hansel, W. (1975b). *Proc. Soc. Exp. Biol. Med.* **148,** 243.
Shemesh, M., and Hansel, W. (1975c). *Biol. Reprod.* **13,** 448.
Shemesh, M., Bensadoun, A., and Hansel, W. (1976). *Proc. Soc. Exp. Biol. Med.* **151,** 667.
Shille, V. M., and Stabenfeldt, G. H. (1979). *Biol. Reprod.* **21,** 1217.
Shinada, T., Yokota, Y., and Igarashi, M. (1978). *Fertil. Steril.* **29,** 84.
Shiota, K., and Wiest, W. G. (1979). *Adv. Exp. Med. Biol.* **112,** 169.
Shirley, A., and Stephenson, J. (1973). *J. Endorcinol.* **58,** 345.
Short, R. V. (1967). *Arch. Anat. Microsc. Morphol. Exp.* **56** (Suppl) 258.
Shutt, D. A., Shearman, R. P., Lyneham, R. C., Clarke, A. H., McMahon, G. R., and Goh, P. (1975). *Steroids* **26,** 299.
Shutt, D. A., Clarke, A. H., Fraser, I. S., Goh, P., McMahon, G. R., Saunders, D. M., and Sharman, R. P. (1976). *J. Endocrinol.* **71,** 453.
Siiteri, P. K., Febres, F., Clemens, R., Chang, R. J., Gondos, B., and Stites, D. (1977). *Ann. N.Y. Acad. Sci.* **286,** 384.
Silbiger, M., and Rothchild, I. (1963). *Acta Endocrinol.* **43,** 521.
Singh, E. J., Baccarini, I. M., and Zuspan, F. P. (1975). *Am. J. Obstet. Gynecol.* **121,** 1003.
Smith, M. S., and McDonald, L. E. (1974). *Endocrinology* **94,** 404.
Smith, M. S., and Neill, J. D. (1976). *Endocrinology* **98,** 696.
Smith, M. S., Freeman, M. E., and Neill, J. D. (1975). *Endocrinology* **96,** 219.
Smith, W. L., Huslig, R. L., Rollins, T. E., and Fogwell, R. L. (1980). *Adv. Prostagl. Thrombox. Res.* **8,** 1345.
Snook, R. B., Brunner, M. A., Saatman, R. R., and Hansel, W. (1969). *Biol. Reprod.* **1,** 49.
Snook, R. B., Saatman, R. R., and Hansel, W. (1971). *Endocrinology* **88,** 678.
Spies, H. G., and Quadri, S. K. (1967). *Endocrinology* **80,** 1127.
Spies, H. G., Slyter, A. L., and Quadri, S. K. (1967a). *J. Anim. Sci.* **26,** 768.
Spies, H. G., Warren, D. R., and Grier, H. T. (1967b). *Endocrinology* **81,** 1435.
Spies, H. G., Hilliard, J., and Sawyer, C. H. (1968a). *Endocrinology* **83,** 291.
Spies, H. G., Hilliard, J., and Sawyer, C. H. (1968b). *Endocrinology* **83,** 354.
Spilman, C. H., Beuving, D. C., Forbes, A. D., and Kimball, F. A. (1977). *Prostaglandins* **14,** 477.
Stabenfeldt, G. H., Holt, J. A., and Ewing, L. L. (1969). *Endocrinology* **85,** 11.

Stabenfeldt, G. H., Drost, M., and Franti, C. E. (1970). *Endocrinology* **90,** 144.
Stevens, V. C., Sparks, S. J., and Powell, J. E. (1970). *Endocrinology* **87,** 658.
Stouffer, R. L., Tyrey, L., and Schomberg, D. W. (1976). *Endocrinology* **99,** 516.
Stouffer, R. L., Nixon, W. E., and Hodgen, G. D. (1977). *Endocrinology* **101,** 1157.
Stouffer, R. L., Bennett, L. A., and Hodgen, G. D. (1980). *Endocrinology* **106,** 519.
Strauss, J. F., III, and Flickiger, G. L. (1977). *Endocrinology* **101,** 833.
Strauss, J. F., III, and Stambaugh, R. L. (1974). *Prostaglandins* **5,** 73.
Surve, A. H., Bacso, I., Brinckerhoff, J. H., and Kirsch, S. (1976). *Biol. Reprod.* **15,** 343.
Suzuki, A., Mori, T., and Nishimura, T. (1977). *J. Endocrinol.* **75,** 355.
Swanston, I. A., McNatty, K. P., and Baird, D. T. (1977). *J. Endocrinol.* **73,** 115.
Takahashi, M., Shiota, K., and Suzuki, Y. (1978). *Endocrinology* **102,** 494.
Takahashi, M., Shiota, K., and Suzuki, Y. (1979). *Biol. Reprod.* **21,** 813.
Takahashi, M., Murakami, N., Naito, H., and Suzuki, Y. (1980). *Biol. Reprod.* **22,** 423.
Takayama, M., and Greenwald, G. S. (1973). *Endocrinology* **92,** 1405.
Tam, W. H. (1973). *J. Reprod. Fertil.* **35,** 105.
Tanaka, K., and Nakada, T. (1974). *Poultry Sci.* **53,** 2120.
Taylor, I. M., and Padykula, H. A. (1978). *Nature (London)* **271,** 588.
Terranova, P. F. (1980). *Endocrinology* **106,** 758.
Terranova, P. F., and Greenwald, G. S. (1978). *Endocrinology* **103,** 845.
Terranova, P. F., and Greenwald, G. S. (1979a). *Endocrinology* **104,** 1013.
Terranova, P. F., and Greenwald, G. S. (1979b). *Endocrinology* **104,** 1020.
Terranova, P. F., Conner, J. S., and Greenwald, G. S. (1978). *Biol. Reprod.* **19,** 249.
Terranova, P. F., Saidapur, S. K., and Greenwald, G. S. (1980). *J. Endocrinol.* **84,** 101.
Thorburn, G. D., and Challis, J. R. G. (1979). *Physiol. Rev.* **59,** 863.
Thorburn, G. D., and Mattner, P. E. (1971). *J. Endocrinol.* **50,** 307.
Thorburn, G. D., Cox, R. I., and Shorey, C. D. (1971). *J. Reprod. Fertil.* **24,** 139.
Thwaites, C. J., and Edey, T. N. (1970). *Am. J. Anat.* **129,** 439.
Turksoy, R. N., and Safaii, H. S. (1975). *Fertil. Steril.* **26,** 634.
Tyndale-Biscoe, C. H. (1973). "The Life of Marsupials." Academic Press, New York.
Tyndale-Biscoe, C. H. (1979). *Ciba Found. Symp.* No. 64, p. 173.
Tyndale-Biscoe, C. H., and Hawkins, J. (1977). *In* "Reproduction and Evolution (J. H. Calaby and C. H. Tyndale-Biscoe, eds.), p. 245. Australian Academy of Science.
Tyndale-Biscoe, C. H., Hearn, J. P., and Renfree, M. B. (1974). *J. Endocrinol.* **63,** 589.
Uchida, K., Kadowaki, and Miyake, T. (1969). *Endocrinol. Jpn.* **16,** 227.
Uchida, K., Kadowaki, M., and Miyake, T. (1970a). *Endocrinol. Jpn.* **17,** 99.
Uchida, K., Kadowaki, M., and Miyake, T. (1970b). *Endocrinol. Jpn.* **17,** 509.
Uchida, K., Kadowaki, M., Miyake, T., and Wakabayashi, K. (1972). *Endocrinol. Jpn.* **19,** 323.
van der Schoot, P., and de Greef, W. J. (1976). *J. Endocrinol.* **70,** 61.
van der Schoot, P., Lankhorst, R. R., De Roo, J. A., and de Greef, W. J. (1978). *Endocrinology* **103,** 949.
Vande Wiele, R. L., Bogumil, J., Dyrenfurth, I., Ferin, M., Jewelewicz, R., Warren, M., Rizkallah, T., and Mikhail, G. (1970). *Recent Prog. Horm. Res.* **26,** 63.
Van Thiel, D. H., Bridson, W. E., and Kohler, P. O. (1971). *Endocrinology* **89,** 622.
Veomett, M. J., and Daniel, J. C. Jr., (1971). *J. Reprod. Fertil.* **26,** 415.
Veomett, M. J., and Daniel, J. C. Jr. (1975a). *J. Reprod. Fertil.* **44,** 513.
Veomett, M. J., and Daniel, J. C. Jr., (1975b). *J. Reprod. Fertil.* **44,** 519.
Veomett, M. J., and Daniel, J. C. Jr. (1975c). *J. Reprod. Fertil.* **44,** 529.
Verhage, H. G., Beamer, N. B., and Brenner, R. M. (1976). *Biol. Reprod.* **14,** 579.
Vickery, G., and McRae, G. (1980). *Biol. Reprod.* **22,** 438.
Vogt, W. (1978). *Adv. Prostagl. Thrombox. Res.* **3,** 89.

Walker, E. P. (1968). "Mammals of the World," 2nd Ed. Johns Hopkins Press, Baltimore, Maryland.

Walsh, S. W., Wolf, R. C., Meyer, R. K., Aubert, M. L., and Friesen, H. G. (1977). *Endocrinology* **100,** 851.

Walton, J. S., McNeilly, J. R., McNeilly, A. S., and Cunningham, F. J. (1977). *J. Endocrinol.* **75,** 127.

Watson, J., and Maule Walker, F. M. (1977). *J. Reprod. Fertil.* **51,** 393.

Watson, J., Shepherd, T. S., and Dodson, K. S. (1979). *J. Reprod. Fertil.* **57,** 489.

Weems, C. W. (1979). *Prostaglandins* **17,** 873.

Weems, C. W., Pexton, J. E., Butcher, R. L., and Inskeep, E. K. (1975). *Biol. Reprod.* **13,** 282.

Weems, C. H., Huecksteadt, T. P., Sjahli, H., and Lavelle, P. (1979). *Prostaglandins* **17,** 891.

Weiss, G., Dierschke, D. J., Karsch, F. J., Hotchkiss, J., Butler, W. R., and Knobil, E. (1973). *Endocrinology* **93,** 954.

Weiss, G., O'Byrne, E. M., Hochman, J. A., Goldsmith, L. T., Rifkin, I., and Steinetz, B. G. (1977). *Obstet. Gynecol.* **50,** 679.

Weiss, T. J., Janson, P. O., Porter, K. J., and Seamark, R. F. (1978). *Acta Endocrinol.* **89,** 158.

Welschen, R., Osman, P., Dullaart, J., de Greef, W. J., Uilenbroek, J.Th J., and de Jong, F. H. (1975). *J. Endocrinol.* **64,** 37.

Westfahl, P. K., and Kling, O. R. (1981). *In* "Dynamics of Ovarian Function" (N. B. Schwartz and M. Hunzicker-Dunn, eds.). Raven Press, New York (in press).

Wiest, W. G. (1970). *Endocrinology* **87,** 43.

Wiest, W. G., Kidwell, W. R., and Balogh, K. (1968). *Endocrinology* **82,** 844.

Wildt, D. E., Danko, W. B., and Seager, W. J. (1979). *Prostaglandins* **18,** 883.

Wilks, J. W. (1977). *Biol. Reprod.* **16,** 474.

Wilks, J. W. (1979). *Adv. Exp. Med. Biol.* **112,** 621.

Wilks, J. W., Forbes, K. K., and Norland, J. F. (1972). *In* "Prostaglandins" (E. M. Southern, ed.), p. 47. Futura, New York.

Williams, M. T., Roth, M. S., Marsh, J. M., and LeMaire, W. J. (1979). *J. Clin. Endocrinol. Metab.* **48,** 437.

Willman, E. A., and Collins, W. P. (1976). *J. Endocrinol.* **69,** 413.

Wilson, L., Jr., Butcher, R. L., Cenedella, R. L., and Inskeep, E. K. (1972a). *Prostaglandins* **1,** 183.

Wilson, L., Jr., Cenedella, R. J., Butcher, R. L., and Inskeep, E. K. (1972b). *J. Anim. Sci.* **34,** 93.

Wolf, R. C., O'Connor, R. F., and Robinson, J. A. (1977). *Biol. Reprod.* **17,** 228.

Wood-Gush, D. G. M., and Gilbert, A. B. (1964). *Anim. Behav.* **12,** 451.

Woody, C., and Ginther, O. J. (1968). *J. Anim. Sci.* **27,** 1387.

Woody, C., Ginther, O. J., and Pope, A. L. (1967). *J. Anim. Sci.* **26,** 1113.

Wu, D. H., and Wiest, W. G. (1978). *Endocrinology* **103,** 513.

Wuttke, W., and Meites, J. (1971). *Proc. Soc. Exp. Biol. Med.* **137,** 988.

Yaron, Z. (1972). *Gen. Compar. Endocrinol.* Suppl. No. 3, p. 663.

Yogev, L., and Terkel, J. (1978). *Endocrinology* **102,** 160.

Yoshinaga, K., Grieves, S. A., and Short, R. V. (1967). *J. Endocrinol.* **38,** 423.

Young, I. R., and Renfree, M. B. (1979). *J. Reprod. Fertil.* **56,** 249.

Yuh, K.-C. (1980). *Annu. Meet. Soc. Study Reprod.* **13,** Abstr. No. 86.

Yuthasastrakasol, P., Palmer, W. M., and Howland, B. E. (1975). *J. Reprod. Fertil.* **43,** 57.

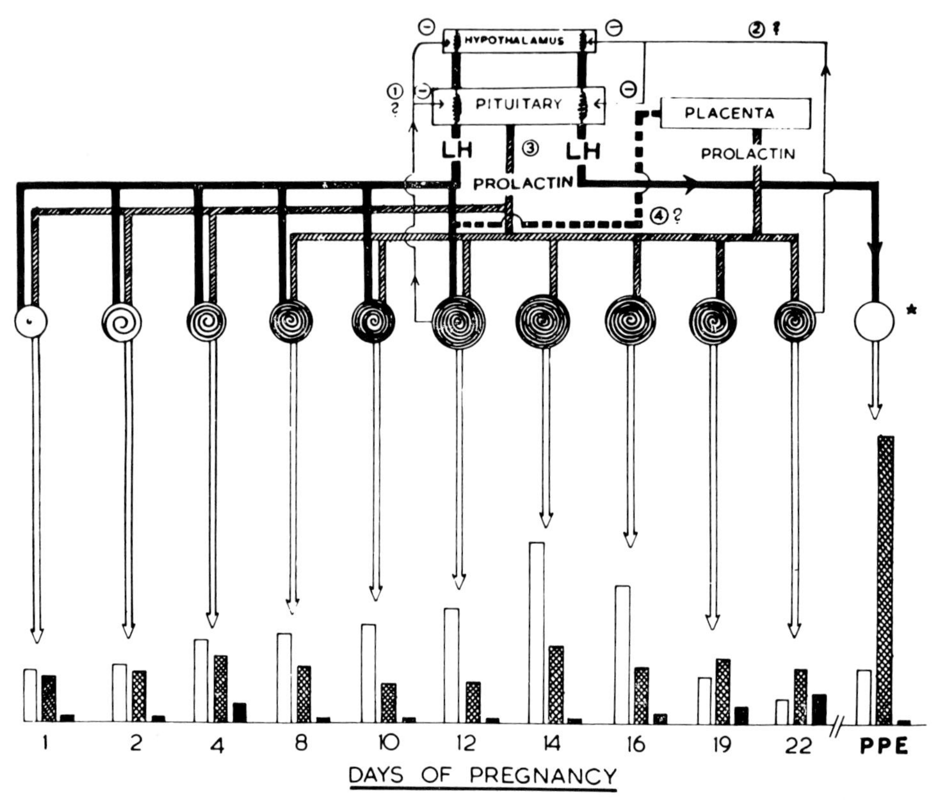

FIG. A. Proposed model for hormonal control of pregnancy in the intact rat. (From Raj and Moudgal, *Endocrinology* **86**, 874–889, 1970.) This model was proposed from the then available data on hormone levels and our work using LH antiserum. (a) Feedback effect of high progesterone and low estrogen titers on pituitary and hypothalamus to cut off LH. (2) Feedback effect of low progesterone and high estrogen titers on the pituitary and hypothalamus to reinitiate LH release. (3) Prolactin from the pituitary and hypothalamus to reinitiate LH release. (3) Prolactin from the pituitary and placenta facilitating conservation of progesterone. (4) Nature of luteotropin from twelfth day placenta had not been clearly established at the time this model was proposed, hence a question mark. It was proposed to be LH like. Open squares, progesterone; solid squares, estrogen; hatched squares, 20α-OH-P. Synthesis under tropic stimulation of LH. Secretion of 20α-OH-P, however, is inversely related to prolactin stimulus due to the ability of PRL to initiate 20α-hydroxysteroid dehydrogenase and conserve progesterone. PPE, Postpartum estrus. Asterisk indicates effect of LH on the corpora lutea of PPE and pregnancy. Pattern of steroid output would once again change with the initiation of suckling-induced prolactin stimulus.

DISCUSSION

H. G. M. Raj: I have one figure which rather refreshes our memory in the evolution of ideas on the control of corpus luteum and the luteotrophic hormone. This (Fig. A) shows a working hypothesis that we proposed exactly 10 years ago and was published in *Endocrinology* (**86,** 814, 1970) at a time when prolactin was being considered to be the sole luteotrophic hormone. While parts of this model were based on our observations, many aspects were hypothesis that served to promote further work in the field. However, our work using LH antiserum in the pregnant rat clearly showed that LH is required for normal maintenance of pregnancy and progesterone synthesis, during pregnancy. I wouldn't take the time to explain all the features of the model, but we clearly demonstrated the need for LH to maintain pregnancy. In the preimplantation period, especially on day 4, LH is the tropic stimulus that induces estrogen production necessary for implantation. However, administration of LH antiserum between day 8 and 12 induces abortion and this was not reversed by various doses of estrogen or prolactin. Only progesterone could reverse the abortificiant effect. This certainly implicates LH as a luteotropic hormone necessary for progesterone production. This work was extended later by Morishige and Rothchild who demonstrated that LH dependency sets in between day 6 and 8, as mentioned in the talk. While LH is not the sole luteotrophic hormone, it certainly is the only hormone capable of stimulating side-chain cleavage and conversion of cholesterol to pregnenolone. From this viewpoint, and using the then available data from other investigators, we proposed that LH is the only tropic influence that stimulates steroidogenesis (i.e., progesterone synthesis per se). Further, we proposed that prolactin modulates and conserves the progesterone from being catabolized. As you presented, your group, as well as Drs. Keyes and Gibori, have, in recent years, elegantly demonstrated that LH acts via intraluteal estrogen formation. However, I am concerned that it has lead to the "nomination" of intraluteal estrogen as a luteotrophic hormone, to the exclusion of LH. Clasically the term luteotropic hormone has been used to denote pituitary and placental hormones that impinge on the ovary from outside to exert this tropic action. If we are going to say that intraluteal estrogen is to be called a luteotropic hormone and not LH, this quite leaves the door open for considering other metabolites like LH-induced testosterone as luteotropic hormone and LH-induced cAMP as luteotropic. By the same reasoning, estrogen-induced mRNA (through which estrogen itself exerts its action) also will have to be considered as luteotropic.

I. Rothchild: As far as the luteotrophic effect of LH is concerned, it is incorrect, I think, to talk about LH as the *primary* luteotrophin in the rat or any other species. For example, if the rat's corpus luteum is not exposed to LH after it has been formed, it does *not* depend on LH at all to maintain its progesterone secretion. The pattern of progesterone secretion in the pituitary-autotransplanted rat (test Figs. 9 and 10) shows this very nicely, and other findings, such as those of Takahashi *et al.* and of Macdonald (see References) fit with this conclusion. This and other evidence I've discussed indicate that it is LH itself which induces the need for its luteotrophic effect. I've discussed LH dependency in the rat in detail in the article, and there is not enough time to do so here, but very briefly, my point is this. The need for the luteotrophic action of LH arises in the rat (and probably in other polyestrous eutheria also) as a result of the action of LH on the prostaglandin (PG)-producing part of the corpus luteum, but because LH also probably acts as a luteotrophin because it can raise the rate of progesterone secretion, it is the *luteolytic* action which later makes the CL depend on the luteotrophic action to continue secreting progesterone. In the absence of the luteolytic effect, the need for the luteotrophic one doesn't arise.

As far as defining a luteotrophin is concerned, I think this can be reduced to the very simple statement that anything can be a luteotrophin if it stimulates progesterone secretion. I've included a set of definitions in the article, not just for luteotrophin but luteolysis, etc. An essential part of my theory is that progesterone stimulates its own secretion; anything, therefore, which facilitates this, acts luteotrophically and anything which hinders it acts luteolytically. The basic underlying factor within the CL that accounts for its typical short life span is the dichotomy between how progesterone secretion is regulated and how PG production is regulated. Any substance or process, therefore, that can act on these can regulate the corpus luteum. We've identified only a few—LH, prolactin, estrogens, placental hormones, uterine PGs—but there may be others still unidentified, perhaps because we haven't thought of looking for them.

K. Savard: The point I would like to make is that there is no question of the episodic existence of the corpus luteum and that this is unique in endocrinology—at least among the steroid-secreting tissues. Nevertheless the corpus luteum cannot be set apart from the other steroid-producing tissues, insofar as its intrinsic biochemical properties are concerned. All steroid-producing tissues share the capability of transforming cholesterol into progesterone and/or obligatorily, its immediate precursor pregnenolone. The enzymes of this critical step, and all other enzymes associated with it, are found only in this family of tissues, and this one fact reflects a read-out of unique genetic information which is not transcribed in other cells. Consequently we can say that all steroid-producing cells form progesterone (or at least its immediate precursor, pregnenolone) from cholesterol and therefore, the formation of progesterone is not necessarily unique.

However, in most cells this progesterone serves as a precursor for other transformations into corticosteroids (the adrenal cortex) or androgens or estrogens; very little if any progesterone is actually released or secreted as such (an exception to this is the adrenal of a certain strain of mouse, I've forgotten the reference to this observation published in *Nature* some years ago). What is unique to the corpus luteum of most species is that much of the steroidogenic process stops at progesterone and this is what is secreted. In certain species as we know, C_{19} steroids and estrogens are also formed. We biochemists have yet to explain the basis for this selective accumulation and secretion of progesterone by such tissues as the human corpus luteum, which also has the capability of synthesizing estrogens.

I do not wish to detract from the thesis which you present, but I must call attention to the biochemical dogma which requires the corpus luteum to possess certain biochemical properties (i.e., enzymes etc.) in common with all other steroidogenic cells. I must admit that the luteolytic process which the corpus luteum undergoes is quite unique and cannot be explained as yet in biochemical terms.

When we consider the many factors which bear on corpus luteum formation, its function and lysis, on the variety of steroidal products formed, among the species studied and reviewed, we are faced with the realization that the process of evolution has certainly impinged heavily upon this essential element of the reproductive–endocrine system. We can be thankful at least for the fact that in all the species, LH, LTH, progesterone, estrogen are discernible in their usual and accepted roles, and that we are not faced with a vast array of varied chemical factors having similar physiological roles. We can be greateful that all we have to unravel is their interplay.

I. Rothchild: One of the greatest difficulties in studying biology and especially reproductive biology is to grasp the fact that there is no purpose in a process which is obviously moving toward a specific goal. Doing without the idea of purpose is not easy, but it must be done if one is to try to understand how the process arose and changed. The story, as I've tried to tell it to you, is that each of the changes in CL function and regulation that took place in the progression from its earliest form in reptiles to the kinds of CL we see in modern mammals was the result of an accident that happened to be valuable for reproduction, or at least not incompatible with it, and so was retained. We don't see the ones that were incompatible with reproduction. I'm sure, for example, that the descendants of the first eutheria included some whose CL became responsive to the effects of LH, and whose CNS–pituitary system went through the changes associated with polyestrous breeding, before they had evolved an endocrine trophoblastic placenta. We don't see these today because they would have been unable to reproduce. We see only the ones in which the endocrine placenta evolved before the return to polyestry, and so its easy for us to say that the endocrine placenta evolved "in order to" prevent regression of the CL, etc., thus injecting the idea of purpose, however innocently and unconsciously it's done, into a process totally devoid of purpose.

What you say about the biochemical characteristics of all steroid-producing tissues helps of course to explain some of the vagaries of the CL, but they also help us lose sight of what a CL really is. I don't think it was "designed" as a progesterone secretor originally, but as a PG producer. PGs were nice and easy to make and they did a good job of getting rid of the postovulatory follicle, which, having nursed its egg and released it, was no longer valuable to the organism, and in fact was probably a nuisance especially in forms which either released millions of eggs, as in swarmers, or made very large eggs. When the accident of progesterone secretion appeared in the postovulatory follicle, it delayed the PG-induced regression and expulsion of the egg, and so it also began the long pathway toward viviparity and the mammalian corpus luteum as such.

P. W. Concannon: First, I would like to compliment you, Dr. Rothchild, on your presentation, particularly as regards the large number of diverse species you have considered in addressing luteal regulation from the aspects of intrinsic luteal autonomy and ephemerality. I would also like to take this opportunity to report some results from my laboratory on two of the species which you cited as examples of animals that experience "long-lived" luteal phases in the absence of pregnancy—namely, the dog and the mink.

In the dog, luteal function is dependent on the presence of the pituitary and LH administration will elevate plasma progesterone levels (Concannon, *J. Reprod. Fertil.* **58,** 407, 1980). We also have additional data demonstrating the luteotrophic function of LH in the dog. Around day 45 of the cycle pregnant or nonpregnant bitches were each given a single injection (10 ml) of an equine antibovine LH serum similar in potency to the antiserum used in your studies on rats. In each bitch serum progesterone levels declined abruptly for 24–48 hours after injection and then returned to control values within 4–6 days. More recently, however, we have obtained evidence that prolactin, also, functions as a luteotropin in the dog. Luteal-phase serum progesterone levels were measured in bitches administered the prolactin-suppressor ergocryptine (CB-154) or control vehicle, daily, for 6 days (Fig. B). The doses of CB-154 were 0.1 mg/kg/day. As shown in the middle panel of Fig. B, the CB-154 treatment initiated on day 42 of the cycle in nonpregnant bitches caused an abrupt decline in progesterone levels to below 1 ng/ml. Progesterone levels remained below 1–3 ng/ml throughout the treatment. After termination of treatment levels increased transiently prior to a final decline and a foreshortening of the luteal phase. CB-154 injections initiated on day 42 in pregnant bitches induced similar rapid declines in progesterone and resulted in abortions within 3–4 days. Results for one such pregnancy are shown in the bottom right panel of Fig. B. When the CB-154 treatment was initiated on day 22 of the cycle the results suggested that the CL may be less dependent on prolactin (or perhaps more "autonomous") during the early luteal phase than during the late luteal phase. The ergocryptine-induced suppression of progesterone was not as severe or protracted as that observed in the bitches treated in the late luteal phase, as shown in the lower left panel of Fig. B, and was followed by recovery of progesterone levels to control values. This observation, in addition to the relative resistance of canine corpora lutea to the luteolytic effects of prostaglandin in the early luteal phase (Concannon and Hansel, *Prostaglandins* **13,** 533, 1977), suggests that the developing corpus luteum in the dog may have a certain degree of autonomy.

Our observations in the mink may be of greater interest to you in that they point to the evolution in this species of a dependence of luteal function on prolactin as a mechanism to regulate the time of implantation (and thus of parturition) in response to seasonal changes in the daily photoperiod. As indicated in Fig. C, in control pastel mink, following mating and induced ovulation in the first week of March, progesterone levels remain low until activation

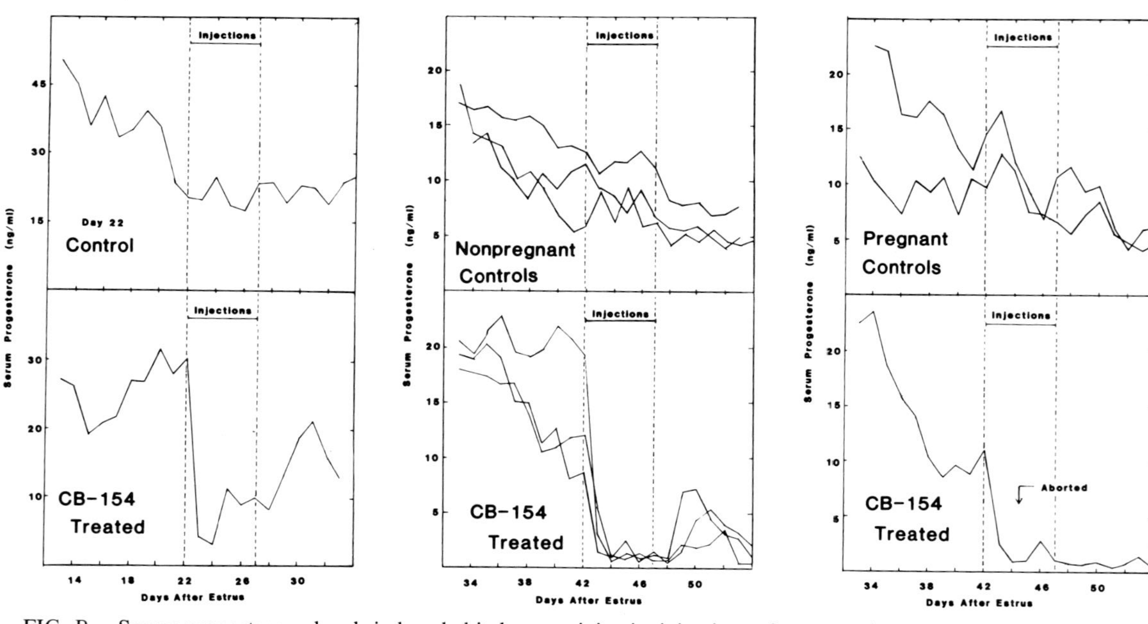

FIG. B. Serum progesterone levels in beagle bitches receiving im injections of ergocryptine (0.1 mg CB-154/kg/day) or control vehicle (20% ethanol, 0.1 ml/kg/day) daily for 6 days.

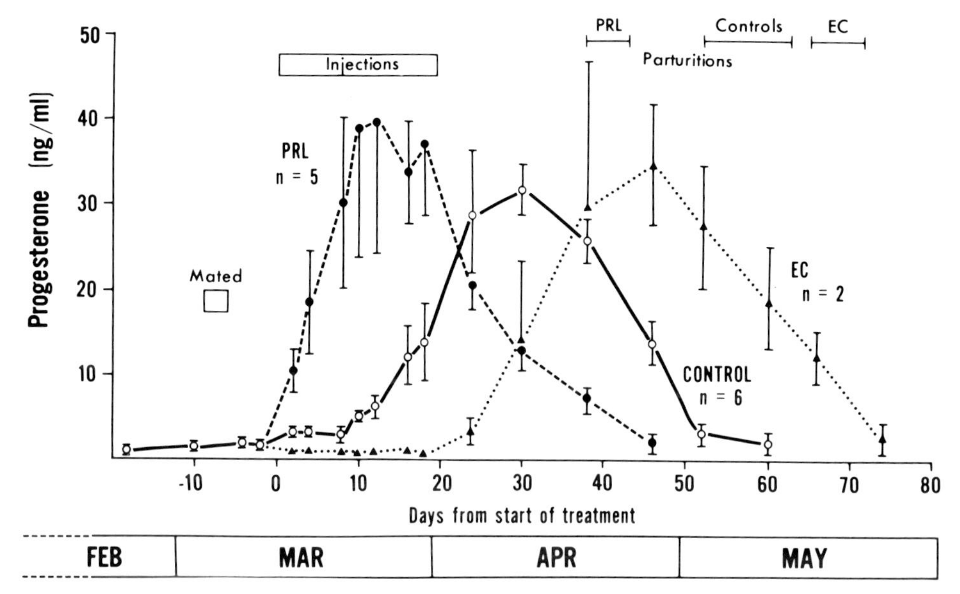

FIG. C. Mean (± SEM) serum progesterone levels in control (○), prolactin-treated (●), and ergocryptine-treated (▲) mink that whelped litters. The ranges of parturition dates are indicated for each group. (From Papke, Concannon, Travis, and Hansel, *J. Animal Sci.* **50**, 1102, 1980.)

of luteal function during the fourth week of March, at or shortly after the vernal equinox. We have found that the rise in progesterone occurs at the same time in mink mated to either intact or vasectomized males in the last week of February, in the first week of March, or in the second or third week of March. An artificial increase in hours of light per day following early matings can advance the rise in progesterone and subsequent implantation (Allais and Martinet, *J. Reprod. Fertil.* **54,** 133, 1978). I think this photoperiod-sensitive control mechanism may be mediated by prolactin. As you can see in Fig. C treatment with prolactin (0.5 mg NIH-B3/day) during embryonic diapause advanced the times of the rise in progesterone levels and of parturition. Conversely, administration of CB-154 inhibited luteal function and the subsequent delayed rise in progesterone resulted in delayed parturitions. However, prolactin may not be the only luteotrophic requirement in mink. Recently, in collaboration with Dr. Bruce Murphy, we have observed that prolactin NIH-S13 administered daily (0.5 mg/kg) to mink hypophysectomized during delayed implantation caused a rise in progesterone levels for 1–2 weeks and resulted in apparently normal implantations. However, continued prolactin treatment was not capable of maintaining progesterone secretion and implanted embryos underwent degeneration and partial resorption. Finally, I would like to report a related observation that is particularly interesting. In both of the studies involving prolactin administration to mink during delayed implantation we observed an immediate and dramatic shedding of the winter fur and initiation of the summer molt. Thus it seems that the fur molt and the activation of luteal progesterone secretion that normally occur in response to increasing daylight after the vernal equinox may both be initiated by an increased secretion of prolactin. This idea is supported by the recent finding of Martinet; she has measured an increase in circulating prolactin levels in mink at the time of luteal activation and has evidence that the timing of this increase can be advanced by increasing the daily photoperiod. Our observations on the possible involvement of pituitary prolactin secretion in the initiation of the summer fur molt can be considered in agreement with the results of Rust, Shackelford, and Meyer (*J. Mammal.* **46,** 549, 1965) insofar as they found that hypophysectomy caused the retention of winter pelage and prevented the development of the summer pelage. However, as I recall, they suggested that ACTH might be the hormone involved. Although we have not tested the effects of ACTH and they did not consider the role of prolactin, perhaps the differences in results reflect differences in the purity of hormone preparations available then and now.

Dr. Rothchild, perhaps you could comment on these observations on factors regulating luteal progesterone secretion in the dog and mink in light of your present ideas on the regulation of the mammalian corpus luteum.

I. Rothchild: Most of my comments are probably in the article, but I'll try. The effect of prolactin on the pelage of the mink reminds me of what I think is somewhat similar effect on molting in birds, in relation to or associated with the transition from ovulation and lay of a clutch to brooding the eggs. This can be a behavior-induced change. In the mink its obviously one connected with a seasonal change. In spite of the differences in the specific stimulus that sets off the change in prolactin secretion, both are again examples of the close connection between the secretion of prolactin and the postovulatory aspects of the reproduction cycle, a connection discussed in great detail by Riddle 17 years ago (see References), and one—though by no means the only one—of the reasons that I've postulated that responsiveness to prolactin was probably the first step in the transition from the metatherian to the eutherian corpus luteum.

Your evidence for the dog and mink and Murphy's for the ferret were some of the other things that persuaded me that the long luteal phase of the monestrous breeders is probably primarily dependent on prolactin. That doesn't mean that LH isn't involved at all; your evidence shows that it has a luteotrophic effect in the dog, and the inability of prolactin by itself to maintain the mink's CL for more than a few weeks after hypophysectomy suggests that maybe LH may also be involved in controlling the mink's CL. But there isn't enough, at least in comparison with polyestrous breeders, after each season's ovulaton in a monestrous breeder for LH to be more than a synergist with prolactin, and probably also not enough to induce a luteolytic effect, i.e., increase the CL's ability to make PGs equal to that induced in a polyestrous breeder. So, prolactin, through it anti-PG effect, can keep progesterone secretion going for a long time, very much as it does, perhaps, in the pituitary autotransplanted rat.

Your information about the mink adds another item to the list of peculiarities of the CL, since it shows us that even among the monestrous breeders things aren't uniform. The dog's CL may not need prolactin crucially until it is well past its third week of life, while the mink's CL seem to need prolactin even to get started! I wonder what the whole picture will be like when we've made a few more comparisons of this kind.

S. Cohen: I'm a little bit suspect of whether there is an involved stimulation and an inhibition occurring simultaneously, because to me that sounds too much like driving a car with one foot on the accelerator and the other on the brake, and pushing them both at the same time, and second, about autonomy, how can you be sure that if the corpus luteum can be formed only by LH hormone then how do you know that the so-called autonomous progesterone production may not be a residue of the LH stimulation?

I. Rothchild: The answer to your first question is one I've given a lot of thought to. One of the important points I'd like to make about the CL is that almost anything (probably everything) that can act on a CL can have two effects, a stimulatory one and an inhibitory one. That's true for LH, for prolactin, for estrogens, for progesterone, for PGs, for placental hormones, etc. That's one of the reasons I postulated what I did, i.e., to fit this particular peculiarity of the corpus luteum with its ability to make both progesterone and PGs. So it isn't really a matter of stepping on the brake pedal and the accelerator at the same time. To mix metaphors a little, it depends on what else the CL is doing at any particular time.

For example, LH, through its activation of cholesterol esterases can increase the concentration of both free cholesterol and arachidonic acid within the corpus luteum, as Kuehl pointed out several years ago (see References). Whether this leads to more progesterone because there's more of its substrate available, or to more PGs because there's more of its substrate available will depend on the state of the corpus luteum at the moment when both these substrates become available in increased amounts. I can't, and in fact I don't want to try to specify what such conditions are right now because it isn't necessary to do so to grasp the idea that the diametrically opposite effects of a hormone like LH don't have to be exerted with equal force at all times. What happens within the CL, in other words, depends on which of these two effects is dominant at the time we look at it. In the end, because of the difference between the progesterone and PGs production system, as I pointed out, the PGs will always win.

Your second question I believe was about how one could be sure that what I called autonomy was not the residual effect of the LH that induced ovulation and luteinization. I suppose we will always argue that question but I think several findings indicate, to me, at least, that the ability to secrete progesterone in the absence of the pituitary is not due to any residual effect of the preovulatory LH. The best comes from the tamar wallaby, in which, even as late as 10 months after ovulation, the quiescent CL responds to hypophysectomy by becoming activated. All the evidence from the behavior of granulosa cells in tissue culture, cited in the article, fits with the interpretation that the preovulatory LH is not involved in progesterone secretion of these cells. In the rat's estrous cycle the short period of autonomous progesterone secretion is actually prolonged by treatment with LHAS, as the experiment by Sanchez-Criado in my lab has shown. As far as we know the turnover of hormones bound to a receptor is just too rapid to account for the prolonged duration of progesterone secretion, after withdrawal of pituitary hormones, on the basis of hormones like LH remaining within the CL. No, the findings, as I see them, are most reasonably interpreted as evidence of a capacity for autonomy.

S. Cohen: And yet in the human they sometimes speak of progesterone production beginning before the LH surge.

I. Rothchild: There is no question that an increased secretion of progesterone occurs in some species before ovulation, and in others, only after the CL has been formed. In the first, the increase comes from the preovulatory follicle, and it may progress without a dip into the pattern of secretion of the definitive CL, as, e.g., in the dog. In others, the preovulatory rise is followed by a dip, and this in turn by the rise of the definitive CL, as for example, in the rat and the human. In the cow, there is apparently no preovulatory rise. I don't yet know how to account for these variations.

B. G. Steinetz: This question has to do with the problem of luteolysis. If hamsters are treated with 1 μg of $PGF_{2\alpha}$ on day 8 of pregnancy there will occur a marked decrease in plasma progesterone levels. If the corpus luteum is examined 24 hours later, it will show histological signs of involution. The animals will abort if nothing else is done. On the other hand, if at the time the $PGH_{2\alpha}$ is injected one also administers a small dose of progesterone, say 1 or 2 mg, there of course is no drop in plasma progesterone levels since you provided it, but there is also no change in the histology of the corpus luteum and the pregnancy continues uneventfully. How would your theories fit the results of this experiment?

I. Rothchild: Your findings are very similar to several others that were done on rats during the similar period of pregnancy except that luteolysis and the abortion that followed it were induced either by hypophysectomy or by treatment with an LHAS. For example, Raj prevented luteolysis after LHAS treatment by giving the rats dydrogesterone a synthetic that acts very much like progesterone. Ahmad prevented luteolysis after hypophysectomy by treatment with progesterone together with a dose of estrogen that was probably too small to have a direct effect on the CL. Loewit and Zambelis prevented the LHAS-induced rise in intraluteal 20α-OHSDH by treatment with progesterone, even in the absence of the pregnant uterus, suggesting very much that this was a direct effect of progesterone. All of these are in the article and I touched on them lightly in discussing the possibility that progesterone stimulates its own secretion. One of the interesting tie-ins with your experiment may be a preliminary experiment Sanchez-Criado has done in my lab in which this luteolytic effect of LHAS was prevented by indomethacin treatment. This probably means that there is little difference in the mechanism of luteolysis induced in your hamsters by PGF_2 for example, and in the rats by LHAS; this in turn suggests that your findings are another bit of evidence for a direct luteotrophic action of progesterone.

J. Weisz: I'd like to make a point in connection with Ken Savard's interesting statement that the peculiar aspect of the corpus luteum is its ability to secrete progesterone and prevent it from going further. Of course there are biochemical bases for it, but there may be proponents of the idea that the corpus luteum secretes progesterone and does a little bit of what we used to consider the prerogative of the protein secretory hormone secretors; they may be right and that would raise some interesting possibilities. Therefore it might be of interest to look at this question of packaging in different species and at different stages of the corpus luteum—what is your feeling about this?

I. Rothchild: Gemmel, the one who lent me the information about the bandicoot, has been much involved in the EM study of the CL and of packaging of progesterone within it. All I can say is that I don't know how to fit it with the rest of the secretion process, and that we'll have to wait to see how widespread this particular form of secretion packaging is. But to come back to the point that you and Ken Savard touched on: how come the CL is such a good progesterone producer? What is it that distinguishes it from other steroid-producing tissue in which the progesterone is used as a precursor for other steroids and is not the typical secretion product of the tissue. Why does this not happen in the CL? As I've already tried to show in my reply to Ken, the solution isn't in looking at the phenomenon teleologically, but in trying to define the characteristics of the CL. One way is by comparing the luteinized granulosa cell with the follicular granulosa cell, and the perhaps not so surprising thing about this is that the major difference between them is in how much progesterone they make, not in what they do with it after it is made. Neither cell can turn the progesterone into androgens very well, and the only reason the follicular granulosa cell makes lots of estrogens and the CL cell doesn't is because the former has a supply of androgens coming to them from the theca and the CL does not. Both cells can turn the androgens into estrogens very easily. But another even more important factor is the great increase in the cell's capacity to make progesterone that takes place when it luteinizes, and here is where the real mystery lies, i.e.: what is luteinization? I've tried to describe what I think happens after the CL is formed, and what was the path of evolution to the CL of modern mammals, but in case you haven't noticed, I avoided saying anything about luteinization, because I have so far only the barest glimmer of an idea about the nature of luteinization where the whole thing started.

L. Birnbaumer: It has been shown by Iqbal Khan in K. Ahren's laboratory, as well as by others, that pseudopregnant rats are refractory to the luteolytic action of $PGE_{2\alpha}$ during the first 3 days. Full responsiveness to $PGE_{2\alpha}$ was shown to be established by day 7 of pseudopregnancy.

Dr. Howard Kirchick and I wondered whether perhaps the luteolytic effect of LH in rabbits is mediated by prostaglandins formed *in situ* under the influence of LH. We therefore injected 6-day pseudopregnant rabbits with hCG to induce luteolysis and tested whether simultaneous administration of indomethacin would interefere with the progesterone-decreasing effect of hCG as seen 18 hours later in the serum of the tested animals. The dose of indomethacin used was such to block the ovulatory effect of hCG known from work by Marsh and LeMaire to require prostaglandins. We found that indomethacin treatment, though blocking ovulation, did not alter progesterone production by the corpora lutea, both in control or in hCG-treated animals. As expected, the latter showed reduced serum levels of progesterone, indicative of initiation of luteolysis. Being aware of the fact that estradiol is essential for rabbit corpus luteum survival and taking into consideration the possibility that hCG treatment might result in a decreased estradiol secretion by neighboring follicles, we repeated the above described experiment in rabbits that had Silastic implants with estradiol of such a size as to increase basal estradiol levels about 3-fold. Again, indomethacin treatment did not interefere with the hCG-induced decrease in serum progesterone levels. It would appear, therefore, that prostaglandins are not the second messenger in the luteolytic effect of hCG. In addition, we also determined that indomethacin did not interfere with the desensitizing effect of hCG as seen in measurements of LH-stimulable adenylyl cyclase activity on corpus luteum homogenates.

I should like to ask you for your opinion as to what the mechanism might be by which LH is luteolytic in ultra-short cycle and in long cycle animals.

I. Rothchild: Wasn't this a desensitization effect?

L. Birnbaumer: The desensitization of the adenylyl cyclase system precedes the initiation of decreased progesterone production by several hours (up to 10 in the rabbit). However, I do not know whether there is a cause–effect relationship between hCG-induced desensitization and hCG-induced luteolysis. The two effects may also be parallel responses. Thus, receptor occupancy by hCG may result in both increased levels of cAMP and desensitization, i.e., interruption of the receptor-cyclase coupling process. If the luteolytic response is mediated by cAMP, then clearly desensitization and luteolysis, though correlated, are not dependent on each other.

I. Rothchild: As I say, I'm not sure that desensitization, or rather, the luteolysis that goes with it, is an effect of PGs. It doesn't seem to be. We have some preliminary evidence that the luteolysis that follows withdrawal of prolactin in the rat also cannot be prevented by PG inhibitors, so it's conceivable that luteolysis could occur following the acute withdrawal of a luteotrophin because an action of the luteotrophin might be to facilitate a crucial step in the production of progesterone. The luteolytic effect of a large desensitizing dose of LH might in some way lead to such a condition, but the luteolytic effect of LH that I was referring to is one which I think happens only in response to a continuous low level rate of LH secretion, and is probably the result of the potentiation of luteal PG production by this level of LH. We're about to set up experiments with indomethacin treatment to test this idea.

J. Nolin: I must add my congratulations to the many others which have been offered you this evening. I also want to offer a bit of new information that we've come across recently. I think there can be no doubt that the ideal place to study hormonal regulatory activity would be in the target itself. Hormone in transit can at best tell us what might be available to a target and at worst, absolutely nothing about hormone–target interaction (J. M. Nolin and E. M. Bogdanove, *Biol. Reprod.* **22,** 393–416, 1980). We think we have had some success over the last few years in actually looking at some of the peptidal hormones, particularly prolactin, in their targets and we invariably find positive correlations between response and the presence in individual target cells. Not long ago we were able to identify prolactin in the forming corpus luteum during the rat estrous cycle. I think this may not fit your hypothesis, if I understood it correctly.

I. Rothchild: The question really is whether the ability of the rats CL to secrete progesterone during the estrus cycle diestrus independently of the pituitary is because it has some prolactin within it as it is being formed. Two findings argue against a dependency on this prolactin at this time in the CL's life. One is an old experiment of Alloiteau and Acker (cited in the article), in which they hypophysectomized the rats early in proestrus, and induced ovulation with a single dose of LH. Their findings were the first to show that the CL formed under these conditions functioned autonomously. Uchida and his co-workers (see References) made similar findings. The other is from the studies of Smith and Neill and Day and Brinbaumer (see References) which show in the one case indirectly and in the other directly, that the rat's CL doesn't respond to prolactin until after its "autonomous" progesterone secretion has reached its peak value, i.e., between the second and third day after ovulation. But the main things about my idea of autonomy is that there is much more evidence for it than just the way progesterone is secreted during the rat's estrus cycle.

J. Nolin: Hypophysectomy, whether done before or after ovulation, involves removing only the source of prolactin. The question is: how long after hypophysectomy does any prolactin remain available to the ovary? We might also ask whether there might be any intercompartmental transfer of prolactin already present in the ovary.

As for the CB-154 approach, this drug produces a relatively precipitous decline in prolactin release from the pituitary gland but not obliteration of release.

Your third point, that treatment with exogenous prolactin doesn't change progesterone secretion until after day 2 of the luteal phase, at first glance, seems to be a strong argument for your hypothesis. Nevertheless, since it does not take into account the presence of endogenous prolactin already in the corpus luteum, it would seem to me that the question of prolactin involvement in corpus luteum function during the rat estrus cycle has not yet been altogether resolved.

G. MacDonald: My only response is that prolactin must be given to hypophysectomized rats quite soon after surgery to maintain progesterone secretion. This is independent of the day of the cycle that the animal is operated.

L. Birnbaumer: Dr. Sharon Day's experiments in my laboratory showed that the critical initial PRL surge, which rescues the CL of the cycle from regression allowing them to become CL of pseudopregnancy, is one that occurs on the morning of diestrus-2. These studies confirmed a similar conclusion made earlier by both M. S. Smith in Dr. J. Neill's laboratory and B. Fluchinger. It follows from this that the previous surges are there probably only because it is simpler to set the hypothalamic clock on the afternoon of proestrus (i.e., mating), to initiate surges immediately, as opposed to setting it in such a manner as to start 3 days later.

G. MacDonald: So that implies the data Dr. Rothchild quoted suggesting prolactin has to be applied within 24 hours of hypophysectomy are incorrect.

I. Rothchild: That's in the pseudopregnant rat. The general rule is that depriving rat CL which are actively secreting progesterone of prolactin for 24 hours or more leads to a luteolytic effect of the prolactin when it again acts on the CL. But if the CL have never been exposed to prolactin, as in the experiment of Alloiteau and Acker I just mentioned, they are not sensitive to this luteolytic action of prolactin for as much as 5 days after hypophysectomy. I think it may have to do with the ability to secrete progesterone autonomously. We also find the same resistance to the luteolytic effect of prolactin in the CL of pregnant rats during the period after day 12 (Lam and Rothchild, 1973), when the CL secrete progesterone in the absence of the pituitary and placentas for at least 3 days (Rothchild *et al.*, 1973).

R. O. Greep: How do you think your theory fits with or helps us understand the basis of the persistent corpus luteum in women?

I. Rothchild: I'm glad you asked that because I think it makes an interesting comparison with the others shown in Figs. 9 and 10. One can show the effect of changing the regression process in the guinea pig and rat on the life span of the CL and its pattern of progesterone secretion because of the specific roles of the uterus and the pituitary in this process in these forms, but the uterus has no effect in primates. Perhaps phenothiazine treatments could reproduce in primates the conditions that prolong the life span in the pituitary-autotransplanted rat, but that can't be done ethically in women and nobody's tried it in monkeys. The persistent corpus luteum, however, seems to be the result of a change that resembles what has happened in the hysterectomized guinea pig and the pituitary-autotransplanted rat, and I'd be willing to bet that if one could measure progesterone levels in these women from the time the CL was formed until its eventual regression (usually about 3–4 months later) one would see a pattern essentially the same as those shown in Fig. 10B. It would also be interesting to see what effect treatment with either CB-154 or a $PGF_{2\alpha}$ analog would have; my guess is that either treatment would induce CL regression and a resumption of ovulation cycles.

H. Adlercreutz: I would like to discuss a new class of compounds in man and animals which is closely connected to gonadal function and especially to the corpus luteum phase of the menstrual cycle and early pregnancy. Others involved in these studies include K. D. R. Setchell, A. M. Lawson, F. L. Mitchell, D. N. Kirk, and M. Axelson.

During studies of steroid excretion by the vervet monkey, a number of phenolic compounds were consistently detected in polar steroid extracts during gas chromatography–mass spectrometric analysis. Although their mass spectra were atypical of steroids, the major compound was found to exhibit a cyclic pattern of excretion during the menstrual cycle in which a maximum and approximately 4-fold increase occurred in the luteal phase (Setchell, Bull, and Adlercreutz, *J. Steroid Biochem.* **12,** 375, 1979).

Previous observations of the presence of these compounds in human urine prompted an investigation of their behavior during the human menstrual cycle. Preliminary results from a limited number of subjects confirmed the initial observation of the cycling behavior and demonstrated a maximum and 4-fold increase during the early luteal phase of the menstrual cycle of human (Setchell and Adlercreutz, *J. Steroid Biochem* **12,** xv, 1979). The excretion of the two major phenolic compounds (compounds 180/442 and 180/410) in one subject in relation to estrone-glucuronide and pregnanediol-3α-glucuronide during a menstrual cycle can be seen in Fig. D.

Measurements of the major compound (180/442) in urine samples collected during pregnancy showed that the maximum excretion occurred between 14 and 22 weeks of gestation, thereafter levels declined. No significant difference in the urinary excretion in an anencephalic pregnancy was seen (Fig. E) and the extremely low levels in newborn infants indicate a maternal origin for these compounds during pregnancy. These preliminary findings were presented at the IXth International Study Group for Steroid Hormones, Rome 1979 (Setchell, Lawson, Axelson, and Adlercreutz, "Research on Steroids IX," 1980, in press).

An intensive investigation of the distribution of these compounds has led to their recognition as urinary constituents in human, baboons, and vervet monkeys and they have also been identified in human plasma and bile. Many of the general physicochemical and chromatographic characteristics in addition to the mass spectrum of the trimethylsilyl ether derivatives of the two principal phenolic compounds were reported recently (Setchell *et al.*, 1979).

Gas chromatography–mass spectrometry, nuclear magnetic resonance spectroscopy, infrared spectroscopy, and wet chemical techniques have shown that these compounds belong to a class known as lignans which contain a 2,3-dibenzylbutane skeleton as their basic structure. The two compounds were definitely identified, following the chemical synthesis of reference compounds: (1) 2,3-bis(3′-hydroxybenzyl)butyrolactone (previously referred to as compound 180/442), and (2) 2,3-bis(3′-hydroxybenzyl)butane-2,4-diol (previously referred to as compound 180/410). The chemical formulae of these two compounds are shown in Fig. F,

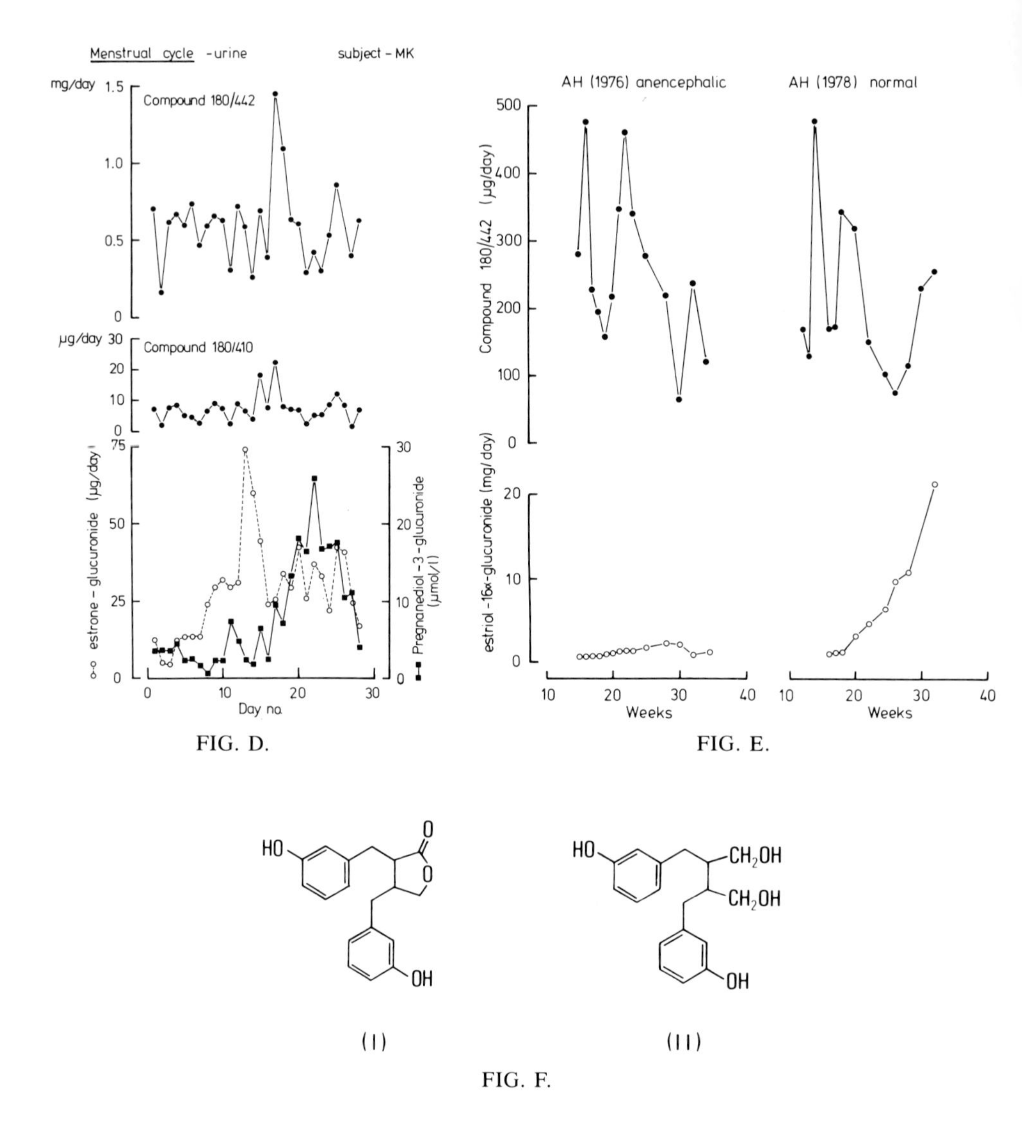

FIG. D.

FIG. E.

FIG. F.

and a comparison of the mass spectra of the trimethylsilyl ether derivatives of the natural (first and third panels) and authentic compounds are shown in Fig. G (Setchell, Lawson, Mitchell, Kirk, Adlercreutz, and Axelson, *Nature* (*London*) 1980, in press). These compounds have been found in urine conjugated to glucuronic acid.

The biosynthesis of these lignans in humans has not yet been determined but their highly aromatic nature might suggest a dietary origin or their formation by intestinal bacteria. Our preliminary results, however, indicate that they may be ovarian in origin or that their production is influenced by ovarian function. The cyclic behavior in the menstrual cycle, the much lower levels in newborn infants and children, and the reduced excretion in post-

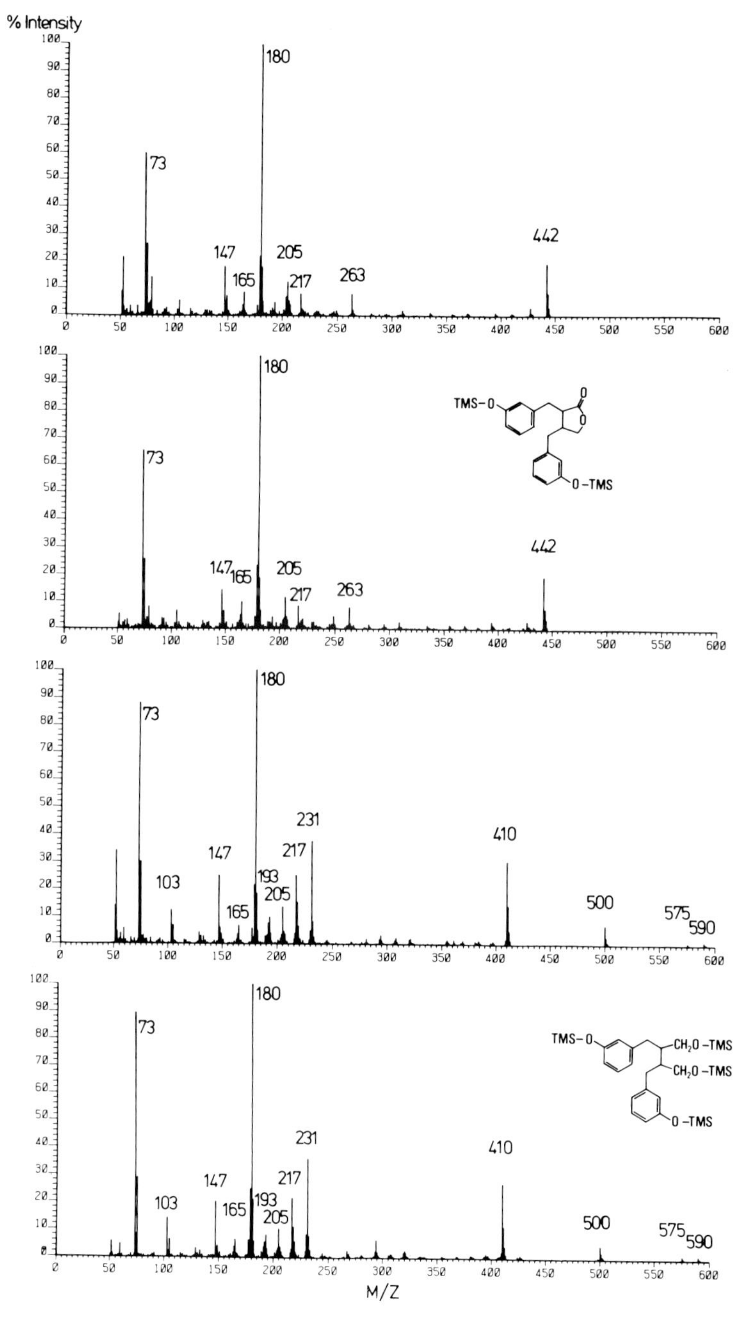
% Intensity
180
73
147
165
205
217
263
442
TMS–O
O
O
O–TMS
231
103
193
410
500
575
590
CH₂O –TMS
CH₂O –TMS
O –TMS
M/Z

FIG. G.

menopausal and ovariectomized women would support this view. Both compounds have, however, been detected in adult males.

The occurrence of lignans in humans and our preliminary observations on their disposition pose questions as to their physiological and biological significance. Lignans are a group of uncommon plant constituents which have only been found in higher plants of the orders Gynerospermophytina and Angiospermophytina. They have been extensively investigated by the natural products chemists because of the known antimitotic activity of many plant and synthetic lignans and their potential anticancer activity. The structures of the lignans described here, however, have never been identified in plant species which presumably reflects differences in pathways of biosynthesis or metabolism. The diphenolic and highly aromatic nature of these compounds are characteristic of many substances which possess properties which are either highly estrogenic or antiestrogenic. Although it is yet to be determined if these lignans possess any biological activity, their cyclic excretion may suggest they play an important role in the regulation of the menstrual cycle.

Mechanism of Calcium Action and Release of Vesicle-Bound Hormones during Exocytosis

HARVEY B. POLLARD, CHRISTOPHER J. PAZOLES, AND CARL E. CREUTZ

Section on Cell Biology and Biochemistry of the Clinical Hematology Branch, National Institute of Arthritis, Metabolism, and Digestive Diseases, National Institutes of Health, Bethesda, Maryland

I. Introduction

The term "exocytosis" is primarily an anatomic word, and was invented by George Palade nearly 20 years ago to describe release of zymogen granule contents from exocrine cells. The data supporting the concept have been mainly ultrastructural and have been summarized recently by Palade (1975) in his Nobel address. He showed that prior to exocytosis the storage organelle membrane attached to the inner aspect of the plasma membrane of the secretory cell. Subsequently the two membranes became closely juxtaposed, forming a "pentalaminar structure" which eventually became a single bilayer separating vesicle contents from the external medium. Finally, this bilayer underwent "fission" or breakage and the vesicle contents were released. This concept, together with an extension to "compound" or "piggyback" exocytosis in which a vesicle also interacts with the membrane of a previously secreted vesicle, is schematically described in Fig. 1. An enormous amount of work has been performed asking whether this mechanism might also underlie release of hormones, transmitters and enzymes.

The biochemical data supporting the exocytosis hypothesis have primarily come from studies on the bovine adrenal medulla, in which storage organelles (called chromaffin granules) contain catecholamines, ATP, and specific peptides, proteins, and enzymes. The data are simply that vesicle contents but not the vesicle membranes are released when the cell is stimulated (Smith, 1968; Viveros, 1974; Winkler, 1977; Pollard *et al.*, 1979a).

For many years it has been appreciated that calcium plays a critical role in regulating exocytosis both in the adrenal medulla and in a number of other systems. In particular, an increase in intracellular free calcium concentration often seems to be a prerequisite for secretion, and it is presently thought that calcium might mediate the initial interaction between

ISBN 0-12-571137-9

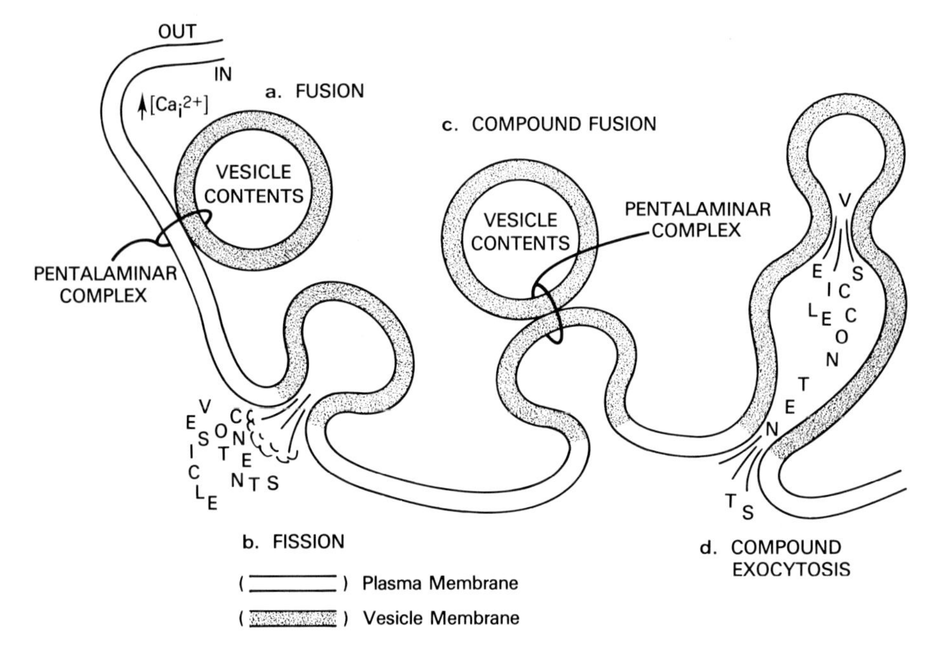

FIG. 1. Schematic outline of fusion and fission steps during regular and compound exocytosis in a hypothetical cell.

the storage organelle and the plasma membrane just prior to secretion. Among the best evidence for this concept is kinetic data from studies by Llinas and his colleagues (1976) on the squid stellate ganglion showing that calcium penetrates the presynaptic nerve terminal and elicits secretion over a time interval that is too short to allow calcium to diffuse more than a short distance from the plasma membrane. Parsegian (1977) has computed this distance to be less than 10 nm.

Numerous proposals have focused on the question of how calcium might act, once free on the cytoplasmic side of the plasma membrane. For example, independent Ca^{2+} action as well as mediation by specific proteins such as calmodulin, actomyosin, and tubulin have been considered (Pollard *et al.,* 1979a). However, in our article we will describe in some detail a new protein which we have discovered called "synexin" which induces Ca^{2+}-dependent formation of pentalaminar complexes between secretory granule membranes.

We will also describe our investigation into the process of membrane breakage or "fission" that finally results in release of secretory vesicle contents outside the cell. This remains a poorly understood problem which we have approached experimentally over the last several years by supposing it might occur by local osmotic rupture at the fusion site, a process analogous to the chemiosmotic lysis of isolated chromaffin granules. In this article we will describe studies testing this hypothesis by comparing the granule lysis reaction to the predicted behavior of secreting chromaffin and other cells.

II. Synexin: A Possible Mediator of Calcium Action

The molecular details of the regulatory role of Ca^{2+} have not been elucidated, in spite of the long history and generality of the observation that Ca^{2+} is required for exocytosis. The lack of biochemical assays for the morphological events which define exocytosis, particularly the fusion of the secretory vesicle to the plasma membrane, has been a major difficulty. However, in many secretory systems, secretory vesicles fuse not only with the plasma membrane but also with the membranes of other vesicles, forming channels to the exterior of the cell in a process called "compound exocytosis." We have recently observed such an extensive system of channels in chromaffin cells after exposure to veratridine, a potent secretagogue. Examples of this phenomenon are shown in Fig. 2 (unstimulated) and Fig. 3 (stimulated with veratridine). It, therefore, seemed likely to us that the interaction between vesicles in this process might be controlled by the same molecular factors that regulated the interaction between the secretory vesicle and the plasma membrane, and that the chromaffin cell might be a suitable system for analysis. Our approach was to examine the role of Ca^{2+} and soluble cytoplasmic factors in causing purified secretory vesicles to agglutinate, and to monitor this activity by turbidity measurements of chromaffin granule suspensions (Creutz *et al.*, 1978, 1980).

Chromaffin granules, the secretory vesicles from the adrenal medulla, were particularly suitable for this study in as much as the Ca^{2+} requirement for exocytosis in this system had been well documented, compound exocytosis had been observed in chromaffin cells (Fenwick *et al.*, 1978), and the vesicles themselves could be readily isolated in large quantities. For our studies chromaffin granules were isolated by either of two procedures: differential centrifugation in isotonic sucrose solution (Pollard *et al.*, 1976), or equilibrium density gradient centrifugation in isotonic mixtures of sucrose and metrizamide (Pollard *et al.*, 1979b). The latter procedure gave greater yields of more highly purified chromaffin granules.

It had previously been reported that isolated chromaffin granules would attach to one another when exposed to high concentrations of divalent cations (Schober *et al.*, 1977). However, in contrast to secretion *in vivo*, this type of interaction showed no specificity for Ca^{2+} as opposed to Mg^{2+}, and the concentrations of cation required (several millimolar) seemed too

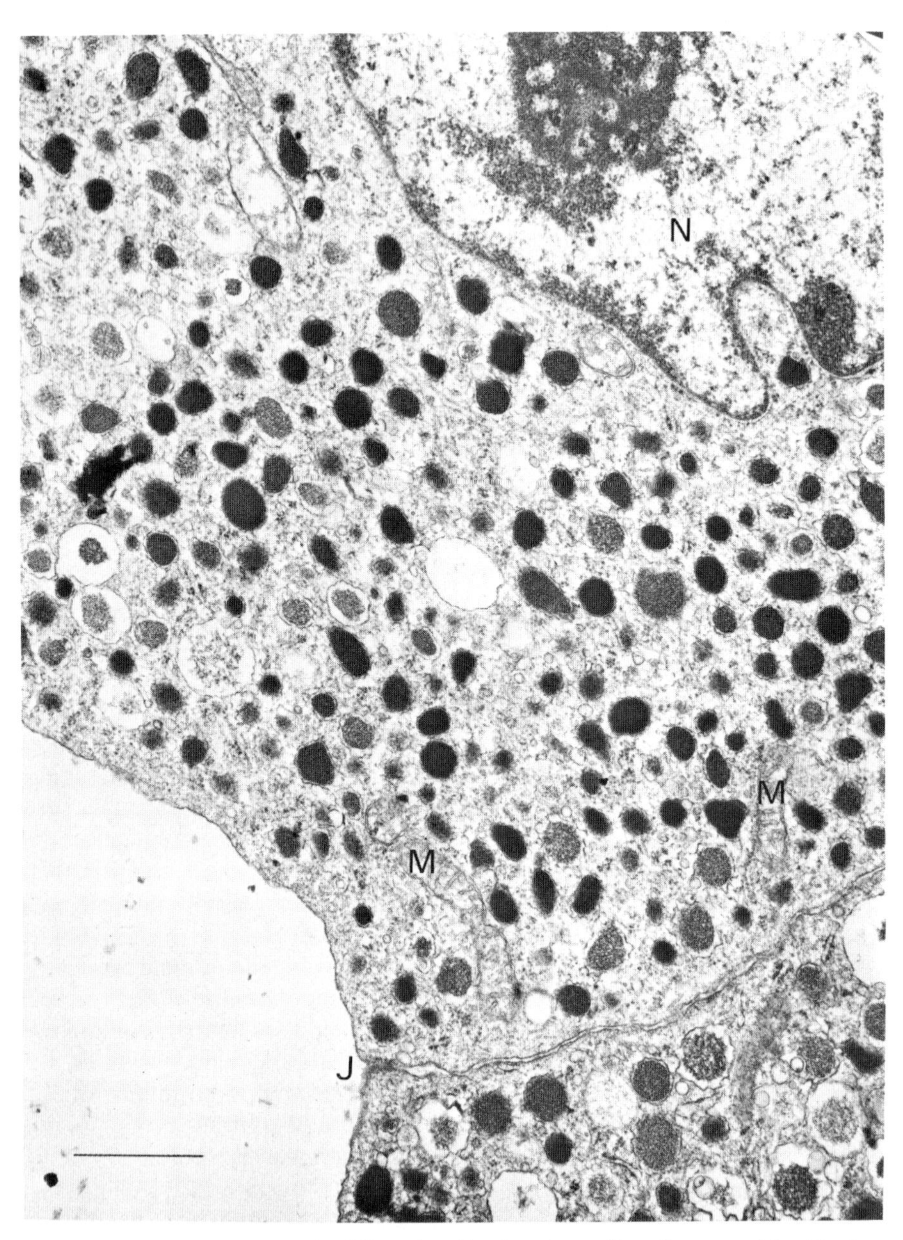

FIG. 2. Electron micrograph of dissociated bovine chromaffin cells exposed for 10 minutes to a medium containing a standard salt solution and 1% DMSO. The cells come as clusters of 5–7 cells attached by specialized junctions (J). N marks the nucleus of one chromaffin cell, while M marks the location of several typical tubular mitochondria. The bar represents 1 μm, and the magnification was $\times 25{,}000$.

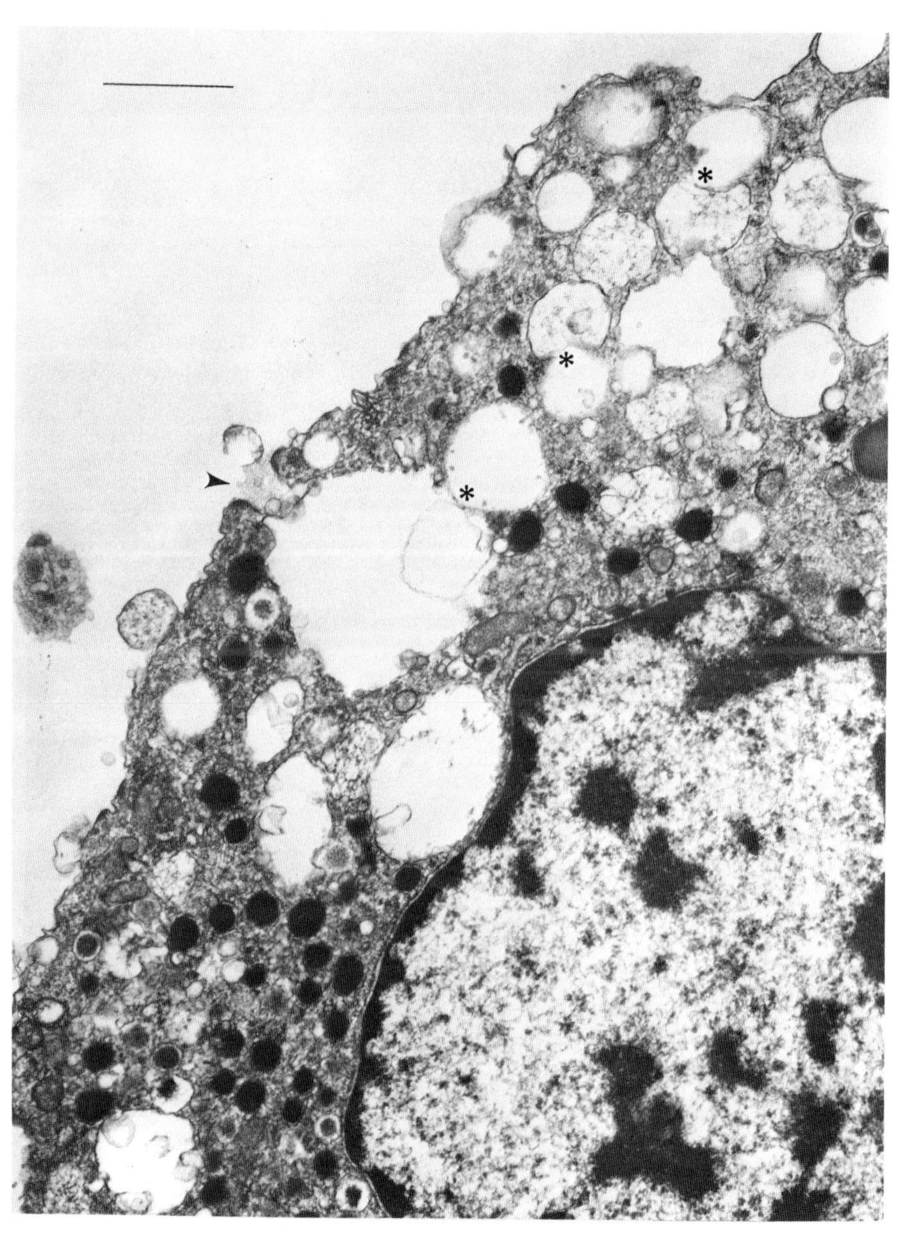

FIG. 3. Electron micrograph of a dissociated bovine chromaffin cell exposed for 10 minutes to a medium containing 100 μM veratridine in 1% DMSO. The cytoplasm of the cell suddenly became filled with large vacuoles. One of the large vacuoles closely related to the surface of the cell appeared to be connected to some extent to the external medium (see large arrow). Some of the lesser vacuoles appeared to be connected to one another (*). Many of the vacuoles appeared to be festooned with unexpended chromaffin granules. The bar represents 1 μm, and the magnification was $\times$25,000.

high to be relevant to an intracellular process. We found, however, that a very sensitive Ca^{2+}-specific aggregation process could be induced if granules were incubated at 37°C in the presence of the postmicrosomal supernatant from homogenized chromaffin tissue. The soluble factor responsible for this Ca^{2+}-dependent process was heat and trypsin sensitive, suggesting it was protein in nature, and we named the factor "synexin," from the Greek word *synexis* which means "meeting," because of its ability to bring chromaffin granules together.

We were able to devise an isolation scheme for synexin, using as an assay for the protein its ability to cause an increase in the turbidity of a chromaffin granule suspension. As shown in Fig. 4, the scheme involved

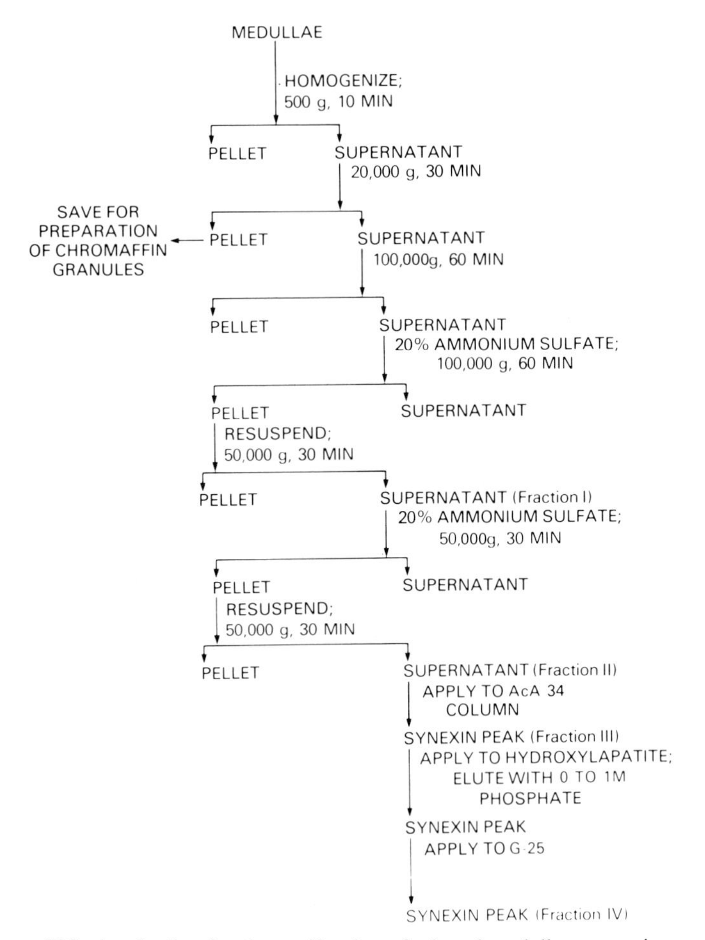

FIG. 4. Outline for the purification of adrenal medullary synexin.

(i) preparation of the postmicrosomal supernatant and precipitation of the factor in 20% $(NH_4)_2SO_4$; (ii) repetition of this precipitation step, which proved important for removing serum albumin; (iii) gel filtration on Ultrogel AcA34; and (iv) hydroxylapatite chromatography. (Complete details are given in Creutz *et al.*, 1978.) After the final chromatographic step the preparation appeared as a single band on an SDS gel with an apparent molecular weight of 47,000, although the preparation after gel filtration, about 85% pure, was found to be suitable for many studies.

The influence of synexin on the turbidity of a granule preparation is illustrated in Fig. 5. This assay was conducted at 37°C in the presence of 240 m*M* sucrose, 30 m*M* KCl, 28 m*M* histidine/HCl (pH 6.0), 2.5 m*M* EGTA, and sufficient $CaCl_2$ to obtain the desired free Ca^{2+} concentration. The turbidity increase began immediately and was complete in 8 to 10 minutes. Barium, strontium, or magnesium could not be substituted for Ca^{2+}. The calcium appeared to be titrating a site with a dissociation con-

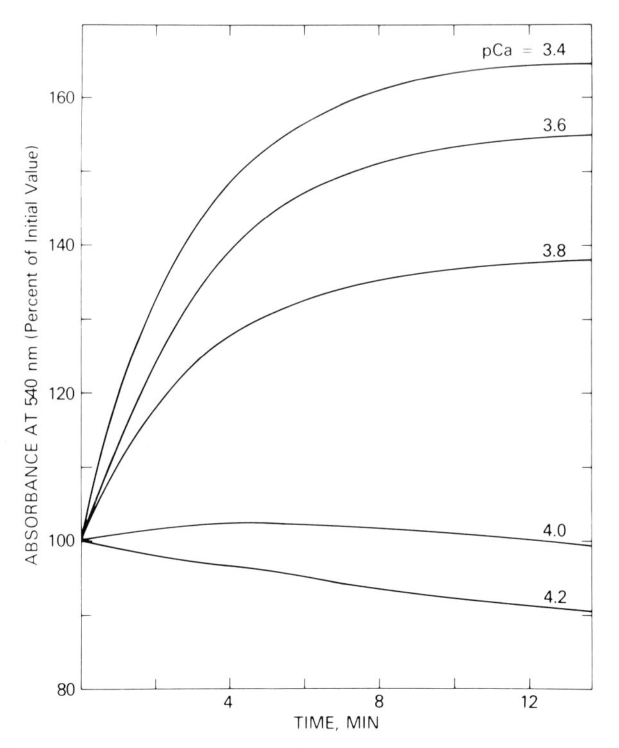

FIG. 5. Time course of turbidity changes induced by synexin (3.4 mg) in a 1 ml chromaffin granule suspension in the presence of different concentrations of free calcium. Initial absorbance ≃0.3 (130 μg of granule protein).

stant of 200 μM, thereby stimulating the reaction. The reaction occurred as well as 25°C, but below 25°C it exhibited a Q_{10} of 2; and the reaction did not occur at 0°C. The reaction was only partly reversible in that the removal of Ca^{2+} by chelation with EGTA after the reaction was complete resulted in a 10–20% reversal of the turbidity increase. During the reaction synexin appeared to bind to the granules in a Ca^{2+}-dependent manner as defined by the fact that the protein could be removed from solution by sedimenting aggregating granules. From such binding studies we calculated that there appeared to be approximately 90 synexin binding sites on each granule.

When chromaffin granules that had been exposed to Ca^{2+} and synexin were examined in thin sections it was seen that nearly all of the granules became attached to at least one another granule at Ca^{2+} concentrations as low as 6 μM. At higher Ca^{2+} concentration larger aggregates of granules formed, but in all cases the granules appeared to be separated at their regions of mutual contact by a pentalaminar structure formed by the close apposition of their trilaminar limiting membranes. This pentalaminar structure appeared similar to those observed in electron microscopic studies of living cells undergoing exocytosis. Under the conditions of our assay the pentalaminar structures appeared stable as vesicles did not fuse to give larger structures with common lumena. Therefore, it appeared that synexin could only be responsible for an initial step in exocytosis, although it might be the critical step at which Ca^{2+} regulated the entire process.

In order to investigate the site of action of Ca^{2+}, we examined the structure of purified synexin in the presence of varying concentrations of free Ca^{2+}. Using 90° light-scattering measurements we determined that Ca^{2+} caused synexin to self-associate (Creutz *et al.*, 1979). The calcium dependence and cation specificity of the self-association reaction was identical to that of synexin-induced chromaffin granule aggregation, strongly suggesting that the mechanism of granule aggregation included a step in which Ca^{2+} became bound to synexin and caused the protein in turn to self-associate. By negative staining of purified synexin with sodium phosphotungstate we determined that Ca^{2+} caused synexin to self-associate into rod-like particles of dimensions 50 by 150 Å. These rods subsequently rapidly associated with one another to form bundles of parallel rods. The native molecular weight of synexin in the absence of Ca^{2+} is such that the rods may consist of 4 or 5 synexin monomers. Whether the rods actually form or line up side by side when chromaffin granules are present, or whether synexin monomers interact individually with the membranes is not known at present. However, Fig. 6 schematically out-

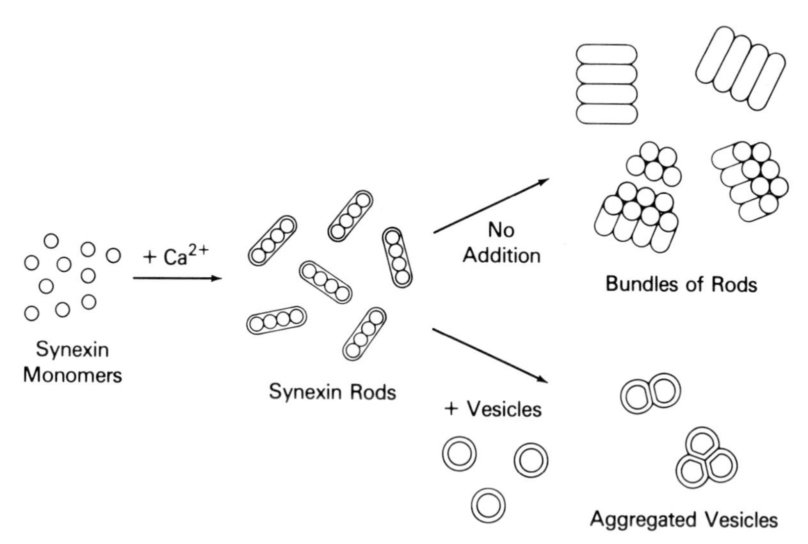

FIG. 6. A schematic interpretation of the events occurring when Ca^{2+} activates synexin to cause the aggregation of secretory vesicles.

lines one possible interpretation of the steps that occur when Ca^{2+} activates synexin to cause membrane interaction.

In other studies we examined the possibility that the popular protein, calmodulin, might enhance or otherwise affect synexin action. However, calmodulin had no effect at all on any aspect of the system. We also found that chlorpromazine as well as a number of related analogs such as trifluoperazine, at $\sim 30\ \mu M$ concentration, markedly inhibited synexin-induced granule aggregation. Hitherto, these drugs were considered by many to inhibit calmodulin activity exclusively.

In order to further examine the morphological relationships of synexin in the intact chromaffin cell and to assist our search for synexin-like proteins in other secretory tissues, we have recently prepared an antibody to synexin. To prepare the antibody, synexin was partially purified by precipitation in ammonium sulfate and gel filtration. This material was then run on a preparative SDS slab gel and the major band on the gel, migrating with an apparent molecular weight of 47,000 and comprising 80% of the protein, was cut from the gel and the protein removed from this slice by electrophoresis. The eluted protein was emulsified with complete Freund's adjuvant and injected into rabbits. The presence of anti-synexin IgG in the serum of a rabbit was detected by the ability of the IgG to inhibit the aggregation of chromaffin granules by synexin (Fig. 7). We have also used the anti-synexin IgG to determine the localization of syne-

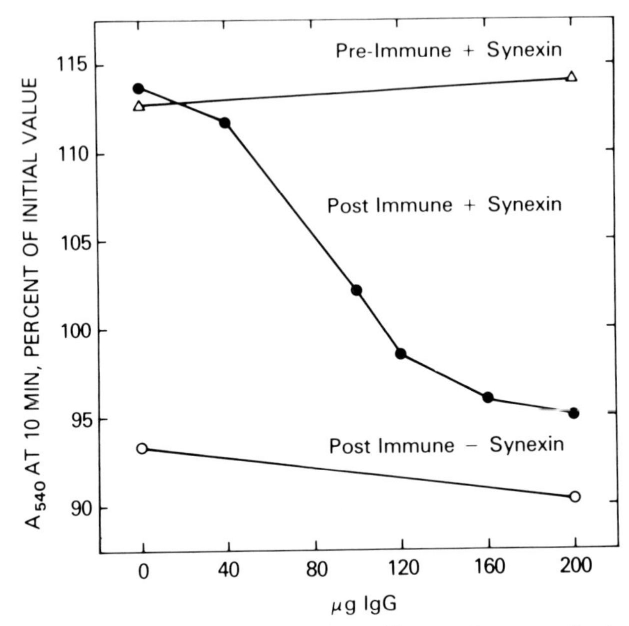

FIG. 7. Inhibition of synexin-dependent chromaffin granule aggregation by rabbit anti-synexin IgG. Approximately 1 μg of synexin was incubated with 130 μg of chromaffin granules in 1 ml in the presence of various amounts of preimmune or antisynexin IgG. The antisynexin has blocked the aggregation of the granules which is monitored as a turbidity change in 10 minutes.

xin in chromaffin cells by indirect immunofluorescence. Chromaffin cells, isolated from medullary tissue by collagenase digestion, were fixed in 2% formaldehyde for 20 minutes at room temperature, then spread on glass slides, air dried, and further fixed and permeabilized in 95% ethanol. The cells were then incubated with the anti-synexin antibody and, subsequently, with a fluorescein-tagged goat anti-rabbit-IgG immunoglobulin. An excess of normal goat IgG was included in the immune reagent to saturate nonspecific binding sites. As illustrated in Fig. 8, specific anti-synexin staining occurred in a diffuse manner throughout the cytoplasm of the chromaffin cell. In some cells the degree of staining was noticeably enhanced near the cell surface.

To summarize our results with synexin, we have found that it is a Ca^{2+} binding protein that, *in vitro,* causes a Ca^{2+}-specific association of chromaffin granule membranes at levels of Ca^{2+} that may occur near the plasma membrane when the chromaffin cell is stimulated. Furthermore, synexin is present in the cytoplasm of the cell. These facts suggest that the *in vivo* role of synexin may be to act as an intracellular receptor for Ca^{2+} which

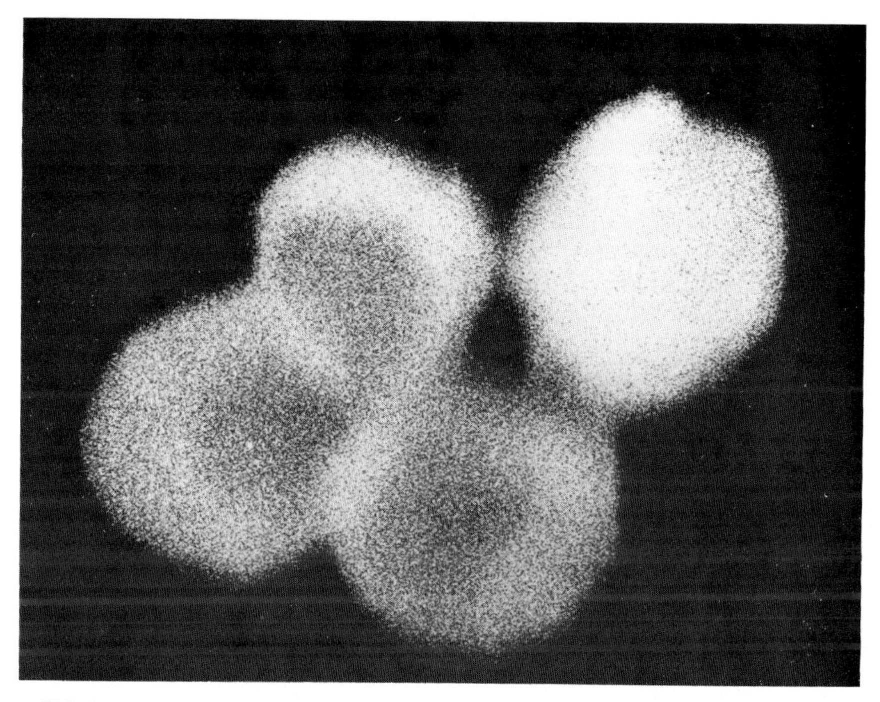

FIG. 8. A small cluster of bovine adrenal chromaffin cells stained by the immunofluorescence technique for the presence of synexin. Specific staining is seen here throughout the cytoplasm, leaving darker areas at the positions of the cell nuclei.

initiates the process of exocytosis. Consistent with this concept is recent work from our laboratory that has shown synexin to attach in a calcium-dependent manner to the inside aspect of the chromaffin cell plasma membrane, but not to the inside of red cell ghosts (Pollard *et al.*, 1980).

In further work on this protein it will be of particular importance to determine whether synexin will indeed attach secretory vesicles to the inner surface of the plasma membrane. It will also be of interest to characterize synexin-like proteins in other tissues, as we have already determined that Ca^{2+}-dependent chromaffin granule aggregation activity exists in crude preparations obtained from the parotid gland, whole brain, and blood platelets.

III. Chemiosmotic Lysis of Chromaffin Granules: A Possible Model for Fission

It was apparent that while synexin might induce formation of pentalaminar complexes, it did not cause breakage or "fission" of the adjacent membranes. A plausible alternate candidate for a process related to fission was the ATP-driven lysis of isolated chromaffin granules in an isoosmotic medium, a reaction first described in 1965 by Oka *et al.* (1965). Such lysis results in the release of granule contents including catecholamines, dopamine-β-hydroxylase, ATP, and chromogranins, and is greatly potentiated by the presence of permeant anions such as chloride. In recent years it has become evident that the loss of granule integrity is due to osmotic lysis subsequent to the coupled influx of protons and permeant anions via two granule membrane activities: a proton pumping Mg-ATPase and a selective anion transport site (summarized in Pollard *et al.*, 1979a). Our understanding of this granule lysis process led us to postulate, by analogy, that the mechanism of fission in exocytosis might involve local osmotic lysis of the fused secretory granule. We sup posed the process might utilize intracellular ATP and the concentration gradient of chloride ions which exists across most cell membranes. We therefore studied the characteristics of the chromaffin granule lysis reaction in detail in order to generate specific, testable predictions regarding the secretory behavior of chromaffin and other cells.

In our experiments, granule lysis was monitored by measuring the release of epinephrine from suspensions of bovine adrenal chromaffin granules. The procedure involved the addition of 250 μl of a suspension of granules (250–500 μg protein) in 0.3 *M* sucrose (4°C), prepared as described earlier, to 1.5 ml of prewarmed (37°C) medium containing various substances of interest (salts, drugs, ATP, etc.). After a 10-minute incubation at 37°C, the granules were sedimented by centrifugation and released epinephrine was assayed in the supernatant by a fluorometric method (Pazoles and Pollard, 1978).

Using this protocol, we examined the effects of Mg^{2+}-ATP and various salts on granule lysis (Table I). We found that epinephrine release was potentiated by Mg^{2+}-ATP and was greatly influenced by the nature of the anion, but not the cation present. Permeant anions such as Cl^-, Br^-, and I^- supported release whereas impermeant anions such as isethionate and PO_4^{3-} did not. In addition, the ATP-dependent release rate was a saturable function of $[Cl^-]$ and was competitively inhibited by isethionate ions, suggesting that an anion-selective membrane transport site might be involved (Pazoles and Pollard, 1978). To pursue this possibility, we made use of a number of compounds which had been previously shown to block anion transport in erythrocytes. These compounds included SITS (a stilbene disulfonate), probenecid, and pyridoxal phosphate (Fig. 9). These drugs contained both anionic and hydrophobic moieties in keeping with their inhibitory function and were impermeant under our conditions. As expected, these compounds all inhibited Mg-ATP-chloride mediated

TABLE I

Influence of Mg^{2+}-ATP and Various Salts on Epinephrine Release from Chromaffin Granule

Salt (80 m*M*)	Percentage epinephrine released/10 minutes[a] $-Mg^{2+}$-ATP	Percentage epinephrine released/10 minutes[a] $+Mg^{2+}$-ATP
None (335 m*M* sucrose)	10.6 ± 0.8[b]	11.4 ± 0.1
KCl	19.5 ± 2.1	65.9 ± 5.2
NaCl	17.3 ± 1.8	66.4 ± 6.6
Choline Cl	14.2 ± 0.7	63.3 ± 2.9
Tetraethylammonium Cl	15.1 ± 1.3	60.4 ± 4.2
K Br	19.9 ± 2.3	86.1 ± 4.4
K Isethionate	10.4 ± 0.2	14.6 ± 1.0
K HPO_4	10.9 ± 1.1	11.6 ± 0.4

[a] Incubations were at 37°C in isotonic media buffered with 50 m*M* MES, pH 6.0.
[b] ± SD ($n \geq 4$).

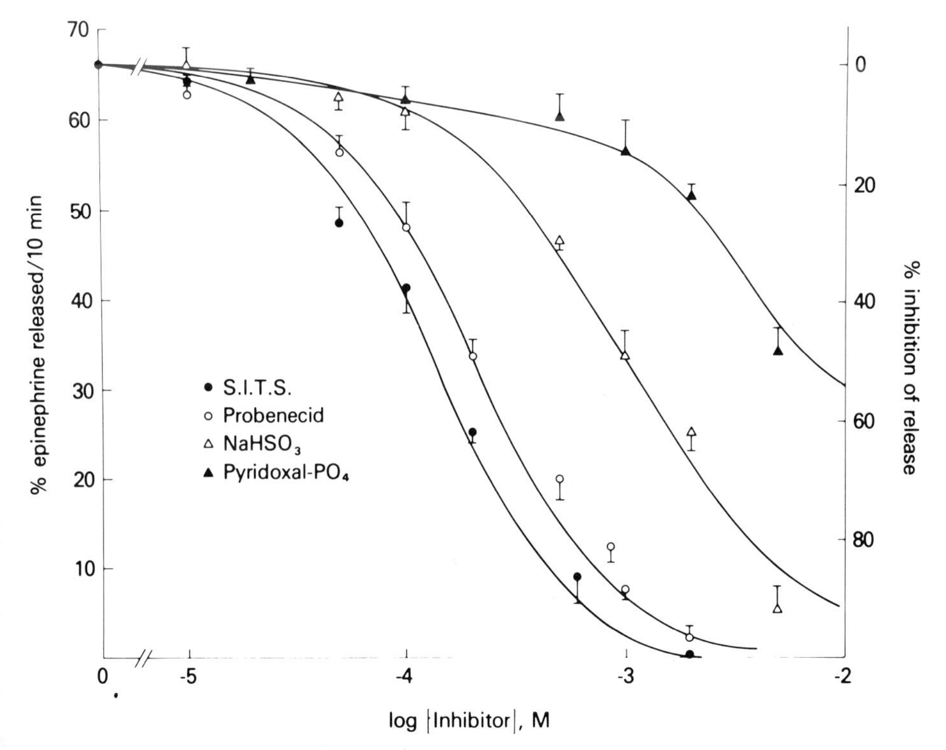

FIG. 9. Inhibition of Mg^{2+}-ATP, Cl^--mediated epinephrine release by anion transport inhibiting drugs. The medium contained 1 m*M* $MgSO_4$, 1 m*M* Na_2ATP, 90 m*M* KCl, 50 m*M* HEPES/NaOH, pH 6.0, and sufficient sucrose to adjust the final osmolarity to 335 mOsm.

epinephrine release with potencies that were very similar to those reported for inhibition of anion transport in erythrocytes (Cabantchik and Rothstein, 1974). Using kinetic analysis, we were also able to show that the mechanism of inhibition in each case was competitive with respect to $[Cl^-]$ (Pazoles and Pollard, 1978). Finally, we demonstrated that SITS directly inhibited entry of $^{36}Cl^-$ into granules in the presence of Mg-ATP (Pazoles and Pollard, 1978). We concluded from these experiments that the mechanism of Mg-ATP-anion induced granule lysis involved anion transport through a selective and saturable membrane site. We are currently attempting to identify the specific granule membrane components involved in anion transport.

We, and others, have also studied the role of ATP in the granule lysis process. It had been known for sometime that the granule membrane contained an externally oriented Mg^{2+}-ATPase (Palade, 1975), and subsequent studies indicated that it might function to pump protons into the granule interior (Casey *et al.*, 1976, 1977; Njus and Radda, 1978). If this were the case, then granule lysis might involve entry of both protons and anions into the granule. This possibility was especially attractive since some cation entry was required to maintain electroneutrality upon anion entry, and since we had shown that uptake of the cation of the added chloride salt did not occur (Pazoles and Pollard, 1978). Our approach to the study of this proton pumping ATPase was to examine the effects of Mg-ATP addition on the electrical and pH gradients across the granule membrane. The transmembrane electrical potential was determined by first measuring the distribution of a lipophilic anion, $[^{14}C]$thiocyanate, across the granule membrane as described in detail elsewhere (Pollard *et al.*, 1976; Pazoles and Pollard, 1978). The potential (ΔE) was then calculated from this distribution via the Nernst equation. Chromaffin granules in an isoosmotic buffered sucrose medium (pH 6.0) exhibited an ΔE of $+28.6 \pm 1.0$ mV, positive inside. Upon addition of 1 mM Mg-ATP, ΔE increased to $+66.4 \pm 6.3$ mV. These data were obtained at 0°C to minimize granule lysis, but qualitatively similar results were found at 37°C. These findings were consistent with the suggestion that the granule ATPase acted to move protons electrogenically into the granule, and supporting this conclusion was the additional finding that FCCP, a proton ionophore, strongly inhibited Mg^{2+}-ATP, Cl^--induced granule lysis, presumably by counteracting the inward proton pump.

The transmembrane proton concentration gradient (ΔpH) was determined by measuring the intragranular pH under conditions of known external pH. To do this, Pollard *et al.* (1979b) and others (Njus *et al.*, 1978) have made use of the facts that ATP is an endogenous component of the granule core and that the ^{31}P NMR resonance signal from the γ-phosphate of ATP is sensitive to its local pH. By artificially setting the internal pH to known values, we were able to calibrate the chemical shift of this resonance with the known value of intragranular pH (Pollard *et al.,* 1979b). These studies showed that the intragranular pH was buffered to approximately 5.7, a value consistent with data from methylamine distribution (Pollard *et al.,* 1976, 1979b; Njus *et al.,* 1978; Johnson and Scarpa, 1976). Addition of Mg-ATP had no effect on this value because of substantial intragranular buffering. If, however, a permeant anion were also present, the granule interior was progressively acidified, as shown in Fig. 10, suggesting that the granule ATPase was capable of sustaining proton movement into the granule against the H^+ concentration gradient only in the form of electroneutral coupled transport with anions.

To further test this hypothesis we repeated the above experiment but replaced the ATPase as the driving force for proton entry with an inward proton concentration gradient created by incubating the granules at pH 5.2. Once again, intragranular acidification depended upon the presence of permeant anions (see Fig. 11). These recent data were obtained with the aid of Jack S. Cohen and Heisaburo Shindo at the NIH, as described in Pollard *et al.* (1979b). If performed in an isoosmotic medium, the combination of low pH and permeant anions resulted in granule lysis. This lysis, like that in the presence of MgATP and permeant anions at higher pH, was also inhibited by anion transport blockers (Fig. 12).

From these experiments it was apparent that in presence of permeant anions and either Mg-ATP or low external pH, there was net accumulation of ions within the granule leading to osmotic lysis. This was confirmed experimentally by demonstrating that Mg-ATP-induced epinephrine re-

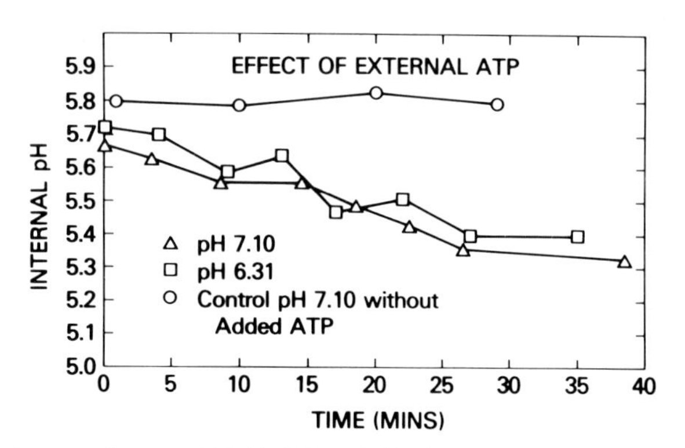

FIG. 10. Influence of external Mg^{2+}-ATP and chloride on the acidification of the chromaffin granule interior. The reaction mixture contained 100 m*M* KCl, 7.5 m*M* $MgSO_4$, 7.5 m*M* Na_2ATP, 50 m*M* PIPES/NaOH buffer, pH 7.10, or 50 m*M* MES/NaOH buffer, pH 6.31, and sufficient sucrose to bring the osmotic strength to 970 mOsm.

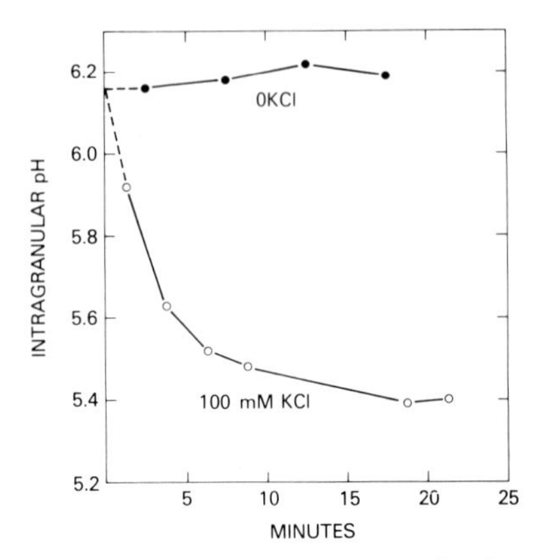

FIG. 11. Intragranular acidification induced by incubation in a chloride medium with a pH lower than the intragranular pH. Media contained either zero or 100 mM KCl, 50 mM MES/NaOH buffer, pH 5.2, and enough sucrose to adjust the osmotic strength to 970 mOsm.

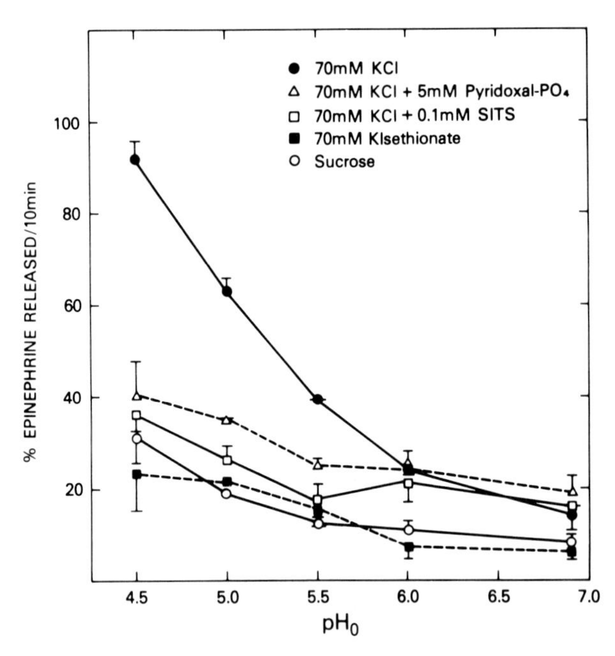

FIG. 12. Influence of anions and anion transport blocking drugs on H^+, Cl^--mediated epinephrine release from chromaffin granules. The medium was buffered with 50 mM MES/NaOH and was brought to 335 mOsm with sucrose.

lease was progressively inhibited by increasing the osmotic strength of the medium (Fig. 13). Similar osmotic suppression was also found for release occurring at low pH.

Taken together, our studies and those of others have led to a chemiosmotic model of the granule lysis process. According to this model, in the presence of an inward concentration gradient of permeant anions, such as chloride, the activity of a granule membrane proton pumping Mg-ATPase results in the electroneutral, bulk uptake of protons and anions. The resulting increase in granule osmotic content induces water entry and subsequent lysis.

We have recently described the successful construction of a mathematical model for the release process that depends on ATP and Cl^- (Creutz and Pollard, 1980). This model incorporates the basic concepts set forth above of an ATP-dependent proton pump and the concurrent influx of Cl^- into the granule via a specific transport site. Since the release event is hypothesized to be due to osmotic lysis, the model relates the influx of osmotically active particles to a degree of lysis within a granule preparation by referring to an experimentally determined osmotic fragility curve for that same population. Such a fragility curve, as determined by incubating granules in hypotonic media and monitoring lysis as a drop in turbidity or a release of epinephrine, is illustrated in Fig. 14. Based on this fragility

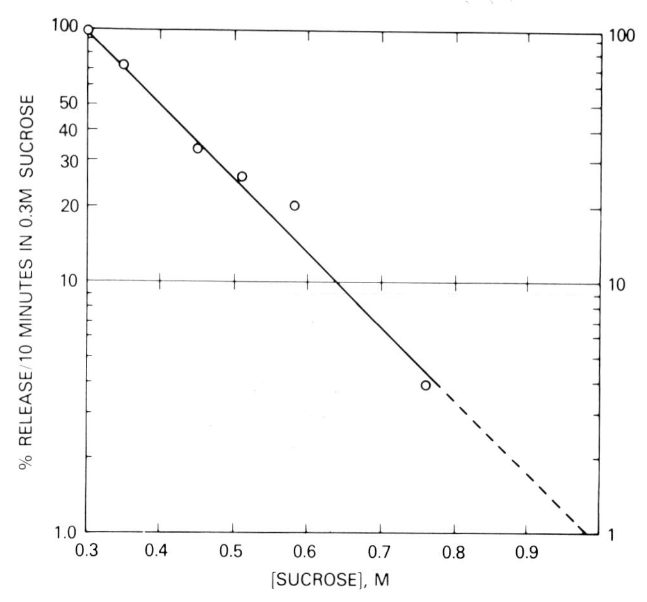

FIG. 13. Suppression of Mg^{2+}-ATP, Cl^--mediated epinephrine release from chromaffin granules by elevation of the extragranular osmotic strength.

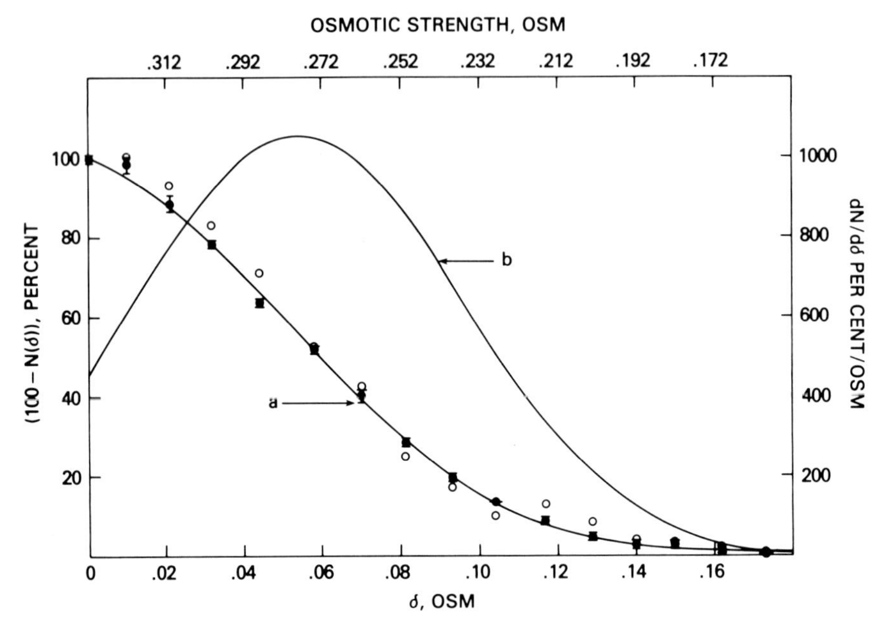

FIG. 14. Osmotic fragility curve of chromaffin granules prepared in 0.3 *M* sucrose. Curve a is $100 - N(\delta)$, the normalized turbidity of the suspension in percent, where 100% corresponds to the turbidity in 0.332 osmolal medium ($A_{540} \simeq 0.3$), and 0% corresponds to the minimum turbidity seen after hypotonic lysis ($A_{540} \simeq 0.9$). The curve is plotted as a function of the total osmolality of the incubation medium, or of δ, the deviation from 0.332 Osm. The points are measurements of turbidity in duplicate ± SD; the open circles are the percentage of total epinephrine remaining in the granules; the solid curve is 100 − the integral of curve b. Curve b is $dN/d\delta$, a Gaussian of the form $Ce^{-(\delta-A)2/B}$ with A, B, and C chosen so that the integral of the curve b gives the best least squares fit to the turbidity data ($A = 0.0540$ Osm; $B = 3.51 \times 10^{-3}$ Osm^2; $C = 1052$ percent/OsM). This curve is referred to as the osmotic fragility curve (Creutz and Pollard, 1980).

curve, the model was able to accurately describe the kinetics of the release reaction with different levels of Cl^- present, as illustrated in Fig. 15. In addition, the model was able to make accurate predictions about the ATP dependence of the reaction, and the suppression of the reaction by increased osmotic strength. The predictions concerning osmotic strength suppression were also accurate when applied to observations on exocytosis from whole cells (see subsequent sections). The success of this modeling effort provided support for the conception of the roles of ATP, anions, and osmotic lysis in the chromaffin granule release reaction and also supported the notion that the same events might be involved in the process of exocytosis from cells.

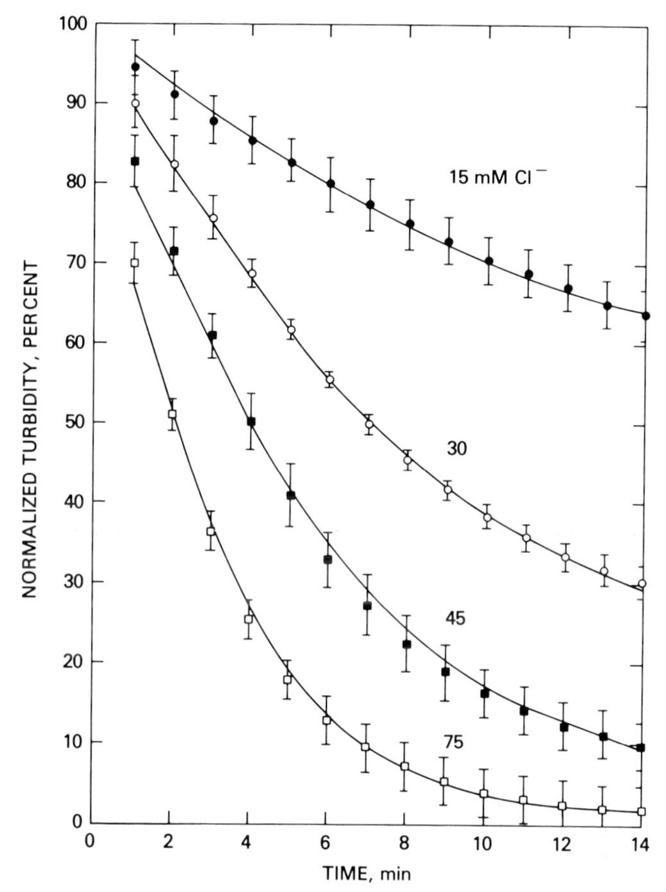

FIG. 15. Time course of turbidity change for chromaffin granule suspensions undergoing the Mg-ATP and Cl^--dependent release reaction at 37°C with different levels of Cl^-. Turbidity axis is in percent with 100% corresponding to the initial turbidity of $A_{540} \simeq 0.3$ and 0% corresponding to the turbidity at 15 minutes with 90 m*M* Cl^-. The Mg-ATP concentration is 5 m*M*. The error bars represent SD for triplicate determinations. The solid lines represent the best simultaneous fit to the data of the model for the release reaction described in detail in Creutz and Pollard (1980).

IV. Exocytosis from Chromaffin Cells: A Test of the Chemiosmotic Model

We have considered the mechanism of chemiosmotic lysis of isolated chromaffin granules, described in detail in the preceding section, to be a possible model for the release event during exocytosis (Pollard *et al.*, 1979a). In fact this was our primary reason for characterizing this process so extensively over the last few years, and we anticipated being able to test our hypothesis with chromaffin and other cell types if we understood the chemistry of granule lysis in some detail.

As a possible scenario of secretion from the viewpoint of the chromaffin granule we imagined that the average granule within the chromaffin cell might be immersed in ~1 m*M* Mg^{2+}-ATP, so that the proton pump might be functioning at all times. Should the local calcium concentration rise the granule might become closely juxtaposed to the plasma membrane, perhaps via synexin action, thereby bringing it into proximity with the greatly elevated chloride concentration outside the cell. If the anion transport site on the granule membrane were in some way introduced into the membrane region separating granule interior and external milieu, then net H^+ and Cl^- transport could cnsuc and osmotic rupture, as in the *in vitro* granule system, might occur.

If this scenario were correct, then several experimental predictions could be made for chromaffin cells. For example, increasing the osmotic strength of the medium might suppress exocytosis. Perhaps replacing chloride by an impermeant anion such as isethionate or adding an anion transport blocker might suppress exocytosis. Finally, drugs which interfered with ATP synthesis or depleted proton gradients might be expected to suppress exocytosis.

To test these predictions we prepared chromaffin cells by treating adrenal medullary tissue with collagenase, by a variation of the method described by Hochman and Perlman (1976) and others (Fenwick *et al.*, 1978; Schneider *et al.*, 1977; Brooks, 1977). These cells, in our hands, were found to secrete epinephrine and dopamine-β-hydroxylase when incubated with cholinergic agonists (acetylcholine or carbachol), the calcium ionophore A23187, or with veratridine, a drug which activates action potential sodium channels. Tetrodotoxin, a drug which specifically blocks veratridine action on nerves, was also found to block epinephrine secretion induced by veratridine. This cell preparation thus appeared to be secreting as expected, and we proceeded to test our chemiosmotic hypothesis.

As expected, progressive elevation of the osmotic strength of the medium with either NaCl or sucrose lead to suppression of epinephrine secretion induced with either veratridine (75 μM) or acetylcholine (500 μ*M*). In fact, the osmotic suppression curve for cells was essentially very similar to that observed with isolated chromaffin granules in the presence of ATP and chloride (cf. Fig. 13). A23187 could not be studied under hypertonic conditions because it induced virtually complete cell lysis above 450 mOsm.

We also studied the relative levels of epinephrine release when different monovalent anions were substituted for chloride in the medium. Using both veratridine and A23187 as secretagogues, NaBr and NaI were found to support higher levels of epinephrine secretion than NaCl while Na acetate supported a lower level and Na isethionate essentially supported very little release (see Table II). This relationship was quite similar to that observed for relative rates of ATP-driven lysis of isolated chromaffin granules, and we concluded that the predictions about anions made on the basis of chromaffin granule studies also appeared to be borne out in studies on cells.

We also analyzed release from cells suspended in low ionic strength media, in which 90% of the NaCl was replaced by isoosmolar sucrose. Veratridine-induced release was substantially suppressed under these conditions, as expected. Yet, carbachol-activated release in such sucrose media was observed in 6 of 10 experiments, casting doubt on the apparently critical need for permeant anions such as Cl^- during exocytosis. More detailed analysis revealed, however, that unexpectedly low amounts of dopamine-β-hydroxylase (DBH), a 280,000 MW, intragranular enzyme, were released in sucrose media, while substantial amounts were released in standard NaCl media. Therefore, release observed in sucrose media was not typically "exocytotic," but of another, hitherto unanticipated variety. Blumenthal and his colleagues have recently described differential release of small components from artificial liposomes, and have called it "leakage" or "appositional" transfer (Blumenthal, 1979). The relevance of this process to the phenomenon described in chromaffin cells is as yet not known.

Finally, we examined the influences of various drugs affecting both anion and proton transport in granules on secretion for intact cells. Proton ionophores such as FCCP (carbonylayanide-*p*-trifluoromethoxyphenylhydrazone) and TTFB (4,5,6,7-tetrachloro-2-trifluoromethylbenzimidazole) inhibited veratridine-activated release by almost 90% at 5 μM concentration, and the dose–response curves were quite similar to that

TABLE II

Influence of Different Anions on Release of Epinephrine from Chromaffin Cells

Na^+ $Anion^-$	(Release relative to that in chloride media) Veratridine	A23187
Br^-	178	311
I^-	158	279
Cl^-	100	100
Ac^-	78	83
Isethionate	6	21

observed for inhibition of chromaffin granule lysis. However, profound inhibition was observed with other metabolic inhibitors which did not affect the granule system. The other inhibitors included rotenone, CN^-, and azide, which affect mitochondrial function, and 2-deoxyglucose, which affects glucose metabolism. We concluded that ATP production was probably important for secretion, but that a specific interpretation in terms of a direct action of ATP on the fused granule prior to secretion seemed necessarily precluded. A variety of anion transport inhibitors were also tested; stilbene disulfonates (such as SITS or DIDS) were inactive, while probenecid and pyridoxal phosphate inhibited secretion at higher concentrations. These findings may reflect the specific geometry of granules in a fused state, or perhaps, a heterogeneity of anion transport sites which we have begun to detect and study in isolated chromaffin granules (Pazoles *et al.*, 1980).

These studies appeared to indicate that it was possible to make predictions about secretion from chromaffin cells based on what was known about chemiosmotic lysis of isolated chromaffin granules. An important question to consider then was how general this effect might be. During and preceding our studies on chromaffin cells and granules we did have the opportunity to study serotonin secretion from human platelets (Pollard *et al.*, 1977) and parathormone (PTH) secretion from bovine parathyroid cells (Brown *et al.*, 1978). Both cell types had general similarities to the chromaffin cell system but a few specific differences as described in the next sections.

V. Secretion from Human Platelets

Secretion of serotonin from human platelets was also found to exhibit many similarities to the chromaffin granule lysis reaction (Pollard *et al.*, 1977). For example, anion transport-blocking drugs were found to inhibit secretion, regardless of whether release was stimulated by A23187, a calcium ionophore, or thrombin, a physiological agonist. However, replacement of sodium chloride by either sucrose or sodium isethionate did not inhibit secretion. Instead, a reduction in pH was found to inhibit both thrombin- and A23187-induced release, and the blocking drugs were found to be apparent competitive inhibitors with respect to OH^- concentration. Suramin was found to be the most effective agent with a K_i of 0.9 μM, while the K_i values for SITS, probenecid, and pyridoxal phosphate in the platelet system were 22, 56, and 350 μM, respectively, with respect to $[OH^-]$. HCO_3^-, which also varied necessarily with pH, did not appear to be involved. In contrast, suramin was not a good inhibitor of PTH secretion by parathyroid cells (see next section) or indeed of Cl, Mg^{2+}-ATP-induced chromaffin granule lysis. FCCP, a proton ionophore, was also found to inhibit platelet secretion completely at a concentration of 4 μM.

As anticipated, hypertonic media inhibited platelet secretion and a semilogarithmic plot of these data showed a remarkable similarity to the homologous curve for osmotic suppression previously shown for chromaffin granule epinephrine release (cf. Fig. 13) and for secretion from chromaffin cells. We concluded that the platelet system appeared to resemble the chromaffin granule in terms of the osmotic basis of release, apparently differing terms of the specific anions involved in secretion.

VI. Secretion from Bovine Parathyroid Cells

PTH is stored in dense-cored secretory granules, and secretion can be stimulated by exposure of the dissociated parathyroid cell to low calcium (0.5 mM), isoproterenol, dopamine, and other agonists. Probenecid and SITS were found to have similar inhibitory potencies and inhibited secretion almost completely, while replacement of sodium chloride by either sucrose or sodium isethionate caused a 70% reduction in PTH secretion. Various cation replacements for sodium were without influence on release, and kinetic analysis of both SITS and probenecid inhibition showed a strong competitive character with respect to Cl^-, each with K_i = 4–6 × 10^{-4} M. FCCP (4 μM) completely inhibited stimulated PTH secretion, as did raising the osmotic strength of the medium from 300 to 1000 mOsm.

We were initially puzzled by the observation that, while anion transport inhibitors blocked PTH release essentially completely, the omission of Cl^- or replacement of Cl^- by isethionate left 30% of the total release unaffected. One interpretation was that the medium might contain an alternative anion to Cl^-. We considered both HCO_3^- and OH^-, since both were known to be transported by the erythrocyte anion channel (Tosteson *et al.*, 1973). We found that simply lowering the pH from 7.5 to 7.0 resulted in a substantial reduction in PTH secretion and that the reduction was not reversed by raising the [HCO_3^-]. Probenecid was also found to be a competitive inhibitor with respect to [OH^-], and we concluded that OH^- might also be a permeant anion for this system. An alternative explanation was that a membrane component was being protonated and therefore inhibited PTH release. This would have meant, however, that probenecid acted in a very similar manner on both a Cl^--interacting site and on a H^+-interacting site, both of which were involved in PTH release. At present we still do not consider this a very likely possibility.

VII. Studies on Other Secreting Cells

A few other cell types have been shown to behave in some respects as predicted by the chemiosmotic chromaffin granule model. Dogfish phagocytes, which release lysosomal enzymes during phagocytosis of opsonized sea urchin eggs, have been shown to depend upon chloride and to be inhibited by several stilbene disulfonate drugs (Korchak *et al.*, 1980). Human polymorphonuclear leukocytes have also been shown to secrete lysosomal enzymes by a mechanism sensitive to osmotic strength and stilbene disulfonates (Weissmann *et al.*, 1978). However, polymorphonuclear leukocytes, like platelets, did not seem to be dependent upon extracellular chloride. Poisner and Hong (1974) have shown vasopressin release from anterior pituitary nerve terminals to be sensitive to chloride and other permeant anions and to variations in external osmotic strength. Finally, F. Rickles and P. Armstrong (personal communication to H. B. Pollard) have shown endotoxin-stimulated secretion from the *Limulus* amoebocyte to be dependent upon chloride in the medium (blocked by replacement of NaCl by Na-isethionate) and to be inhibited by stilbene disulfonates.

VIII. Conclusions

Exocytosis, as viewed from the perspectives of electron microscopy and chemistry, seems to require mechanisms for formation of a calcium-dependent complex between plasma membrane and secretory vesicles and mechanisms for subsequent breakage of the complex to allow vesicle contents to escape from the cell. Insofar as the initial complex formation is concerned, our new protein synexin appears to satisfy many of the expected requirements of such a catalyst for this process. Not only is it a calcium-binding protein, but it also binds to the inner aspect of chromaffin cell plasma membranes. No other type of protein that we know of appears to be capable of this constellation of membrane effects.

Calmodulin, a popular protein that has been touted as a possible mediator of secretion for example has none of these properties. One interesting property that both synexin and calmodulin share, however, is a similar sensitivity to higher concentration of phenothiazine drugs such as trifluperazine and chlorpromazine. Perhaps this latter property relates in some fashion to recent observations that many secreting cells are inhibited by these drugs.

The final event in secretion, that of breaking the membrane-separating vesicle contents from the external milieu, is still far from understood, although we have been attracted to the possibility that chemiosmotic properties of secretory granules might be related to the process. The primary reason for our interest in this concept, as described above, is that the granule lysis mechanism was at least one example of how the granule membrane could lose its integrity by a mechanism related to intrinsic granule chemistry. The fact that many of the properties of the granule lysis reaction can be found in the intact cell when secretion is occurring indicates that this hypothesis may indeed be valid. It is important to note, however, that our chemiosmotic hypothesis for exocytosis remains circumstantial inasmuch as we have shown parallels only between cell secretion and granule lysis. Nonetheless, it is of interest to note that the osmotic part of the hypothesis has been tested in a purely physical model of membrane fusion in recent experiments described by Zimmerberg *et al.* (1980) and Cohen *et al.* (1980) from Finkelstein's laboratory. These studies showed that fluorescein-filled multilamellar liposomes could fuse with and transfer liposome contents across a black lipid membrane (BLM), provided that an osmotic gradient initially existed across the BLM. Similar dependences have been shown by others in more biological systems.

However, it is evident that we are far from having good experimental approaches to all of the processes involved in secretion, particularly in chromaffin cells. Nonetheless, the system seems ideal for discovering other experimental paradigms. For example, we are at a quandary as to how the pentalaminar complex formed between adjacent granules or granules and plasma membranes might, indeed, proceed to the breakage point, or why breakage should occur at any specific point. Spontaneous rearrangement of synexin-aggregated membranes does not occur *in vitro*, as we have shown, and is thus unlikely to occur *in vivo*. One possibility, however, discussed by Dr. Carl Creutz in detail in the following discussion, is that specific free fatty acids such as arachidonic acid, may be involved in changes in membrane integrity. He has found, for example, that addition of arachidonic acid to synexin-aggregated chromaffin granules induces them to fuse into a rather large ($\leq$ 10 μm diameter) bags containing diffuse granule contents. Possibly arachidonic acid or related compounds may prove to be important additional factors in controlling and directing the membrane remodeling process occurring during exocytosis.

REFERENCES

Blumenthal, R., Ralston, E., Dragston, P., and Weinstein, J. N. (1979). *Biophys. J.* **25,** 291A.

Brooks, J. C. (1977). *Endocrinology* **101,** 1360–1378.

Brown, E. M., Pazoles, C. J., Creutz, C. E., Aurbach, G. D., and Pollard, H. B. (1978). *Proc. Natl. Acad. Sci.* U.S.A. **75,** 876–880.

Cabantchik, Z. I., and Rothstein, A. (1974). *J. Membr. Biol.* **15,** 207–226.

Casey, R. P., Njus, D., Radda, G. K., and Sehr, P. A. (1976). *Biochem. J.* **158,** 583–588.
Casey, R. P., Njus, D., Radda, G. K., and Sehr, P. A. (1977). *Biochemistry* **16,** 972–978.
Cohen, F. S., Zimmerberg, J., and Finkelstein, A. (1980). *J. Gen. Physiol.*
Creutz, C. E., and Pollard, H. B. (1980). *Biophys J.* **31,** 255–270.
Creutz, C. E., Pazoles, C. J., and Pollard, H. B. (1978). *J. Biol. Chem.* **253,** 2858–2866.
Creutz, C. E., Pazoles, C. J., and Pollard, H. B. (1979). *J. Biol. Chem.* **254,** 553–558.
Creutz, C. E., Pazoles, C. J., and Pollard, H. B. (1980). *in* "Catecholamines: Basic and Clinical Frontiers" (I. Kopin and E. Usdin, eds.), Vol. 1, pp. 346–349, Pergamon, Oxford.
Fenwick, E. M., Fajdiga, P. B., Howe, N. B. S., and Livett, B. G. (1978). *J. Cell Biol.* **76,** 12–30.
Hochman, J., and Perlman, R. L. (1976). *Biochim. Biophys. Acta* **421,** 168–175.
Johnson, R. G., and Scarpa, A. (1976). *J. Biol. Chem.* **241,** 2189–2191.
Korchak, H. M., Eisenstatt, B. A., Hoffstein, S. T., and Weissman, G. (1980). *Proc. Natl. Acad. Sci.* U.S.A., in press.
Llinas, R., Steinberg, I. Z., and Walton, K. (1976). *Proc. Natl. Acad. Sci. U.S.A.* **73,** 2918–2922.
Njus, D., and Radda, G. K. (1978). *Biochim. Biophys. Acta* **463,** 219–244.
Njus, D., Sehr, P. A., Radda, G. K., Ritchie, G. A., and Seeley, P. J. (1978). *Biochemistry* **17,** 4337–4343.
Oka, M., Ohuchi, T., Yoshida, H., and Imaizumi, R. (1965). *Biochim. Biophys. Acta* **97,** 170–171.
Palade, G. E. (1975). *Science* **189,** 347–357.
Parsegian, V. A. (1977). *in* "Soc. for Neuroscience Symposia" (W. M. Cowan and J. A. Ferrendelli, eds.), Vol. II, pp. 161–194. Soc. for Neuroscience, Bethesda, Maryland.
Pazoles, C. J., and Pollard, H. B. (1978). *J. Biol. Chem.* **253,** 3962–3969.
Pazoles, C. J., Creutz, C. E., Ramu, A., and Pollard, H. B. (1980). *J. Biol. Chem.* **255,** 7863–7869.
Poisner, A. M., and Hong, J. S. (1974). *Adv. Cytopharm.* **2,** 303–310.
Pollard, H. B., Zinder, O., Hoffman, P. G., and Nikodijevik, O. (1976). *J. Biol. Chem.* **251,** 4544–4550.
Pollard, H. B., Tack-Goldman, K. M., Pazoles, C. J., Creutz, C. E., and Shulman, N. R. (1977). *Proc. Natl. Acad. Sci.* U.S.A. **74,** 5295–5299.
Pollard, H. B., Pazoles, C. J., Creutz, C. E., and Zinder, O. (1979a). *Internatl. Rev. Cytol.* **58,** 159–197.
Pollard, H. B., Shindo, H., Creutz, C. E., Pazoles, C. J., and Cohen, J. S. (1979b). *J. Biol. Chem.* **254,** 1170–1177.
Pollard, H. B., Creutz, C. E., Pazoles, C. J., and Scott, J. H. (1980). *Proc. Electron Microsc. Soc. Am.* **38,** 594–597.
Schneider, A. S., Herz, R., and Rosenheck, K. (1977). *Proc. Natl. Acad. Sci.* U.S.A. **74,** 5036–5040.
Schober, R., Nitsch, C., Rinne, U., and Morris, S. J. (1977). *Science* **195,** 495–497.
Smith, A. D. (1968). *in* "The Interaction of Drugs and Subcellular Components in Animal Cells" (P. N. Campbell, ed.), pp. 239–292. Churchill, London.
Tosteson, D. C., Gunn, R. B., and Wieth, J. O. (1973). *in* "The Organization of Energy Transducing Membranes" (M. Nakao and L. Packer, eds.), pp. 345–354. University Park Press, Baltimore, Maryland.
Viveros, O. H. (1974). *Handbook Physiol. Sect. 7: Endocrinol.* **6,** 389–426.
Weissmann, G., Finkelstein, M. C., Csernonsky, J., Quigley, J. P., Quinn, R. S., Techner, L., Troll, W., and Dunham, R. B. (1978). *Proc. Natl. Acad. Sci. U.S.A.*

Winkler, H. (1977). *Neuroscience* **2,** 657–683.
Zimmberberg, J., Cohen, F. S., and Finkelstein, A. (1980). *J. Gen. Physiol.* **75,** 241–250.

DISCUSSION

C. Creutz: I would like to briefly describe some observations I made this summer which suggest that chromaffin granules that have been aggregated, or brought into close apposition, by synexin and Ca^{2+} can subsequently fuse to form larger structures with a common interior space. Dr. Pollard showed an electron micrograph of a chromaffin cell that had been exhaustively stimulated to secrete (see Fig. 3). In the cytoplasm of that cell were large vacuoles apparently formed by the coalescence of numerous chromaffin granules undergoing compound exocytosis. It occurred to us that these vacuoles might be large enough to see in the light microscope. Indeed we found that in stained thick sections of these cells the vacuoles were plainly visible with the light microscope. We became interested in looking for the formation of such structures *in vitro* from isolated chromaffin granules and synexin. Accordingly, I incubated chromaffin granules with synexin for an extended period of time, until very large clusters of granules were formed that could be easily seen in the phase microscope. A picture of such aggregates is shown in Fig. A (A). However, these aggregates seemed to be quite stable indefinitely and did not appear to form any sort of vacuole. However, I subsequently found that if a particular cofactor was added to the incubation medium the aggregates did transform into a new type of structure, shown in Fig. A (B, C, and D). These structures form in 1 or 2 minutes and have the appearance of large, spherical vacuoles similar to those that formed in the intact cell. They vary in size depending upon the size of the original granule aggregate, with the largest having diameters up to 10 μm.

The cofactor that was necessary to induce this remarkable transition was simply a free, unsaturated fatty acid. Several naturally occurring fatty acids were effective in this regard, but arachidonic acid worked best. Other compounds that have been traditionally used, at much higher concentrations, to fuse cells did not cause this fusion to occur. A particularly interesting example is lysolecithin, which many people have speculated, because of its detergent-like properties, could be involved in biological membrane fusion. However, lysolecithin was ineffective in this system.

The threshold concentration for arachidonic acid to cause this transition was in the range of 5 to 10 μM. Interestingly, this concentration, when compared with the total amount of membrane phospholipid in the incubation mixture, is the same amount of arachidonic acid, relatively speaking, as is released from a blood platelet by phospholipases acting on membrane phospholipids when the platelet is stimulated to secrete serotonin. In the case of the platelet, the released arachidonic acid is known to serve as a precursor for the formation of prostaglandins. However the present observation suggests it may also play a direct role in membrane fusion.

When the clumps of chromaffin granules fuse to form vacuoles there is a corresponding decline in the turbidity of the suspension. Accordingly, it was possible to develop a turbidimetric assay for the fusion event and thus make quantitative statements about the relative effectiveness of the various fatty acids. In addition to arachidonic acid the 18-carbon unsaturated fatty acids also caused fusion—linolenic, linoleic, and oleic acids. However their effectiveness declined as their degree of saturation increased. Now consider oleic acid, which has a single double bond between the ninth and tenth carbon atoms. If this acid is esterified to glycerol to form glycerol monooleate, which has been used at high concentrations to fuse cells, the compound is completely ineffective at inducing fusion of the chromaffin granules. If the double bond of oleic acid, which is in the cis-configuration, is instead in

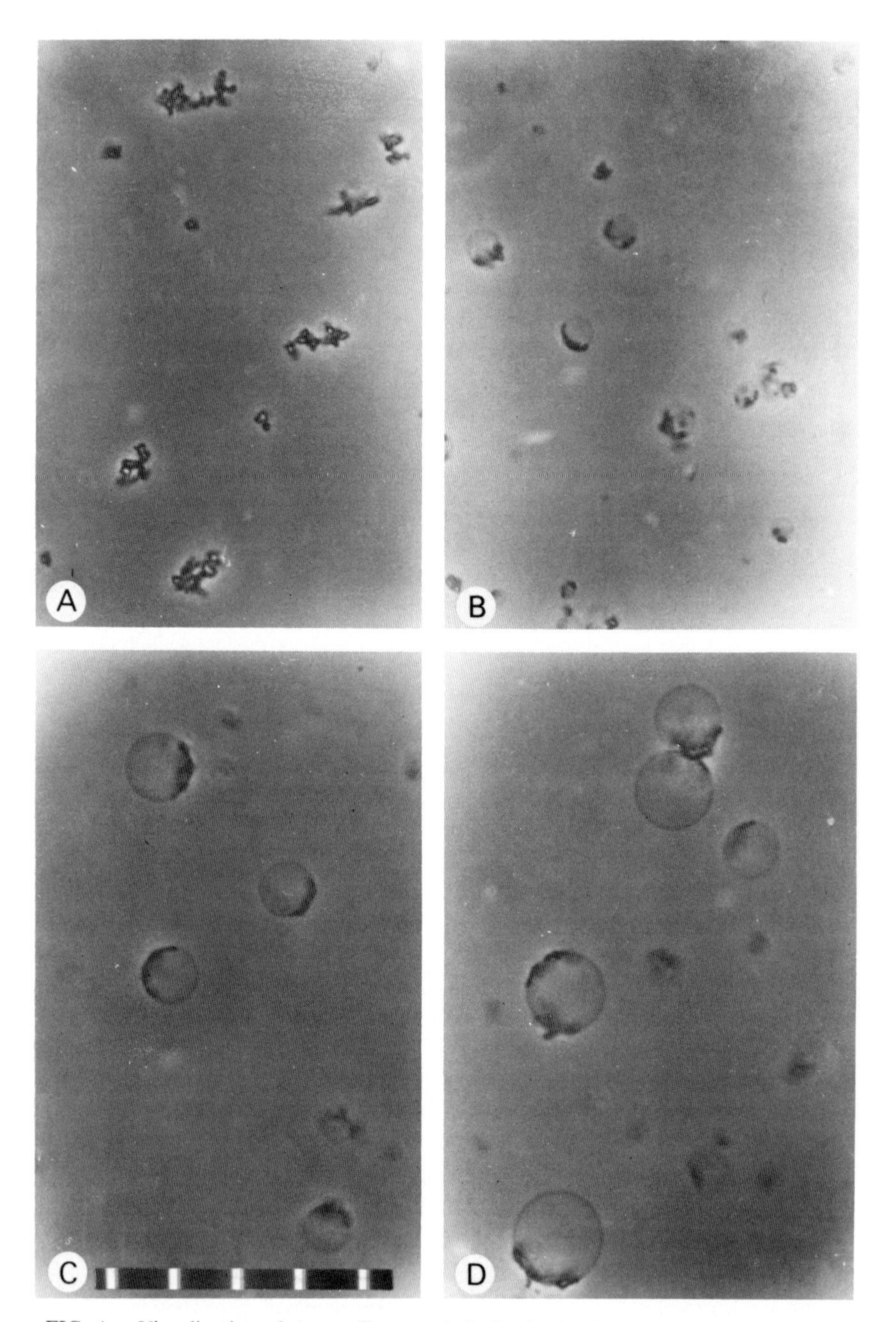

FIG. A. Visualization of chromaffin granule fusion in the phase microscope. (A) Clumps of granules that have been aggregated by incubation with synexin and Ca^{2+} for ~40 minutes. (B,C,D) Vesicles of various sizes formed after further incubation of the preparation for ~15 minutes in the presence of 4 μg/ml arachidonic acid. Graticule marks are 10 μm apart.

the transconfiguration, the compound is also ineffective. If the double bond is moved to the 6,7 position, closer to the head group, the compound again is completely ineffective. In fact it is quite remarkable that the only fatty acids that seem to work are the very ones that are present in the membrane phospholipids and can potentially be released by the action of a phospholipase—as is indeed the case with arachidonic acid in platelets and chromaffin cells.

I would also like to mention that this fusion reaction appears to have a specific requirement for synexin. There are other ways to form large aggregates of chromaffin granules. The granules have a negative surface charge and can be aggregated by basic proteins such as polylysine or histidine-rich glycoprotein from blood serum. Although very large aggregates of granules can be formed this way, when arachidonic acid is added, no fusion is seen.

We may also wonder what role the chemiosmotic properties of the chromaffin granule might play in this fusion event. We think that an osmotic swelling of the granules may provide a driving force for the reaction. It is clear that there is a considerable increase in the volume contained within the granule membranes when this fusion occurs. Consider a large number of small spheres clumped together—let the number of these spheres be X. Then take the total surface area of these spheres and combine them to make a single large sphere. The volume of this single sphere will be the square root of X times larger than the original, collective volume of the small spheres. The largest of the vacuoles we have seen formed by fusing chromaffin granules is 10 μm in diameter. Such a vacuole has the surface area of 2500 granules, from which it was apparently formed. Thus the volume contained within the membranes of these granules has been increased 50-fold. This may have resulted, at least in part, from the entry of water into the vesicles as a consequence of an increased internal osmotic content, due either to the inward movement of Cl^- as Dr. Pollard has described, or perhaps in addition, solubilization of some of the contents of the granules.

As the observations I have described are only preliminary at this point, we have many things to determine before we can be sure just what has occurred during this fascinating transition. However, we feel it is a provocative observation and one that suggests many experiments.

H. Pollard: The question was why the vesicle should lyse in any particular direction. We think that there's an evolutionary problem here because obviously the system was designed to secrete out. Therefore there must be something critically arranged so that secretion would actually occur outward. The question now is what the critical arrangement might be, and there are several ways you can actually think about this. First, consider an automobile tire which has a worn spot in a particular place. By analogy the place that the secretory granule interacts with another granule or plasma membranes might be disorganized or weakened. There may even be a special molecular mechanism, as Dr. Creutz has alluded to in his discussion, involving the production of a disruption in the phospholipid organization making the membrane somewhat weak. Breakage might occur only at the weak spot. A second viewpoint is based on the physics of curved structures. If a spherical structure such as a vesicle is pushed in a bit at one point then the radius of curvature varies about the resulting anular defect. The region with the smaller radius of curvature has higher energy and is more likely to break. Thus when you push a secretory granule into a plasma membrane, that place where it's interacting has a different radius of curvature and is therefore less stable. Finally, it is possible that release in the wrong direction can occur. Dr. Robert Allen at Dartmouth College has been studying secretion from platelets using optical methods and he has been loading platelet secretory vesicles with mepacrine, a fluorescent compound, and has then observed secretion of the fluorescent compound upon specific stimulation. One of the curiosities is that he finds some examples of mepacrine flooding back into the cell, as well as many showing the compounds coming out too. Therefore I will suggest that possibly the idea that you brought up of wrong direction release rupture may well occur in some cases.

However, I have a feeling that what happens in most cells is that they probably have a nice evolutionarily arrived at mechanism for making sure that secretion usually goes in the direction that it's supposed to go.

R. Chatterton: I was wondering about the orientation of the vesicles at the membrane surface. Is there any evidence that the anion transport site is aligned through a process involving microfilaments or microtubules and does vincristine or vinblastine disrupt that process? Also, I was wondering about conservation of the membrane. Thinking about the epithelial cells of the mammary gland, we have a process by which the membrane is lost on secretion of lipid, and then increased in the exocytosis process by which protein and carbohydrate are released. This results in a net conservation of the membrane. Is there some process such as that occurring in these cells?

H. Pollard: Let's see—I'm trying to remember the first question.

R. Chatterton: I was wondering about the orientation of the vesicles.

H. Pollard: The vesicle membrane probably contains multiple anion transport sites. There are many, many submembrane particles in granule membranes that you can see by freeze-fracture and perhaps these particles are related to anion transport. We do know that transport sites in the red cell membrane are represented by such particles and occur in similar numbers. Therefore I think that the orientation of vesicles is probably not critical. The second question as I recall had to do with the nature of actin or tubulin or synexin in the membrane and whether they oriented or interacted with the secretory granules—is that right?

R. Chatterton: Yes, that's right.

H. Pollard: We have not really looked very carefully, in chromaffin cells, but Dr. Dominique Aunis from Strasbourg has found rod-shaped objects connecting chromaffin granules with plasma membranes. The size of these objects was approximately 100 Å long and 50 Å wide, very reminiscent by the way of the synexin polymer. Furthermore, there may be a subcortical web underneath the plasma membrane which clearly seems to go away when the secretion process occurs. Actin per se does not appear to inhibit the release in this case, and perhaps it depolymerizes thereby allowing the secretory vessel to come up to and touch the plasma membrane. There is one other example of this sort in the *Limulus* amoebocyte that has been studied by Tom Reese and Richard Ornberg. Under the plasma membrane of the cell there is actually a cortical web about 1 μm in depth which disappears whenever secretion begins. I don't know anything else about actin and the secretion process. You also asked about recovery of expended membrane?

R. Chatterton: Yes, I was asking about the increase in the plasma membrane by exocytosis as opposed to the loss through lipid secretion which occurs in some other tissues.

H. Pollard: All I can say is that it is an interesting question, and we don't know anything about it.

H. Friesen: Is the synexin self-association a reversible event with, for example, calcium chelating agents? Second, you mentioned that the liver was an especially rich source of synexin; what is its role and distribution in the liver?

H. Pollard: Synexin self-association can be reversed with EGTA, for example. However, the membrane association that's induced by it cannot be reversed, so there is a fundamental reorganization which occurs upon synexin-induced vesicle association. The new complexes are now independent of calcium for their stability. One possibility is that EGTA can't reach the complex, but at present there is no evidence for such a hypothesis. Liver is really not a particularly richer source than is adrenal medulla. However, there is a lot of it. You can go to a slaughter house and pick up a few kilos while adrenal glands take a lot more work. You asked what synexin might be doing in the liver. Liver cells, like all cells, have a lot of fusion processes going on. In a recent lecture by George Palade, in the thirty-sixth annual meeting of the Electron Microscopy Society of America in Reno, Nevada, he described secretion of very low-density lipoproteins (VLDLs) from liver. VLDL is packaged in large membrane-bound organelles and is secreted by exocytosis. In some cases one can actually get the liver cell interiors to be jammed with these VLDL vesicles. Thus, this is only one example of a secretory process in the liver which appears to occur by a fusion of an intracellular membrane with the plasma membrane. There are probably a lot of others since the liver is a significant secretory organ.

C. Monder: Is the synexin molecule found throughout the various phyla, and if so, is the structure of the molecule conserved?

H. Pollard: We have not done a very extensive phylogenetic study of synexin. However, the structure of a synexin-like molecule from human platelets appears to be slightly different from that of the cow. For example, our present antibody against cow synexin does not react against human synexin. Furthermore the human platelet synexin seemed to be somewhat larger than bovine synexin and has an affinity constant for calcium which is about 10 μM, not 100 μM as the cow material.

B. I. Posner: Did you look at the effect of colchicine, an inhibitor of exocytosis in a number of systems, on either the self-association of synexin or the synexin vesicle interaction?

H. Pollard: Colchicine did not have any action either on granule association or synexin self-association. Now I would like to mention some caveats about colchicine. Colchicine is not as good an inhibitor of exocytosis as you might believe. For example, in the beta cell system colchicine will block only the second phase of insulin secretion, but not the first phase of insulin secretion. One way of thinking about it is that perhaps the vesicles already closely juxtaposed to the plasma membrane are released during the first phase and are not blocked by colchicine. The second phase may represent the recruitment and moving in of vesicles from some deeper sites and perhaps it is this movement that is blocked by colchicine. Furthermore, colchicine is not a very good inhibitor of release from the adrenal medulla, and there may be some question about its mechanism of action since one investigator believes it may block acetylcholine receptors. In sum, there is at present no evidence that tubulin is involved in synexin action. I might also mention that when we began this work we thought that various proteins such as calmodulin, actin, tubulin, myosin, and other proteins might be involved. However, all attempts to "shoehorn" these factors into membrane fusion were failures. We then discarded these approaches and began to look for other factors; that is, in fact, how synexin came to be discovered.

B. I. Posner: May I ask a second question? Chloroquine has been used to alter the pH in lysosomes, perhaps by influencing the proton pump. Since you are postulating that a proton pump is involved in the osmotic-induced lysis of these vesicles, perhaps looking at the effect of chloroquine would be of interest.

H. Pollard: I will begin by saying that chloroquine is really not an inhibitor of the proton pump. It actually enters the interior of lysosomes as an uncharged species, binds protons, and form an impermeant charged species, which is trapped like ammonia. Now ammonia is a compound with which I have had considerable experience. It inhibits release from granules, but at higher concentrations will cause the ΔpH to go to zero causing lysis of the granules. Ammonium chloride, a good lysis agent for red cells, is also an excellent lysis agent for chromaffin granules because of the intrinsic chloride transport system and the endogenous proton gradient. We haven't worked much with chloroquine, but I would anticipate many ammonia-like properties for that compound.

K. Sterling: This was a very intriguing presentation.

I was particularly interested in the observations on the magnesium ATPase. If I understood it correctly, dinitrophenol (DNP) and FCCP the classic examples of uncouplers of oxidative phosphorylation also blocked the phenomena you have described. Now we know that ATPase as it exists in the "knobs" of the inner chondrial membrane functions for ATP formation as well as splitting ATP, and I was thinking, in view of the vectorial composition of these granules, and the ion movements that you proposed, whether there may not be ATP formation involved perhaps prior to the inhibition of solutes and swelling up. Are you planning to explore this in the future?

H. Pollard: Good question. It is possible that there in fact may be synthesis and the vectorial organization of the granule may be important. As you may be aware mitochondria pump protons out, into the cytoplasm, and that is the basis of energy production. Chloroplasts, on the other hand, pump protons in, just as do chromaffin granules. Chromaffin granules and chloroplasts are very similar in this regard and in fact I can tell you parenthetically that I got my whole insight into how to study the energetics of chromaffin granules by studying the chloroplast literature. Regarding the question of whether ATP synthesis could occur perhaps you might expect that this would be a case if you allowed protons to come out and run the ATPase in reverse. This has been studied by others, including Dr. Taugner from Germany, who claims to have been able to create conditions for ATP synthesis by granules. One other thing that is interesting about these secretory granules is that they also contain an electron transport system. They have a b-type cytochrome and the granules are red in color because of this heme protein. In this sense the granules are somewhat similar to mitochondria. As you know, membrane proteins in mitochondria are defined by nuclear and cytoplasmic genes. Indeed, the F_0 protein involved in proton translocation in mitochondria has its structural analog in chromaffin granules and F_0 is defined by an organelle gene in both mitochondria and chloroplasts. We have been wondering as you have suggested how close to the mitochondrial system we are. Are the secretory granules in fact another kind of degenerate microorganism? If not, how did they obtain their F_0-like factors? Did they steal them from their rightful owners, the mitochondria? Are some F_0's defined by nuclear genes? These are all very interesting questions, and close examination may actually lead us to a better understanding of how cells are put together.

H. Burrows: I would like to thank Dr. Pollard and his group for developing this model of the release process in which the granule itself plays an active role. This model can be tested using systems of isolated granules. I have been working in Dallas with Drs. Barnea and Porter characterizing the release of luteinizing hormone releasing hormone (LHRH) from granules isolated from the hypothalamus of the male rat. Some of the data we have collected are shown in the following figures.

In the presence of 0.15 *M* KCl, the addition of either magnesium ATP or magnesium chloride stimulates the release of LHRH from isolated granules. However, if the KCl in the incubation medium is substituted with sucrose, magnesium chloride stimulates the release of LHRH but magnesium ATP does not (Fig. B). Similarly, magnesium chloride stimulates the release of LHRH in the presence of KCl at 4°C, yet magnesium ATP does not. From these data it appears that the mechanism through which magnesium ATP stimulates the release of LHRH is separate from the mechanism through which magnesium chloride stimulates the release of LHRH.

In its sensitivity to decreased temperature and in its dependence on ionic environment, the magnesium ATP-induced release of LHRH appears to be similar to the magnesium ATP-induced release of epinephrine from isolated chromaffin granules. However, in contrast to the effects observed in chromaffin granules, when LHRH granules are incubated in the presence of an elevated concentration of sucrose, the magnesium ATP-induced release of LHRH is unaffected (Fig. C). We have also measured the release of LHRH in the presence of an elevated concentration of KCl (0.45 *M*), but find a large KCl-induced release of LHRH. Have you observed any effects of sucrose, KCl, or magnesium chloride in the systems of isolated granules which you have studied which might help to explain the mechanism of the effects which we have observed in our studies of the isolated LHRH granule?

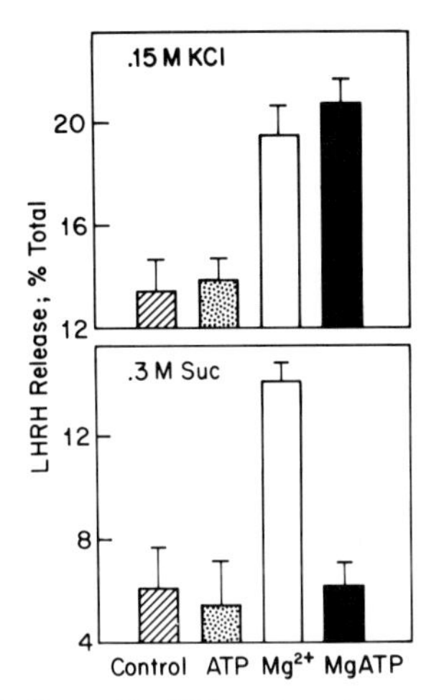

FIG. B. Effect of ATP, $MgCl_2$, or MgATP on the release of LHRH from isolated storage granules in the presence and absence of KCl.

H. Pollard: I think that's interesting that the LHRH release is analogous to the granule system. However they are not chromaffin granules, and so they shouldn't exactly behave like chromaffin granules. Instead they should behave like LHRH granules. I would ask whether LHRH granules themselves are sensitive to osmotic pressure or ATP. What happens when you start doing these experiments, both to the terminals, and to the granules? The only thing I can say at this point is that we will learn more as more people do similar experiments on different systems. I think that experiments that are sometimes most productive are those where things turn out not exactly as you would expect. So I think that your data are really fascinating and I'm glad you have showed them.

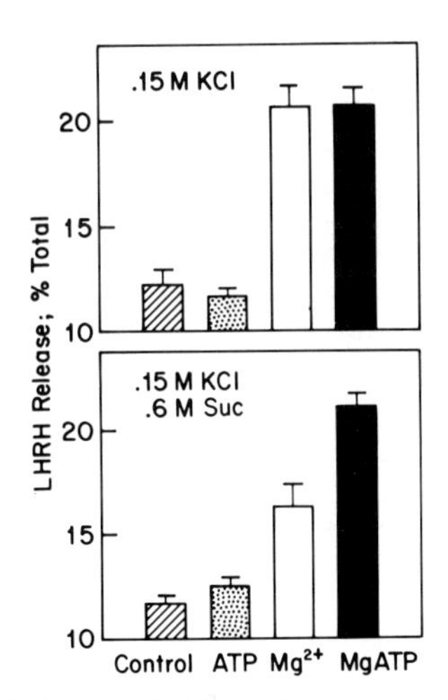

FIG. C. Effect of elevated concentrations of sucrose on the release of LHRH from isolated granules in the presence of 0.15 *M* KCl.

L. Bullock: There are several syndromes associated with an abnormality in secretory granules or secretory lysosomes. Do you know if synexin could be involved in any of these syndromes. If it is, the limited scope of the abnormality, involving only certain organelles or tissues, suggests that synexin function could be regulated differently in different cells. Do you have any data that it is?

H. Pollard: The first syndrome that comes to mind is Chediak Higashi and I hasten to add that we don't know anything about that particular disease. A second entity is of course diabetes. In the pancreas of those with relatively recent maturity onset diabetes there is quite a lot of insulin. It is just not secreted "enough." We don't know what that word "enough" means, but it might be that there is an aspect of some of the secretory mechanisms which I have discussed which might be important (see Note Added in Proof). I hope I have skirted that issue widely enough. I can't remember the next to last point.

L. Bullock: Just whether secretory function or synexin could be regulated differently in different cells.

H. Pollard: In the case of the cow we have examined brain, parotid, adrenal cortex, and liver. The synexin molecule in each tissue appears to be similar in every regard. However, the human platelet synexin-like activity turned out to be different. In terms of sensitivity to calcium and in terms of size, one might suppose that different tissues would have different cofactors which could influence synexin action. So far we have found none.

C. Monder: I find this absolutely fascinating so I'm going to ask another question. First, is synexin stable in the cell and does it turn over rapidly? A related question is what controls the decision-making process for secretion to occur? Is it not a fact that the adrenal medulla continuously secretes at a constant rate?

H. Pollard: I would think that the decision-making process would be regulated by the intercellular calcium level. With low intracellular calcium levels the synexin would be generally distributed in the cytoplasm. Evidence came from the fluorescent antibody studies. However, when calcium levels rise upon activation the distribution would necessarily change. For example, we know the synexin becomes a membrane bound protein in elevated Ca^{2+}, and so perhaps that is your "decision-making" event. Regarding the turnover of synexin I can't tell you anything. We do have access to cultured chromaffin cells, to which we could introduce radioactive amino acids, and experiments you have proposed could be done. I thank you very much for your suggestions.

Note Added in Proof. Since the conference two fascinating papers have been published showing that the chemiosmotic hypothesis for secretion may apply to insulin secretion from rat islets and perfused rat pancreas [Somers, Sener, Devis, and Malaisse (1980). *Pflügers Arch.* **388,** 249–253; Orci and Malaisse (1980). *Diabetes* **29,** 943–944]. Further chemical studies on islets and islet components will reveal whether these remarkable parallels are based on analogous biochemical relationships to chromaffin cells or are fortuitous.

Calmodulin: Properties, Intracellular Localization, and Multiple Roles in Cell Regulation[1]

ANTHONY R. MEANS

Department of Cell Biology,
Baylor College of Medicine,
Houston, Texas

I. Introduction

Peptide hormones regulate a variety of intracellular events characteristic of endocrine cells. These events include the secretion of steroid hormones and proteins, the movement of cells, cell division, and cell to cell communication. It has been recognized for some time that the peptide hormones act through a series of second messengers. The first such messenger to be clearly demonstrated was cyclic AMP. The mechanism of action of cyclic AMP is reasonably well understood. In all instances it binds to a receptor. This receptor is a component of one of the two nucleotide-dependent protein kinases. Thus a common intermediate in all events known to be affected by cyclic AMP is the activation of protein kinase via cyclic nucleotide binding to a protein component (Krebs and Beavo, 1979; Nimmo and Cohen, 1977). The second messenger system that has been well established is calcium. For many years it was suggested that calcium ion was unique in that it could regulate a variety of intracellular events in its ionic form (Kretsinger, 1980). In recent years it has been shown that a family of calcium-binding proteins exists (Goodman *et al.*, 1979; Kretsinger, 1980). The one most studied in skeletal muscle is troponin C which is the calcium-binding protein involved in muscle contraction. It is now recognized that all cells contain a calcium-binding protein that has recently been termed calmodulin (Means and Dedman, 1980). Indeed calmodulin is an intracellular calcium receptor. In analogy with the steroid hormone receptor systems, it binds calcium with high affinity and high specificity. It is the major calcium-binding protein in smooth and nonmuscle cells. It has no alternate function so far discovered except to bind calcium. There are multiple binding or acceptor proteins for the

[1] Supported by NIH Research Grant HD-07503 and the Baylor Center for Reproductive Biology and Population Research.

ISBN 0-12-571137-9

calmodulin–calcium cmplex. Finally this protein is ubiquitous and structurally conserved.

Calmodulin has been shown to regulate a variety of intracellular processes. Again this protein is unique because first it had been known in every instance that the event was calcium regulated. Only subsequently was it shown that the calcium regulation was mediated by the binding of this ion to calmodulin. Several reviews on calmodulin have recently appeared (Means and Dedman, 1980; Cheung, 1980; Wang and Waisman, 1979; Klee *et al.*, 1980). In general these reviews cover the physical properties of the protein, the regulation of cyclic nucleotide metabolism via activation of phosphodiesterase and some adenylyl cyclases, regulation of protein phosphorylation which includes proteins involved in the nervous system as well as the myosin light chain kinase in non and smooth muscle systems. Calmodulin has been shown to mediate the calcium sensitivity of microtubules both *in vivo* and *in vitro* (Means and Dedman, 1980; Marcum *et al.*, 1978). Glycogen metabolism is affected by calmodulin. Philip Cohen and his co-workers have revealed that the long missing calcium-binding subunit of phosphorylase kinase is calmodulin (Cohen *et al.*, 1979). More recently Payne and Soderling (1980) have demonstrated that there exists a calmodulin-sensitive glycogen synthase kinase that is distinct from the form of this enzyme regulated by cyclic AMP and also distinct from the form that is independent from either calcium or cyclic nucleotide regulation. Calcium flux is regulated by calmodulin. This includes the active movement of calcium out of cells via the calcium magnesium ATPase (Gopinath and Vincenzi, 1977) as well as the transport of calcium down axons in the nervous system (Iqbal and Ochs, 1978), the movement of calcium between organelles within cells, and possibly the release of calcium from mitochondria.

The far-reaching consequences of calmodulin in cells should be apparent from the preceding paragraph. It is also clear that many of the processes discussed are absolutely required for secretion and secretion is one of the most salient features of an endocrine cell. It has been demonstrated that calmodulin is involved in intestinal ion secretion from brush border epithelial cells (Ilundian and Naftalin, 1979), insulin release from the beta cells of the pancreas (Schubart *et al.*, 1980), and possibly neurotransmitter release from isolated synaptosomes (DeLorenzo *et al.*, 1979). Calcium regulation of many other secretory systems is likely to be demonstrated in the near future to require calmodulin. Thus it seems appropriate in the context of this meeting to discuss calmodulin as an intracellular calcium receptor and the importance this protein may play in the regulation of cell function.

II. Purification and Physical Properties

Our own studies on calmodulin arose from our interest in understanding how cyclic nucleotides and calcium control the function of the testicular Sertoli cell. Our interest was stimulated by the report that a calcium-binding protein was involved in the stimulation of phosphodiesterase in a variety of tissues (Waisman *et al.*, 1975; Smoake *et al.*, 1974). At this time calmodulin was called an activator protein of phosphodiesterase. A tissue survey by Smoake *et al.* (1974) revealed that testes contained high concentrations of this protein. We therefore decided to purify the protein, determine its physical properties, and make an affinity column. The affinity column was then to be used to purify the various proteins from the Sertoli cell including, hopefully, the calcium-dependent cyclic AMP phosphodiesterase. As it turned out, the purification of calmodulin from rat testis is one of the easiest procedures known (Dedman *et al.*, 1977a). Purification requires only the preparation of a homogenate, heat treatment of this homogenate which denatures a variety of proteins but does not affect calmodulin, separation of the heat-treated extract by ion exchange chromatography, and finally a sizing step on a gel filtration column. These three steps result in a 700-fold purification. The protein is homogeneous as determined by several electrophoretic procedures and the yield is an incredible 90%. Thus one can recover over 100 mg of calmodulin from 1 kg of rat testis (Table I).

The pure protein was used to characterize a variety of physical properties (19) that are listed in Table II. First the protein is quite resistant to elevated temperatures. One can heat a solution containing calmodulin for 5 minutes at 90°C with no appreciable loss of activity. It should be pointed out, however, that calmodulin is heat-resistant and not truly heat-stable.

TABLE I
Purification of Rat Testis Calmodulin[a]

	Protein (mg)	Activity (U/mg)	Purification (fold)	Yield (%)
Homogenate	50,000	35	—	100
Heat	625	2,508	76	95
DEAE-cellulose	65	22,196	673	88
Gel filtration	63	22,751	690	85

[a] 500 gm of frozen rat testes was homogenized and fractionated as described by Dedman *et al.* (1977) except that 200-ml aliquots were heated in a microwave oven for 90 seconds followed by rapid cooling in a methanol–dry ice mixture.

TABLE II
Physical Properties of Calmodulin

Property	Specific value	Reference
Heat resistance	$t_{1/2}$ = 7 minutes at 100°C	Beale *et al.* (1977)
Molecular weight	16,700 (148 amino acids)	Dedman *et al.* (1977)
Trimethyllysine	Lysine 115	Jackson *et al.* (1977)
Isoelectric pH	3.9	Dedman *et al.* (1977)
Ca^{2+} binding	4 mol/mol; K_d = 2.4 μM	Dedman *et al.* (1977)
Conformation	40–55% α-helix	Dedman *et al.* (1977)
Sequence homology	50% to troponin C	Watterson *et al.* (1980)
Drug binding	Phenothiozines	Weiss *et al.* (1980)
	W-compounds	Hidaka *et al.* (1979a,b)
Hydrophobicity	Increased by Ca^{2+}	LaPorte *et al.* (1980)

The half-life of the protein at 100°C is 7 minutes (Beale *et al.*, 1977). Calmodulin has a molecular weight of 16,700 and consists of 148 amino acids. We have sequenced the protein from rat testis (Dedman *et al.*, 1977b). It has also been sequenced from bovine brain (Watterson *et al.*, 1980) and bovine uterus (Grand and Perry, 1978) as well as from a marine coelenterate *Renilla reniformis* (Vanaman and Scharief, 1979). The incredible fact about this protein is its highly conserved nature. Thus of all the sequences known so far, there are only seven amino acid substitutions and they have all resulted from a point mutation and thus a conservative amino acid change. Position 115 is a lysine. The unique property of this lysine is that it is trimethylated (Jackson *et al.*, 1977). Trimethylation is uncommon among animal cell proteins. Indeed there are very few proteins that have been shown to have this particular posttranslational modification. One known protein is cytochrome c isolated from both plants and yeast (Palasto *et al.*, 1978). In this case it has been demonstrated that trimethylation markedly enhances the affinity of cytochrome c for cytochrome oxidase. To date such studies have not been performed on the physiological significance of this modification for calmodulin. However, van Eldik and colleagues (1980) have revealed that the translation of messenger RNA from spinach leaves result in a calmodulin that apparently does not contain trimethyllysine. Thus it should be possible in the near future to determine whether this modification has any role in the binding of calcium to the protein or in the interaction of this protein with its various binding proteins. Finally calmodulin is a highly acidic protein demonstrating an isoelectric pH of 3.9 (Dedman *et al.*, 1977a).

The calcium-binding properties of calmodulin are also rather interesting if somewhat controversial. There is no question that calmodulin contains 4 metal-binding sites. In studies carried out in our laboratory by equilibrium dialysis, it was suggested that the 4 calcium-binding sites were all calcium specific and were equivalent; thus analysis of the binding data by Scatchard plots revealed a single slope and a K_d of 2.4 M (Dedman *et al.*, 1977a). These studies were carried out in concert with equivalent experiments on troponin C. The troponin C data were found to be exactly what had been published in the literature whereas the calmodulin data were clearly different. Others have reported that the binding of metal ions to calmodulin depends upon the salt concentration (Klee, 1977; Klee *et al.*, 1980; Wolff *et al.*, 1977). Thus by altering the salt concentration it has been reported that some magnesium binding occurs. The only way this will be resolved is by successfully crystallizing the protein and determining its three-dimensional structure. In collaboration with W. Cook and C. Bugg we have succeeded in crystallizing calmodulin from 2-methyl 2,4-pentanediol in the presence of 5 mM calcium chloride (Cook *et al.*, 1980). The crystals demonstrate one calmodulin molecule per unit cell and are triclinic in space group P-1. Analysis by X-ray defraction reveals a resolution beyond 2.5 Å. So far the data accumulated have suggested calmodulin to contain 4 metal-binding sites. The specificity and location of these sites require further studies where calcium is replaced by other ions and derivatives are used to accumulate sufficient reflections to build a space-filling model.

It is clear that calmodulin is a highly coiled molecule. In the absence of metal 40% of the protein exists in an α-helical configuration (Dedman *et al.*, 1977a). Binding of calcium to calmodulin increases the helicity to greater than 50%. This change in conformation is mandatory for the regulation of all enzyme molecules so far described by calmodulin. It should also be pointed out that the regulation of an enzyme by calmodulin can be affected in two ways. One is to increase the calcium concentration in the presence of a fixed amount of calmodulin. The second is to increase the calmodulin concentration in the presence of a fixed amount of calcium. As one increases the calmodulin concentration the amount of calcium required to stimulate a reaction is markedly reduced.

The sequence of calmodulin from rat or bovine demonstrates nearly 50% direct sequence homology with rabbit skeletal muscle troponin C (Dedman *et al.*, 1977b; Watterson *et al.*, 1980). Somewhat more amazing however is the internal homology demonstrated by calmodulin. As mentioned earlier calmodulin binds 4 moles of calcium per mole. Thus one can divide the protein into 4 metal-binding domains. When this is done and the domains are compared it can be seen in Table III that domain 1 (beginning at the N terminus) is highly homologous with domain 3, whereas domain 2 is highly homologous with domain 4 (the C terminal portion of the protein). Indeed 70% of the amino acids in domains 1 and 3 are identical and 70% of the amino acids in domains 2 and 4 are identical.

TABLE III
Internal Homology of Calmodulin[a]

	11											40
I	E F K E A F	S	L F D K D G N G	T	I T T	K	E L	G T	V M	R S	L G	
III	E I R E A F	R	V F D K D G N G	Y	I S A	A	E L	R H	V M	T N	L G	
	84											113

	47													75
II	E L Q D M I	N	E V D A D E	N	G	T	I D F	P	E F L	T	M M A	R	K	
IV	E V D E M I	R	E A N I D E	D	G	E	V N Y	E	E F V	Q	M M T	A	K	
	120													148

[a] The amino acid sequence of rat testis calmodulin was determined by Dedman *et al.* (1978). Amino acids are numbered from N to C termini. Domain I is, therefore, the first Ca^{2+}-binding region from the N-terminus. This domain begins with amino acid 11 which is Glu. The one-letter code is A Ala, B Asx, C Cys, D Asp, E Glu, F Phe, G Gly, H His, I Ile, K Lys, L Leu, M Met, N Asn, P Pro, Q Gln, R Arg, S Ser, T Thr, V Val, W Trp, Y Tyr, and Z Glx. The numerals refer to positions in the calmodulin protein sequence. The boxed areas indicate positions at which the two domains compared are either identical or related by functionally conservative replacements.

This strongly suggests that calmodulin has arisen by gene duplication. The protein is present in virtually all species including the lowest eukaryotes (Waisman *et al.*, 1975; Chafouleas *et al.*, 1979). Therefore it is a likely possibility that troponin C has evolved from calmodulin at about the time that the vertebrates appeared. Our laboratory has recently succeeded in isolating and partially purifying messenger RNA for calmodulin from the electroplax of the electric eel *Electrophorous electricus* (Munjaal *et al.*, 1980). This partially purified messenger RNA has been used to isolate a structural gene copy by cloning in bacterial plasmids. The sequence of the double-stranded complementary DNA reveals no differences between eel and rat. In addition this probe recognizes specific sequences in the DNA from 5 representative phyla. Again these data point to the highly conserved nature of calmodulin.

The final physical property of calmodulin that is likely to prove useful is that fact that it binds rather specifically a variety of pharmacologic agents. The first such agent to be demonstrated were the phenothiozines. Weiss and colleagues (1980) revealed that phenothiozines bound to calmodulin in a calcium-dependent fashion and the interaction of the drugs with calmodulin prevented the stimulation of phosphodiesterase activity. Studies have been extended which demonstrate that the binding of phenothiozines by calmodulin prevents the stimulation of a variety of enzymes by this protein. One curious property was why the binding was calcium dependent. It has recently been revealed that the interaction of calcium with calmodulin exposes a highly lipophilic region of the molecule (LaPorte *et al.*, 1980). It is this lipophilic region that binds to phenothiozine and it is also this region of the protein that interacts with phosphodiesterase, myosin light chain kinase, and calcium magnesium ATPase. Another series of pharmacologic tools have recently been developed by Hidaka *et al.* (1979a). These are considerably less hydrophobic but have similar affinities to the best phenothiozines, that is K_ds for calmodulin of 10^{-6} to 10^{-7} M. The advantage of the Hidaka compounds is that they more readily enter cells so that the incubation of cells with such drugs may lead to an indication of various reactions that require calmodulin as a regulatory component. It must be stressed however that the use of these drugs cannot be taken as absolute proof of a calmodulin-dependent process. Certainly all of the drugs do have many different actions within cells including binding to cell surfaces and alteration of transport properties. Nonetheless pharmacologic agents can be used with discretion as a first approximation of events that may be calmodulin dependent.

III. Preparation and Purification of Antibody

Once we had characterized calmodulin from rat testis and determined many of its physical properties, we prepared an affinity column by coupling calmodulin to cyanogen bromide activated sepharose and attempted to isolate phosphodiesterase. The experiments were performed by passing an extract of Sertoli cells through the column in the presence of calcium. Once no more protein could be removed from the column by this buffer EGTA was added to specifically release those proteins bound to calmodulin in a calcium-dependent fashion. Several protein components were eluted by this procedure. However phosphodiesterase was not among them. Subsequently it has been shown that the calcium-dependent phosphodiesterase in testis is not calmodulin-dependent. We were then left with high concentrations of a calcium-binding protein in testis that did not perform the expected function, that is stimulation of phosphodiesterase. The approach we took was to prepare antibodies to the protein, localize the protein in cells by indirect immunofluorescence microscopy, and utilize the localization to attempt to determine specific functions calmodulin might play in Sertoli and other cells.

Preparation of antibody proved to be a difficult task. Calmodulin is small, acidic, and highly conserved. Our first attempts utilized rabbits as the animal and rat calmodulin as the immunogen. No antibody was found upon analysis by double immunodiffusion. We then decided to use a larger animal and chose a goat. It was also pointed out by a colleague that not all antibodies needed to be precipitating ones. We therefore decided to utilize our calmodulin affinity columns to purify any calmodulin antibody from the bulk of the IgG in serum. These experiments were accomplished by passing serum over the column and then eluting bound protein by a pH shift. In our case we used glycine buffer pH 2.7. We were happy to find that protein was eluted by the pH shift. This material was demonstrated to be IgG by gel electrophoresis and was shown to specifically block the stimulation of bovine brain cyclic AMP phosphodiesterase by calmodulin giving us a suggestion that the antibody was reasonably specific (Dedman *et al.*, 1978). The antibody has now been used to develop a sensitive and specific radioimmunoassay (Chafouleas *et al.*, 1979) and to localize calmodulin in cells both in interphase and during mitosis (Dedman *et al.*, 1978; Welsh *et al.*, 1978, 1979). It should also be pointed out that subsequent to our successful isolation of antibodies, several groups have reported antibodies to calmodulin. However to date ours is the only antibody that was prepared using undenatured protein as the immunogen. Other investigators have modified the protein by precipitation with alum (Andersen *et al.*, 1978) or by treating the protein with dinitrophenol (Wallace *et al.*, 1979).

IV. Development of Radioimmunoassay

The development of a radioimmunoassay also proved to be reasonably difficult. This is because calmodulin contains only 2 tyrosines and one of these is inaccessible in the absence of calcium. Indeed one way to demonstrate conformational changes upon binding of calcium to calmodulin is by measuring tyrosine fluorescence (Dedman *et al.*, 1977a). When we utilized the lactoperoxidase and chloramine T procedures to iodinate calmodulin, we recovered low specific radioactivity material and found that a great deal of the biologic activity, assessed by the ability to stimulate phosphodiesterase, had been lost (Chafouleas *et al.*, 1979). We eventually resorted to the use of the procedure described by Bolton and Hunter (1973) that attaches an iodinatable derivative to the epsilon amino groups of lysine. Protein labeled in this manner revealed a specific activity of 2400 Ci/mmol and was completely biologically active. After a great deal of trial and error, it was determined that the radioimmunoassay was most sensitive using iodinated rat testis calmodulin as a tracer, affinity purified antibody, and pansorbin as a means of precipitating the iodinated protein–antibody complex (Chafouleas *et al.*, 1979). Under such conditions it was possible to precipitate 90% of the total iodinated tracer. Eventually we chose an antibody dilution of 1 to 20 which resulted in 40% of the tracer being bound which, under these conditions, was 4000 to 5000 cpm. The immunoassay was then fit to a computer program based on the assay statistics derived by Midgley *et al.* (1969) and Duddleson *et al.* (1972). The immunoassay was shown to have an interassay variability of less than 5% and an intraassay variability of less than 3%. The statistical assay sensitivity was 150 pg whereas the limit of detection was 15 pg. In all cases the background was less than 100 cpm.

The radioimmunoassay was first used to confirm the highly conserved nature of calmodulin. When pure calmodulin isolated from bovine brain, rat testis, *Renilla reniformis,* and the peanut (*Arachis hypogea*) was used to obtain standard dilution curves it was found that all 4 proteins described the same curve (Chafouleas *et al.,* 1979). On the other hand troponin C from rabbit skeletal muscle required 660-fold greater protein concentration to achieve 50% competition and demonstrated a statistically different slope. Again this emphasized the fact that although troponin C and calmodulin are homologous, they are not identical. Another small molecular weight calcium-binding protein parvalbumin demonstrated no cross reactivity even at 50,000-fold protein excess. In order for the immunoassay to be useful one would have to be able to detect calmodulin in tissue extracts. For these studies varying dilutions of heat-treated supernatant solutions from a variety of tissues were assayed. As shown by the representative data presented in Fig. 1, all samples, regardless of the source, described the same curve (Chafouleas *et al.,* 1979). Tissues and organisms examined to date include rat, eel, rabbit, bovine, human, amphibian, reptile, slime mold, plants, algae, coelenterate, paramecium, tetrahymena, and ameba. These data once again illustrate the fact that the immunologic nature of calmodulin is highly conserved between the most primitive unicellular organism and man.

The radioimmunoassay was utilized to illustrate another very interesting point regarding the nature of calmodulin's interaction with its various binding proteins. The most usual assay to determine the amount of calmodulin in a sample is the ability to stimulate a partially purified preparation of bovine brain cyclic AMP phosphodiesterase or chicken gizzard myosin light chain kinase. When we compared the amount of calmodulin found in various tissues and species by radioimmunoassay and the phosphodiesterase assay, it was found that in all instances the radioimmunoassay yielded higher values (Chafouleas *et al.,* 1979). In fact in organisms such as *Dictyostelium* and *Chlamydomonas,* no calmodulin could be detected by the phosphodiesterase assay whereas significant concentrations were found by radioimmunoassay. The reason for these discrepancies seem clear. In the biologic assays one is using only partially purified preparations of the enzyme as well as heat-treated extracts containing the calmodulin preparation. There are multiple calmodulin-binding proteins in

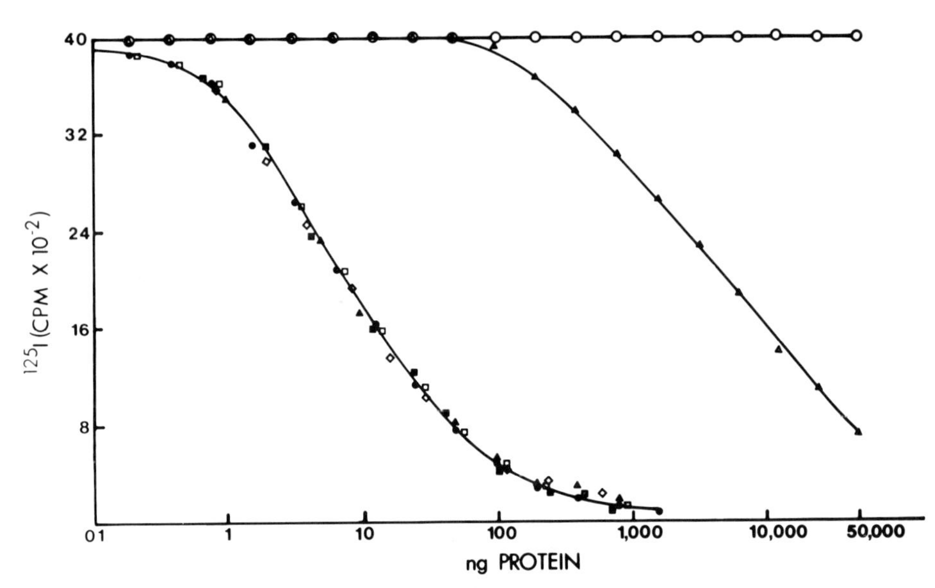

FIG. 1. Relative immunological cross reactivity of homologous calcium-binding proteins. The results were obtained using the radioimmunoassay of Chafouleas *et al.* (1979) using pure rat testis calmodulin as both tracer and standard (●—●). Other pure proteins include *Arachis hypogea* (peanut) calmodulin (■—■), troponin C (△—△), and parvalbumin (○—○). Heat-treated extracts containing calmodulin were from *Tetrahymena* (□—□), electroplax of *E. electricus* (◇—◇), and *C. reinhardtii* (▲—▲).

cells and tissues. Some exist in heat-treated extract and others exist in the enzyme preparation. Thus the assay for calmodulin by enzyme activation depends upon the ability of calmodulin to bind and activate the enzyme. Preparation of other calmodulin-binding proteins with similar or greater affinities would markedly interfere with the determination of quantitative values for this protein. Indeed it has subsequently been demonstrated that when calmodulin is isolated and purified from the two species mentioned before it will stimulate bovine brain phosphodiesterase. Thus it seems clear that the only accurate way for determining quantitative values for calmodulin in cell tissue extracts is radioimmunoassay.

V. Intracellular Localization

A. INTERPHASE

To localize calmodulin in cells in tissue culture we utilized the indirect immunofluorescence procedure described by Fuller *et al.* (1975). This procedure consists of growing the cells on glass coverslips, fixing them in 3% glutaraldehyde, and then treating with an agent such as acetone to poke holes in the plasma membrane. Cells are then incubated with the antibody, in this case anticalmodulin. The excess antibody is removed and a second antibody is added that has been conjugated to a fluorescent dye such as fluorescein or rhodamine. Cells are then viewed under a light microscope equipped with ultraviolet optics. Under these conditions the fluorescein-tagged antibody is seen as green on a black background and rhodamine will be seen as red on a black background. In interphase, calmodulin was found to be associated with the stress fibers (Dedman *et al.*, 1978a). A typical distribution in 3T3 cells is illustrated in Fig. 2. Stress fibers are actin-containing microfilaments. That is also the location for other contractile proteins in nonmuscle cells such as myosin and tropomyosin. Initially these data seemed strange. Why would calmodulin be localized on stress fibers? Subsequently a variety of laboratories

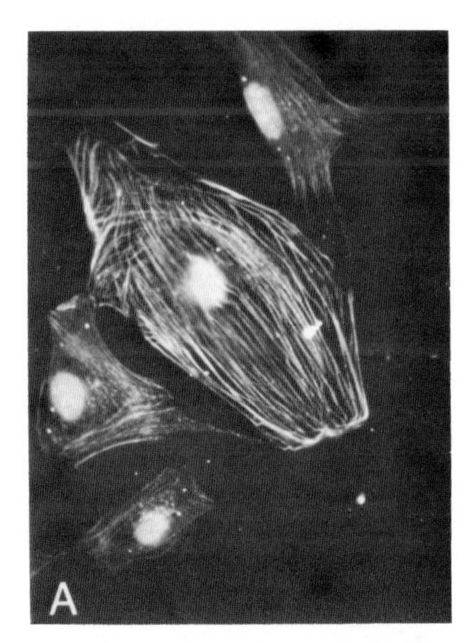

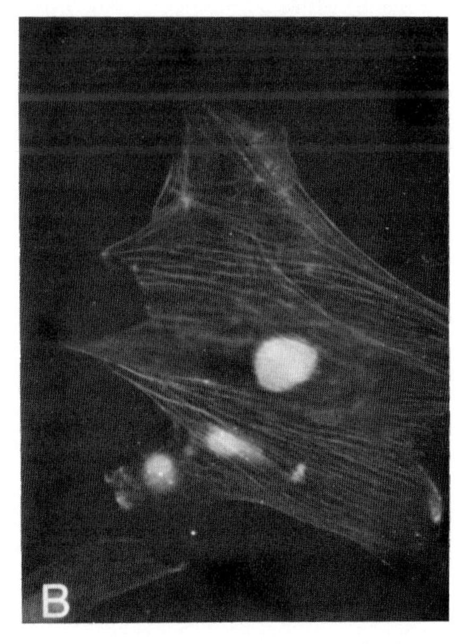

FIG. 2. Intracellular localization of calmodulin and myosin light chain kinase by indirect immunofluorescence microscopy. Swiss mouse 3T3 cells were grown and fixed as described by Dedman *et al.* (1978). A shows interphase calmodulin localization. Sheep anticalmodulin was incubated with acetone-treated fixed cells followed by incubation with fluorescein-conjugated rabbit antisheep IgG. B shows the localization of myosin light chain kinase. Rabbit anti-myosin light chain kinase was incubated with the cells followed by fluorescein-conjugated goat anti-rabbit IgG. The cells were processed identically and in parallel, exposed for the same length of time (Leitz Fl Oel 54/0.95) using Tri-X film rated at ASA 1000 and developed in Acufine developer. Magnifications are ×440.

showed biochemically that this localization is of considerable physiologic importance. This is because the contractility of smooth and nonmuscle cells does not operate through the troponin system that occurs in skeletal muscle. Rather the activation of myosin ATPase activity by actin requires phosphorylation of one of the light chains of myosin (LC20). Dabrowska *et al.* (1978) as well as Hathaway and Adelstein (1979) demonstrated that calcium binds to calmodulin and associates with an enzyme called myosin light chain kinase. This calcium-dependent interaction activates the enzyme leading to the phosphorylation of the 20,000 molecular weight light chain of myosin. This phosphorylation results in a conformational change so that actin can come into contact with the myosin head group stimulating myosin ATPase leading to the development of tension and presumably motility. This effect of calmodulin is the only one that has been demonstrated to date to have physiologic relevance (Manning *et al.*, 1980). Several investigators have now demonstrated that the degree of myosin light chain phosphorylation is directly proportional to tension development and that dephosphorylation is directly proportional to relaxation. This relationship has been shown in isolated cells, in skinned muscle fibers, and in isolated strips of smooth muscle. More recently we have succeeded in isolating the myosin light chain kinase from chicken gizzard, prepared an antibody to this enzyme, and have revealed a similar localization in interphase cells (Fig. 2). Thus calmodulin, actin, myosin, tropomyosin, and myosin light chain kinase are all present on the same actin-containing microfilaments in nonmuscle cells.

The indirect immunofluorescence technique is limited by its resolving power. One is visualizing a fluorescent molecule by light microscopy. The use of a sandwich-type procedure results in considerable enhancement of the image but there is no question that the only localization that is revealed are those structures that contain high concentrations of the particular protein. Therefore we decided to attempt localization of calmodulin in interphase cells at the electron microscopic level. For this we resorted to the use of immunoelectron microscopy procedures (Lin *et al.*, 1980). To obviate the problem with large antibody molecules entering cells Fab fragment of the antibody were prepared by papain digestion of the IgG. The Fab fragments were labeled with horseradish peroxidase and utilized for the experiments. Tissues were fixed with 2% paraformaldehyde by vascular perfusion. Tissues were then removed, washed, and 50-μm sections were prepared. The sections were incubated with the Fab peroxidase conjugant against calmodulin and then refixed in 2.5% glutaraldehyde. The sections were then incubated with the substrate for the peroxidase which is 3,3′-diaminobenzidine. Sections were then postfixed in 1% OsO_4. After dehydration the sections were imbedded and examined under a light microscope to identify areas containing positive reaction product. Thin sections were observed under the electron microscope without further staining. One of the tissues that demonstrated the best calmodulin stain was the rat cerebellum (Fig. 3). Specifically the Purkinje cells demonstrated intensive peroxidase reaction product. Several controls were used to guard against nonspecific staining. These included (1) goat Fab peroxidase against another protein which was chicken ApoVLDLII, (2) sheep Fab peroxidase conjugate against calmodulin was preabsorbed with a 5-fold molar excess of protein, and (3) horseradish peroxidase alone was substituted for the Fab peroxidase conjugate.

In the Purkinje cell body calmodulin could be found associated with virtually all membranes (Lin *et al.*, 1980). Thus reaction product was noted on the plasma membrane, on rough and smooth endoplasmic reticulum, associated with polyribosomes, with small membranous vesicles, and with nuclear membrane. Both inner and outer membranes of mitochondria showed reaction product. As one examined the dendrite region of the Purkinje cells calmodulin could be found as a granular mass in the middle of the process. This could be in keeping with the suggestion by Iqbal and Ochs (1978) that calmodulin may be involved in fast axonal transport. In the region of the synapse calmodulin was found associated with the synaptic boutons with a rather intense stain associated with the postsynaptic density. This association with the postsynaptic density membranes confirms a previous report by Wood *et al.* (1980) using mouse basal ganglia and also by Grab *et al.* (1979) where postsynaptic densities were isolated and calmodulin was purified from the isolated membranous factions. Thus the electron microscopy localization data suggest that calmodulin is a component of virtually all membranes.

To convince ourselves that these data were correct, we isolated each of the fractions that calmodulin was found to be associated with by electron microscopy. It was found that all subcellular fractions including homogenate, nuclei, mitochondria, microsomes, plasma membranes, and postmicrosomal supernate contain between 0.4 and 2% calmodulin as a fraction of total protein concentration (Lin *et al.*, 1980). Polyribosomes isolated by the procedure of Means *et al.* (1971) were also shown to contain approximately 0.4% calmodulin. The question arose as to whether this represented the site of synthesis of the protein or whether calmodulin might be a structural ribosomal protein. This question was resolved by incubating the isolated polyribosomes in a cell-free protein-synthesizing system in the presence of puromycin. This causes the nascent peptide chains to be released from the ribosomes. Ribosomes can then be reisolated by ultracentrifugation. Determination of calmodulin content in the nascent chains versus the polyribosomes demonstrated that all of the

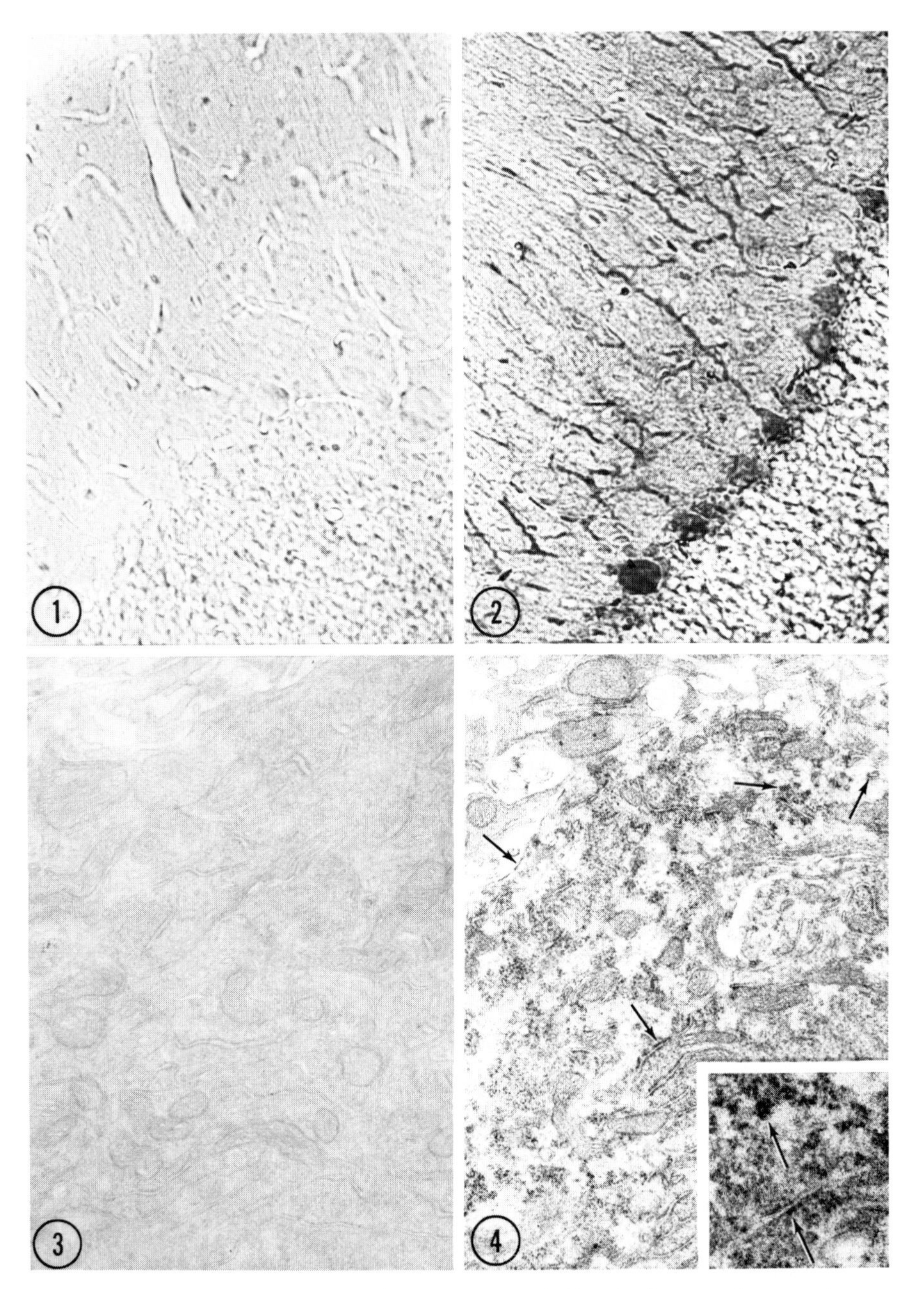

FIG. 3. Localization of calmodulin in the rat cerebellum by immunoelectron microscopy. The procedure has been previously described by Lin *et al.* (1980). (1) Control rat cerebellum treated with an Fab-peroxidase conjugate against chicken apo VLDL-II. No reaction product can be seen. × 1000. (2) Rat cerebellum was treated with an Fab-peroxidase conjugate against calmodulin. The reaction product (dark staining) is shown in Purkinje cell

polyribosomes associated with calmodulin were present in the supernatant fluid. These data would suggest that calmodulin localization on polyribosomes represents the site of synthesis and that this protein is not a structural component of the ribosome.

Isolated microtubules from cerebellum contain no detectable calmodulin by radioimmunoassay (Lin *et al.*, 1980). However synaptic plasma membranes did contain 1 μg of calmodulin per milligram of protein. When postsynaptic densities were prepared this value increased to 3%. Thus virtually every subcellular fraction contained calmodulin and the only fraction where an enrichment might be evident was the postsynaptic membrane. The postsynaptic membrane is also the locale of neurotransmitter receptors. We thought it would be interesting to ask whether in cholinergic neuromuscular junctions calmodulin and acetylcholine receptors were similarly localized. In experiments undertaken with Dr. Zach Hall we have revealed both in inervated and denervated muscle that acetylcholine receptor localized by rhodamine-labeled α-bungarotoxin and calmodulin localized by fluorescein-labeled anticalmodulin are coincident. As one might suspect from the previously described data the localization is found in the postsynaptic region of the neuromuscular junction. The purpose of calmodulin localization in the same region as neurotransmitter receptors remains to be established but it is likely that the calcium release of neurotransmitter substances may be mediated by calmodulin (DeLorenzo *et al.*, 1979).

B. MITOSIS

Examination of mitotic cells revealed a distribution that had been completely unexpected (Welsh *et al.*, 1978). In metaphase calmodulin was localized in association with the mitotic spindle. In anaphase calmodulin was found only in the region of the spindle between the centrioles and the chromosomes and was completely absent from the interzonal region. The distribution of calmodulin throughout the mitotic cycle of PtK_2 cells is shown in Fig. 4. Several control experiments were performed which demonstrated this localization to be specific to calmodulin (Welsh *et al.*, 1978). Electron microscopic localization using the Fab fragment also revealed

---

bodies and dendrites. ×1000. (3) Rat cerebellum treated exactly as in (2) but the antibody was first preabsorbed with a 5 *M* excess of calmodulin. Again no reaction product can be seen. ×23,000. (4) Again rat cerebellum was treated as in (2). Here is shown part of a Purkinje cell body that reveals electron-dense reaction products (arrows) associated with plasma membrane, free polyribosomes, rough endoplasmic reticulum, and smooth endoplasmic reticulum. ×15,700. The inset shows higher magnification (×27,500) of free and bound polyribosomes.

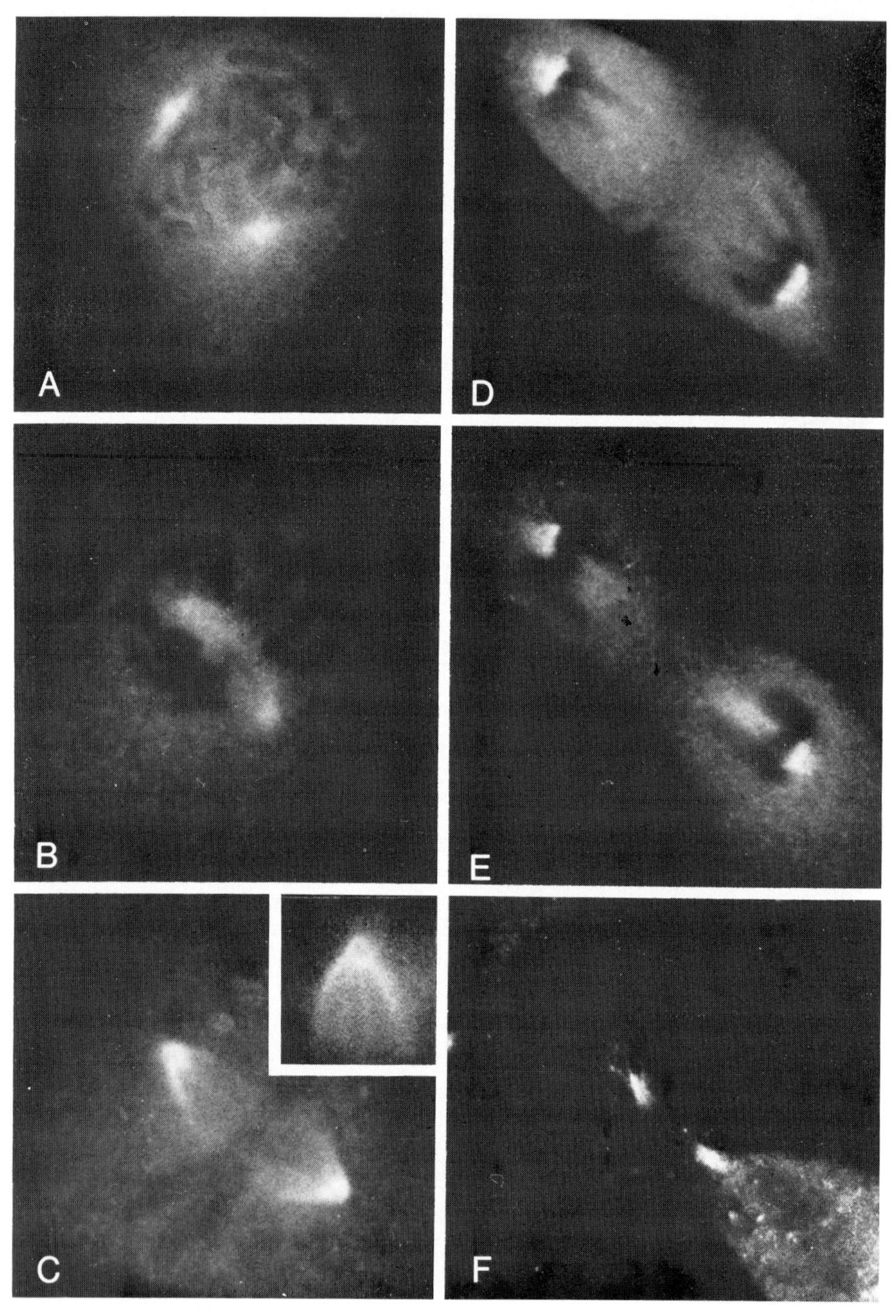

FIG. 4. Calmodulin localization in mitotic rat kangaroo PtK_2 cells. The indirect immunofluorescence procedure and growth of the cells were as described by Welsh *et al.* (1979). (A) Prophase; (B) prometaphase; (C) metaphase. The inset illustrates one-half of a mitotic spindle (×2200); (D) anaphase; (E) late anaphase; (F) telophase. All figures × 1660.

that the localization of calmodulin was associated with the half mitotic spindles.

The initial localization studies in mitotic cells suggested a similarity between calmodulin localization and that of microtubules. Therefore a series of experiments were undertaken to evaluate the similarities and differences between the localization of calmodulin and tubulin during mitosis in several types of cells maintained in tissue culture (Welsh *et al.*, 1979). As cells enter prophase tubulin and calmodulin specific fluorescence first appeared near the centrioles. Through prometaphase and metaphase tubulin and calmodulin continue to show similar patterns of localization. At metaphase however calmodulin was primarily concentrated at the poles of the mitotic spindle with strands of fluorescence projecting toward the chromosome. The pattern suggests a gradient with the highest concentrations close to the poles and the lowest concentrations close to the chromosomes. Tubulin however was much more uniform throughout the mitotic apparatus. During interphase tubulin was present both between the poles of the chromosomes and in the region between the separating chromosomes. In contrast, calmodulin was found only in the half spindle, that is, between the poles and chromosomes. Through cytokinesis calmodulin immunofluorescence was conspicuously absent from the contractile ring of the cleavage furrow. This is an area demonstrated to contain actin, myosin, and myosin light chain kinase. At late anaphase or early telophase tubulin remained present in both half spindles and interzonal regions. During this stage calmodulin was transiently observed on each side of the chromosomes as two distinct areas on either side of the cleavage furrow. Finally in very late telophase tubulin was found throughout the midbody except for a narrow band at the center of the structure corresponding to the cleavage furrow. Calmodulin distributed at each end of the midbody region in a pattern clearly different from that of tubulin. A series of drugs was then used to determine which component of the mitotic apparatus was most closely associated with calmodulin (Welsh *et al.*, 1979). Treatment with cytochalasin B, a drug known to disrupt microfilaments, caused no change in either the concentration or localization of calmodulin or tubulin. However when cells were treated with agents known to disrupt microtubules, spindle structure was altered and tubulin and calmodulin specific fluorescence were equally affected. Colcemid treatment completely disrupted the spindle as reflected by tubulin immunofluorescence and equally abolished calmodulin localization in the mitotis apparatus. Treatment of cells with nitrous oxide, which causes disorganization of the spindle but does not cause disassembly of spindle microtubules, disrupted spindle structure as visualized by tubulin-specific fluorescence. However calmodulin was still concentrated in the cell center in the same region as the microtubules of the disorganized spindle. Finally it is known that two types of microtubules exist in the mitotic apparatus. The microtubules from pole to chromosome are known to be stable to cold temperatures whereas lowering the temperature to 4°C disrupts those microtubules present in the interzone region that extend from pole to pole (Brinkley and Cartwright, 1975). As expected treatment of cells at 4°C resulted in the disruption of the pole to pole microtubules as visualized by antitubulin immunofluorescence. However the pole to chromosome tubules were cold stable. No change in the distribution of calmodulin was found upon exposure of the cells to cold temperatures suggesting that if calmodulin is associated with microtubules during mitosis, the most likely components are the pole to chromosome microtubules which comprise the half spindles. Subsequent studies by Andersen *et al.* (1978) confirm this localization pattern using an antibody that had been prepared against alum-precipitated calmodulin. In addition de May and deBrabander (1980) have localized calmodulin in mitotic mammalian cells by an electron microscopy method. Again the distribution pattern described above was shown to be the case. Thus a gradient of calmodulin concentration was seen being most concentrated at the pole and least concentrated at the chromosome.

VI. Calmodulin Effects on Microtubule Assembly

Taken together the distribution data suggest that calmodulin is almost entirely localized in the mitotic apparatus between the chromosomes and the poles. This pattern is altered only very late in anaphase or early telophase where a transient association of calmodulin is seen between the chromosomes and the developing cleavage furrow. In all instances the distribution pattern is consistent with the presence of high concentrations of calmodulin in regions where microtubules must depolymerize; first in order for chromosomes to move from the metaphase plate to the poles and second for the daughter cells to divide. These experiments suggested that the calcium lability of microtubules may be mediated by calmodulin. In order to test this hypothesis microtubules were isolated by four cycles of polymerization/depolymerization as described by Borisy *et al.* (1975). Microtubule formation was monitored by a change in absorbancy at 320 nm and polymerization was initiated by the addition of GTP (Marcum *et al.*, 1978). As shown in Fig. 5 the presence of 0.3 μM calcium had no effect on microtubule polymerization. Increasing the concentration to 11 μM caused only about a 10% reduction in the extent of microtubule polymerization. When calmodulin was added in calcium–EGTA buffer systems so that the free concentration of calcium was again 0.3 μM little effect on

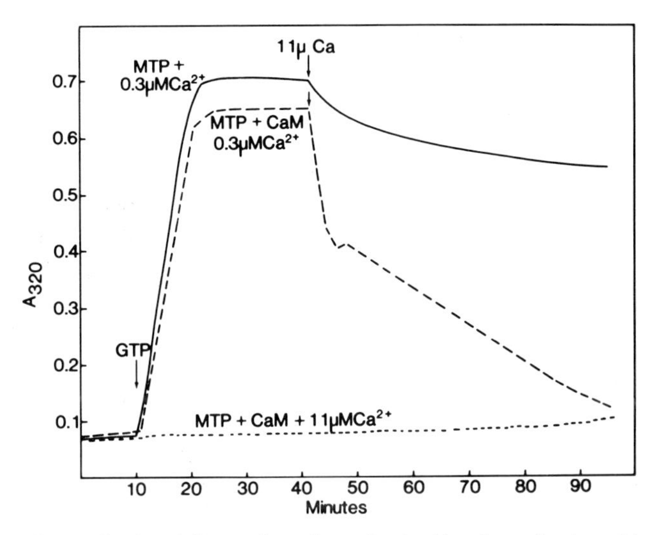

FIG. 5. Effects of calmodulin on the polymerization/depolymerization of bovine brain microtubules. Microtubules were isolated as described by Borisy *et al.* (1975). Polymerization was monitored by light scattering at 320 nm in a Gilford recording spectrophotometer. The reactions were carried out at 37°C and were initiated by the addition of GTP (Marcum *et al.*, 1978). Calcium–EGTA buffers were utilized to calculate free calcium concentrations (Dedman *et al.*, 1977). MTP, Microtubule protein; CaM, calmodulin.

polymerization was seen. However the addition of 11 μM calcium in the presence of calmodulin completely prevented microtubule polymerization. Similarly addition of 11 μM calcium plus 2.5 mg/ml calmodulin to polymerized microtubules resulted in a complete depolymerization of these structures. Further examination of this effect revealed that it was not all or none. Rather the presence of calmodulin caused a shift in the concentration of calcium required for microtubule polymerization (Dedman *et al.*, 1980). Thus in the absence of calmodulin the amount of calcium required for depolymerization was millimolar. However in the presence of calmodulin the concentration of calcium required for complete depolymerization of microtubules was $10^{-5} M$. Therefore a 100-fold change in sensitivity of calcium was achieved by the addition of calmodulin.

The difficulty with this series of experiments was that the ratio of calmodulin to tubulin required for microtubule depolymerization was 6: 1. For most effects of calmodulin so far described the stoichiometry is 1: 1. We reasoned that the isolation of microtubules by polymerization/depolymerization selected for those components involved in microtubule assembly and selected against those proteins that might be involved in microtubule depolymerization. Thus when calmodulin levels were measured in microtubules isolated by polymerization cycles little was found (Lin *et al.*, 1980). It seemed logical to assume that other proteins could be lost during this procedure. We therefore turned to a second system to evaluate the effects of calcium calmodulin on microtubule polymerization. This was the detergent permeabilized cell system described by Brinkley *et al.* (1980). In this system isolated tissue culture cells are incubated in the presence of colcemid to disrupt the cytoplasmic microtubule complex. The cells are then permeabilized by treatment with Triton X-100 and washed to remove depolymerized 6 S tubulin and the colcemid. Visualization of these cells by indirect immunofluorescence microscopy using antitubulin reveals that the only structures seen in the cells represent the single organizing center associated with the centrosomal region of each interphase cell. Addition of 6 S tubulin to this preparation results in the specific nucleation of microtubule assembly from the single nucleating site. Experiments were next conducted equivalent to those described above for the isolated microtubules (Means and Dedman, 1980; Tash *et al.*, 1980). Figure 6 illustrates that incubation of these lysed cells with 11 μM free calcium caused no difference in the degree of microtubule polymerization. However if calmodulin was added to these cells in the presence of 11 μM calcium, complete abolition of microtubule polymerization was achieved. Brinkley *et al.* (1980) established that the optimal concentration of tubulin for microtubule assembly was 1 mg/ml. Assuming a molecular weight of 110,000 for the 6 S dimer, this results in a concentration of tubulin of approximately 10^{-5} M. The optimal concentration of calmodulin in this system was 6 μM. Thus the ratio of calmodulin to tubulin required for optimal effects was much closer to 1 : 1 than the concentrations required in the *in vitro* microtubule polymerization experiments.

Taken together these experiments suggest that there should be an inverse relationship between the concentration of calmodulin in the cell and the number of polymerized microtubules. Several systems have been developed to examine this possibility. The first was achieved by first determining the distribution of anticalmodulin in mitotic cells by fluorescence microscopy and then serially sectioning them for electron microscopy (Dedman *et al.*, 1980). Each of the sections was evaluated for the number of microtubule profiles as described by Brinkley and Cartwright (1971). In metaphase when high concentrations of calmodulin were found at the poles no polymerized microtubules were counted in those sections. However as the gradient of calmodulin decreased toward the poles the number of polymerized microtubules increased reaching the highest numbers at the kinetochore plates of the chromosomes. An inverse relationship was seen on the other side of the chromosomes, thus again high concentra-

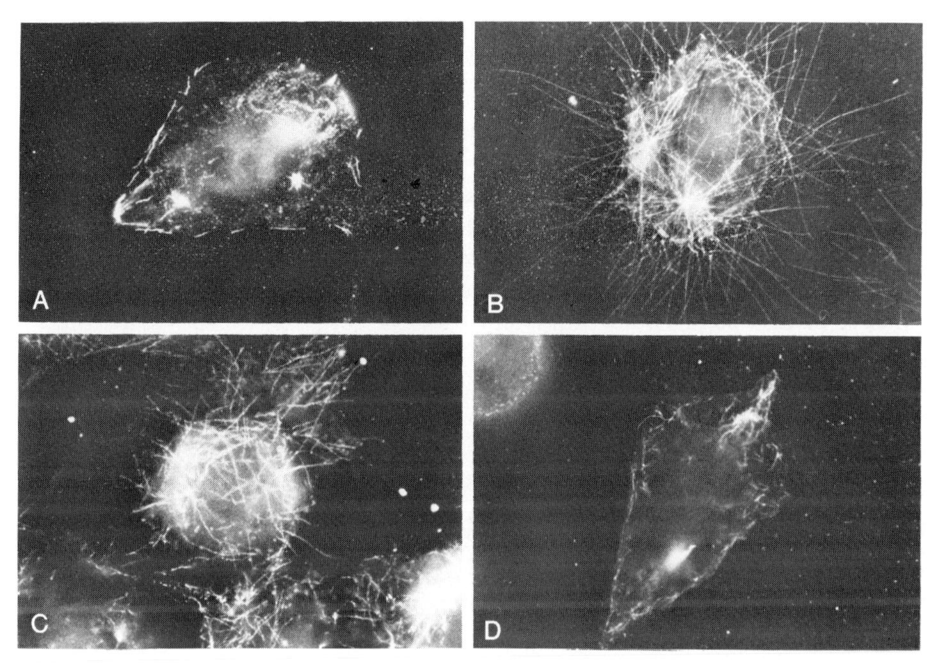

FIG. 6. Effect of calmodulin on the polymerization of 6 S tubulin in detergent-permeabilized 3T3 cells. The permeabilized cell system has been described by Brinkley *et al.* (1980). Microtubules were prepared from bovine brain (Borisy *et al.*, 1975) and 6 S tubulin purified by phosphocellulose chromatography. Tubulin was added at 1 mg/ml (10^{-5} M) and calmodulin at 6×10^{-6} M. Polymerization was allowed to continue for 15 minutes at 37°C. Calcium–EGTA buffers were utilized to calculate free calcium concentrations (Dedman *et al.*, 1977). (A) Colcemid-treated cell with no tubulin added; (B) tubulin; (C) tubulin plus 11 μM calcium; (D) tubulin plus 11 μM calcium plus calmodulin.

tions were observed close to the kinetochore followed by a decreasing gradient achieving no polymerized microtubules at the opposite pole. This relationship held throughout mitosis even in late anaphase where calmodulin was found to be transiently associated on both sides of the chromosomes. In such cells the only polymerized microtubules were found in the middle of the cell corresponding to the position of the developing cleavage furrow. Once again, therefore, there was an inverse relationship between the concentration of calmodulin and the number of polymerized microtubules.

The second approach was to isolate mitotic spindles from sea urchin eggs as described by Salmon and Segall (1980). These spindles demonstrate micromolar sensitivity to calcium and were found to contain calmodulin by radioimmunoassay (Dedman *et al.*, 1980). Staining of the metaphase mitotic spindle by antitubulin demonstrated that the entire mitotic spindle contained tubulin including the asters at each pole. Examination of the fluorescence pattern of calmodulin revealed localization only in the region of the centrioles. When serial sections were made of the mitotic spindles it was again found that only in association with the poles where sections of the centriole could be seen were there no polymerized microtubules. As the distance increased from pole to chromosome the number of polymerized microtubules increased. Again in this system there is an association between the calmodulin concentration and the number of polymerized microtubules. Finally Cande *et al.* (1974) have developed a eukaryotic mammalian cell system in which they can study the rate of metaphase–anaphase chromosome movement. This movement is markedly enhanced by the addition of micromolar calcium. In collaborative experiments we have recently shown that this movement can be blocked by incubation of the mitotic spindles with anticalmodulin antibody or the anticalmodulin agent W13 described by Hidaka *et al.* (1979b). It seems reasonable to assume, therefore, that calmodulin may be involved in the regulated depolymerization of microtubules that occurs during metaphase–anaphase chromosome movement. It should also be pointed out that in those systems where calcium concentration has been measured micromolar concentrations of calcium are not achieved in the spindle. Therefore high concentrations of calmodulin would be required in order to assure proper depolymerization of microtubules. These data support the immunofluorescent localization patterns. However the exact mechanism by which calmodulin affects microtubule depolymerization remains to be determined.

VII. Regulation

The results presented in the preceding section suggest that elevation of calmodulin in cells should lead to a decrease in polymerized microtubules unless the amount of tubulin is also increased. For that reason we have investigated a variety of hormonally regulated systems to determine whether calmodulin is selectively elevated (Chafouleas *et al.*, 1980c). The systems so far investigated have been estrogen and progesterone stimulation of chick oviduct, androgen and rat prostate, corticosteroids in GH_1 cells, FSH and Sertoli cells, ACTH and Y1 adrenal tumor cells, TSH and thyroid slices, and GnRH in pituitary cells. In no instance has calmodulin shown to be selectively elevated. This is even true in the chicken oviduct where estrogen results in a remarkable cytodifferentiation and the appearance of many new protein products. However in the immature undifferentiated oviduct, in the oviduct during primary differentiation, withdrawal from hormone or secondary stimulation the amount of calmodulin per cell is constant.

In the peptide hormone systems it is known that calcium is important for the secretion of various products. Since calmodulin levels were unaltered we decided to determine whether the peptide hormones resulted in a redistribution of calmodulin within the cell. In collaboration with Dr. Michael Conn we undertook a study to evaluate the distribution of calmodulin in pituitary cells stimulated by GnRH (Chafouleas *et al.*, 1980a). It was found that GnRH did promote a redistribution of calmodulin whether cells were fractionated in the presence or absence of calcium (Table IV). This change in distribution preceded the secretion of LH as assessed by a specific radioimmunoassay. Whereas no changes were seen in nuclei or mitochondrial fractions, GnRH promoted significant redistribution of calmodulin in plasma membrane fractions. These changes could be accounted for by reciprocal changes in either microsomal or cytoplasmic fractions. The data suggest the possibility that calmodulin-mediated enzymes may be regulated due to a hormone-dependent redistribution of the calcium-binding protein. It is likely that this redistribution is promoted by alterations in the net flux or distribution of calcium within the cell rather than by changes in the cellular content of calmodulin.

In 1976 Watterson and colleagues reported that transformation of chick embryo fibroblasts by Rous sarcoma virus resulted in an elevation in the activator protein of phosphodiesterase. In these experiments the protein

TABLE IV

Effect of GnRH on Subcellular Distribution of Calmodulin in Pituitary Cells[a]

Fraction	Control	GnRH	Difference (%)
	(% of total CaM)		
Homogenate	100	100	—
Nuclei	5.0	5.3	—
Mitochondria	10.4	9.8	—
Microsomes	6.0	10.4	+4.4
Plasma membrane	14.8	18.4	+3.6
Cytosol	63.2	54.9	−8.3

[a] Pituitary cells were isolated from estrogen-treated rats and enriched for gonadotrophs. Cells were incubated in the absence or presence of GnRH for 20 minutes at 37°C, homogenized, then fractionated. Each fraction was assayed for purity by marker enzymes and found to contain less than 7% contamination. Calmodulin was assayed by radioimmunoassay as described by Chafouleas *et al.* (1979).

was quantitated by densitometric scanning of polyacrylamide gels. A similar report appeared by LaPorte *et al.* (1979) 3 years later. Again the system was the same, chick embryo fibroblasts and those cells transformed by Rous sarcoma virus. In this case calmodulin was assayed by its ability to stimulate cyclic AMP phosphodiesterase. Both reports suggested a doubling in the concentration of calmodulin in the transformed relative to the nontransformed cell. We decided to evaluate whether this might be a more general phenomenon associated with transformation of cells to the malignant state (Chafouleas *et al.*, 1980b,c). When calmodulin was quantitated by radioimmunoassay it was revealed that SV40 transformed 3T3 cells contained more calmodulin than did 3T3 cells. In addition normal rat kidney (NRK) cells transformed by Rous sarcoma virus contained more calmodulin than their nontransformed counterparts. Finally, mouse mammary epithelial cells contained much less calmodulin than those cells present in mouse mammary epithelial tumors. In all three instances, the ratio of calmodulin in the transformed to the normal cell was 2–3:1. Chafouleas *et al.* (1980b) then evaluated the mechanism for the increase in both 3T3 and NRK cell systems. Calmodulin was quantitated by radioimmunoassay or by immunoprecipitation with a monospecific antibody. In the same samples total protein was measured by acid precipitation and tubulin was quantitated by cholchicine binding or by immunoprecipitation using monospecific antibody to tubulin. The experimental design was to determine the rate of synthesis of calmodulin, tubulin, and total protein in exponentially growing cells by evaluating the rate of incorporation of ^{35}S-labeled methionine into the specific proteins. The rate of turnover of the proteins was then established by incubating cells with [^{35}S]methionine for 1 hour then adding a 4000-fold excess of unlabeled methionine and removing cells for analysis at various times thereafter. The data revealed that the rate of synthesis of calmodulin, tubulin, and total protein is elevated in the transformed cells compared to the nontransformed counterpart. In addition the rate of degradation was faster in transformed cells than in nontransformed cells. However whereas the rate of synthesis of calmodulin is elevated 3-fold, only a 50% change in the rate of degradation is noted. This resulted in a 2- to 2.5-fold increase in the amount of calmodulin per cell (Table V). On the other hand tubulin synthesis was stimulated by 2-fold whereas degradation was also enhanced by 2-fold. Thus the amount of tubulin in the cells did not vary.

Brinkley and colleagues (1978) have established that the cytoplasmic microtubule complex in 3T3 cells is markedly different than the complex in SV40 transformed 3T3 cells. The diminished cytoplasmic microtubule network occurs even though the amount of tubulin in each cell is identical (Chafouleas *et al.*, 1980b; Hiller and Weber, 1978). When the per-

TABLE V

Calmodulin and Tubulin Ratios in Virally Transformed Cells and Their Nontransformed Counterparts[a]

Cell type	Total protein (mass ratios in pg/cell)	Tubulin (mass ratios in pg/cell)	Calmodulin (mass ratios in pg/cell)	CaM/tubulin (molar ratios)
SV3T3/3T3	1.20	1.10	2.63	2.3
SR-NRK/NRK	1.23	1.24	3.20	2.6

[a] Swiss mouse 3T3 cells and 3T3 cells transformed by the DNA virus simian 40 as well as normal rat kidney cells and those cells transformed by the RNA virus Rous sarcoma were maintained in tissue culture as described by Welsh *et al.* (1978). Rate of synthesis and degradation of calmodulin and tubulin were measured in exponentially growing cells using incorporation of [^{35}S]methionine into the specific proteins. Calmodulin was quantitated by radioimmunoassay and tubulin by colchicine binding as described by Chafouleas *et al.* (1979).

meabilized cell system mentioned earlier was used to nucleate the assembly of microtubules from organizing centers of 3T3 and SV3T3 cells it was found that the 3T3 cells nucleated more microtubules and those microtubules were longer than in the transformed counterpart (Brinkley *et al.*, 1980). Together these data suggested the possibility that the elevated levels of calmodulin might be preventing the establishment of a complete cytoplasmic microtubule complex. To test this hypothesis SV40 transformed cells were treated with detergent and then preincubated with the antibody to calmodulin (Fig. 7). When 6 S tubulin was added microtubules grew from the organizing centers in a manner indistinguishable from what occurred in the 3T3 cell under identical conditions. Thus neutralization of the elevated level of calmodulin allowed microtubules to grow in a normal fashion. This experiment suggests that indeed elevated levels of calmodulin do lead to a diminished cytoplasmic microtubule complex. This effect is not due to the lack of tubulin in the cells but rather to an inhibition of microtubule polymerization.

VIII. Summary and Conclusions

The information presented in this manuscript illustrates the important role of calmodulin in cell function. Calcium and calmodulin are intimately involved with the cytoskeleton (Dedman *et al.*, 1979). On the one hand microfilaments are controlled by the effect of calmodulin on myosin light chain kinase and the subsequent phosphorylation of myosin light chain. On the other hand calmodulin seems to be involved in promoting de-

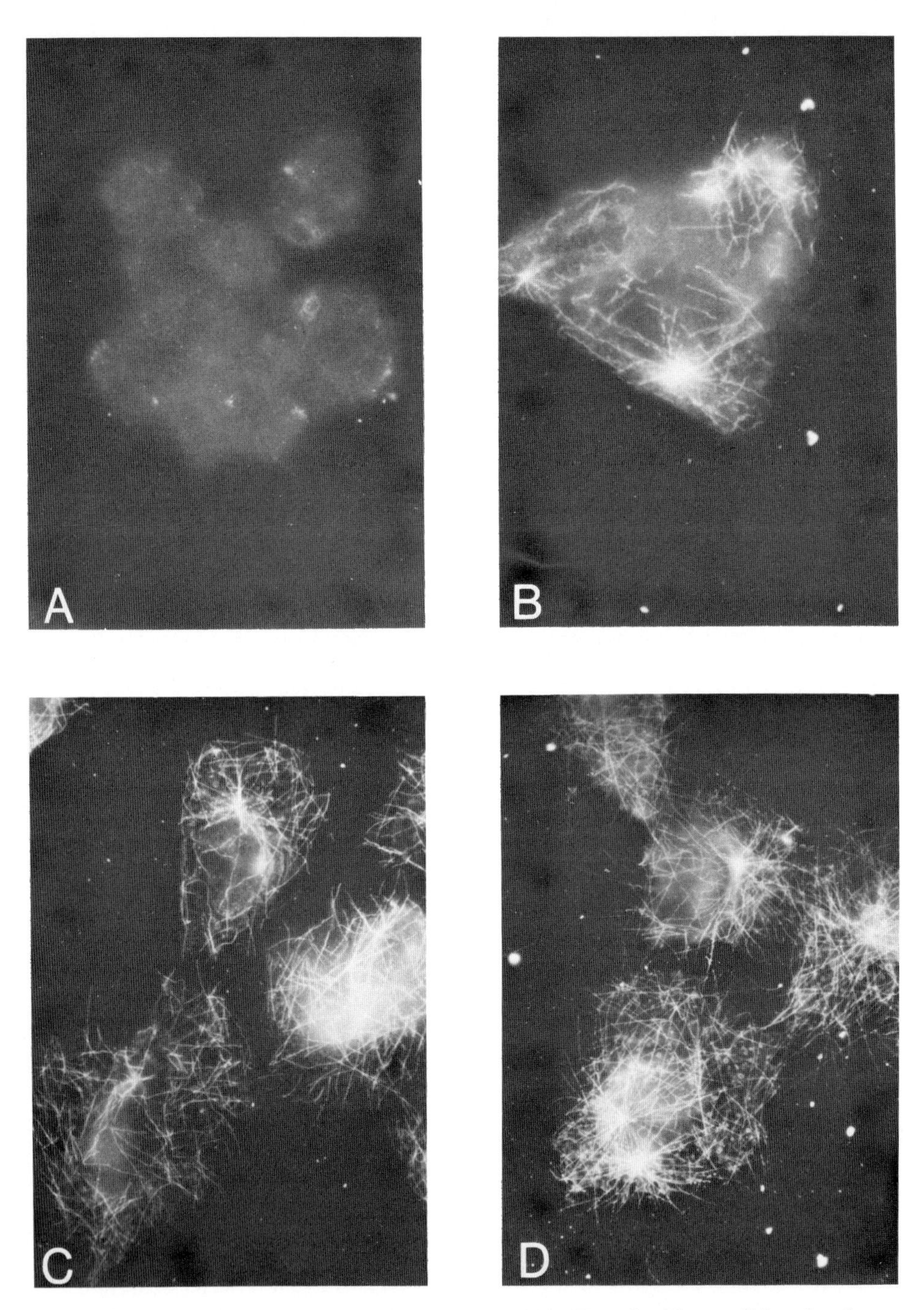

FIG. 7. Microtubule polymerization in 3T3 and SV-3T3 cells. The conditions for the permeabilized cell system, isolation of components, and incubation were as described in Fig.

polymerization of microtubules either due to elevated levels in the cytoplasm of transformed cells or because of the high concentration of calmodulin in the area of the mitotic spindle of normal cells. Microtubules and microfilaments are involved in the regulation of secretion. It is likely that microtubules are needed to define and orient the flow of secretory granules from packaging in the Golgi apparatus to the plasma membrane. Microfilaments are required to provide the motive force for this movement and also possibly for the discharge of the contents of secretory vesicles into the media. Calcium is also involved in receptor mediated endocytosis (Goldstein *et al.*, 1979). One of the calcium requirements is in maintaining the structure of the clathrin-coated vesicles. It has recently been shown that these vesicles are involved not only in the endocytotic process but also in exocytosis (Rothman *et al.*, 1980). In hormone-regulated systems this has been most clearly demonstrated with respect to the acetylcholine receptor and we have already discussed the fact that acetylcholine receptor and calmodulin share common locales in neuromuscular junctions. Linden *et al.* (1980) have demonstrated that calmodulin is an important component of clathrin-coated vesicles. The precise role of calmodulin in the coated vesicle is unclear. It does not seem to be associated with clathrin but does seem to be associated with other proteins that constitute the vesicle structure. It is possible that the interaction of calcium with the vesicles results in a change in structure leading to either fusion of the vesicles with plasma membrane or the pinching off of the vesicles from the plasma membrane. Certainly this will be an important area for investigation in the future.

Much of what has been published concerning calmodulin to date must be considered as phenomenological. It is unknown precisely how calmodulin regulates most of the proteins that it affects. The major exception to this is the myosin light chain kinase. In this case it is known that calmodulin interacts on a one to one basis with the inactive enzyme in a calcium-dependent fashion. This interaction results in a conformational change that allows the enzyme to phosphorylate myosin light chains and leads to tension development. Similar experiments concerning the physiologic regulation of calcium magnesium ATPase, phosphodiesterase, and microtubule organization must be undertaken. Phosphorylation seems to be the one area of metabolism most often regulated by calmodulin (Cheung, 1980; Means and Dedman, 1980a). It seems possible,

6. (A) Colchicine-treated SV-3T3 cell with no tubulin added; (B) SV-3T3 plus tubulin; (C) SV-3T3 cell was preincubated for 30 minutes with 200 μg/ml of sheep anticalmodulin and then for 15 minutes with tubulin; (D) 3T3 cell incubated with tubulin. Note the similarities in the number and length of microtubules demonstrable in (C) and (D).

therefore, that calcium-calmodulin may share a common mode of action to that of cyclic AMP and regulatory subunit of protein kinase. In both instances the interaction of the ligand with the regulatory protein leads to enhanced protein kinase activity. There is no question that calmodulin is very important in the regulation of endocrine cells. Precisely how important and by what mechanisms should constitute the efforts of a large number of laboratories over the next several years.

ACKNOWLEDGMENTS

I am indebted to my colleagues Drs. B. R. Brinkley, J. G. Chafouleas, J. R. Dedman, M. J. Welsh, T. Lin, V. Guerriero, and R. P. Munjaal for they carried out many of the experiments described in this article. The able assistance of Ms. E. MacDougall, S. Cox, L. Wible, and Mr. C. R. Mena is also gratefully acknowledged. Finally I appreciate the efforts of Ms. G. Laird who typed this manuscript.

REFERENCES

Anderson, B., Osborn, M., and Weber, K. (1978). *Cytobiologie* **17,** 354–364.

Beale, E. G., Dedman, J. R., and Means, A. R. (1977). *Endocrinology* **101,** 1621–1634.

Bolton, A. E., and Hunter, W. M. (1973). *Biochem. J.* **133,** 1014–1021.

Borisy, G. G., Marcum, J. M., Olmstead, J. B., Murphy, D. B., and Johnson, K. A. (1975). *Ann. N.Y. Acad. Sci.* **253,** 107–132.

Brinkley, B. R., and Cartwright, J. (1971). *J. Cell Biol.* **50,** 416–431.

Brinkley, B. R., and Cartwright, J. (1975). *Ann. N.Y. Acad. Sci.* **253,** 428–439.

Brinkley, B. R., Miller, C. L., Fuseler, J. W., Pepper, D. A., and Wible, L. J. (1978). *In* "Cell Differentiation and Neoplasia" (G. F. Saunders, ed.), pp. 419–450. Raven, New York.

Brinkley, B. R., Pepper, D. A., Cox, S. M., Fistel, S., Brenner, S. L., Wible, L. J., and Pardue, R. L. (1980). *In* "Microtubules and Microtubule Inhibitors" (M. deBrabander and J. deMey, eds.), pp. 281–296. Elsevier, Amsterdam.

Cande, Z., Snyder, J., Smith, D., Summers, K., and McIntosh, R. (1974). *Proc. Natl. Acad. Sci. U.S.A.* **71,** 1559–1653.

Chafouleas, J. G., Dedman, J. R., Munjaal, R. P., and Means, A. R. (1979). *J. Biol. Chem.* **254,** 10262–10267.

Chafouleas, J. G., Conn, P. M., Dedman, J. R., and Means, A. R. (1980a). *Endocrinology* **106,** 289a.

Chafouleas, J. G., Pardue, R. L., Brinkley, B. R., Dedman, J. R., and Means, A. R. (1980b). *Proc. Natl. Acad. Sci. U.S.A.* (in press)

Chafouleas, J. G., Pardue, R. L., Brinkley, B. R., Dedman, J. R., and Means, A. R. (1980c). *In* "Calcium Binding Proteins and Calcium Function in Health and Disease" (F. L. Siegel *et al.*, eds.), pp. 189–196. Elsevier, Amsterdam.

Cheung, W. Y. (1980). *Science* **207,** 19–27.

Cohen, P., Cohen, P. T., Shenolikar, S., Nairn, A., and Perry, S. V. (1979). *Eur. J. Biochem.* **100,** 329–337.

Cook, W. J., Dedman, J. R., Means, A. R., and Bugg, C. E. (1980). *J. Biol. Chem.* **255,** 8152–8153.

Dabrowska, R., Aromatorio, D., Sherry, J. M. F., and Hartshorne, D. J. (1978). *Biochemistry* **17,** 253–258.
Dedman, J. R., Potter, J. D., Jackson, R. L., Johnson, J. D., and Means, A. R. (1977a). *J. Biol. Chem.* **252,** 8415–8522.
Dedman, J. R., Jackson, R. L., Schreiber, W. E., and Means, A. R. (1977b). *J. Biol. Chem.* **253,** 343–346.
Dedman, J. R., Welsh, M. J., and Means, A. R. (1978). *J. Biol. Chem.* **253,** 7515–7521.
Dedman, J. R., Brinkley, B. R., and Means, A. R. (1979). *Adv. Cyclic Nucleotide Res.* **11,** 131–174.
Dedman, J. R., Lin, T., Marcum, J. M., Brinkley, B. R., and Means, A. R. (1980). *In* "Calcium Binding Proteins and Calcium Function in Health and Disease" (F. L. Siegel *et al.*, eds.), pp. 181–188. Elsevier, Amsterdam.
DeLorenzo, R. J., Freedman, S. D., Yohe, W. B., and Mauree, S. C. (1979). *Proc. Natl. Acad. Sci. U.S.A.* **76,** 6471–6475.
de Mey, J., and deBrabander, M. (1980). *In* "Microtubules and Microtubule Inhibitors" (M. deBrabander and J. deMey, eds.), pp. 227–241. Elsevier, Amsterdam.
Duddleston, W. G., Midgley, A. R., Jr., and Niswender, G. D. (1972). *Comput. Biomed. Res.* **5,** 205.
Fuller, G. M., Brinkley, B. R., and Boughter, J. M. (1975). *Science* **187,** 948–950.
Goldstein, J. L., Anderson, R. G. W., and Brown, M. S. (1979). *Nature (London)* **279,** 679–685.
Goodman, M., Pechere, J.-F., Haiech, J., and Demaille, J. G. (1979). *J. Mol. Evol.* **13,** 331–352.
Gopinath, R. M., and Vincenzi, F. F. (1977). *Biochem. Biophys. Res. Commun.* **77,** 1203–1209.
Grab, D. J., Berzins, K., Cohen, R. S., and Siekevitz, P. (1979). *J. Biol. Chem.* **254,** 8690–8698.
Grand, R. J. A., and Perry, S. V. (1978). *FEBS Lett.* **92,** 137–142.
Hathaway, D. R., and Adelstein, R. S. (1979). *Proc. Natl. Acad. Sci. U.S.A.* **76,** 1653–1657.
Hidaka, H., Naka, M., and Yamaki, T. (1979a). *Biochem. Biophys. Res. Commun.* **90,** 694–699.
Hidaka, H., Yamaki, T., Naka, M., Tanaka, T., Hayashi, H., and Kobayashi, R. (1979b). *Mol. Pharmacol.* **17,** 66–72.
Hiller, G., and Weber, K. (1978). *Cell* **14,** 795–804.
Ilundian, A., and Naftalin, R. J. (1979). *Nature (London)* **279,** 466–468.
Iqbal, Z., and Ochs, S. (1978). *J. Neurochem.* **31,** 409–418.
Jackson, R. L., Dedman, J. R., Schreiber, W. E., Bhatnagar, P. K., Knapp, R. D., and Means, A. R. (1977). *Biochem. Biophys. Res. Commun.* **77,** 723–729.
Klee, C. B. (1977). *Biochemistry* **16,** 1017–1024.
Klee, C. B., Crouch, T. H., and Richman, P. G. (1980). *Annu. Rev. Biochem.* **49,** 489–516.
Krebs, E. G., and Beavo, J. A. (1979). *Annu. Rev. Biochem.* **48,** 923–961.
Kretsinger, R. H. (1980). *Crit. Rev. Biochem.* **8,** 119–174.
LaPorte, D. C., Gidwitz, S., Weber, M. J., and Storm, D. R. (1979). *Biochem. Biophys. Res. Commun.* **86,** 1169–1177.
LaPorte, D. C., Wierman, B. M., and Storm, D. R. (1980). *Biochemistry* **19,** 3814–3819.
Lin, C. T., Dedman, J. R., Brinkley, B. R., and Means, A. R. (1980). *J. Cell. Biol.* **85,** 473–480.
Linden, C. D., Dedman, J. R., Chafouleas, J. G., Means, A. R., and Roth, T. F. (1981). *Proc. Natl. Acad. Sci. U.S.A.* **78,** 308–312.
Manning, D. R., DiSalvo, J., and Stull, J. T. (1980). *Mol. Cell. Endocrinol.* **19,** 1–19.

Marcum, J. M., Dedman, J. R., Brinkley, B. R., and Means, A. R. (1978). *Proc. Natl. Acad. Sci. U.S.A.* **75**, 3771–3775.
Means, A. R., and Dedman, J. R. (1980). *Nature (London)* **285**, 73–77.
Means, A. R., and Dedman, J. R. (1980a). *Mol. Cell. Endocrinol.* **19**, 215–227.
Means, A. R., Abrass, I. B., and O'Malley, B. W. (1971). *Biochemistry* **10**, 1561–1570.
Midgley, A. R., Jr., Niswender, G. D., and Rebar, R. W. (1969). *Acta Endocrinol. Suppl.* **142**, 247.
Munjaal, R. P., Chandra, T., Woo, S. L. C., Dedman, J. R., and Means, A. R. (1981). *Proc. Natl. Acad. Sci. U.S.A.* (in press)
Nimmo, H. G., and Cohen, P. (1977). *Adv. Cyclic Nucleotide Res.* **8**, 145–266.
Payne, M. E., and Soderling, T. R. (1980). *J. Biol. Chem.* **255**, 8054–8056.
Polasto, E., Schneck, A. G., Leonis, J., Kim, S., and Paik, W. K. (1978). *Int. J. Biochem.* **9**, 795–801.
Rothman, J. E., Burstzyn-Pettegrew, H., and Fine, R. E. (1980). *J. Cell. Biol.* **86**, 162–171.
Salmon, E. D., and Segall, R. R. (1980). *J. Cell Biol.* **86**, 355–365.
Schubart, U. K., Erlichman, J., and Fleischer, N. (1980). *J. Biol. Chem.* **255**, 4120–4124.
Smoake, J. A., Song, S. Y., and Cheung, W. Y. (1974). *Biochim. Biophy. Acta* **341**, 402–411.
Tash, J. S., Means, A. R., Brinkley, B. R., Dedman, J. R., and Cox, S. M. (1980). *In* "Microtubules and Microtubule Inhibitors" (M. deBrabander and J. deMey, eds.), pp. 269–279. Elsevier, Amsterdam.
van Eldik, L. J., Grossman, A. R., Iverson, D. B., and Watterson, D. M. (1980). *Proc. Natl. Acad. Sci. U.S.A.* **77**, 1912–1916.
Vanaman, T. C., and Scharief, F. (1979). *Fed. Proc. Fed. Am. Soc. Exp. Biol.* **38**, 788.
Waisman, D. M., Stevens, F. C., and Wang, J. H. (1975). *Biochim. Biophys. Acta* **163**, 349–358.
Wallace, R. W., and Cheung, W. Y. (1979). *J. Biol. Chem.* **254**, 6564–6571.
Wang, J. H., and Waisman, D. M. (1979). *Curr. Top. Cell. Reg.* **15**, 47–107.
Watterson, D. M., van Eldik, L. J., Smith, R. E., and Vanaman, T. C. (1976). *Proc. Natl. Acad. Sci. U.S.A.* **73**, 2711–2715.
Watterson, D. M., Sharief, F., and Vanaman, T. C. (1980). *J. Biol. Chem.* **255**, 962–975.
Weiss, B., Prozialeck, W., and Cimino, M. (1980). *Adv. Cyclic Nucleoditde Res.* **12**, 213–225.
Welsh, M. J., Dedman, J. R., Brinkley, B. R., and Means, A. R. (1978). *Proc. Natl. Acad. Sci. U.S.A.* **75**, 1867–1871.
Welsh, M. J., Dedman, J. R., Brinkley, B. R., and Means, A. R. (1979). *J. Cell. Biol.* **81**, 624–634.
Wolff, D. J., Poirer, P. G., Brostrom, C. O., and Brostrom, M. (1977). *J. Biol. Chem.* **252**, 4108–4117.
Wood, J. G., Wallace, R. W., Whitaker, J. N., and Cheung, W. Y. (1980). *J. Cell. Biol.* **84**, 66–76.

DISCUSSION

H. Adlercreutz: I just want to ask you: has vitamin D any effect on calmodulin?

A. R. Means: That's a very good question, one that many people have asked. At this moment there's nothing that I know of but several people have begun to examine this problem. We do know that the vitamin D induced calcium-binding protein in chickens and calmodulin are not the same. We have traded samples with A. Norman and evaluated potential cross-reactivity in the respective radioimmunoassays. However, the possibility that calmodulin plays some role in vitamin D action is a very likely possibility and should constitute a fruitful avenue of investigation.

R. Chatterton: I wonder if you would be willing to expand on the observation that transformed cells contain more calmodulin than their nontransformed counterparts. The other question I had was: I think you showed earlier that the binding is very specific for calcium and that magnesium does not bind. Can you explain some of the antagonistic roles that magnesium exerts physiologically in the system, and do you think there's a mag-modulin?

A. R. Means: The first question dealt with the difference in calmodulin levels in normal and transformed cells. The answer is that on a per cell basis, calmodulin levels are still elevated. Second, the rate of synthesis is indeed a rate point, thus a 30 minute point is not very long when considering that the cell cycle is 14–20 hours in transformed or normal cells, respectively. But more recently, Jim Chafouleas has conducted experiments to evaluate, in both cell types, at what stages calmodulin is synthesized during the cell cycle. It is fascinating that synthesis is extremely tightly coupled to the G/S boundary. The only proteins that I know that are coupled in such a tight fashion are the histones. Almost everything else is synthesized reasonably randomly through G_1 and some synthesis may occur in G_2. When we evaluated the same experiments using the cDNA probe for calmodulin we found exactly what one would expect—that is a very rapid increase and then a very rapid fall-off. So this message is extremely short-lived during the cell cycle and we can show that during this time the concentration of the messenger RNA in the transformed cells is higher than in the normal. I think these data suggest that it's a real effect and not due to the growth of the cells.

The second question dealt with ion binding to calmodulin. Claude Klee at the NIH has been interested for some years in the calmodulin. Her results show that one can achieve almost any results depending on the conditions. In the absence of salt, Mg^{2+} will compete for one of the 4 Ca^{2+}-binding sites. However, in the presence of 35 mM salt (or higher), Ca^{2+} ion binding specificity is absolute. It is difficult to imagine the precise salt concentration *in vivo* so I would be reluctant to try to extrapolate from these *in vitro* experiments to what happens in the cell. Also, magnesium is present in much higher concentrations in a "cytoplasmic extract" than is calcium. We are talking about millimolar concentrations of magnesium versus micromolar levels of calcium. Most people that are interested in metal ion action have suggested because of these large differences there's no need to evoke a "mag-modulin" if you will, but to my knowledge no one has very carefully investigated the possibility.

H.-C. Blossey: I've also a question concerning the difference in the concentration between of calmodulin between normal and transformed cells. Would you think that calmodulin may act or may serve as a marker for the genetic activity of the cell?

A. R. Means: If I might rephrase your question to ask whether or not calmodulin might be involved in the initiation of DNA synthesis in cells, I would say I think it does. In fact, there's a recent paper by MacMannis and colleagues (*Biochem. Biophys. Res. Commun.* **95,** 745, 1980) that presents evidence that calmodulin may be important in initiation of DNA synthesis in tissue culture cells.

K. Sterling: Earlier in the talk you showed by fluorescent stains the calmodulin is in the mitochondria, presumably in the inner membrane. About a year ago A. L. Lehnimger showed rapid calcium ion movements during oxidative phosphorylation using the calcium electrode. We've observed a similar phenomenon happening rapidly within a matter of seconds using 45 calcium ($^{45}Ca^{2+}$) during oxidative phosphorylation. If calmodulin is in the inner membrane, can you say any more about it, and whether it's related to the ATPase assemblies and exactly where it is situated in the inner membrane?

A. R. Means: That is not an area we've worked on, however, it is being actively investigated in several laboratories. Howard Rasmussen has demonstrated that if mitochondria are isolated, preloaded with calcium-45, and then transferred to fresh media, a very rapid equilibrium ensues where the concentration of external calcium achieves a certain level and then is maintained. When mitochondria are removed to fresh media, the same thing happens and a similar Ca^{2+} concentration is achieved in the medium. The evidence that calmodulin is involved in this system stems from the use of anticalmodulin drugs such as the phenothiazines. As I pointed out earlier, there's some problems with these; however, the point is that if such experiments are performed and mitochondria are preincubated with these drugs, this equilibrium does not occur. That is all I know about what has been done with mitochondria. The second thing germain to your question is that there's a bacteria called azotobacter and it has a very primitive calcium pump in that it's a calcium proton pump. Eugene Barnes in the Biochemistry Department at Baylor works on this pumping mechanism and we thought it might be interesting to determine whether or not calmodulin was present in these azotobacter. When we looked by the radioimmunoassay initially we found nothing, but the procedure that we used was a heat-treatment, lysis of the bacteria, and centrifugation. We then decided to use what's now called the "Eastern" gel transfer technique. In this case, the entire bacteria is solubilized and the proteins are distributed on a gel by electrophoresis. The proteins are then transferred to nitrocellulose paper followed to incubation with the calmodulin antibody. In order to show where cross-reactive proteins exist one utilizes iodiated protein A. This protein will bind most species of immunoglobulin. The apper is then washed and subjected to autoradiography. Two protein components were found to stain specifically with the anti-calmodulin antibody; one is about 120,000 daltons whereas the other is nearly 200,000 daltons. If one performs exactly the same experiment with mitochondria isolated from rat liver, one finds that calmodulin itself is there, of course, in rather high concentrations, but one also finds a 200,000 dalton protein. So it is possible that in bacteria and possibly in mitochondria there is a membrane-associated protein that contains calmodulin as an integral subunit or at least an immunoreactive homolog.

C. R. Kahn: From a personal interest point of view, I would hope to see some interest of calmodulin on the problem of insulin action. Insulin is one of many hormones for which calcium has been suggested to play a role in the mechanism of action, both in possibly causing changes in total calcium, but more importantly shifting membrane-bound or protein-bound calcium. Has anybody looked at the alterations of calmodulin or its calcium binding in cells which have been insulin-treated versus not?

A second related question which is of more general nature is, can you give us some idea, in the normal physiologic state, either based on direct measurement or on calculation in the normal cell, whether the four calcium-binding sites of calmodulin are occupied or is there a chance for this to serve a regulatory role by binding calcium?

A. R. Means: With respect to insulin action, there have been two papers by Malaisse and colleagues. The first dealt with stimulation of adenylylcyclase in the membranes of pancreatic beta cells. The authors maintain that cyclase is stimulated by calmodulin in the Ca^{2+}-dependent fashion. Second, calmodulin was shown to bind to plasma membranes from beta cells and this too was Ca^{2+}-dependent. The problem with both of these I discussed earlier, that is, the lipophilic nature of calmodulin being as it is, I'm not sure whether these results can really be considered specific effects of calmodulin. There was also a paper by Fleischer and colleagues that appeared recently (*J. Biol. Chem.* **255,** 4120, 1980). These authors have shown calmodulin dependent phosphorylation of a 98K cytoplasmic protein in a hamster insulinoma. Phenothiozines prevented the phosphorylation and also inhibited insulin secretion. Thus these authors conclude that calmodulin is important in insulin secretion. The final piece of information comes from Larner's laboratory. As you know, he and Jarrett have evidence that when cells are incubated with insulin a small molecular weight peptide is released presumably from the plasma membrane. This peptide seems to stimulate the pyruvate dehydrogenase complex in the mitochondria. It is well known that the phosphatase activity is the calcium-sensitive subunit of the pyruvate dehydrogenase complex. The phosphatase is approximately 40,000 daltons in size and can be phosphorylated. Bennet and Lynch working with blood platelets have shown phosphorylation of a 40K protein that is calmodulin dependent. These authors suggest that the 40K protein may represent the phosphatase of pyruvic dehydrogenase. If these data prove to be true, calmodulin can be clearly related to insulin action. However, the definitive experiments remain to be accomplished.

C. R. Kahn: The second part was related to any estimation of the amount of saturation of the calcium binding under normal physiologic conditions and its variability.

A. R. Means: In general the free concentration of calcium in cells differs about 2 orders of magnitude from a baseline of about 10^{-7} to about 10^{-5} *M* under stimulated conditions. The minimal concentration of calmodulin in a cell is 10^{-6} *M*, so in theory all of the calcium should be bound in an unstimulated cell. Upon stimulation, 1 μM calmodulin could bind 4 μM calcium. The possibility exists that at least in the resting cell there may be very little free ionic calcium. One of the problems is that you can't really measure the calcium in cells very well except in the giant amoeba which is large enough to be sampled with a calcium electrode. Lansing Taylor has done some of these experiments. An interesting point comes from evaluation experiments I discussed concerning calmodulin using calcium-EGTA buffer systems to determine how many calcium ions are required in order to stimulate the activity of a specific enzyme. For instance, in order for calmodulin to stimulate phosphoesterase only 1 calcium is needed that can be bound to any one of the 4 equivalent sites. The microtubule effect requires all 4 sites to be filled. Thus the fractional occupancy of Ca^{2+}-binding sites on calmodulin may dictate various physiological roles. Moreover, phenothiozines block calmodulin stimulation of phosphodiesterase but not microtubule depolymerization. Thus, there may be multiple ways for calmodulin to function. On the one hand, it may be via a conformational change resulting in a protein–protein interaction whereas on the other hand, it may deliver calcium more effectively to a particular structure.

S. Cohen: My questions is somewhat based on that asked by Dr. Adlercreutz but it's a little more generalized—is the formation of calmodulin in any way influenced by the levels of calcium, magnesium phosphorus or any other mineral in the stimulation of tissue?

A. R. Means: It's a very good question, and I don't think that's really been evaluated. Your question would be if you load a cell with calcium is the synthesis of calmodulin elevated? I don't believe anyone had done such studies. They would be good ones to do.

H.-C. Blossey: One other question concerning the protein of 200,000 molecular weight to the membrane. As there are many genetic similarities between bacteria and mitochondria, might it be that this protein is a candidate of the rare mitochondrial proteins coded by mitochondrial DNA?

A. R. Means: Anything is possible.

C. Monder: I'd like to ask two questions. One is related to Dr. Cohen's question about the effect of calcium on the level of calmodulin in the cell. One way to test this would be to look at bone cells: osteocytes, osteoblasts, or osteoclasts. Has this been done and if so, what were the results.

A. R. Means: To my knowledge, such experiments have not been completed. However, there are three groups to whom we have provided both calmodulin and antibody that work in this area. I know experiments are underway but I have no idea of any results at the moment.

C. Monder: Is there any indication that trimethyllysine serves a specific function in the calmodulin molecule?

A. R. Means: I guess the answer to that has to be no at the moment. When you isolate the protein from the tissue it's impossible with present technology to separate trimethylated from nontrimethylated forms. One approach to the problem has been taken by M. Watterson and colleagues at Rockefeller (*P.N.A.S.* **77,** 1912, 1980). These authors have shown that calmodulin synthesized in a cell-free protein translation system from spinach poly(A) does not contain trimethyllysine. Large amounts of protein cannot be prepared in this manner. However, it should be possible to determine whether trimethylation is important for Ca^{2+} binding or interaction with calmodulin-dependent enzymes.

C. Monder: Is trimethyllysine unique to calmodulin or is it found in other protein molecules?

A. R. Means: As I think I mentioned it's a very rare modification. Finn Wold at Minnesota who is an expert in posttranslational modifications of proteins believes that the trimethylation preserves the positive charge on the E-amino group because there is no known enzyme that will reverse the reaction. Kim and Paik have shown yeast and plant cytochrome c to be trimethylated and suggest it is important for the interaction of this protein with cytochrome oxidase. I know of no other protein in animal cells that has been shown to be trimethylated but that does not mean that there aren't some.

T. Fujii: I would like to report that a hypocalcemic state produced by parathyroidectomy causes a marked alteration in the testicular function in rats. Bilateral parathyroid glands were removed surgically at 4 weeks of age and serum testosterone was determined at 7 weeks and 3 months of age using radioimmunoassay. The serum testosterone levels in parathyroidectomized rats showed a marked decrease as compared with those in normal controls at the ages examined. Serum LH levels in these parathyroidectomized rats were also lower than those seen in normal controls, while serum FSH did not show any significant change. When parathyroidectomy was performed at 3 months of age, serum testosterone level tended to decrease 3 months later but it was not statistically significant.

Although the serum FSH levels did not show any significant change following parathyroidectomy, the histological appearance of the testicular tissue of the parathyroidectomized rats operated at 4 weeks of age demonstrated a marked alteration. The slide shows a transverse section of a testis from a parathyroidectomized rat sacrificed at 3 months of age. We can see degenerative features of the seminiferous epithelium. No sperms and very few spermatocytes are demonstrated in some seminiferous tubuli, though many seminiferous tubuli are life intact.

We are interested in the content and biological activities of calmodulin in the testis under the hypocalcemic condition induced by parathyroidectomy.

A. Amsterdam: If phenothiazines are found to prevent a specific hormone-dependent event, is it safe to presume that event is calmodulin-dependent?

A. R. Means: The interaction of the phenothiazines with calmodulin is absolutely dependent upon calcium. This is why people began to think that they could use these compounds as pharmacologic tools to investigate calmodulin action. The problem is that the binding of calcium to calmodulin produces a conformational change exposing a highly lipophilic surface. It is this surface that interacts with the drugs. Troponin C also binds Ca^{2+} and undergoes conformational changes but no lipophilic surface is exposed. Therefore, troponin C does not bind phenothiazines. Thus, troponin C will not mimic the action of calmodulin that require this hydrophobic region such as stimulation of phosphodiesterase or myosin light chain kinase. However, phenothiazines do not affect the effect of calmodulin on microtubules *in vitro*. In this case the effect can be mimicked by troponin C implying that the hydrophobic surface of camodulin is not required for this interaction.

A. Amsterdam: I would like to ask whether calmodulin binds to 6 S tubulin?

A. R. Means: Calmodulin does not bind to 6 S tubulin, under any circumstances that we or several other laboratories have been able to evaluate. There's no interaction so it's likely that calmodulin is binding to one of the microtubular associated proteins (maps). When people isolate microtubular protein containing tubulin and associated protein there's very little evidence for the true nature of the so-called maps, except in brain where clearly there are two large molecular weight proteins that are always present. These map proteins are present from nonbrain tissue when microtubules are isolated. Almost every enzyme you can think of is associated with microtubules when they're prepared by the polymerization depolymerization cycle method. One finds Ca^{2+}-protein kinase, phosphodiesterase, protein kinase inhibitor, cyclic nucleotide-dependent protein kinase, magnesium calcium ATPase, and Margolis and Wilson have even reported adenyl cyclase to be present (*Cell,* 1980). I think from *in vitro* experiments it's extremely difficult to extrapolate because we really don't know whether these are specific or nonspecific components. We should also remember that indirect immunofluorescent microscopy is a reasonably crude technique. We can only demonstrate localization when the calmodulin concentration is sufficiently high to allow resolution at light microscopic level. As you saw from the interphase cells we see microfilament localization by light microscopy whereas by electron microscopy the distribution is markedly different. I would like to think that the reason that calmodulin appears to be present in the mitotic spindle is because that's where the membranes are. Plant cells have no centrioles but still have spindles. Moreover, plants still show a similar calmodulin distribution to that of animal cells. Peter Hepler (*J. Cell Biol.,* 1980) has shown that the localization of smooth membrane structures during plant mitosis is similar to that of calmodulin. So my hypothesis would be that calmodulin in this system may be regulating the calcium concentration in the microenvironment of the spindle. Thus, the localization data may not indicate a direct interaction of calmodulin with the microtubules per se but possibly with membranous structures that are juxtaposed to the tubules.

H. G. M. Raj: You showed that the relatively short-term effects of administering FSH did not change calmodulin levels in Sertoli cells; do you expect chronic effects of FSH would involve any change?

A. R. Means: They do not, either in hypophysectomized adult animals or in immature animals where FSH has been administered *in vivo* (Beale *et al., Endocrinology* **101,** 1634, 1977).

A. M. Spiegel: I wonder if we could pursue the question of the mechanism of calmodulin interaction with so many different enzymes and protein effectors—specifically with regard to adenyl cyclase that you mentioned. Is it known with what component of the cyclase system calmodulin interacts—do you believe that this interaction is limited to brain cyclase, or do you think that it's more general than that?

A. R. Means: I'm always a little reluctant to comment on this point because, in my opinion, cyclic nucleotide metabolism is going to be a very minor role for calmodulin in many eukaryotic cells. There are, for example, many phosphodiesterases that require calcium but do not require calmodulin such as that present in the Sertoli cell of the testes. In the cyclase system the studies are to my mind, less clear than any of the other proposed roles for calmodulin that have been described. Jim Potter (*J.B.C.* **255,** 4176, 1980) maintains even that the decreased activity of cyclase found in many tissues in response to calcium is a calmodulin-modulated event. So I don't know whether it's going to be important in general or not. I think there are a lot of cyclase activities that are not modulated by calmodulin or by calcium. Certainly there's no evidence that I'm aware of concerning which component of the brain cyclase is regulated by calmodulin.

Current Status of Thymosin and Other Hormones of the Thymus Gland[1,2]

ALLAN L. GOLDSTEIN, TERESA L. K. LOW, GARY B. THURMAN, MARION M. ZATZ, NICHOLAS HALL, JIEPING CHEN, SHU-KUANG HU, PAUL B. NAYLOR,* AND JOHN E. MCCLURE

*Department of Biochemistry, The George Washington University School of Medicine and Health Science, Washington, D.C., and *Department of Biological Chemistry, Harvard University Medical School, Boston, Massachusetts*

I. Introduction

It has been 10 years since our initial Laurentian Hormone Conference presentation documenting the endocrine role of the thymus gland (Goldstein *et al.*, 1970a). At that time, we reported that an acetone powder extract of calf thymus termed "thymosin fraction 3" could stimulate lymphocytopoiesis, prevent wasting, and reconstitute immune function in neonatally thymectomized mice. We hypothesized that the thymus regulated lymphoid tissue growth and function via an endocrine mechanism and proposed a potentially important role for thymic hormones in the treatment of diseases associated with immunodeficiencies. We also indicated that determination of the number of hormones secreted by the thymus would have to await the purification and chemical characterization of the biologically active molecules in the thymic preparations under investigation.

In the time that has elapsed since that report, it has been firmly established that the endocrine thymus, as illustrated in Fig. 1, produces a family of hormonal-like peptides which controls development of the thymic-dependent lymphoid system and participates in the process of immune regulation.

In this article, we will focus on the current status of the chemistry, biology, and clinical applications of the well-defined thymic hormones.

[1] Supported in part by grants from the National Institutes of Health, CA 24974 and AG 01531, and from Hoffmann-La Roche, Inc.

[2] This paper is dedicated to the memory of Dr. Abraham White, an extraordinary scientist and teacher whose inspiring leadership helped guide the development of the new field of thymic endocrinology.

ISBN 0-12-571137-9

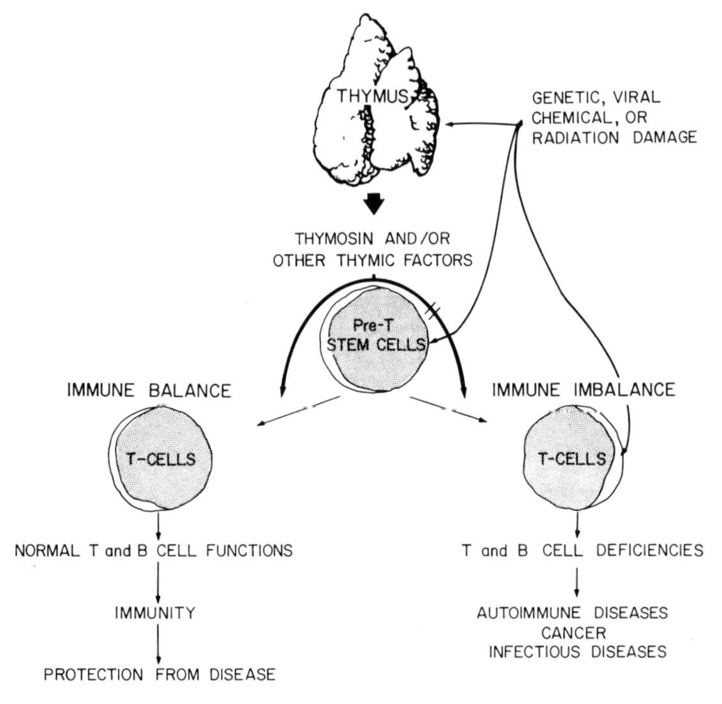

FIG. 1. Role of the endocrine thymus in immune regulation.

We will not attempt to review the extensive historical literature of the thymus, but refer you to our paper in the 1970 Proceedings of these meetings (Goldstein *et al.*, 1970a) and other comprehensive review articles (Friedman, 1975; Trainin, 1974; White and Goldstein, 1974; Bach and Carnaud, 1976; Bach, 1977, 1979; Goldstein *et al.*, 1978; Low and Goldstein, 1978; Trivers and Goldstein, 1980; White, 1980), which document the development of modern approaches toward understanding the cellular and endocrine roles of the thymus gland.

II. Chemistry of the Thymosins and Other Thymic Hormones

A. PURIFICATION AND CHEMICAL CHARACTERIZATION OF THYMOSIN AND ITS COMPOSITE PEPTIDES

The presence of a lymphopoietic factor in rat and mouse thymus extracts was first described in our laboratory by Klein *et al.* (1965, 1966). Later, a biologically active fraction was prepared from calf thymus which was termed thymosin (Goldstein *et al.*, 1966). In 1975, a standardized fraction termed thymosin fraction 5 was prepared in larger quantities for clinical trials (Hooper *et al.*, 1975). Thymosin fraction 5 has been the parent preparation used for the further purification and characterization of most of the hormonal-like peptides that have been isolated from the thymus to date. Several other laboratories have now reported the isolation of biologically active fractions from thymus tissue using isolation procedures similar to those described for thymosin fraction 5 (Aleksandrowicz *et al.*, 1975; Skotnicki, 1978; Falchetti *et al.*, 1977; Aiuti *et al.*, 1979; Jin *et al.*, 1979; Liu *et al.*, 1978; Liu, 1979).

B. ISOLATION PROCEDURE FOR THYMOSIN FRACTION 5

Thymosin fraction 5 is prepared from calf thymus, as described by Hooper *et al.* (1975). The thymus tissue is homogenized and centrifuged. The supernatant is filtered through glass wool. The filtrate is then processed through an 80°C heat step, an acetone precipitation step, and an ammonium sulfate precipitation step. The 25–50% ammonium sulfate precipitate is further subjected to ultrafiltration in Amicon DC-2 hollow fiber system and desalted on Sephadex G-25 column to yield fraction 5.

C. NOMENCLATURE AND ISOELECTRIC POINTS OF THE THYMOSIN POLYPEPTIDES AND OTHER PURIFIED THYMIC PEPTIDES

Analytical isoelectric focusing of thymosin fraction 5 has revealed the presence of a number of components in the preparation. A nomenclature, based on the isoelectric focusing pattern of thymosin fraction 5 in the pH range of 3.5–9.5, has been described (Klein *et al.*, 1966) and is illustrated in Fig. 2. The separated polypeptides are divided into three regions: The α region consists of polypeptides with isoelectric points below 5.0; the β region 5.0–7.0; and the γ region above 7.0. The subscript numbers α_1, α_2, β_1, β_2, etc. are used to identify the polypeptides from each region as they are isolated. The purified polypeptides are tested in various assay systems to study their biological efficacy, and the active polypeptides are then given the prefix "thymosin"; the components which are inactive and are believed not to be involved specifically in controlling T-cell maturation and function are given the prefix "polypeptide." For comparative purposes, the location of FTS, thymopoietin, and THF on the gel and their isoelectric points are shown. It has been reported that trace amounts of FTS (Dardenne *et al.*, 1980) and thymopoietin (Gershwin *et al.*, 1979) are found in thymosin fraction 5. In the case of FTS, we have indeed found

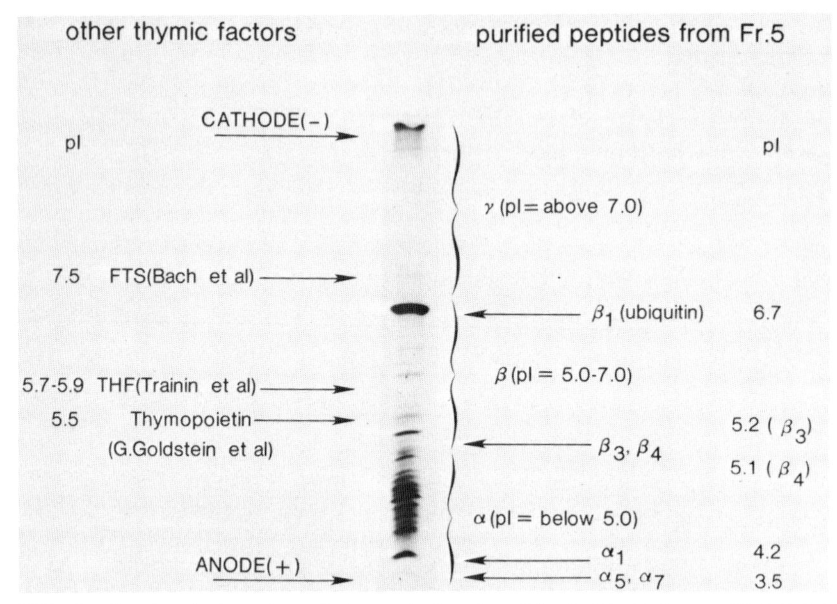

FIG. 2. Isoelectric focusing of thymosin fraction 5 in LKB PAG_{plate} (pH 3.5–9.5). Purified thymosin peptides from the α, β, and γ regions are identified. The isoelectric points of several other well-characterized thymic factors are illustrated for comparison.

that there is a trace amount of FTS-like material in thymosin fraction 5 as measured by RIA. However, the levels are about the same as those found in fraction 5 preparations of calf spleen, liver, or kidney.

D. PURIFICATION AND CHARACTERIZATION OF THE COMPONENT PEPTIDES IN FRACTION 5

Twenty of the 40 to 50 peptide components of fraction 5 have been purified to homogeneity or near homogeneity. Three of these peptides, thymosin α_1 (Goldstein *et al.*, 1977; Low *et al.*, 1979; Low and Goldstein, 1979), thymosin β_4 (Low *et al.*, 1980), and polypeptide β_1 (Low *et al.*, 1979; Low and Goldstein, 1979) have been fully characterized and sequenced.

Thymosin α_1, α_7, β_3, and β_4 are four of the component peptides of thymosin fraction 5 with biological activity in modulating immunological responses *in vitro* and *in vivo,* and in regulating the differentiation of thymic-dependent lymphocytes. Polypeptide β_1 has been found to be homologous with ubiquitin (Goldstein *et al.*, 1978) and the N-terminal 74 amino acids of A-24, a nonhistone chromosomal protein (Hunt, 1977). We have found this peptide to be inactive in bioassays reflective of thymic hormone activity (Low *et al.*, 1979). Most recently Wilkinson *et al.* (1980) have shown the β_1 peptide to be homologous with AFP, an ATP-dependent coupling factor involved in proteolysis. This observation of a general role for the β_1 peptide may account for its ubiquitous distribution.

E. THYMOSIN α_1

The first biologically active polypeptide to be isolated from among the highly acidic components of bovine thymosin fraction 5 has been termed thymosin α_1 (Goldstein *et al.*, 1977). This peptide is highly active in amplifying T-cell immunity (Low *et al.*, 1979; Ahmed, 1979) and is active in modulating the expression of terminal deoxynucleotidyl transferase (TdT) (Hu *et al.*, 1980a). Thymosin α_1 was isolated from fraction 5 by ion-exchange chromatography on CM-cellulose and DEAE-cellulose, as well as by gel filtration on Sephadex G-75. The yield of thymosin α_1 from fraction 5 is about 0.6%. Thymosin α_1 is a polypeptide with a molecular weight of 3108 consisting of 28 amino acid residues and a p*I* of 4.2. The complete amino acid sequence of this peptide is shown in Fig. 3. The amino terminus of thymosin α_1 is blocked by an acetyl group.

Comparison of the sequence of thymosin α_1 with the published sequence of other thymic factors (Fig. 3), such as thymopoietin II (Schlesinger and Goldstein, 1975) and facteur thymique serique (FTS) (Pleau *et al.*, 1977) reveals no homology. Computer analysis of the sequence of α_1 has established that α_1 contains very little homology with any of the protein sequences that have been published to date (Low and Goldstein, 1979).

Thymosin α_1 has been chemically synthesized by several laboratories, including Wang *et al.* (1978) and Birr and Stollenwerk (1979) using solution synthesis procedures, and Folkers (1979), Wang *et al.* (1980), and Wong and Merrifield (1980) using solid phase procedures. The synthetic material prepared by Wang *et al.* (1978) has been tested in our laboratories and has been found to have activities similar to the natural α_1.

Studies by Freire *et al.* (1978) suggest that thymosin α_1 is produced in the thymus as part of a larger protein. These investigators have translated messenger RNA isolated from calf thymus and carried out synthesis studies in cell-free wheat germ system. Radioactive products that were immunoprecipitable with antisera against thymosin fractions were analyzed and found to be identical to those expected for tryptic peptides from thymosin α_1. Most recently, Freire *et al.* (1981) have been able to purify the mRNA fraction from calf thymus polysomes by preparative polyacrylamide disc electrophoresis.

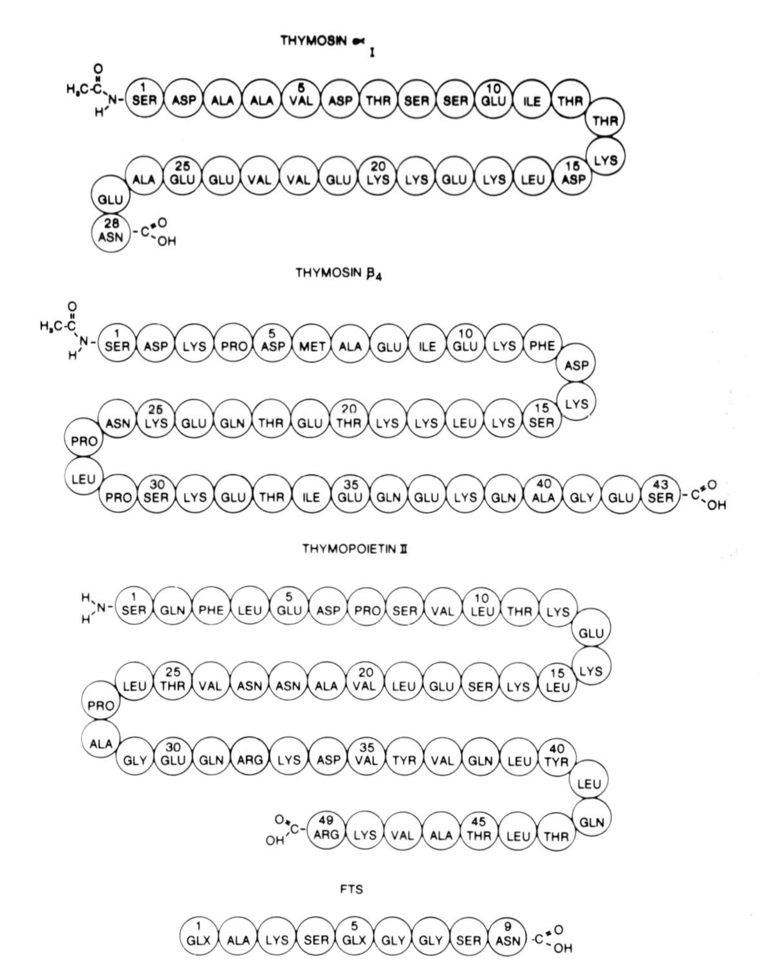

FIG. 3. Sequence analysis of well-characterized thymic hormones: Thymosin α_1, thymosin β_4, thymopoietin II, and facteur thymique serique (FTS).

The results of these studies suggest that thymosin α_1 is synthesized in the thymus as a longer peptide chain of 16,000 daltons and may be further processed (or degraded) to form the peptide detected in preparations isolated from the thymus.

Recently, Wetzel *et al.* (1980) have reported the isolation and complete chemical characterization of a N^{α}-desacetyl thymosin α_1 utilizing recombinant DNA procedures. In this important new development, the gene for thymosin α_1 (shown in Fig. 4) was synthesized, inserted into a plasmid, and cloned in a strain of *E. coli,* as illustrated in Fig. 5. The primary

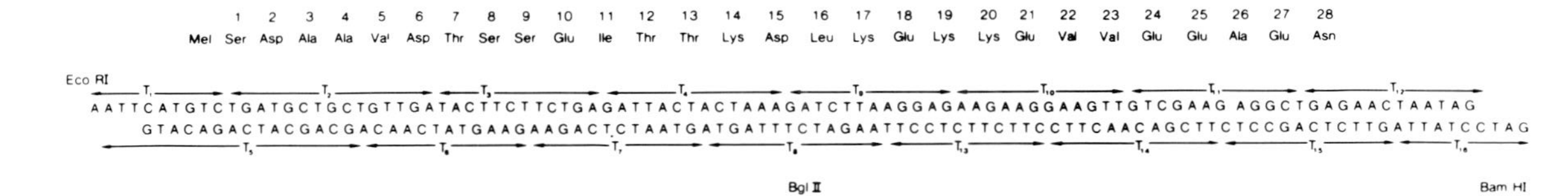

FIG. 4. Design of the gene for thymosin α_1.

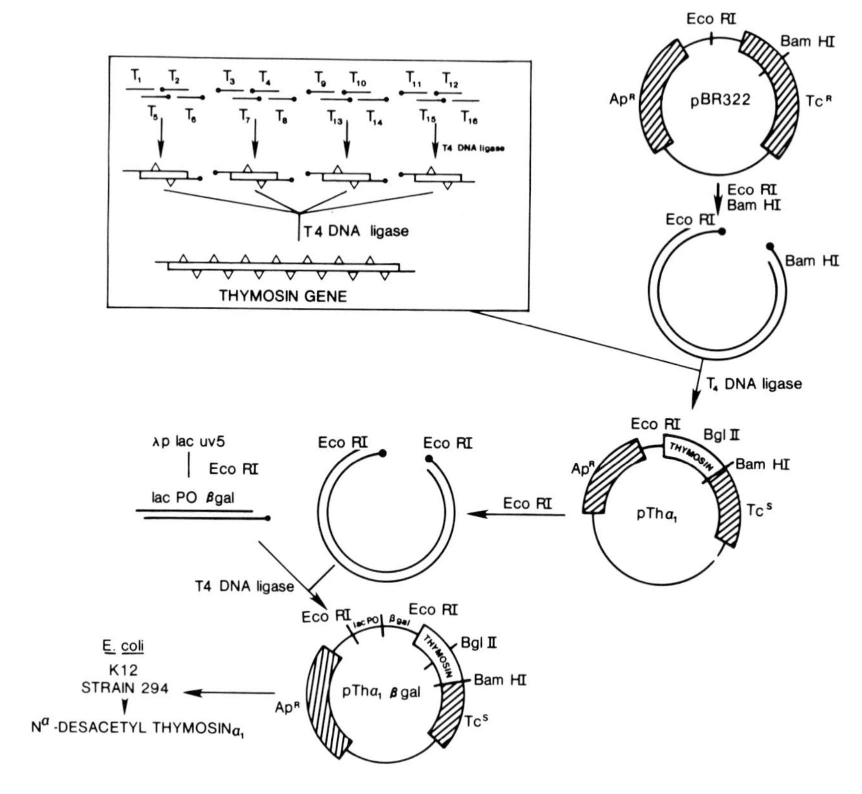

FIG. 5. Construction of the gene and plasmid for N^{α}-desacetyl thymosin α_1. The primary sequence of the gene was accomplished using preferred prokaryotic codons with elimination of codons with multiple specificity and minimization of AT or GC regions. The gene was ligated into plasmids and placed under *lac* operon control and expressed as part of a β-galactosidase chimeric protein.

nucleotide sequence required for the gene was constructed using prepared prokaryotic codons with elimination of codons of multiple specificities and minimization of AT and GC-rich regions. In cloning the α_1 gene, the gene was inserted under *lac* operon control into the plasmid and expressed as part of a β-galactosidase chimeric protein. The structure of the N^{α}-desacetyl thymosin α_1 was confirmed by sequence analysis and, as indicated in Tables I and II, the molecule was found to be as biologically active *in vitro* as the chemically synthesized thymosin α_1. A method for aminoacetylation of the N^{α}-desacetyl thymosin α_1 has been reported by Kido *et al.* (1981) using a transacetylase associated with a wheat germ ribosomal preparation.

TABLE I

Reconstitution of MIF Production in PBLs of TX Guinea Pigs by N^{α}-Desacetyl Thymosin α_1

Preparation	Concentration (μg/ml)	Percentage specific inhibition (MIF production)			
		Exp 1	Exp 2	Exp 3	Exp 4
Thymosin	200	24.7	29.1	28.9	38.9
Fraction 5	20	14.1	19.5	15.9	12.5
(Lot C 100496)	2	9.5	12.1	15.5	1.7
Thymosin α_1	1	52.3	46.8	48.4	59.1
Chemically	0.1	34.6	37.3	39.7	51.4
Synthesized	0.01	11.0	27.2	25.5	33.4
	0.001	N.T.	N.T.	10.6	7.8
N^{α}-Desacetyl Thymosin α_1	1	50.8	48.2	53.2	39.7
From transformed *E. coli*	0.1	29.4	33.3	34.4	32.2
	0.01	27.5	27.6	16.0	23.5
	0.001	N.T.	N.T.	8.6	14.4
No thymosin, PPD only		4.7	−3.4	5.0	5.0

F. THYMOSIN β_4

Thymosin β_4 is the first of the biologically active polypeptides from the β region of thymosin fraction 5 to be completely characterized (Low *et al.*, 1981). Thymosin β_4 was isolated by ion-exchange chromatography on a column of carboxymethyl-cellulose (CM-52) in 10 m*M* NaOAC, 1 m*M* 2-mercaptoethanol, pH 5.0. Two stepwise linear gradients of 0–0.5 *M* NaCl and 0.5–1.0 *M* NaCl were used for the elution. Thymosin β_4 was derived from the second retained peak of the carboxymethyl-cellulose

TABLE II

Suppression of TdT Activity by Chemically Synthesized and E. coli N^{α}-Desacetyl Thymosin α_1 in Murine C57BL/6J Thymocytes[a]

	Concentration (μg/ml)	Percentage decrease[b]
Thymosin α_1	0.02	20
(Chemically synthesized)	0.2	62
	0.4	23
N^{α}-Desacetyl thymosin α_1	0.02	8
(From *E. coli*)	0.2	55
	0.4	34

[a] Cells are incubated with thymosin for 20 hours at 37°C in HRPMI and 10% FCS.

[b] TdT activity relative to cell cultures without thymosin.

column. It was further purified by gel filtration on Sephadex G-50 in 6 *M* guanidinium–HCl. The third protein peak was pooled and desalted on a Sephadex G-10 column in sterile water. The purified sample so obtained is identified as thymosin β_4. The complete sequence of β_4 is shown in Fig. 3. Thymosin β_4 is composed of 43 amino acid residues and has a molecular weight of 4982 and p*I* of 5.1. The N-terminal end of the peptide is blocked by an acetyl group.

This molecule induces TdT expression in TdT-negative murine bone marrow cells *in vivo* and *in vitro*. It also increases TdT activity in thymocytes from hydrocortisone immunosuppressed mice *in vivo*. Thus, it appears that thymosin β_4 is acting on lymphoid stem cells and may influence the early stages of the maturation process of thymus-dependent lymphocytes.

A computer search for possible sequence homology between the sequence of thymosin β_4 and other published protein sequences has been conducted (personal communication through the National Biomedical Research Foundation, Georgetown University Medical Center, Washington, D.C. 20007). The results do not indicate a statistically significant relationship of thymosin β_4 to any other sequenced protein currently stored in the data bank. However, there is an interesting internal duplication between residues 18 to 30 and 31 to 43 as illustrated in Fig. 6.

G. THYMOSIN β_3

Thymosin β_3 is isolated from fraction 5 and 5A by ion-exchange chromatography and gel filtration (Low and Goldstein, unpublished). Like β_4, it induces the expression of TdT-positive cells in several different model systems. Thymosin β_3 has an isoelectric point of 5.2 and a molecular weight of approximately 5500. Thymosin β_3 shares an identical sequence with β_4 through most of its amino-terminal portion and differs only at the carboxyl-terminal ends. Its complete sequence has not been determined.

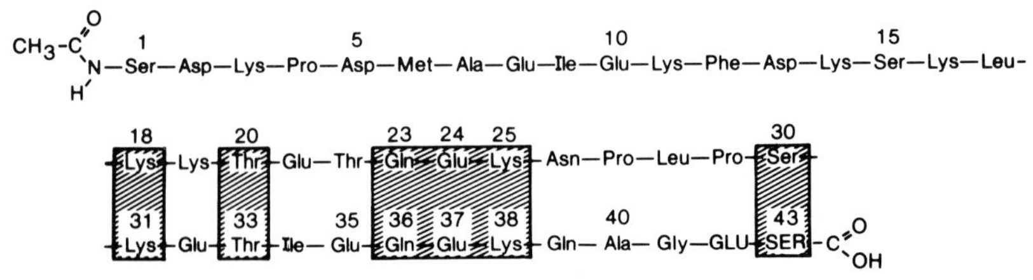

FIG. 6. Regions of internal duplication of thymosin β_4.

H. THYMOSIN α_7

Thymosin α_7 has been isolated from fraction 5 by ion-exchange chromatography on CM-cellulose and DEAE-cellulose and by gel filtration on Sephadex G-75 (Low and Goldstein, unpublished). It is highly acidic with an isoelectric point around 3.5, and is free of carbohydrate and lipid. Thymosin α_7 has a molecular weight of approximately 2200. Thymosin α_7 has been found to be a potent inducer of suppressor cells (S. Horowitz, personal communication) and is also active in inducing T-cell markers (Ahmed, 1979).

I. OTHER THYMIC HORMONES

The thymus appears to synthesize and secrete several biochemically distinct hormone-like products. In addition to the thymosins, a number of factors with thymic hormone-like activity have been isolated from thymus tissue and blood. These preparations, as listed in Table III, are in various stages of characterization and include: thymosin fraction 5, thymopoietin II (TP), thymic humoral factor (THF), facteur thymique serique (FTS), and thymic factor X (TFX). As shown in Fig. 3, the four thymic hormones that have been sequenced to date (thymosin α_1, MW 3108; thymosin β_4, MW 4982; thymopoietin II, MW 5562; and FTS, MW 857) appear to be chemically unrelated.

The demonstration that several different agents are produced by the thymus immediately raises the question of whether a single thymic hormone can elicit all of the potential biological functions of the thymus gland, or whether each hormone acts to regulate selective aspects of T-cell differentiation. This last possibility would not only explain the diverse nature of the products that have been reported with thymic hormone-like activity, but would also have significance in the development of more precise application of these substances for the amelioration of various types of impaired immunological states.

III. Biology of the Thymosins

A. EXPERIMENTAL STUDIES IN ANIMAL MODELS

Partially purified thymosin preparations and purified thymosin polypeptides have been found to be effective in regulating immune function in a variety of animal models (Goldstein *et al.*, 1970a, 1978; White and Goldstein, 1974; Low and Goldstein, 1978; Trivers and Goldstein, 1980; White,

TABLE III

Thymic Preparations and Their Biological Effects

Thymic preparations	Principal references	Chemical properties	Biological effects
From Thymus Tissue			
Thymosin fraction 5	Hooper *et al.* (1975); Goldstein *et al.* (1975)	Family of heat stable, acidic polypeptides, MW 1000–15,000	Induces T-cell differentiation, and enhances immunological function in animal models and in humans
Thymosin α_1	Goldstein *et al.* (1977); Low *et al.* (1979); Low and Goldstein (1979)	Polypeptide of 28 residues MW 3108, p*I* 4.2, sequence determined	Increases mitogenic responsiveness of murine lymphocytes; induces enhancement of MIF production; increases Thy 1.2 and Lyt 1,2,3 positive cells and helper T cells; modulates TdT activity
Thymosin β_4	Low *et al.* (1981)	Polypeptide of 43 residues, MW 4982, p*I* 5.1, sequence determined	Induces TdT *in vivo* and *in vitro* in bone marrow cells from normal and athymic mice; *in vivo* induction of TdT in thymocytes of immunosuppressed mice
Thymosin α_7	Low *et al.* (in preparation); Ahmed *et al.* (1979)	Acidic polypeptide, MW 2500, p*I* 3.5	*In vitro* enhancement of suppressor T cells; expression of Lyt 1,2,3 positive cells
Thymic humoral factor (THF)	Trainin *et al.* (1975)	Polypeptide of MW 3200, p*I* 5.7, amino acid composition determined	Restoration of ability of spleen cells from neonatally thymectomized donors to induce an *in vivo* graft vs host reaction; enhancement of ability of normal spleen cells to respond to PHA and Con A
Thymopoietin	Schlesinger and Goldstein (1975)	Polypeptide of 49 residues, MW 5562, p*I* 5.7, sequence determined	Causes delayed impairment of neuromuscular transmission *in vivo;* induces bone marrow cells to develop into intrathymic lymphocytes

Thymic factor X (TFX)	Aleksandrowicz and Skotnicki (1976)	Polypeptide, MW 4200, amino acid composition reported	*In vitro* restoration of the azathioprine sensitivity of spleen rosette-forming cells from adult thymectomized mice; *in vivo* increase in blood T-cell number and return of delayed hypersensitivity
Thymostimulin (TS)	Falchetti *et al.* (1977)	Mixture of polypeptides	Induces markers and specific functions of T lymphocytes both in immunosuppressed animals and in immunodeficient patients; stimulates interferon production in mice following challenge with poly(I) : poly(C)
Porcine thymic preparation	Jin *et al.* (1979)	Mixture of polypeptides, MW 9000–68,000 p*I* 5.0–7.5	Increases rosette formation in fetal thymocytes
Bovine thymic preparation	Liu *et al.* (1979)	Mixture of polypeptides	Increases rosette formation in umbilical cord blood lymphocytes
Homeostatic thymic hormone (HTH)	Comsa (1973)	Glycopeptide, MW 1800–2500	Suppression of deleterious consequences of thymectomy in young guinea pigs; restoration of delayed hypersensitivity of thymectomized rats
Lymphocytopoietic factors (LSH_h and LSH_r)	Luckey *et al.* (1973)	Polypeptides, MW 8000 (LSH_r) and 15,000 (LSH_h); an amino acid composition of LSH_r is available	Enhances antibody production to sheep erythrocytes and induces a lymphocytosis
Hypocalcemic and lymphocytopoietic substances (TP_1 and TP_2)	Mizutani *et al.* (1973)	Polypeptides	Enhances production of antibody to sheep erythrocytes in neonatal mice; hypocalcemic activity in normal rabbits
Thymic polypeptide preparation (TP)	Milcu and Potop (1973)	Mixture of polypeptides and amino acids	Elevation of serum calcium concentration and decrease in serum inorganic phosphate; stimulation of antibody synthesis in immunized X-ray irradiated rabbits

(*Continued*)

TABLE III (*Continued*)

Thymic preparations	Principal references	Chemical properties	Biological effects
Thymosterin	Potop and Milcu (1973)	Lipids or lipoproteins, one purified component termed IIB_3 is C_{28} steroid with methyl groups at C-21 and C-28	Antiproliferative action on KB tumor cells in culture; repairs the specifically altered metabolism of normal or thymectomized tumor-bearing animals
From Blood			
Facteur thymique serique (FTS)	Dardenne *et al.* (1977); Pleau *et al.* (1977)	Nonapeptide, MW 857, p*I* 7.5, sequence determined	Enhancement of generation of effector cytotoxic T cells both *in vitro* and *in vivo;* inhibition of contact sensitivity in normal mice
Protein fraction from human plasma	Burton *et al.* (1978); White *et al.* (1980)	Protein, MW 57,700; properties analogous to prealbumin	Enhanced ability of neonatally thymectomized mice to reject an allogeneic skin graft, enhanced MLR of mouse spleen cells incubated with the blood fraction
Human serum factor (SF)	Astaldi *et al.* (1977)	Adenosine (possibly other small molecular weight components)	Increases the intracellular cyclic AMP level of human and mouse thymocytes; increases the population of hydrocortisone-resistant cells
From Thymic Epithelial Supernatants			
Thymic epithelial supernatant (TES)	Kruisbeck *et al.* (1978)	Crude extract, chemical nature not characterized	Augmented the proliferative responses of rat thymocytes to PHA or Con A; stimulated mixed lymphocyte reactivity and antibody production to sheep erythrocytes by spleen cells from nude mice
Human thymic epithelial medium (HTEM)	Kater *et al.* (1979)	Crude extract, chemical nature not clear	Augmented mitogen responses of thymocytes

1980). Table III summarizes the major biological properties of thymosin. Thymosin treatment has been shown to increase the survival of neonatally thymectomized mice (Asanuma *et al.*, 1970; Goldstein *et al.*, 1972), accelerate skin graft rejection (Hardy *et al.*, 1968, 1972; Goldstein *et al.*, 1970a), restore graft vs host reactivity (Law *et al.*, 1968), and accelerate development of immune functions in newborn mice (Asanuma *et al.*, 1970; Goldstein *et al.*, 1972; Law *et al.*, 1968) and reconstitution of suppressor T-cells in adult thymectomized mice (Asherson *et al.*, 1976). Thymosin affects the responsiveness of lymphocytes from nude (Ahmed *et al.*, 1977, 1978), normal (Thurman *et al.*, 1975; Scheid *et al.*, 1973), and tumor-bearing mice and rats (Zisblatt *et al.*, 1970), and causes immature lymphoid cells to acquire distinctive T-cell surface antigens (Scheid *et al.*, 1973; Ahmed *et al.*, 1978a,b; Cohen *et al.*, 1975).

Several animal models have been utilized to assess the influence of thymosin administration on immune perturbations associated with old age and autoimmune disorders. Thymosin treatment of NZB mice reconstituted suppressor cell and other T-cell functions and temporarily induced remissions in the autoimmune disease which these animals develop (Gershwin *et al.*, 1974; Talal *et al.*, 1975; Dauphinee *et al.*, 1974). Administration of thymosin to casein-treated mice reduced the incidence of amyloidosis (Scheinberg *et al.*, 1976b). In aged mice, thymosin administration *in vivo* has been found to significantly increase hemagglutinin responses against sheep RBCs (Strausser *et al.*, 1971), antihapten responses to TNP (D'Agostaro *et al.*, 1980), and delayed hypersensitivity responses to oxazolone (Bruley-Rosset, 1979). *In vitro* thymosin has been found to correct the cell cycle of lymphocytes from aging thymectomized rats (Dabrowski and Goldstein, 1976).

Recent experimental approaches utilizing thymosin peptides have shown their effectiveness in inducing the differentiation of specific subclasses of T lymphocytes (killer, helper, and suppressor cells) (Goldstein *et al.*, 1978; Ahmed, 1979; Marshall *et al.*, 1980, and unpublished observations) and have shown that specific thymosin peptides isolated from thymosin fraction 5 can induce the expression of certain T-cell markers (TdT, Thy-1, and Lyt) and functional activity associated with lymphocyte maturation (Ahmed, 1979; Scheid *et al.*, 1973; Ahmed *et al.*, 1978a,b; Pazmino *et al.*, 1978a; Hu *et al.*, 1979; Goldschneider *et al.*, 1980). For example, thymosin fraction 5 and thymosin β_3 and β_4 have been shown to induce TdT activity *in vitro* and *in vivo* in precursor cells from normal and nude mice (Pazmino *et al.*, 1978a; Hu *et al.*, 1979). Most recently, as shown in Table IV, we have found that thymosin fraction 5 and thymosin β_4, given *in vivo*, significantly accelerate the recovery of cell numbers and TdT positive cells in the involuted thymus of steroid treated mice. We

TABLE IV
In Vivo Induction of TdT by Thymosin in Hydrocortisone Acetate (HCA)-Treated C57BL/6J Mice

Agent[a]	Dose[b] (μg)	Enzyme unit[c]	Percentage increase
Control saline	—	17.99	—
Spleen fraction	100	15.88	0
Thymosin fraction 5	100	28.54	58.6
Thymosin β_4	1	28.07	56.0
Spleen β_4-like peptide[d]	1	19.81	10.1

[a] Mice (8/group) were treated with 1.25 mg HCA followed by daily injection of various agents for 11 days and sacrificed on day 12.
[b] Amount used per injection.
[c] TdT unit is expressed as nmoles dGTP/10^8 cells/hour.
[d] Isolated from spleen fraction 5.

have also observed, as shown in Table V, that thymosin fraction 5, when given daily for 14 days (100 μg/day) *in vivo,* increases the number of cells in the thymus and glucocorticoid binding sites on thymocytes from steroid suppressed mice. In contrast, as shown in Table VI, incubation of thymocytes *in vitro* with thymosin fraction 5 decreases the number of glucocorticoid receptors. This latter observation is in agreement with the report of Osheroff (1980) and points to a direct role for thymosin in inducing the maturation of steroid-sensitive immature T cells. However, thymosin α_1, a potent inducer of helper T cells (Goldstein *et al.,* 1977; Ahmed, 1979), decreases TdT expression in thymocytes *in vitro* when used at low concentrations (Table I and Wetzel *et al.,* 1980; Hu *et al.,* 1980), as shown in Table VII, and induces TdT expression when used at high concentrations (Goldschneider *et al.,* 1981). These results suggest that the individual thymosin polypeptides probably act at different steps in promoting the differentiation of precursor cells into functionally mature thymocytes. The thymosin peptides β_3 and β_4 appear to act both before and at the prothymocyte state, whereas α_1 appears to act at both early and late stages of thymocyte maturation. The present working model for the proposed role of the various polypeptides in T-cell maturation is shown in Fig. 7.

B. RADIOIMMUNOASSAY FOR THYMOSIN α_1

We have recently succeeded in developing a radioimmunoassay (RIA) for thymosin α_1 (McClure *et al.,* 1981). Antiserum to synthetic thymosin α_1 was produced in rabbits by immunization with the synthetic peptide

TABLE V

In Vivo Induction of Glucocorticoid Receptors by Thymosin in Hydrocortisone Acetate (HCA)-Treated BALB/c Mice

Treatment	Number of animals	Cells/thymus	Glucocorticoid receptors	
			cpm/10^7 cells	fmoles/10^6 cells
Normal[a]	15	73.3×10^6	1719	5.83
HCA + saline[b] (6 days)	14	13.6×10^6	1747	5.93
HCA + thymosin fraction 5[b] (6 days)	14	16.5×10^6	1722	5.84
Normal[a]	15	41.9×10^6	1919	6.56
HCA + saline[b] (14 days)	12	19.8×10^6	2326	7.26
HCA + thymosin fraction 5[b] (14 days)	12	34.7×10^6	2676	8.33

[a] Normal mice (not treated with HCA, saline, or thymosin) were housed in the animal room for the same number of days as saline or thymosin-treated groups.

[b] Animals were injected with 1.25 mg HCA, followed by daily injection of saline or 100 μg thymosin fraction 5 (intraperitoneally) for 6 or 14 days. The animals were sacrificed 24 hours after the last injection, thymus glands removed, and glucocorticoid receptors determined.

TABLE VI

In Vitro Modulation of Glucocorticoid Receptors by Thymosin in Murine Thymocytes[a]

Thymosin fraction 5 added (μg/ml)	Total binding (cpm/2 × 10^7 cells)	Nonspecific binding (cpm/2 × 10^7 cells)	Specific binding[b] (cpm/2 × 10^7 cells)	Glucocorticoid receptors (fmole/10^6 cells)	Percentage decrease
—	1574	321	1253	4.24	—
0.02	1569	337	1232	4.17	1.6
0.2	1256	218	1038	3.51	17.2
2.0	1026	322	704	2.38	43.8
20.0	926	245	681	2.31	45.5

[a] Thymus glands from 20 5-week-old BALB/c male mice were used. Cells were incubated with thymosin fraction 5 for 23 hours at 37°C. Levels of glucocorticoid receptors were determined by binding with [^{3}H]dexamethasone.

[b] Specific binding = total binding − nonspecific binding.

TABLE VII

Induction of Terminal Transferase in nu/+ C57BL/6 Mouse Spleen and Bone Marrow Cells[a]

Cell source	Fraction (%)[b]	Percentage TdT cells after incubation with (mean SE)[c]		
		Spleen fraction 5[d]	Thymosin fraction 5[d]	Thymosin α_1[e]
Spleen	A 9	0.4 ± 0.3	9.4 ± 2.6	8.1 ± 1.2
	B 16	0.5 ± 0.2	6.3 ± 0.8	6.8 ± 1.0
	C 53	0.2 ± 0.1	0.3 ± 0.1	0.2 ± 0.2
	D 22	0.1 ± 0.1	0.0 ± 0.0	0.2 ± 0.2
	Unfractionated	0.3 ± 0.2	2.3 ± 0.1	2.0 ± 0.3
Bone marrow	A 17	3.8 ± 1.3	11.5 ± 0.8	5.4 ± 1.6
	B 48	3.6 ± 0.2	9.5 ± 2.1	7.8 ± 2.6
	C 15	1.6 ± 0.9	4.4 ± 1.9	4.4 ± 2.3
	D 19	2.2 ± 1.2	2.4 ± 1.4	2.8 ± 1.6
	Unfractionated	3.3 ± 0.4	8.0 ± 0.2	6.0 ± 2.2

[a] Determined by indirect immunofluorescence for TdT.

[b] Cells separated by albumin density gradient centrifugation. Numbers indicate mean percentage of total nucleated cells recovered per fraction. Fraction A, least dense cells; fraction D, most dense cells.

[c] Mean of 3 experiments; 500–1000 cells counter per point per experiment. Similar results were obtained with spleen fraction 5-treated and untreated control suspensions.

[d] 10 μg of thymosin fraction 5 or spleen fraction 5/2 × 10^6 cells/ml.

[e] 1 μg of thymosin fraction 5 or spleen fraction 5/2 × 10^6 cells/ml.

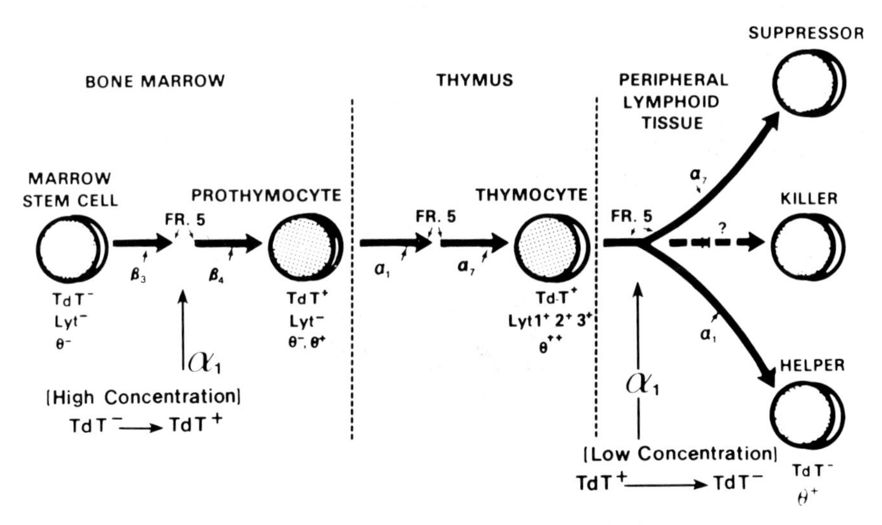

FIG. 7. Proposed role of thymosin peptides in T-cell maturation. β_3 and β_4 promote early stem cell differentiation to the prothymocyte stage. α_1 promotes both early and late steps of T-cell differentiation. α_7 is associated with the generation of functionally mature suppressor T cells and α_1 with the generation of helper T cells.

coupled to hemocyanin by means of glutaraldehyde and was used in the RIA without purification at final dilutions between 1 : 10,000 and 1 : 20,000. Labeled thymosin α_1 of high specific activity (approximately 300 μCi/μg) was purified by gel filtrations on Sephadex G-10 and G-50 and found to retain immunoreactive integrity as assessed by incubation with excess antibody. The assay conditions included incubation of standard or unknown samples with antiserum in phosphate-buffered saline for 1 hour, addition of radioactive thymosin α_1, and successive incubations at 37°C (1 hour) and 4°C (48 hours). A second antibody (goat anti-rabbit γ-globulins) was used to precipitate the immune complexes formed during competitive binding. By using the highly purified synthetic thymosin α_1 standard, a calibration curve was generated which had a minimal detectable dose of 30–50 pg and an ED_{50} (50% response) of 150–400 pg. Measurements of the radioactivity bound in the immunoprecipitate were reduced by a four-parameter logistics computer program to a graph of counts bound at defined dose divided by counts bound at zero dose ($B_i/B_0 \times 100$) vs $\log_{10}$ dose of peptide.

Using the RIA, we have found a high degree of homology and immunological cross-reactivity in all species of thymosin α_1 examined, including man, cattle, sheep, mouse, rat, and guinea pig. In man, thymosin α_1 concentrations are highest in the fetal circulation (2–4 ng/ml) and, as seen in Fig. 8, decline significantly with age. In mice, thymosin α_1 levels appear to be maximal between 10 and 18 days of age and also decrease significantly with age. Blood samples obtained at midnight were 2–3 times higher than those obtained at midday, suggesting a diurnal rhythm. Preliminary studies in genetically athymic (nu/nu) BALB/c mice indicate that absence of the thymus is associated with significantly lower thymosin α_1 levels compared to normal littermates. The RIA studies indicate that thymosin α_1 levels decrease with age and may reflect the capacity of the thymus to regulate immune balance.

C. LOCALIZATION OF THYMOSIN α_1, β_3, AND β_4 IN THYMIC EPITHELIAL CELLS

Using indirect immunofluorescence, Hirokawa *et al.* (1980) have studied the site of synthesis and localization of thymosin α_1 and thymosin β_3 and β_4 in thymus glands of human individuals ranging in age from newborn to 62 years. As shown in Figs. 9 to 13, thymosin α_1 was detected specifically in thymic epithelial cells of the medulla and in cells covering the cortical surface. Thymosin β_3 and β_4 was detected almost exclusively in cells covering the cortical surface. Hirokawa *et al.* (1980) have found that epithelial cells in the medulla, which were positive for thymosin α_1,

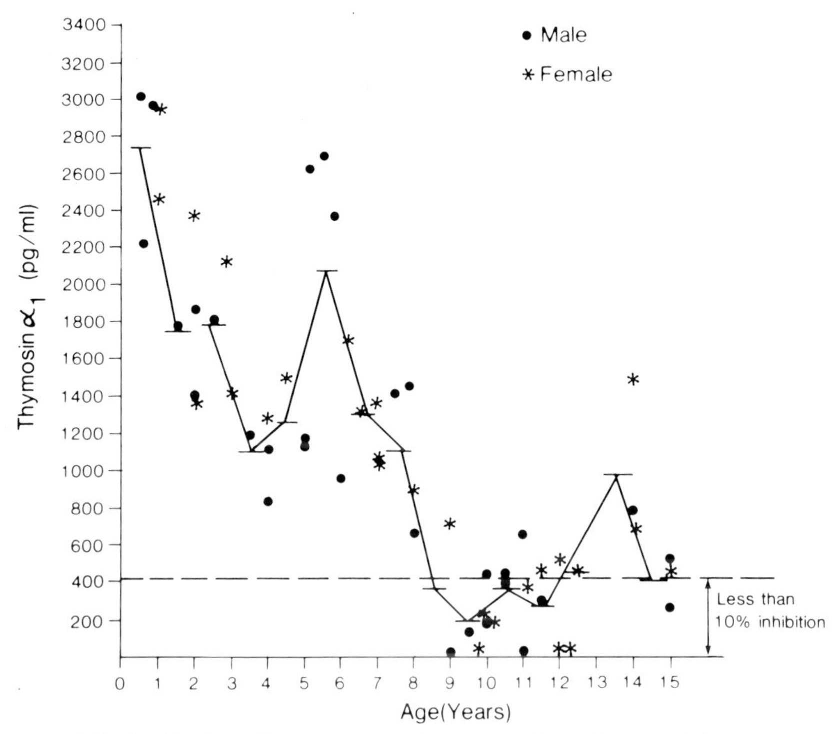

FIG. 8. Decline with age in serum thymosin α_1 levels in normal children.

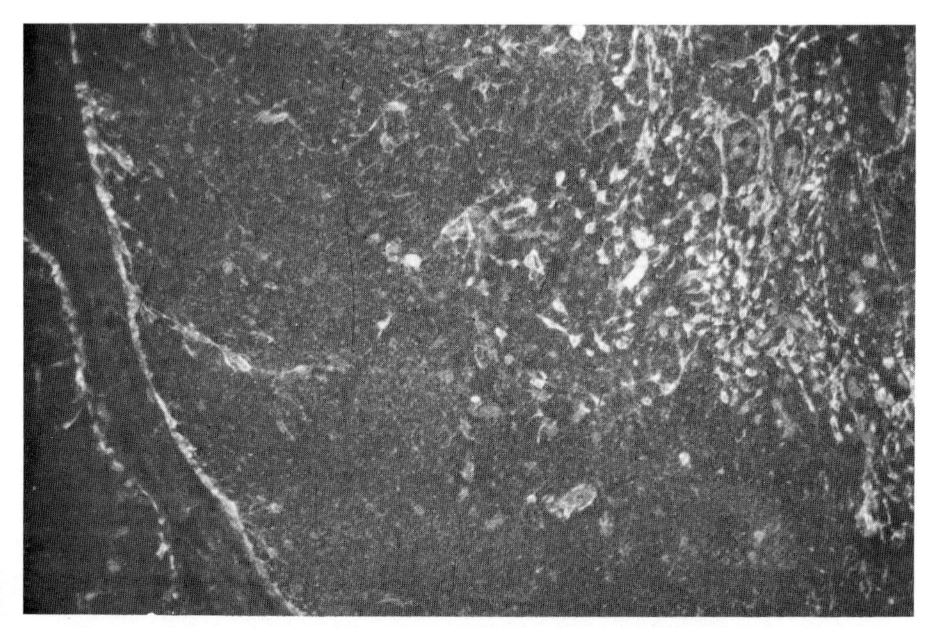

FIG. 9. Localization of thymosin α_1 in the thymus obtained from a 2-year-old male. Positive cells are present in the medulla and in the superficial layer of the cortex.

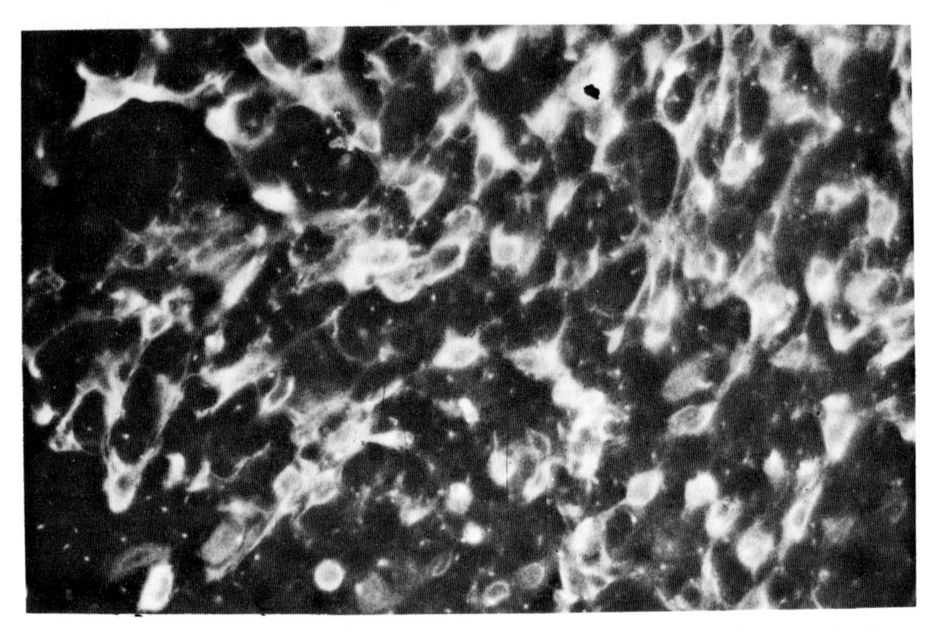

FIG. 10. Higher magnification of the medulla in Fig. 9. Thymosin α_1 is present in the cytoplasm of thymic epithelial cells which are interconnected with each other by long cytoplasmic processes. A distinct border is formed around the vascular area by the lining of positive epithelial cells.

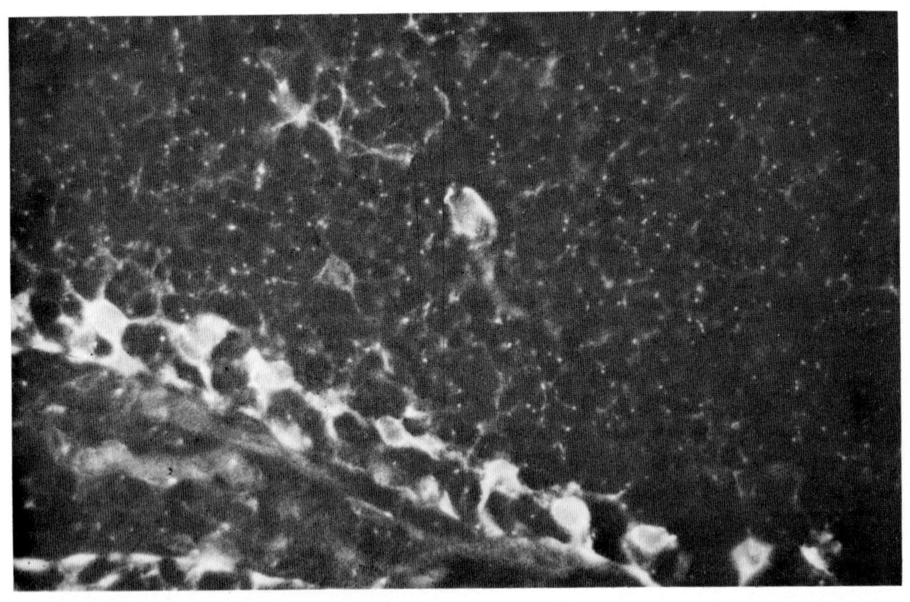

FIG. 11. Higher magnification of the cortex in Fig. 9. Thymosin α_1 is also present in long cytoplasmic processes between unstained thymocytes in the cortex.

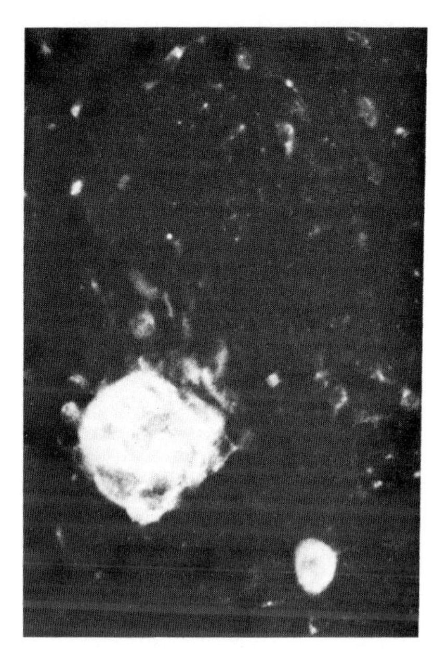
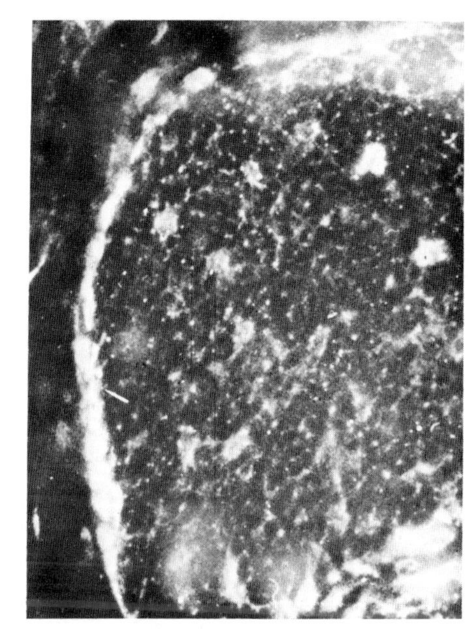

FIG. 12. Localization of thymosin β_3 in the thymus. Positive cells are present in the superficial layer of the cortex but almost none in the medulla.

progressively decreased in number with age, beginning at around 13 years. The anti-β_3 serum cross-reacts to a great extent with thymosin β_4.

These studies confirm the earlier reports of Kater *et al.* (1979) and Van den Tweel (1979) of the epithelial origin of thymosin α_1, and indicate a further segregation of thymosin peptide production within the thymus, which may be related to the individual peptides' roles in T-cell differentiation. It is interesting to note that thymosin β_3 was almost exclusively present in the cells covering the cortical surface. This finding is compatible with the known biological activity of thymosin β_3 in induction of TdT expression and the fact that TdT-positive cells are predominant in the thymic cortex. Similarly, thymosin α_1-producing cells are found in the thymic medulla where the cells are predominantly TdT negative, and thymosin α_1 at physiological concentrations is associated primarily with the suppression of TdT expression on thymocytes (Hu *et al.,* 1980a,b).

D. REGULATION OF THE THYMUS BY THE CENTRAL NERVOUS SYSTEM

Successful orchestration of the diverse and specialized facets of host defense depends upon the central nervous system and a balanced endo-

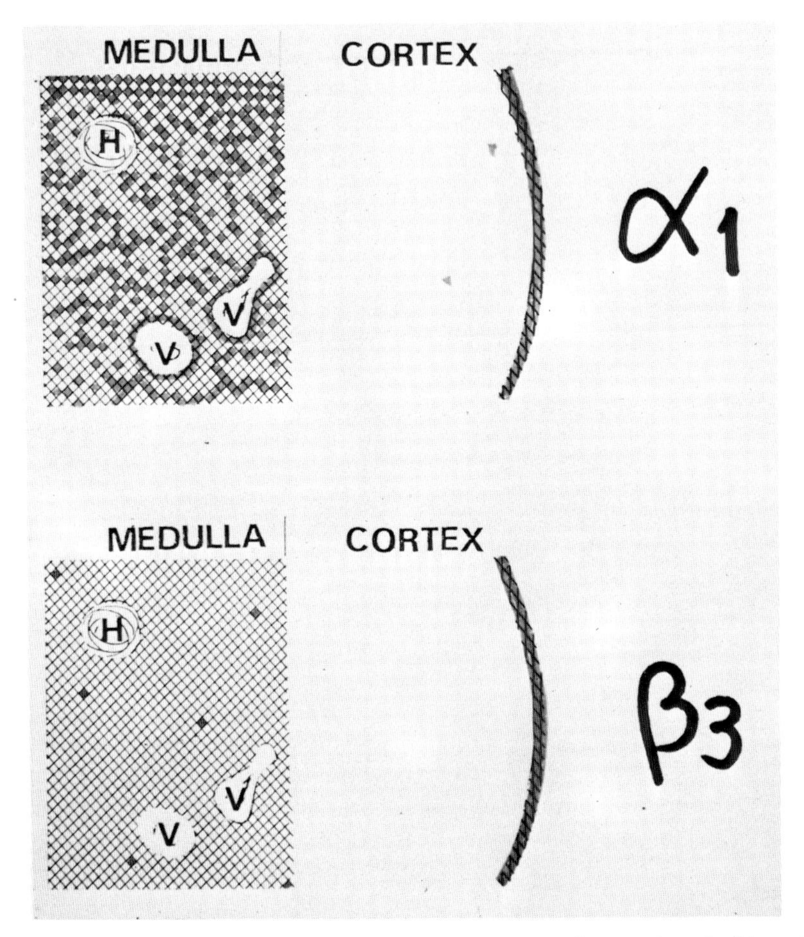

FIG. 13. Schematic presentation of thymosin α_1 and thymosin β_3 and β_4. Positive cells are indicated as black points. Thymosin α_1-positive cells are present in both medulla and superficial cortex, but thymosin β_3 positive cells are present almost exclusively in the superficial cortex. H, Hassall's corpuscle; V, vascular area.

crine environment. Several recent articles have reviewed the evidence implicating both autonomic and neuroendocrine output channels in modulating the immune system (Spector, 1980; Hall, 1980; Hall and Goldstein, 1980; Stein *et al.*, 1980). This article will summarize those data that implicate the endocrine thymus as being part of a central nervous system–immune system axis.

Figure 14 illustrates the manner by which the central nervous system might influence the endocrine thymus. Neural innervation of the thymus is suggested by neuroanatomic and pharmacologic evidence. Injection of

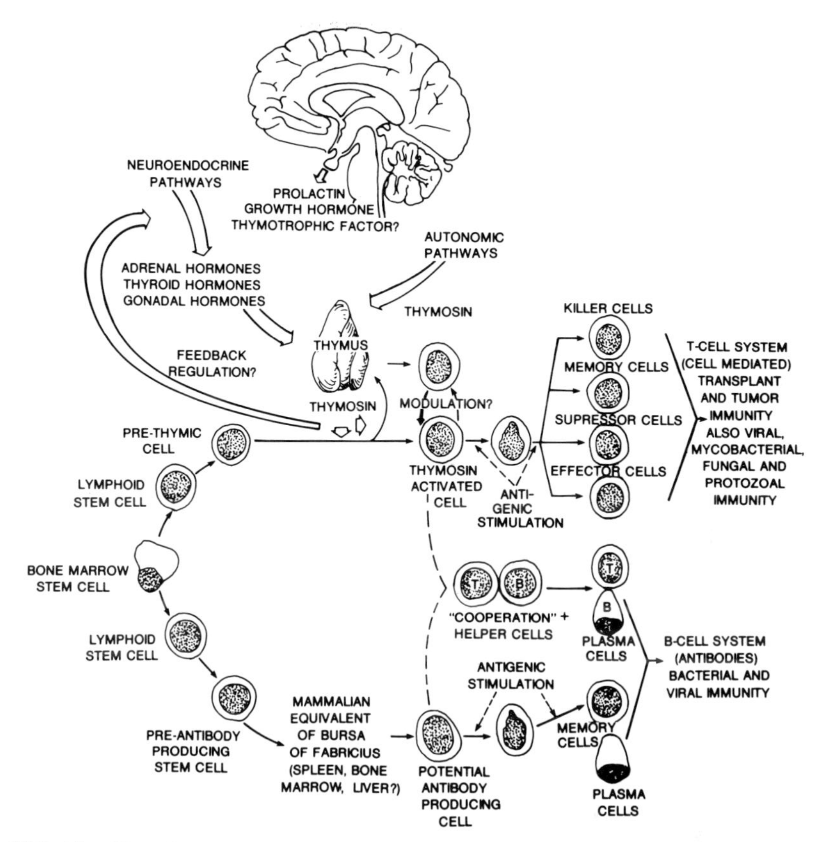

FIG. 14. Hypothetical model illustrating the major interactions between the central nervous system and the neuroendocrine thymus.

horseradish peroxidase into the thymus of both rats and mice has been found to result in reaction products in neurons of the nucleus ambiguus, as well as in anterior horn cells of the cervical spinal cord (Bulloch and Moore, 1980; Kearns and Hall, unpublished observations). The presence of cholinergic receptors on the surface of thymosin-producing epithelial cells (Engel *et al.*, 1977) and of both cholinergic and β-adrenergic receptors on the surface of T lymphocytes (Bourne *et al.*, 1974; Fuchs *et al.*, 1980) raises the distinct possibility that both cell types can be influenced by neurotransmitters. A modulatory role for catecholamines is suggested by pharmacologic evidence. Depletion of synaptic vesicle catecholamines, using the drug 6-hydroxydopamine, has been correlated with profound alterations of thymic-dependent immunity. Antibody titers to sheep red blood cells are significantly depressed (Kasahara *et al.*, 1977), and thymocyte TdT levels are significantly elevated (Hall *et al.*, 1980).

Preliminary evidence from our laboratory indicates that serum levels of thymosin α_1 are also altered following chemical sympathectomy.

In addition to cholinergic and catecholaminergic influences upon the endocrine thymus, there is also evidence of a possible GABAergic influence. Detectable levels of GABA have been found in the thymus, but the role, if any, that this neurotransmitter might play in the ontogeny of the immune response is not known. A significant change in thymic levels of GABA has been detected during the course of the primary immune response to a T-dependent antigen (Hall *et al.*, in preparation).

Evidence that the CNS is able to modulate the immune system through a neuroendocrine output channel is considerable and has been reviewed elsewhere (White and Goldstein, 1972; Ahlquist, 1980). The possibility that various hormones are able to directly influence thymosin production has to be considered as part of the neuroendocrine–immune axis. Growth hormone has recently been found to result in a several fold increase in serum levels of thymosin α_1 when given to growth hormone deficient patients (D. W. Wara, personal communication). Interactions between thymosin peptides and other hormonal systems must also be considered.

No direct evidence has been obtained to implicate thymic hormones in the feedback control of immunity at the level of the CNS. Nonetheless, preliminary evidence from our laboratory does not preclude the existence of such a regulatory mechanism. Thymosin α_1 can be detected in homogenized brain tissue and CSF by RIA and radiolabeled thymosin α_1 is able to accumulate in discrete subcortical brain regions. Investigations are being conducted to determine if specific receptors are present in the CNS for thymosin peptides and the effect that intracerebral thymic hormones have upon thymic-dependent immunity.

E. MECHANISM OF ACTION OF THYMIC HORMONES

As illustrated in Fig. 15, a second messenger mechanism for thymic hormone-mediated lymphocyte maturation has been demonstrated both by pharmacological manipulation and direct measurement of cyclic nucleotides and calcium (Naylor, 1979). One of the earliest detectable effects of thymosin fraction 5 on thymocytes is to increase their intracellular cGMP levels (Naylor *et al.*, 1976). Using an acetylation RIA procedure to measure cGMP (Harper and Brooker, 1975), stimulation of cGMP can be seen as early as 1 minute after *in vitro* incubation with thymosin, and is maximal between 5 and 10 minutes. Thymosin causes an influx of calcium into thymocytes, consistent with the fact that the increase in cGMP is calcium dependent (Naylor *et al.*, 1979). No stimulatory effect of thymosin on cAMP levels has been observed.

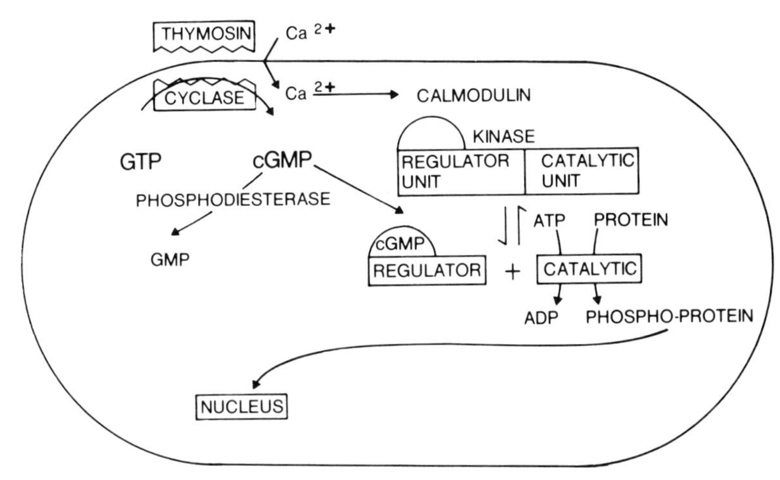

FIG. 15. Mechanism of action of thymosin.

These observations are consistent with the hypothesis that a calcium-dependent increase in cGMP mediates the maturation and activation of more mature or "committed" lymphocytes in the thymus and spleen (Fig. 15). Whether the calcium influx acts directly on the cyclase or phosphodiesterase or via a calcium-binding protein (calmodulin) is not known. Also, the mechanism through which the increases in cGMP and intracellular calcium mediate lymphocyte maturation remains to be determined. Consistent with this hypothesis is the evidence that cAMP increases may be involved in earlier commitment steps, while cGMP and calcium mediate the later stages of differentiation (Naylor, 1979). In contrast to our findings with thymosin fraction 5, Kook and Trainin (1974) using THF, and Scheid *et al.* (1975) using thymopoietin, have reported that these thymic factors increase cAMP levels.

These studies suggest that both cGMP and cAMP may be important secondary messengers for specific T-cell responses. It is an anomaly that thymosin does not stimulate cAMP directly. Yet, cAMP can mimic thymosin in some *in vitro* systems, e.g., the induction of spontaneous rosette-forming cells in the adult thymectomized mouse spleen (Bach *et al.,* 1971b), the appearance of TL and Thy-1 antigens (Ag) in pre-T-cell enriched bone marrow (Scheid *et al.,* 1975), the induction of differentiation of human E-rosette forming cells, phytohemagglutinin, and mixed lymphocyte culture responses (Kaplan and Peterson, 1978), and the differentiation of null cells (Low and Goldstein, 1978). In addition, studies by Astaldi *et al.* (1978) have shown that thymosin can induce a factor in the serum of immunodeficient patients which can stimulate cAMP production in mouse thymocytes; however, thymosin does not have this effect directly.

The complexity of the events involved in the maturation of stem cells to functional T lymphocytes is just beginning to be appreciated. Certainly studies linking cyclic nucleotide levels with T-cell differentiation under the influence of the endocrine thymus are providing significant input into the eventual deciphering of the puzzle. Especially important will be studies utilizing purified thymus peptides and well-characterized lymphocyte subpopulations. In light of our studies suggesting a calcium dependence of the cGMP response of lymphocytes to thymosin (Naylor *et al.*, 1979), calcium-binding proteins become likely candidates for playing key roles in the mechanism of activation of T cells.

IV. Clinical Trials

A. *IN VITRO* STUDIES

Several studies have documented that the *in vitro* incubation of thymosin with peripheral blood lymphocytes (PBL) from patients with certain primary or secondary immune deficiencies results in a significant enhancement of T-cell number and function. Thymosin-induced augmentation of E-rosette forming cells (E-RFC) has proven to be a useful diagnostic assay for identifying patients who may respond to thymosin therapy *in vivo* based on their capacity to respond to thymosin *in vitro*. Thymosin increases both the percentage and absolute number of E-rosettes, formed by PBL from patients with primary immunodeficiencies (Hirokawa *et al.*, 1980; Goldstein *et al.*, 1975, 1976; Rossio and Goldstein, 1977; Goldstein and Rossio, 1978; Wara and Ammann, 1978; Astaldi *et al.*, 1978; Barrett *et al.*, 1980; Wara *et al.*, 1980; Sharp and Peterson, 1978; Ammann *et al.*, 1978; Rubenstein *et al.*, 1979), cancer (Costanzi *et al.*, 1977, 1978; Cohen *et al.*, 1979; Lipson *et al.*, 1979; Chretien *et al.*, 1978; Schafer *et al.*, 1976), allergies (Byrom *et al.*, 1978a), asthma (Byrom *et al.*, 1978b), severe burns (Ishizawa *et al.*, 1978), viral infections (Scheinberg *et al.*, 1976a), liver disease (Mutchnick and Goldstein, 1979), tuberculosis (Vladiminsky *et al.*, 1978), Kwashiorkor (Olusi *et al.*, 1980), systematic lupus erythematosus, and rheumatoid arthritis (Scheinberg, 1975; Moutsopoulos *et al.*, 1976; Lavastida, 1978) and in aged normal individuals (Rovensky *et al.*, 1977). Thymosin α_1 is up to 100 times as active as fraction 5 in increasing the percentage and the absolute numbers of T-cell rosettes (Goldstein *et al.*, 1977; Thurman *et al.*, 1979). Thymosin does not exhibit a marked effect on E-RFC of most normal individuals or of patients with initial T-cell levels within the normal range (Rossio and Goldstein, 1977). In a study of 388 patients with head and neck, mediastinal, and pelvic malignancies, and of 277 normal adults, the *in vitro* response to thymosin correlated inversely with initial T-cell levels for each group, including the normal individuals (Kenady *et al.*, 1977). Following radiation therapy, PBL from patients with mediastinal malignancies exhibited the most significant increase in E-RFC following thymosin injection. It was suggested that mediastinal radiation had resulted in specific impairment of thymus gland function in such individuals, thus leading to greater numbers of circulating thymosin-sensitive precursor cells (Kenady *et al.*, 1977).

In normal adults, putative stem cells express E-rosette receptors following incubation with thymosin fraction 5 (Horowitz and Goldstein, 1978). Peripheral blood null lymphoid cells isolated by bovine serum albumin density gradients (Kaplan, 1978) or by nylon column filtration and E-rosette depletion (Kaplan and Peterson, 1978) can be induced to form E-RFC after *in vitro* exposure to thymosin. No changes in B cells, monocytes, or in Fc or C_3 receptor-bearing cells could be documented. Therefore, thymosin appears to act selectively on T-cell precursors. The thymosin-induced T cells exhibit enhanced responsiveness to phytohemagglutinin (PHA) and to allogeneic cells (MLC) (Horowitz and Goldstein, 1978). It is noteworthy that PBL from patients with severe combined immunodeficiency diseases do not respond to thymosin *in vitro* (Maahinney *et al.*, 1979). Such patients are felt to lack a population of thymosin-responsive stem cells.

In vitro thymosin treatment has been shown to significantly alter the proportions of several different subsets of T cells in cancer patients. A subpopulation of human T cells, representing approximately 26% of the lymphocyte pool of healthy individuals, is able to bind autologous red blood cells and are called autologous rosette-forming cells (ARFC) (Caraux *et al.*, 1978). In cancer patients, this population of T cells is significantly reduced (Caraux *et al.*, 1979). Recently, it has been shown (Caraux *et al.*, 1980) that a short-term incubation with thymosin α_1 produced a significant and constant increase in ARFC percentages in cancer patients with solid tumors.

Lowell *et al.* (1980), using a solid phase radioimmunoassay to detect *in vitro* secretion by human peripheral blood lymphocytes (PBL) of IgG, IgM, and IgA directed against specific bacterial antigens have found that thymosin fraction 5 and thymosin α_1 stimulate secretion of antibacterial antibodies *in vitro*. When PBL obtained from individuals who had been immunized with tetanus toxoid (TT) vaccine were cultured with pokeweed mitogen (PWM), addition of either thymosin fraction 5 or synthetic thymosin α_1 markedly enhanced the secretion of specific anti-TT antibodies, anti-Mgc, and/or anti-GP antibodies. Similar results have been observed with group C meningicoccal polysaccharide (Mgc) and gonococcal pilus (GP) vaccines. The total amount of polyclonal antibody secreted, however, was not necessarily enhanced and was often suppressed. Thymosin also stimulated specific antibody secretion by PBL, which had been highly depleted of mature cells. These results support the concept that thymosin can potentiate the development of functional specific helper T cells among human PBL.

B. *IN VIVO* STUDIES

Most clinical studies of thymic preparations have been performed with bovine thymosin fraction 5 (Wara *et al.*, 1975, 1980; Goldstein *et al.*, 1975, 1976; Rossio and Goldstein, 1977; Goldstein and Rossio, 1978; Wara and Ammann, 1978; Astaldi *et al.*, 1978; Barrett *et al.*, 1980; Sharp and Peterson, 1978; Ammann *et al.*, 1978; Rubenstein *et al.*, 1979; Costanzi *et al.*, 1977, 1978; Cohen *et al.*, 1979; Lipson *et al.*, 1979; Chretien *et al.*, 1978; Schafer *et al.*, 1976), thymic humoral factor (Shohat *et al.*, 1978; Dolfin *et al.*, 1976; Handzel, 1977, 1978, 1979; Varsano, 1976, 1977), and several thymosin fraction 5-like preparations, such as thymostimulin (TS) (Aiuti *et al.*, 1979; Tovo *et al.*, 1980), porcine (Jin *et al.*, 1979), and bovine (Liu *et al.*, 1978; Liu, 1979), thymic preparations studied in China, and TFX (Aleksandrowicz *et al.*, 1975; Aleksandrowicz and Skotnicki, 1976). Thymosin fraction 5 has been utilized in the largest number of clinical trials to date. This fraction has been chosen for therapeutic studies because it contains a number of different biologically active polypeptides. It is also apparent that thymosin injections in man and animals result in detectable serum thymic hormone activity as measured in the assays of Bach (Bach *et al.*, 1977) and Astaldi *et al.* (1978) for FTS and SF, respectively.

Most of the reported thymic hormone trials in patients with a variety of disorders cannot be critically evaluated at present since either the number of treated patients with a clinical syndrome was too small to permit proper statistical analysis of the findings, or subjects receiving placebo were not included. Nonetheless, thymic hormone replacement therapy is proving to be of significant benefit in treating children with primary immunodeficiency diseases. In these patients, clinical trials with thymosin, now entering their seventh year, have resulted in significant improvements in T-cell numbers and function (Wara *et al.*, 1975, 1980; Goldstein *et al.*, 1975, 1976; Rossio and Goldstein, 1977; Goldstein and Rossio, 1978; Wara and Ammann, 1978; Astaldi *et al.*, 1978; Barrett *et al.*, 1980; Sharp and Peterson, 1978; Ammann *et al.*, 1978; Rubenstein *et al.*, 1979).

In cancer patients, phase I toxicity studies and a limited number of phase II trials in patients with advanced disease have been carried out over the past 5 years. Thymosin appears to be relatively nontoxic and to induce increased T-cell numbers and function. The recent positive phase II trials of Chretien and colleagues (Cohen *et al.*, 1979; Lipson *et al.*, 1979; Chretien *et al.*, 1978) in patients with oat cell carcinoma of the lung have provided the stimulus for further therapeutic investigations using thymosin and other thymic factors in cancer patients.

C. IMMUNODEFICIENCY PATIENTS

Over 80 children have received thymosin fraction 5 for a variety of primary immunodeficiency diseases (Wara *et al.*, 1975, 1980; Goldstein *et al.*, 1975, 1976; Rossio and Goldstein, 1977; Goldstein and Rossio, 1978; Wara and Ammann, 1978; Astaldi *et al.*, 1980; Sharp and Peterson, 1978; Ammann *et al.*, 1978). These patients have been treated with injections of thymosin up to 400 mg/m^2 for periods of over 6 years (usually daily for 2 to 4 weeks, then once per week). Most of the patients have received 60 mg/m^2 thymosin by subcutaneous injection. There has been no evidence of liver, kidney, or bone marrow toxicity in this group due to thymosin administration. There was a close correlation between the number of patients whose cells responded *in vitro* in the E-rosette assay and those patients who have also responded *in vivo* with increased absolute T-cell numbers and clinical improvement.

In a more recent study of 17 immunodeficient patients in whom other forms of therapy either were unsuccessful or could not be utilized, Wara and Amman (1978) have reported significant clinical improvement in patients treated with thymosin. The patients all had *in vitro* evidence of enhanced E-RFC percentages following incubation with thymosin fraction 5 and/or enhanced lymphocyte function as assayed in MLC.

In a follow-up report of the work of Barrett *et al.* (1980), Wara *et al.* (1980) have correlated in a group of 18 patients changes in MLC reactivity *in vivo* following thymosin therapy with pretherapy enhancement of MLC reactivity by *in vitro* thymosin incubation. In this retrospective analysis, they found that in those patients who had normal MLC reactivity after therapy, pretherapy lymphocyte incubation with thymosin *in vitro* had resulted in greater than 119% enhancement of MLC reactivity. Conversely, in those patients who did not develop normal MLC responses after therapy, pretherapy lymphocyte incubation with thymosin resulted in 7–99% enhancement of MLC reactivity. Wara *et al.* (1980) observed that if the criteria for a positive enhancement *in vitro* is greater than 100%, 6 of 8 patients' positive *in vitro* response correlated with subsequent response to therapy. Thus, it is possible that pretherapy augmentation of MLC with thymosin can be used as an indicator of the *in vivo* efficacy of thymosin to enhance T-cell function. A prospective study in larger numbers of patients is necessary to better define "significant" percentage enhancement of MLC reactivity with thymosin incubation.

In a subsequent study, Barrett *et al.* (1980) observed that T-cell numbers were increased to normal with thymosin *in vitro* in 3 of 5 DiGeorge patients. When thymosin was given *in vivo,* the same 3 patients responded by an improvement in T-cell numbers and function. Similarly, in a single case report, Sharp and Peterson reported a significant improvement of cellular immunity in a DiGeorge patient treated with thymosin fraction 5 (Sharp and Peterson, 1978).

In one patient with thymic hypoplasia and nucleoside phosphorylase deficiency who was treated for 9 months with thymosin at a dose of 1 mg/kg/week, Ammann *et al.* (1978) reported an increase in the percentage of E-rosettes and the total number of T cells and a return of the PHA and MLC response to greater than 50% of normal control values. However, with the development of systemic type 1 hypersensitivity reactions following thymosin administration, therapy was discontinued. Immunologic parameters returned to previous abnormally low values.

In a case report by Rubenstein *et al.* (1979) in a patient with adenosine deaminase deficiency and combined immunodeficiency, it was found that thymosin therapy improved the clinical course of the disease when given with red cell transfusions. The *in vivo* improvement in cell-mediated immunity correlated with the *in vitro* response to thymosin.

D. AUTOIMMUNE DISORDERS

Doctors Lavastida and Daniels (University of Texas Medical Branch, Galveston) have conducted a small phase I trial in patients with autoimmune disease. To date, six patients with autoimmune diseases have been treated with thymosin fraction 5 for periods ranging from 4 to 16 months (Lavastida, 1978). Five of the patients had systemic lupus erythematosus (SLE), and the sixth rheumatoid arthritis.

As indicated in Table VIII, while receiving thymosin, significant changes were seen in peripheral blood T-cell and null cell percentages. There was also a major decrease in a cytotoxic serum factor that causes the lysis of murine thymocytes in the presence of complement and is present in many patients with autoimmune diseases. Based on these encouraging findings, a phase II randomized trial is planned by Dr. Daniels to determine the efficacy of thymosin therapy in SLE.

TABLE VIII

Changes in Lymphocyte Subpopulations and Decreased Serum Cytotoxicity following in Vivo Administration of Thymosin in Patients with Autoimmune Diseases [a]

		Percentage T cells		Percentage Null cells		Percentage B cells		Percentage cytotoxicity[c]	
Disease[b]	Patient	Pre Rx	On Rx	Pre Rx	On Rx	Pre Rx	On Rx	Pre Rx	On Rx
S.L.E.	A.B.	31	67	58	9	11	24	27	0
S.L.E.	M.L.	49	51–71	N/D	0	N/D	29	10	0
S.L.E.	J.A.R.	24[d]	71	60[d]	12	16[d]	17	76	0
R.A. and S.S.	J.W.	45	68	17	0	38	33	57	0
S.L.E.	E.H.	37[d]	52–62	48[d]	36	15	12	18	0

[a] Lavastida *et al.* (1978).

[b] S.L.E., systemic lupus erythematosus; R.A., rheumatoid arthritis; S.S., Sjögrens syndrome.

[c] Normal values = 0 to 10%. Capacity of patients' serum to lyse murine thymocytes in the presence of complement.

[d] Early Rx.

Although the possible mechanism of immune reconstitution with thymosin fraction 5 in patients with SLE is not as yet defined, it may be related to induction of a subpopulation of thymosin-activated suppressor or regulator T cells. Such a population of cells can be induced, *in vitro,* by incubation of PBL from SLE patients with thymosin or cultured thymic epithelium (Horowitz *et al.,* 1977).

Recently, Dalakas *et al.* (1980), using antibodies against thymosin α_1 and an indirect immunofluorescence, compared normal thymus glands of human subjects of different ages with hyperplastic, thymomatous, or "involuted" thymus of patients with myasthenia gravis. Thymosin α_1 was localized only in the epithelial cells, lying singly or grouped at the periphery of Hassall's corpuscles, and such cells increased in numbers in thymomas. In contrast to normal thymuses, which had fewer and more weakly stained cells, thymuses from patients with myasthenia gravis had many strongly positive epithelial cells. The presence of these cells was markedly evident in thymomas. All thymic lymphocyte-containing areas, including germinal centers, were unstained. Atrophic "involuted" thymuses from older patients with myasthenia gravis had small islands of brightly stained epithelial cells lying within the fatty tissue.

Because there is evidence suggesting that thymosin α_1 can affect the early stages of T-lymphocyte maturation and influence the transformation of precursors to helper T lymphocytes, these findings raise the possibility that excess thymosin α_1 secretion may exacerbate myasthenia gravis by facilitating overproduction of helper T lymphocytes sensitized against nicotinic acetylcholine receptors (NAChR); such specifically sensitized-helper T lymphocytes would stimulate B lymphocytes to produce the specific anti-NAChR antibodies. This hypothesis is in accord with the observations in experimental myasthenia gravis, in which T lymphocytes sensitized to NAChR are demonstrable before the onset of symptoms and that the presence of helper T lymphocytes is required for development of the disease (Livingston, 1978). These findings may partially explain the beneficial effect of thymectomy in patients with myasthenia gravis of any age, including the older group with "involuted" thymuses (Dalakas *et al.*, 1980).

E. PHASE I AND PHASE II CANCER TRIALS

More than 200 cancer patients have been treated according to Phase I or Phase II protocols. Cancer patients have been treated for periods of up to 4 years. As with pediatric patients, no major side effects have been seen in the majority of patients treated with thymosin fraction 5. In addition, Dr. A. Ommaya (National Institute of Neurological Diseases) and P. Chretien (National Cancer Institute) have just completed a small Phase I trial in patients with brain tumors using synthetic thymosin α_1 prepared by Hoffmann-La Roche (Nutley, N.J.). Twleve patients with malignant gliomas, who had received surgical and radiation treatments with and without concurrent intratumoral 8-azaguanine therapy, were entered into a Phase I trial testing thymosin α_1 versus thymosin fraction 5. Three patients received fraction 5 at 60 mg/m^2 subcutaneously twice weekly for 4 weeks; and nine patients received α_1 in escalating doses, 300, 600, 900 μg/m^2 twice weekly for 4 weeks.

Prior to treatment, all patients had low levels of T cells and α_2HS-glycoprotein and elevated levels of immunosuppressive glycoproteins (α_1-acid glycoprotein, haptoglobin, and α_1-antitrypsin). During fraction 5 or α_1 administration, low α_2HS-glycoprotein levels rose higher than control levels. At the end of agent administration, the levels continued to rise. T cell levels were either stable or rose during agent administration and were influenced by chemotherapy and steroid therapy. The elevated levels of immunosuppressive glycoproteins declined significantly during agent administration, then either stabilized or began to rise. Prior to study, α_1 levels were either normal or elevated, which is consistent with the effects of steroids on thymic hormones. The α_1 levels rose significantly during administration of both thymosin fraction 5 and α_1. Hematocrit,

CBC, and serum albumin levels did not change significantly in any patient during the study. No toxicity attributable to the agents was observed.

The data indicate that in this Phase I study, both thymosin fraction 5 and the synthetic thymosin α_1 peptide of fraction 5 improved parameters of cellular immunity after combined modality therapy for malignant glioma. The results provide rationale for Phase II trials to evaluate the clinical effects of these thymic hormones as immune adjuvants in the treatment of these tumors.

The need for proper immune evaluation prior to thymosin-containing chemoimmunotherapy was established by Patt *et al.* (1979) in a small, nonrandomized study of patients with stage IIIB melanoma. Twenty-eight patients were immunologically evaluated and then treated with thymosin fraction 5, plus either BCG alone or BCG with DTIC. Immune competence was assessed by delayed-type hypersensitivity skin testing, enumeration of E-RFC in the blood, and assessment of PBL proliferative responses to PHA and Con A.

Thymosin treatment consisted of various schedules using subcutaneous injections of either a low dose (4 mg/m^2) or a high dose (40 mg/m^2) of the hormone. These investigators found that immunocompetent melanoma patients treated with high dose thymosin, plus BCG relapsed earlier than those treated with low dose thymosin and BCG. However, high dose thymosin treatment significantly improved the disease-free survival of the immunoincompetent patient group, whereas low dose thymosin was not detrimental to this group. This investigation appeared to confirm the numerous *in vitro* studies with thymosin which had suggested that immunoincompetent cancer patients were the ones most likely to benefit therapeutically from high dose thymosin administration (Rossio and Goldstein, 1977).

The first randomized Phase II trials of thymosin were designed by Dr. Paul Chretien, Associate Chief of Surgery and Head of Tumor Immunology at the NCI and carried out by Dr. Martin Cohen and his colleagues at the Washington VA Hospital. The trial was a three-arm study in 55 patients with oat cell carcinoma of the lung. Carried out from February 1976 to January 1977, chemotherapy included 6 weeks of an intensive phase using a regimen comprised of cytoxan, methotrexate and CCNU, followed by a 6 week course of less intensive chemotherapy consisting of vincristine, adriamycin, and procarbazine. Surviving patients received one or two courses of maintenance chemotherapy using alternating combinations of these drugs and/or several other agents. All patients were randomized to receive subcutaneous injection of thymosin fraction 5—60 mg/m^2, thymosin fraction 5—20 mg/m^2, or placebo twice weekly during the first 6 weeks of intensive chemotherapy. The results of this trial have recently been reported (Chretien *et al.*, 1978; Cohen *et al.*, 1979) and are illustrated in Fig. 16. Overall tumor response did not differ significantly among the three treatment groups. However, thymosin (60 mg/m²) significantly prolonged survival in patients who had eradication of all detectable disease by chemotherapy (median survival chemotherapy plus placebo, 240 days, versus 450 days for chemotherapy plus thymosin at 60 mg/m²). The median survival is now over 500 days. Six of the original 21 patients in the high dose thymosin group were alive and tumor free at over 2 years (M. Cohen, personal communication).

As indicated in Tables IX and X, prolonged survival of the lung cancer patients was found to correlate directly with initial low levels of T cells

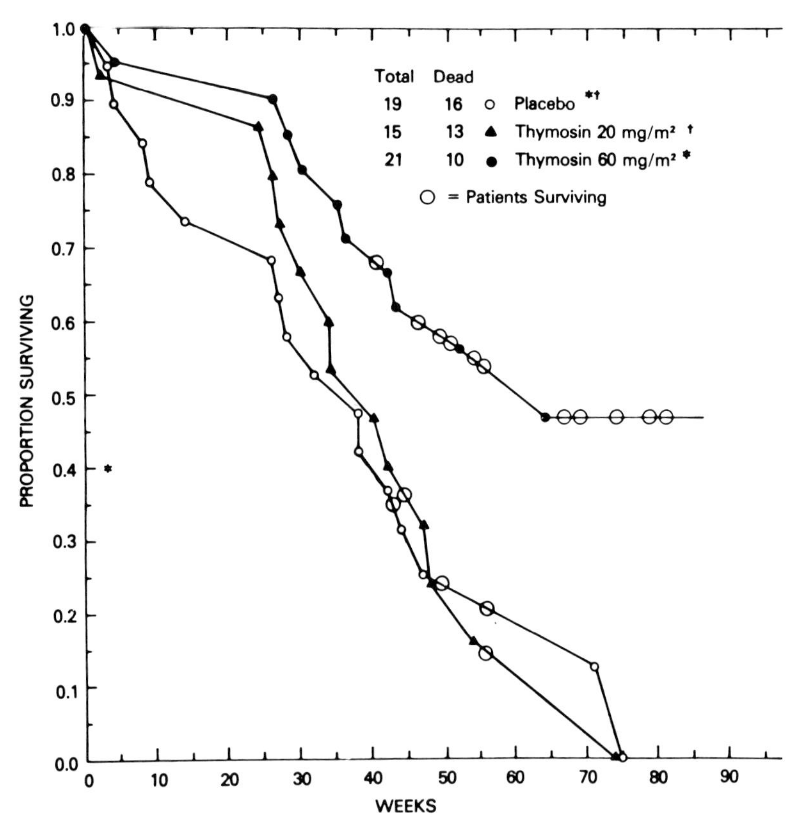

FIG. 16. Effect of thymosin on survival of patients with oat cell carcinoma of the lung (after Cohen *et al.*, 1979). Thymosin, in chemotherapy of cancer patients. Survival kinetics of oat cell carcinoma patients given 60 mg/m² thymosin (●), 20 mg/m² thymosin 5 (▲) twice weekly subcutaneously during the first 6 weeks of intensive chemotherapy. Thymosin increased median survival from 240 days to over 450 days.

TABLE IX
Relation of Pretreatment Total T Cells and Survival in Lung Cancer Patients Receiving Thymosin

Total T-cell level	Median survival in days		Comparison between treatment groups by life-table analysis (Genan's Test)
	Chemotherapy and thymosin (60 mg/m^2)	Chemotherapy alone	
High: >775/mm^3	350 (9)[a]	285 (11)	$p = 0.28$ (1-sided)
Low: <775/mm^3	405 (12)	180 (8)	$p = 0.006$ (1-sided)

[a] Values in parentheses represent number of patients; from Lipson *et al.* (1979).

and low levels of α_1HS glycoproteins (Lipson *et al.*, 1979; Chretien *et al.*, 1978). The patients who benefited most from thymosin were those with relatively low immune reactivity. Thus, this study was interpreted to indicate that whereas thymosin had no detectable direct antitumor effect, it may have ameliorated the immune defects secondary to the tumor or the chemotherapy.

Although more effective chemotherapy regimens will no doubt be developed for small cell lung cancers (Livingston, 1978), this lung cancer trial with thymosin is significant as it was the first positive controlled trial involving a thymic hormone preparation or, for that matter, any biological modifier, in the treatment of oat cell carcinoma. This study has provided the stimulus for several other Phase II trials utilizing thymosin and other thymic factors as adjuncts to conventional chemotherapy.

V. Future Prospectives for Thymic Hormones in Clinical Medicine

The ultimate application of the thymosins and other thymic hormones and factors in cancer treatment should be in providing a means of safely augmenting specific T lymphocyte functions in patients with diminished thymic-dependent immunity. In anergic cancer patients, the thymic hor-

TABLE X
Relation of Pretreatment Serum α_2-HS Glycoprotein Levels and Survival

α_2-HS glycoprotein	Median survival in days		Comparison between treatment groups by life-table analysis (Genan's Test)
	Chemotherapy and thymosin (60 mg/m^2)	Chemotherapy alone	
High: >60.5 mg/dl	300 (10)[a]	262 (11)	$p = 0.17$ (1-sided)
Low: <60.5 mg/dl	495 (10)	180 (8)	$p = 0.039$ (1-sided)

[a] Values in parentheses represent number of patients; from Lipson *et al.* (1979).

mones may be of importance as an adjunct to conventional treatments by increasing T-cell function in response not only to tumor cells, but also to pathogens, thus reducing the high incidence of infection that often accompanies cancer treatment.

The positive clinical trials to date with thymosin fraction 5 in children with immunodeficiency diseases, the positive oat cell trial of Chretien and his colleagues, and the positive studies reported with THF and several thymosin fraction 5-like preparations offer a strong rationale for rapidly confirming the clinical studies and expanding the basic research programs with the goal of further purifying, characterizing, and increasing the availability of the various thymic factors. Confirmatory clinical trials using thymosin fraction 5 in lung cancer patients are already in progress in several centers. The clinical studies are being conducted at institutions that have the capability of performing detailed immunological profiles on the treated patients. In the completed oat cell and melanoma trials, such assays appeared to identify the patients that benefited most from thymosin therapy.

Several pharmaceutical companies have standardized the procedures for increased production of thymic factors such as thymosin fraction 5. However, further clinical assessment of the synthetic thymosins and thymosin-like polypeptides is needed. The availability of active agents that can be synthesized in the laboratory will circumvent the technical problems associated with the isolation of various thymic hormones from bulk quantities of thymus tissue or serum.

It will also be important to develop experimental animal models which can be used to explore the efficacy of administering thymic hormones by various routes (locally, systemically) and in combination with other biological response modifiers, such as lymphokines, adjuvants, interferons, or with tumor cell antigens. It is to be anticipated that over the next decade, well-planned clinical trials will help to determine the optimal conditions for employing thymic hormones as a therapeutic modality in the treatment of a wide variety of diseases associated with immune deficiency. It is also anticipated that unraveling the endocrine thymus interrelationships with other systems will provide new approaches for treatments of many endocrine disorders associated with thymic malfunction.

REFERENCES

Ahlquist, J. (1981). *In* "Psychoneuroimmunology" (R. Ader, ed.). Academic Press, New York.

Ahmed, A., Smith, A. H., Sell, K. W., Steinberg, A. D., Gershwin, M. E., Thurman, G. B., and Goldstein, A. L. (1977). *Immunology* **33,** 757.

Ahmed, A., Smith, A. H., and Sell, K. W. (1978a). *In* "Immune Modulation and Control of Neoplasia by Adjuvant Therapy" (M. A. Chirigos, ed.), p. 293. Raven, New York.
Ahmed, A., Smith, A. H., Wong, D. M., Thurman, G. B., Goldstein, A. L., and Sell, K. W. (1978b). *Cancer Treat. Rep.* **62,** 1739.
Ahmed, A., Wong, D. M., Thurman, G. B., Low, T. L. K., Goldstein, A. L., Sharkis, S. J., and Goldschneider, I. (1979). *Ann. N.Y. Acad. Sci.* **332,** 81.
Aiuti, F., Ammirati, P., Fiorilli, M., D'Amelio, R., Franchi, F., Calvani, M., and Businco, L. (1979). *Pediatr. Res.* **13,** 797.
Aleksandrowicz, J., and Skotnicki, A. B. (1976). *Acta Med. Pol.* **17,** 1.
Aleksandrowicz, J., Turowski, G., Czarnecki, J., Szmigiel, Z., Cybulski, L., and Skotnicki, A. B. (1975). *Ann. Immunol.* **7,** 97.
Ammann, A. J., Wara, D. W., and Allen, T. (1978). *Clin. Immunol. Immunopathol.* **10,** 262.
Asanuma, Y., Goldstein, A. L., and White, A. (1970). *Endocrinology* **86,** 601.
Asherson, G. B., Sembala, M., Nayhew, B., and Goldstein, A. L. (1976). *Eur. J. Immunol.* **6,** 699.
Astaldi, G. C. B., Astaldi, A., Groenwoud, M., Wijermans, P., Schellekens, P. T. A., and Eijsvoogel, V. P. (1977). *Eur. J. Immunol.* **7,** 836.
Astaldi, A., Astaldi, G. C. B., Wijermans, P., Groeneuond, M., Schellikens, P. Th. A., and Eijsvogel, V. P. (1978). *J. Immunol.* **119,** 1106.
Bach, J. F. (1977). *Annu. Rev. Pharmacol. Toxicol.* **17,** 281.
Bach, J. F. (1979). *J. Pharmacol.* **1,** 277.
Bach, J. F., and Carnaud, C. (1976). *Prog. Allergy* **21,** 418.
Bach, J. F., and Dardenne, M. (1973). *Immunology* **25,** 353.
Bach, J. F., Dardenne, M., and Davis, A. J. S. (1971a). *Nature (London) New Biol.* **231,** 110.
Bach, J. F., Dardenne, M., Goldstein, A. L., Guha, A., and White, A. (1971b). *Proc. Natl. Acad. Sci. U.S.A.* **68,** 273.
Barrett, D. J., Wara, D. W., Ammann, A. J., and Cowan, M. J. (1980). *J. Pediatr.* **97,** 66.
Birr, C., and Stollenwerk, U. (1979). *Angew. Chem.* **91,** 422.
Bourne, H. R., Lichtenstein, L. M., Melmon, K. L., Henney, C. S., Weinstein, Y., and Shearer, G. M. (1974). *Science* **184,** 19.
Bruley-Rosset, M., Florentin, I., Kiger, N., Schulz, J., Davigny, M., and Mathe, G. (1979). *In* "The Immune System, Functions and Therapy of Dysfunction" (H. Faraitre, ed.). Academic Press, New York.
Bulloch, K., and Moore, R. Y. (1980). *Anat. Rec.* **196,** 25A.
Burton, P., Iden, S., Mitchell, K., and White, A. (1978). *Proc. Natl. Acad. Sci. U.S.A.* **75,** 823.
Byrom, N. A., Staughton, R. C., Campbell, M. A., Timlin, D. M., Chooi, M., Lane, A. M., Copeman, P. W. N., and Hobbs, J. R. (1978a). *Br. J. Dermatol.* **100,** 499.
Byrom, N. A., Caballero, F., Campbell, M. A., Chooi, M., Lane, A. M., Hugh-Jones, K., Timlin, D. M., and Hobbs, J. R. (1978b). *Clin. Exp. Immunol.* **31,** 490.
Caraux, J., Thierry, C., and Serrou, B. (1978). *Biomedicine* **29,** 151.
Caraux, J., Thierry, C., and Serrou, B. (1979). *J. Natl. Cancer Inst.* **63,** 593.
Caraux, J., Goldstein, A. L., Esteve, C., and Serrou, B. (1980). *Biomedicine* (in press).
Chirigos, M. A. (1978). *In* "Immune Modulation and Control of Neoplasia by Adjuvant Therapy" (M. A. Chirigos, ed.), p. 305. Raven, New York.
Chretien, P. B., Lipson, S. D., Makuch, R., Kenady, D. E., Choen, M. H., and Minna, J. B. (1978). *Cancer Treat. Rep.* **62,** 1787.
Cohen, G. H., and Goldstein, A. L. (1975). *In* "The Biological Activity of Thymic Hormones" (D. W. van Bekkum, ed.), p. 257. Kooyker Scientific Publ., Rotterdam.
Cohen, G. H., Hooper, J. A., and Goldstein, A. L. (1975). *Ann. N.Y. Acad. Sci.* **249,** 145.

Cohen, M. H., Chretien, P. B., Ihle, D. C., Fossicek, B. E., Makuch, R., Bunn, P. A., Johnston, A. V., Shackney, S. E., Matthews, M. J., Lipson, S. O., Kenady, D. E., and Minna, J. D. (1979). *J. Am. Med. Assoc.* **241,** 813.

Costanzi, J. J., Gagliano, R. G., Loukas, D., Delaney, F., Sakai, H., Harris, N. S., Thurman, G. B., and Goldstein, A. L. (1977). *Cancer* **40,** 14.

Costanzi, J. J., Harris, N., and Goldstein, A. L. (1978). *In* "Immune Modulation and Control of Neoplasia by Adjuvant Therapy" (M. A. Chirigos, ed.), p. 373. Raven, New York.

Dabrowski, M. P., and Goldstein, A. L. (1976). *Immunol. Commun.* **5,** 695.

D'Agostaro, G., Frasca, D., Garavini, M., and Doria, G. (1980). *Cell. Immunol.* **53,** 207.

Dalakas, M. C., Engel, W. K., McClure, J. E., and Goldstein, A. L. (1980). *N. Engl. J. Med.* **302,** 1092.

Dardenne, M., Pleau, J. M., Man, N. K., and Bach, J. F. (1977). *J. Biol. Chem.* **252,** 8040.

Dardenne, M., Monier, J. C. Pleau, J. M., and Bach, J. F. (1980). *Proc. Int. Congr., 4th, Immunol.* 3.3.05.

Dauphinee, M. J., Talal, N., Goldstein, A. L., and White, A. (1974). *Proc. Natl. Acad. Sci. U.S.A.* **71,** 2637.

Dolfin, Z., Handzel, A. I., Altman, Y., Hahn, T., Levin, S., and Trainin, N. (1976). *Isr. J. Med. Sci.* **12,** 1259.

Engel, W. K., Trotter, J. L., McFarlin, D. E., and McIntosh, C. L. (1977). *Lancet* **1,** 1310.

Falchetti, R., Bergesi, G., Eishfof, A., Cafiero, G., Adorini, L., and Caprino, L. (1977). *Drugs Exp. Clin. Res.* **3,** 39.

Folkers, K. (1979). *Miles Int. Symp. Polypeptide Horm., 12th* (in press).

Freire, M., Crivellaro, O., Isaacs, C., Moschera, J., and Horecker, B. L. (1978). *Proc. Natl. Acad. Sci. U.S.A.* **75,** 6007.

Freire, M., Hannappel, E., Rey, M., Freire, J. M., Kido, H., and Horecker, B. L. (1981). *Proc. Natl. Acad. Sci. U.S.A.* **78,** 192.

Friedman, G., ed. (1975). *Ann. N.Y. Acad. Sci.* **249.**

Fuchs, S., Schmidt-Hopfeld, I., Tridente, G., and Tarrab-Hazdai, R. (1980). *Nature (London)* **287,** 162.

Gershwin, M. E., Ahmed, A., Steinberg, A. D., Thurman, G. B., and Goldstein, A. L. (1974). *J. Immunol.* **113,** 1068.

Gershwin, M. E., Kruise, W., and Goldstein, G. (1979). *J. Rheumatol.* **6,** 610.

Goldschneider, I., Ahmed, A., Bollum, F. J., and Goldstein, A. L. (1981). *Natl. Acad. Sci. U.S.A.* (in press).

Goldstein, A. L., and Rossio, J. L. (1978). *Comp. Ther.* **4,** 49.

Goldstein, A. L., Slater, F. D., and White, A. (1966). *Proc. Natl. Acad. Sci. U.S.A.* **56,** 1010.

Goldstein, A. L., Asanuma, A., and White, A. (1970a). *Recent Prog. Horm. Res.* **26,** 505.

Goldstein, A. L., Asanuma, Y., Battisto, J. R., Hardy, M. A., Quint, J., and White, A. (1970b). *J. Immunol.* **104,** 359.

Goldstein, A. L., Guha, A., Zatz, M. M., Hardy, M., and White, A. (1972). *Proc. Natl. Acad. Sci. U.S.A.* **69,** 1800.

Goldstein, A. L., Wara, D. W., Ammann, A. J., Sakai, H., Harris, N. S., Thurman, G. B., Hooper, J. A., Cohen, G. H., Goldman, A. S., Costanzi, A. S., and McDaniel, M. C. (1975). *Transplant. Proc.* **7,** 681.

Goldstein, A. L., Cohen, G. H., Rossio, J. L., Thurman, G. B., Brown, C. N., and Ulrich, J. T. (1976). *Med. Clin. Na. Am.* **60,** 591.

Goldstein, A. L., Low, T. L. K., McAdoo, M., McClure, J., Thurman, G. B., Rossio, J. L.,

Lai, C.-Y., Chang, D., Wang S.-S., Harvey, C., Ramel, A. H., and Meienhofer, J. (1977). *Proc. Natl. Acad. Sci. U.S.A.* **74,** 725.
Goldstein, A. L., Thurman, G. B., Low, T. L.K., Rossio, J. L., and Trivers, G. E. (1978). *J. Reticuloendothel. Soc.* **23,** 253.
Hall, N. R. (1981). *In* "Molecular and Behavioral Neuroendocrinology" (C. B. Nemeroff and A. J. Dunn, eds.). Spectrum, New York.
Hall, N. R., and Goldstein, A. L. (1981). *In* "Psychoneuroimmunology" (R. Ader, ed.). Academic Press, New York.
Hall, N. R., McClure, J. E., Hu, S.-K., Tick, N. T., Seals, C. M., and Goldstein, A. L. (1980). *Neurosci. Abstr.* **26,** 4.
Handzel, Z. T., Levin, S., Ashkenazi, A., Hahn, T., Altman, Y., Czernohislky, B., Schecter, B., and Trainin, N. (1977). *Isr. J. Med. Sci.* **13,** 347.
Handzel, Z. T., Levin, S., Hahn, T., Altman, Y., Ashkenazi, A., Trainin, N., and Schecter, B. (1978). *Isr. J. Med. Sci.* **11,** 1391.
Handzel, Z. T., Dolfin, Z., Levin, S., Altman, T., Hahn, T., Trainin, N., and Godot, N. (1979). *Pediatr. Res.* **13,** 803.
Hardy, M. A., Quint, J., Goldstein, A. L., State, D., and White, A. (1968). *Proc. Natl. Acad. Sci U.S.A.* **61,** 875.
Hardy, M. A., Zisblatt, M., Levine, N., Goldstein, A. L., Lilly, F., and White, A. (1971). *Transplant. Proc.* **3,** 926.
Hardy, M. A., Goldstein, A. L., and White, A. (1972). *Surg. Forum XXIII* **23,** 305.
Harper, J. F., and Brooker, G. (1975). *J. Cyclic Nucleotide Res.* **1,** 207.
Hirokawa, K., and Saitoh, K. (1980). *Int. Congr. Immunol., 4th* 3.3.14 Abstr.
Hirokawa, K., McClure, J. E., and Goldstein, A. L. (1981). Submitted.
Hooper, J. A., McDaniel, M., Thurman, G. B., Cohen, G. H., Schulof, R. S., and Goldstein, A. L. (1975). *Ann. N.Y. Acad. Sci.* **249,** 125.
Horowitz, S. D., and Goldstein, A. L. (1978). *Clin. Immunol. Immunopathol.* **9,** 408.
Horowitz, S., Borcherding, C. O., Moorthy, A. V., Chesney, R., Schulte-Wisserman, H., and Hong, R. (1977). *Science* **197,** 4307.
Hu, S.-K., Low, T. L. K., and Goldstein, A. L. (1979). *Fed. Proc. Fed. Am. Soc. Exp. Biol.* **38,** 1079A.
Hu, S.-K., Low, T. L. K., and Goldstein, A. L. (1980a). *Fed. Proc. Fed. Am. Soc. Exp. Biol.* **39,** 1133.
Hu, S.-K., Thurman, G. B., Low, T. L. K., McClure, J., and Goldstein, A. L. (1980b). *New Trends Immunol. Cancer Ther.* (in press)
Hunt, L. T., and Dayhoff, M. O. (1977). *Biochem. Biophys. Res. Commun.* **74,** 650.
Ishizawa, S., Sakai, H., Sarles, H. E., Larson, D. L., and Daniels, J. C. (1978). *J. Trauma* **18,** 48.
Jin, Y., Xu, X., Zhu, J., Wang, Y., Zhu, A., and Zhang, H. (1979). *J. Nanking Univ.* **1,** 115.
Kaplan, J. (1978). *Cancer Treat. Rep.* **62,** 1757.
Kaplan, J., and Peterson, W. D. (1978). *Clin. Immunol. Immunopathol.* **9,** 436.
Kasahara, K., Tanaka, S., Ito, T., and Hamashima, Y. (1977). *Res. Commun. Chem. Pathol. Pharmacol.* **16,** 687.
Kater, L., Oosterom, R., McClure, J. E., and Goldstein, A. L. (1979). *Int. J. Immunopharmacol.* **1,** 273.
Kenady, D. E., Chretien, P. B., Potvin, C., Simon, R. M., Alexander, J. C., and Goldstein, A. L. (1977). *Cancer* **39,** 642.
Khaw, B. A., and Rule, A. H. (1973). *Br. J. Cancer* **28,** 288.
Kido, H., Vita, A., Hannappel, E., and Horecker, B. L. (1981). *Arch. Biochem. Biophys.* (in press).

Klein, J. J., Goldstein, A. L., and White, A. (1965). *Proc. Natl. Acad. Sci. U.S.A.* **53,** 812.
Klein, J. J., Goldstein, A. L., and White, A. (1966). *Ann. N.Y. Acad. Sci.* **135,** 485.
Kook, A. I., and Trainin, N. (1974). *J. Exp. Med.* **139,** 193.
Kruisbeck, A. M., Astaldi, G. C. B., Blankwater, M. J., Ziglstra, L. A., Leverb, L. A., and Astaldi, A. (1978). *Cell. Immunol.* **35,** 134.
Lavastida, M. T., and Daniels, J. C. (1978). *Fed. Proc. Fed. Am. Soc. Exp. Biol.* **37,** 1669.
Law, L. W., Goldstein, A. L., and White, A. (1968). *Nature (London)* **219,** 1391.
Lipson, D. S., Chretien, P. B., Makuch, R., Kenady, D. E., and Cohen, M. H. (1979). *Cancer* **43,** 863.
Liu, S.-L. (1979). *Peking Med.* **1,** 219.
Liu, S.-L., Hsu, C.-S., Tsuel, L.-H., Yang, K.-C., and Chang, S.-C. (1978). *Acta Biochem. Biophys. Sin.* **10,** 413.
Livingston, R. B. (1978). *Semin. Oncol.* **5,** 299.
Low, T. L. K., and Goldstein, A. L. (1978). *In* "The Year In Hematology" (R. Silber, J. Lobuc, and A. S. Gordon, eds.), p. 281. Plenum, New York.
Low, T. L. K., and Goldstein, A. L. (1979). *J. Biol. Chem.* **254,** 987.
Low, T. L. K., Thurman, G. B., McAdoo, M., McClure, J. E., Jr., Rossio, J. L., Naylor, P. H., and Goldstein, A. L. (1979). *J. Biol. Chem.* **254,** 981.
Low, T. L. K., Hu, S.-K., and Goldstein, A. L. (1981). *Proc. Natl. Acad. Sci. U.S.A.* **78,** 1166.
Lowell, G. W., Smith, L. F., Klein, D., and Zollinger, W. P. (1980). *Proc. Int. Congr. Immunol., 4th* **17,** 2, 23.
Maahinney, H., Gleadhill, V. F. D., and McCrea, S. (1979). *Clin. Immunol. Immunopathol.* **14,** 196.
McClure, J. E., and Goldstein, A. L. (1980). *Proc. Int. Congr. Immunol. 4th* **17,** 2, 26.
McClure, J. E., Wara, D., Cameris, C., and Goldstein, A. L. (1981). Submitted.
Marshall, G. D., Thurman, G. B., Rossio, J. L., and Goldstein, A. L. (1980). *J. Immunol.* (in press)
Milcu, S. M., and Potop, I. (1973). *In* "Thymic Hormones" (T. D. Luckey, ed.), p. 97. Univ. Park Press, Baltimore, Maryland.
Mizutani, A. (1973). *In* "Thymic Hormones" (T. D. Luckey, ed.), p. 193. Univ. Park Press, Baltimore, Maryland.
Moutsopoulos, H., Fye, K. H., Sawada, S., Becker, M. J., Goldstein, A. L., and Talal, N. (1976). *Clin. Exp. Immunol.* **26,** 563.
Mutchnick, M. G., and Goldstein, A. L. (1979). *Clin. Immunol. Immunopathol.* **12,** 271.
Naylor, P. H., and Goldstein, A. L. (1979). *Life Sci.* **25,** 301.
Naylor, P. H., Sheppard, H., Thurman, G. B., and Goldstein, A. L. (1976). *Biochem. Biophys. Res. Commun.* **73,** 843.
Naylor, P. H., Thurman, G. B., and Goldstein, A. L. (1979). *Biochem. Biophys. Res. Commun.* **90,** 810.
Olusi, S. O., Thurman, G. B., and Goldstein, A. L. (1980). *Immunol. Immunopathol.* **15,** 687.
Osheroff, P. L. (1981). *Cell. Immunol.* (in press).
Patt, Y. Z., Hersh, E. M., Schafer, L. A., Smith, T. L., Burgess, M. A., Gutterman, J. U., Goldstein, A. L., and Mavligit, G. M. (1979). *Cancer Immunol. Immunother.* **7,** 131.
Pazmino, N. H., Ihle, J. N., and Goldstein, A. L. (1978a). *J. Exp. Med.* **147,** 708.
Pazmino, N. H., Ihle, J. H., McEwan, R. N., and Goldstein, A. L. (1978b). *Cancer Treat. Rep.* **62,** 1749.
Pleau, J. M., Dardenne, M., Blouquit, Y., and Bach, J. F. (1977). *J. Biol. Chem.* **252,** 8045.

Potop, I., and Milcu, S. M. (1973). *In* "Thymic Hormones" (T. D. Luckey, ed.), p. 205. Univ. Park Press, Baltimore, Maryland.

Rossio, J. L., and Goldstein, A. L. (1977). *World Surg.* **1,** 605.

Rovensky, J., Goldstein, A. L., Holt, P. J. L., Pekarek, J., and Mistina, T. (1977). *Casopis Lekara Ceskych* **116,** 1063.

Rubenstein, A., Hirschorn, R., Sicklick, M., and Murphy, R. A. (1979). *N. Engl. J. Med.* **300,** 387.

Schafer, L., Gutterman, J. W., Hersh, E. M., Mavligit, G. M., Dandridge, K., Cohen, G., and Goldstein, A. L. (1976). *Cancer Immunol. Immunother.* **1,** 259.

Scheid, M. P., Hoffman, M. K., Komuro, K., Hammerling, H., Boyse, E. A., Cohen, G. H., Hooper, J. A., Schulof, R. S., and Goldstein, A. L. (1973). *J. Exp. Med.* **138,** 1027.

Scheid, M. P., Goldstein, G., Hammerling, U., and Boyse, E. A. (1975). *In* "Membrane Receptors of Lymphocytes" (M. Seligmann, J. L. Preudhomme, and F. M. Kourilsky, eds.), p. 353. Elsevier, Amsterdam.

Scheinberg, M. A., Cathcart, E. S., and Goldstein, A. L. (1975). *Lancet* **22,** 424.

Scheinberg, M. A., Blacklow, W. R., Goldstein, A. L., Parrimo, T. A., Rose, F. B., and Cathcart, E. S. (1976a). *N. Engl. J. Med.* **294,** 1208.

Scheinberg, M. A., Goldstein, A. L., and Cathcart, E. S. (1976b). *J. Immunol.* **115,** 156.

Schlesinger, D. H., and Goldstein, G. (1975). *Cell* **5,** 361.

Sharp, M. R., and Peterson, D. A. (1978). *Clin. Res.* **26,** A818.

Shohat, B., Spitzer, S., Topilsky, M., and Trainin, N. (1978). *Biomed. Exp.* **29,** 91.

Skotnicki, A. B. (1978). *Pol. Tyg. Lek.* **28,** 1119.

Spector, N. H. (1980). *In* "Handbook of the Hypothalamus" (P. Morgane and J. Panksepp, eds.). Dekker, New York.

Stein, M., Keller, S., and Schleifer, S. (1980). *In* "Psychoneuroimmunology" (R. Ader, ed.). Academic Press, New York.

Talal, N., Dauphinee, M., Philarisetty, R., and Goldblum, R. (1975). *Ann. N.Y. Acad. Sci.* **249,** 438.

Thurman, G. B., Silver, B. B., Hooper, J. A., Giovanella, B. C., and Goldstein A. L. (1974). *In* "Proceedings, First International Workshop on Nude Mice" (J. Rygaard and C. O. Polvsen, eds.), p. 105. Fishcer Verlag, Stuttgart.

Thurman, G. B., Steinberg, A. P., Ahmed, A., Strong, D. M., Gershwin, M. E., and Goldstein, A. L. (1975). *Transplant. Proc.* **7,** 299.

Thurman, G. B., Marshall, G. D., Low, T. L. K., and Goldstein, A. L. (1979). *In* "Cell Biology and Immunology of Leukocyte Function" (M. R. Quastel, ed.), p. 189. Academic Press, New York.

Tovo, P. A., Bernengo, M. G., Cordero di Montezemolo, L., Del Piano, A., Saitta, M., and Nicola, P. (1980). *Thymus* **2,** 41.

Trainin, N. (1974). *Physiol. Rev.* **54,** 272.

Trivers, G. E., and Goldstein, A. L. (1980). *In* "Cancer Biology Reviews" (J. J. Marchalonis, M. G. Hanna, and I. J. Fidler, eds.), Vol. 1, p. 49. Dekker, New York.

Van Den Tweel, J. G., Taylor, C. R., McClure, J., and Goldstein, A. L. (1979). *Adv. Exp. Med.* **114,** 512.

Varsano, I., Danon, Y., Jaber, L., Livni, E., Shohat, B., Yakir, Y., Schneyoun, A., and Trainin, N. (1976). *Isr. J. Med. Sci.* **12,** 1168.

Varsano, I., Shofeld, M., Matoth, M., Shohat, B., Englander, T., Rotter, V., and Trainin, N. (1977). *Acta. Paediatr. Scand.* **66,** 329.

Wang, S. S., Kulesha, I. D., and Winter, D. P. (1978). *J. Am. Chem. Soc.* **101,** 253.

Wang, S. S., Makofske, R., Bach, A. E., and Merrifield, R. B. (1980). *Int. J. Pept. Protein Res.* **15,** 1.

Wara, D. W., and Ammann, A. J. (1978). *Transplant. Proc.* **10,** 203.
Wara, D. W., Barrett, D. J., Ammann, A. J., and Cowan, M. J. (1980). *Ann. N.Y. Acad. Sci.* **332,** 128.
Wetzel, R., Heyneker, H. L., Goeddel, D. V., Jhurani, P., Shapiro, J., Crea, R., Low, T. L. K., McClure, J. E., and Goldstein, A. L. (1980). *Biochemistry* (in press)
White, A. (1980). *In* "Biochemical Actions of Hormones" (G. Litwack, ed.), Vol. VIII, pp. 1–46. Academic Press, New York.
White, A., and Goldstein, A. L. (1974). *Adv. Metab. Disorders* **8,** 359.
Wilkinson, K. D., Urban, M. K., and Haas, A. L. (1980). *J. Biol. Chem.* **255,** 7529.
Wong, T. W., and Merrifield, R. B. (1980). *Biochemistry* **19,** 3233.
Zisblatt, M., Goldstein, A. L., Lilly, F., and White, A. (1970). *Proc. Natl. Acad. Sci. U.S.A.* **66,** 1170.

DISCUSSION

J. George: Twenty to thirty years ago the thymus of infants was irradiated for respiratory problems. Now these people are being called back for possible thyroid cancer. Are you aware of any immunologic problems that they might have?

A. Goldstein: We're very much interested in this group. It was thought that the sudden death syndrome was due to a disease termed thymostatus lymphaticus. An enlarged thymus was thought to press against the trachea and cause death. Since the thymus was felt to be useless and since it was so sensitive to radiation, the obvious way to prevent the syndrome was to shrink the thymus by X-irradiation. Well, we now recognize the flaws in that logic and the medical community has to now deal with the long-term radiation damage in these patients. It appears that more than just thyroid problems are developing in this group. Increasing numbers of patients with immunological problems and cancers whose thymus glands were irradiated in infancy are being reported, and I suspect the number of patients with serious complications will increase as the patient population grows older.

P. Naylor: Dr. Goldstein, as usual, despite the fact that we talk to each other frequently, I always learn more everytime I hear you give a lecture on the exciting field that we're both interested in. In our laboratory, we've had an opportunity to study rats which I thymectomized at 4 to 6 weeks of age. They were given DMBA because we're interested in studying the mammary tumor which is induced by this carcinogen in these animals. At sacrifice we took the opportunity to measure the levels of prolactin in these animals. The rats which had been thymectomized whether they were fed high fat or low fat diets had lower levels of prolactin than the animals which were sham operated. While this does not say that the thymus directly controls the levels of prolactin it certainly suggests that there is indeed some effect of the thymus on the endocrine control of prolactin levels.

A. Goldstein: I think this is a very exciting observation. There are some early studies that we have reviewed (cf. White and Goldstein, *Perspect. Biol. Med.* **11,** 475–489) that support your data and suggest an important role for the thymus in influencing other endocrine systems.

J. Geller: I wondered if the early figure you showed with the decline in thymosin, measured as a crude extract by bioassay, had been dissected to give us any information as to whether there was a component in the crude thymosin that might be responsible for immune surveillance and which in turn might be related to the ability of the organism to destroy tumor clones; and also whether such a specific thymus factor that might be related to tumorigenesis has been measured in aging or in patients with tumors to see whether it in fact declines from young to old age or is different in tumor patients than nontumor patients of the same age.

A. Goldstein: That's a very important point. The RIA for thymosin α_1 is a very recent development. We are just beginning to address the question you have raised. Data, primarily from the laboratory of J. F. Bach, using a bioassay to measure thymic hormone levels in the blood, point to a strong correlation between disease states and circulating thymic hormones. With the development of a RIA, we hope to be able to quantitate and define normal thymosin levels in the blood and to correlate changes that are seen with disease state.

J. Geller: Is there any relationship between transfer factor and any of the thymosin components?

A. Goldstein: Yes. One of the major problems that has been associated with transfer factor (TF) is its multiplicity of biological properties. There is a specific component in TF capable of transferring immunity from one individual to another and a nonspecific component capable of turning on the immune system of immunosuppressed individuals. Using the RIA for thymosin α_1, we've studied purified TF preparations from the laboratories of Drs. C. Kirkpatrick (University of Colorado, Denver) and Dr. A. Kahn (Wadley Institute, Dallas) and have identified significant levels of thymosin α_1 in both preparations.

A. Wentz: Premature ovarian failure is thought to have several etiologies, including autoimmunity. The athymic nude mouse develops hypergonadotropinemia and premature ovarian failure. Would you comment on the potential mechanism and tell us if the nude mouse might be a model to study premature ovarian failure in the human.

A. Goldstein: I think there are a number of individuals studying the problem. I would suggest another model, the neonatally thymectomized mouse, as well. A group in Japan, led by Dr. Nishizuka (Y. Nishizuka and T. Sakakura, *Science* **166**, 753, 1969), and more recently Dr. Sandy Michael (S. P. Michael, *Arth. Rheum.* **22**, 1241, 1979) at SUNY in Binghamton have demonstrated that some strains of neonatally thymectomized mice develop an ovarian dysgenesis. Dr. Michael has been able to prevent or correct this ovarian dysgenesis with thymus transplants and/or thymosin. In addition, Dr. Rebar and his colleagues at the University of California in San Diego (Rebar, personal communication) have found a significant deficiency in LH and FSH levels in athymic (nu/nu) mice. The findings from both of these groups suggest an important role for the thymus in the regulation of gonadal function.

S. Cohen: My question concerns myesthenia gravis which most of you probably know has been transferred from a neurological disease to an autoimmune disease. Practically all cases of myesthenia gravis have enlarged thymuses. The first part of the treatment is removal of the thymus gland. Do you know whether thymosin has been used in such patients?

A. Goldstein: Well, Dr. Cohen, very recently Drs. Dalakas and Engel at the NIND have reported, using immunohistofluorescence techniques and a thymosin α_1 antibody, that patients with myasthenia gravis appear to have increased numbers of epithelial cells in the thymus producing α_1 (Dalakas *et al., N. Eng. J. Med.* **302,** 1092, 1980). This observation might account for the beneficial effect of thymectomy seen in about 23% of patients with myasthenia gravis. It is now thought that the major problem in myasthenia is antibodies directed against acetylcholine receptors. It is also thought that patients with this disease have too many helper T cells. Since it is known that thymosin α_1 is a potent inducer of helper cells, it is possible that elevated α_1 levels play a role in the immunological components of this disease.

S. Cohen: I had an occasion to observe one case of a close friend of mine and he is now completely off prostigmine and he is now on corticoids only and this is gradually being reduced. His only trouble is he has to watch for infections and I wondered whether thymosin might help this?

A. Goldstein: Well, it's theoretically possible. One of the most potentially important areas of clinical application for the thymic hormones, I believe, will be in the treatment of opportunistic infections. In several of the pediatric and cancer patients treated with thymosin, dramatic improvements in chronic opportunistic infections have been seen.

G. Campbell: I'd like to make several comments regarding the possible interactions between the thymus and the anterior pituitary. We have been using the neonatally thymectomized rat instead of the neonatally thymectomized mouse, primarily because of the availability of homologous radioimmunoassays for rat gonadotropins, prolactin, and growth hormone. In the normal strain of rat, we've had some difficulty in finding any alterations in LH, FSH, prolactin, or growth hormone secretion or any evidence of premature ovarian dysgenesis. However, this may not be the case if the strain of rat used is particularly susceptible to the development of autoimmune disorders. If you use that particular type of rat, as in the case of Michael *et al.* with the neonatally thymectomized mouse, then you may very likely find an alteration in prolactin secretion occurring at a preweening age. The other comment I would like to make is that we have had an opportunity to transplant the anterior pituitary of the hamster and the rat into several areas which have been reported to be immunologically priviliged sites. Contrary to at least my expectation, and the dogma of endocrinology, when these pituitaries are transplanted into an immunologically privileged site, they have almost every pituitary cell type with one exception, and that is the prolactin cell. These pituitaries have essentially no prolactin cells, and they most likely do not secrete much prolactin at all. I'm very interested and excited to see the immunologists try to push endocrinologists forward into studying what interactions there are between the anterior pituitary and the thymus gland.

A. Goldstein: I second your own observation about strain, as well as species differences. Dr. S. Michael's work indicates that the strain is very important in determining whether the thymectomized animals will develop an ovarian dysgenesis. Your work with privileged sites is very interesting. It would be worthwhile to look at thymic hormones in your animal model.

H. Friesen: It was difficult for me to try to make a comparison of the results obtained with fraction five and some of the purified thymosin factors in a number of assays. If you use an antibody to thymosin how much of the activity of fraction five is lost in the various bioassays.

A. Goldstein: We have not yet done the antibody experiment you suggest. We are in the process of preparing thymosin fraction 5 minus α_1, and we could do the same with β_3 and β_4. Thymosin α_1 is about 1% of fraction 5 on a weight basis. We have yet to sort out how much of the activity in fraction 5 is due to α_1, β_3, β_4, etc. It is my feeling that it may be necessary to use a mixture of peptides in order to get full immunological reconstitution. However, a number of thymic deficiency diseases may be found where only one or two of the biologically active thymosin peptides are deficient. This, however, remains to be established.

H. Friesen: Two other quick questions if I may. In the animals that generated the antibodies to thymosin were there any deficiencies of the immune system noted? Second, do you know anything about the turnover rates of thymosin.

A. Goldstein: With regard to the first question, the rabbits injected with thymosin coupled to haptenes have done reasonably well. Some of our immunized rabbits, however, have died. We haven't done pathology on these animals. In general, some of our best antisera producers have remained alive for considerable periods of time. With regard to your second question, the pharmacological studies are only now being done with the purified peptides.

I. Rothchild: One question is whether you have any thoughts about the role of thymus-mediated immunity in the lack of immune rejection of the embryo by the mother and a possible relation to the effects of progesterone. Another is whether if you have any ideas about the way prolactin might affect immunity-rejection phenomena.

A. Goldstein: Well, I think it is an important question that can now be addressed. Yacob Weinstein from the Weizman Institute has reported that thymocytes, as well as spleen cells and bone marrow cells, contain significant amounts of 20α steroid dehydrogenase, an enzyme that reduces progesterone to 20α-dihydroprogesterone (Y. Weinstein *et al.*, *Nature* (*London*) **266**, 632, 1977). What are these thymocytes doing with this enzyme? In mice, the thymocytes with 20α steroid dehydrogenase are found primarily in the medullary region of the thymus and have the highest enzyme levels at birth. These observations suggest that the thymus might be playing a more active role during pregnancy than we now recognize.

B. Dobyns: In Grave's disease the thymus becomes very large. It is often most impressive. It has been described for many years. It is sometimes associated with the profound myasthenia of Graves' disease. I wonder if you can tell us anymore about the relationship of the thymus to this disease.

A. Goldstein: I think it is going to be very important to take a fresh look at some of these endocrine disorders and to attempt to correlate thymic function with disease process.

K. Sterling: Well I dare say there are one or two others who didn't happen to know that. Among your lymphokines, I saw that MIF and MAF were included. I was guessing that MIF is migration inhibition factor. What is MAF?

A. Goldstein: Macrophage activation factor. I should mention that the nomenclature is changing very rapidly and, with the proliferation of new factors, may have to be updated in the near future.

R. Miller: If you infuse acetylcholine or norepinephrine or some other transmitter do you find an increase in thymosin α_1?

A. Goldstein: These areas are just being investigated. Preliminary results following chemical sympathectomy with 6-OHDA point to a significant elevation in α_1 levels.

K. Sterling: I have a few questions. I was sitting next to our illustrious chairman and neither he nor I were sure what TdT positive and negative meant; I guessed it meant thymus-dependent T cells or something like that.

A. Goldstein: No, TdT is terminal deoxynucleotidyl transferase, a nontemplate directed DNA polymerase.

R. Miller: Would you speculate on the regulation of the secretion of thymasin A, and comment on the evidence for the role of the autonomic nervous system in this regulation.

A. Goldstein: About 6 months ago, Dr. Nick Hall, a young postdoctoral student, joined my group specifically to begin to address the question of autonomic and neuroendocrine regulation of thymosin fraction. Our studies are too preliminary to comment on. However, Dr. C. Bulloch (University of California at San Diego) has recently described a direct innovation of the thymus to the cerebellum (personal communication). This observation is of interest since it appears that there are receptors for α_1 in the cerebellum as well (Hall and Goldstein, unpublished observations). We haven't yet characterized the specificity of the receptors, but we are very interested in pursuing this line of research.

K. Sterling: There was a question about myasthenia gravis. To pursue what Dr. Cohen started, I think in some series, as many as a quarter to a third of them actually have thymus tumors. Even when they've been explored, these tumors may be inapparent until after the thymus has been ressected, so I was interested in your thinking that they may indeed have too much thymosin α_1. I wonder if you've had the opportunity to study any of this by the serum RIA.

A. Goldstein: We're just starting to do that. We've spent the better part of the past year establishing normal levels in mouse and in human blood.

K. Sterling: One last question. Mid-way through your talk you showed immunofluorescence figures on normal human thymus glands, I wondered how you got permission to sample those: were the patients kind enough to be the cadavers?

A. Goldstein: No. The study was done in Japan at the University of Tokyo. The patients were undergoing open heart surgery for various reasons, and it was necessary to remove a lobe of thymus for the surgical procedure. The patients were, to the best of my knowledge, immunologically normal.

K. Sterling: I believe the "thyroid" gland means "shield" or thymus-like, and if I'm correct in my Greek, you have an endocrine precursor.

RECENT PROGRESS IN HORMONE RESEARCH, VOL. 37

Biosynthesis and Mechanism of Action of Nerve Growth Factor

ERIC M. SHOOTER, BRUCE A. YANKNER, G. E. LANDRETH, AND ARNE SUTTER

Department of Neurobiology, Stanford University School of Medicine, Stanford, California

I. Introduction

It is becoming increasingly clear that cells require one or more growth factors or hormones before they can express and maintain their fully differentiated function. One of the earliest growth factors to be recognized was nerve growth factor (NGF) because of its ability to stimulate the growth of certain embryonic sensory and sympathetic nerve cells (Levi-Montalcini and Angeletti, 1968). When circulating levels of NGF are increased in neonatal animals massive increases in neuronal and ganglionic volume occur and an extensive overgrowth of sympathetic fibers as well as a large increase in the innervation of sympathetic tissue is observed (Levi-Montalcini and Angeletti, 1968). Conversely appropriate doses of antibody to NGF reduce sympathetic ganglionic volume and cell number to only a few percent of their original values in most species (Levi-Montalcini and Booker, 1966). Similarly inhibition of the development of embryonic sensory neurons is observed in rat fetuses when NGF antibody production is induced in pregnant rats by injection of NGF (Gorin and Johnson, 1979). Both sympathetic and embryonic sensory neurons are dependent on NGF for survival and morphological differentiation in culture. Recently several NGF-responsive lines have been established from a transplantable rat pheochromocytoma and one of them, the PC12 clone, responds reversibly to NGF (Greene and Tischler, 1976). In the absence of NGF this line displays many of the features of their nonneoplastic counterparts, adrenal chromaffin cells (Tischler and Greene, 1978). When exposed to NGF the PC12 cells slowly cease cell proliferation and acquire a number of the properties of sympathetic neurons including neurite outgrowth and increased electrical excitability. Withdrawal of NGF results in disintegration of the neurites and recommencement of cell proliferation (Greene and Tischler, 1976).

NGF plays other roles, some of which are important throughout the life cycle of the responsive neurons. The growth of axons from developing

ISBN 0-12-571137-9

sensory and sympathetic neurons *in vivo* (Hendry, 1976) and the maintenance of the differentiated state of these neurons require NGF (Stöckel and Thoenen, 1975). The neurites of sympathetic neurons in culture continue to grow when exposed to NGF but regress when NGF is removed (Campenot, 1977). Although the *in vivo* source of the NGF has not yet been clarified the retrograde flow of NGF from nerve terminal to cell body has been amply documented (Hendry *et al.*, 1974; Paravicini *et al.*, 1975) and it is clear that an interruption of this flow has significant consequences in both developing and mature sensory and sympathetic neurons. There is also growing evidence that NGF may have a chemotactic role in guiding the direction of growth of axons (Menesini-Chen *et al.*, 1978; Gunderson and Barrett, 1979).

Whether these several roles of NGF arc thc result of a single mechanism of action is not known but it is reasonably clear that they are all initiated by the interaction of NGF with specific receptors on the cell soma or nerve endings. Some of the details of this interaction and its consequences are now understood and those which relate to the ability of NGF to induce morphological differentiation of sensory and sympathetic neurons or of PC12 cells are discussed in a later section. In the next section, however, we describe briefly the biochemistry of the NGF proteins and show how a knowledge of their structure has led to a model for the biosynthesis of the biologically active NGF dimer.

II. Biochemistry and Biosynthesis of NGF

The stable form of NGF in the adult male mouse submaxillary gland is the multisubunit-containing protein 7 S NGF (Fig. 1). This was the first NGF protein to be purified (Varon *et al.*, 1967) and it followed from the demonstration by Cohen (1960) of the protein nature of the growth factor. The biologically active NGF dimer is part of the 7 S complex and it is readily isolated after the complex is dissociated at acid pH (Varon *et al.*, 1968). It is a remarkably stable dimer, the equilibrium dissociation constant being less than 10^{-13} M (Bothwell and Shooter, 1977). The complex also contains two copies of a trypsin-like enzyme, the γ subunit (Greene *et al.*, 1979; Au and Dunn, 1977), two copies of an acidic protein, the α subunit, and two zinc ions (Pattison and Dunn, 1975) and the zinc ions contribute greatly to the stability of 7 S NGF (Bothwell and Shooter, 1978). The biological activity of the NGF dimer is inhibited in 7 S NGF as shown by both the lack of activity of the cross-linked complex (Stach and Shooter, 1979) and the inability of ^{125}I-labeled NGF to interact with the NGF receptors when stabilized in 7 S NGF (Harris-Warrick *et al.*, 1980). Similarly the enzymatic activity of the γ subunit is inhibited in the com-

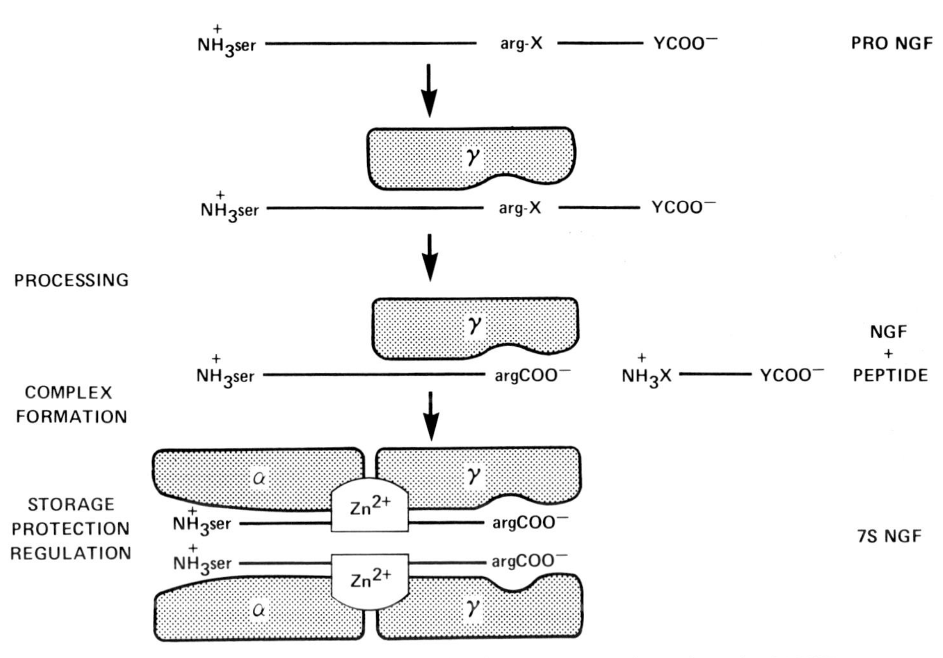

FIG. 1. A model for the biosynthesis of NGF and the formation of 7 S NGF.

plex with the interactions between the C-terminal arginine residues of the NGF chains and the active site of the γ subunit being the key features in this inhibition (Greene *et al.*, 1968; Bothwell and Shooter, 1978). The NGF dimer is susceptible to two limited proteolytic cleavages by enzymes in the submaxillary gland. A carboxypeptidase-B-like enzyme removes the C-terminal arginine residues (Moore *et al.*, 1974) while an endopeptidase, kallikrein (Bothwell *et al.*, 1978), releases the N-terminal octapeptide sequences (Angeletti *et al.*, 1973; Mobley *et al.*, 1976). Neither of these enzymes is able to attack the NGF dimer when it is present in the 7 S NGF complex (Moore *et al.*, 1974; Mobley *et al.*, 1976). The 7 S NGF complex, therefore, not only protects the NGF dimer from proteolytic degradation in the gland but acts also as a very stable storage complex. The NGF activity in the gland is secreted into mouse saliva as 7 S NGF (Burton *et al.*, 1978) and it is likely that this is also the form in which NGF is secreted initially into the circulation. The 7 S NGF complex dissociates at some stage after secretion in the circulation because the NGF dimer is finally found bound to α_2-macroglobulin in plasma (Ronne *et al.*, 1979). The new forms of NGF described for both mouse saliva (Murphy *et al.*, 1977) and the mouse submaxillary gland (Young, 1979) have, on further analysis, been found to be identical to 7 S NGF (Burton *et al.*, 1978; D. Estell and E. M. Shooter, unpublished data).

The structure and properties of 7 S NGF suggest that the complex arises during the processing of a precursor, proNGF, to NGF by the action of the γ subunit (Fig. 1). A similar argument can be made for the formation of another growth factor complex in the mouse submaxillary gland, the high-molecular-weight epidermal growth factor (HMW-EGF) complex (Fig. 2). The latter also contains besides the EGF dimer, two copies of another trypsin-like enzyme, the EGF-binding protein (EGF-BP) and two zinc ions (Taylor *et al.*, 1970; M. A. Bothwell and E. M. Shooter, unpublished data). In both instances the trypsin-like subunit recognizes, and binds to, the sequence around the arginine residue which ultimately becomes the C-terminal residue of the growth factor chain. The liberation of the extrapeptide material from the C-terminus of both precursors, coupled with the continued binding of the enzymes to their products (in analogy with the formation of a trypsin–trypsin inhibitor complex) initiates the formation of the two respective complexes. Like the γ subunit in 7 S NGF the activity of the enzyme EGF-BP is also inhibited in HMW-EGF and again the C-terminal arginine residues of the EGF chains are the key binding domains for the active site of the enzyme (Server and Shooter, 1977). The finding that, in spite of their considerable similarities in structure and activity, one trypsin-like enzyme, EGF-BP, will not substitute for the other, the γ subunit, in the formation of 7 S NGF suggests that these enzymes should be specific for the processing of their respective precursors (Server and Shooter, 1977). This has now been shown to be correct for at least one of the models. The precursors, proNGF (Berger

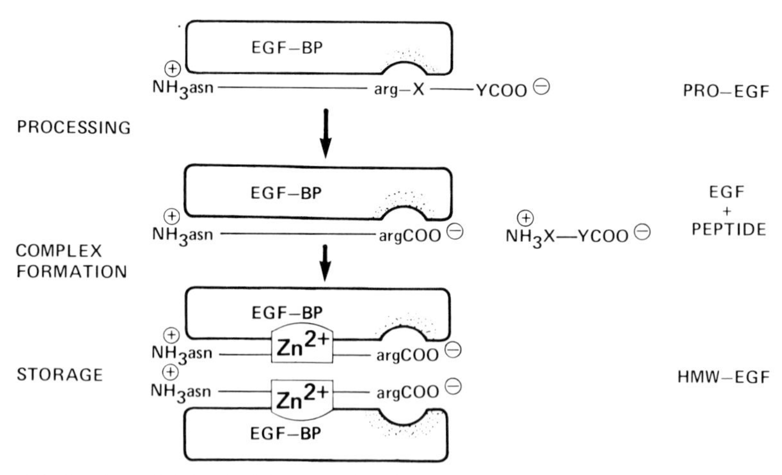

FIG. 2. A model for the biosynthesis of EGF and the formation of HMW-EGF.

and Shooter, 1977) and proEGF (Frey *et al.*, 1979), have been identified and characterized by the kinetics of labeling of the growth factor proteins in slices of the submaxillary glands, by their tryptic peptide composition, and by their enzymatic conversion to NGF and EGF, respectively. Because of the ability to proEGF to withstand heat denaturation the specificity of its processing in the gland extract can be examined after first denaturing the endogenous proteases. Using this method Frey *et al.* (1979) found that only EGF-BP, and specifically not the γ subunit or trypsin, is able to carry out the conversion of labeled proEGF to EGF. The same experiments were repeated with native proEGF isolated from the gland extract, where it accounts for 0.3% of the EGF proteins in the extract, with the same results, and as predicted by the model the EGF was recovered in the form of the complex HMW-EGF. By labeling the free amino-terminal residue of proEGF with ^{125}I it was also possible to show that the extrapeptide material was released from the C-terminus of proEGF as predicted. The determination of the specificity of the processing of native proNGF awaits its isolation but the fact that NGF is formed from a precursor like proNGF suggests analogies with the biosynthesis of other hormones and emphasizes the relationship between NGF and the insulin-like family of hormones and growth factors (Bradshaw, 1978).

III. The Mechanism of Action of NGF

A. NGF RECEPTORS WITH TWO AFFINITIES

The presence of NGF receptors on responsive sensory and sympathetic cells was established by several groups (Banerjee *et al.*, 1973; Herrup and Shooter, 1973; Frazier *et al.*, 1974) but the characteristics of the receptors reported in these investigations were not the same. In particular Frazier *et al.* (1974) noted heterogeneous binding affinities and their data supported the idea of a negatively cooperative binding. In more recent work (Sutter *et al.*, 1979a) NGF receptors with two different affinities have been described and the interconversion of one receptor to the other now demonstrated (Landreth and Shooter, 1980; Cohen *et al.*, 1980).

The development of a method for the preparation of ^{125}I-labeled NGF which retained full biological ativity and which displayed low nonspecific binding permitted the identification of a class of NGF receptors with high affinity while the use of a rapid centrifugation assay allowed the characterization of NGF-NGF receptor complexes with short half-lives (Sutter *et al.*, 1979a). The steady state binding of [^{125}I]NGF to viable cell dissociates of sensory ganglia of 8-day-old chick embryos over a wide range of [^{125}I]NGF concentrations is shown in Fig. 3. Specific binding approaches saturation at 3 n*M* and half saturation at approx. 1 n*M* [^{125}I]NGF indicating one class of NGF receptors with an equilibrium dissociation constant of approx. 1 n*M* (Site I in Sutter *et al.*, 1979a). At concentrations less than 0.1 n*M* [^{125}I]NGF nonspecific binding is virtually zero and a second class of receptors with a dissociation equilibrium constant of approx. 0.01 n*M* is evident (Site II). Scatchard analysis of the binding data (Fig. 4) gives more precise values of 1.4×10^{-9} *M* for the equilibrium dissociation constant of the low-affinity receptor and 2×10^{-11} *M* for the high-affinity receptor, affinities which differ by about two orders of magnitude. As judged from the Scatchard analysis the low-affinity receptors predominate being present in approx. 10-fold greater numbers than the high-affinity receptors.

The two receptors differ mainly in the rate at which they release bound [^{125}I]NGF. The dissociation of [^{125}I]NGF from the high-affinity receptor can be determined independently of dissociation from the low-affinity receptor by preequilibrating the cells at concentrations below 10^{-11} *M* where binding is predominantly to the high-affinity receptor. The release of [^{125}I]NGF from these receptors is first order (Fig. 5 top curve) with a half-life of approx. 10

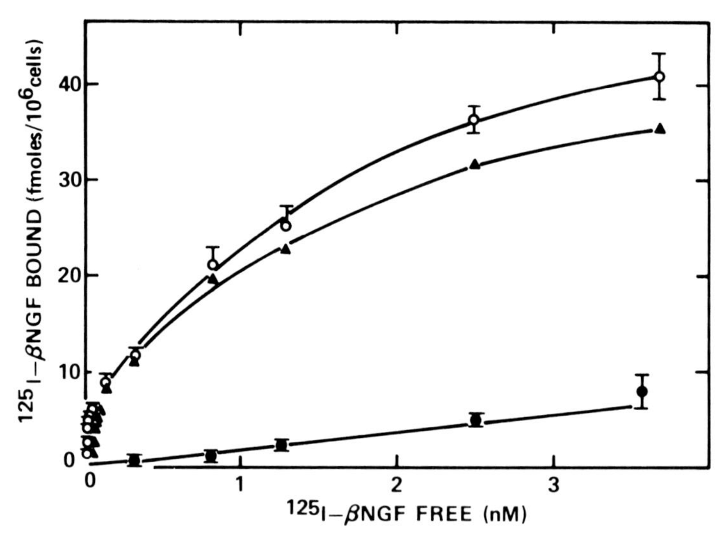

FIG. 3. Binding of [^{125}I]βNGF to sensory ganglion cells of 8-day-old chick embryos as a function of concentration. Cells (0.6×10^6/ml) were incubated at 37°C for 45 minutes with various concentrations (3 p*M* to 3.7 n*M*) of [^{125}I]βNGF. For each point, 3 aliquots of 100 μl each were processed. Nonspecific binding of [^{125}I]βNGF was measured in the presence of 10 μg/ml of unlabeled βNGF. ○, Total binding; ▲, specific binding; ●, nonspecific binding. Reproduced with permission from Sutter *et al.* (1979a).

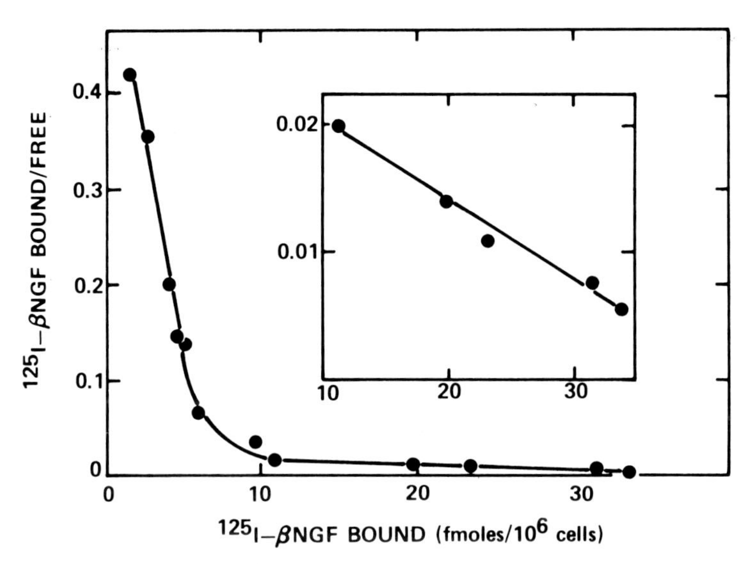

FIG. 4. Scatchard analysis of the data shown in Fig. 3. Binding data for the low-affinity region are expanded in the inset. Reproduced as for Fig. 3.

minutes. The dissociation of [^{125}I]NGF from the low-affinity receptor can, in turn, be observed by preequilibrating the cells at higher concentrations to obtain significant occupation of these receptors. As shown by the lower two curves in Fig. 5 the dissociation of [^{125}I]NGF from cells loaded under these conditions is biphasic. Part of the labeled NGF is released rapidly and part at a rate which corresponds to the rate of release from the high-affinity receptors. Since the fraction which is released rapidly increases when the occupancy of the low-affinity receptor is increased in the preloading it follows that the rapid phase represents release from the low-affinity receptors. Although the actual rate is too fast to measure by the sedimentation technique where the average sedimentation time for the cell-bound [^{125}I]NGF is approx. 3 seconds the half-life must be of the order of a few seconds or less. It is clear therefore that the approx. 100-fold difference in the equilibrium dissociation constants of the two receptors is reflected in a similar difference in the rates of dissociation. The high-affinity receptor binds NGF more tightly by releasing it more slowly than does the low-affinity receptor. The dissociation curves also allow the calculation, from the intercepts on the ordinate, of the fractional occupancy of high- and low-affinity receptors at any preloading [^{125}I]NGF concentration. These calculated occupancy rates are close to those predicted from the steady-state binding data.

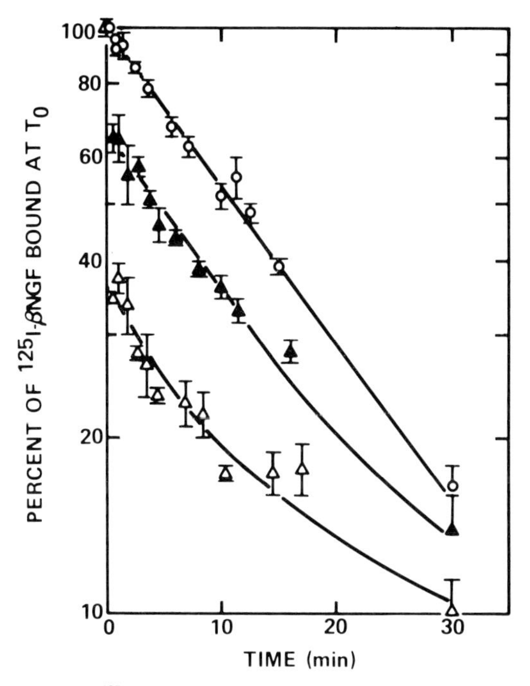

FIG. 5. Dissociation of [^{125}I]βNGF after preequilibration with different [^{125}I]βNGF concentrations at 37°C. Cells (3×10^6/ml) were preincubated for 30 minutes with 0.6×10^{-11} *M* (○), 1.6×10^{-10} *M* (▲), and 1.36×10^{-9} *M* (△) [^{125}I]βNGF. The dissociation of [^{125}I]βNGF was induced by the addition of 3.8×10^{-7} *M* unlabeled βNGF. The specific binding at t_0 was measured in sextuplets and after different times of dissociation in triplicates of 100 μl each. The data are corrected for nonspecific binding. Reproduced with permission from Sutter *et al.* (1979a).

Are these two NGF receptors characterized by steady-state and kinetic criteria independent populations of receptors or is one population generated from the other? The biphasic behavior of the dissociation of [^{125}I]NGF argues against the generation of the low-affinity receptors from high-affinity receptors by a process of negative cooperativity. All three dissociation curves shown in Fig. 5 were obtained in the presence of a large excess (3.8×10^{-7} *M*) of unlabeled NGF. The addition of the unlabeled NGF results in the very rapid saturation of all unoccupied receptor sites and if the NGF induces a conversion of high-affinity to low-affinity receptors then only one dissociation rate (that characteristic of the low-affinity state) should be observed. Rather is the converse true, the pattern of dissociation is dependent on the relative occupancy of the two receptors prior to the induction of dissociation by addition of unlabeled NGF indicating that the phenomenon of negative cooperativity cannot be invoked to explain the existence of the two receptor states.

It should be noted that the release of [^{125}I]NGF from the high-affinity receptor is accelerated by addition of excess unlabeled NGF (Frazier *et al.*, 1974; Sutter *et al.*, 1979a), a result normally interpreted as showing negative cooperativity because of the increased receptor occupancy. However the rate of dissociation is also accelerated when the concentration of added unlabeled NGF is chosen so as to decrease rather than increase receptor occupancy during dissociation, a result opposite to that predicted on the basis of negative cooperativity. It appears that at least part of the explanation for the effect of unlabeled NGF in increasing the rate of dissociation of bound [^{125}I]NGF lies in the presence of an "unstirred layer" around cell or membrane surfaces. The same phenomenon of an increased dissociation rate in the presence of unlabeled NGF is also seen with NGF receptors on membrane fragments from sensory ganglia (Riopelle *et al.*, 1980). When these fragments are vigorously stirred the release of [^{125}I]NGF is increased over that from unstirred fragments even in the absence of added unlabeled NGF. Although the increased rate is not as high as that obtained in the presence of unlabeled NGF this experiment does show that stirring can disrupt the "unstirred layer" to some extent and reduce the rebinding of [^{125}I]NGF trapped in this layer.

The reasonable agreement between the equilibrium dissociation constants determined from equilibrium and kinetic data, respectively (Sutter *et al.*, 1979a) suggests that the interaction of NGF with its receptors on sensory cells in suspension is reversible, at least over a 45-minute period, and that internalization by endocytosis is not a major contributor to the binding characteristics. This is confirmed by the negligible lysosomal degradation which occurs under these conditions and by the finding that both kinetic and steady state binding data show the same two receptors at 2°C as well as 37°C (Sutter *et al.*, 1979a). It is of interest to note that while the affinities of the two receptors are similar at the low as compared to the high temperature the number of high-affinity receptors is significantly less at 2°C than at 37°C. The implications of these results in terms of the generation of high from low-affinity receptors are discussed later.

Both receptors are specific for NGF since only NGF of a variety of hormones tested (insulin, proinsulin, somatomedins A and C, and epidermal growth factor) competes with the binding of [^{125}I]NGF to either receptor (Sutter *et al.*, 1979a). The same two receptors are found on chick sympathetic neurons in similar numbers (Godfrey and Shooter, 1979; Olender and Stach, 1980) and on PC12 pheochromocytoma cells after the latter have been exposed to NGF (Landreth and Shooter, 1980). The binding of one, well-characterized derivative of NGF has been analyzed in some detail to determine if alterations in the binding to one receptor are paralleled by similar changes in the binding to the other receptor. Such a result would support the idea that the two receptors reflect different states of a single receptor. The Trp-21 residue is the most reactive of the three tryptophan residues in the NGF monomer and is readily oxidized by *N*-bromosuccinimide (Frazier *et al.*, 1973). The dose–response curves for the NGF-induced neurite outgrowth on sensory or PC12 pheochromocytoma cells show that 20- to 30-fold higher concentrations of this particular oxidized derivative of NGF are required to elicit half-maximum biological response than native NGF (Cohen *et al.*, 1980). This decrease in biological activity is paralleled by a decreased binding to NGF receptors on both types of cells. On sensory cells the affinity of the derivative for the high-affinity receptor is 2.5% and on PC12 cells 1.2% of that of native NGF. The derivative also shows exactly the same relative affinities for the low-affinity receptors on the two cells. In other words the binding of the derivative to the low-affinity receptors is decreased to the same extent as the binding to the high-affinity receptors supporting the idea that the receptors share common structural features in their binding sites which are equally sensitive to changes in the NGF structure.

The interpretation of the residual activity of the modified NGF relies on the proof that this activity is not due to 1–3% residual native NGF in the oxidized preparation. Although this is unlikely from the way in which the oxidized derivative is prepared it is possible to measure the actual amount of residual native NGF by a cytotoxicity assay. In this assay sensory cells carrying the high-affinity NGF receptor are lysed in the presence of NGF, anti-NGF antiserum, and complement. The proportion of sensory ganglion cells which are lysed increases with increasing NGF concentration until it reaches a maximum at 3.8×10^{-11} *M* NGF (Zimmermann *et al.*, 1978). Since no lysis is detected with amounts of the oxidized NGF 500-fold greater than concentrations of NGF which give significant lysis this places the maximum level of residual native NGF at 0.2%. Lysis was detected at a 1000-fold ratio suggesting the actual fraction of unmodified NGF in the preparation is between 0.1 and 0.2% and therefore insufficient to account for the residual activity of this derivative.

B. THE CONVERSION OF LOW- TO HIGH-AFFINITY RECEPTORS

As noted earlier steady-state binding experiments with PC12 pheochromocytoma cells indicate that NGF binds to these cells with two differing affinities (Yankner and Shooter, 1979; Landreth and Shooter, 1980). In contrast to these experiments which assess binding characteristics after exposure of the cells to NGF for 30 minutes or longer, competition assays show only one type of receptor on naive PC12 cells, the low-affinity receptor (Cohen *et al.*, 1980). Competition assays, in which varying proportions of unlabeled and labeled NGF are added to PC12 cells, reflect the state of the receptor at the moment of addition and therefore suggest that PC12 cells initially possess only low-affinity receptors (see also Herrup and Thoenen, 1979). This point was proved by taking advantage of the fact that the rate of release of NGF from the high-affinity receptor on PC12 cells is very slow at 0°C. A brief wash of the cells with unlabeled NGF-containing medium at any time during the binding of [^{125}I]NGF therefore removes only [^{125}I]NGF bound to low-affinity receptors and allows an assessment of both types of binding. Using this protocol it is clear that only low-affinity receptors are initially found on PC12 cells and that the high-affinity receptors appear only after a time lag (Landreth and Shooter, 1980). The continued generation of high- from low-affinity binding is also observed on PC12 cells when [^{125}I]NGF is removed from the medium after initiating binding (Fig. 6). That the phenomenon of receptor conversion occurs on the cell surface is evident from the fact that a major fraction of [^{125}I]NGF bound to the high-affinity receptors can be recovered by dissociation at 37°C. The conversion also confers a limited trypsin resistance to the high-affinity receptor and its bound NGF. Even at high NGF concentrations only a limited fraction (approx. 10%) of the low-affinity receptors undergo conversion. Whether this reflects the need for binding of the receptor to another membrane protein present in limiting amount or the probability of receptor cross-linking by the bivalent NGF dimer is not yet known. It seems likely that the conversion reflects in some way the clustering of receptors resulting from their lateral diffusion in the membrane, a phenomenon described for other hormones and growth factors (Schlessinger *et al.*, 1978; Haigler *et al.*, 1979). Of particular interest is the finding that the clustering of the EGF-EGF receptor complexes on A431 carcinoma cells is seen after about 30 seconds (Haigler *et al.*, 1979), a time which is similar to the lag observed in the appearance of high-affinity receptors on PC12 cells. Also it is known that the cross-linking of occupied insulin receptors by insulin antibodies converts the receptor from a low- to a high-affinity state (Schecter *et al.*, 1979) and that membrane glycoproteins from liver plasma membranes interact with solubilized insulin receptors and increase their affinity (Maturo and Hollenberg, 1978).

C. THE FATE OF THE RECEPTOR-BOUND NGF

1. Internalization

Why are the low-affinity receptors converted by NGF to a higher affinity form? First it should be noted that one biological response to NGF, the outgrowth of neurites from sensory neurons, occurs at very low NGF

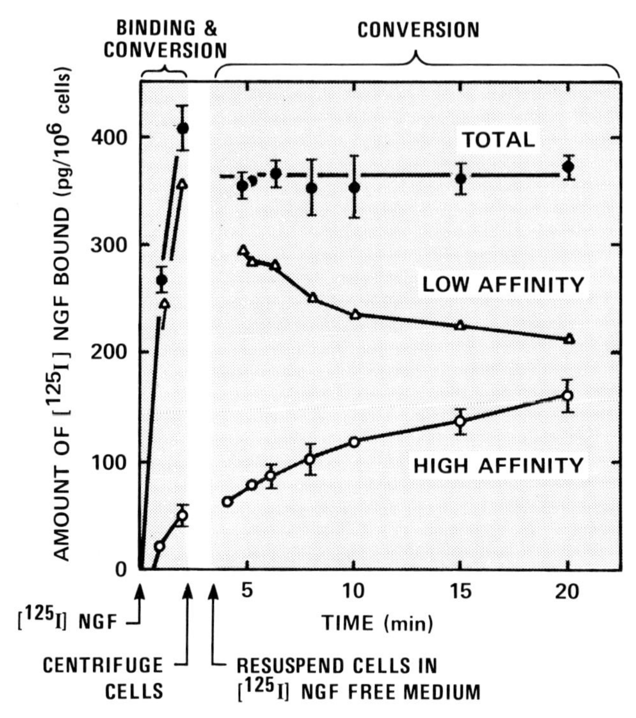

FIG. 6. Effect of removal of [^{125}I]NGF from the medium on NGF binding to PC12 cells. PC12 cells were incubated with 35 p*M* [^{125}I]NGF at 37°C for 2 minutes. The cells were centrifuged for 1 minute at 1000 *g*, the [^{125}I]NGF-containing medium was aspirated, and the cells were resuspended in the same volume of fresh medium (arrow). Total binding (●), high-affinity binding (○), and low-affinity binding (△) were determined. Each point represents the mean ± SD of triplicate determinations. Reproduced with permission from Landreth and Shooter (1980).

concentrations (Sutter *et al.*, 1979b). Half-maximal response for neurite outgrowth from sensory neurons is found at 2×10^{-12} *M* NGF, a concentration which formally corresponds to an occupancy of about 8% of the high-affinity receptors but only 0.1% of the low-affinity receptors. If the biological response is mediated solely by the low-affinity receptors then the mechanism must be exquisitely sensitive. A more likely possibility is that the response correlates with occupancy of high-affinity receptors and this in turn emphasizes the importance of the conversion to the higher affinity state of the receptor. In support of this are the observations from both binding data (Sutter *et al.*, 1979b) and a cytotoxic assay (Zimmermann *et al.*, 1978) that the high-affinity receptor is restricted to the neurons in dissociates of embryonic sensory ganglion dissociates.

Recent observations suggest that the conversion is intimately linked to the internalization of NGF on its receptor, at least on PC12 cells. As shown in Fig. 7A down regulation of NGF binding is manifest by a decrease in the number of low-affinity receptors. High-affinity binding is maintained at steady state when the external concentration of [^{125}I]NGF is high (Fig. 7A) but decreases when the concentration is low (Fig. 7B) suggesting that high-affinity receptors are internalized.

This can be demonstrated directly by removing the low-affinity receptors and their bound NGF by limited trypsin digestion after maximum binding is attained (as noted above the high-affinity receptors are resistant to such treatment). The down regulation of the high-affinity receptors is then observed over the next 2 to 3 hours and results in the loss of approx. two-thirds of the receptors. The apparent steady state of high-affinity binding at high external [^{125}I]NGF concentrations can therefore be explained by a balance between the internalization of high-affinity receptors and their replenishment by the conversion of low-affinity receptors. Fur-

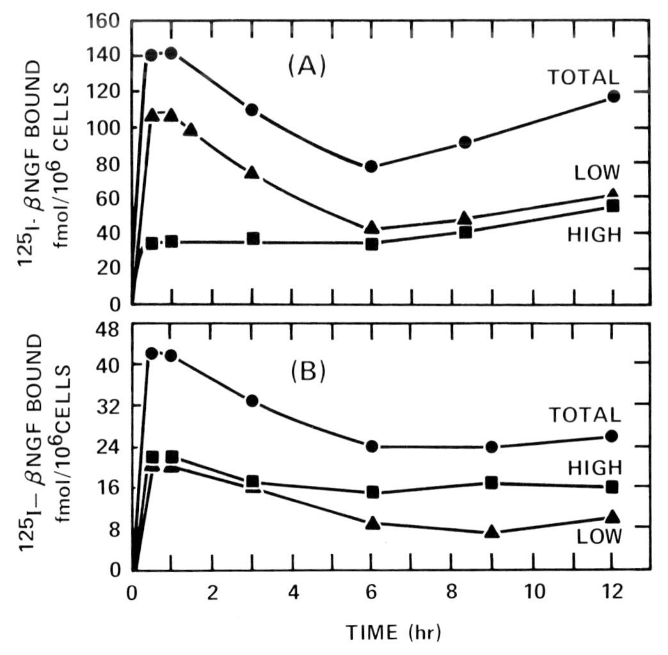

FIG. 7. Time course of the total (●), low-affinity (▲), and high-affinity (■) binding of [^{125}I]βNGF to the PC12 cell. Cells were incubated with [^{125}I]βNGF at 37°C and binding was determined at specified times. Each point represents the means of three determinations from which nonspecific binding has been subtracted. (A) 100 ng/ml [^{125}I]βNGF. (B) 5 ng/ml [^{125}I]βNGF.

thermore it is possible that the conversion of the low-affinity receptors serves to establish a new rate of receptor internalization.

2. Intracellular Transport

Upon subfractionation of the PC12 cell specific receptors for NGF are found associated with the nucleus (Yankner and Shooter, 1979). The nuclear receptors are localized to the membrane and are not found on chromatin. The equilibrium dissociation constant of the higher affinity nuclear receptor is similar to that of its plasma membrane counterpart. Two lines of evidence suggest that nuclear high-affinity receptors may arise by insertion of the internalized surface receptor–NGF complex into the nuclear membrane. First an increase in the high-affinity receptor content of the nucleus is observed after incubation of PC12 cells with NGF (Yankner and Shooter, 1979) and second the high-affinity receptor is simultaneously absent from both the cell surface and the nucleus of a nonresponding mutant of the PC12 cell (B. A. Yankner and E. M. Shooter, unpublished data). Although the high-affinity nuclear receptor may be translocated from the cell surface it differs from the latter in its resistance to solubilization by the nonionic detergent Triton X-100, a property which may be used to assay the translocation of NGF to the nucleus. It is important to note that the detergent does not promote transfer of receptors from cell membranes to the nucleus since if membranes and nuclei, both with bound [^{125}I]NGF, are combined and extracted with Triton X-100 the residual Triton-resistant binding of [^{125}I]NGF represents the initial contribution of the nuclei (Yankner and Shooter, 1979).

The translocation of NGF to the nucleus of PC12 cells is most readily observed when the cells are held in suspension and are unable to develop neurites. Nuclear accumulation of NGF on high-affinity receptors begins after a lag period of about 20 minutes and continues steadily over a further period of 20 hours long after the total high-affinity binding to the cell reaches steady state. At this stage nuclear NGF accounts for about two-thirds of the total high-affinity cell bound NGF. The translocation is temperature dependent and does not occur at 4°C. In contrast to the behavior of PC12 cells in suspension cells in monolayer on plastic can extend neurites and, as noted above (Section III,C,1), show significant down regulation of high-affinity NGF receptors. This down regulation is accompanied by lysosomal degradation of the internalized NGF as is apparent from the chloroquine-sensitivity of the down regulation and the release of ^{125}I-labeled tyrosine into the medium (P. Layer and E. M. Shooter, unpublished observations). It is only after this initial degradative period which lasts between 1 and 5 hours that NGF is detected in the nucleus (Figs. 8 and 9). That sequestration of NGF in the lysosomes is indeed an initial

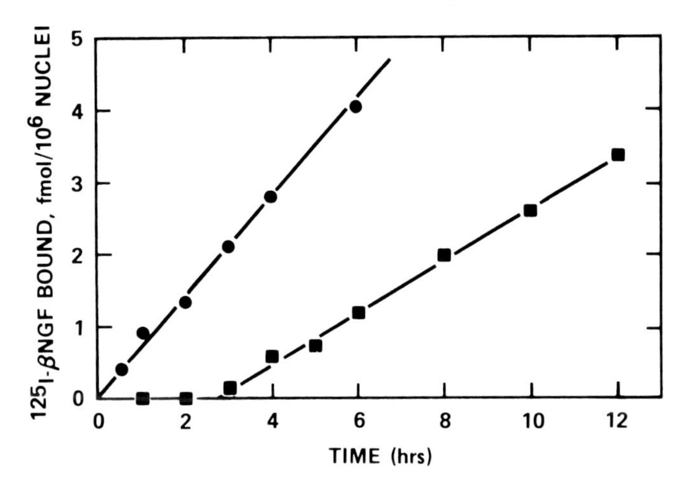

FIG. 8. Time course of the initial appearance of NGF in the nucleus of the PC12 cell in the presence (●) or absence (○) of 0.1 mM chloroquine. Cells were incubated with 100 ng/ml of [^{125}I]βNGF at 37°C. Each point represents the mean of three determinations from which nonspecific binding has been subtracted.

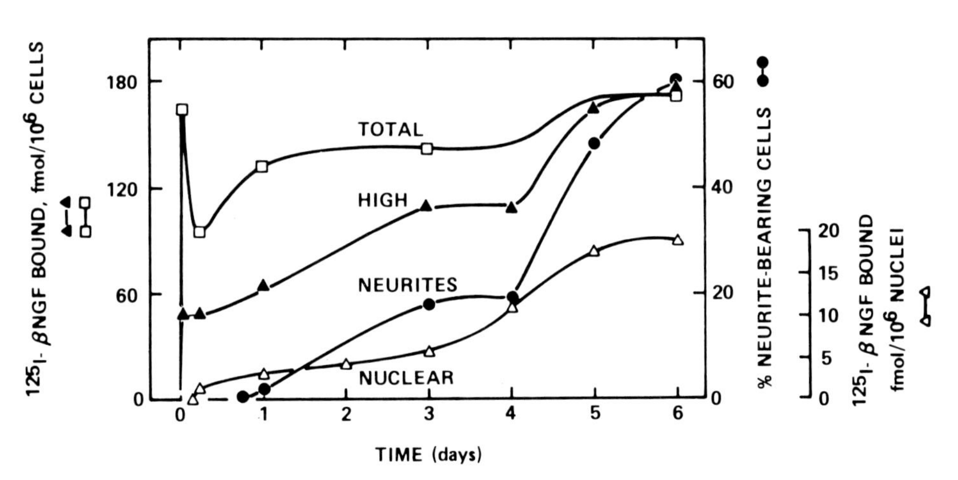

FIG. 9. Long-term time course of total binding (□), high-affinity binding (▲), nuclear binding (△), and neurite outgrowth (●). PC12 cells were continuously incubated with 100 ng/ml of [^{125}I]βNGF for 6 days in DMEM/BSA with a change of medium and [^{125}I]βNGF on days 2 and 4. Each point represents the mean of three determinations from which nonspecific binding has been subtracted. Neuritic processes which extended one cell diameter or more in length were scored in the assay for neurite outgrowth. Each point represents the mean of four determinations of at least 300 cells each. All of the above parameters were determined on the same cells as described in experimental procedures.

barrier to nuclear translocation is supported by the finding that chloroquine abolishes the delay in the appearance of NGF in the nucleus and accelerates the rate of nuclear accumulation (Fig. 8). The transloca-tion of NGF to the nucleus of PC12 cells in monolayer is a slow process which begins to saturate after 5 to 6 days of incubation (Fig. 9). Nuclear translocation precedes neurite outgrowth and there is an approximate correlation between nuclear accumulation of NGF and the number of cells committed to neurite outgrowth. The NGF which reaches the nucleus is intact as judged by electrophoresis under denaturing conditions. In addi-tion it retains its biological activity as determined by the ability of NGF dissociated from isolated nuclei to elicit the neurite outgrowth response when readded to PC12 cells.

The differences between the lysosomal degradation of NGF by PC12 cells in monolayer, where they flatten by adhesion to the substratum, and in suspension, where they are more spherical, suggest an involvement of the cytoskeleton in the translocation of NGF to the lysosomes. While pretreatment of cells with 1 μM cytochalasin D did not alter the binding of NGF nor the subsequent down regulation, lysosomal degradation was in-hibited approx. 90% and translocation to the nucleus enhanced. Since cytochalasin D is effective in the disruption of actin filaments it would appear that translocation of internalized NGF to lysosomes is mediated by actin microfilaments (Fig. 10). The microtubule-disrupting agent col-chicine has little effect on the lysosomal degradation of NGF but enhances nuclear binding. Thus translocation to the nucleus is mediated by neither actin microfilaments nor microtubules and may involve passive diffusion of the NGF-containing vesicles and their subsequent fusion with nuclear membrane (Fig. 10). These data suggest an ordered temporal sequence in the translocation of NGF within the cell as depicted in the model in Fig. 10 with NGF-containing vesicles being initially directed toward the lyso-somes. The lysosomotropic drug chloroquine promotes the accumulation of ligand-containing vesicles within the cell (Libby *et al.*, 1980) and this may be the reason for the rapid appearance of NGF in the nucleus in the presence of chloroquine. Antipain and leupeptin do not promote such an accumulation and have only a slight effect on the rate of appearance of NGF in the nucleus. They do significantly inhibit lysosomal degradation (Umezawa, 1976) over a period of 2 days but this has no effect on neurite outgrowth, suggesting that the products of NGF degradation are not in-volved in its mechanism of action.

3. *The Significance of Nuclear Binding*

The translocation of NGF to the nucleus of the PC12 cell is a process which is regulated by events within the cell and the data in the previous

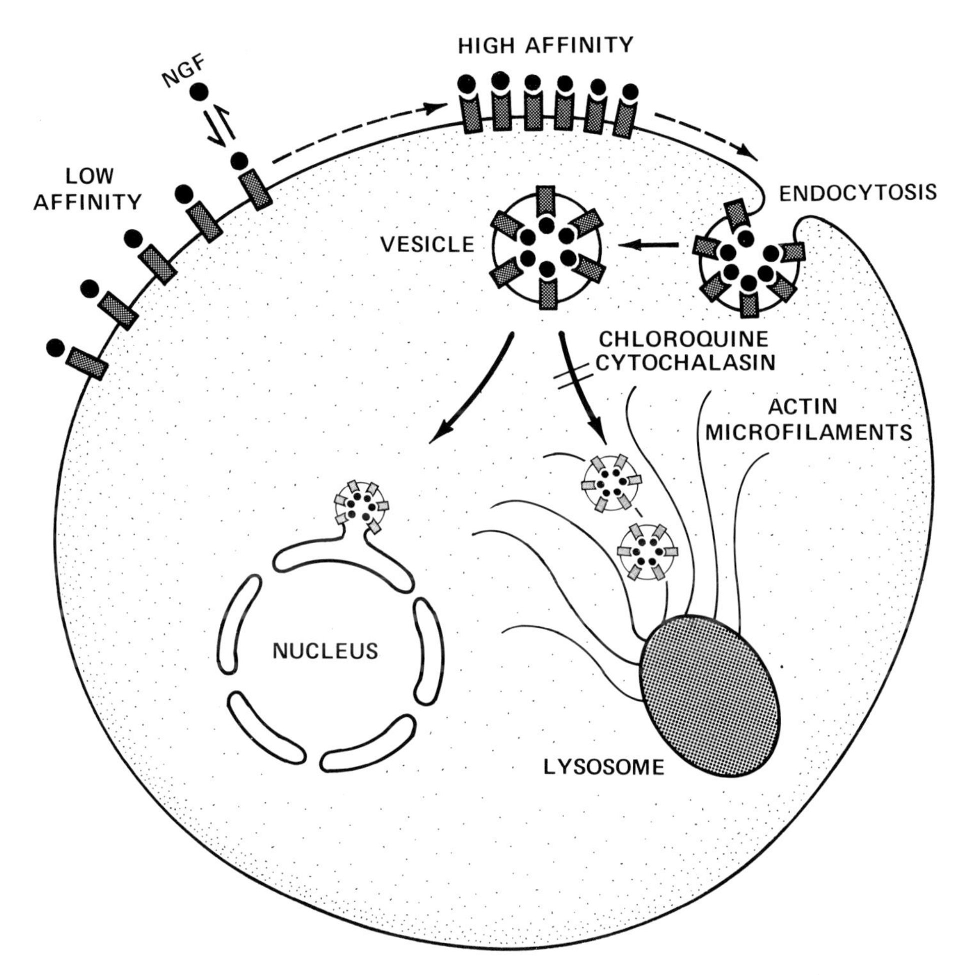

FIG. 10. Steps in the binding, internalization, and intracellular transport of NGF.

section emphasize how this regulation can be modulated. Is the translocation essential for the morphological biological response, the outgrowth of neurites? This is a particularly important question because morphological studies, albeit in different systems, have thus far not produced evidence to parallel the biochemical data discussed above. It is well known, for example, that NGF is internalized at sympathetic nerve endings and transported retrogradely to the cell body (Hendry *et al.*, 1974; Campenot, 1977). The NGF which reaches the cell body is intact (Stöckel *et al.*, 1976; Johnson *et al.*, 1978) and biologically active (Paravicini *et al.*, 1975). Autoradiographic studies with the electron microscope (Schwab and

Thoenen, 1977) show that the majority of the transported NGF is associated with smooth endoplasmic reticulum and in vesicles and a smaller fraction in secondary lysosomes. No NGF was observed in the nucleus. Experiments using horseradish peroxidase-coupled NGF gave the same results (Schwab, 1977). The characterization of the properties of the nuclear-bound NGF now offer some explanation for these differences and suggest its importance in the biological response.

A rapidly responding variant of the PC12 cell, the PCR cell, selected in medium containing 1% horse serum, shows significant neurite outgrowth after 24 hours in NGF as well as significant nuclear accumulation of NGF. The amount of NGF translocated to the nucleus can be manipulated by adding anti-NGF IgG to the incubation medium at increasing time intervals after the initial addition of ^{125}I-labeled NGF. Addition of this antibody at any time in the first 4 hours of incubation prevents translocation of NGF to the nucleus (Fig. 11A). With longer pulse times of [^{125}I]NGF incubation before addition of antibody increasing levels of NGF are detected in the nucleus after 24 hours. The response of these populations of cells with respect to neurite outgrowth at 24 hours is shown in Fig. 11B. No neurite outgrowth is observed when no NGF reaches the nucleus but increasing response is seen with increasing levels of NGF in the nucleus. These data suggest that internalization of NGF relevant to nuclear transport does not occur until approx. 4 hours after the start of the incubation (the time during which down regulation of receptors and degradation of NGF are maximal) and that these is a correlation between the amount of NGF reaching the nucleus and the extent of commitment of the PCR cells to neurite outgrowth. It is of interest to note that this delayed response, presumably resulting from a delayed internalization relevant to this response, is observed with another growth factor. At least 6 hours of continuous incubation of 3T3 fibroblasts is required to elicit a mitogenic response (Schechter *et al.*, 1978).

PC12 cells induced in NGF for 5 days acquire the capacity to regenerate neurites much more rapidly than naive cells (Greene, 1977). They lose this capacity when NGF is withdrawn slowly with a half-life of about 32 hours (Burstein and Greene, 1978). The PCR cells show the same characteristics and interestingly the rate of loss of NGF from the nucleus of PCR cell bodies previously incubated with [^{125}I]NGF for 5 days follows the same time course (Fig. 12A) and parallels the decay in the regenerative capacity of these cells (Fig. 12B). These results therefore suggest the involvement of the nuclear pathway in the biological response to NGF. Moreover the long life-time of NGF in the nucleus means that little or no [^{125}I]NGF will reach the nucleus of the cell unless the length of the pulse with the labeled NGF is also very long and this may explain, in part, why the autoradio-

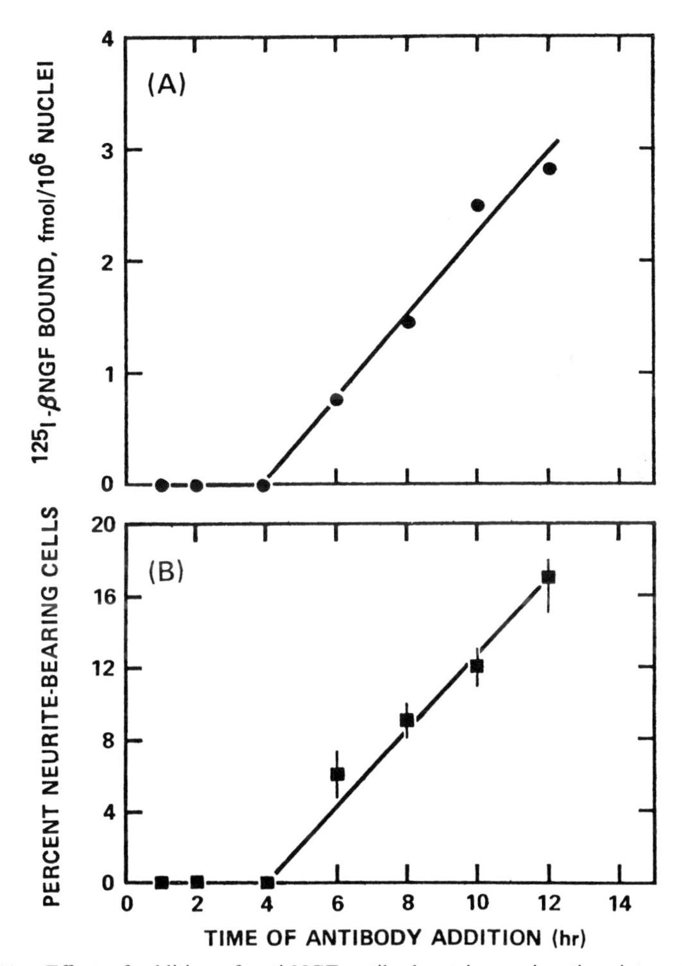

FIG. 11. Effect of addition of anti-NGF antibody at increasing time intervals on the translocation of NGF to the nucleus and the outgrowth of neuritic processes. PCR cells in monolayer on 6.5 cm plastic tissue culture dishes were incubated with 100 ng/ml of [^{125}I]βNGF in DMEM/0.1% BSA for 24 hours during which time anti-NGF IgG was added after increasing time intervals. Control cultures were coincubated with [^{125}I]βNGF and antibody from the start. (A) Translocation of [^{125}I]βNGF to the nucleus. After 24 hours of incubation, the cells were dislodged from the plate by trituration and extracted with 1% Triton X-100. Each point represents the mean of three determinations from which nonspecific binding derived from the control incubation has been subtracted. (B) Extension of neuritic processes. After 24 hours of incubation, the cells were scored for NGF-mediated neurite outgrowth. Neurites which extended one cell diameter or more in length were counted. Each point represents the mean of five determinations of at least 300 cells each.

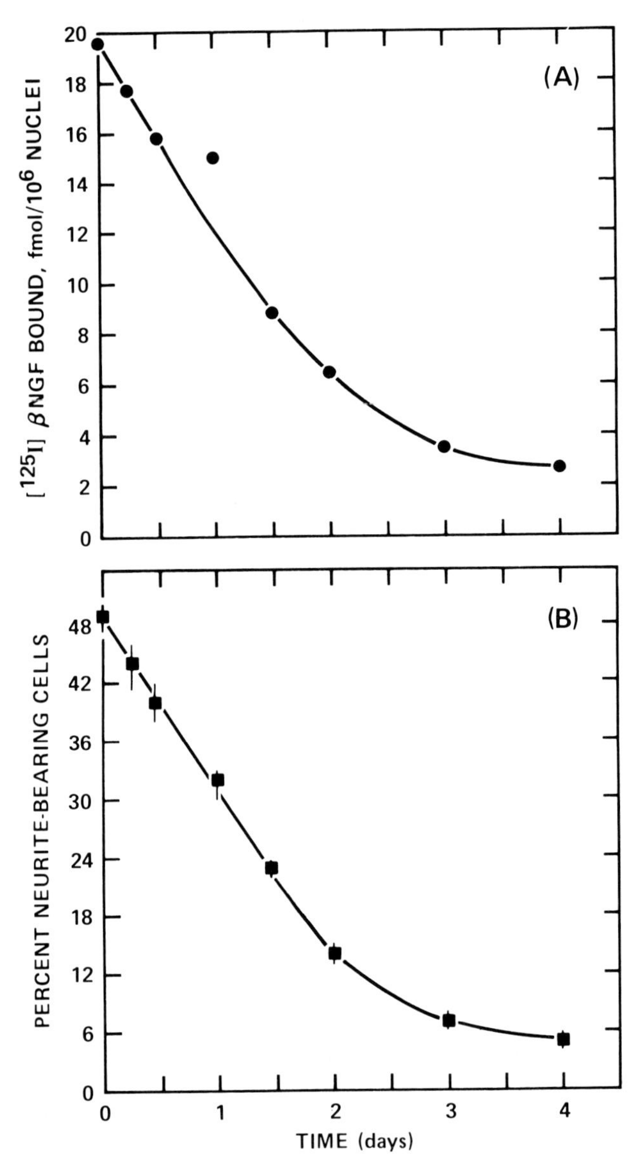

FIG. 12. (A) Dissociation of NGF from the nucleus in the intact cell. PCR cells were incubated with 100 ng/ml of [^{125}I]βNGF in DMEM/0.1% BSA for 5 days with a change of medium and NGF on days 2 and 4. On day 5, the medium was removed and the cells were washed 8 times with DMEM/0.1% BSA by centrifugation and resuspension. The cells were then replated in DMEM containing 5% horse and 10% fetal calf serum in the presence of anti-NGF IgG. At increasing time intervals after the removal of NGF, the [^{125}I]βNGF remaining in the nucleus was determined. Control cultures previously coincubated with 100

graphic studies have thus far failed to find [^{125}I]NGF in the nucleus. Nuclear receptors for other hormones have been described, for example insulin (Goldfine and Smith, 1976), which share many of the properties of the NGF nuclear receptor and the translocation of EGF to the nucleus of cultured pituitary cells (Johnson *et al.*, 1980) shows many similarities to the accumulation of NGF in the nuclei of PC12 cells. It will be of considerable interest to attempt to elucidate the nature of the regulatory processes which control the intracellular pathways for hormones and growth factors, the identity of the membrane proteins which may be carried into the cell with the ligand, and the molecular consequences of the interaction of NGF with the nucleus. At least one of the latter may be the phosphorylation of specific nuclear proteins (Halegoua and Patrick, 1981) and of microtubule associated proteins (C. Richter-Landsberg, G. E. Landreth, and E. M. Shooter, unpublished data).

ACKNOWLEDGMENTS

Original research described in this article was supported by grants from NINCDS (NS-04270), NIAMDD (AM-25434), NSF (BNS 79-14088), the American Cancer Society (BC-325), and an NIH Training Grant GM-07365.

REFERENCES

Angeletti, R. H., Hermodson, M. A. and Bradshaw, R. A. (1973). *Biochemistry* **12**, 100.
Au, M. J., and Dunn, M. F. (1977). *Biochemistry* **16**, 3958.
Banerjee, S. P., Snyder, S. H., Cuatrecasas, P., and Greene, L. A. (1973). *Proc. Natl. Acad. Sci. U.S.A.* **70**, 2519.
Berger, E. A., and Shooter, E. M. (1977). *Proc. Natl. Acad. Sci. U.S.A.* **74**, 3647.
Bothwell, M. A., and Shooter, E. M. (1977). *J. Biol. Chem.* **252**, 8532.
Bothwell, M. A., and Shooter, E. M. (1978). *J. Biol. Chem.* **253**, 8458.
Bradshaw, R. A. (1978). *Annu. Rev. Biochem.* **47**, 191.
Burstein, D. E., and Greene, L. A. (1978). *Proc. Natl. Acad. Sci. U.S.A.* **75**, 6059.
Burton, L. E., Wilson, W. H., and Shooter, E. M. (1978). *J. Biol. Chem.* **253**, 7807.
Campenot, R. B. (1977). *Proc. Natl. Acad. Sci. U.S.A.* **74**, 4516.
Cohen, S. (1960). *Proc. Natl. Acad. Sci. U.S.A.* **46**, 302.
Cohen, P., Sutter, A., Landreth, G., Zi-mermann, A., and Shooter, E. M. (1980). *J. Biol. Chem.* **255**, 2949.

---

ng/ml of [^{125}I]βNGF and 10 μg/ml of unlabeled NGF were used to determine nonspecific binding. Each point represents the mean of three determinations from which nonspecific binding has been subtracted. (B) Loss of the capacity for spontaneous regeneration of neurites after the removal of NGF. PCR cells were incubated with NGF and treated as in (A). At increasing time intervals after the removal of NGF, the cells were replated on polylysine-coated dishes and scored 1 day later for neurite regeneration. Each point represents the mean of five determinations of at least 300 cells each.

Frazier, W. A., Angeletti, R. A. H., Sherman, R., and Bradshaw, R. A. (1973). *Biochemistry* **12,** 3281.

Frazier, W. A., Boyd, L. F., and Bradshaw, R. A. (1974). *J. Biol. Chem.* **249,** 5513.

Frey, P., Forand, R., Maciag, T., and Shooter, E. M. (1979). *Proc. Natl. Acad. Sci. U.S.A.* **76,** 6294.

Godfrey, E. W., and Shooter, E. M. (1979). *Soc. Neurosci.* **5,** 767.

Goldfine, I. D., and Smith, G. J. (1976). *Proc. Natl. Acad. Sci. U.S.A.* **73,** 1427.

Gorin, P., and Johnson, E. M. (1979). *Proc. Natl. Acad. Sci. U.S.A.* **76,** 5382.

Greene, L. A. (1977a). *Brain Res.* **133,** 350.

Greene, L. A., and Tischler, A. S. (1976). *Proc. Natl. Acad. Sci. U.S.A.* **73,** 2424.

Greene, L. A., Shooter, E. M., and Varon, S. (1968). *Proc. Natl. Acad. Sci. U.S.A.* **60,** 1383.

Greene, L. A., Shooter, E. M., and Varon, S. (1969). *Biochemistry* **8,** 3735.

Gundersen, R. W., and Barrett, J. N. (1979). *Science* **206,** 1079.

Haigler, H. T., McKanna, J. A., and Cohen, S. (1979). *J. Cell Biol.* **81,** 382.

Halegoua, S., and Patrick, J. (1981). *Cell* (in press).

Harris-Warrick, R. M., Bothwell, M. A., and Shooter, E. M. (1980). *J. Biol. Chem.* (in press)

Hendry, I. A. (1976). *Rev. Neurosci.* **2,** 149.

Hendry, I. A., K. Stöckel, Thoenen, H., and Iversen, L. L. (1974). *Brain Res.* **68,** 103.

Herrup, K., and Shooter, E. M. (1973). *Proc. Natl. Acad. Sci. U.S.A.* **70,** 3384.

Herrup, K., and Thoenen, H. (1979). *Exp. Cell Res.* **121,** 71.

Johnson, E. M., Andres, R. Y., and Bradshaw, R. A. (1978). *Brain Res.* **150,** 319.

Johnson, L. K., Vlodavsky, I., Baxter, J. D., and Gospodarowicz, D. (1980). *Nature* (*London*) **287,** 340.

Landreth, G. E., and Shooter, E. M. (1980). *Proc. Natl. Acad. Sci. U.S.A.* **77,** 4751.

Levi-Montalcini, R., and Angeletti, P. U. (1968). *Physiol. Rev.* **48,** 534.

Levi-Montalcini, R., and Booker, B. (1960). *Proc. Natl. Acad. Sci. U.S.A.* **46,** 384.

Libby, P., Bursztajn, S., and Goldberg, A. L. (1980). *Cell* **19,** 481.

Maturo, J. M., and Hollenberg, M. D. (1979). *Proc. Natl. Acad. Sci. U.S.A.* **75,** 3070.

Menesini-Chen, M. G., Chen, J. S., and Levi-Montalcini, R. (1978). *Arch. Ital. Biol.* **116,** 53.

Mobley, W. C., Schenker, A., and Shooter, E. M. (1976). *Biochemistry* **15,** 5543.

Moore, John B., Jr., Mobley, W. C., and Shooter, E. M. (1974). *Biochemistry* **13,** 833.

Murphy, R. A., Saide, J. D., Blanchard, M. H., and Young, M. (1977). *Proc. Natl. Acad. Sci. U.S.A.* **74,** 2672.

Olender, E. J., and Stach, R. W. (1980). *J. Biol. Chem.* **225,** 9338.

Paravicini, U., Stöckel, K., and Thoenen, H. (1975). *Brain Res.* **84,** 279.

Pattison, S. E., and Dunn, M. F. (1975). *Biochemistry* **14,** 2733.

Riopelle, R. J., Klearman, M., and Sutter, A. (1980). *Brain Res.* (in press).

Ronne, H., Anundir, H., Rask, L., and Peterson, P. A. (1979). *Biochem. Biophys. Res. Commun.* **87,** 330.

Schechter, Y., Chang, K.-J., Jacobs, S., and Cuatrecasas, P. (1979). *Proc. Natl. Acad. Sci. U.S.A.* **76,** 2720.

Schlessinger, J., Schechter, Y., Willingham, M. K., and Pastan, I. (1978). *Proc. Natl. Acad. Sci. U.S.A.* **75,** 2659.

Schwab, M. E. (1977). *Brain Res.* **130,** 190.

Schwab, M. E., and Thoenen, H. (1977). *Brain Res.* **122,** 459.

Server, A. C., and Shooter, E. M. (1977). *Adv. Prot. Chem.* **31,** 339.

Stach, R. W., and Shooter, E. M. (1980). *J. Neurochem.* **34,** 1499.

Stöckel, K., and Thoenen, H. (1975). *Brain Res.* **85,** 337.

Stöckel, K., Guroff, G., Schwab, M., and Thoenen, H. (1976). *Brain Res.* **109,** 271.

Sutter, A., Riopelle, R. J., Harris-Warrick, R. M., and Shooter, E. M. (1979a). *J. Biol. Chem.* **254,** 5972.

Sutter, A., Riopelle, R. J., Harris-Warrick, R. M., and Shooter, E. M. (1979b). "Transmembrane Signalling" (M. Bitensky, R. J. Collier, D. F. Steiner, and C. F. Fox, eds.), pp. 659. Liss, New York.

Taylor, J. M., Cohen, S., and Mitchell, W. M. (1970). *Proc. Natl. Acad. Sci. U.S.A.* **67,** 164.

Tischler, A. S., and Greene, L. A. (1978). *Lab. Invest.* **39,** 77.

Umezawa, H. (1976). *Methods Enzymol.* **55,** 678.

Varon, S., Nomura, J., and Shooter, E. M. (1967). *Biochemistry* **6,** 2202.

Varon, S., Nomura, J., and Shooter, E. M. (1968). *Biochemistry* **7,** 1296.

Yankner, B. A., and Shooter, E. M. (1979). *Proc. Natl. Acad. Sci. U.S.A.* **76,** 1269.

Young, M. (1979). *Biochemistry* **18,** 3050.

Zimmermann, A., Sutter, A., Samuelson, J., and Shooter, E. M. (1978). *J. Supramol. Struct.* **9,** 351.

DISCUSSION

W. Schrader: Do you feel that the low-affinity and high-affinity binding sites on the cell surface have a precursor–product relationship, or do you mean that there's a transport or shuffling of the ligand from the low-affinity to the high-affinity sites?

E. Shooter: The data that we have so far simply tell us that there is a change when NGF binds to low-affinity receptors which results in a receptor of higher affinity. We don't yet know the mechanism behind this change. One possible model is that the binding of ligand to low-affinity receptors allows the receptor to subsequently bind to an "effector" protein in the membrane and that this binding then induces a conformational change in the receptor effector which gives rise to the high affinity. It is also possible that the high affinity is a result of the micro-patching of the receptors, a manifestation of the first step in the internalization process.

W. Schrader: You mentioned that trypsinization of the cells destroyed the low-affinity binding sites but not the high affinity binding sites. If the occupancy of the low-affinity sites were obligatory for action, one would predict from that trypsin experiment that trypsinized cells would not respond. Alternatively, if only occupancy of the high-affinity binding sites were required, one would predict that trypsinized cells would respond. Have you done that experiment, and what were the results?

E. Shooter: Trypsinization of PC12 cells before binding of NGF eliminates all the cell surface receptors. However limited trypsinization after exposure of cells to NGF eliminates the low- but not the high-affinity receptors and its bound NGF. These cells when maintained in NGF will grow neurites but the time scale is sufficiently long (> 24 hours) for newly synthesized low-affinity receptors to be reinserted in the cell membrane. The critical experiment here would be to see if trypsinized cells will grow neurites when new receptor synthesis is inhibited and this has not yet been done.

C. R. Kahn: I also found this a very interesting talk and noted that there are many similarities to some of the processes regarding insulin action and processing. I have a couple of questions along the line that Dr. Schrader introduced, namely related to the issue of whether you are postulating a conversion between the low-affinity and high-affinity receptor or whether the change in binding could be due to some other factor. Most of the diagrams that you showed suggested that this was an induced confirmational change which occurred on NGF binding. If that were so, then one would predict positive cooperativity in binding curves and one would certainly predict that if one did Scatchard analysis at different times after binding one would see progressive increases in the amount of high affinity sites. Thus, one question is, if one looks at the binding characteristics at different times after binding does one see a change in the nature of the binding characteristics suggesting an induced change following the binding process? A second related question regarding the possible mechanism would be: does this occur in the broken cell or is the intact cell required? That is, if you solubilize the cell can you see the same changes? Finally, since there is internalization which is occurring concomitantly is part of the increased affinity binding which is being interpreted as binding really internalization or is this a subsequent and separate process which must be considered?

E. Shooter: Scatchard analysis of binding experiments at times shorter than the usual 45 minutes does show decreased high-affinity binding as the model predicts. However the analysis of these data is complicated by the fact that the rate of conversion to high-affinity receptors changes with the NGF concentration. The conversion of receptor affinity appears to be largely a surface phenomenon because at least 90% of the NGF bound to the high-affinity receptor can be recovered by dissociation in the presence of unlabeled NGF. The conversion also occurs at low temperature, although more slowly, and preliminary experiments show that it also takes place on isolated membranes.

C. R. Kahn: And in the solubilized preparation of the receptor do you see similar biphasic scattered plots suggesting that the same conversion can occur?

E. Shooter: We have not done these experiments.

A. Amsterdam: The question that I want to raise is, first, when you have synchronization of the NGF do you have any evidence that the receptor is internalized, in other words, if you get internalization can you also show transition in the number of receptors that you find in the nuclei, and the second question is what is really the structure that you have.

E. Shooter: We have no direct evidence that the receptor is internalized along with NGF; the model was developed by analogy with other hormone and growth factor systems where there is such evidence. Indirect evidence for the internalization of the receptor comes from the finding that the increase in the numbers of nuclear high-affinity NGF receptors on exposure of PC12 cells to NGF is roughly paralleled by a similar decrease in the numbers of cell surface high-affinity receptors. In answer to your second question there are no morphological experiments which, at the moment, parallel the biochemical ones reported here. Internalization of rhodamine-labeled NGF or of [^{125}I]NGF has been demonstrated in different cells in several laboratories. None of the internalized NGF was found associated with the nucleus but this may be a result, partly of using too short a time for the pulse of the labeled NGF and also of the relatively small proportion of NGF which reaches the nucleus and it is likely that quite long exposure of cells to labeled NGF will be required to discern nuclear translocation by autoradiography or visually.

H. B. Pollard: It seems to me to be still unclear whether the low-affinity receptor becomes converted to a high-affinity receptor or if in fact there are two receptors. There is a simple experiment that you can do, namely, to cross-link NGF to the low-affinity receptor and then ask if high-affinity receptors could later be developed.

E. Shooter: Attempts to cross-link NGF to its receptor have not yet been successful. One further piece of evidence in favor of the conversion is that at low NGF concentrations (10 p*M*) all the initially, low-affinity receptors on PC12 cells are converted to high-affinity receptors. This is deduced from the fact that the dissociation of NGF from PC12 cells loaded at low NGF concentrations is first-order with the rate characteristic of the high-affinity receptors.

H. B. Pollard: Are there any examples of a conversion of both kinds, a transfer of a peptide or other hormones from one low-affinity receptor to another different high-affinity receptor?

E. Shooter: Not that I know of, no. At least not the direct observation of the increase in affinity. There are several examples where the rate of dissociation of a ligand decreases with time and one interpretation of this phenomenon is that it reflects an increase in receptor affinity.

I. Rothchild: Among the very fascinating things that you told us about, the thing that fascinated me most of all was the question of how the cell decides between using the low-affinity and high-affinity receptor and I wonder whether you have any speculation on this and particularly whether the important factors that determine what happens to the NGF once it becomes bound to the cell might be the rate of production of its neurotransmitter or whatever active agent the cell uses to do its work. What is the relationship between the activity of the cell and the pathway of utilization of the NGF once it enters the cell?

E. Shooter: A very good question and one to which we have few, if any, answers. At the stage at which NGF is known to control neurotransmitter synthesis in the sympathetic nerve cell it is not acting to control neurite growth because the cell has a mature axon and synaptic connections. One assumption, therefore, is that the mechanisms underlying these two functions of NGF are separate. How the cell regulates the intracellular transport of NGF-containing vesicles is also an open question. It could be done at the cell surface or, as suggested here, intracellularly. If regulation is at the cell surface it is possible that low-affinity receptors and their bound NGF are internalized for transport to one location which is different to the location for the high-affinity receptor-containing vesicles. If regulation is within the cell then it follows from the experiments reported here that the primary pathway involves translocation of the NGF-containing vesicles to the lysosomes with transport to the nucleus coming later. This might imply that the lysosome or some aspects of the degradative activity of the lysosome has a regulatory function with respect to intracellular transport. However, other possibilities remain since when one pathway, that to the lysosomes, is inhibited by chloroquine a build up of vesicles occurs within the cell and the nuclear pathway is used.

S. Cohen: I'm a little bit concerned about your NGF antibody causing the death of the cell. I'm not sure that any committee has set up a set of criteria that determines when the cell shall be considered dead or alive. Does the nerve survival depend on growth of the axon or can it survive for a while, wait for the effect of the antibody to wear off, and later be responsive?

E. Shooter: The PC12 cells are resistant to antibody to NGF provided no complement is present in the medium. The experiment described above has its own internal control in the sense that neurite outgrowth is observed from cells exposed to antibody for times up to 20 hours. It is reasonable to conclude therefore that no neurite outgrowth is observed from cells exposed to anti-NGF IgG for 20 to 24 hours because no NGF reaches the nucleus rather than the cells are being killed by a few extra hours in the antibody-containing medium. In addition cells exposed to NGF and anti-NGF IgG for 24 hours will respond to fresh NGF after removal of the antibody.

S. Cohen: So the death of the cell does not necessarily follow the failure of the axon to grow. Does the life of the cell body depend on the growth of an axon?

E. Shooter: For primary cells such as embryonic sensory and sympathetic nerve cells the survival of the cell body ultimately depends on the growth of axons and the ability of these developing fibers to sequester NGF. The PC12 cell, on the other hand, can survive quite well in the absence of neurite growth and indeed of NGF and this makes it an ideal cell for the antibody experiments.

E. Peck: I am curious about the localization of the high-affinity receptor at the level of the nucleus. You have suggested it is on the inner nuclear membrane and that it is not solubilized by Triton. I am curious whether it is associated with the nuclear matrix as defined by Don Coffey instead of the nuclear membrane. Have you done any experiments along that line?

E. Shooter: No, we haven't. The use of the term "inner nuclear membrane" is based simply on the basis of the insolubility of the nuclear NGF receptor in Triton X-100. One interesting point is the increasing evidence for the location of the replisome of eukaryotic cells on inner nuclear membranes or matrices. The translocation of NGF to the nucleus of a PC12 cell at least brings it close to the replication apparatus.

L. Birnbaumer: I would like to ask you for verification of one of your experiments if I may, and that is the one that dealt with the interconversion of the receptors. If I understood well, if you wash your membranes, you lose your low-affinity binding, yet you had to wash to see the subsequent interconversion into high-affinity binding in the absence of NGF in the medium. Shouldn't you have lost low-affinity binding upon washing leaving you with nothing bound to interconvert into high-affinity binding?

E. Shooter: One can readily be confused by this. Dissociation curves for characterizing the release of [^{125}I]NGF from PC12 cells are done in the presence of a large excess of unlabeled NGF. The half-life for the high-affinity receptors is about 30 minutes and for the low-affinity receptors about 30 seconds at 37°C. However when the cells are diluted into an NGF-free medium the rate of release of [^{125}I]NGF from both receptors is very much slower. During the course of centrifugation and a brief wash in NGF-free medium only about 10% of the total or low-affinity bound [^{125}I]NGF is lost. These cells can then be resuspended in medium lacking [^{125}I]NGF and the fate of the [^{125}I]NGF bound to both low- and high-affinity receptors followed in the absence of further binding. Why the dissociation of [^{125}I]NGF in an NGF-free environment is so slow is not yet clear.

L. Birnbaumer: I should like to comment on the existence of receptor interconversion reactions of the type you describe here, i.e., low-affinity into high-affinity form. Although not specifically labeled interconversion, it seems to me that the basic phenomenon has been described by others. Best, perhaps, by Ross, Gilman, and collaborators in a paper published in 1977 (*J. Biol. Chem.*) on the kinetics of binding of the β-adrenoceptor antagonist [^{125}I]hydroxybenzylpindolol. These authors showed unequivocally a time-dependent transition (transformation?) of a readily reversible initial binding event to a much slower reversing higher affinity binding form. The process was mathematically modeled and may be similar to what you observe with NGF receptors. Also, in my laboratory, studying specific binding of glucagon to liver plasma membranes, we observe two-step kinetics. In this system, however, the high-affinity, second form, can be reversed to the initial low-affinity form by addition of guanine nucleotides. In this context I should like to ask you, whether you tested, studying NGF binding to isolated membranes, if guanine nucleotides affect the NGF–receptor interaction. If so, this might be construed as suggestive evidence for NGF's potential connection to the cAMP forming adenylyl cylase system.

E. Shooter: We haven't explored possible mechanisms such as you suggest. It is possible that the altered kinetics of binding in other systems are due to changes in receptor affinity but other explanations are also possible.

L. Bullock: I was interested in the similarities between insulin EGF and NGF and the fact that they all contain zinc. A unique characteristic of guinea pig pancreatic insulin is that in contrast to insulins from many other species, it lacks zinc and there is little reactivity between guinea pig insulin and antibodies raised against bovine insulin. I was wondering if there is anything known about the structures of the growth factors from the guinea pig or their reactivity with anti-mouse EGF or NGF antibodies.

E. Shooter: Little is known about the structure of the guinea pig NGF (isolated from the prostate) other than it does cross react with mouse NGF. Thoenen and his colleagues have however shown that it has some antigenic sites which are different to those in mouse NGF. The structure of the larger NGF-containing molecule in the guinea pig prostate is not known but it would be of interest to see if, like mouse 7 S NGF, it contained zinc ions. The analogy between the properties of insulin and of NGF have recently been extended to include the zinc ions. Dunn and his colleagues have shown that the binding domains of the zinc ions in 7 S NGF are similar if not identical to those in the zinc–insulin hexamer.

J. E. Rall: Three brief questions, one: the hexamer of the $\alpha_2\gamma_2$ βNGF, I think you said had a dissociation constant to the order of 10^{-12}. When does it dissociate. Is it presumably just the NGF itself which is active or is the whole hexamer active? If it is only the NGF dimer how in the world does it dissociate with the concentrations you are likely to have in the cell? Second, perhaps you did not have time to say something about the fact that NGF is not just a proteolytic enzyme which was discussed in *Nature* a year or so ago. Third, do you have any data on the binding of the NGF receptor complex with DNA versus chromatin?

E. Shooter: The equilibrium dissociation constant of zinc-containing 7 S NGF is 10^{-12} *M* and you are correct in supposing that the complex must dissociate to produce the biologically active NGF dimer. The activity of the NGF dimer is inhibited in 7 S NGF. The important point to be borne in mind about the dissociation is that the equilibrium dissociation constant of 7 S NGF increases dramatically as the free zinc ion concentration is reduced, to reach a value of 10^{-7} *M* in zinc-free conditions. Presumably therefore conditions in the circulation or in the environment of the responsive nerve cells have sufficiently low free zinc ion concentrations to promote dissociation of the complex.

I am happy to comment on the recent publications which suggested that NGF is a plasminogen activator as well as a growth factor. The preparations used in this work were the so-called high-molecular-weight NGF (HMW-NGF) isolated from the mouse submaxillary gland by Young and his colleagues. These workers suggested that HMW-NGF represented a new form of NGF in the gland from which the biologically active NGF dimer was released by autocatalysis. This is not correct. When the isolation of HMW-NGF is repeated according to the published procedures the protein which is obtained is 7 S NGF. Since 7 S NGF contains the trypsin-like γ subunit, which itself expresses a low level of plasminogen activator activity, it is a reasonable conclusion that the plasminogen activator activity of HMW-NGF (i.e., 7 S NGF) is a trivial activity of the γ subunit which it contains. The key experiment which was thought to support the idea that the NGF dimer was released by an autocatalytic proteolysis rather than by a simple dissociation of the complex has also been shown to be invalid. Briefly it can be shown that the HMW-NGF preparation does reversibly dissociate into its constituent subunits, like 7 S NGF, and the failure to observe this phenomenon in the published experiment can be attributed to precipitation of the dissociated subunits during the attempt to reconcentrate the sample to bring about reassociation. The precipitated subunits do not recombine to reform HMW-NGF (7 S NGF) but they are solubilized and do recombine when the salt concentration in the concentrate is lowered appropriately.

In answer to your third question, we have not done any of these experiments but they represent an interesting and potentially most useful route to follow.

R. Chatterton: William Pratt (W. B. Pratt, J. L. Kaine, and D. V. Pratt, *J. Biol. Chem.* **250,** 4584–4591, 1975) has described a two-step model for the binding of glucocorticoids to their soluble receptor. He has also described a process in which the higher affinity binding substance appears to be the activated form which is necessary for binding to the nucleus. I think there is also other evidence among the soluble receptors that the activated form may have higher affinity, and I wonder whether this model might fit with the kind of change that you see in terms of the selectivity process. In other words, is the lower affinity binding, that which goes to the lysosome and that which becomes activated in the sense that it is transformed by a change to the high affinity that which goes to the nucleus?

E. Shooter: The analogies with the mechanism of action of steroid hormones which you emphasized are of considerable interest. We had earlier considered a model in which the binding affinity of the receptor determined which intracellular pathway the vesicles traveled, i.e., low-affinity to the lysosomes and high-affinity to the nucleus. It still is a possible model although the actual mechanisms present some problems. On the other hand it is now clear that vesicles containing high-affinity receptors are transported to the lysosomes and degraded.

G. Weiss: Since NGF is functioning as a local hormone, is there any information about its local source, the stimulus for its release, and whether it circulates.

E. Shooter: There is no good evidence identifying the *in vivo* sources of NGF especially during development and this is one of the gaps in the NGF story; as Bob Jaffe also emphasized this is true for EGF and FGF. The hypothesis predicts that all target organs should synthesize and secrete NGF and the mouse submaxillary gland fits into this picture because of its sympathetic innervation. At least one other target organ, the iris, also secretes NGF in culture and indeed Young and his colleagues have convincingly demonstrated that many different types of cultured cells have this capacity. However an *in vivo* demonstration of this capacity for most target organs has not yet been made.

With respect to NGF in the circulation, as noted earlier, the conditions required to promote dissociation of secreted 7 S NGF are low 7 S NGF and low zinc ion concentrations. NGF is finally found bound to α_2-macroglobulin in plasma, this may be another way of promoting dissociation of the complex because α_2-macroglobulin also binds trypsin and trypsin-like enzymes (e.g., the γ subunit). Several cells have receptors for α_2-macroglobulin raising the further possibility that NGF could be sequestered by cells along with α_2-macroglobulin.

K. Sterling: I have to confess I am still having some difficulty about the transformation of low- to high-affinity receptors. Now in the biophasic Scatchard plot that you showed it appeared that perhaps two-thirds of the ligand was bound to the high-affinity sites, though the low-affinity might have been five times as abundant in number of sites. Could I ask you if that was a typical or testing cell or what was it?

E. Shooter: The Scatchard plot gives the extrapolated maximum numbers of both types of receptors and as you comment there are about 10 times as many low- as high-affinity receptors when all receptors are saturated. If the conversion of the low- to the high-affinity receptor involves an "effector" protein in the membrane and if the molar concentration of this protein is about one-tenth that of the NGF receptor then only this fraction of low-affinity receptors can undergo conversion even at high NGF concentration. However at very low NGF concentrations all the occupied low-affinity receptors can undergo conversion and this is what you see in the dissociation curves. The dissociation of NGF from cells loaded at very low concentrations is monophasic with a rate characteristic of the high-affinity receptor. Similarly in the experiment showing conversion after removal of free [^{125}I]NGF in the medium the occupancy of total receptors is very low and the fraction of high-affinity receptors which are generated comes close to one-half of the total.

K. Sterling: If one had cells with an invariant proportion of these two classes of sites under the ordinary theory of molecular collisions with the high-affinity having a K_a 2 decades higher than the low-affinity even though they are only one-tenth as abundant the initial binding would be better than 90% of the high-affinity rather than what you have just said. I suppose that the difficulty is that these are in a state of flux. One thing that I wanted to ask you, you used the term "patching" or "micropatching" in the membrane to describe this conversion; I wonder if you could say a little more as to what it implies.

E. Shooter: The question raises the important issue of the two affinities of receptors found on sensory and sympathetic nerve cells as opposed to PC12 cells. Unlike the latter high-affinity binding is found even at the earliest measurable times on sensory and sympathetic nerve cells. Does this mean that cells which have been previously exposed to NGF have a population of high-affinity receptors which after conversion from the low-affinity form are reasonably stable or does it mean that the conversion rate is very much faster than on PC12 cells? We have no answer to this question at the moment but it does, in turn, raise the further question as to what is being measured when the initial rate of NGF binding is determined at low NGF concentration. Is it binding to the high-affinity or to the low-affinity receptor? I used the term patching in the model by analogy with other better defined systems in which the clustering of surface receptors and their subsequent internalization can be visualized by using an appropriately fluorescently labeled ligand. These studies have illustrated very well the transport of ligand to the lysosomes. It would be of considerable interest to extend the time scale of these experiments to see if the fluorescently labeled ligand could eventually be detected in the nucleus.

H.-C. Blossey: I am also interested in the distribution of the receptor on the cell surface; are there preexisting clusters or are they built up during the binding of the hormone and have you any idea how many of the receptor molecules are transported in the vesicles.

E. Shooter: Judging again from work in other systems it appears that some hormone receptors are initially diffusely distributed over the cell surface. There is evidence also for clusters of small numbers of receptors perhaps reflecting differences in the hormonal states of the cell. It is generally agreed that endocytosis of receptors and bound ligand in vesicles is preceded by significant clustering of receptors. The amount of NGF which is transported to the nucleus is a small fraction of the total cellular NGF. After 5 days in culture PC12 cells accumulate about 10% of the cell-bound NGF in their nuclei.

J. Nolin: Thank you for a very nice paper, very well presented. I find it startling to see the number of similarities between your findings for NGF and ours for prolactin. However, I want to mention one apparent difference. In the milk secretory cell, although we find translocation of prolactin to nuclei, the major second pathway appears to be transcellular transport. Although the prolactin transported through this target retains biologic activity (R. R. Gala, I. A. Forsyth, and A. Turvey, *Life Sci.* **26,** 987–993, 1980), as far as the cell itself is concerned, this pathway serves an "inactivation" process just as the lysosomal pathway appears to do for NGF in nerve cells. I think the whole concept of two or possibly more pathways for handling peptide hormones in their target cells is a very important one. It may help resolve some of the current controversy about why peptide hormones are incorporated by their targets and I thank you for bringing it to us.

E. Shooter: The similarities with the translocation of prolactin are indeed striking. Also I think there is much that we can learn from the research on virus assembly and release in cells where different pathways of intracellular transport are so critical.

B. Moyle: I would like to make a comment and follow it with a question. The "sequential binding" you observed might also be explained by reorientation of the ligand and/or receptor in the complex. A simple example of "reorientation" may be the recombination of gonadotropin α and β subunits to form the intact molecule (Bewley *et al., Arch. Biochem. Biophys.* **163,** 625, 1974; Reichert *et al., J. Biol. Chem.* **249,** 6472, 1974). Apparently the subunits bind to one another and then the complex undergoes a molecular rearrangement resulting in a higher affinity state. In a "reorientation" type of model, formation of the high affinity complex would be seen following a characteristic time lag. In addition, dissociation of the complex would occur with two or more rate constants. Thus a "reorientation model" would account for the lag in binding and the multiple rates of dissociation shown by some of your data. However, in contrast to the curvilinear Scatchard plots you described, a simple "reorientation" model would predict a linear Scatchard plot.

This leads to my question. Do your data provide evidence for negative cooperativity in binding? For example, when you added excess cold hormone, the "low-affinity receptors" dissociated within 5 seconds. On the other hand, when you removed the labeled hormone from solution, the "low-affinity receptor complexes" had a much longer half-life. This may have provided sufficient time for "reorientation" to the high-affinity state. Thus the complex model you use to describe sequentital binding could be replaced with a model as simple as recombination of gonadotropin subunits provided the initial binding was negatively cooperative.

E. Shooter: The analogy to the gonadotropin system is a good one and the sequential binding model would indeed explain the data. Although I have previously emphasized NGF receptor clustering with another receptor or another membrane protein as a basis of the conversion, a reorientation of receptor subunits is also a plausible mechanism behind the change in affinity. You are correct in pointing out that the very substantial increase in the rate of dissociation of NGF from its receptor in the presence of unlabeled NGF is compatible with negative cooperativity. However we also found an increase in the rate of dissociation when the amount of unlabeled NGF resulted in a decrease rather than an increase in receptor occupancy and this is the opposite to what you would expect from negative cooperativity. Also the biphasic dissociation curves are obtained in the presence of a large excess of unlabeled NGF and yet they still reflect the receptor occupancy at the end of the binding period rather than after addition of the unlabeled NGF to promote dissociation. For all these reasons the NGF receptor is not behaving in a negatively cooperative manner and I outlined in my talk the direct evidence for our conclusion that the opposite is indeed true, i.e., NGF binds first to receptors of low affinity and the binding in some way converts the receptor to a higher affinity form. One partial explanation for the dissociation behavior is the presence of an "unstirred layer" around the PC12 cell which prevents the released NGF from entering the medium and this promotes rebinding. Dr. R. Riopelle and his colleagues have shown that the unstirred layer around PC12 membranes fractions can be disturbed by vigorous shaking with a concomitant increase in the rate of NGF dissociation.

R. O. Greep: I'm curious as to the basis of your retention of the term "factor." When I extended the invitation for you to speak here I believe I used the term growth hormone. You were out of the country and I was dealing with your secretary. A few days later I got a call from her stating that the professor prefers the term "factor." It is a common practice in endocrinology to use the term "factor" when one is dealing with a biological activity whose structure has not yet been determined. We used the term factor for the pituitary hormone-releasing activities of hypothalamic origin (TSF and LRF) until their structure was known, then they were termed hormones, i.e., TSF and LHRH etc. Since you obviously have the structure of NGF very clearly demonstrated why do you continue to use the term factor? Is it the definition of a hormone that bothers you?

E. Shooter: You remember the events of last September very well. I was lost on the Italian railways at the time the invitation arrived! Your comment is very appropriate and NGF is indeed a perfectly good hormone as well as a factor. I retained the term "factor" because I thought that this was the way that most people would recognize nerve growth factor and therefore have some idea about the subject of my lecture.

RECENT PROGRESS IN HORMONE RESEARCH, VOL. 37

Immunochemical Studies Relating to Cholecystokinin in Brain and Gut

EUGENE STRAUS,*,† STEVEN W. RYDER,† JOHN ENG,† AND ROSALYN S. YALOW*,†

** The Department of Clinical Sciences, Albert Einstein College of Medicine at Montefiore Hospital and Medical Center, Bronx, New York, and † The Solomon A. Berson Research Laboratory, Veterans Administration Hospital, Bronx, New York*

I. Introduction

The list of central nervous system (CNS) peptides, several of which are common to the gastrointestinal tract, is expanding far more rapidly than our understanding of the significance of the findings. Cholecystokinin (CCK), a relative newcomer on this list, is an outstanding example. It is outstanding in its high brain concentration, far exceeding the brain concentrations of other brain–gut peptides, and remarkable in its abundance and broad distribution throughout the cerebral cortex. It is further unusual in the variety of its heterogeneous molecular forms and the finding that these are distributed differently in brain and gut tissues. Our initial studies with CCK demonstrated that both intact CCK-33 and its COOH-terminal fragments are found in the brain as well as in the gut. Those findings led us to attempt to discover what cells in the cerebral cortex contain immunoreactive CCK, the nature of the enzymes responsible for posttranslational cleavage of intact CCK peptides, the distribution of CCK immunoreactivity within neuronal cells, and finally, whether brain CCK plays some role in satiety behavior.

II. Background

In 1928 the cross-circulation experiments of Ivy and Oldberg (1928) extended the earlier observation of Okada who, working in Starling's laboratory, had found that intestinal acidification resulted in contraction of the gallbladder (Okada, 1914/15). Active material was extracted from duodenal mucosa and was named cholecystokinin (CCK). Fifteen years later Harper and Raper (1943) demonstrated that intravenous injection of intestinal extracts stimulated the secretion of pancreatic enzymes. They

ISBN 0-12-571137-9

named the hormonal material responsible for this activity pancreozymin (PZ). Jorpes and Mutt (1966) purified the crude material and demonstrated that CCK and PZ were the same peptide with both cholecystokininic and pancreozyminic activities. It is now conventional to use the term CCK.

A great deal has been learned about the chemistry and pharmacology of CCK (Mutt, 1980) and the hormone has found clinical application in radiographic and other noninvasive studies of gallbladder function. Nonetheless, until recently only limited efforts had been made to develop immunochemical methods which could be applied to studies of tissue and circulating CCK. In the past decade much more immunochemical work was done with the closely related gastrin peptides. The source of gastrin's appeal was in its applicability to the study of acid-peptic disorders. No such obvious rewards were available to underwrite the more arduous technical work required for sensitive and specific measurement of CCK peptides since no clinical states of excessive secretion of pancreatic enzymes, hepatic bile flow, and gallbladder contractility have been defined or postulated.

Two discoveries have contributed to the current surge of interest in immunochemical studies of CCK. The first was Mutt's discovery in 1976 of a variant form in porcine intestine. The original purification and structural analysis accomplished by Mutt and Jorpes (1971) described a basic 33 amino acid peptide with a COOH-terminal pentapeptide (Gly-Trp-Met-Asp-Phe-NH_2) which is identical to that of gastrin. The phenolic group of the tyrosine residue (in position 27) was esterified with sulfuric acid and unlike the sulfated tyrosine located next to the pentapeptide in gastrin II, this sulfation is required for the CCK peptides to exert biologic activity. Furthermore the COOH-terminal tryptic dodecapeptide and octapeptide fragments (CCK-12 and CCK-8) were shown to be considerably more potent in their actions on the gallbladder and on enzyme secretion from the pancreas than is the intact CCK-33 (Rubin *et al.*, 1969).

These observations are of fundamental interest and importance. In the context of previously known structure–activity relationships they clarified the pharmacologic relationship between CCK and gastrin (Grossman, 1973) and provided the basis for current concepts of the evolution of these, and related peptides (Dockray, 1979). The discovery of big gastrin (G-34) (Yalow and Berson, 1970, 1971; Berson and Yalow, 1971) and the emerging significance of peptide hormone heterogeneity coupled with these findings clearly opened the way for an appreciation of a family of biologically active CCK peptides. It was therefore of special interest when Mutt (1976) described the variant form of CCK, containing the sequence of CCK-33 but extended at the NH_2 terminus by a hexapeptide having an unsulfated NH_2-terminal tyrosine. The analogy to the gastrin situation was again clear; this was big CCK, if not big, big CCK. Furthermore, the NH_2-terminal unsulfated tyrosine offered a possible gambit for immunoassayists since the difficulty in obtaining a satisfactory ^{125}I-labeled CCK of high specific activity (Straus, 1978, 1980) had been ascribed to difficulty in iodinating the already sulfated tyrosine of CCK-33.

The second discovery which added greatly to our knowledge and harnessed much energy in the area of immunochemical studies of CCK was the finding of Vanderhaeghen *et al.* (1975) of a new peptide in the vertebrate central nervous system (CNS) which reacts with antibodies against gastrin, and the subsequent suggestion by Dockray (1976) that the brain material resembled a COOH-terminal CCK-like peptide more closely than a gastrin-like peptide on the basis of its elution volume on Sephadex G-25 and its reactivity with several antisera. Our initial studies confirmed and extended these data by demonstrating that both intact CCK-33 and its COOH-terminal fragments are found in the brain as well as in the gut (Muller *et al.*, 1977; Straus and Yalow, 1978). These observations came in the midst of considerable interest and speculation generated by earlier findings of peptides common to the brain and gut, and, more importantly, at a time when the emerging significance of peptides in neurobiology appears vast (Brownstein *et al.*, 1980). As a venerable gastrointestinal hormone CCK inspired respect but little enthusiasm. Found in a new and unexpected location it seemed more exciting.

III. Methods of Investigation

The research approaches which we have attempted require well characterized radioimmunoassay systems, efficient extraction techniques, and reliable methods for separating and measuring the several immunoreactive molecular forms of CCK in tissue extracts. That each of these has presented difficulties is reflected in the relatively slow progress that has been made with immunochemical studies of CCK. Radioimmunoassay has been used to identify and quantitate CCK immunoreactivity in tissues and biologic fluids, and to characterize the antisera used in immunohistochemical studies. The COOH-terminal identity with gastrin, the strong positive charge of the larger forms, and the sulfation of the tyrosine in the biologically active portion of the peptide have resulted in considerable difficulty for the immunoassayist. Early assays were not well validated and questions were raised with regard to their sensitivity and specificity (Straus, 1978). Because methodologic questions continue to complicate the interpretation of data we will begin with a discussion of CCK radioimmunoassays, methods of extracting CCK from tissues, and procedures used to estimate the relative concentrations of CCK forms in extracts.

A. RADIOIMMUNOASSAY

We have used two antisera with different immunochemical specificities. One was prepared in a goat by immunization with porcine CCK-33 (pCCK-33). It appears to be directed toward the NH_2-terminal portion of the molecule, since it does not cross-react with CCK-8 or the gastrins (big G-34 or little G-17) in spite of their shared COOH-terminal pentapeptide. This antiserum does not cross-react with other gastrointestinal peptides. In this assay ^{125}I-labeled CCK-33 is used as tracer and pure natural pCCK-33 is used as standard (Muller *et al.*, 1977). The other antiserum was prepared by immunization of a rabbit (Rabbit B) with the COOH-terminal gastrin–CCK tetrapeptide amide. Using ^{125}I-labeled gastrin as tracer, the cross-reactivities of pCCK 33, CCK-12, and CCK-8 are virtually identical on a molar basis, G-17 is more immunoreactive and CCK-39 is less immunoreactive than CCK-33 in this system.

Using the carboxy-terminal assay system we observed that in 0.1 *N* HCl extracts of monkey, dog, and pig cerebral cortex the immunoreactive contents averaged 0.05, 0.1, and 0.2 μg CCK-8 eq/gm of tissue, respectively, compared to 0.4, 0.7, and 0.6 μg/gm for extracts of the guts of these species, respectively (Straus and Yalow, 1978). Our recent finding that acid solvents extract only one-third to one-half the immunoreactive CCK which is removed by alkaline solvents makes it necessary to revise these concentrations upward (Ryder *et al.*, 1980a). The absence of gastrin peptides in our tissue extracts was demonstrated by assay with a sensitive gastrin-specific antiserum which cross-reacts only very weakly with CCK peptides. As an incidental finding we noted that in the homologous porcine CCK assay no immunoreactivity was detected in the same monkey and dog extracts which were readily measurable in the carboxy-terminal assay although the immunoreactivities in pig gut and brain were quite comparable when measured in either assay system (Straus and Yalow, 1978). We have interpreted these data as suggesting that there are major structural differences between pig and other animal CCKs in the NH_2-terminal portion of the molecule. Since full biologic potency resides in the CCK-8 portion of the molecule, it is not surprising that the COOH-terminal sequence has been conserved while the NH_2-terminal portion has diverged during the course of evolution.

The COOH-terminal approach has been preferred for the measurement of CCK peptides in gastrin-free tissue extracts but is not applicable to the measurement of plasma CCK because of the relative abundance of gastrin peptides in plasma, and their strong cross-reactivity in this assay. Most other investigators have also used antisera directed toward the COOH-terminus which cross-react to some degree with gastrin peptides (Vanderhaeghen *et al.*, 1975; Dockray, 1976, 1977; Schneider *et al.*, 1979). Rehfeld (1978a) has a series of antisera each of which is apparently "specific" for a short sequence within the COOH-terminal half of CCK-33. One of these antisera, 4698, appears to have appropriate specificity for measuring circulating CCK peptides in that it reacts with CCK-33 and CCK-8 without reacting with G-17. However, the apparently low energy of this antiserum probably limits its usefulness for assay of plasma hormone.

The labeled hormones used in the various assay procedures differ somewhat. We have used a chloramine T method to prepare ^{125}I-labeled CCK-33 and ^{125}I-labeled G-17 for the Goat I and Rabbit B assays, respectively (Muller *et al.*, 1977). The sulfated tyrosine of CCK-33 is iodinated and the labeled peptide is purified by adsorption to and elution from Quso G-32. The GIH CCK preparation is generally supplied in vials containing milligram quantities of cysteine and cannot be readily iodinated because the cysteine is preferentially oxidized. ^{125}I-labeled CCK-39 prepared by the chloramine-T method does not bind as well to Goat I. ^{125}I-labeled CCK-8 (sulfated or unsulfated) does not offer any advantage over ^{125}I-labeled G-17 in the Rabbit B system. Most other groups have also prepared suitable labeled gastrin or CCK peptides with the chloramine-T method (Vanderhaeghen *et al.*, 1975; Dockray, 1976, 1977; Schneider *et al.*, 1979). Rehfeld has found chloramine-T-labeled CCK peptides to be poorly immunoreactive with his antisera and therefore has labeled CCK-33 by conjugating ^{125}I-labeled hydroxyphenylpropionic succinimide ester to the free NH_2 groups according to the method of Bolton and Hunter (1973). Varying degrees of conjugation may result in heterogeneous products containing the rather bulky iodinated ester conjugated mainly to lysyl side chains (Knight *et al.*, 1978). These groups may mask some immunoreactive sites. Differences in antibody specificity and/or the choice of tracer may explain the discrepant results obtained with this method (Sankaran *et al.*, 1979).

We have used pure natural CCK-33 as standard in our Goat I assay and synthetic CCK-8 (Squibb) as standard in the Rabbit B system. We have observed significant batch to batch differences in the immunopotency of synthetic CCK-8 and some batches of CCK-8 appear to be heterogeneous in their migration in starch-gel electrophoresis. This is in agreement with heterogeneity of this preparation observed on high pressure liquid chromatography (Pradayrol *et al.*, 1979). Other investigators have also used Squibb CCK-8 as standard (Schneider *et al.*, 1979; Dockray, 1980). Variations in the potency of standards may account for some of the discrepancies in determinations of the concentration of CCK peptides in tissues. However differences in the efficiency of extraction and the nature of hormonal forms extracted must also be considered.

B. EXTRACTION METHODS

In the classic studies of Jorpes and Mutt the methods for the initial extraction of secretin and CCK were identical, that is, boiling the first meter of intestine and reextracting with dilute acetic acid at room temperature (Mutt and Jorpes, 1973). Most investigators have therefore continued to use some variation of neutral or acid extractants to recover CCK from gut as well as brain. One might expect secretin and intact CCK (CCK-39 and CCK-33) to havc similar cxtractability properties since they are similar in molecular weight and charge. Nonetheless, we have found that CCK peptides are most efficiently extracted from rat gut and brain in 0.1 *N* NaOH and that other alkaline extractants such as 100 m*M* Tris buffer (pH 10) are also superior to acid or neutral extractants (Ryder *et al.*, 1980a). As shown in Table I the efficiency of extraction of CCK immunoreactivity from rat brain depends strikingly on the extraction method. In contrast, virtually identical amounts of enkephalin are recovered with boiling HCl or boiling NaOH extractants. Whereas boiling does not increase the efficiency of extraction in acid or alkaline extractants, the results shown in Table II indicate that extraction in distilled water at room temperature is only about 10% as efficient in extracting CCK immunoreactivity as is boiling water. Furthermore, these differences in the amount of immunoreactivity extracted from tissues appear to be due simply to failure to remove the immunoreactivity and not to loss because

TABLE I

Effect of Extractant on Recovery of CCK and Enkephalin Immunoreactivity from Rat Brain

Extractant	CCK-8 equivalents (ng/gm) Total	CCK-8 equivalents (ng/gm) QUSO Eluate	Leu-Enkephalin (pmoles/gm)
0.5 *M* Acetic acid	57 ± 15 (2)[a,c]	—	—
0.1 *N* HCl	97 ± 10 (9)[c]	11 ± 2 (6)[b]	76 ± 13 (5)
H_2O	129 ± 14 (8)[c]	11 ± 2 (4)[b]	—
Tris (100 m*M*, pH 10)	213 ± 14 (6)[b]	14 ± 3 (6)[b]	—
0.1 *N* NaOH	273 ± 8 (13)	49 ± 8 (7)	69 ± 11 (5)

[a] Mean ± SEM (number of extractions).

[b] $p < 0.01$.

[c] $p < 0.001$ level of significance compared to NaOH.

TABLE II
Reextraction of CCK Immunoreactivity from Residual Pellets

	CCK-8 equivalents (ng/gm)	
Room temperature H_2O	13 ± 3 (6)[a,b]	
Boiling H_2O extraction of tissue pellet		102 ± 5 (2)
Total CCK extracted		115 ± 13 (2)
Boiling NaOH extraction of tissue pellet		222 ± 48 (2)
Total CCK Extracted		235 ± 48 (2)
Boiling H_2O	111 ± 3 (2)	
NaOH extraction of tissue pellet		133 ± 8 (2)
Total CCK Extracted		244 ± 9 (2)

[a] Mean ± SEM (number of extractions).
[b] $p < 0.001$ level of significance, unboiled vs boiled extractant.

of proteolytic degradation or other factors since reextraction of the residual pellets with NaOH resulted in total recovery comparable to that with an initial alkaline extraction. The alkaline extraction appears to be more efficient for all hormonal forms. Similar results were obtained in studies of extraction from rat gut so that extractability depends on the chemical nature of the peptide, not on different properties of the tissues.

Proper interpretation of dynamic changes of tissue CCK in response to fasting, feeding, and other laboratory manipulations requires efficient extraction of total immunoreactivity. For instance, if one hormonal form is preferentially extracted by a particular solvent, changes in the apparent amount of that form extracted could arise from changes in conversion among hormonal forms, as well as from differences in the total amount of CCK stored in the tissue. Nonetheless, since the precursor forms, CCK-39 and CCK-33, have lower biologic potencies than the COOH-terminal fragments the extractant should inhibit conversion among these forms.

C. FRACTIONATION OF IMMUNOREACTIVE CHOLECYSTOKININ

Fractionation of immunoreactive CCK peptides has been accomplished in a variety of systems which separate on the basis of size and/or change, including Sephadex gel and ion-exchange chromatography, as well as electrophoresis on starch gel and other supporting media. Dockray (1976), for example, used Sephadex gel chromatography for the initial demonstration that the immunoreactivity recovered from brain tissue did not correspond in molecular radius to known gastrin peptides. While the separation systems used by various groups have tended to be similar, the elution buffers frequently differ (Dockray, 1976; Muller *et al.*, 1977; Straus and Yalow, 1978; Rehfeld, 1978b). Of special importance with regard to fractionation of CCK peptides is the fact that the more basic larger forms, CCK-39 and CCK-33, tend to adsorb to many inert surfaces, such as glass and plastic, and recoveries of these peptides are often quite poor. Thus, fractionation techniques requiring exposure to such adsorbing surfaces generally underestimate the amount of these peptides. For instance, the NH_2-terminal immunoreactivity in acid extracts of brain tissue elutes from Sephadex G-50 columns and migrates on starch gel electrophoresis in the same region as authentic pCCK-33 but only approximately 30% of either of these starting materials is recovered (Muller *et al.*, 1977). On the other hand the COOH-terminal CCK peptides are efficiently recovered from Sephadex and starch gels (Ryder *et al.*, 1980a).

We have developed a simple method for the quantitative separation of the larger basic CCK-33 and CCK-39 peptides from the CCK-12 and CCK-8 fragments (Straus *et al.*, 1979). The method depends on adsorption of the basic peptides to inert materials such as Quso G-32 (microfine precipitated silica) and talc. A typical study in which the peptides were studied alone or in combination is shown in Table III. The peptides were dissolved in 2.5 ml of a 1 : 5 dilution of plasma in barbital buffer (0.02 *M*, pH 8.5). The CCK-33 is quantitatively adsorbed onto talc or Quso but CCK-8 or CCK-12 are not. The adsorbed immunoreactivity is quantitatively extracted from Quso but not from talc with 0.1 *N* HCl.

The method is rapid and simple but does not permit distinction between CCK-39 and CCK-33 or between CCK-12 and CCK-8. However since the

TABLE III

Extraction and Elution of CCK Peptide from QUSO and Talc

	Immunoreactive CCK (ng/ml)			
	Residual in supernatant		Recovered in neutralized 0.1 *N* HCl eluate from pellet	
	QUSO (5 mg)	Talc (25 mg)	QUSO (5 mg)	Talc (25 mg)
CCK-33 (35 ng/ml)	0	0	33	4
CCK-12 (80 ng/ml)	80	80	0	0
CCK-8 (80 ng/ml)	80	80	0	0
CCK-33 (15 ng/ml) + CCK-8 (40 ng/ml)	36	37	15	2

biologic activities of the larger peptides are quite similar but much lower than those of the carboxy-terminal fragments, it is evident that this separation method should prove useful for bioassay as well as for immunoassay of mixtures of the peptides.

IV. Heterogeneity of CCK Immunoreactivity Extracted from Brain and Gut

There have been numerous reports describing the heterogeneity of CCK in brain and gut (Dockray, 1976, 1980; Muller *et al.,* 1977; Straus and Yalow, 1978; Ryder *et al.,* 1980a; Rehfeld and Goltermann, 1979; Rehfeld and Larsson, 1979; Schneider *et al.,* 1979; Lambers *et al.,* 1980). As yet there is not uniform agreement among the various laboratories concerning the relative concentrations of the different hormonal forms. Discrepancies may occur because of the use of different extractants, losses of the larger hormonal forms due to their adsorption to inert surfaces, and antisera with different sensitivities for the various hormonal forms.

There is general agreement that in water extracts of the brain CCK-8 is the predominant form (Muller *et al.,* 1977; Straus and Yalow, 1978; Ryder *et al.,* 1980a; Dockray, 1976, 1980; Rehfeld, 1978b; Schneider *et al.,* 1979). Our studies (Straus and Yalow, 1978) confirm the earlier report of Dockray (1976) demonstrating a minor void volume component on Sephadex G-50 gel filtration. Whether this represents a larger form than CCK-39 or a polymerized form has not been determined. A major disagreement exists in estimates of the absolute or relative amounts of CCK-33. Dockray originally reported no immunoreactivity in the CCK-33 region in water extracts of hog brain and Rehfeld reported only 2 to 5% of the total immunoreactivity in hog and human brains were in this region. There is general agreement that acid is more efficient for the extraction of CCK-33 than is boiling water. Nonetheless even when the same acetic acid extractant is used some workers find very little (Rehfeld, 1978b) or no (Dockray, 1977) CCK-33 in brain while others report that similar extracts contain exclusively CCK-33 (Lamers *et al.,* 1980). In our recent study comparing various extracts using rat brain we found that 15% of the immunoreactivity in 0.1 *N* NaOH extracts was attributable to CCK-33 or CCK-39 (Ryder *et al.,* 1980a). These forms accounted for 10 and 8%, respectively, in 0.1 *N* HCl and boiling water extracts. We had earlier reported that Sephadex gel filtration of 0.1 *N* HCl extracts of pig and dog brains showed that about 25 to 30% of the immunoreactivity could be attributed to CCK-33 (Straus and Yalow, 1978). Thus some of the discrepancies may be due to species differences.

Similar discrepancies are reported for the distribution of hormonal forms in the gut. We earlier reported that about half the immunoreactivity in 0.1 *N* HCl extracts of monkey, dog, and pig gut elutes in the region of CCK-33 on Sephadex gel filtration (Straus and Yalow, 1978). However in recent studies using the Quso extraction and acid elution method we found that only about 15% of the immunoreactivity in 0.1 *N* HCl extracts of rat gut is attributable to the larger forms (Ryder *et al.*, 1980a). These differences may be methodologic or due to species differences. Clearly much additional work is required to resolve these discrepancies.

Recently Rehfeld *et al.* (Rehfeld and Goltermann, 1979; Rehfeld and Larsson, 1979) have suggested that the COOH-terminal tetrapeptide amide (G-4) common to gastrin and CCK is the predominating molecular form in gut and brain. This differs from the first report from this laboratory (Rehfeld, 1978b) which concluded that CCK-8 was the predominant form in brain. G-4 or CCK-4, as it could also be called, is without significant biologic activity since the minimum fragment for CCK-like activity is CCK-7 and G-4 has only about 1/6 to 1/30 the potency of G-17 (Tracy and Gregory, 1964). The differences in the concentrations of G-4 between the earlier (Rehfeld, 1978b) and later papers (Rehfeld and Goltermann, 1979; Rehfeld and Larsson, 1979) from Rehfeld's laboratory is due to the fact that the antiserum they used, 2609, reacts poorly with G-4 and in the later paper they multiplied their observed immunoreactivity in the G-4 region by a factor of 30. The antiserum we use, Rabbit B, was prepared by immunization with G-4 and therefore reacts quite strongly with this peptide. With some bleedings G-4 is equally as immunoreactive as CCK-8 and larger fragments; with other bleedings it was only 3- to 4-fold less reactive than CCK-8. Using this antiserum we have found no G-4 in rat brain and only a minor component attributable to this peptide in rat gut. Whether the G-4 results from the action of specific converting enzymes as is the case for CCK-8 or simply from the action of nonspecific proteases has not been determined.

V. CCK-Converting Enzyme in the Brain

The finding of multiple but well-defined hormonal forms of CCK in brain and gut suggested the possibility that there might be specific enzyme(s) involved in the conversion from CCK-39 or CCK-33 to the COOH-terminal fragments which account for the major fraction of immunoreactivity at least in the brain. Conversion to CCK-8 could be effected by a tryptic-like enzyme such as has been reported to effect conversion of proinsulin (Zuhlke *et al.*, 1976) and proparathyroid hormone (Macgregor *et al.*, 1976) to their smaller forms. As yet the tryptic-like enzymes involved in these conversions have not been well-characterized.

Enzymatic activity which converts CCK-33 to the COOH-terminal fragments is found in distilled H_2O, 0.9% NaCl, or phosphate (0.25 *M*, pH 7.5) extracts of porcine, canine, and other mammalian cerebral cortical tissue. We have not yet found similar converting activity in splenic extracts or even in extracts of the gut. Studies using the latter tissues have been complicated by the high concentrations of other nonspecific proteases.

A rapid screening test for degrading activity is based on the use of paper chromatoelectrophoresis (Straus *et al.,* 1978). ^{125}I-labeled CCK-33, in common with many peptides such as insulin, secretin, etc., binds to paper at the site of application while the serum proteins and other more acidic peptides such as gastrin, CCK-8, and the iodotyrosines migrate anodally. Radioiodide is usually the most anodal component. Treatment of ^{125}I-labeled CCK-33 with whole brain extracts effected conversion to a migrating component which was not iodide (Fig. 1). Fractionation of the brain extract on G-75 or G-50 Sephadex columns revealed that only the void volume eluates contained converting activity so that it differs in molecular size from trypsin (Straus *et al.,* 1978). This method, while very convenient for screening purposes, does not permit determination of the

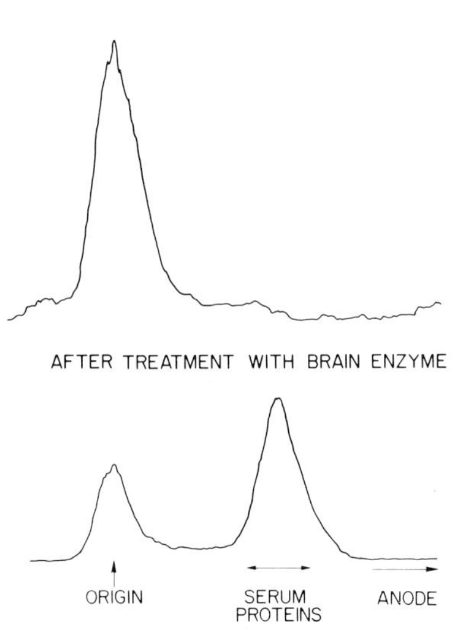

FIG. 1. Paper chromatoelectrophoresis of ^{125}I-labeled CCK before (top) and after (bottom) treatment with active fraction (void volume eluate after Sephadex G-50 gel filteration) of extract of pig cerebral cortex. Intact ^{125}I-labeled CCK remains at the site of application; the ^{125}I-labeled fragments migrate with the serum proteins. Reproduced from Straus *et al.* (1978).

nature of the final product(s). It could be used to demonstrate that the brain enzyme differs from trypsin not only in molecular size but also in temperature sensitivity. Trypsin remains fully active in converting CCK-33 to the smaller fragments at temperatures up to 55°C for 1 hour while the brain enzyme is inactivated in 1 hour at 45°C. Furthermore, lima bean trypsin inhibitor does not inhibit the brain enzyme at concentrations sufficient to inhibit trypsin at a concentration of 1 mg/ml. The brain enzyme is inactive at pH 6 or below but like trypsin it is fully active in the pH range from 6.5 to 9.

The enzyme does not manifest a high degree of species specificity since canine and other mammalian brain extracts appear to be highly active in conversion of porcine CCK to the smaller fragments.

Starch gel electrophoresis was employed to identify the nature of the fragments as well as to demonstrate that the converting enzyme is not trypsin since it fails to convert G-34 to G-17 although this conversion is readily effected with trypsin (Fig. 2) (Straus *et al.,* 1978). One product of enzymatic conversion is found on starch gel to have the same electrophoretic mobility as sulfated CCK-8. In this system unsulfated CCK-8 and CCK-12 have the same electrophoretic mobility so that at present we have not as yet been certain of the distribution of these peptides in the immunoreactivity identified as a second component. There appears to be at least two enzymes involved in the conversion process. The G-75 void volume eluate converts CCK-33 to a peptide resembling CCK-12 but does not appear to alter CCK-12 (Malesci *et al.,* 1980). Treatment of CCK-33 with whole brain extract yields primarily CCK-8 and does convert CCK-12 in part to CCK-8 (Fig. 3). Furthermore, sucrose gradient ultracentrifugation of whole brain extracts revealed that the activity is contained in two fractions (Ryder *et al.,* 1980b). Fraction A is heavier than γ-globulin; Fraction B has a sedimentation velocity between γ-globulin and bromophenol-stained albumin. Treatment of CCK-33 with either Fraction A or the G-75 void volume eluate yields a product resembling CCK-12 (Fig. 4). Treatment with Fraction B, like treatment with whole brain extracts, yields a CCK-12-like product and in addition, CCK-8. Production of CCK-8 requires cleavage of an Arg-Asp bond. Fraction A and the G-75 void volume eluate do not cleave this bond in the dipeptides although whole brain extract and Fraction B do (Fig. 5). Production of CCK-12 requires cleavage of an Arg-Ile bond. Whole brain extract, the G-75 void volume eluate, Fraction A and Fraction B all can cleave this bond in the dipeptide Arg-Ile (Fig. 6). They appear to be equally active in cleaving the dipeptides Arg-Val or Arg-Leu. Thus we have demonstrated that there are brain enzymes capable of cleaving the Arg-Ile and Arg-Asp bonds whether incorporated in CCK-33 or free as dipeptides (Ryder *et al.,*

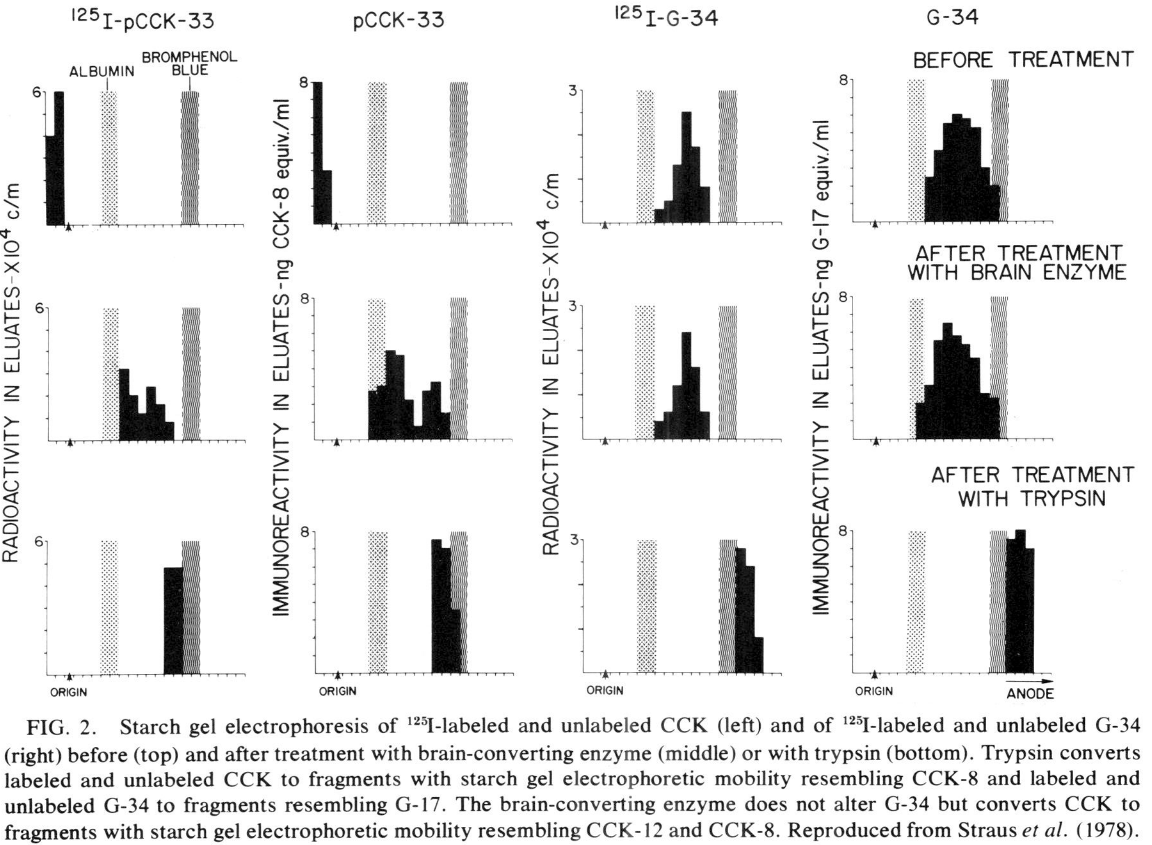

FIG. 2. Starch gel electrophoresis of ^{125}I-labeled and unlabeled CCK (left) and of ^{125}I-labeled and unlabeled G-34 (right) before (top) and after treatment with brain-converting enzyme (middle) or with trypsin (bottom). Trypsin converts labeled and unlabeled CCK to fragments with starch gel electrophoretic mobility resembling CCK-8 and labeled and unlabeled G-34 to fragments resembling G-17. The brain-converting enzyme does not alter G-34 but converts CCK to fragments with starch gel electrophoretic mobility resembling CCK-12 and CCK-8. Reproduced from Straus *et al.* (1978).

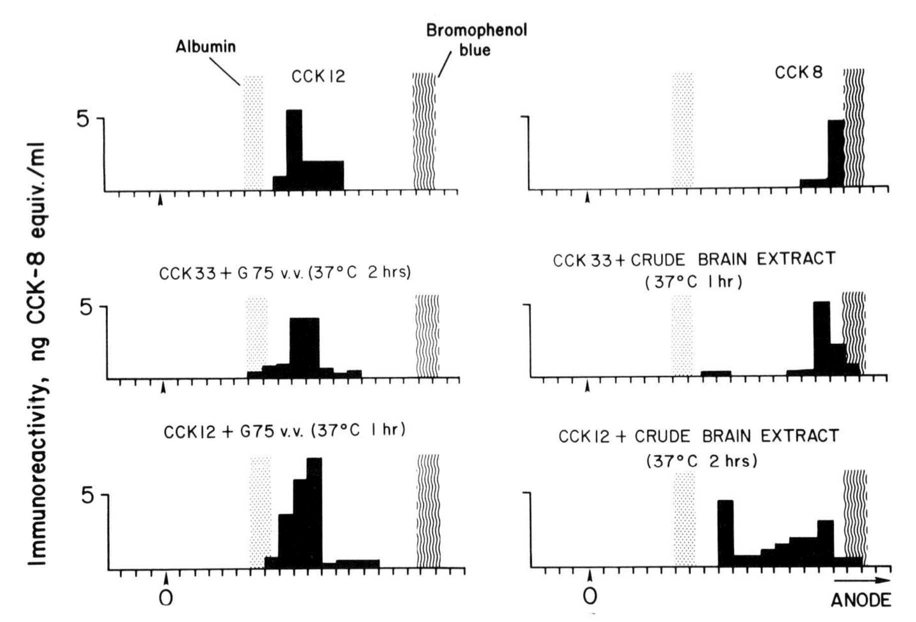

FIG. 3. Starch gel electrophoresis of synthetic CCK-12 (upper left); synthetic CCK-8 (upper right); the reaction products after treatment of CCK-33 with the Sephadex G-75 void volume fractions (G-75 vv) of crude brain extract (middle left) or with crude brain extract (middle right). In this system intact CCK, which is a very basic peptide, migrates slightly cathodally from the origin. At the highest concentration of G-75 vv and more prolonged exposure the final product of CCK-33 conversion resembles CCK-12; the final product of treatment with crude brain extract resembles CCK-8. Treatment of synthetic CCK-12 with G-75 vv produces no alteration in starch gel electrophoretic pattern (bottom left); CCK-12 is converted in part to CCK-8 by treatment with crude brain extract (bottom right). Reproduced from Malesci *et al.* (1980).

1980b). Further study is required to be certain that it is the same enzyme involved in each of the specific cleavages. However since bonds between arginine and neutral or acidic amino acids are quite common in peptide hormones, it is interesting to speculate whether the enzymes we have characterized cleave these bonds in other peptide hormones as well.

Since the unsulfated CCK-8 cannot be readily distinguished from CCK-12 on starch gel electrophoresis we cannot at this time conclude what fraction of immunoreactivity in this region may be due to a biologically inactive desulfated peptide. Such studies are in progress. We have however demonstrated that some portion of the immunoreactivity in this region is biologically active and therefore is likely to correspond to CCK-12 (unpublished observation).

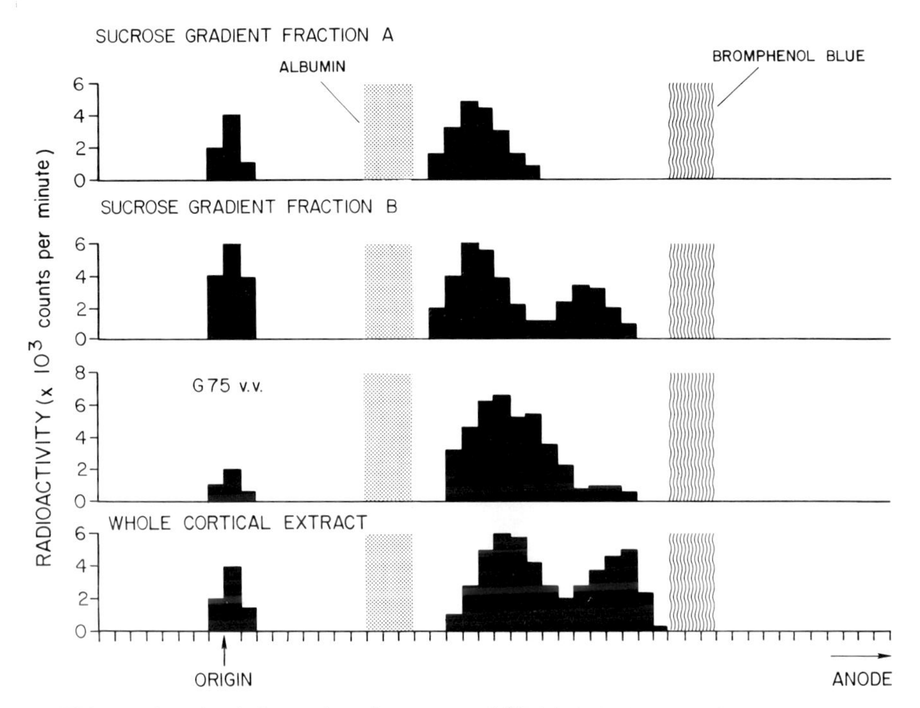

FIG. 4. Starch gel electrophoretic patterns of ^{125}I-labeled pCCK-33 after treatment with (top to bottom) sucrose gradient Fraction A (molecular weight greater than γ-globulin); sucrose gradient Fraction B (molecular weight between human serum albumin and γ-globulin); Sephadex G-75 void volume eluate; crude unfractionated bovine cortical extract from which the various enzymes were partially purified. Marker peptides run on similar gels confirm that intact porcine cholecystokinin (pCCK-33) remains at the site of application, or on occasion, migrates slightly cathodally; the dodecapeptide (CCK-12) migrates just anodally to albumin and the octapeptide (CCK-8) migrates anodally to CCK-12 and cathodally to bromphenol blue. Reproduced from Ryder *et al.* (1980b).

VI. Distribution of CCK Immunoreactivity in Brain and Gut

In the original studies of Vanderhaeghen *et al.* (1975) the highest concentrations of gastrin-like immunoreactivity were found in cortical gray matter of all cerebral lobes. The concentrations in hypothalamus, brain stem, and spinal cord were much lower, averaging only approximately 3% of the cortical concentration. Most other studies of the distribution of CCK immunoreactivity have confirmed that the highest concentrations are found in cerebral cortical tissues. Some have reported hypothalamic concentrations to be in the range of 10% (Rehfeld, 1978b) to 30% (Schneider *et al.*, 1979) of the cortical concentration with much lower

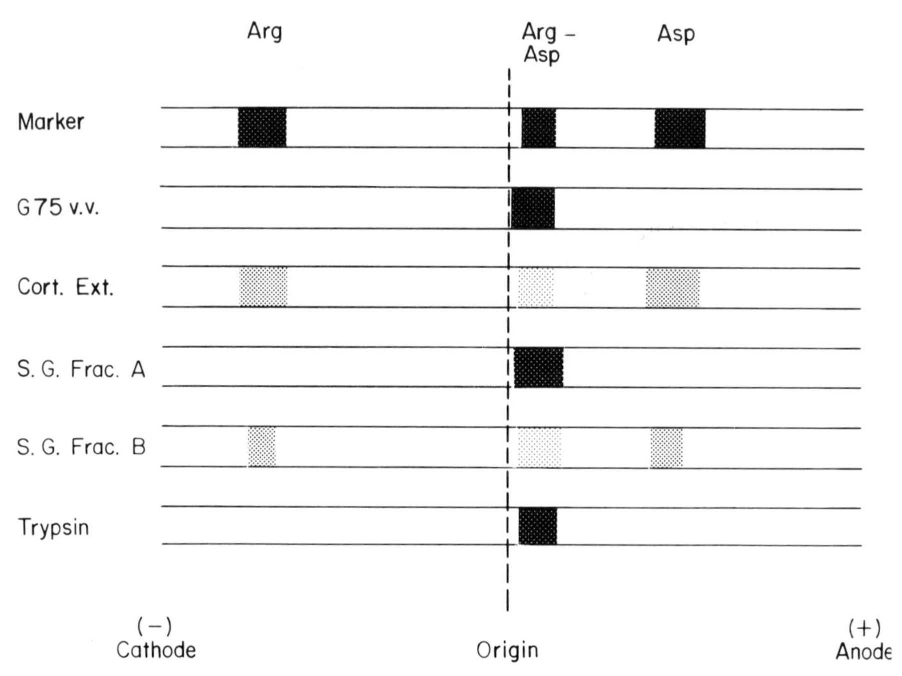

FIG. 5. Typical paper electrophoretic patterns of the products following treatment of Arg-Asp with G-75 vv, cortical extract, sucrose gradient Fraction A, and sucrose gradient Fraction B. Paper chromatography does not permit resolution of Arg and Asp from Arg-Asp. However, these are readily separated by electrophoresis because of marked differences in charge. The marker molecules are shown in the top frame. Reproduced from Ryder *et al.* (1980b).

relative concentrations in the brain stem and spinal cord. However, Lamers *et al.* (1980) have reported hypothalamic concentrations to be greater than cortical concentrations. No difference between right and left sides of the brain has been reported with respect to CCK concentrations.

The finding of specific peptides in extracts of brain tissues cannot fail to provoke speculation regarding their functions. The very high CCK concentrations in the cortex clearly suggested that it was synthesized within the brain. Immunohistochemical studies are required to define the cellular elements within the brain that contain CCK immunoreactivity. Our studies of rabbit cortical tissues (Straus *et al.*, 1977) employing Rabbit B antiserum and the unlabeled antibody-enzyme method of Sternberger *et al.* (1970) revealed staining of many cortical neurons throughout the cortical grey matter (Fig. 7). This finding has been confirmed and extended by several groups and positive cell bodies and fibers have been observed in hippocampal areas, in the olfactory bulb, and in hypothalamic, preoptic,

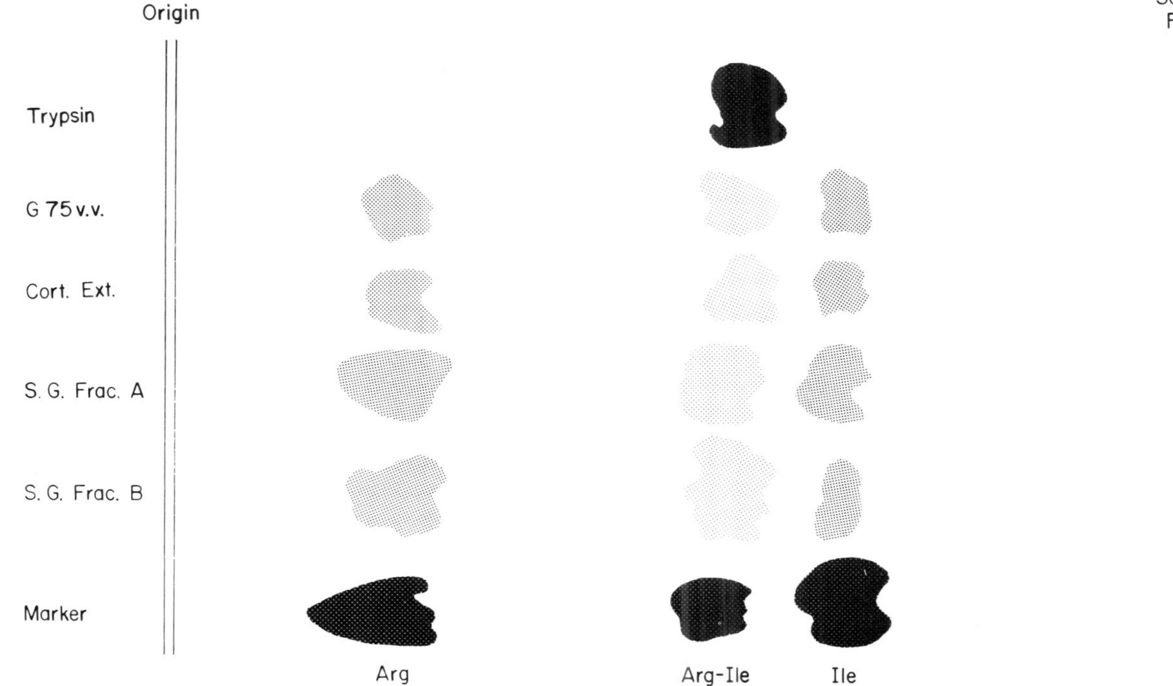

FIG. 6. Typical paper chromatography patterns of the products following treatment of the dipeptide Arg-Ile with (top to bottom) trypsin; Sephadex G-75 void volume eluate; crude unfractionated bovine cortical extract; sucrose gradient Fraction A; sucrose gradient Fraction B. The lowest frame shows the patterns of authentic marker molecules. Reproduced from Ryder *et al.* (1980b).

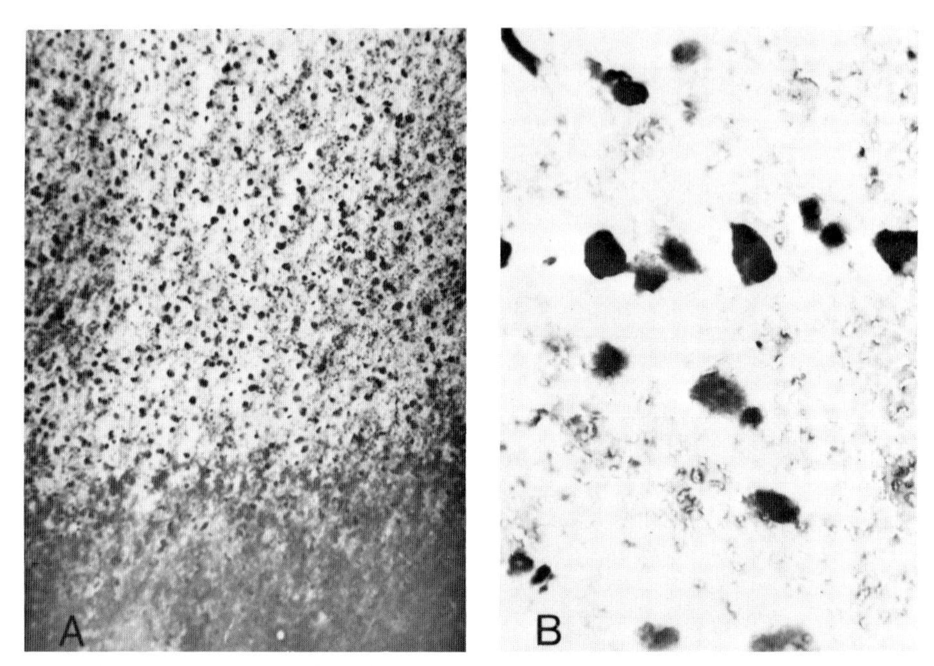

FIG. 7. (A) Low-power photomicrograph of rabbit cerebral cortex (frontal lobe). The tissue was stained by the immunoperoxidase technique using rabbit B antiserum in a 1 : 10 dilution. Staining of individual cell bodies can be seen in all layers of cortical gray matter and diffuse staining can be seen at the bottom in subcortical white matter (×33). (B) High-power photomicrograph showing staining of cell bodies in cortical grey matter (×208). Reproduced from Straus *et al.* (1977).

and amygdaloid nuclei, as well as in the dorsal horn of the spinal cord (Hokfeldt *et al.,* 1978; Larsson and Rehfeld, 1979; Vanderhaeghen *et al.,* 1978, 1980; Loren *et al.,* 1979; Innis *et al.,* 1979).

The finding that the abundant CCK immunoreactivity in cortical gray matter was restricted to neurons stimulated our studies of the distribution of CCK peptides in subcellular fractions of rat cerebral cortex prepared according to the method of Whittaker (1969). These studies demonstrated the presence of immunoreactive CCK in the pellet identified by electron microscopy to contain a high proportion of synaptic vesicles. The recovery in this pellet of 40% of the total immunoreactivity in the initial cortical extract (Fig. 8) is quite comparable to that of other peptides such as vasoactive intestinal peptide (VIP) (Giachetti *et al.,* 1977) and somatostatin (Epelbaum *et al.,* 1977) which have also been reported to localize in the synaptosomes. Immunoreactive CCK was released from synaptosomes incubated in solutions containing K^+ and Ca^{2+} according to the paradigms

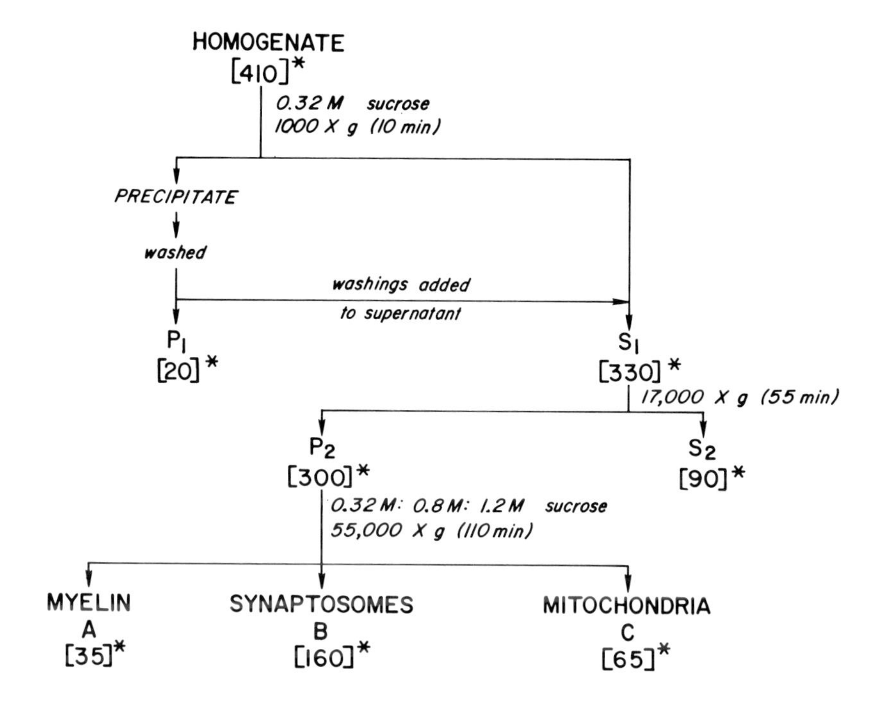

FIG. 8. Flow diagram and recovery of CCK-like immunoreactivity for subcellular fractionation of a rat cerebral cortical extract. Reproduced from Pinget *et al.* (1978).

usually employed to evaluate neuronal chemicals purported to have a role in synaptic physiology (Pinget *et al.*, 1979). These findings have recently been confirmed by Emson *et al.* (1980).

Immunoreactive CCK in the gut has been identified throughout the proximal small intestine (Straus and Yalow, 1978; Rehfeld, 1978b) with significant amounts residing in both mucosal and muscle layers (unpublished observations). Immunohistochemical studies have demonstrated that mucosal CCK immunoreactivity is located in endocrine-type cells (Buchan *et al.*, 1979) while that in the muscle layer is found in neuronal cells (Schultzberg *et al.*, 1980). It is interesting to note that while CCK cells in the brain are so numerous, CCK staining neurons in the intestine are sparce in comparison with those containing VIP and other brain–gut peptides (Schultzberg *et al.*, 1980). They are most abundant in the colon, primarily in the submucous plexus with fewer cells in the myenteric plexus. Recently, Rehfeld *et al.* (1980) have reported that nerves containing G4 have been observed in and around pancreatic islet cells. On the basis of this immunohistochemical localization of G-4 in pancreatic tissue these authors have suggested that the secretion of insulin and other islet hormones is under neural control by G-4. While this finding is of potential importance, it should be pointed out that recent studies have emphasized the considerable technical difficulty in eliminating nonspecific binding of immunoglobulins by ionic interaction to gastroenteropancreatic (GEP) endocrine cells. The early immunohistochemical finding of abundant gastrin within pancreatic islets (Greider and McGuigan, 1971; Lomsky *et al.*, 1969) was not confirmed by radioimmunoassay data (Nilsson *et al.*, 1973). Similarly, Grube (Grube and Weber, 1980; Grube, 1980) has called into question his own finding of CCK within A cells of pancreatic islets (Grube *et al.*, 1978), and has suggested a series of extended specificity controls for immunohistochemical studies.

VII. Functions of Cholecystokinin

The hormonal effects of CCK peptides presumably released from the so-called I cells of intestinal mucosa in response to meal and other secretogogues has been extensively studied (Mutt, 1980). Yet, it now appears that in large-brained animals the major portion of CCK is found in the CNS and not in the gut. The physiologic significance of CCK in the CNS is yet to be clearly defined.

Nonetheless, it is now known that CCK peptides are abundant in cortical and other neurons, and that they are concentrated in, and can be released from synaptosomes. These findings are consistent with a role as a neurotransmitter or neuromodulator. The very broad distribution of the peptides suggests that they may be involved in a variety of functions. It should be cautioned, however, that a neurotransmitter role has not yet been proven. Proof will require the demonstration of presynaptic concentration and release, and postsynaptic electrophysiologic response at the synapse in question. The peripheral nervous system presents less complexity for this type of study than the CNS.

We have investigated the possibility that brain CCK may have some part in the regulation of appetite. A role for CCK in affecting satiety was suggested first by the findings of Gibbs *et al.* (1973a) that injection of purified CCK or CCK-8 in fasted mice evoked satiety although pentagastrin and secretin did not. Since the doses employed were clearly pharmacologic and animal discomfort per se may have prompted discontinuance of feeding, the significance of these findings could be questioned. The later observations of Stern *et al.* (1976) that intraventricular caerulein (which shares six of the seven C-terminal amino acids with CCK and has equivalent CCK-like activity) is more effective in limiting eating than was systemic caerulein and of Maddison (1977) that the operant response to feeding was modulated with intracranial doses of CCK 10-fold smaller than intraperitoneal doses are consistent with a central nervous system role for CCK in appetite regulation. Della-Fera and Baile (1979) have recently demonstrated that injections of as little as 0.01 pmol per minute in the lateral cerbral ventricles of fasted sheep inhibit feeding. These studies taken together are consistent with a role for intracranially administered exogenous CCK in appetite suppression but they throw no light on whether endogenous neuronal CCK has such a role.

It has long been known that there are several inbred strains of rodents which manifest hyperphagia, hyperglycemia, and obesity and that damage in and around the ventromedial hypothalamus is followed by a similar clinical syndrome. It seemed of interest to determine whether the unrestrained appetite of hyperphagic rodents is related to abnormalities in brain CCK. The Obese (ob) and Diabetes (db) strains are known to be single gene mutants with different loci whose mode of inheritance is autosomal recessive. Acid extracts of the brain of ob/ob mice contain about one-third the immunoreactive CCK of their nonobese littermates (Straus and Yalow, 1979a). Similar extracts of the brains of db/db mice have slightly but not significantly higher CCK content and those from gold-thioglucose lesioned mice with obesity have significantly higher CCK than control nonlesioned mice of the same age and strain (Fig. 9) (Straus and Yalow, 1979b). We interpret these data as suggesting that the hyperphagia of ob/ob mice might be due to a deficient signal to the hypothalamic satiety center because of diminished cortical CCK. An interrupted feed-back loop, due to lesioning of the ventromedial hypothalamus as a consequence of treatment with gold-thioglucose, appears to result in an increase in cortical CCK. Perhaps the defect in the db/db also resides at the hypothalamic receptor site. We have also shown that brain CCK is diminished in 2 to 5 day fasted mice (Straus and Yalow, 1980) suggesting the possibility that CCK may be implicated even in acute regulation of appetite. Schneider *et al.* (1979) failed to confirm our findings in ob/ob or fasted mice. Additional work is required to resolve these differences.

VIII. Conclusion

It is less than 5 years since it was first suggested that there was a gastrin-like peptide in the brain. In the intervening years much progress has been made in demonstrating that the peptides are CCK-like not gastrin-like, that there are several different hormonal forms of CCK, that CCK immunoreactivity is concentrated in neuronal tissues, and that specific enzymes appear to be involved in conversion of the precursor

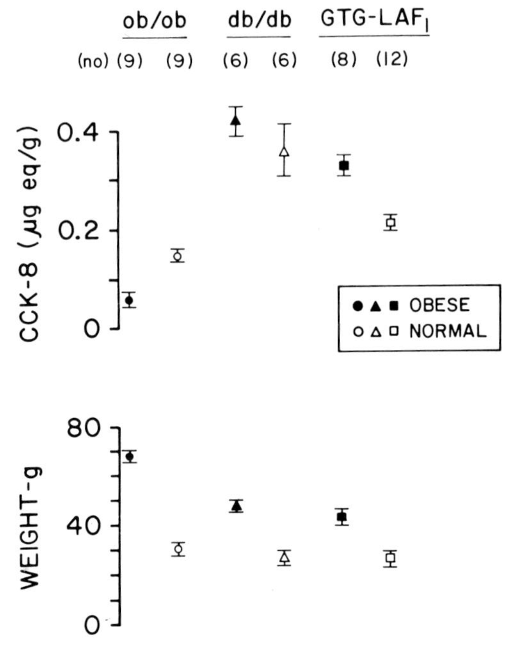

FIG. 9. Weight and brain immunoreactive CCK content in obese, hyperphagic mice, and their control littermates. The Obese (ob/ob) and Diabetes (db/db) strains are single-gene mutants with different loci whose mode of inheritance is autosomal recessive. The LAF_1 mice developed obesity and hyperphagia subsequent to gold-thioglucose (GTG) lesioning of the ventromedial hypothalamus. Reproduced from Yalow and Straus (1979).

molecules to the smaller forms. These data suggest but do not prove a role for CCK as a neuroregulator. However there is much left to be done. The methodology needs to be improved so that there is better agreement among laboratories concerning concentrations and distribution among hormonal forms. Although there is suggestive evidence that CCK is involved in the regulation of appetite, a full range of functions for CCK in the various portions of the brain where it is found needs to be defined. The enzymes involved in specific conversion to the smaller hormonal forms of CCK are still not yet fully characterized. Furthermore there remains some disagreement as to what are the end-products of degradation; CCK-8, desulfated CCK-8, or G-4 are among the likely candidates. Is the biologic activity of brain CCK modulated by regulation of its concentration or the concentration of the converting enzymes or both? The turnover time of CCK in the periphery is measured in minutes, but still unknown is its turnover time in the brain. The study of CCK in the brain is but in its infancy. We look forward with great interest to its growth and maturity.

REFERENCES

Berson, S. A., and Yalow, R. S. (1971). *Gastroenterology* **60,** 215.

Bolton, A. E., and Hunter, W. M. (1973). *Biochim. Biophys. Acta* **251,** 363.

Brownstein, M. J., Russell, J. T., and Gainer, H. (1980). *Science* **207,** 373.

Buchan, A. M. J., Polak, J. M., Solcia, E., and Pearse, A. G. E. (1979). *Nature (London)* **277,** 138.

Della-Fera, M. A., and Baile, C. A. (1979). *Science* **206,** 471.

Dockray, G. J. (1976). *Nature (London)* **264,** 568.

Dockray, G. J. (1977). *Nature (London)* **270,** 359.

Dockray, G. J. (1979). *Annu. Rev. Physiol.* **41,** 83.

Dockray, G. J. (1980). *Brain Res.* **188,** 155.

Emson, P. C., Lee, C. M., and Rehfeld, J. F. (1980). *Life Sci.* **26,** 2157.

Epelbaum, J., Brazeau, P., Tsang, D., Brawer, J., and Martin, J. B. (1977). *Brain Res.* **126,** 309.

Giachetti, A., Said, S.-I., Reynolds, R. C., and Koniges, F. C. (1977). *Proc. Natl. Acad. Sci. U.S.A.* **74,** 3424.

Gibbs, J., Young, R. C., and Smith, G. P. (1973a). *J. Comp. Physiol. Psychol.* **84,** 488.

Gibbs, J., Young, R. C., and Smith, G. P. (1973b). *Nature (London)* **245,** 323.

Greider, M. H., and McGuigan, J. E. (1971). *Diabetes* **20,** 389.

Grossman, M. I. (1973). *In* "Frontiers in Gastrointestinal Hormone Research" (S. Anderson, ed.), p. 17. Almqvist & Wiksell, Stockholm.

Grube, D. (1980). *Histochemistry* **66,** 149.

Grube, D., and Weber, E. (1980). *Histochemistry* **65,** 223.

Grube, D., Maier, V., Raptis, S., and Schlegel, W. (1978). *Histochemistry* **56,** 13.

Harper, A. A., and Raper, H. S. (1943). *J. Physiol.* **102,** 115.

Hökfelt, T., Elde, R., Fuxe, K., Johansson, O., Ljungdahl, A., Goldstein, M., Luft, R., Efendic, S., Nilsson, G., Terenius, L., Ganten, D., Jeffcoate, S. L., Rehfeld, J., Said, S., Perez de la Mora, M., Possani, L., Tapia, R., Teran, L., and Palacios, R. (1978). *In* "The Hypothalamus" (S. Reichlin, R. J. Baldessarini, and J. B. Martin, eds.), p. 69. Raven, New York.

Innis, R. B., Correa, F. M. A., Uhl, G., Schneider, R., and Snyder, S. H. (1979). *Proc. Natl. Acad. Sci. U.S.A.* **76,** 521.

Ivy, A. C., and Oldberg, E. (1928). *Ann. J. Physiol.* **86,** 599.

Jorpes, E., and Mutt, V. (1966). *Acta Physiol. Scand.* **66,** 196.

Knight, L. C., and Welch, M. J. (1978). *Biochim. Biophys. Acta* **534,** 185.

Lamers, C. B., Morley, J. E., Poitras, P., Sharp, B., Carlson, H. E., Hershman, J. M., and Walsh, J. H. (1980). *Am. J. Physiol.* (in press)

Larsson, L. I., and Rehfeld, J. E. (1979). *Brain Res.* **165,** 201.

Lomsky, R., Langr, F., and Vortel, V. (1969). *Nature (London)* **223,** 618.

Loren, I., Alumets, J., Hakanson, R., and Sundler, F. (1979). *Histochemistry* **59,** 249.

Macgregor, R. R., Chu, L. L. H., and Cohn, D. V. (1976). *J. Biol. Chem.* **21,** 6711.

Maddison, S. (1977). *Psychol. Behav.* **19,** 819.

Malesci, A., Straus, E., and Yalow, R. S. (1980). *Proc. Natl. Acad. Sci. U.S.A.* **77,** 597.

Muller, J. E., Straus, E., and Yalow, R. S. (1977). *Proc. Natl. Acad. Sci. U.S.A.* **74,** 3035.

Mutt, V. (1976). *Clin. Endocrinol. Suppl.* **5,** 175s.
Mutt, V. (1980). *In* "Gastrointestinal Hormones" (G. B. J. Glass, ed.), p. 169. Raven, New York.
Mutt, V., and Jorpes, E. (1971). *Biochem. J.* **125,** 57.
Mutt, V., and Jorpes, J. E. (1973). *In* "Methods in Investigative and Diagnostic Endocrinology, Part III" (S. A. Berson, and R. S. Yalow, eds.), p. 1059. Elsevier, Amsterdam.
Nilsson, G., Yalow, R. S., and Berson, S. A. (1973). *In* "Frontiers in Gastrointestinal Hormone Research" (S. Anderson, ed.), p. 95. Almqvist & Wiksell, Stockholm.
Okada, S. (1914/15). *J. Physiol. (London)* **49,** 457.
Pinget, M., Straus, E., and Yalow, R. S. (1978). *Proc. Natl. Acad. Sci. U.S.A.* **75,** 6324.
Pinget, M., Straus, E., and Yalow, R. S. (1979). *Life Sci.* **25,** 339.
Pradayrol, L., Vaysse, N., Cassigneul, J., and Ribet, A. (1979). *In* "Hormone Receptors in Digestion and Nutrition" (G. Rosselin, F. Fromageot, and S. Bonfils, eds.), p. 95. Elsevier, Amsterdam.
Rehfeld, J. F. (1978a). *J. Biol. Chem.* **253,** 4016.
Rehfeld, J. F. (1978b). *J. Biol. Chem.* **253,** 4022.
Rehfeld, J., and Goltermann, N. R. (1979). *J. Neurochem.* **32,** 1339.
Rehfeld, J., and Larsson, L. (1979). *Acta Physiol. Scand.* **105,** 117.
Rehfeld, J. F., Larsson, L. T., Goltermann, N. R., Schwartz, T. W., Holst, J. J., Jensen, S. L., and Morley, J. S. (1980). *Nature (London)* **284,** 33.
Rubin, B., Engel, S. L., Drungis, A. M., Dzetzkalns, M., Grizas, E. O., Waugh, M. H., and Yiacas, E. (1969). *J. Pharm. Sci.* **58,** 955.
Ryder, S. W., Eng, J., Straus, E., and Yalow, R. S. (1980a). *Biochem. Biophys. Res. Commun.* **94,** 704.
Ryder, S., Straus, E., and Yalow, R. S. (1980b). *Proc. Natl. Acad. Sci. U.S.A.* **77,** 3669.
Sankaran, H., Deveney, C. W., Goldfine, I. D., and Williams, J. A. (1979). *J. Biol. Chem.* **254,** 9349.
Schneider, B. S., Monahan, J. W., and Hirsh, J. (1979). *J. Clin. Invest.* **64,** 1348.
Schultzberg, M., Hokfelt, T., Nilsson, G., Terenius, L., Rehfeld, J. F., Brown, M., Elde, R., Goldstein, M., and Said, S. (1980). *Neuroscience* **5,** 689.
Stern, J., Cudillo, C. A., and Kruper, J. (1976). *J. Comp. Physiol. Psychol.* **90,** 484.
Sternberger, L. A., Hardy, P. H., Cuculis, J. J., and Meyer, H. G. (1970). *J. Histochem. Cytochem.* **18,** 315.
Straus, E. (1978). *Gastroenterology* **74,** 141.
Straus, E. (1980). *In* "Clinics in Gastroenterology" (W. Creutzfeldt, ed.), No. 9, p. 555. Saunders, Philadelphia, Pennsylvania.
Straus, E., and Yalow, R. S. (1978). *Proc. Natl. Acad. Sci. U.S.A.* **75,** 486.
Straus, E., and Yalow, R. S. (1979a). *Science* **203,** 68.
Straus, E., and Yalow, R. S. (1979b). *Endocrinology (Suppl.)* **282,** A-837.
Straus, E., and Yalow, R. S. (1980). *Life Sci.* **26,** 969.
Straus, E., Muller, J. E., Choi, H.-S., Paronetto, F., and Yalow, R. S. (1977). *Proc. Natl. Acad. Sci. U.S.A.* **74,** 3033.
Straus, E., Malesci, A., and Yalow, R. S. (1978). *Proc. Natl. Acad. Sci. U.S.A.* **75,** 5711.
Straus, E., Malesci, A., Pinget, M., and Yalow, R. S. (1979). *Life Sci.* **25,** 343.
Tracy, H. J., and Gregory, R. A. (1964). *Nature (London)* **204,** 790.
Vanderhaeghen, J. J., DeMev, J., Lotstra, F., and Gilles, C. (1978). *Acta Neurol. Belg.* **79,** 62.
Vanderhaeghen, J. J., Signeau, J. C., and Gepts, W. (1975). *Nature (London)* **257,** 604.
Vanderhaegen, J. J., Lotstra, F., DeMey, J., and Gilles, C. (1980). *Proc. Natl. Acad. Sci. U.S.A.* **77,** 1190.
Whittaker, V. P. (1969). *In* "Handbook of Neurochemistry" (A. Laitha, ed.), Vol. 2, p. 327. Plenum, New York.

Yalow, R. S., and Berson, S. A. (1970). *Gastroenterology* **58**, 609.
Yalow, R. S., and Berson, S. A. (1971). *Gastroenterology* **60**, 203.
Zuhlke, H., Steiner, D. F., Lernmark, A., and Lipsey, C. (1976). *Ciba Found. Symp.* No. 41, p. 183.

DISCUSSION

T. J. McDonald: In 1971 Anastasi *et al.* (*Experientia* **27**, 166, 1971) reported the sequences of two structurally related tetradecapeptides, bombesin and alytesin, which they had isolated from the skin of two European frogs. Interest in these amphibian peptides was stimulated when bombesin was shown to have potent and diverse pharmacological effects on the mammalian gastrointestinal tract [see P. Melchiorri, *in* "Gut Hormones" (S. R. Bloom, ed.), p. 534. Churchill Livingstone, 1978] and the central nervous system (M. Brown and W. Vale, *Trends Neurosci.* **2**, 95, 1979). Erspamer and Melchiorri [*in* "Gastrointestinal Hormones" (J. C. Thompson, ed.), p. 575. University of Texas Press, 1975] first provided evidence for the existence of an endogenous mammalian bombesin-related peptide by demonstrating bombesin-like immunoreactivity (BLI) in extracts of mammalian gut. This finding was confirmed by Polak *et al.* (*Lancet* **1**, 1109, 1976) in a study on human gastrointestinal tissue and extended by Brown *et al.* (*Life Sci.* **23**, 2721, 1978) by the demonstration of BLI in the mammalian central nervous system. At the Karolinska institute we found that a chromatographic fraction derived from porcine gastric tissue extracts on injection into test animals resulted in increased plasma immunoreactive gastrin and increased gastric acid and pepsin secretion (*Gut* **19**, 767, 1978). The active peptide [originally named the gastrin releasing peptide (GRP) after the bioactivity used as the bioassay during isolation] has been isolated and sequenced (*Biochem. Biophys. Res. Commun.* **90**, 227, 1979). The porcine peptide having 27 amino acid residues is larger than bombesin but the two peptides have nine identities in their 10 C-terminal residues; the one deviation being a histidine/glutamine interchange (porcine/amphibian) at the eighth position from the C-termus (Fig. A). This C-terminal homology undoubtedly accounts for the similar bioactivity of the two peptides.

Erspamer *et al.* (*Adv. Exp. Med. Biol.* **106**, 51, 1978) demonstrated the presence of considerable amounts of BLI in avian gastric (proventricular) tissue. We have recently isolated and sequenced such a bombesin-related peptide from the chicken proventriculus (McDonald *et al.*, submitted for publication) which has considerable structural homology with the porcine GRP (Fig. A). The porcine and chicken GRPs have 27 residues, identical N- and C-terminal residues, and identical tryptic cleavage points. There are 18 identities in the 27 residues with eight of the

Porcine GRP Ala-Pro-Val-Ser-Val-Gly-Gly-Gly-Thr-Val-Leu-Ala-Lys-
Chicken GRP Ala-Pro-Leu-Gln-Pro-Gly-Gly-Ser-Pro-Ala-Leu-Thr-Lys-

Bombesin Pyr-Gln-Arg-Leu-Gly-Asn-Gln-Trp-Ala-Val-Gly-His-Leu-Met-NH_2
Porcine GRP -Met-Tyr-Pro-Arg-Gly-Asn-His-Trp-Ala-Val-Gly-His-Leu-Met-NH_2
Chicken GRP -Ile-Tyr-Pro-Arg-Gly-Ser-His-Trp-Ala-Val-Gly-His-Leu-Met-NH_2
Alytesin Pyr-Gly-Arg-Leu-Gly-Thr-Gln-Trp-Ala-Val-Gly-His-Leu-Met-NH_2

FIG. A. Structural comparison of the porcine GRP, chicken GRP, bombesin, and alytesin. The peptides are aligned at their C-termini. Identical residues in the porcine GRP, chicken GRP, and the amphibian peptides are enclosed with solid lines.

nine nonidentities occurring in the N-terminal 14 residues. In the C-terminal 13 residues, the one nonidentity is an asparagine/serine interchange (porcine/chicken) at the ninth position from the C-terminus. Interestingly, alytesin also has a hydroxyl-containing residue (threonine) at the equivalent position and in this respect, the chicken GRP is slightly more alytesin-like than bombesin-like. Also of interest, the chicken like the porcine GRP has a histidine residue in position eight from the C-terminus instead of the glutamine residue present in the amphibian peptides.

Hence, the chicken and porcine GRPs are the first chemically characterized nonamphibian members of the bombesin-like family of peptides. At least in the case of the mammalian members of the family, these peptides appear to be present in both brain and gut. The physiological significance, if any, of these peptides in their respective species is at present unknown but considerable study is being directed toward their ability to cause elevation of plasma gastroenteropancreatic hormone levels.

W. D. Odell: If you use identical extraction methods for identical immunochemical localization methods, do you find other tissues outside the gut and the brain (for example, liver, lung, kidney) contain CCK-related peptides?

E. Straus: We have looked at a variety of other tissues other than the gut and brain and have found no significant immunoreactivity in tissue such as kidney, lung, heart. At this point there's been a very positive or healthy development in terms of our concept of "gastrointestinal" peptides. It is important to look all over the place. I think the same thing has been suggested for insulin and other peptides, to look all over for possible other sources. While it is striking to find CCK in new places it is not ubiquitous in its distribution. It certainly is distributed in neural tissues, it is for example very abundant in the central nervous system, as I indicated, and it is also found in the vagus nerve and other neural elements.

B. Posner: I have several questions and a comment. Could you give us some information on the distribution of CCK in different parts of the brain? What are the relative concentrations in the cortex, the thalamus, and the hypothalamus? Have you examined subdivisions of the hypothalamus?

E. Straus: I can tell you that the original report of Vanderhaeghen *et al.* of gastrin-like immunoreactivity indicated that by far the highest concentrations were in the cerebral cortex and that the hypothalamus and more caudal structures contained approximately 3% of that in the cortex. Other workers have found essentially similar data in that the concentration in the cortex has been agreed to be the highest. Now Rehfeld has done the most extensive anatomic radioimmunoassay survey of brain CCK and you can probably best refer to his papers to look at those differences. Again, by far the most immunoreactivity was found in the cortex with other areas having approximately 10% or less. Lamers *et al.* in acid and neutral extracts of brain found that the hypothalamus had an even greater concentration than the cortex but that report is outstanding in its disagreement from the other published work. There are immunohistochemical studies—several to try to quantitate the brain content in various areas—I wouldn't try to inform you as to that although I'll give you those references if you're interested, and I think that it's difficult to be quantitative, or I feel it's difficult to be quantitative about CCK content from the immunohistochemical studies. It remains to have careful studies of immunoreactive material by radioimmunoassay I think, for the study of much larger brained animals where I think these nuclei can be better extracted, can be obtained in greater tissue weights and be extracted more efficiently. I also think that the extraction, as I indicated, the alkaline extraction is a much better, more uniform, and more efficient method and this finding is rather new and I think that these kinds of data should be forthcoming but are not available now.

B. Posner: Are there any differences that you can determine in concentration or distribution of CCK in relationship to rapidity or method of sacrifice of the animal?

E. Straus: We have looked at that to some extent because, of course, this is important with a variety of peptides when one is looking at human tissues since we rely primarily or exclusively on autopsy material. We are looking at methods of sacrifice such as the guillotine and also rapid microwave oven fixation or cooking of brain tissues, and as yet we really don't have definitive findings. As far as that's concerned, we do think it's important of course to be as rapid as possible in obtaining the tissue and extracting those tissues, but I can't give you any real quantitation with respect to CCK. We have found, however, that opening the peritoneal cavity at autopsy somehow accelerates the degradation of secretin and gastrin.

B. Posner: Did you also have an opportunity to look at receptor or binding site distribution for CCK?

E. Straus: We have not done that sort of work, but Dr. John Williams at the University of California in San Francisco has looked at receptors using a Bolten-Hunter labeled preparation. Essentially what his data suggest is that everywhere that you find CCK you find CCK receptors.

B. Posner: Mark vanHouten, in my laboratory, has been studying peptide–brain interactions. He's observed that a number of intravenously administered peptides including insulin, angiotension, calcitonin, ACTH, and lactogen undergo receptor-mediated uptake into brain tissue. The sites of uptake have been restricted, by and large, to the circumventricular areas of the brain including the median eminence. No uptake of blood-borne peptide has been seen into cortical tissue where the blood–brain barrier is intact. It is thus possible that at least in certain areas of the brain, perhaps in the hypothalamic region, some of the CCK may be derived from receptor-mediated uptake into that area.

E. Straus: I think that's a good point. The very high concentrations of CCK in the cerebral cortex certainly suggests that it's synthesized in those cortical neurons. The blood–brain barrier should and in fact when one uses labeled peptides does prevent the entry of significant amounts of the material from the circulation.

K. Sterling: I think we are grateful for your shedding some light on what was previously a rather murky area—there was just one thing that was rather astonishing—if I understood you correctly—human CCK does not have a structure that's known to us and it's not available. I wanted to ask you is that for technical reasons, or simply the difficulty in getting sufficient autopsy tissues, or why is this?

E. Straus: It's simply because of the way in which Victor Mutt has purified cholecystokinin and secretin. It's very impressive if you go to his laboratory. He takes the upper meter of intestine from 30,000 or so hogs which he gets frozen from a slaughter house and he makes these tremendous extracts and puts it over immense Sephadex columns and takes very great losses. It is possible that in the initial water boiling he discards a significant amount of CCK, and there might even be a greater yield if it was extracted in alkaline medium. In any event, he needs a tremendous amount of starting material and he takes tremendous losses to get pure CCK peptides and because of that and the abundance of the porcine tissue we have the porcine secretin and CCK and a number of other porcine intestinal peptides. All of us working with intestinal peptides have relied almost entirely upon Dr. Mutt. He is our source. I think that in the future it should be possible to monitor purifications by radioimmunoassay to improve efficiency.

J. Dupre: Would you comment further on your own comments regarding the difficulties of immunofluorescent techniques in relation to the figure you showed us, because of the possibility of that obscuring of localization that may be more important?

E. Straus: Yes, I am not an immunohistochemist and the studies that I showed here were our first and the first immunohistochemical studies of CCK in neural tissues. But in any case, we were so interested to see whether this material was in the neurons that we undertook to do these studies. The finding that immunoglobulins bind nonspecifically by certain ionic interactions with cells was restricted by Grube and Weber to the endocrine type cells of the gastroenteropancreatic tissues. Whether or not that same sort of nonspecific binding may be present in neuronal tissues hasn't been determined, but I think it certainly would be well for immunohistochemists to employ the suggestions which they have made about extended specificity controls, which one can find in their papers, in order to reexamine by immunohistochemical methods neuronal tissues. I'm sure that this will be done. I think that there's no doubt in my mind that the initial finding of abundant gastrin in the pancreas by immunohistochemical methods reflected that artifact. As far as our finding is concerned, and those findings of others in terms of the cerebral cortex in other neuronal tissues, I certainly hope that that's not artifact. I think that in view of these recent findings about the restrictions in specificity with these kinds of cells and they are similar, at least in terms of their content of the CCK-like material, that this really has to be done. It must be pointed out, however, that in this case immunohistochemical and radioimmunoassay data are in agreement.

E. Rall: I presume if you have a variety of clearly homologous polypeptides that you get out of tissues and can be derived one from the other that there perhaps are three possibilities, as to how this might happen. You might actually have separate genes for the different peptides as a result of some genetic recombination event.

Second, in different tissues you might have different concentrations of reasonable specific proteolytic enzymes so that you'd start off with single gene product, but depending on the concentration of the proteolytic enzymes you might get a different ratio of the different fragments. A third possibility is that the method of extraction might artifactually give you different polypeptides and in reality if you could look at the cell freed from any artifact there would really only be a single peptide. Would you like to choose among those possibilities?

E. Straus: I think that, of course, is absolutely true and very relevant. It is precisely why we were so concerned initially about whether or not neuronal tissue actually contained any CCK-33 because in the initial description it appeared clear that there was only the single form—the C terminal octapeptide. Our finding that there is CCK-33 and our finding that there is at least proteolytic activity which is capable of affecting these kinds of cleavages suggests perhaps that your first possibility is unlikely. The finding of the same CCK forms, although we haven't been able to detect the same enzymatic activities in gut tissue primarily I think, because there's so much other proteolytic activity in gut tissue that we can't recover these enzymes, the finding that the same forms are in the two tissues and the finding of these enzymes suggests to me that there aren't two modes of synthesis. What regulates the conversion, or the actual concentration of the more biologically active (at least for those activities that we know) C terminal peptides, whether it's synthesis or enzyme availability I don't know. The other point that you made about artifacts of extraction of course is equally important. This is why we have tried and are continuing to try to determine the efficiency of extraction with various extractants. It's certainly true that there are differences in terms of what one recovers with different extractants. I think it is clear, however, that both forms are present and that there is proteolytic activity which is capable of making these conversions and I think that's about as far as I can go with these data.

C. R. Kahn: I share with others the enthusiasm for this general area of research and I had just two small questions concerning the method of extraction. Having had some experience extracting tissues for insulin-like activity, I became aware that there are great differences in extraction rates—and I wondered if you could tell us a little bit more about the absolute extraction efficiency versus the relative extraction efficiency. Obviously the alkaline method did yield higher absolute amounts of CCK but if one adds tracer to the system, do you have any estimate of the absolute extraction efficiency or are you still looking only at the tip of the iceberg. There may still be a lot of immunoreactive material that isn't being extracted even with this method.

E. Straus: I think that's a very good question, but I don't have any data relative to that. I would not comment on it. I think it's a very important point, however. The experiments which you suggest might not reflect the difficulty in extracting the peptides from their locations within the cell, or might reflect losses onto extracting vessels, rather than absolute extraction efficiency. The important question is what tracer or tracers to add. CCK-33 and the C-terminal peptides behave differently on extraction and there may be enzymatic conversion. This is much more complicated than insulin extraction from tissues.

C. R. Kahn: A second point relates to the nature of the material in brain versus the gut. You were primarily stressing the similarity and certainly in the early figure you showed with a series of gel filtration patterns lined up one on top of the other; they look quite similar on initial inspection. But I noticed that in both the pig and monkey extracts, there was considerable difference in the migration of the central peak—the peak that corresponds to the 33–39 amino acid cholecystokinin when one compared the material from the brain and the gut. I wondered if you had had further characterization perhaps using methods such as polyacrylamide gel electrophoresis or isoelectric focusing.

E. Straus: As I indicated both columns are 1 by 50 cm Sephadex columns and I think that the resolution that we obtained as shown there is about the best that we can do in that system. I think that clearly one of the areas in which work has to be done in this field is to develop better, finer, more precise separation systems. I think one could suggest a variety of them. There are those who use Sephadex G-50 as we do, but use much longer columns and have essentially found in different species that the larger forms elute from these columns rather similarly among species. But again, particularly with the 33 amino acid forms, there are certainly species differences in the structure near the NH_2-terminus which might relate to how they would elute in these columns.

J. M. George: Is there gastrin or other polypeptides in brain that cross-react to CCK immunologically?

E. Straus: I think gastrin is remarkable in its absence from the brain. There is some gastrin, rather low in concentration, in porcine pituitary gland but not in bovine pituitary gland where there is CCK, but as far as we and others have determined there is essentially no gastrin in the brain if you accept our finding that there is no G-4 which you could call gastrin or CCK. But there is no G-17 or what we generally call gastrin, or G-34, that we can determine in neural tissues. There is an exception to that in that Rehfeld has found that the vagus nerve contains very significant G-17. Others have found that that C-terminal type immunoreactivity is CCK-8 for the most part. Other than that I think that in neural tissue gastrin is remarkable in its comparison with CCK in its absence, certainly from brain tissue. Now you asked about several other peptides.

J. M. George: Were there any others that you were aware of?

E. Straus: Of any other cross-reacting gastrin-CCK family peptides? Well the only other major one that we think about is Caerulein which is, of course, from the frog skin and is a decapeptide almost structurally identical to the C-terminus of CCK and has the same biological activities and potencies in various biological systems. To the best of my knowledge, and John may correct me about this, unlike bombesin which has been found in mammalian tissues, to my knowledge Caerulein has not been found in any mammalian tissues at all, and not in the brain of the frog either as far as I know.

RECENT PROGRESS IN HORMONE RESEARCH, VOL. 37

Insulin Receptors, Receptor Antibodies, and the Mechanism of Insulin Action

C. RONALD KAHN, KATHLEEN L. BAIRD, JEFFERY S. FLIER,
CARL GRUNFELD, JOAN T. HARMON, LEN C. HARRISON,
F. ANDRES KARLSSON, MASATO KASUGA, GEORGE L. KING,
URSULA C. LANG, JUDITH M. PODSKALNY, AND
EMMANUEL VAN OBBERGHEN

Section on Cellular and Molecular Physiology, Diabetes Branch, National Institute of Arthritis, Metabolism and Digestive Diseases, National Institutes of Health, Bethesda, Maryland

I. Introduction to the Problem of Insulin Action

Since the discovery of insulin, many investigators have devoted considerable effort in attempting to unravel the mechanism of action of this hormone. Insulin and its precusors have been completely sequenced, and their three-dimensional structure determined (Sanger, 1959; Steiner *et al.*, 1969; Blundell *et al.*, 1972). The first step in insulin action, the interaction of insulin with its plasma membrane receptor, has been well characterized and considerable progress has been made toward purification of the receptor and identification of its subunit components. Many of the effects of insulin on enzymes and pathways involved in carbohydrate, protein, and lipid metabolism are also well studied (Cahill, 1971). However, how the interaction of insulin with the cell is transformed into a final biological response remains a mystery (Czech, 1977; Kahn, 1979). The complexity of this problem is evidenced by the fact that since the conception of the Laurentian Hormone Conference in 1943, no fewer than 23 papers have been presented on topics related to insulin chemistry and/or the mechanism of insulin action.

There are several reasons why unraveling the mechanism of insulin action has been difficult. First, insulin exerts a wide spectrum of effects at the cellular level (Table I). These include effects at the membrane level, e.g., stimulation of glucose and amino acid uptake; effects on both membrane and cytoplasmic enzymes; and effects on protein synthesis, DNA synthesis, cell growth and differentiation.

In addition, the effects of insulin vary both in time course and dose–response (Fig. 1). Some effects of insulin, such as stimulation of glucose transport, occur within seconds after hormone exposure, whereas others,

ISBN 0-12-571137-9

TABLE I
Classification of the Actions of Insulin by Time-Course and Dose–Response

Effect	Classification by[a]		Requires protein synthesis
	Time	Dose–response	
Stimulation of glucose transport (and utilization)	1	A	−
Stimulation of amino acid transport	3	B	+
Stimulation of enzymes			
Glycogen synthase	1–2	A–B	(−)
Acetyl-CoA carboxylase	1–2	A–B	(−)
Pyruvate dehydrogenase	1–2	A–B	(−)
Tyrosine aminotransferase	3	A–B	+
Lipoprotein lipase	4	A	+
Inhibition of lipolysis	1	A	−
Stimulation of protein synthesis	2–3	A–B	+
Alteration in protein phosphorylation	1	A	(−)
Stimulation of RNA synthesis	3	B	+
Stimulation of DNA synthesis	4	C	+

[a] The letters and numbers correspond to the curves shown in Fig. 1.

such as stimulation of DNA synthesis, require hours; effects on most cytoplasmic enzymes lie somewhere between these two extremes (Fig. 1A). In all cases, there is a lag before the onset of a measurable, biological effect, and with many of the effects which have more prolonged time courses, removing insulin early after the cells are exposed stops or prevents the insulin action. For example, the earliest time at which one can detect an effect of insulin on DNA synthesis in human fibroblasts is 4 to 6 hours after exposure, and the effect is maximal at 16–20 hours (Fig. 1A, curve 4) (Rechler *et al.*, 1974). If, however, cells which have been exposed to insulin for 3 hours are washed to remove the hormone, it is as if the cells had never been insulin-treated at all, i.e., there is no subsequent stimulation of DNA synthesis at any time over the next 24 hours.

Likewise, effects of insulin occur with widely varying concentration dependence, ranging from 10^{-11} M for production of the antilipolytic effect of insulin to 10^{-7} M for the growth-promoting action (Fig. 1B). In fact it is possible to classify insulin's actions by these two characteristics (Table I). In general, the more delayed actions of insulin require the higher hormone concentrations; however, this is not always the case. Of course, insulin's actions can also be classified by other criteria, such as whether there is a requirement for protein synthesis, a dependence on glucose transport, etc. Any proposed mechanism for hormone action, if it is to be solitary, must take into account all of these variations.

Another problem which has plagued investigators interested in studying

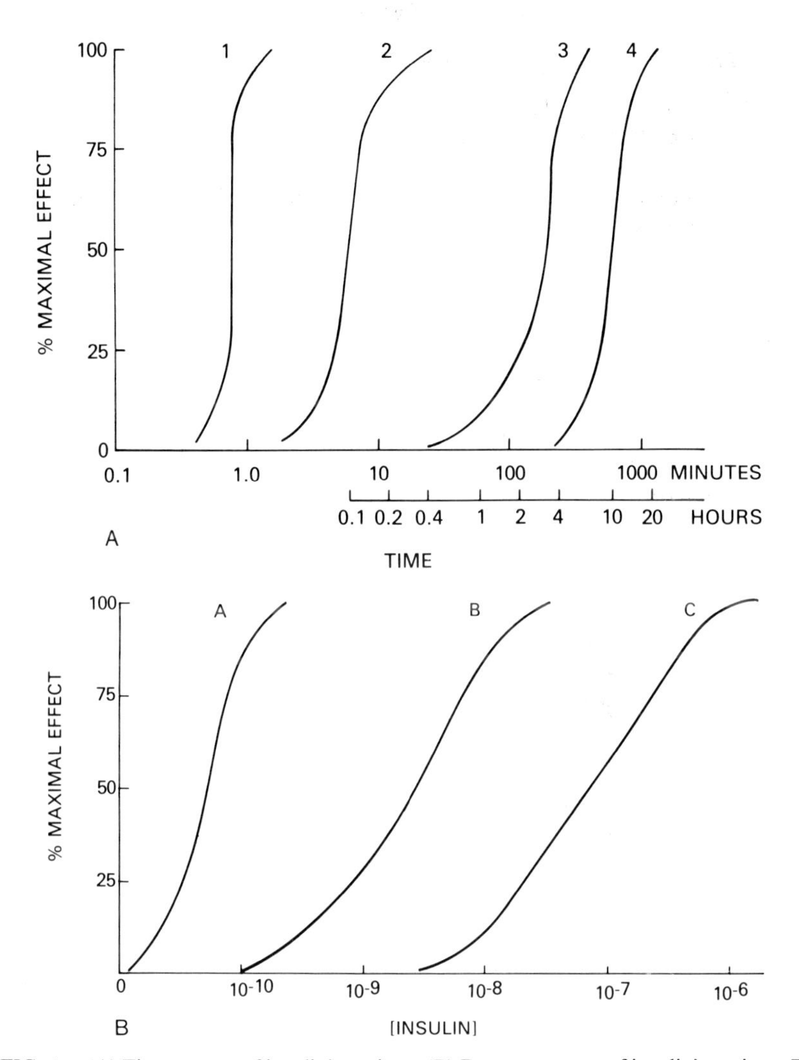

FIG. 1. (A) Time course of insulin's actions. (B) Dose–response of insulin's actions. The letters and numbers indicating the different curves correspond to those in Table I.

insulin action has been the difficulty of detecting any effect of the hormone in broken cell systems. Thus, it is well known that insulin stimulates glucose transport, and this effect persists in membrane vesicles even after the cell is broken (Martin and Carter, 1970). However, if the cell is first broken to form the membrane vesicles, and the vesicles treated with insulin directly, no effect is observed. Recently, this problem seems closer to a solution by the exciting work from the laboratories of Jarett (Jarett and Seals, 1979; Seals and Jarett, 1980; Popp *et al.*, 1980) and Larner *et al.* (1979). These workers have shown that insulin's effects on certain enzymes can be produced either using a soluble extract of cells treated with insulin or in a broken cell preparation containing some plasma membrane elements. However, it is important to keep in mind that the effects being studied represent only a very small part of the range of all of insulin's actions, and thus we are still uncertain as to the extent to which these observations can be generalized in our overall picture of insulin action.

Finally, in any study of insulin's effects, one must by necessity also consider another group of peptide hormones with a similar spectrum of activities called insulin-like growth factors or IGFs. These are a family of polypeptides which are immunologically distinct from insulin, but are capable of mimicking all of insulin's biological actions, albeit with different dose–response curves (Zapf *et al.*, 1978; Van Wyk and Underwood, 1978). The IGFs include insulin-like growth factor I (IGF-I), insulin-like growth factor II (IGF-II), somatomedin A, somatomedin C, and multiplication stimulating activity (MSA) (Table II). In general, the insulin-like growth factors are more potent in growth-promoting actions, such as stimulation of DNA synthesis, whereas insulin is more potent in metabolic effects, such as stimulation of glucose oxidation (Fig. 2). At least a part of this overlapping spectrum of activities can be accounted for by structural similarities between the insulin-like growth factors and insulin. IGF-I and IGF-II have been sequenced and shown to have about 50% sequence homology with insulin (Rinderknecht and Humbel 1978a,b). In addition, however, these peptides have their own receptors, which differ in specificity from the insulin receptor (vide infra). Again any comprehensive scheme for the mechanism of insulin action must take into account these peptides and their receptors.

Recently several new probes have become available which have shed some light on the problem of insulin action. These include cultured cell

TABLE II
Insulin-Like Growth Factors (IGF)

	Molecular weight	Isoelectric point	Source
IGF-1	7650	Basic	Human plasma
IGF-2	7470	Basic	Human plasma
Somatomedin A	~7500	Neutral–acid	Human plasma
Somatomedin C	~7600	Basic	Human plasma
Multiplication stimulating activity (MSA)	7000–8700	Neutral–basic	Calf serum Liver-cell culture

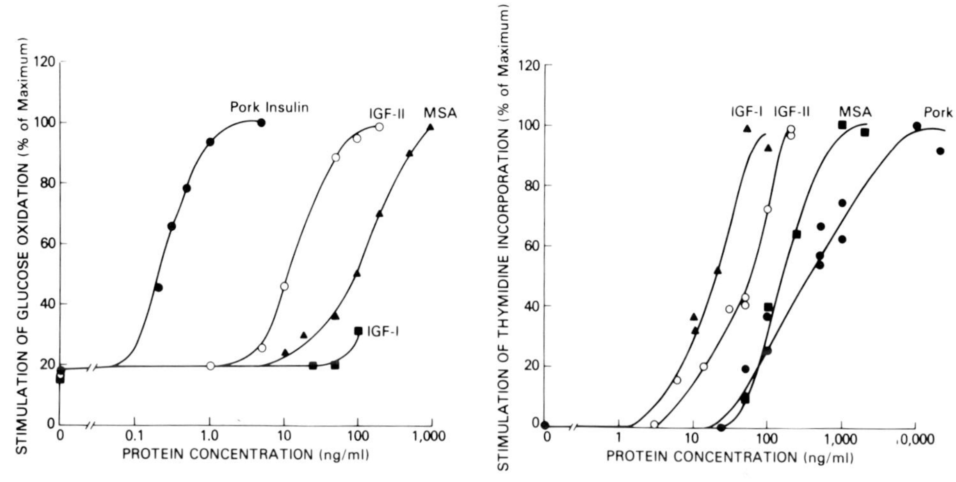

FIG. 2. Comparison of the potencies of insulin and the insulin-like growth factors (IGF-I, IGF-II, and MSA) to stimulate glucose oxidation in adipocytes (left) and thymidine incorporation into DNA of fibroblasts (right).

systems which are highly responsive to insulin, new methods for studying receptor structure, mutant cell lines that possess defects in either the insulin receptor or pathways of insulin action, and antibodies to the insulin receptor (anti-R) which block insulin binding and mimic insulin action. In this article, we will briefly attempt to review some of the data concerning the use of these probes and their implications regarding insulin action. We will particularly concentrate on the antibodies to the receptor since they have been uniquely useful in many of these studies.

II. The Insulin Receptor

The concept that cells possess "receptive substances" or receptors whose primary function is specific recognition and binding of another molecule arose nearly a century ago. This was well before the isolation of insulin, and even predated the formalized concept of hormones as circulating regulators of cell function by several years (Langley, 1978; Ehrlich, 1906). Over the past 30 years, evidence has come from a variety of sources that the first step in the action of insulin is binding to specific receptor sites on the plasma membrane of the cell (reviewed in Roth, 1973; Kahn and Roth, 1975). Direct studies of the insulin–receptor interaction were attempted as early as 1953 (Stadie *et al.*, 1953), however, these were fraught with many problems, particularly related to the preparation of biologically active tracer and defining biologically specific binding (Newerly and Berson, 1957). Almost simultaneously these problems were overcome when Freychet *et al.* (1971) and Cuatrecasas (1971) showed that insulin could be labeled with ^{125}I and remain active, and using this they could define hormone binding that had the property of biological specificity. Since that time insulin receptors have been demonstrated on almost all cells or tissues of vertebrate species (Ginsberg, 1977).

Until recently the insulin receptor had not been isolated, even in a partially purified form, and thus in most studies it has been necessary to define the insulin receptor by its binding characteristics (Kahn, 1976). These include a high affinity for insulin, rapid and reversible binding, and saturability. The keystone to the functional definition of any receptor, however, is specificity. For the insulin receptor, the affinity of insulin and insulin analogs is proportional to their biological activities. Thus, the insulin-like growth factors (such as MSA) which are about 1% as active as insulin in glucose oxidation bioassays, compete for labeled insulin binding at 100-fold higher concentration than insulin (Fig. 3, left).

The major insulin degrading activity is also functionally distinct from the insulin receptor as judged by its affinity for insulin and specificity for insulin analogs (Freychet *et al.*, 1972). There may, however, be a component of receptor related degradation (Terris and Steiner, 1975; Kahn and Baird, 1978; Gliemann and Sonne, 1978).

The quantitative aspects of the insulin-receptor interaction are complex and the subject of some controversy. While almost all investigators agree that Scatchard plots are curvilinear (see Fig. 11), there remains little in the way of agreement as to whether this is due to negative cooperativity in insulin binding as suggested by DeMeyts *et al.* (1973, 1976), two classes of binding sites of differing affinity (Pollet *et al.*, 1977), or some combination of cooperativity and heterogeneity of binding sites (see recent review by DeLean and Rodbard, 1980). Certainly, at present, no investigator has succeeded in purifying two populations of receptors corresponding to two receptors of differing affinity although it has been possible by several purification procedures to obtain receptors which have lost some of the complex binding characteristics (Krupp and Livingston, 1978; Maturo and Hollenberg, 1978; Hedo *et al.*, 1980).

In general, we have found that the cooperative model is capable of fitting our data quite well, and it has therefore been useful in comparing receptors in animals or cells in differing physiologic or pathologic states (Kahn *et al.*, 1978b). Since it is now clear that there may be regulatory proteins associated with the insulin receptor in addition to the binding components, and there may be degradation of insulin and uptake of insulin and its degradation products by cells, it seems likely that with further

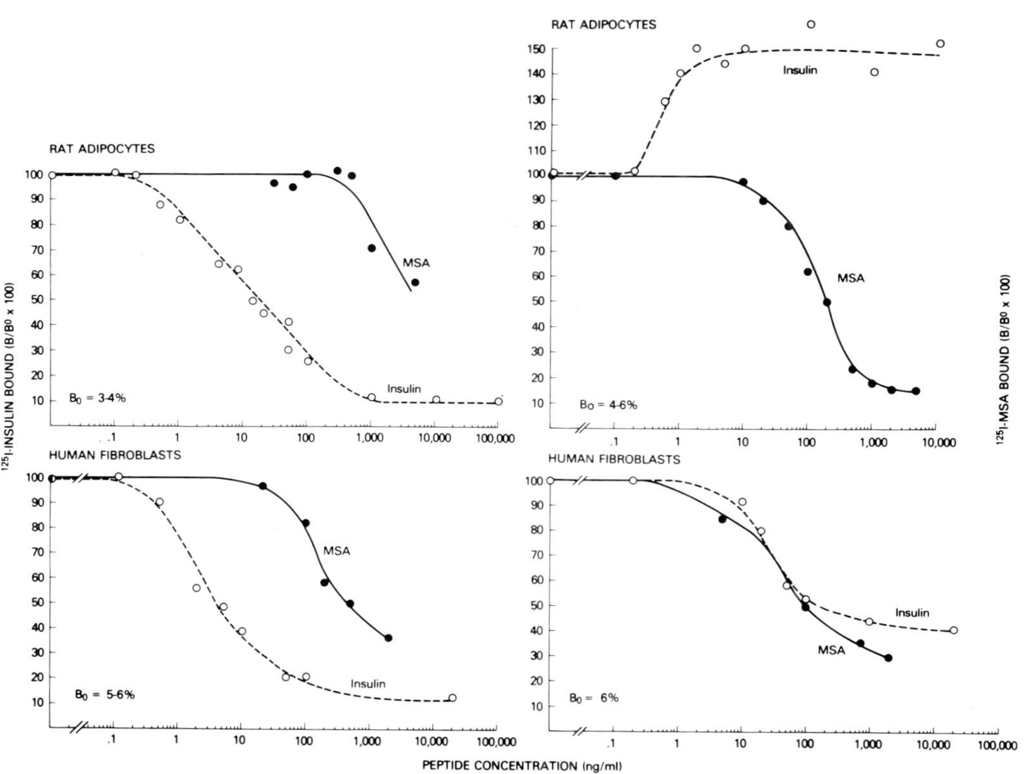

FIG. 3. Comparison of receptors for insulin and the insulin-like growth factors. The panels on the left show the typical binding inhibition curves observed when ^{125}I-labeled insulin is bound to its receptors on adipocytes (top) or fibroblasts (bottom). On the right are data from studies of receptors for the insulin-like growth factors obtained using [^{125}I]MSA as tracer. Note the very different competition curves obtained with adipocytes (top) and fibroblasts (bottom) for this receptor. From King *et al.* (1980).

study the quantitative analysis of binding data will become more complex rather than simpler.

III. Receptors for Insulin-Like Growth Factors

As already noted, the insulin-like growth factors have a weak affinity for the insulin receptor (Fig. 3, left). In addition, however, the IGFs have receptors of their own (Fig. 3, right). The latter were first demonstrated by using a crude preparation of IGFs by Megyesi *et al.* (1974) and have subsequently been more extensively characterized by Zapf *et al.* (1978), Hall and Fryklund (1979), Van Wyk and Underwood (1978), and Rechler, Nissley, and their co-worker (1980).

It is important to note that in contrast to the insulin receptors, which are virtually identical from tissue to tissue and species to species, there appear to be several types of receptors for insulin-like growth factors (Rechler *et al.*, 1980). In some cases, such as in the human fibroblast insulin competes for the binding of labeled insulin-like growth factors with the same affinity as the unlabeled insulin-like growth factor (Fig. 3, lower right). With other cell types, insulin usually shows a much lower affinity for the IGF receptor; in some cases, insulin may actually produce an increase in binding of the labeled insulin-like growth factor (Fig. 3, upper right). In studies where several different labeled IGFs have been compared, it appears that on some tissues there may be more than one type of IGF receptor.

Although the specificity of the IGF receptors is more complex than that of insulin receptors, quantitative aspects of the binding data appear somewhat simpler. Thus far there is no evidence for cooperativity in binding to these receptors, and what few Scatchard plots have been performed suggest a single class of noninteracting receptors.

IV. Regulation of Insulin Receptors in Disease

For the physiologist and physician, the most important advance which has been derived from direct studies of the insulin–receptor interaction has been the appreciation that receptors are not static—rather these are dynamic molecules whose affinity and concentration are regulated by many factors in health and disease (Roth *et al.*, 1975; Kahn *et al.*, 1977b; Bar *et al.*, 1979; Olefsky, 1976). An important role for modulation of hormone action at the level of the receptor has been demonstrated in obesity, non-insulin-dependent diabetes, states of growth hormone, and glucocorticoid excess and deficiency, as well as a variety of other physiologic and pathologic circumstances.

From these studies it also became apparent that there were many substances which could serve as regulators of receptor-affinity or concentration. A major regulator of the concentration of insulin receptors is insulin itself. Thus both *in vivo* and *in vitro* there is often a close inverse relationship between the ambient concentration of insulin and that of its receptors, a phenomenon which has been termed homologous receptor regulation or "down-regulation" (Gavin *et al.*, 1974; Blackard *et al.*, 1978; Livingston *et al.*, 1978). Other modulators of receptor concentration and/or affinity include heterologous hormones, ions, drugs, nucleotides, and the state of growth and differentiation of the cell. Most recently, it has also been appreciated that cell surface receptors can be altered in immune-mediated disease processes by the development of autoantibodies which alter receptor binding and/or function (Kahn *et al.*, 1977b; Harrison and Kahn, 1980).

V. Antibodies to the Insulin Receptor

A. CLINICAL ASPECTS

Antibodies to the insulin receptor were first discovered during evaluation of patients with insulin resistance (Flier *et al.*, 1975). At that time we were studying a group of patients with marked insulin resistance, hyperinsulinemia, and glucose intolerance; most were also noted to have the skin disorder acanthosis nigricans. Two subgroups could be defined based on clinical features and studies of insulin receptors (Kahn *et al.*, 1976; Bar *et al.*, 1980) (Table III). One group was composed of young females with signs of virilization. These patients were found to have a marked defect in insulin binding to receptors on their circulating monocytes due to a decrease in receptor number. This syndrome was termed the Type A syndrome of insulin resistance and acanthosis nigricans. Recent studies of cells from these patients have demonstrated that a binding defect persists after the cells have been placed in long-term culture suggesting a genetic basis for this syndrome (Podskalny and Kahn, 1980; S. Taylor, personal communication).

The second subgroup of patients had evidence of a systemic immune disease manifest by elevated serum globulins, anti-nuclear and anti-DNA antibodies. In about one-third of the cases these immune manifestations could be classified into a clinically defined autoimmune disease, such as

TABLE III
Syndromes of Insulin Resistance and Acanthosis Nigricans

	Type A	Type B
Age	12–21	21–65
Sex	All female	Predominately female
Glucose tolerance	Usually abnormal	Usually severely abnormal
Other features	Hirsutism	High ESR
	Virilization	+ ANA and anti-DNA
	Polycystic ovaries	Leukopenia
	Accelerated early growth	Alopecia
		Arthralgias
		Nephrotic syndrome
Insulin receptor defect	Decreased number	Decreased affinity
Anti-receptor antibodies	Absent	Present

systemic lupus erythematosis, ataxia telangectasia, etc. (the detailed clinical features of these patients are reviewed in Kahn and Harrison, 1981). Studies of circulating lymphocytes from these patients showed a marked decrease in insulin binding (Fig. 4), however, on Scatchard analysis this appeared to be due to a decrease in receptor affinity rather than a change in receptor number. These patients were designated as having the Type B syndrome of insulin resistance and acanthosis nigricans.

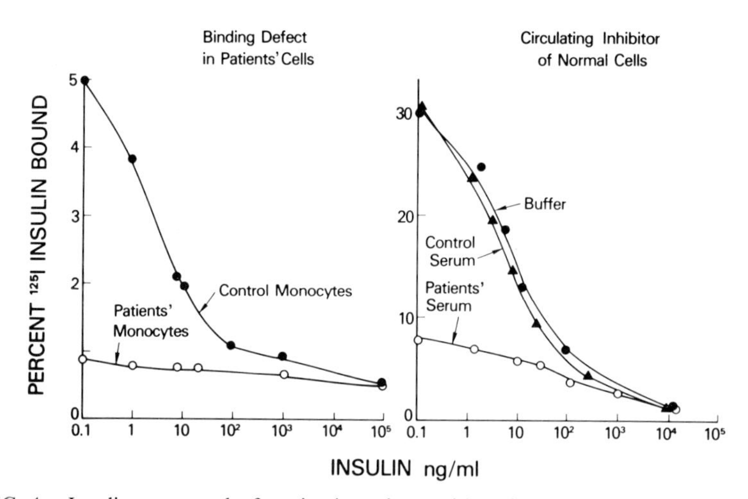

FIG. 4. Insulin receptor dysfunction in patients with anti-receptor antibodies. The panel on the left shows decreased binding of insulin to peripheral monocytes isolated from a patient with the Type B syndrome of insulin resistance and acanthosis nigricans. The panel on the right shows the effect of this patient's serum to inhibit insulin binding to normal cultured human lymphocytes.

Evidence that Type B syndrome was due to antibodies to the insulin receptor first came in 1975 when Flier *et al.* found that sera from these subjects inhibited the binding of insulin to a variety of normal tissues, thus mimicking *in vitro* the defect observed with the patient's cells *in vivo* (Fig. 4 and Fig. 5, left). This property continues to be the principal assay for their detection. The anti-receptor sera are approximately equipotent against receptors on a variety of human tissues including monocytes, cultured (IM-9) lymphocytes (Flier *et al.*, 1975), fat cells (Kasuga *et al.*, 1978b), fibroblasts (King *et al.*, 1980), and placental membranes (Harrison *et al.*, 1979b); they also impair binding to receptors from a variety of heterologous tissues, although in general the titers for inhibition of insulin binding to receptors on nonmammalian tissues are lower than to mammalian receptors (Flier *et al.*, 1975; Muggeo *et al.*, 1979a).

Antibodies to the insulin receptor can also be detected by their ability to immunoprecipitate solubilized insulin receptors (Harrison *et al.*, 1979b) Fig. 5, right). Although this assay is more cumbersome, it has the theoretical advantage of increased sensitivity, since it can detect antibodies directed at sites on the receptor other than the insulin binding site. It is interesting to note that antibodies raised in animals to partially purified receptor preparations have many of the properties of the naturally occurring antibodies, i.e., they immunoprecipitate the receptor and have insulin-like activity, however, they do not bind to the receptor in such a way as to inhibit insulin binding (Jacobs *et al.*, 1978).

In almost all cases, the antibody activity is either exclusively or predominately of the IgG class (Flier *et al.*, 1976). The activity has also been shown to be due to the Fab, rather than Fc portions of the molecule. Naturally occurring IgM antibodies to the insulin receptor have also been found in the serum of one patient with the Type B syndrome, in sera from some patients with ataxia telangectasia (Bar *et al.*, 1978; Harrison *et al.*, 1979a), and in the sera of New Zealand Obese mice (Harrison and Itin, 1979). In general, however, these have been low titer and therefore of limited usefulness as probes of receptor structure and function.

All available data suggest that the autoantibodies observed in Type B patients have arisen as part of a generalized autoimmune process and that the underlying receptor in these patients is normal (Muggeo *et al.*, 1979b). Thus, there is no apparent preferential effect of the patients' anti-receptor sera on their own tissues compared to normal human tissues, and the binding defect on the patients' cells can be at least partially reversed by an acid-wash procedure, designed to elute surface immunoglobulins. In addition, the patients' fibroblasts in culture have normal insulin-binding properties.

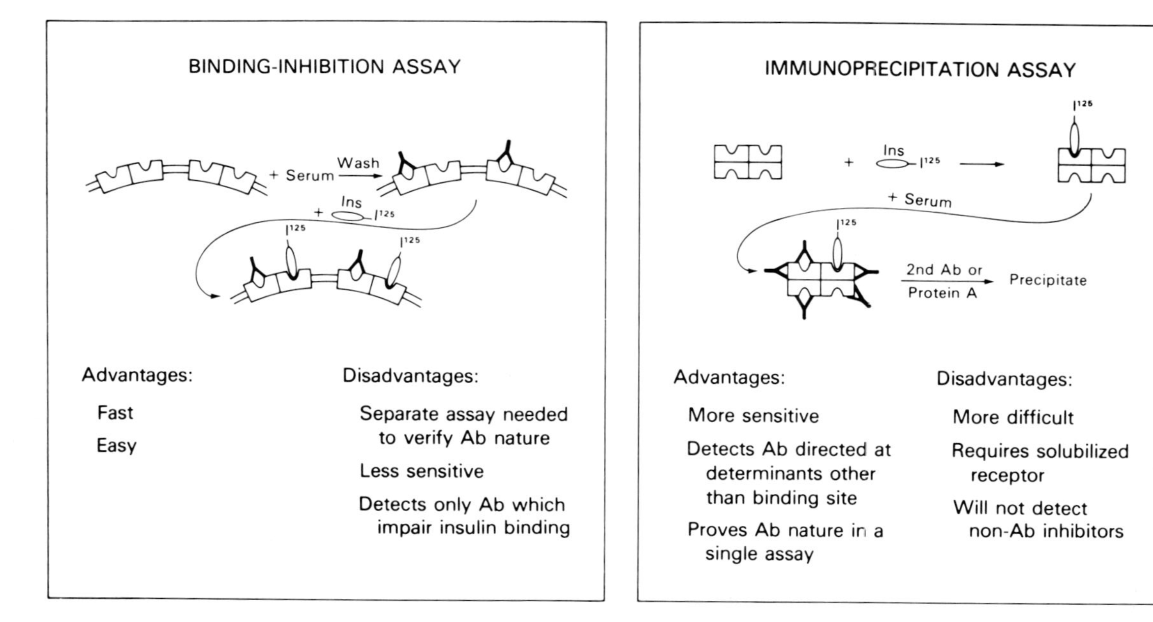

FIG. 5. Direct assays for antibodies to the insulin receptor.

B. EVIDENCE THAT THE ANTIBODIES BIND DIRECTLY TO THE RECEPTOR

In addition to their ability to block insulin binding, several other bits of evidence suggest that the antibodies derived from these patients bind directly and specifically to the receptor. First, as noted above, the antibodies block insulin binding in virtually all cell types and tissues from all species that have been tested (vide supra). Thus, if the antibodies were not recognizing the receptor directly, it would have to be some other membrane component which is extremely well conserved both in structure and linkage to the insulin receptor. The autoantibodies to the insulin receptor do not inhibit the binding of other hormones including glucagon, growth hormone, epidermal growth factor, and in most cases, the insulin-like growth factors (King *et al.,* 1980; Kahn and Harrison, 1981). Likewise, the anti-receptor antibodies do not inhibit insulin degradation (Flier *et al.,* 1977b).

Second, ^{125}I-anti-receptor antibody binds to a variety of cells in direct proportion to their insulin receptor concentration, and this binding was specifically competed for by insulin and insulin analogs (Jarrett *et al.,* 1976). Thus, not only is the antibody a competitive inhibitor of insulin binding, but conversely, insulin is an inhibitor of antibody binding—a feature which has proven extremely useful in providing specificity. Furthermore, as noted above, anti-receptor IgG will quantitatively precipitate the solubilized insulin receptor (Harrison *et al.,* 1979b). Again, this is specific, with no depletion of receptors for growth hormone, prolactin, or insulin-like growth factors, and no depletion of insulin degrading activity.

The most convincing evidence that the antibodies bind to the receptor is structural. Thus by affinity labeling, iodination, and incorporation of [^{35}S]methionine, Van Obberghen, Kasuga, and Harrison have shown that the antibodies recognize the same receptor subunits detected by other approaches. These data are reviewed in more detail in the following section.

Since the insulin receptor molecule has a complex subunit structure and will probably turn out to have functionally distinct components subserving insulin binding, cooperativity, affinity regulation, and biological signal transduction, it would not be surprising if the antibodies recognize a variety of distinct determinants on the receptor. In fact, there are some data, albeit indirect, to this effect. Thus, some of the anti-receptor sera decrease insulin binding by reducing receptor affinity, others by altering available receptor number. In some cases the change in affinity is due to a change in association rate, in some changes in dissociation rate, and in some changes in both (Flier *et al.,* 1977a). Also, pretreatment of cells with trypsin blocks the bioactivity of different antisera to a varying extent suggesting differential sensitivity of the antibody-binding sites to trypsin (Kahn *et al.*, 1977a). As more precise data on the structure of the insulin receptor become available and the exact sites of antibody binding become known, the studies with anti-receptor antibodies should provide important insights into structure–activity relationships in the receptor.

VI. The Structure of the Insulin Receptor

Despite the fact that direct studies of insulin receptors have been possible for nearly a decade, the structure of the insulin receptor has been difficult to determine. For convenience, studies into the structure of the insulin receptor can be divided into those in which the receptor is studied in an active form, i.e., a form in which insulin binding is retained; and studies of subunit structure in which the receptor may be reduced to its fundamental subunits, with loss of its insulin binding activity. The latter usually involves electrophoresis in a detergent such as sodium dodecyl sulfate (SDS).

A. THE SOLUBILIZED, NONDENATURED RECEPTOR

The insulin receptor retains both insulin binding and immunologic reactivity when solubilized in neutral detergents such as Triton X-100 and in this form has been characterized by gel filtration (Gavin *et al.*, 1972; Cuatrecasas, 1972; Harrison *et al.*, 1978; Ginsberg *et al.*, 1976; Maturo and Hollenberg, 1978) and more recently by gel electrophoresis (Krupp and Livingston, 1978, 1979; Lang *et al.*, 1980a) (Fig. 6). The estimated molecular radius of the insulin receptor in Triton is 68–72 Å, and depending on the assumptions made regarding shape and detergent binding, this corresponds to an estimated molecular weight of 300,000–1,000,000. The extent to which the Triton micelle and the sphere of hydration add to this molecular size estimate is unknown, but certainly a factor which must be kept in mind when these numbers are considered. From Ferguson plot analysis, Lang *et al.* (1980a) have also suggested that the native receptor is highly charged (nearly 100 net charge units/molecule). The unusually large valence may be due, in part, to the association of multiple copies of the receptor within the relatively large Triton X-100 micelle or the association of the receptor with other membrane proteins.

The insulin receptor is a glycoprotein, and this may alter its behavior in various procedures to determine size and change. Receptors solubilized from several tissues have been shown to bind to lectins that bind *N*-acetylglucosamine (wheat germ agglutinin), mannose (concanavalin A,

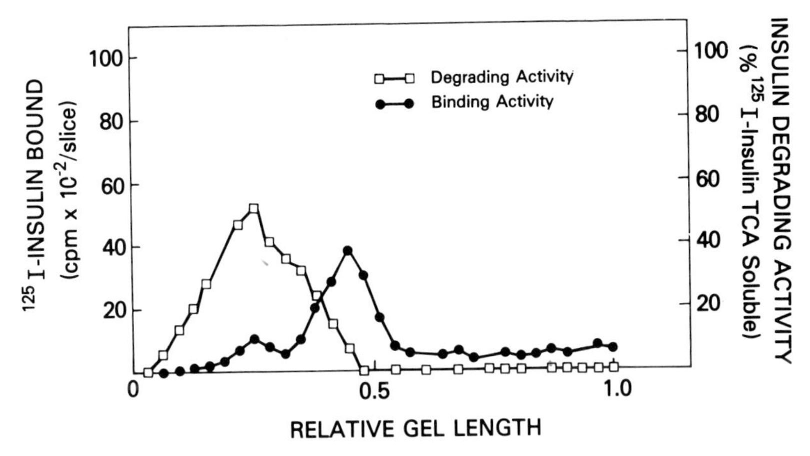

FIG. 6. Separation of the insulin receptor and insulin-degrading activity from cultured human lymphocytes by polyacrylamide gel electrophoresis in Triton X-100. From Lang *et al.* (1980a).

lentil lectin, and pea lectin), and galactose (ricin I and II) (Cuatrecasas and Tell, 1973; Hedo *et al.*, 1980). These lectins also exert insulin-like effects, and most, but not all, compete for insulin binding (Cuatrecasas and Tell, 1973; H. Katzen, personal communication). These lectins are also useful for aiding in purification of the receptor. Lectins that bind *N*-acetylgalactosamine, fucose, and galactose do not retain solubilized insulin receptor, suggesting the content of these saccharides is very low (Hedo *et al.*, 1980).

At least three investigators (Ginsberg *et al.*, 1976; Krupp and Livingston, 1978, 1979; Lang *et al.*, 1980a) have found that under some conditions an active receptor of smaller size can be detected, suggesting that the high molecular weight receptor is a complex composed of more than one component. Using gel filtration in Triton X-100, Ginsberg *et al.* (1976) showed that in the presence of 25–50 ng/ml insulin, the soluble insulin receptor from avian erythrocytes (72 Å) dissociated into a smaller component (40 Å) which still bound insulin. Krupp and Livingston (1979, 1980) have also noted two components of the solubilized insulin receptor from adipocytes which are interconvertible in the presence of insulin. These appear to have somewhat different binding properties as judged by both Scatchard plots and studies with analogs.

With these techniques, the major insulin-degrading enzyme activity appears completely distinct from the major part of the insulin-binding activity by both size and charge (Fig. 6). These results support other observations that the two activities are largely independent and unrelated (Freychet *et al.*, 1972; Gameltoff and Gliemann, 1973). Although it is possible that the degrading and binding activities are functionally linked as mentioned above.

B. THE SUBUNIT STRUCTURE OF THE RECEPTOR BY SDS–GEL ELECTROPHORESIS

Characterization of the insulin receptor after denaturation to its subunits was slow to develop due to difficulty in both receptor purification and techniques for direct identification. As early as 1977, Jacobs *et al.* had studied a partially purified preparation of insulin receptor by SDS–polyacrylamide gel electrophoresis and reported a single band at 135K. However, since this preparation was only partially pure and since SDS destroys irreversibly all insulin-binding activity, it was impossible to be certain if this band was in fact the receptor, or if some minor component not seen on the gel accounted for the insulin binding.

A major breakthrough in receptor structure came in the past 2 or 3 years with the development of photoaffinity probes (Yip *et al.*, 1978, 1980; Wisher *et al.*, 1980), and the use of chemical cross-linking agents (Pilch and Czech, 1979; Massague and Czech, 1980; Kasuga *et al.*, 1981) to covalently link radiolabeled insulin to its receptor. The data obtained with such probes are summarized in Table IV. With these affinity approaches combined with SDS–gel electrophoresis in the presence of reducing agents virtually all investigators have found heavy labeling of a protein of about 130K (Fig. 7). In addition, many investigators have found lighter and variable labeling of a protein of 90K. Labeling of both bands is specific as judged by the ability of both insulin and anti-receptor antibody to inhibit binding (Fig. 7). On nonreduced SDS gels, these subunits are joined together and the apparent molecular weight of the receptor is 350K. An intermediate form of 210K has also been found after partial reduction (Massague and Czech, 1980). This had led to the suggestion that the native receptor may have an immunoglobulin-like structure with heavy (α) and light (β) chains held together by disulfide bonds (Massague *et al.*, 1980; Jacobs *et al.*, 1980; Kasuga *et al.*, 1981) (also see Fig. 12).

Further studies of the structure of the partially purified insulin receptor by SDS gels have lead to relatively similar conclusions. Both Jacobs *et al.* (1977) and Harrison and Itin (1981) have found a major protein band of about 130K in a preparation of insulin receptors purified from rat liver by combinations of lectin and affinity chromatography with insulin or anti-receptor antibody. Proteins of about 90K and 45K were also apparent, especially if the receptor was iodinated and autoradiography performed (Jacobs *et al.*, 1979, 1980; Harrison and Itin, 1981). Preliminary studies have suggested that the latter are not derived from the 130K receptor

TABLE IV

The Subunit Structure of the Insulin Receptor

Method	Tissue	Major subunits	Minor subunits	Reference
Gel filtration	Turkey RBC	40 Å (75–100K)		Ginsberg *et al.* (1976)
SDS–polyacrylamide gel				
Electrophoresis after				
Purification	Liver	135K	90K, 75K, 45K	Jacobs *et al.* (1979)
	Placenta	125K and 90K	82K, 66K, 55K, 42K	Harrison and Itin (1981)
Photoaffinity labeling	Adipocyte	130K > 90K		Yip *et al.* (1978)
	Liver, placenta	135K		Jacobs *et al.* (1979)
	Liver	90K	30K	Wisher *et al.* (1980)
Chemical affinity labeling	Adipocyte	125K	(225K)	Pilch and Czech (1979, 1980)
Immunoprecipitation				
+Surface iodination	Lymphocyte	90K > 130K	67K, 56K, 34K	Lang *et al.* (1980); Harrison *et al.* (1981)
+[^{35}S]Methionine incorporation	Lymphocyte	90K > 130K		Van Obberghen *et al.* (1981)
+Chemical affinity labeling	Lymphocyte	130K > 90K		Kasuga *et al.* (1981)
Radiation inactivation	Liver, adipose	90K, 250–300K		Harmon *et al.* (1980)

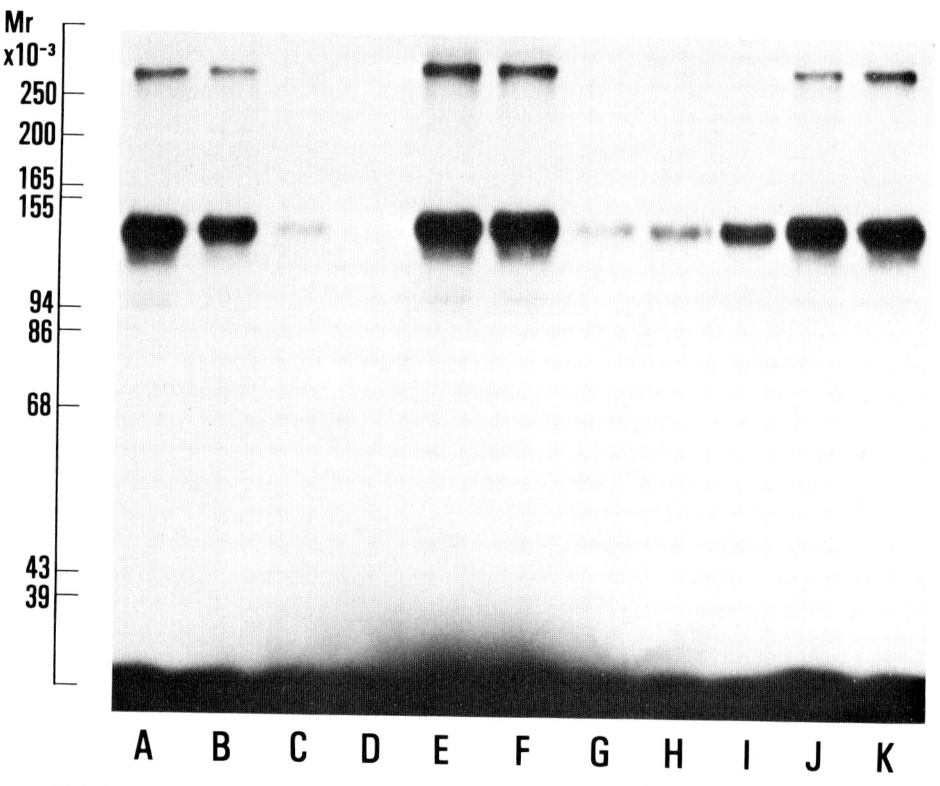

FIG. 7. Autoradiogram showing affinity-labeling of the insulin receptor. Crude lymphocyte membranes were incubated with 5 n*M* ^{125}I-labeled insulin in the absence or presence of various peptides, cross-linked by dissuccinimidyl suberate by the method of Pilch and Czech (1980), electrophoresed in a 7.5% polyacrylamide gel using a discontinuous buffer with 0.1% SDS and 100 m*M* dithiothreitol. From left to right the lanes represent ^{125}I-labeled insulin alone (A), ^{125}I-labeled insulin in the presence of insulin (B, 5×10^{-9} *M*; C, 5×10^{-8} *M*; D, 5×10^{-6} *M*), human growth hormone (E, 5×10^{-6} *M*), ovine plancental lactogen (F, 5×10^{-6} *M*), 0.2 mg/ml of anti-receptor IgG (G, patient B-2; H, patient B-5; I, patient B-8; J, patient B-6) or 0.2 mg/ml normal IgG (K). From Kasuga *et al.* (1981).

subunit as judged by both peptide mapping and immunological studies (Jacobs *et al.*, 1980; M. Kasuga, personal communication). Since the intact receptor appears to have a molecular weight between 310 and 350K Jacobs has suggested that the native receptor contains two 135K and two 45K (rather than two 135K and two 90K) subunits; certainly this point deserves further study. All three subunits appear to be glycoproteins based on changes in relative mobility following neuraminadase treatment.

C. ANTI-RECEPTOR ANTIBODY AND RECEPTOR SUBUNITS

Recently, we have taken advantage of the anti-receptor antibody to study the insulin receptor subunits after labeling by either surface iodination (Lang *et al.*, 1980b; Harrison *et al.*, submitted) or biosynthetically with [^{35}S]methionine (Van Obberghen *et al.*, 1981). The basic principle for the surface iodination is shown in Fig. 8; biosynthetic labeling is much the same except that in the latter case the cells are grown for 6–18 hours in

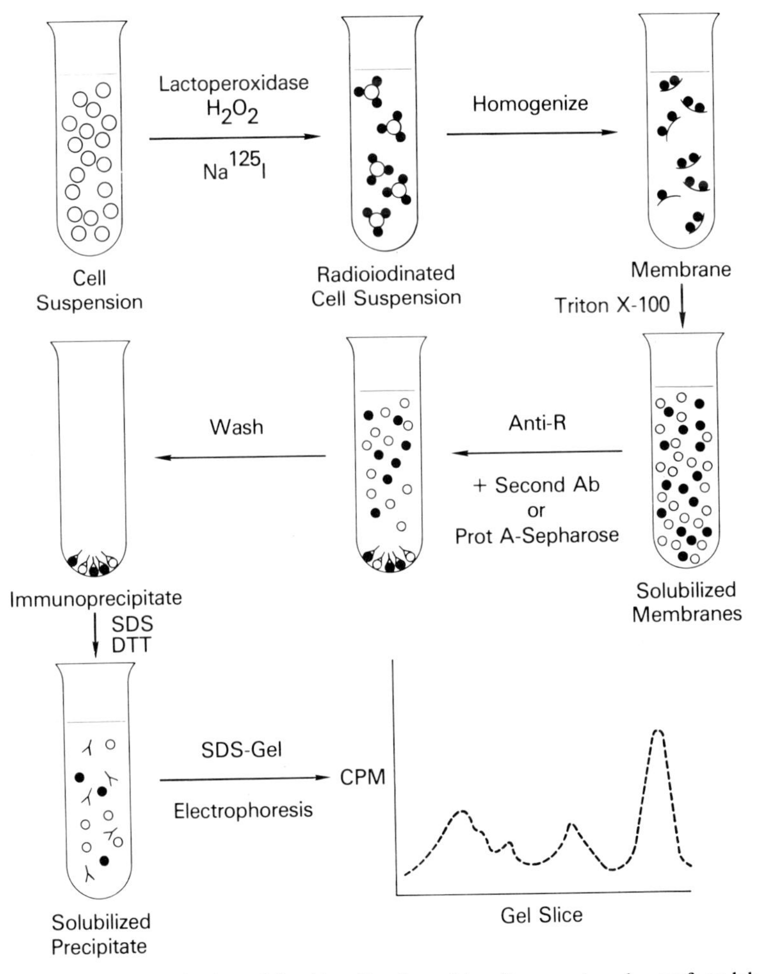

FIG. 8. General method used for identification of insulin receptors by surface labeling and gel electrophoresis.

medium containing the radioactive amino acid. The procedure may be modified to study total cellular insulin receptors by simply deleting the membrane fractionation or to study only the "fully glycosylated" receptor by adding a lectin purification step before immunoprecipitation. This latter procedure has proven especially useful since it provides a 20-fold purification of the receptor and reduces nonspecific immunoprecipitated

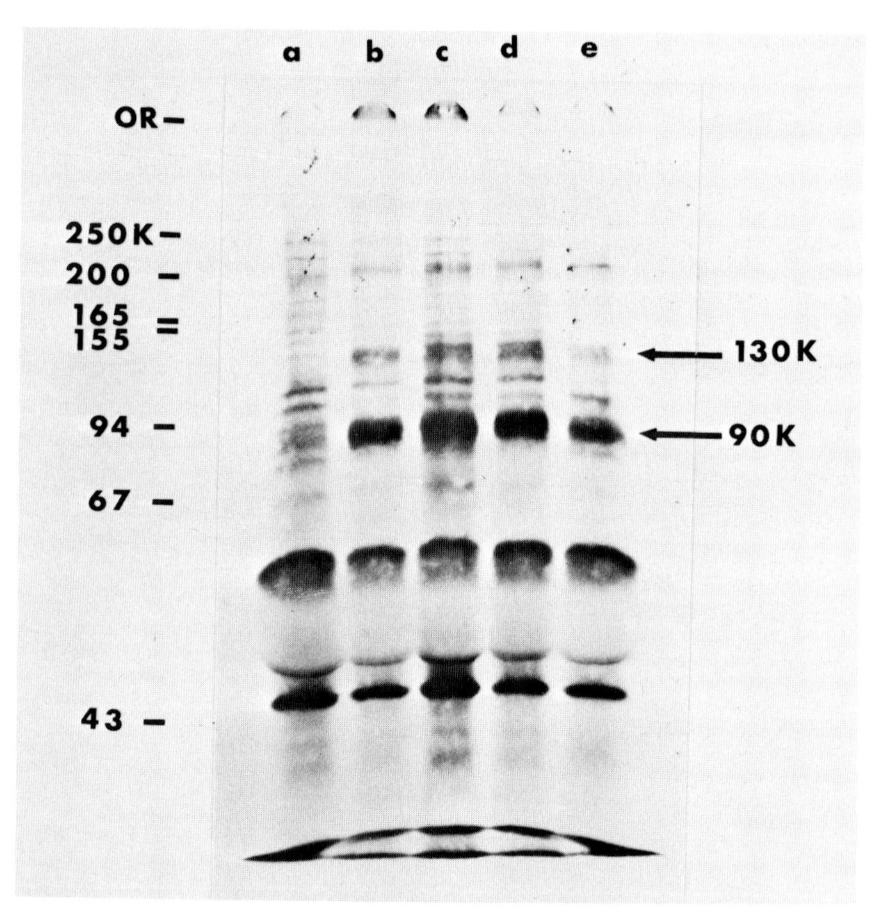

FIG. 9. Identification of the insulin receptor by [^{35}S]methionine labeling and immunoprecipitation. Cells were labeled with [^{35}S]methionine and solubilized in Triton X-100. The insulin receptors were partially purified and immunoprecipitated as shown in Fig. 8. The precipitate was solubilized in SDS with dithiothreitol, electrophoresed as in Fig. 7, and an autoradiogram prepared. The lanes from left to right represent: a, normal IgG; b–e, antireceptor IgG (b, B-2; c, B-5; d, B-6; e, B-8). All IgGs were used at 120 μg/ml. From Van Obberghen *et al.* (1981).

material simultaneously. The results of such an experiment using [^{35}S]methionine labeling is shown in Fig. 9.

When the solubilized [^{35}S]methionine-labeled glycoproteins are immunoprecipitated with serum from a normal individual, a few minor bands ranging from 25 to 150K are observed (Fig. 9, lane a). Immunoprecipitation with sera containing autoantibodies against the insulin receptor reveals two major additional bands of apparent molecular weight 130K and 90K and a minor band of molecular weight 210K (Fig. 9, lane b). Similar bands are observed if the cells are surface iodinated rather than grown in [^{35}S]methionine. In contrast to the studies where affinity labels are used, the intensity of the 90 and 130K bands in these studies is approximately equal.

Evidence that these bands are in fact subunits of the insulin receptor includes the fact that their immunoprecipitation is blocked by unlabeled insulin and all are lost after "down-regulation" of cells which markedly decreases insulin receptor number (Van Obberghen *et al.*, 1981; Harrison *et al.*, submitted). Interestingly, sera from four different patients with anti-receptor antibodies all precipitate the same two major bands (Fig. 9, lanes b–e). This provides the most direct proof that these antibodies are directed against the insulin receptor itself rather than some other membrane protein. In addition, recent studies by Jose Hedo, in which labeled sugars have been substituted for methionine, have shown that both bands are indeed glycoprotein (personal communication).

An important caveate in these studies is the possible effect that endogenous proteases may play in interpretation of data for these studies. Thus, in the initial studies from our laboratory by Lang *et al.* (1980b) the major subunit was 90K, with some smaller subunits of 67K, 56K, and 35K. Recently, these studies have been repeated using high concentrations of protease inhibitors (Harrison *et al.*, submitted), and under these conditions there is also a major subunit of 130K and decreased amounts of the smaller proteins, suggesting that the previous observation may have been, at least in part, spurious due to receptor degradation. On the other hand, it is also clear that some protease inhibitors may alter insulin receptor binding properties (Osbourne *et al.*, 1978), and thus it is possible that the data obtained in the presence of protease inhibitors may also be altered from the native state. Further studies may be necessary to verify these molecular weights as those of the true receptor subunits.

VII. The Structure of the Insulin Receptor by Radiation Inactivation

In all of the studies described above, the insulin receptor has been extracted from the membrane, a process which obviously may result in significant changes in the structure of the receptor from its normal environment. In an attempt to characterize the native insulin receptor in its membrane environment, we turned to the technique of radiation inactivation. For many years, ionizing radiation has been utilized to inactivate soluble enzymes and viruses. However, it has only been recently that scientists interested in examining membrane function have begun to recognize the potential of this technique as an analytical tool to determine the size of hormone receptors (Housley *et al.*, 1977; Schlegel *et al.*, 1979; Harmon *et al.*, 1980).

This technique offers several advantages over other approaches. The major advantage is that one can examine active membrane complexes *in situ*, i.e., in the membrane. Further, the purity of the membrane preparation is of no concern, unless one of the contaminants interferes in the assay for activity. Finally, since one measures loss of functional activity with increasing doses of radiation, the measured target size of a specific membrane component is the size of the intact functional unit. For example, for enzymes with multiple subunits, the estimated size will be the size of the entire complex if all interacting units are required for activity, or the size of a single subunit if each is active alone.

The application of classical target theory to radiation inactivation data may be explained in terms of mathematical probability. When a sample is irradiated using high energy electrons, the ionizations resulting from the interaction of ionizing radiation with the sample are random along the path of the electron. Hence, the loss of biological activity with increasing radiation exposure can be expressed as an exponential function of radiation dose; i.e.,

$$A = A_0 e^{-V \cdot D}$$

where A is the biological activity measured after the sample has received a given radiation dose (D); A_0 is the biological activity of the unirradiated sample (zero dose); and V is the "radiation sensitive volume" which is related to the size of the functional unit. Thus, the inactivation curve for a system in which there is only one component responsible for the biological activity will be a single exponential line described by the equation

$$\ln \frac{A}{A_0} = -V \cdot D$$

The slope is related to the size (volume) of the functional unit. The larger the volume is, the steeper the slope of the decay line is. With the appropriate conversions the volume can be converted to molecular weight. Such is the case for the binding of the insulin-like growth factor, MSA, to its receptor in rat liver membranes (Fig. 10). From the slope of this line

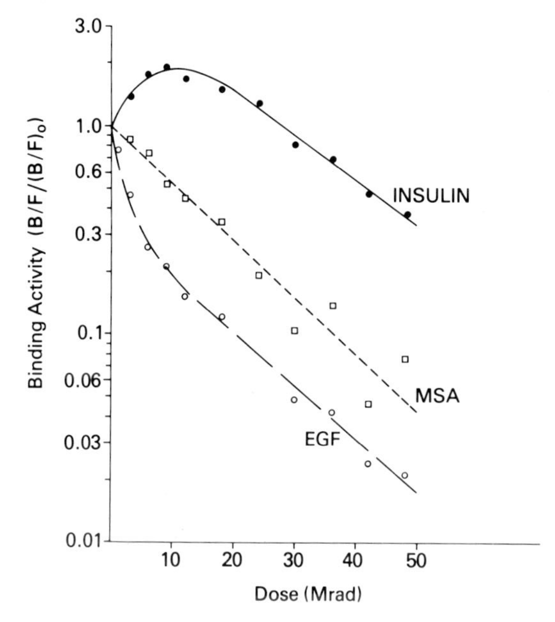

FIG. 10. Radiation inactivation profiles for the binding of several peptide hormones. Rat liver membranes which had received between 0 and 48 Mrad of ionizing radiation were used in hormone binding assays to measure specific binding of insulin, MSA, or EGF. The fraction of specific binding remaining at any dose of radiation [bound/free, B/F, at a given dose divided by $(B/F)_0$ of nonirradiated samples] was plotted versus dose of radiation received by the samples. The irradiations were performed at less than $-100°C$ as previously described (Harmon *et al.*, 1980a).

the functional size of this receptor can be calculated to be 115,000 daltons.

In a more complicated system, when the total activity is contributed to by multiple components of differing sizes, the resulting inactivation curve will be multiexponential; the multiexponential line can be resolved to obtain the functional size and relative activity contributed by each component. Epidermal growth factor (EGF) binding to its receptor on rat liver plasma membranes demonstrates a multiexponential inactivation curve consistent with a two-component system (Fig. 10). The initial rapid loss of EGF binding seen on membranes exposed to very low doses of radiation can be accounted for by a functional unit with a molecular weight of approximately 1,000,000; and the second phase of the inactivation curve would be consistent with another functional unit with a molecular weight of approximately 100,000.

When insulin binding to its receptor was measured on irradiated membranes, the anticipated loss in insulin-binding activity was not observed

(Fig. 10) (Harmon *et al.*, 1980a). Rather there was a biphasic curve with an increase in the amount of specifically bound insulin reaching a maximum at 9–12Mrad followed by a decrease in the binding activity. Such an increase in activity with radiation has not been previously reported.

To further characterize this unusual effect of ionizing radiation on insulin binding, we examined the effect of radiation on the affinity and number of insulin-binding components as determined by analysis of binding data by the method of Scatchard (Fig. 11). Assuming a cooperative model, we found that with increasing radiation exposure, the affinity of the insulin receptor, $\bar{K}_e$, increased from 0.7×10^8 to $2.6 \times 10^8 \ M^{-1}$. This effect occurred at low radiation doses reaching its maximum by 12 Mrad. On the other hand, receptor concentration (R_0), which was initially 12 pmol/mg protein, decreased at all exposure doses. Thus, the inactivation profile of the insulin receptor can be viewed as consisting of two phenomena which are occurring concomitantly: an increase in affinity in proportion to the loss of an apparent large-molecular-weight component (an affinity regulator) and a decrease in receptor concentration in proportion to the loss of the smaller component (binding component). The estimated molecular weights of these two components are about 300,000 and 90,000, respectively (Harmon *et al.*, 1980a).

Several other findings are worth noting. First, the increase in affinity

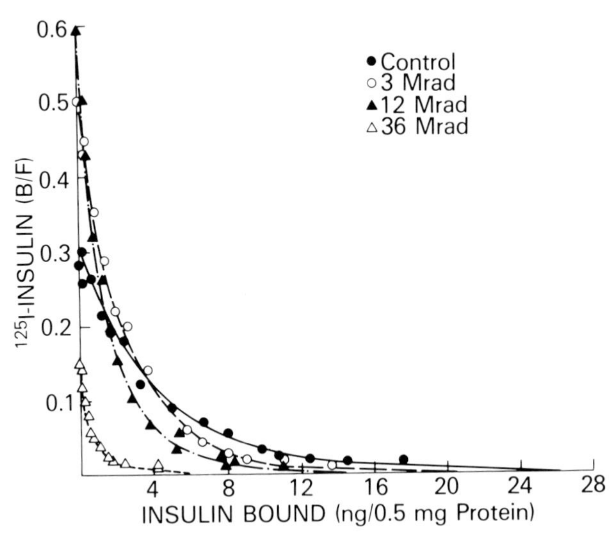

FIG. 11. Scatchard plots of insulin binding to liver membranes after irradiation. Rat liver membranes were exposed to 0, 3, 12, and 36 Mrads and specific binding was measured as previously described (Harmon *et al.*, 1980). The protein concentration in all assay tubes was 0.5 mg/ml.

after irradiation is due to an increase in the association rate of insulin with its receptor rather than a change in the rate of dissociation (Harmon *et al.*, 1980a). With increasing doses of radiation, the effect of insulin to increase the rate of dissociation of prebound ^{125}I-labeled insulin, i.e., negative cooperativity, is lost. However, because of the lack of sensitivity of this assay using rat liver membranes, we were unable to determine the molecular weight of the membrane component which is associated with the cooperative interactions. Grossly, the loss of cooperativity appears to correlate more closely with the loss of the binding component of the receptor, rather than the affinity regulator.

Second, when the irradiated membranes are studied by ^{125}I-antireceptor antibody binding, a single component of molecular weight 92,000 is observed. This corresponds in size to the "binding component" of the receptor. The inactivation of the higher-molecular-weight "affinity-regulatory component" does not appear to affect antibody binding.

Finally, if the membranes were preincubated in the presence of various concentrations of unlabeled insulin before irradiation, there was a dramatic change in the inactivation profile (Harmon *et al.*, 1980b). The initial phase of the inactivation curve (low doses of radiation) decreased in proportion to the insulin concentration. This was not due to a change in the size of either of the "components" of the receptor, but to a change in their interaction due to insulin binding. This insulin-induced change in the inactivation profile is reminiscent of the changes in gel filtration pattern observed with insulin treatment (see preceding section).

Other factors such as pH and ionic strength, which are known to affect the apparent affinity of the insulin receptor, also have a substantial effect on the inactivation profile. Thus, the lower the apparent affinity of the receptor, the larger the increase in binding observed after the membranes have been irradiated or the greater the interaction of binding and affinity-regulatory components.

As with other methods, the estimated size of the insulin-degrading enzymes using the radiation inactivation approach was different from that of the receptor. With liver membranes a multiexponential decay was observed consistent with two components, one of approximate 1.2×10^6 and the other 1.1×10^5 molecular weight (Harmon *et al.*, 1980a). Under no condition was there an increase in degradation to parallel the increase in binding observed with lower radiation doses.

VIII. Models of the Insulin Receptor

Taking into account the various forms of structural data on the insulin receptor, the results from equilibrium and kinetic experiments, and the results from radiation inactivation studies, one might hope to develop a working model of the insulin receptor. As already noted, the data obtained from the SDS gels of affinity labeled receptor, the purified receptor, and the receptor subunits after immunoprecipitation have suggested a receptor with an immunoglobulin-like structure with two light (90K) and two heavy (130K) chains linked by disulfide bonds (Fig. 12A). There are some problems with the stoichiometry. The total molecular weight of the receptor has not been found to exceed 350K (too low to accommodate two 130K and two 90K chains) and several studies have shown other smaller chains. These could be the result of endogenous proteases, although this has not been conclusively proven.

It has usually been assumed that the insulin binding site is the 130K subunit (Jacobs *et al.*, 1980), since this preferentially labels with most affinity reagents. However, the 90K subunit can be specifically labeled (Yip *et al.*, 1980; Kasuga *et al.*, 1981). Thus, it remains a possibility that both subunits contribute to the insulin binding site, and that the 130K is preferentially labeled for other reasons (Fig. 12A). Certainly, examples of this phenomenon exist in the immunoglobulin literature. Anti-receptor antibody binding sites are presumably present on both subunits, and some antibodies are directed at the insulin binding sites (Fig. 12A).

The data which are most difficult to directly fit with this model are the radiation inactivation data which suggest the presence of proteins associated with the receptor which may serve a regulatory role, a conclusion also reached by Maturo and Hollenburg (1978, 1980) using a combination of lectin and affinity chromatography. In hopes of resolving this problem, we have attempted to quantitatively fit the radiation inactivation data to several models of hormone receptor (Harmon *et al.*, 1980b). These include models in which there are inhibitors which regulate receptor affinity, models in which there are site–site interactions among receptors, models with multiple independent classes of sites, and models in which the receptor can undergo aggregation and/or conformational changes.

In fitting the data to any of these models, one of the most significant and distinguishing attributes of the radiation data is the increase in specific insulin binding observed at low radiation doses which reaches a maximum at approximately 12 Mrad of irradiation. At this radiation dose the derivative of bound/free (B/F) hormone with respect to dose of radiation is equal to zero or

$$\frac{d\ \mathrm{B/F}}{d\ \mathrm{dose}} = 0 \text{ at dose} \cong 12 \text{ Mrad}$$

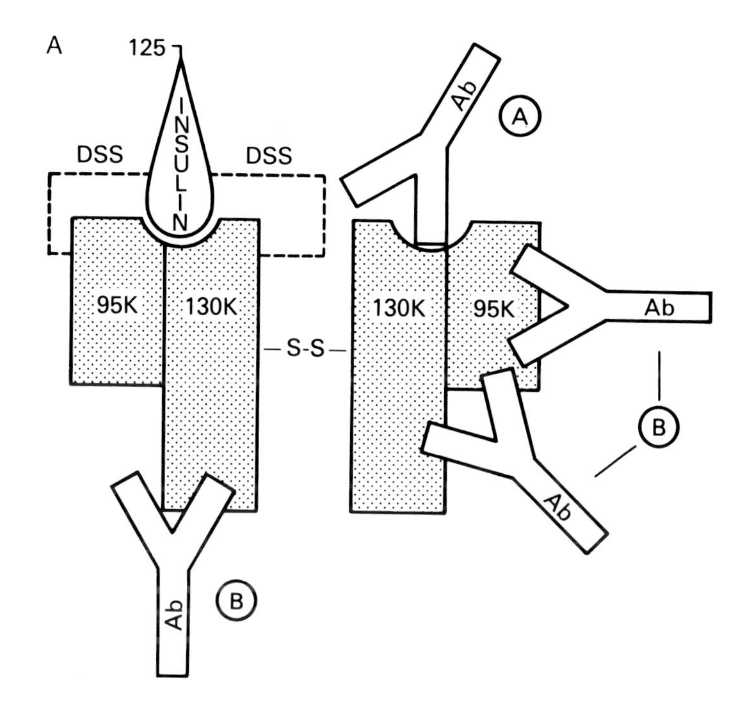

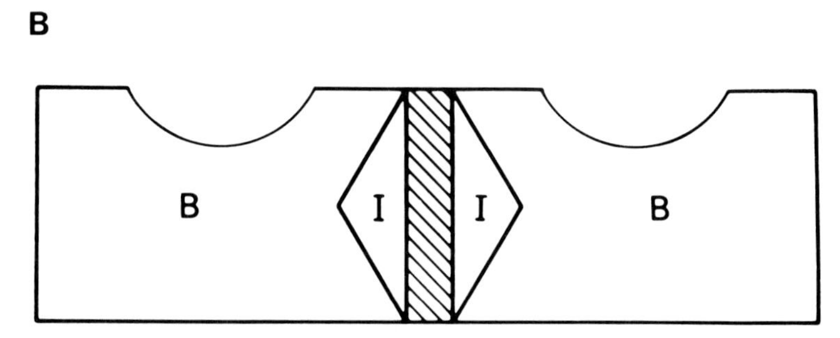

FIG. 12. Models of the insulin receptor. (A) Model of the insulin receptor showing its proposed immunoglobulin-like structure. ^{125}I-labeled insulin is at the insulin binding site and the possible positions of covalent cross-linking by dissuccinimidyl suberate (DSS) are indicated. Anti-receptor antibodies may recognize determinants outside the insulin binding region (situation B) or be directed at the insulin binding site (situation A). (B) Model of the insulin receptor taking into account the radiation inactivation data (see text). B indicates the binding subunit, I, the inhibitor. The oligomeric arrangement shown is arbitrary. It is also possible that these subunits are joined by disulfide bonds as shown in Model A.

Using this equation on the models presented above, we found that the only model which could predict the radiation inactivation was one which included an inhibitor (Fig. 12B). The insulin-binding component may exist in the membrane either free, in which case it has a high affinity for insulin, or associated with the inhibitor, in which case its affinity for insulin is reduced. In light of the structural studies discussed above, and best-fitting the radiation inactivation data, we would suggest that the binding component is 90–130K and the inhibitor is 40–50K. These are tightly associated (perhaps by disulfide bonds). This general model would also predict the results of the equilibrium binding experiments (curvilinear Scatchard plots), but could not predict the observed enhanced dissociation of prebound ^{125}I-labeled insulin by unlabeled insulin (DeMeyts *et al.*, 1976). To account for this kinetic phenomena, it is necessary to also propose an oligomeric receptor, i.e., one which is composed of at least two binding components and presumably two inhibitors and thus the minimum receptor would be about 300K (Fig. 12B). Finally, it seems clear that occupancy of the insulin receptor with insulin causes a change in the conformation of the receptor and in the interaction of the binding component and inhibitor. Exactly how this occurs is as of yet poorly understood, but the data suggest that there is a dissociation of these components. Further studies are obviously needed to clarify this point.

IX. Structure of IGF Receptors

At present few data exist concerning the nature of IGF or somatomedin receptors. Using chromatography on Sepharose 6B of Triton X-100 solubilized placental membranes Bhaumick *et al.* (1980) have reported that there is a marked similarity between the elution profile of insulin-binding activity and the elution profile of the receptor(s) for a partially purified somatomedin preparation. With a photoaffinity labeling technique and SDS–gel electrophoresis these investigators found that the molecular weight of this receptor was >240K in the absence of reducing agents and this was decreased to 140K after reduction. Thus, the somatomedin receptor in placenta appears to be similar in size to the insulin receptor, but slightly larger.

Using radiation inactivation we have found that the IGF receptor in liver (measured by labeled MSA binding) is also slightly larger than the insulin-binding component (115K vs 90K—Fig. 10). In addition this receptor does not exhibit the biphasic inactivation profile observed for the insulin receptor.

Preliminary studies using the chemical cross-linking approach have yielded a similar conclusion, although with this technique an even higher molecular weight component (250K) has been observed (M. P. Czech, personal communication; M. Kasuga, personal communication). Since it is clear that there are several different types of IGF receptors based on binding characteristics, and since they also differ from tissue to tissue, one might expect that with further studies more heterogeneity in structure will be found.

X. The Metabolic Actions of Insulin

A. BIOACTIVITY OF ANTI-RECEPTOR ANTIBODIES

Anti-receptor sera not only bind to the insulin receptor and inhibit insulin binding, but also mimic the many actions of insulin, a property which has made them useful probes in our attempt to understand the possible pathways of insulin action. The insulin-like activity was first shown in experiments studying the effect of whole serum on glucose oxidation by isolated fat cells (Kahn *et al.*, 1977a) (Fig. 13). Like the ability of the serum to inhibit insulin binding, their ability to stimulate glucose utilization was due to the anti-receptor antibodies, not insulin. Thus, the insulin-like activity is blocked by antihuman IgG (but not anti-insulin serum) or can be enriched in purified immunoglobulin fractions. With different sera there are differences in the relative potency in these two fundamental actions. Some sera are more potent in insulin bioassay than

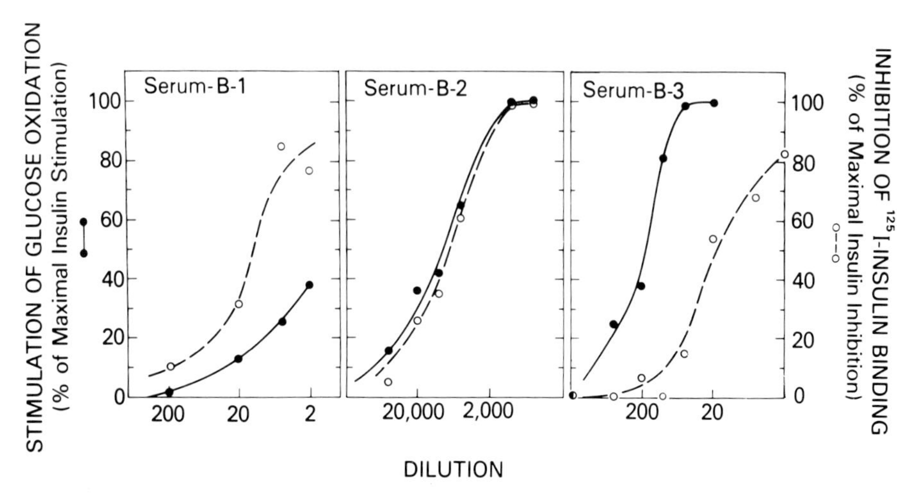

FIG. 13. Effect of three anti-receptor sera to inhibit insulin binding and stimulate glucose oxidation by isolated adipocytes. From Kahn *et al.* (1977a).

in binding inhibition, whereas with others the contrary is true (Fig. 13). This was at least in part due to differences in the population of antibodies which are present. Fractionation of the IgG by DEAE chromatography yields subpopulations of antibodies which vary in activity (Kahn and Harrison, 1980).

It is difficult to precisely compare the anti-receptor antibody with insulin in terms of biological activity. If one estimates the fraction of the total IgG molecules in any serum that are actually binding the receptor (Jarrett *et al.,* 1976), it appears that the anti-receptor antibody may be equipotent with insulin on a molar basis. This estimate must be interpreted with some caution, however, since each anti-receptor antisera is probably a mixture of antibodies with different intrinsic activities.

The insulin-like activity of the anti-receptor antibody has been most extensively studied in the isolated rat adipocyte (Table V). In these cells, the antibodies stimulate glucose transport and metabolism (Kahn *et al.,* 1977a; Kasuga *et al.,* 1978a,b), inhibit lipolysis (Kasuga *et al.,* 1978a,b), stimulate leucine incorporation into protein (Kasuga, 1978a), stimulate pyruvate dehydrogenase and acetyl CoA carboxylase (Belsham *et al.,* 1980), stimulate glycogen synthase (Lawrence, *et al.,* 1978), and alter protein phosphorylation (Belsham *et al.,* 1980). It is worth noting that the antibodies not only mimic effects of insulin dependent on glucose transport, but also those which are independent of glucose transport. Further, the anti-receptor antibodies have been shown to mimic intracellular as well as membrane effects of insulin.

Insulin-like effects of anti-receptor antibodies have also been observed with cells other than adipocytes (Table V). Anti-receptor antibodies have been shown to activate glycogen synthase in three different cell types (adipose, muscle, and liver), although not always with the same dose–response curve (Lawrence *et al.,* 1978; LeMarchand-Brustel *et al.,* 1978; Baldwin *et al.,* 1979b). Anti-receptor antibody also increases lipoprotein lipase activity in the culture 3T3L1 fatty fibroblast (Van Obberghen *et al.,* 1979), an effect of insulin which requires new protein synthesis. This effect, like the effect of the antibody on glycogen synthase in muscle, does not reach the same maximum as insulin (see discussion below). Anti-receptor antibody will also activate tyrosine aminotransferance and stimulate, at least partially, RNA synthesis (Kahn, unpublished observation). The sole exception to the insulin-like activities of the anti-receptor antibody is its lack of ability to stimulate thymidine incorporation into DNA in human fibroblasts (King *et al.,* 1980a); and we believe that this latter effect is mediated by binding of insulin to one of the receptors for the insulin-like growth factors, rather than the insulin receptor itself (vide infra).

TABLE V

Classification of Some of the Actions of Insulin

Effect	Cell type	Classification by		Requires protein synthesis	Mimicked by Anti-R
		Time	Dose–response		
Stimulation of glucose transport	Adipocytes, 3T3-L1	1	A	–	+
(and utilization)	Muscle	1	A–B	–	+
Stimulation of amino acid transport	Hepatocytes, fibroblasts	3	B	+	+
Stimulation of enzymes					
Glycogen synthase	Adipocytes, muscle, liver	1–2	A–B	(–)	+
Acetyl-CoA carboxylase	Adipocytes	1–2	A–B	(–)	+
Pyruvate dehydrogenase	Adipocytes	1–2	A–B	(–)	+
Tyrosine aminotransferase	Hepatocytes	3	A–B	+	+
Lipoprotein lipase	3T3-L1	4	A	+	+
Inhibition of lipolysis	Adipocytes	1	A	–	+
Stimulation of protein synthesis	Adipocytes	2	A	+	+
	Fibroblasts	3	B	+	+
Alteration in protein phosphorylation	Adipocytes	1	A	(–)	+
Stimulation of RNA synthesis	Fibroblasts, hepatocytes	3	B	+	+
Stimulation of DNA synthesis	Fibroblasts	4	C	+	–

The finding that antibody mimics to some extent all actions of insulin with the exception of DNA synthesis suggests that all of insulin's effects have at least some components of their pathways of action in common. At minimum these data suggest that insulin is binding to a single (immunologically speaking) class of receptors which likely generates some common type of transmembrane signal.

B. DESENSITIZATION DUE TO PROLONGED EXPOSURE TO ANTI-RECEPTOR ANTIBODY

While all metabolic actions of insulin are mimicked to some extent by anti-receptor antibody, it is important to note that not all effects are fully mimicked or are mimicked with the same dose–response curve. There are probably several reasons for this. First, it is likely that some of the more complex metabolic effects of insulin are mediated through interacting pathways involving insulin receptors, as well as the receptors for the insulin-like growth factors (vide infra). Furthermore, insulin itself shows different dose–response characteristics for different bioeffects (Fig. 1B). In addition, however, with anti-receptor antibody, there is another variable which must be considered in the evaluation of its biological effects, and that is the effect of desensitization (Karlsson *et al.*, 1979a; Grunfeld *et al.*, 1980).

The clinical syndrome observed in patients with antibodies to the insulin receptor is a syndrome of insulin resistance. Since it was clear that acute exposure of freshly isolated cells to antibody produced insulin-like effects, experiments were performed in cell culture which allowed study of more prolonged effects. For these experiments, the preadipocyte 3T3-L1 cell line has proven useful since it has both insulin receptors and responses similar to the freshly isolated adipocyte but is stable in long-term culture (Rubin *et al.*, 1978; Karlsson *et al.*, 1979b).

As with other systems, anti-receptor antibodies inhibit insulin binding and mimic insulin action with 3T3-L1 cells (Karlsson *et al.*, 1979a; Van Obberghen *et al.*, 1979; Grunfeld *et al.*, 1980). After prolonged exposure, the insulinomimetic activity is lost, and insulin resistance develops (Fig. 14), thus providing an *in vitro* model for the insulin resistance observed in the patients. This change in biological response with time of exposure may explain the inability of the anti-receptor antibody to fully mimic some of insulin's metabolic actions. For example, the antibody effect to stimulate lipoprotein lipase closely follows the insulin effect for the first 6 hours, but then begins to plateau, reaching a significantly lower level than maximal insulin effect (which is observed at 24–48 hours) (Van Obberghen *et al.*, 1979).

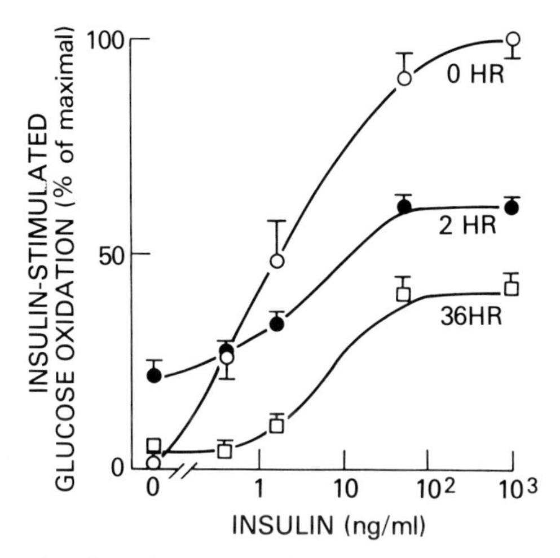

FIG. 14. Effect of prolonged exposure of 3T3-L1 cells to anti-receptor antibody. Note that after 2 and 36 hours there is a decrease in maximal insulin response and a rightward shift of the dose–response curve for insulin-stimulated glucose oxidation.

Desensitization appears to be a complex process involving a decrease in the ability of the receptor to generate a biological response (Grunfeld *et al.*, 1980). Bivalent antibody is required (vide infra), as is an appropriate media composition containing either glucose, pyruvate, or certain other hexoses. Desensitized cells also show a decreased response to concanavalin A, but not to spermine or vitamin K_5, insulinomimetic agents that act independently of the insulin receptor.

XI. Role of Receptor Aggregation in Insulin Action

The biological activity of the antibodies to the insulin receptor depends on their bivalency (Kahn *et al.*, 1978a; Grunfeld *et al.*, 1980). Purified IgG and $F(ab')_2$ fragments are fully bioactive on a molar basis with insulin; monovalent Fab fragments, although able to inhibit binding, have no bioactivity (Fig. 15) and are competitive antagonists of insulin action (vide infra). The bioactivity of the monovalent antibody can be restored by addition of a second antibody. This suggests that receptor occupancy by antibody alone is not a sufficient condition to elicit the insulin effect and that receptor aggregation or cross-linking is needed (Fig. 16). Cross-linking of receptors or receptor subunits has also been demonstrated to be important for other systems including mast cell degranulation induced by

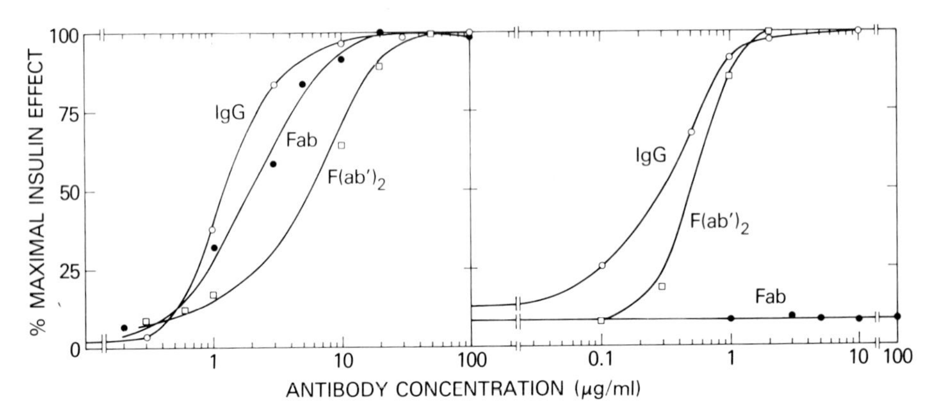

FIG. 15. The role of valence in the action of antibodies to the insulin receptor. The panel at the left shows inhibition of ^{125}I-labeled insulin binding to isolated adipocytes by anti-receptor IgG, F(ab')$_2$, and Fab. The panel at the right shows the ability of these same preparations to stimulate glucose oxidation in these cells.

IgE (Isersky *et al.*, 1978), the mitogenic activity of epidermal growth factor (Shecter *et al.*, 1979), and the degradation of acetylcholine receptors by anti-receptor antibodies in myasthenic sera (Drachman *et al.*, 1978).

The mechanism of activation by anti-receptor antibody also raises the question of whether the action of insulin itself is mediated via receptor aggregation. Although definitive proof is lacking, at least two bits of evidence suggest this may be true. First, cross-linking of prebound insulin by very low concentrations of anti-insulin antibody will augment insulin's biological effects (Kahn *et al.*, 1978a; Schecter *et al.*, 1980). In addition, in a collaborative study (Schlessinger *et al.*, 1980), we have shown that both insulin and anti-receptor antibodies actually patch and cap on the surface of cells (Fig. 17). These two ligands appear to be capping the same proteins. Thus if cells are treated with a low concentration of rhodamine-labeled insulin, then fixed and reacted with fluorescein-labeled antibody, both labels are found in the same "cap." This also suggests that either the receptors are multivalent or that unoccupied receptors co-cap with occupied receptors. Based on structural data discussed above, certainly at least the former seems true.

Since insulin at physiological concentrations (10^{-11}–10^{-9} *M*) is a monomer, the mechanism by which it might induce receptor aggregation remains uncertain. It has been suggested that since insulin receptors are probably oligomeric and at high density on the surface of cells, it is possible that the local concentration of bound insulin may be sufficiently high to permit aggregation due to insulin–insulin interactions. If this is true, however, this must occur in a fashion different from the aggregation which

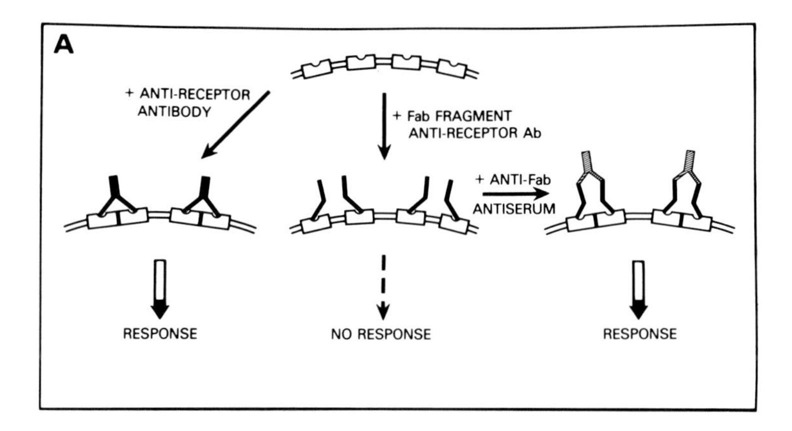

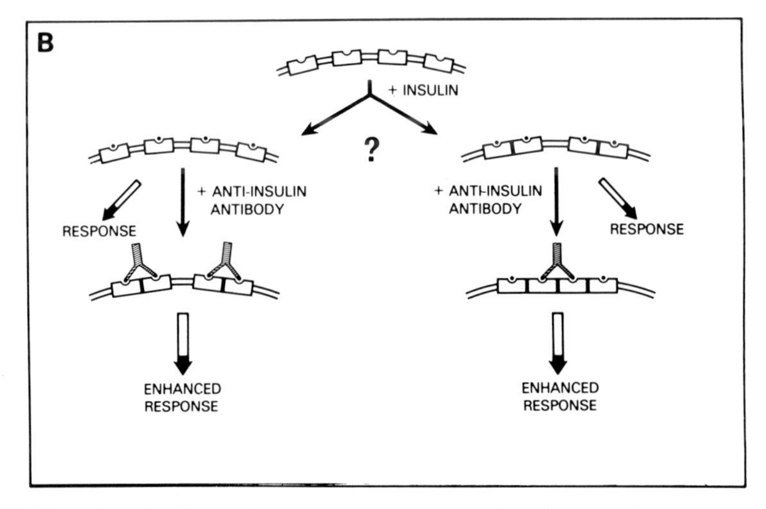

FIG. 16. The role of receptor aggregation or cross-linking in the action of anti-receptor antibody (A) and insulin (B). See text for description.

occurs in solution, since insulins which do not normally dimerize (such as guinea pig and tetranitro-insulin) are still biologically active (DeMeyts *et al.,* 1976).

Alternatively, the receptor aggregation could be achieved through the action of some mechanoskeletal protein. However, at present exactly which protein might serve this role remains unclear. Inhibitors of microtubular and microfilament function do not block insulin action or the insulin-like effect of anti-receptor antibodies (Kahn *et al.,* 1978a). In view of the finding that many receptors, including the insulin receptor are associated with the coated pits (J. L. Carpentier and P. Gorden, personal communication), perhaps a good candidate is clatherin.

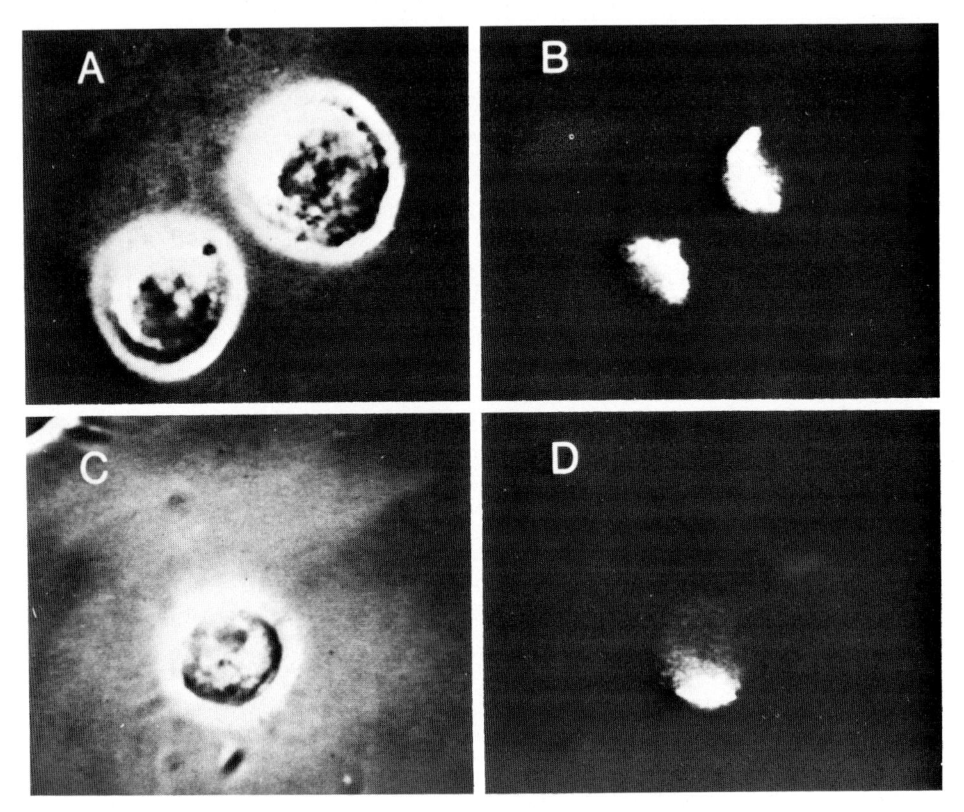

FIG. 17. Capping of insulin and anti-receptor antibody on intact lymphocytes. The upper panels show two cells treated with rhodamine-labeled insulin and the lower panel a cell treated with fluorescein-labeled anti-receptor antibody. Panels A and C use phase microscopy; panels B and D use fluorescence microscopy, both with video intensification. From Schlessinger *et al.* (1980).

It is interesting to note that concanavalin A (Con A), a lectin which binds to the insulin receptor and can mimic many (but not all) of insulin's biological effects (Cuatrecasas and Tell, 1973; Czech and Lynn, 1973; Lawrence and Larner, 1978), is a tetramer and therefore capable of multivalent binding and receptor cross-linking. We have found that the insulin-like action of Con A, like the insulin-like effect of the anti-receptor antibody, depends on this multivalent binding; thus monovalent Con A is without biological effect (Kahn *et al.*, submitted). In contrast to the findings with anti-receptor antibody, however, the insulin-like activity of monovalent Con A cannot be restored by addition of an anti-Con A antibody. Since Con A binds to many membrane glycoproteins in addition to the insulin receptor and the probability of cross-linking two insulin receptors is small, this suggests that the insulin-like effect of multivalent ligands depends on their interactions with specific membrane receptors, not simply any membrane protein. Antibodies to a partially purified glucose transport protein of fat cell membranes has also been shown to have insulin-like activity which depends on bivalent binding (Pillion *et al.*, 1979).

XII. The Growth-Promoting Action of Insulin

As already noted, the pleotypic effects of insulin induce not only a broad spectrum of metabolic actions, but also growth-promoting effects such as stimulation of DNA synthesis. At least two observations suggested that these may be mediated by pathways quite independent of the metabolic actions of insulin. It is well established that there are insulin-like growth factors which have their own receptors and which seem to be more closely allied to growth-promoting actions of insulin. Based on this observation, several years ago Megyesi *et al.* (1974) and others (Van Wyk and Underwood, 1978; Zapf *et al.*, 1978; Hall and Fryklund, 1979) postulated that the metabolic effects of insulin and the IGFs were mediated through the insulin receptor, whereas the growth effects were mediated through a receptor for the insulin-like growth factors (Fig. 18A). Also, it is clear that all of the actions of insulin listed in Table V are at least partially mimicked by the anti-receptor antibody, except for one. The sole exception is the ability of insulin to stimulate thymidine incorporation into DNA in human fibroblasts (King *et al.*, 1980a).

With these observations in mind, three questions concerning the growth-promoting action of insulin are obvious: (1) Is the similar spectrum of biological effects for insulin and the IGFs simply due to the fact that both peptides are capable of binding to each other's receptors, or are both types of receptors able to stimulate the same range of postreceptor events (Fig. 18A)? (2) Can a region on the insulin molecule be mapped that is vital to its growth-promoting effects and is this different from the active site for metabolic actions? (3) Are there any interactions between the insulin receptors and the receptors for IGFs which might be important in the action of these hormones?

A. WHAT IS THE ROLE OF RECEPTORS FOR INSULIN AND IGFS IN THE METABOLIC AND GROWTH EFFECTS OF THESE PEPTIDES?

To answer this question experiments had to be designed where the insulin receptors of target cells were inhibited without the blockade of the IGF receptors. To accomplish this blockade, monovalent Fab fragments

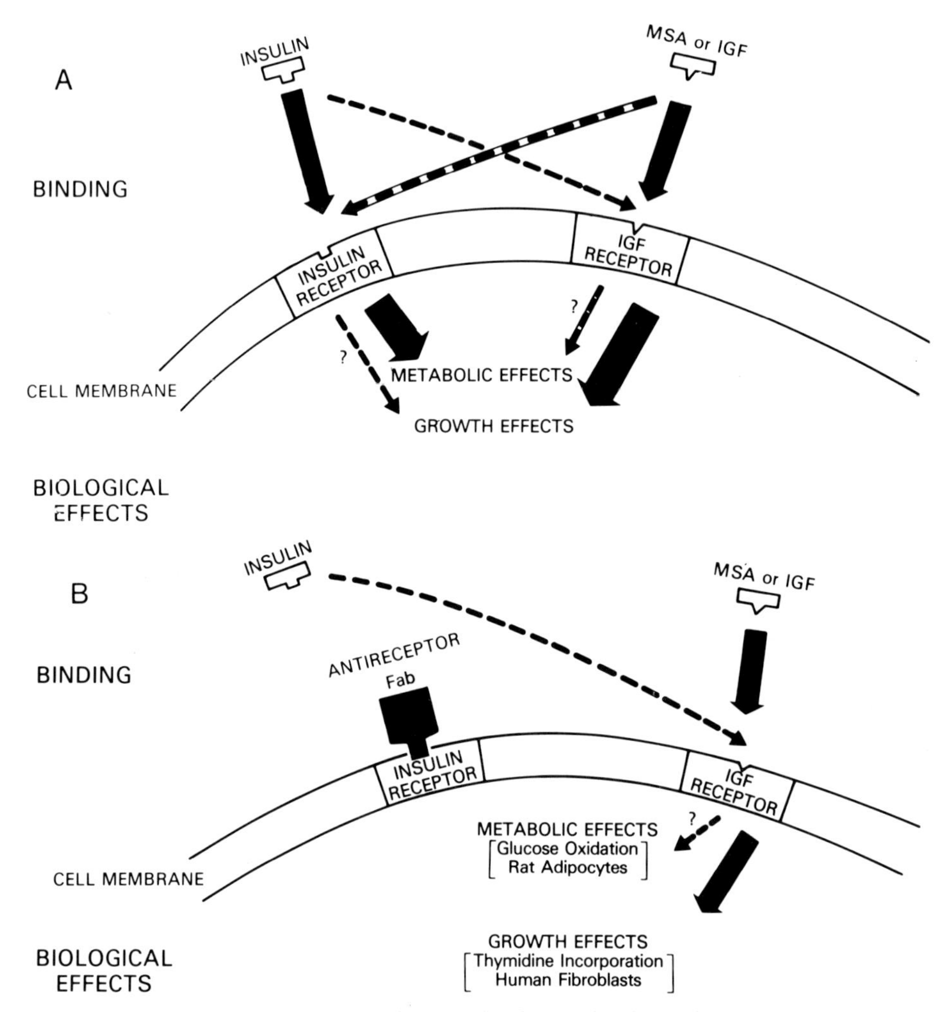

FIG. 18. (A) Two receptor model accounting for overlapping actions of insulin and the insulin-like growth factors. (B) Specific blockade of the receptor for the insulin-like growth factors by anti-receptor Fab.

of antibodies to the insulin receptor were used (Fig. 18B). We have previously shown that like the bivalent anti-receptor antibodies, the monovalent Fab fragment would block insulin binding; however, unlike the bivalent antibody, they are without intrinsic biological activity (Kahn *et al.*, 1978a; King *et al.*, 1980a) thus providing a competitive antagonist of insulin action at the receptor level. This blockade is specific; at Fab concentrations of 10 μg/ml, specific insulin binding can be inhibited by 90–95% with minimal inhibition of labeled MSA binding to the IGF receptor (King *et al.*, 1980a). For our initial experiments we chose to study the stimulation of glucose oxidation in rat adipocytes as representative of the rapid metabolic effects and the stimulation of thymidine incorporation into DNA of human fibroblasts as a growth effect, since they represent extremes of the spectrum of insulin actions.

As shown in Fig. 19A, the addition of Fab fragments antibodies to block the insulin receptor results in a rightward shift of the dose–response curves of both insulin and MSA for glucose oxidation. This inhibition of action is specific to ligands which act through the insulin receptor. Thus, the insulin-like effects of spermine and vitamin K_5 which do not require the insulin receptor are not blocked by anti-receptor antibody, and Con A is only partially inhibited (King *et al.*, 1980a).

On the other hand, Fab fragments had no significant effects on the stimulation of thymidine incorporation into DNA by insulin or MSA (Fig. 19B). These data strongly support the postulate that insulin and the insulin-like growth factors are exerting their metabolic effects through the insulin receptor since both are inhibited by the specific inhibitor of the insulin receptor, whereas their growth effects are mediated by another receptor, presumably one (or more) of the receptors for the insulin-like growth factors, and hence are not blocked by this treatment.

B. IS THERE A SEPARATE SITE ON THE INSULIN MOLECULE FOR THE GROWTH-PROMOTING ACTIVITY?

The original definition of the insulin-like growth factors depended upon their differential activity in growth and metabolic bioassays when compared to insulin (Fig. 2). The bioactive site of insulin for metabolic effects had been well defined and was known to contain both the C- and N-terminal regions of the A chain and the distal part of the B chain of insulin which come together on the surface of the molecule in its three-dimensional folding (Fig. 20) (Blundell *et al.*, 1972). Previous studies using proinsulin had suggested that the growth-promoting action of insulin may show an analog specificity which differs from that for metabolic action (Nissley *et al.*, 1977). To answer questions concerning structure–activity relationships in a more systematic fashion we have now assayed over 30 insulin analogs and compared their ability to stimulate metabolic responses to their growth-promoting potentials (King *et al.*, 1980b). The results thus far obtained have revealed that for most insulin analogs there is a great divergence between these effects. For example, bonito fish insulin, pork proinsulin, and [des-gly, des-phe] insulin have 34, 5, and 0.8%, respectively, of pork insulin's potency to stimulate glucose oxidation in rat adipocytes. By contrast, their growth-promoting activities are 120, 5, and 10% of the pork insulin standard, respectively (Fig. 21).

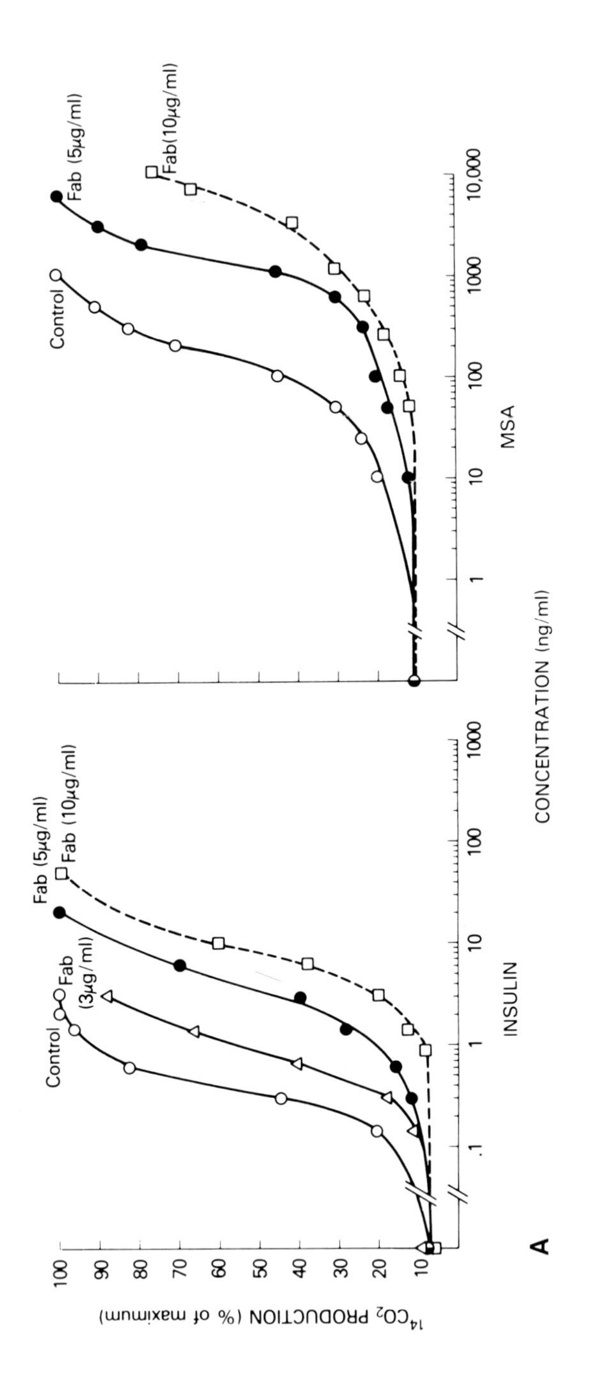

A
$^{14}CO_2$ PRODUCTION (% of maximum)
100
90
80
70
60
50
40
30
20
10
Control
Fab
(3µg/ml)
Fab (5µg/ml)
Fab (10µg/ml)
.1
1
10
100
1000
INSULIN
Control
Fab (5µg/ml)
Fab(10µg/ml)
1
10
100
1000
10,000
MSA
CONCENTRATION (ng/ml)

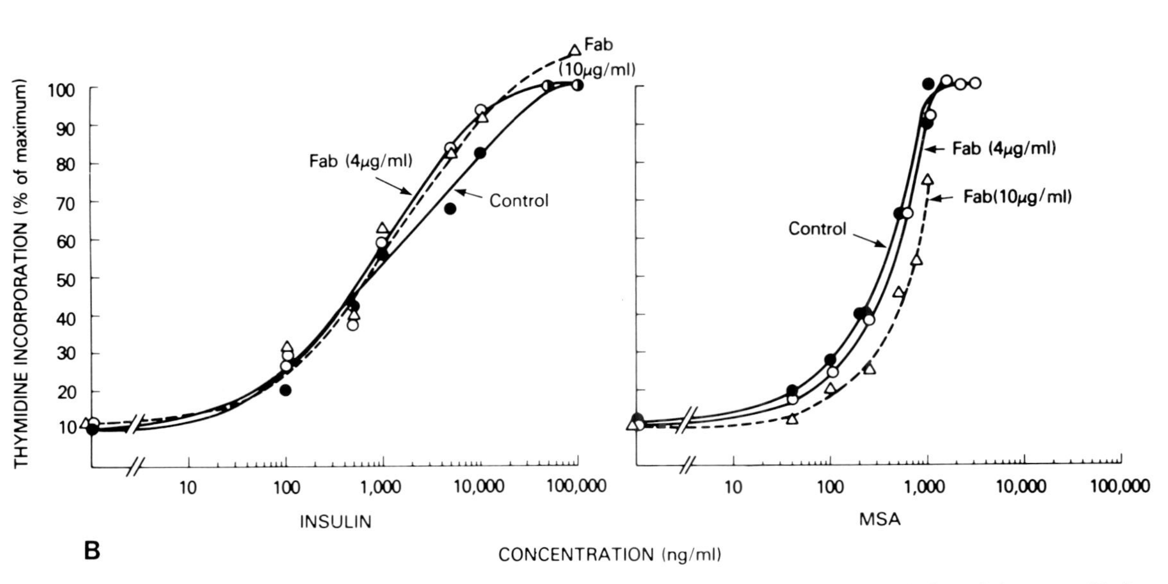

FIG. 19. (A) Effect of anti-insulin receptor Fab to block insulin (left) and MSA (right) stimulation of glucose oxidation in isolated adipocytes. (B) Lack of effect of anti-insulin receptor Fab on stimulation of thymidine incorporation into DNA in fibroblasts. From King *et al.* (1980a).

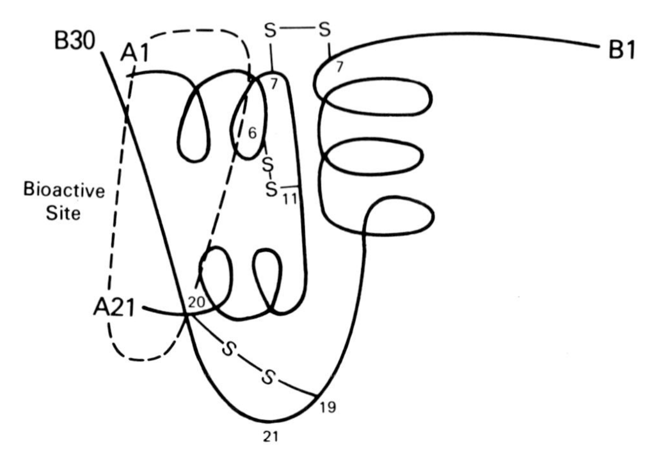

FIG. 20. Schematic representation of the three-dimensional structure of insulin indicating the bioactive site for metabolic effects.

In general, the growth-promoting effects of insulin seemed to be more conserved than metabolic effects, both evoluntionarily and following chemical modification. While it has not yet been possible to map the precise region of the insulin molecule responsible for its growth-promoting effect, several important structure–function statements can be made:

1. The B_{22}–B_{30} region of insulin which is vital for its metabolic activity does not seem crucial for its growth effect. Thus desoctapeptide (DOP) insulin has greatly reduced metabolic activity but is almost fully active in stimulating DNA synthesis.
2. Modification of the A8 residue to histidine (as in turkey or chicken insulins) results in an increase in both metabolic and growth-promoting action.
3. Substitutions at other residues, in particular A4, A20–21, B10, B13, and B26, appear to be important in modifying the growth-promoting action of insulins.

One very surprising observation from these studies was that insulins from species of the hystricomorph family of rodents (the guinea pig, casiragua, porcupine, and coypu) can stimulate thymidine incorporation to a greater maximum than other mammalian insulins. In this respect, the hystricomorph insulins appear to act more as growth factors than regulators of metabolism.

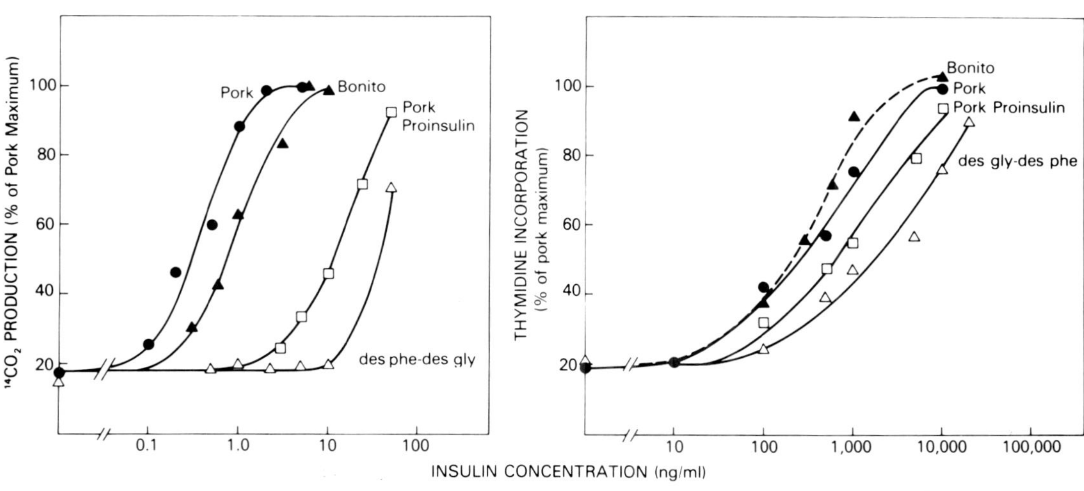

FIG. 21. Comparison of bonito fish insulin, pork proinsulin, and [des-gly, des-phe] insulin in stimulation of glucose oxidation in adipocytes (left) and thymidine incorporation into DNA in fibroblasts (right).

C. ARE THERE ANY INTERACTIONS BETWEEN INSULIN AND IGF RECEPTORS?

Although this is an area which needs further study, several observations have suggested that there may be interactions between receptors for insulin and IGFs at the molecular or physiological level. We have already alluded to two of these: the similarity in structure of the IGFs and insulin, and the overlapping spectrum of biological activities. In addition structural similarities in the receptors may exist, although the data are very sketchy on this point (Bhaumick *et al.*, 1980). We have observed that in human fibroblasts (but not in other tissues) high concentrations of antibody to the insulin receptor will inhibit MSA binding to IGF receptors suggesting immunological similarities of the receptors also (King *et al.*, 1980a).

The most direct evidence for possible interaction has come from the study of IGF receptors in rat adipocytes. We and others found that in these cells insulin did not inhibit binding of [^{125}I]MSA or [^{125}I]IGF; rather there was about a 50% increase in binding when unlabeled insulin was added (Fig. 3, upper right) (King *et al.*, 1980a; Zapf *et al.*, 1979). We found that the ability of unlabeled insulin to enhance [^{125}I]MSA binding occurred at low concentrations of insulin (1×10^{-10} *M*) and was specific; other peptide hormones such as growth hormone and epidermal growth factor (EGF) could not duplicate this effect. In addition, both pork proinsulin and antibody to the insulin receptor can mimic this effect at the concentrations where they stimulate metabolic activities. Thus, insulin can influence the MSA–receptor interaction and increase [^{125}I]MSA binding to its own receptors on the rat adipocytes.

This effect of insulin to increase MSA binding is due to an increase in receptor affinity, rather than receptor number. Further, this effect is blocked by inhibitors of microtubules and microfilaments, as well as low temperature. The low concentrations of insulin which produce this effect suggest it is of physiological importance.

XIII. The Fate of Insulin Bound to Cells or What Happens Next?

Aside from receptor aggregation, what happens after insulin binding to its receptor that ultimately accounts for insulin actions still remains largely unknown. Two general models of insulin action have been considered (Fig. 22) (Kahn, 1979). The first model suggests that insulin action follows a mechanism similar to that for the peptide hormone which activate adenylate cyclase. In this model, insulin binding to its receptor results in an activation of some membrane-associated enzyme or transport

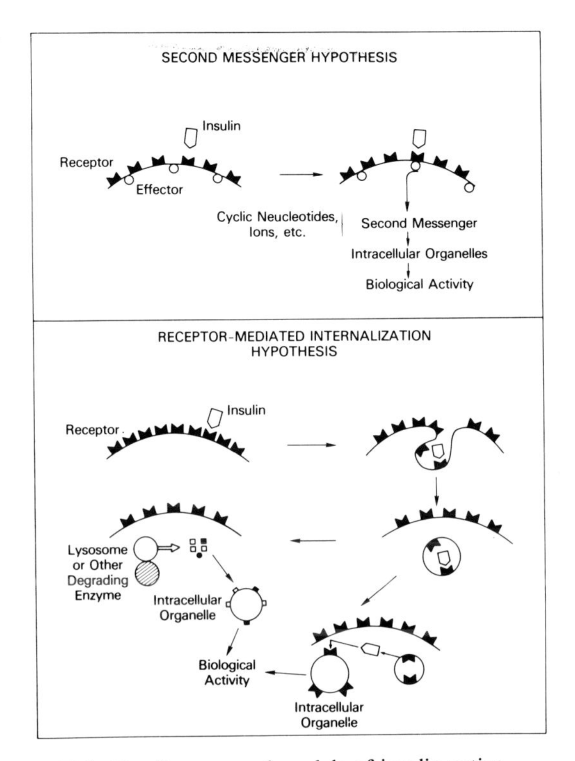

FIG. 22. Two general models of insulin action.

protein which in turn generates an intracellular messenger for hormone action. Recently both Jarett and co-workers (Jarett and Seals, 1979; Seals and Jarett, 1980; Dopp *et al.,* 1980) and Larner et al. (1979) have presented evidence for such messengers. This has become one of the most hopeful new developments in unraveling the problem of insulin action, although the exact chemical nature of these "messengers" remains uncertain. Treatment of cells with anti-receptor antibody results in generation of a "second messenger" which is indistinguishable from that which occurs after insulin treatment (Seals and Jarett, 1980).

The alternative suggestion is that perhaps insulin enters the cell and is itself, in some form, its own second messenger (Steiner, 1977; Goldfine, 1977). The first suggestion that this might be true came from studies in which it was found that there was a time- and temperature-dependent decrease in the ability to dissociate ^{125}I-labeled insulin bound to adipocytes (Kahn and Baird, 1977). Since that time, the fate of insulin bound to cells has been studied by a variety of biochemical and morphological techniques. These have been reviewed by Gorden *et al.* (1980) and include electron microscopic studies with ferritin-labeled insulin, electron microscopic autoradiography with ^{125}I-labeled insulin, and localization of insulin in living cells using fluorescent conjugates and video intensification fluorescense microscopy (Schlessinger *et al.*, 1980).

The results of these observations are summarized pictorially in Fig. 23. Initially, the insulin is on the plasma membrane; in some cells there may even be preferential localization that can be shown to the microvilli (J. L. Carpentier and P. Gorden, personal communications). The receptor-bound insulin then appears to redistribute to form patches or caps, and some ligand, presumably still bound to the receptor, enters the cell by adsorptive pinocytosis. The latter process is thought to involve the coated-pit regions of the cell, although this has not been conclusively proven. The rate and magnitude of this internalization process is different in different cell types and in different studies, but varies from 15 to about 50% of the total ligand at steady state.

Exactly where the internalized insulin goes remains a matter of some debate. Insulin-binding sites have been found on several intracellular organelles and their properties studied (Table VI; also reviewed in Gorden *et al.*, 1980; and Kahn, 1976, 1979). Carpentier and Gorden have found at later time points a preferential localization of the internalized insulin to lysosomes (Gorden *et al.*, 1980), whereas Bergeron *et al.* (1979) find the

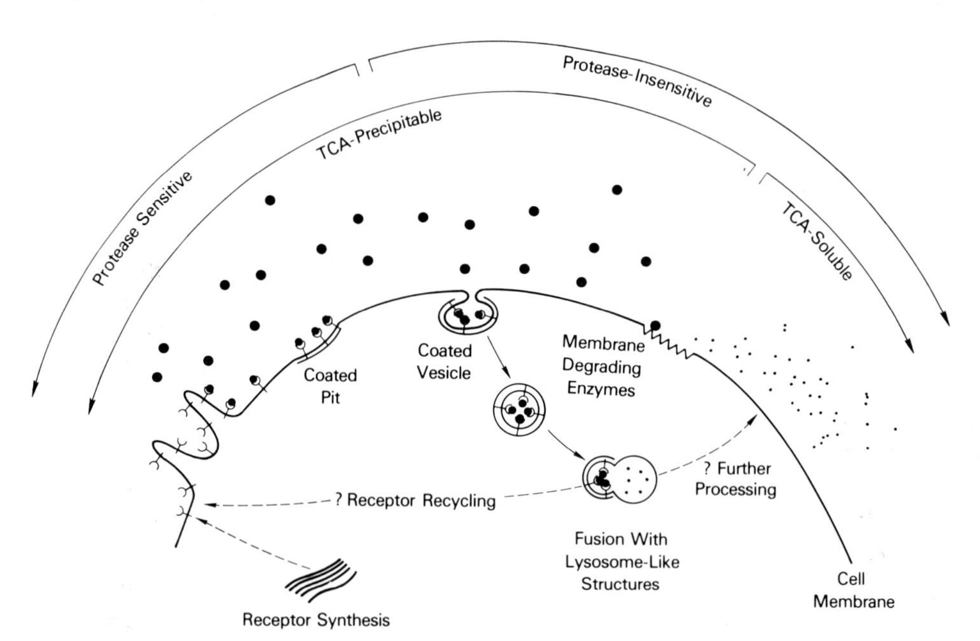

FIG. 23. Schematic representation of the fate of insulin bound to cells.

TABLE VI

Properties of Insulin-Binding Sites on Various Organelles

	General binding properties	Analog specificity	Negative cooperativity: Curved Scatchard	Negative cooperativity: Kinetics of dissociation	Receptor regulation	Antibody reactivity
Plasma membrane	+	++	+	+	+	++++
Golgi Light (vesicular)	+	++	+	+	+	++
Heavy (cisternal)	+	++	+	+	−	++
Smooth endoplasmic reticulum	?	+	+	?	±	−
Rough endoplasmic reticulum	?	+	−	?	±	±
Nuclei	−	++	+	−	+	−

primary intracellular localization is the Golgi elements. Since these two structures are often closely associated, this is only a fine distinction. On the other hand, Goldfine *et al.* (1978) have found preferential localization to nuclear membrane. The explanation for this difference in experimental findings is still unclear.

It is clear that regardless of the exact site of localization, much of the internalized insulin is degraded (Kahn and Baird, 1977; Suzuki and Kono, 1979), and this process can be blocked by inhibitors of lysosomal proteases inhibitors (Terris *et al.*, 1979; Suzuki and Kono, 1979; Marshall and Olefsky, 1979). This has lead to the suggestion that either insulin or a fragment of insulin interacts with other intracellular proteins to produce the final biological response.

In our opinion, there is a significant body of existing data which are rather strongly against this pathway as being a critical step in the pathway of insulin action. First, although some investigators (Weitzel *et al.*, 1973; Steiner, 1977) have suggested that there may be small fragments of insulin B chain which resemble some substrates or inhibitors of protein kinase and have insulin-like biological activity, we and others have been unable to reproduce this finding. Thus, in our hands, B-chain fragments from B21–26 have no intrinsic activity, nor do they modify insulin activity, even at concentrations up to 100 μg/ml (Fig. 24). While it is possible that higher concentrations may have some effect, one could seriously question the significance of such observations.

Second, although insulin receptors have been found on intracellular organelles (Table VI), there is no evidence that these are biologically important in insulin action. In preliminary experiments in which we entrapped insulin in liposomes and fused these liposomes with cells from which surface receptors had been removed by trypsin treatment, no effect of the insulin on metabolic function could be detected (J. Flier, C. R. Kahn, and K. Baird, unpublished observation). Thus, it seems more likely that these intracellular binding sites are receptors in the process of synthesis and degradation.

Another reason for thinking that the internalization and degradation are not critical steps in activation of the cell by insulin is the results of experiments using inhibitors of these processes (Table VII). While occasionally these do alter biological response, more often this is not the case (Fig. 25, Table VII).

Finally, there are the data with anti-receptor antibody. Using electron microscopic autoradiography, Carpentier *et al.* (1979) have found that ^{125}I-receptor antibody bound to cells is internalized and, like insulin, localized to lysosome-like structures. We have found that cell-bound antibody is also degraded by a process which can be blocked by inhibitors of lysosomal degradation (Grunfeld *et al.*, 1980). However, both monovalent

TABLE VII

Internalization, Degradation, and Insulin Action

Cell type	Biological effect	Inhibitor	Effect of inhibitor on: Internalization	Degradation	Bioresponse	Reference
Adipocyte	Glucose transport Phosphodiesterase	DNP, KCN, N_3	+	+	+	Kono *et al*. (1977)
	Phosphodiesterase	Chloroquine, Dibucaine, Tetracaine	−	+	−	Susuki and Kono (1979)
	Glucose oxidation	Chloroquine, Methylamine, bacitracin	+	−	−	Kahn and Baird (unpublished)
	Phosphodiesterase	Antibody to glutathione transhydrogenase	−	+	+	Phelps and Varandani (1977)
Hepatocyte	AIB transport	Methylamine	+	+	−	LeCam *et al*. (1979); Carpentier *et al*. (1980)
	Glycogen synthase	Chloroquine, Bacitracin	−	+	+	Desbuquois *et al*. (personal communication)
Fibroblast	DNA synthesis	Methylamine	+	+	+	King and Kahn (unpublished)

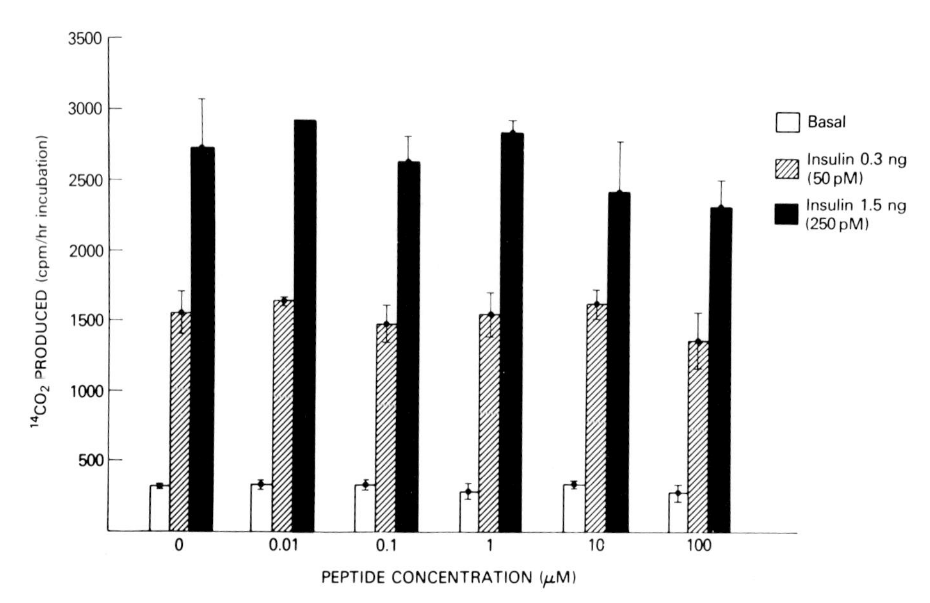

FIG. 24. Effect of the modified B-chain fragment B21–26 (β-Ala-Arg-Gly-Phe-Phe-Tyr-NH_2) on glucose oxidation. The open bars represent basal glucose oxidation, whereas the hatched bars and the solid bars are glucose oxidation stimulated by 0.3 and 1.5 ng/ml of insulin, respectively.

and bivalent antibody are internalized, even though only bivalent antibody is biologically active. Furthermore, even though the internalized antibody is localized to lysosomes in a fashion similar to insulin, it seems unlikely that this could result in production of an active fragment which would resemble an active-fragment of insulin.

XIV. Summary and Conclusions

The action of insulin at the cellular level can be regarded as a cascade of metabolic and growth effects which differ in time course and dose–response to insulin. These events are mediated by the interaction of insulin with at least two distinct types of receptors: the insulin receptor and a receptor (or receptors) for the insulin-like growth factors.

The insulin receptor is a high-molecular-weight integral membrane glycoprotein. There are two major subunits (130K and 90K) which are precipitated by antibodies to the receptor. In affinity labeling experiments the 130K chain is preferentially labeled suggesting that it possesses the insulin binding site or contains more available reactive groups for attachment. There is also an associated membrane component which acts as an

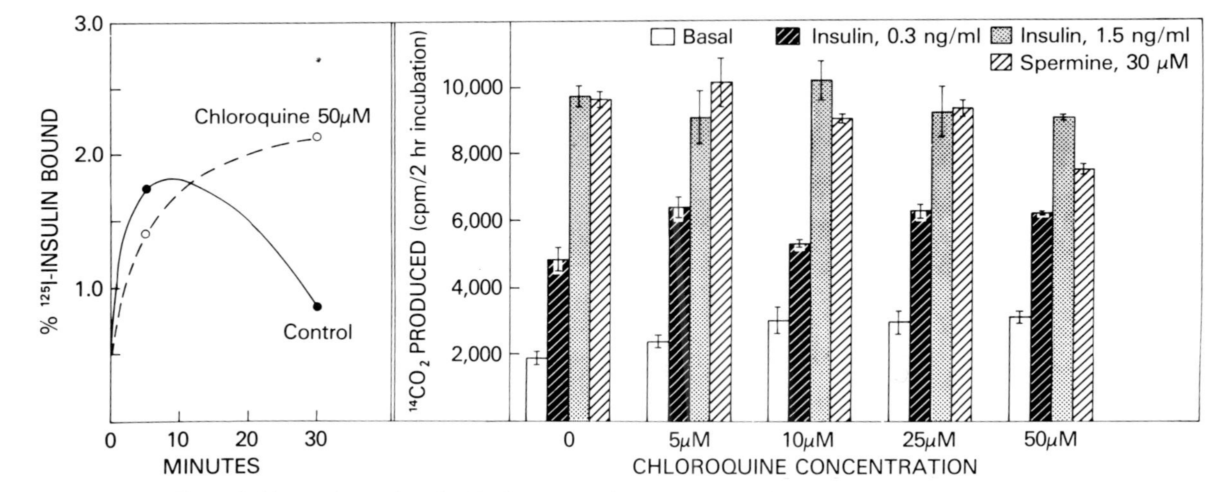

FIG. 25. Effect of chloroquine on insulin binding and action in isolated adipocytes. Note that although chloroquine may increase cell-associated insulin by inhibiting lysosomal degradation (left), it has no systematic effect on basal, insulin-stimulated, or spermine-stimulated glucose oxidation.

affinity regulator for the receptor. In the native state in the membrane, this complex has an apparent molecular weight of about 300K. Interaction of insulin with the receptor produces some conformation change which may be detected by a change in gel filtration and radiation inactivation profiles.

Most cells also have one or more types of receptors for the insulin-like growth factors. These differ from the insulin receptor in binding characteristics and reactivity with anti-receptor antibodies. Preliminary data also suggest structural differences.

Interaction of insulin with the insulin receptor produces the full spectrum of metabolic responses associated with insulin action. Receptor aggregation appears to be required since these actions are mimicked by bivalent anti-receptor antibodies and blocked by monovalent antibodies. The growth-promoting response of insulin (DNA synthesis) is mediated by interaction of insulin with the receptor(s) for the insulin-like growth factors. There is a different set of structural requirements for the growth response, and this effect is neither mimicked nor blocked by anti-receptor antibodies. While we have not yet studied all insulin effects by these techniques, it seems likely that there will be a number of insulin effects which represent hybrids between a simple metabolic or growth response where both receptors and postreceptor events may play interactive roles.

The mechanism of insulin action remains unknown. The fact that ligands such as antibodies or lectins which perturb the insulin receptor appropriately elicit a biological response suggests that the "information" for insulin's actions is "contained" within the receptor rather than the ligand. Receptor-mediated internalization and degradation of both insulin and anti-receptor antibody occur, but there is no evidence that either of these processes is required for insulin's actions.

XV. Future Directions

It should be clear from this article that, while considerable progress has been made in the area of insulin action since the review of Levine and Goldstein (1955) at this meeting 25 years ago, there is still much to be learned. It is evident even now, however, that to develop a comprehensive model for the mechanism of insulin action, it will be necessary to consider the problem in all of its aspects, rather than simply a problem of membrane chemistry or glucose metabolism. In addition to the approaches already discussed, it seems clear that new approaches must be developed and combined with the more classical biochemistry discussed here. Proposed candidates for the "second messenger" of insulin action must be tested in many systems to determine where they fit in the overall scheme of insulin action; hopefully our understanding will progress more in the next 25 years than it has in the past 25.

ACKNOWLEDGMENTS

The authors are deeply indebted to Drs. Jesse Roth and Phillip Gorden for continued support and advice throughout these studies. We also wish to acknowledge Dr. Rachmeil Levine whose contributions to our understanding of diabetes and insulin action are great and who celebrated his 70th birthday at this conference. Finally, we wish to thank Mrs. Nancy Conley for her secretarial assistance in preparation of this manuscript.

REFERENCES

Baldwin, D., Jr., Terris, S., and Steiner, D. F. (1979b). *Diabetes* **28,** 392.

Bar, R. S., Levis, W. R., Rechler, M. M., Siebert, C. W., Podskalny, J. M., Roth, J., and Muggeo, M. (1978). *N. Engl. J. Med.* **298,** 1164–1171.

Bar, R. S., Harrison, L. C., and Muggeo, M. (1979). *Adv. Intern. Med.* **24,** 23–52.

Bar, R. S., Muggeo, M., Kahn, C. R., Gorden, P., and Roth, J. (1980). *Diabetologia* **18,** 209–216.

Belsham, G. J., Browney, R. W., Hughes, W. A., and Denton, R. M. (1980). *Diabetologia* **18,** 307–312.

Bergeron, J. J. M., Sikstrom, R., Hand, A. R., and Posner, B. I. (1979). *J. Cell Biol.* **80,** 427–443.

Bhaumick, B., Hollenberg, M., and Bala, R. M. (1980). *Clin. Res.* **28,** 516A.

Blackard, W. G., Guzelian, P. S., and Small, M. E. (1978). *Endocrinology* **103,** 548–553.

Blundell, T. L., Dodson, G. C., Hodgkin, D. C., and Mercola, D. A. (1972). *Adv. Protein Chem.* **26,** 279–402.

Cahill, G. F., Jr. (1971). *Diabetes* **20,** 785–797.

Carpentier, J. L., Van Obberghen, E., Gorden, P., and Orci, L. (1979). *Diabetes* **28,** 345A.

Cuatrecasas, P. (1971). *Proc. Nat. Acad. Sci. U.S.A.* **68,** 1264–1268.

Cuatrecasas, P. (1972). *J. Biol. Chem.* **247,** 1980–1981.

Cuatrecasas, P., and Tell, G. P. E. (1973). *Proc. Natl. Acad. Sci. U.S.A.* **70,** 485–489.

Czech, M. P. (1977). *Annu. Rev. Biochem.* **46,** 354–384.

Czech, M. P., and Lynn, W. S. (1973). *Biochim. Biophys. Acta* **297,** 368–377.

DeLean, A., and Rodbard, D. (1980). *Fed. Proc. Fed. Am. Soc. Exp. Biol.* **39,** 116–120.

DeMeyts, P., Roth, J., Neville, D. M., Jr., Gavin, J. R., III, and Lesniak, M. A. (1973). *Biochem. Biophys. Res. Commun.* **55,** 154–161.

DeMeyts, P., Bianco, A. R., and Roth, J. (1976). *J. Biol. Chem.* **251,** 1877–1888.

Drachman, D. B., Angus, C. W., Adams, R. N., *et al.* (1978). *N. Engl. J. Med.* **298,** 1116–1122.

Ehrlich, P. (1906). "Studies in Immunity." Wiley, New York.

Flier, J. S., Kahn, C. R., Roth, J., and Bar, R. S. (1975). *Science* **190,** 63–65.

Flier, J. S., Kahn, C. R., Jarrett, D. B., and Roth, J. (1976). *J. Clin. Invest.* **58,** 1442–1449.

Flier, J. S., Kahn, C. R., Jarrett, D. B., and Roth, J. (1977). *J. Clin. Invest.* **60,** 784–794.

Freychet, P., Roth, J., and Neville, D. M., Jr. (1971). *Proc. Natl. Acad. Sci.* **68,** 1833–1837.

Freychet, P., Kahn, C. R., Roth, J., and Neville, D. M., Jr. (1972). *J. Biol. Chem.* **247,** 3953–3961.

Gammeltoft, S., and Gliemann, J. (1973). *Biochim. Biophys. Acta* **320,** 16–32.

Gavin, J. R., III, Mann, D. L., Buell, D. N., and Roth, J. (1972). *Biochem. Biophys. Res. Commun.* **49,** 870–875.

Gavin, J. R., III, Roth, J., Neville, D. M., Jr., DeMeyts, P., and Buell, D. N. (1974). *Proc. Natl. Acad. Sci. U.S.A.* **71,** 84–88.

Ginsberg, B. H. (1977). *In* "Biochemical Actions of Hormones" (G. Litwack, ed.), Vol. 4, pp. 313–349. Academic Press, New York.

Ginsberg, B. H., Kahn, C. R., Roth, J., and DeMeyts, P. (1976). *Biochem. Biophys. Res. Commun.* **73,** 1068–1074.

Gliemann, J., and Sonne, O. (1978). *J. Biol. Chem.* **253,** 7857–7863.

Goldfine, I. D. (1977). *Diabetes* **26,** 148–155.

Goldfine, I. D., Jones, A. L., Hardek, G. T., Wong, K. Y., and Mooney, J. S. (1978). *Science* **202,** 760–763.

Gorden, P., Carpentier, J. L., Freychet, P., and Orci, L. (1980). *Diabetologia* **18,** 263–274.

Grunfeld, C., Van Obberghen, E., Karlsson, F. A., and Kahn, C. R., (1980). *J. Clin. Invest.* **66,** 1124–1134.

Hall, K., and Fryklund, L. (1979). *In* "Hormones and Blood" (C. H. Gray and V. H. T. James, eds.), Vol. 1, pp. 255–278. Academic Press, New York.

Harmon, J. T., Kahn, C. R., Kempner, E. S., and Schlegel, W. (1980a). *J. Biol. Chem.* **255,** 3412–3419.

Harmon, J. T., Kahn, C. R., and Johnson, M. S. (1980b). *Diabetes* **29,** 47A.

Harrison, L. C., and Itin, A. (1979). *Nature (London)* **279,** 334–336.

Harrison, L., and Itin, A. (1981). *J. Biol. Chem.* (in press)

Harrison, L. C., and Kahn, C. R. (1980). *Prog. Clin. Immunol.* **4,** 107–126.

Harrison, L. C., Muggeo, M., Bar, R. S., Flier, J. S., Waldman, T., and Roth, J. (1979a). *Clin. Res.* **27,** 252A.

Harrison, L. C., Flier, J. S., Roth, J., Karlsson, F. A., and Kahn, C. R. (1979b). *J. Clin. Endocrinol. Metab.* **48,** 59–65.

Harrison, L. C., Itin, A., Kasuga, M., and Van Obberghan, E. (1981). Submitted.

Hedo, J. A., Harrison, L. C., and Roth, J. (1980). *Diabetes* **29,** 38A.

Houslay, M. D., Ellory, J. C., Smith, G. A., Hesketh, T. R., Stein, J. M., Warren, G. B., and Metcalf, J. C. (1977). *Biochim. Biophys. Acta* **467,** 208–219.

Isersky, C., Taurog, J. D., Poy, G., *et al.* (1978). *J. Immunol.* **121,** 549–558.

Jacobs, S., Schechter, Y., Bissell, K., and Cuatrecasas, P. (1977). *Biochem. Biophys. Res. Commun.* **77,** 981–988.

Jacobs, S., Chang, K. J., and Cuatrecasas, P. (1978). *Science* **200,** 1283–1284.

Jacobs, S., Hazum, E., Schechter, Y., and Cuatrecasas, P. (1979). *Proc. Natl. Acad. Sci. U.S.A.* **76,** 4918–4921.

Jacobs, S., Hazum, E., and Cuatrecasas, P. (1980). *J. Biol. Chem.* **255,** 6937–6940.

Jarett, L., and Seals, J. R. (1979). *Science* **206,** 1407–1408.

Jarrett, D. B., Roth, J., Kahn, C. R., and Flier, J. S. (1976). *Proc. Natl. Acad. Sci. U.S.A.* **73,** 4115–4119.

Kahn, C. R. (1976). *J. Cell Biol.* **70,** 261–286.

Kahn, C. R. (1979). *Trends Biochem. Sci.* **263,** 4–7.

Kahn, C. R., and Baird, K. L. (1978). *J. Biol. Chem.* **253,** 4900–4906.

Kahn, C. R., and Podskalny, J. M. (1980). *J. Clin. Endocrinol. Metab.* **50,** 1139–1141.

Kahn, C. R., and Roth, J. (1975). *Am. J. Clin. Pathol.* **63,** 656–668.

Kahn, C. R., Flier, J. S., Bar, R. S., Archer, J. A., Gorden, D., Martin, M. M., and Roth, J. (1976). *N. Engl. J. Med.* **294,** 739–745.

Kahn, C. R., Baird, K. L., Flier, J. S., and Jarrett, D. B. (1977a). *J. Clin. Invest.* **60,** 1094–1106.

Kahn, C. R., Megyesi, K., Bar, R. S., Eastman, R. C., and Flier, J. S. (1977b). *Annu. Rev. Intern. Med.* **86,** 205–219.

Kahn, C. R., Baird, K. L., Jarrett, D. B., and Flier, J. S. (1978a). *Proc. Natl. Acad. Sci.* **75,** 4209–4213.

Kahn, C. R., Goldfine, I. D., Neville, D. M., Jr., and DeMeyts, P. (1978b). *Endocrinology* **103,** 1054–1066.

Kahn, C. R., Baird, K. L., and Van Obberghen, E. M. (1981). Submitted.

Karlsson, F. A., Van Obberghen, E., Grunfeld, C., and Kahn, C. R. (1979a). *Proc. Natl. Acad. Sci. U.S.A.* **76,** 809–813.

Karlsson, F. A., Grunfeld, C., Kahn, C. R., and Roth, J. (1979b). *Endocrinology* **104,** 1383–1392.

Kasuga, M., Akanuma, Y., Tsushima, T., Suzuk, K., Kosaka, K., and Kibata, M. (1978a). *J. Clin. Endocrinol. Metab.* **47,** 66–77.

Kasuga, M., Akanuma, Y., Tsushima, T., Iwamoto, Y., Kosaka, K., Kibato, M., and Kawanishi, K. (1978b). *Diabetes* **27,** 938–944.

Kasuga, M., Van Obberghen, E., Yamada, K., and Harrison, L. C. (1981). *Diabetes* (in press).

King, G. L., and Kahn, C. R. (1980). *Diabetes* **29,** 14A.

King, G. L., Kahn, C. R., Rechler, M. M., and Nissley, S. P. (1980). *J. Clin. Invest.* **66,** 130–140.

Kobayashi, M., Olefsky, J. M., Elders, J., Mako, M. E., Given, B. D., Schedwie, H. K., Fiser, R. H., Hintz, R. L., Horner, J. A., and Rubeinstein, A. H. (1978). *Proc. Natl. Acad. Sci. U.S.A.* **75,** 3469–3473.

Kono, T., Robinson, F. W., Sarver, J. A., Vega, F. V., and Pointer, R. H. (1977). *J. Biol. Chem.* **252,** 2226–2233.

Krupp, M. N., and Livingston, J. N. (1978). *Proc. Natl. Acad. Sci. U.S.A.* **75,** 2593–2597.

Krupp, M. N., and Livingston, J. N. (1979). *Nature (London)* **278,** 61–62.

Lang, U., Kahn, C. R., and Chrambach, A. (1980a). *Endocrinology* **106,** 40–49.

Lang, U., Kahn, C. R., and Harrison, L. C. (1980b). *Biochemistry* **19,** 64–70.

Langley, J. N. (1878). *J. Physiol. (London)* **1,** 339–360.

Larner, J., Galasko, G., Cheng, K., DePaoli-Roach, A. A., Huang, L., Daggy, P., and Kellogg, J. (1979). *Science* **206,** 1408–1410.

Lawrence, J. C., Jr., and Larner, J. (1978). *J. Biol. Chem.* **253,** 2104–2113.

Lawrence, J. C., Jr., Larner, J., Kahn, C. R., and Roth, J. (1978). *Mol. Cell. Biochem.* **22,** 153–158.

LeCam, A., Maxfield, F., Willingham, M., and Pastan, I. (1979). *Biochem. Biophys. Res. Commun.* **88,** 873–881.

LeMarchand-Brustel, Y., Gorden, P., Flier, J. S., Kahn, C. R., and Freychet, P. (1978). *Diabetologia* **14,** 311–318.

Levine, R., and Goldstein, M. S. (1955). *Recent Prog. Horm. Res.* **11,** 343–374.

Livingston, J. N., Purvis, B. J., and Lockwood, D. H. (1978). *Nature (London)* **273,** 394–396.

Marshall, S., and Olefsky, J. M. (1979). *J. Biol. Chem.* **254,** 10153–10160.

Martin, D. B., and Carter, J. R. (1970). *Science* **167,** 873–874.

Massague, J., and Czech, M. P. (1980). *Diabetes* **29,** 945–947.

Massague, J., Pilch, P. F., and Czech, M. D. (1980). *Proc. Natl. Acad. Sci. U.S.A.* (in press)

Maturo, J. M., III, and Hollenberg, M. D. (1978). *Proc. Natl. Acad. Sci. U.S.A.* **75,** 3070–3074.

Megyesi, K., Kahn, C. R., Roth, J., Froesch, E. R., Humbel, R. E., Zapf, J., and Neville, D. M., Jr. (1974). *Biochem. Biophys. Res. Commun.* **57,** 307–315.

Muggeo, M., Ginsberg, B. H., Roth, J., Neville, D. M., Jr., DeMeyts, P., and Kahn, C. R. (1979a). *Endocrinology* **104,** 1393–1402.

Muggeo, M., Kahn, C. R., Bar, R. S., Rechler, M., Flier, J. S., and Roth, J. (1979b). *J. Clin. Endocrinol. Metab.* **49,** 110–119, 1979.

Newerly, K., and Berson, S. A. (1957). *Proc. Soc. Exp. Med.,* **94,** 751–755.

Nissley, S. P., Rechler, M. M., Moses, A. C., Short, P. A., and Podskalny, J. M. (1977). *Endocrinology* **101,** 708–716.

Olefsky, J. M. (1976). *Diabetes* **25,** 1154–1162.

Osborne, C. K., Monoco, M. E., Lippman, M. E., and Kahn, C. R. (1978). *Cancer Res.* **38,** 94–102.

Phelps, B. H., and Varandani, P. T. (1977). *Biochem. Biophys. Res. Commun.* **75,** 302–310.

Pilch, P. F., and Czech, M. (1979). *J. Biol. Chem.* **254,** 3375–3381.

Pillion, D. J., Grantham, J. R., and Czech, M. P. (1978). *J. Biol. Chem.* **254,** 3211–3320.

Pollett, R. J., Standaert, M. L., and Haase, B. A. (1977). *J. Biol. Chem.* **252,** 5828–5834.

Popp, D. A., Keichle, F. L., Kotagal, N., and Jarett, L. (1980). *J. Biol. Chem.* **255,** 7540–7543.

Rechler, M., Podskalny, J., Goldfine, I., and Wells, C. (1974). *J. Clin. Endocrinol. Metab.* **39,** 512–521.

Rechler, M. M., Zapf, M., Nissley, S. P., Froesch, E. R., Moses, A. C., Podskalny, J. M., Schilling, E. E., and Humbel, R. E. (1980). *Endocrinology* **107,** 1451–1459.

Rinderknecht, E., and Humbel, R. E. (1978a). *J. Biol. Chem.* **253,** 2769–2776.

Rinderknecht, E., and Humbel, R. E. (1978b). *Fed. Eur. Biochem. Soc. Lett.* **89,** 283–286.

Roth, J. (1973). *Metabolism* **22,** 1059–1073.

Roth, J., Kahn, C. R., Lesniak, M. A., Gorden, P., DeMeyts, P., Megyesi, K., Neville, D. M., Jr., Gavin, J. R., III, Soll, A. H., Freychet, P., Goldfine, I. D., Bar, R. S., and Archer, J. A. (1975). *Recent Prog. Horm. Res.* **31,** 95–139.

Rubin, C. S., Hirsch, A., Fung, C., and Rosen, O. M. (1978). *J. Biol. Chem.* **253,** 7570–7578.

Sanger, F. (1959). *Science* **129,** 1340–1344.

Schilling, E. E., Rechler, M. M., Grunfeld, C., and Rosenberg, A. M. (1979). *Proc. Natl. Acad. Sci. U.S.A.* **76,** 5877–5881.

Schlegel, W., Kempner, E. S., and Rodbell, M. (1979). *J. Biol. Chem.* **254,** 5168–5176.

Schlessinger, J., Van Obberghen, E., and Kahn, C. R. (1980). *Nature (London)* **286,** 729–731.

Seals, J. R., and Jarett, L. (1980). *Proc. Natl. Acad. Sci. U.S.A.* **77,** 77–81.

Shecter, Y., Hernaez, L., Schlessinger, J., and Cuatrecasas, P. (1979). *Nature (London)* **278,** 835–838.

Shecter, Y., Chang, K. J., Jacobs, S., and Cuatrecasas, P. (1980). *Proc. Natl. Acad. Sci. U.S.A.* **76,** 2720–2724.

Shimizu, Y., and Nobuyoshi, S. (1980). *Somatic Cell Genet.* **6,** 585–601.

Stadie, W. C., Haugaard, N., and Vaughn, M. (1953). *J. Biol. Chem.* **200,** 745–751.

Steiner, D. F. (1977). *Diabetes* **26,** 322–340.

Steiner, D. F., Clark, J. L., Nolan, C., Rubenstein, A. M., Margoliash, E., Aten, B., and Oyer, P. E. (1969). *Recent Prog. Horm. Res.* **25,** 207–272.

Suzuki, K., and Kono, T. (1979). *J. Biol. Chem.* **254,** 9786–9794.

Terris, S., and Steiner, D. F. (1975). *J. Biol. Chem.* **250,** 8389–8398.

Terris, S., Hofmann, C., and Steiner, D. F. (1979). *Can. J. Biochem.* **57,** 459–468.

Van Obberghen, E., Spooner, D. M., Kahn, C. R., Chernick, S. S., Garrison, M. M., Karlsson, F. A., and Grunfeld, C. (1979). *Nature (London)* **280,** 500–502.

Van Obberghen, E., Kasuga, M., LeCam, A., Itin, A., Hedo, J. A., and Harrison, L. C. (1981). *Proc. Natl. Acad. Sci. U.S.A.* (in press)

Van Wyk, J. J., and Underwood, L. E. (1978). *In* "Biochemical Actions of Hormones" (G. Litwack, ed.), pp. 101–148. Academic Press, New York.

Weitzel, G., Eisele, K., Schulz, V., and Stock, W. (1973). *Hoppe-Seylers Z. Physiol. Chem.* **352,** 1735–1738.

Wisher, M. H., Baron, M. D., Jones, R. H., Sonksen, P. H., Saunders, D. J., Thamm, P., and Brandenburg, D. (1980). *Biochem. Biophys. Res. Commun.* **92,** 492–498.

Yip, C. C., Yeung, C. W. T., and Moule, M. L. (1978). *J. Biol. Chem.* **253,** 1743–1749.

Yip, C. C., Yeung, C. W. T., and Moule, M. L. (1980). *Biochemistry* **19,** 70–76.

Zapf, J., Rinderknectit, E., Humbel, R. E., and Froesch, E. R. (1978). *Metabolism* **27,** 1803–1828.

DISCUSSION

H. Pollard: I have a question which I think goes directly to the heart of the problem of whether capping and patching have anything to do with the mechanism of insulin action. The fact that the insulin receptor may be multisubunit in nature and the fact that antibody to the receptor can mimic insulin led me to remember a classical experiment done by Boris Rotman on *E. coli* many years ago. The observation was that a mutant form of β-galactosidase was inactive because it could not form the active tetrameric species. However an antibody against β-galactosidase was found to reactivate the enzyme. Therefore my question is this: might it be possible that the role of the anti-receptor antibody would simply be to rearrange the subunits of the receptor or to mimic the polymeric state and that the patching and capping observation would simply be something secondary, occurring incidently because of the added ability of antibodies to induce patching and capping?

C. R. Kahn: I would say that there is no evidence that the microscopically visible patching and capping has anything to do with insulin action. The classic agents which alter these processes do not block most of insulins biological responses. If there is an aggregation step which is required in insulin action, and my bias is that there is either an aggregation step or at least the confirmational change produced by ligand binding that is required, this is at a bimolecular or perhaps tetramolecular level. It is not at the level that we can see with the microscope. I think that the capping which we see is long after the fact.

H. Pollard: One might approach this question with monovalent fragments of IgG. The fragment would be expected to bind to the receptor, creating a polymeric state but not inducing cross linking and subsequent patching and capping.

B. W. O'Malley: My question relates to the insulin-induced capping. As a control, have you created mitogenic-induced capping and then looked to see whether the insulin receptor aggregates also?

C. R. Kahn: We haven't done the experiments that way, but we have done the converse. In the same experiments in which the co-capping of the insulin receptor and the anti-receptor antibody were investigated, we also studied the effect of insulin binding on the distribution of fluorescently labeled concanavalin A. We found that when there is capping of the insulin receptor you do not co-cap the concanavalin A binding sites as determined by this technique. We did not do whether the converse is true; that is we did not know if pretreatment with concanavalin A affects capping of the insulin receptor.

B. W. O'Malley: In your radiation inactivation what role might the surface area or shape of the receptor play? Second, what about the immediate environment? Radiation would produce free radicals and one then might have varying effects depending upon whether the environment has more lipid or water, etc.

C. R. Kahn: In answer to the first question, in our experiments the shape of a molecule has no effect, because there is no way to preferentially orient the molecules with respect to their shape and the radiation field. The measure we have reflects the molecular volume. It would be possible to use this technique in a modified fashion to look at the shape of the molecule if there is a method to preferentially orient the molecules. This has been done with tobacco mosaic virus, for example. One can line up the cigar shape molecules by a variety of techniques and then irradiate using a type of radiation which will be of low enough energy so that it will be able to penetrate only a small distance into the sample. In this case, one can determine something about their shape. Under the conditions of our experiments, however, this is not true.

As far as the free radical problem goes, this is a potential problem and this is the reason that the radiation inactivation must be performed under one or two circumstances, either it must be performed on a lyophilized preparation in which water is removed, because that's the major source of free radicals, or it must be done at liquid nitrogen temperature to minimize the formation of free radicals after the radiation. We have tried both techniques and one observes identical results. Thus within the limits of what can be done, we do not believe that what is observed is due to a secondary radiation phenomenon, but rather to primary radiation of the receptor itself.

B. W. O'Malley: Do you find any antibody internalized in the nucleus? What is your general opinion of experiments purporting to show insulin in the nucleus?

C. R. Kahn: The studies done on internalization, and I should say these were done by Jean Louis Carpentier and Phil Gorden, do not indicate that either insulin or anti-receptor antibody go to the nucleus. One could not, therefore, use this as a differential point in the mechanism of the anti-receptor antibody versus insulin. Ira Goldfine who has been the main proponent of the hypothesis that insulin does go to the nucleus has not studied the fate of anti-receptor antibody. I think we need more data on this point, since at present there are mixed feelings between the investigators who looked at this problem. In the following paper, for example, Barry Posner will describe in some detail his observations concerning the fate of bound insulin. He finds that insulin goes primarily to the Golgi, whereas Phil Gorden and Jean Louis Carpentier think it goes primarily lysosome, and Ira Goldfine believes that internalized insulin goes to the nucleus. Whether this is due to a difference in interpretation or some experimental differences is not clear.

E. Shooter: Do I understand that your thinking now is that insulin binds first to a low-affinity receptor and that through aggragation with other proteins in the membrane, may convert the receptor to high affinity.

C. R. Kahn: No. I'm glad, however, that you asked that question. Although there is certainly still a debate over the nature of the binding isotherm for the insulin receptor reaction, I think that the model most consistent with all of the data must include cooperative interactions among insulin receptors. It must be a type of negative cooperativity in that the binding of insulin causes a decrease in receptor affinity rather than an increase. We do not have any evidence that there is a confirmational change to increase receptor affinity after binding insulin.

B. Posner: Did you point out in your lecture that monovalent Fab fragments were internalized?

C. R. Kahn: Yes, that is true. I don't have the quantitative data from Jean Louis Carpentier yet, but I know that the initial inspection of the photomicrographs have revealed that the monovalent Fab is internalized although the actual grain counts and distribution have not been done; the initial impression is that it would be very similar to that seen with the divalent antibody.

W. Schrader: I want to ask you a couple of questions about the radiation damage experiments. First of all, can you do that technique on either unoccupied receptors or receptors complexed with ^{125}I-labeled insulin?

C. R. Kahn: Yes, I'm sorry if I wasn't clear. The experiment is done by irradiating the membrane first and measuring the insulin binding in a classical binding assay afterward, so that in a normal situation the receptors are unoccupied at the time of irradiation. We have looked at the effect of occupancy because the time has been limited and I, therefore, had to eliminate those data from this presentation.

W. Schrader: I understood that you thought that movement or conformational changes occur in the receptor reducing its target size from two hundred and some thousand to 90,000 during the irradiation. Do you mean to imply that that would occur in liquid nitrogen and/or in the lyophilized state, or do you envision that there would be radiation damage which would then be manifest only upon rehydration or warming?

C. R. Kahn: Again this may have been something that I was not entirely clear about. While the radiation damage occurs in the liquid nitrogen state, we have no way of evaluating until the membranes are thawed and studied. One can detect gross modifications in protein subunit structure of the membrane by SDS–gel electrophoresis, indicating that large numbers of peptide bonds are being broken during this process.

S. Cohen: In an early figure you showed us a demonstration of how the receptor acts. On this figure, there is also a small amount of insulin-degrading enzyme. What is the purpose of such an enzyme?

C. R. Kahn: I did not have time to discuss our studies of insulin-degrading activity in detail. I believe, however, that insulin degradation has at least two components. Most of the insulin degradation that we measure *in vitro* is related, I believe, to cell surface proteases which are independent of the receptor. One can also find a small amount of receptor related degradation which may be occurring through the process of internalization. There is a large amount of interest, but virtually no data, to suggest that this latter component of degradation is related to insulin action. In fact, I would say that if anything, in my opinion, the bulk of data suggest that it is not important for insulin action. Thus, while there are degrading enzymes for insulin their particular role, as I visualize it, would be simply to decrease the free insulin concentration and, therefore, decrease insulin action.

S. Cohen: It would be more economical to produce less insulin.

C. R. Kahn: Well it might be more economical, but I think you need local regulatory mechanisms which can allow the cell to turn on and turn off more rapidly. It's not a great surprise that for this hormone, as for all hormones, almost all of the target tissues which bind insulin are also active degraders. If one tries to do correlations between the degradation process and biological response, it becomes very difficult to say that this is required for activity. Degradation may be required for turning off the signal, but probably not for turning it on.

J. Carter: If I remember correctly, when your colleagues presented your radiation in activation data this spring, they used some calculations based on this to disprove a simple model of negative cooperativity. I'd like you to comment on that. Second, a few years ago Jarrett presented data with ferritin insulin using electron microscopy in which he was able to show that the ability of the cell to respond to insulin did, in fact, depend on the presence of receptor clusters but that insulin itself did not affect those clusters, that they were present before the binding. Would you comment on that?

C. R. Kahn: The radiation inactivation experiments have been used to investigate negative cooperativity, although not in detail. After irradiation one finds that there is a loss of negative cooperativity and this loss of negative cooperativity roughly parallels the loss of receptor sites, it does not appear to be related to this higher molecular weight affinity regulatory component. So that from the radiation inactivation data, we do not conclude that negative cooperativity does not exist, rather what we conclude is that a change in negative cooperativity is not what we are seeing in the early part of the inactivation profile, rather we are seeing a change in affinity due to a change in some other component which affects association rate, not dissociation rate.

As for the second question, Len Jarrett's studies with ferritin insulin have a very direct impact on these studies. Jarrett has presented evidence that insulin receptors exist in preexisting clusters. This study was done using ferritin-labeled insulin complexes. I have no personal experience with this technique, but I know it's a difficult technique, and there is the possibility for artifacts because complexes are not always monomeric complexes, etc. But for the moment, let's accept for face value that what has been observed is representative of the true distribution of receptors. The critical question is, is this important in insulin action? I would say no, not if one considers the big picture. Jarrett has shown that these complexes of insulin receptors can be disaggregated by cytochalasin B, an agent which is known to inhibit glucose transport, but not by cytochalasin D which does not inhibit glucose transport. He has postulated, therefore, that this aggregation is important for the glucose transport phenomenon, and perhaps it is. On the other hand, I would like to point out that cytochalasins B and D do not block other insulin effects, so that if this aggregation being visualized is important and it can be disrupted, then this is not a common step required for all of insulin's actions. At most, it is required only for some effects.

L. Birnbaumer: As you know studies that correlate events do not prove cause–effect relationships and can lend themselves to confusion. In your presentation you first showed data that indicated that solubilized insulin receptors tend to dissociate into smaller forms upon addition of insulin, suggesting this to be perhaps the molecular basis of the negative cooperativity seen in insulin binding to membrane receptors. Later on, you also showed data indicating that insulin binding to receptors in intact cells results in aggregation. How do you reconcile these rather opposing results in terms of gaining information about the mechanism of insulin action?

C. R. Kahn: There is an inconsistency, in one sense, that when you add insulin in high concentration, it definitely causes a dose-dependent disaggregation of the receptor. The concentrations, however, required to observe this are relatively high, that is at least 25 ng, and even at that stage only about 20% of receptors are disaggregated. This increases with further increases in insulin concentration. On the other hand, the concentration of insulin which produces the biological responses, where aggregation may be important, are much smaller. So that it may be there are two phenomena going on simultaneously that are being measured independently. The other limitation in interpretation of these data is that we really don't have a good correlation between what we observe in terms of receptor aggregation and a biological response. Thus, I think at present the best we can do is to try to develop a hypothesis which will somehow encompass the various observations you have to deal with.

L. Birnbaumer: Did you try irradiation inactivation studies with membranes to which you had prebound insulin? If so, how did the results compare to results with membranes that had not "seen" insulin?

C. R. Kahn: Yes, insulin causes a change in the inactivation profile with a loss of the upward component suggesting that either it causes a dissociation of the receptor from a regulatory component or it causes some change in the confirmation of the complex which allows the subunits to be viewed more independently. Although not direct, this would also suggest that a kind of dissociation event occurs at high insulin concentrations. At low physiologic insulin concentrations one cannot observe a change in the inactivation profile.

L. Birnbaumer: I find your studies on the capping of insulin receptors very interesting. However, in terms of correlating them with insulin action, I wonder whether (a) you see this capping phenomenon in all the cell types that are known to respond to insulin and where this can be determined, and (b) are the cells on which you observe capping target cells for insulin's actions?

C. R. Kahn: Very few cell types have been examined. Most of the cells which are attached to surface, such as fibroblasts, seem to form patches, whereas lymphocytes which grow in suspension, form caps, We have looked on the 3T3-L1 cells which grow as fibroblasts and which are insulin responsive under both conditions. When these are attached to a surface, insulin forms patches; however, when these cells are suspended, insulin caps. Thus, one observes patching or capping may depend not only on cell type but on the state of the cell at the time of the study. We really don't know if there is a differential significance to whether one observes patching and capping in this context.

Z. Naor: Regarding the mechanism of action of insulin, would you comment on the possible role of protein phosphorylation in the hormone action.

C. R. Kahn: I can really make only a limited comment. The changes in protein phosphoration that have been observed under insulin exposure are mimicked by the anti-receptor antibody. It is still a matter of debate as to whether all or any of these proteins are required in insulin action. Some of them had been identified, others have not. Whether this is a critical step in insulin action or not is totally unknown.

W. R. Moyle: I'm impressed that insulin may have different kinds of recognition sites for its growth hormone activity and for its metabolic activity. In your studies have you found any evidence that the recognition site of various insulin receptors differ? Have you found that portions of the insulin molecule bind differently to receptors mediating growth than to those mediating metabolic activity?

C. R. Kahn: George King has recently been involved in the very large study of this type looking at the comparison of the growth-promoting and glucose metabolic effects of over 30 insulin analogs. We hope that from this we will be able to map the site for the growth-promoting activity. One thing which is clear at this point is that there is a great difference, as I indicated, between the parts of the insulin molecule required for growth-promoting activity and those required for glucose metabolism. This action of insulin is much better conserved from the point of view of evolution that is the glucose metabolic effect. Some chemically modified insulins which have lost most of their metabolic activity still are quite potent in promoting thymidine incorporative into DNA. Furthermore there are some insulin such as those from the hystrictomorphs (guinea pig, coypu, porcupine, and casargua) which show growth-promoting activity beyond that observed in any other species. This suggests that these insulins may be more closely related to the insulin-like growth factors, then to the classical pancreatic insulin in other species. Some studies being conducted by Jesse Roth and his co-workers looking at nonpancreatic tissue insulins also support this point of view. At present, however, I can't draw a picture to identify the specific residues involved in growth promotion although we are working toward that goal.

W. R. Moyle: Is it possible to quantify the stoichiometry of the insulin receptor aggregation phenomenon? You mentioned that you had 20% of the receptors occupied and you were getting full aggregation. What happens if you only occupy 10%?

C. R. Kahn: We cannot observe the insulin on the cells at such low concentrations of insulin because of the limitations of the technology. There is one correlation which I will mention, but its only a correlation and I would hate to draw any striking conclusion from it. Dr. Van Obberghen and Dr. Schessinger showed that if one looks at the time course of capping on lymphocytes, there is a very close correlation between this phenomenon and the down-regulation phenomenon which has been observed. One of the questions that we would like to explore further is whether this is a prerequisite step in down regulation.

R. Fellows: We are also intrigued by the mediation of the mitogenic action of insulin. In what may only be a semantic difference, we tend to think of two types of insulin receptor rather than an insulin and a growth factor receptor. The question I have is, what evidence is there for physical separation or nonseparation of receptors for the two types of binding activity.

C. R. Kahn: Because the time was limited I did not review for you the direct binding studies using insulin growth factors. There are a variety of kinds of data which suggest that the cells that we are studying have at least two kinds of receptors. Direct binding studies using varieties of the insulin-like growth factors have shown a specific high-affinity receptor for one or more of these substances. By the radiation inactivation technique one finds a different size for the insulin-like growth factor receptor than for the insulin receptor. The receptors also differ in ionic strength and pH dependence, and as I showed you, very markedly in terms of reactivity toward anti-receptor antibody. So that at least by these functional criteria, the receptors are indeed separate. There may be some interactions between these receptors under some circumstances because in some cells binding of insulin receptor appears to effect binding of the insulin-like growth factors to their receptors. In terms of the physical structure of the receptor, however, they appear to be independent. The last point I should make is in some immunoprecipitation experiments done by Len Harrison, which are probably the most clear-cut of all, he found that one could quantitatively immunoprecipitate the insulin receptor of the human placenta without appreciably depleting the receptors from the insulin-like growth factors.

Polypeptide Hormones: Intracellular Receptors and Internalization

BARRY I. POSNER, JOHN J. M. BERGERON,* ZEEV JOSEFSBERG, MASOOD N. KHAN, RAHAT J. KHAN, BARBARA A. PATEL, ROY A. SIKSTROM,* AND ANIL K. VERMA

*Departments of Medicine and *Anatomy, McGill University and the Royal Victoria Hospital, Montreal, Canada*

I. Introduction

The notion that chemicals act on living cells via "receptive substances" was first articulated in the early 1900s most notably by J. N. Langley and P. Ehrlich. The receptor concept became firmly rooted in pharmacology and was elaborated in studies of adrenergic and cholinergic agents and their antagonists. The concept was readily extended to the realm of polypeptide hormone action well before the direct study of polypeptide hormone receptors began around 1970 (Lefkowitz *et al.*, 1970; Goodfriend and Lin, 1970). This latter advance was made possible by the availability of highly purified polypeptide hormones, the development of methods for radioiodinating hormone to high specific activity, while retaining biological activity, and the application of the principle of competition between labeled and unlabeled ligands for specific binding sites, as formulated by Berson and Yalow (1959).

In the past 10 years the direct study of hormone–receptor interactions has led to considerable new knowledge and great refinements in thinking about the mechanisms of hormone action. Receptors for almost every polypeptide hormone have been characterized and shown to have high affinity for the hormone in question and an exquisite specificity which generally parallels the biological activity of the hormone and its analogs (Roth, 1973; Posner, 1975). It has been shown that tissue receptors levels undergo marked modulation in specific physiologic and pathologic states, and that the regulation of receptors constitutes an important mechanism for adjusting target cell sensitivity to hormones (Catt *et al.,* 1979). It has become clear that the binding of hormone to its receptor and the activation of the tissue response are two distinct steps which can be dissociated from one another, and that many hormonal responses are maximally

ISBN 0-12-571137-9

stimulated when only a fraction of the available binding sites are occupied (Kono and Barham, 1971).

Before the era of the direct study of polypeptide hormone receptors a hormone's target tissues were defined as those in which a hormonal response was demonstrable. The limitation of this definition is that it presupposes a knowledge of the particular biological parameters influenced by a hormone. The failure to see a hormonal effect on a particular biological parameter in a tissue simply means the tissue is unresponsive in respect to the function measured but may be responsive in some other untested fashion. It was appreciated rather early that a more general approach to defining hormone target tissues would be to identify those tissues bearing receptors for the hormone (Posner, 1974). Since the presence of receptors is a necessary but not sufficient condition for evoking a hormonal response tissues containing receptors should be regarded as potential target tissues until a specific response to hormone has been either identified or definitively excluded. There are now an increasing number of examples where the identification of tissue receptors preceded an appreciation of the tissue's sensitivity to hormone (e.g., Posner *et al.*, 1974a,b). Furthermore the use of *in vivo* autoradiography for identifying polypeptide hormone receptors in the intact animal has led to an augmented appreciation of how widespread is the distribution of receptors for a number of these hormones (Bergeron and Posner, 1979).

In recent years we have been especially preoccupied with the distribution of receptors within the cell. The same guiding principle (i.e., cell organelles bearing receptors are potential target sites of hormone action) has informed our thinking in this domain, but has been substantially modified by considerations of cell dynamics whereby receptor distribution could reflect aspects of protein catabolism or biosynthesis rather than simply anchored sites at which hormone action is effected. It is our purpose in the present communication to review predominantly our work in respect to the cellular distribution of receptors, the dynamics of their distribution, and the implications of these processes for our understanding of hormone action.

II. Intracellular Receptors for Peptide Hormones

Early studies of peptide hormone binding sites stressed the cell surface location of receptors (Cuatrecasas, 1969, 1974). This conformed to the view of peptide hormone action as being initiated and fulfilled at the cell surface by the stimulation of membrane-associated enzyme(s) (e.g., adenylate cyclase) with the production of second messenger(s) (e.g., cyclic AMP) which produced the intracellular changes characteristic of hormone action (Sutherland *et al.*, 1968). There were observations of peptide hormone binding sites in other subcellular fractions besides plasmalemma. Thus ^{125}I-labeled insulin binding was observed in endoplasmic reticulum (Horvat *et al.*, 1975), Golgi (Bergeron *et al.*, 1973b), and nuclei (Goldfine and Smith, 1976). A fundamental question was to what extent did the observed binding reflect contamination of these subcellular fractions by plasmalemma known to be highly enriched in insulin receptors. At approximately this time I had observed a high concentration of prolactin binding sites in total hepatic microsomes from very hyperprolactinemic rats (Posner, 1976). Since the prevailing circulating prolactin level should have saturated all plasmalemma receptors it seemed likely that the hepatic lactogen receptor sites were sequestered, perhaps intracellularly. In early 1975 John Bergeron and I set out to determine if the insulin binding sites previously described in Golgi fractions (Bergeron *et al.*, 1973b) resided on bona fide Golgi elements. Our preliminary studies quickly encompassed [^{125}I]hGH which showed highly preferential binding to Golgi versus plasmalemma subcellular fractions. Coupled with the development of a method for morphologically evaluating the specific binding of ^{125}I-labeled hormone by electron microscope autoradiography we soon had preliminary data of ^{125}I-labeled peptide hormone binding to true Golgi structures (Posner and Bergeron, 1975; Bergeron and Posner, 1975).

A. PEPTIDE HORMONE RECEPTORS IN GOLGI ELEMENTS

The conclusion that peptide hormone receptors exist on true Golgi elements and not on contaminating plasmalemma was based upon: (1) the pattern of peptide hormone binding to hepatic subcellular fractions (Table I), (2) the direct visualization of the sites of hormone–receptor interaction by electron microscope autoradiography (Fig. 1), and (3) the demonstration that binding was augmented by freeze-thawing Golgi but not plasmalemma fractions (Table II).

Although Golgi fractions showed less insulin binding than plasmalemma it seemed unlikely that the insulin binding sites of Golgi were due to plasmalemma contamination. The level of 5′-AMPase activity (a plasmalemma marker enzyme) in Golgi, if entirely reflecting plasmalemma, could not account for the level of binding sites observed (Bergeron *et al.*, 1978b). Furthermore Golgi levels of 5′-AMPase did not accurately reflect plasmalemma contamination since histochemical analyses of 5′-AMPase in Golgi fractions indicated that a substantial portion of the enzyme activity was intrinsic to bona fide Golgi structures (Farquhar *et al.*, 1974). The striking observation that hGH binding [largely to lactogen-specific sites (Posner *et al.*, 1979b)] was much greater in Golgi than plasmalemma ren-

TABLE I

Pattern of Specific Binding of Different Peptide Hormones to Subcellular Fractions from Rodent Liver[a]

	Insulin[b]	Lactogen[b]	Somatogen[c]	ILAs[d]
Homogenate	0.1	0.2	0.4	n.p.[f]
Plasmalemma	1.0	1.0	1.0	1.0
Total microsomes	0.3	1.0	0.8	7.7
Golgi vesicles[e]	0.4	5.8	7.6	42.6
Golgi heavy	0.3	2.5	1.2	13.4
Smooth microsomes	0.2	0.3	1.0	3.0
Rough microsomes	0.2	0.3	0.3	0.0

[a] The specific binding of each peptide hormone is expressed relative to that of plasmalemma.

[b] From Bergeron *et al.* (1978b).

[c] From Verma and Posner (1979).

[d] ILAs refers to an insulin-like growth factor (IGF) isolated from human plasma by Posner *et al.* (1978). From Posner *et al.* (1980b).

[e] Golgi vesicles refers to the combined Golgi light and intermediate fractions.

[f] n.p., not performed.

dered it very unlikely that plasmalemma contamination was responsible. More recent studies on the distribution of ILAs (an insulin-like growth factor) receptors in rat liver subcellular fractions and on somatogenic receptor distribution in pregnant mouse liver subcellular fractions indicated a striking concentration of receptor in Golgi fractions as compared to plasmalemma (Table I). Similar direct binding studies have shown a 3-fold higher concentration of lectin (Young *et al.*, 1976) and asialoglycoprotein receptors (Pricer and Ashwell, 1976) in rat liver Golgi compared to

TABLE II

Activation of Hormone Binding to Golgi Fractions by Freeze-Thawing[a]

	Golgi light	Golgi intermediate	Plasmalemma
Insulin[b]	2.3	2.5	0.9
hGH[b]	2.0	3.5	n.d.[d]
bGH[c]	3.1	3.2	1.3

[a] Specific binding in subcellular fractions frozen and thawed four times is expressed as a ratio of that in freshly prepared fractions.

[b] From Bergeron *et al.* (1978b).

[c] From Verma and Posner (1979).

[d] n.d., no detectable binding under conditions used.

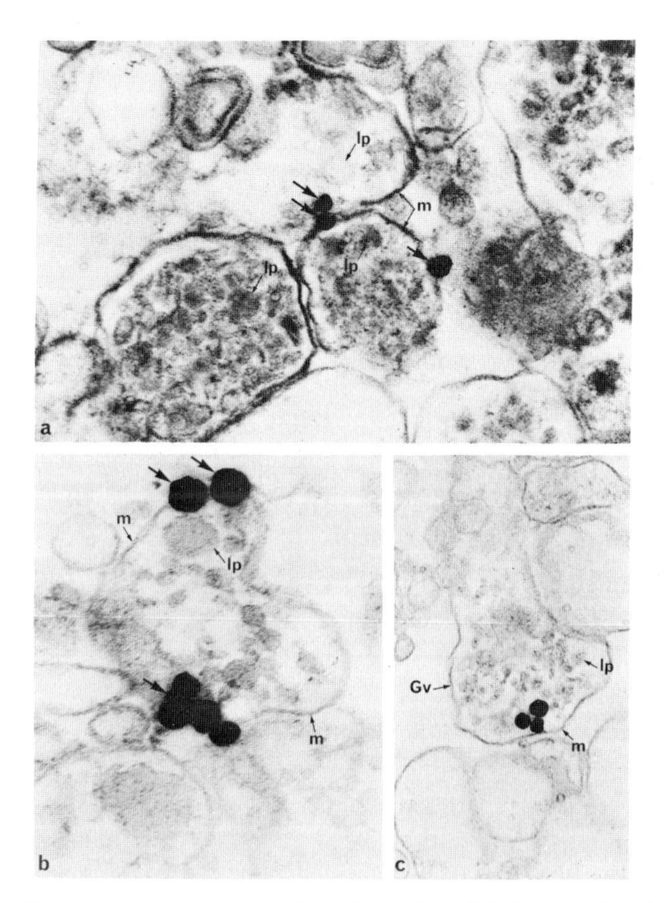

FIG. 1. Electron microscope autoradiography of Golgi light fraction fixed immediately after a direct binding incubation with [^{125}I]hGH. The autoradiographic silver grains (indicated by arrows) are directly over the membrane (m) of Golgi vesicles (Gv) as identified by the characteristic secretory content of very low density lipoprotein particles (lp). Magnification ×60,000. From Bergeron *et al.* (1978b).

plasmalemma. Thus, for a number of ligands the Golgi complex is a region of receptor enrichment greatly exceeding that of plasmalemma. When it is considered further that a substantial contribution to the protein concentration of the Golgi fractions from rat liver is the VLDL protein content of the vesicles it can be seen that receptor enrichment on Golgi membranes is very great indeed (perhaps 10 times greater than the values relative to plasmalemma noted in Table I).

The most convincing data for the identification of receptor sites on true Golgi elements have come from our electron microscope autoradiography studies (Bergeron *et al.*, 1978b). In these studies we were able to visualize directly the hormone–receptor interaction on morphologically defined Golgi vesicles (Fig. 1). Indeed, quantitative analysis of autoradiographic grain distribution showed a striking association of the grains (about 70%) with the membrane of Golgi vesicles (Bergeron *et al.*, 1978b). Furthermore, hormone binding to Golgi fractions but not to plasmalemma was activated by repetitive freezing and thawing (Table II), a process demonstrated to disrupt the Golgi vesicles thus exposing the cisternal surface. This observation suggested to us that the receptors were on the inner aspect of the Golgi vesicles.

Golgi receptors have probably been identified for acetylcholine in cultured chick skeletal muscle cells (Fambrough and Devreotes, 1978), and for both gonadotropins and prostaglandins in bovine corpora lutea (Mitra and Rao, 1978). In this latter study the Golgi but not plasmalemma sites were latent and binding was activated by treatment with alamethacin a channel-forming agent. Specific binding sites were 2–3 times greater in Golgi than plasmalemma, again indicating receptor enrichment in this cellular organelle.

B. PROPERTIES OF GOLGI RECEPTORS

In all cases in which a detailed comparison has been made the binding sites in the Golgi fractions were very similar to those of the plasmalemma (Posner *et al.*, 1978, 1979b). The rates of binding and dissociation were temperature dependent. Binding followed the law of mass action and was, within limits, proportional to both cell fraction protein and hormone concentration. Binding to Golgi and plasmalemma showed similar pH optima. Bound ^{125}I-labeled hormone could be eluted from cell fractions and was found to retain full integrity. The specificity of binding in Golgi and plasmalemma was identical for ^{125}I-labeled insulin and [^{125}I]hGH in female rat liver, and [^{125}I]bGH in pregnant mouse liver fractions. An example of such an analysis is noted in Fig. 2 in which the specificity of the rat liver lactogen receptor was assessed. The inhibitory effect of different lactogens on [^{125}I]hGH binding is the same in both Golgi and plasmalemma. The pattern of inhibition of [^{125}I]oPRL to Golgi is the same as with [^{125}I]hGH further emphasizing the lactogenic character of the receptor under study. By studying binding at 4°C, to minimize degradation, one can analyze the binding quantitatively and determine the concentration and affinity of the sites. Scatchard analyses employed for these estimates revealed that the lactogen and somatogen sites were of one class on both Golgi and plasmalemma. Insulin binding data on both Golgi and plasmalemma fractions gave rise to comparable nonlinear Scatchard plots

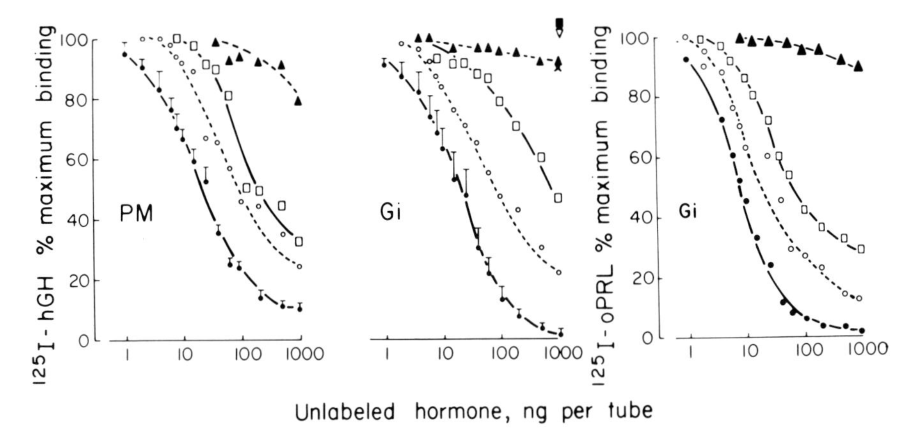

FIG. 2. Specificity of binding of [^{125}I]hGH and [^{125}I]oPRL to Golgi intermediate (Gi) and plasmalemma (PM) subcellular fractions. The peptides studied were hGH (●), oPRL (○), rPRL (□), bGH (▲), glucagon (■), insulin (▽), and ACTH (×). Incubation was for 24 hours at 4°C with 50 μg of cell fraction protein per tube. For details see Posner *et al.* (1979b).

which were interpreted as reflecting comparable degrees of heterogeneity and/or negative cooperativity in Golgi and plasmalemma (Posner *et al.*, 1978).

More recently we have examined the effect of an insulin receptor antibody (Baldwin *et al.*, 1980) on ^{125}I-labeled insulin binding to Golgi and plasmalemma (Patel *et al.*, 1980). Figure 3 illustrates that the antibody produced comparable inhibition of ^{125}I-labeled insulin binding to both Golgi and plasmalemma. This argues for a marked degree of antigenic similarity of the surface-located and intracellular receptors. Further evidence of their similarity is provided by recent studies of C. Yip and colleagues at the University of Toronto in which the insulin receptor in highly purified Golgi fractions and plasmalemma was photoaffinity labeled and analyzed by autoradiography after SDS–gel electrophoresis (Yip *et al.*, 1980). As seen in Fig. 4 the main photolabeled bands in plasmalemma (130K and 90K) are the same as those in the three Golgi fractions. In all fractions the photolabeling was blocked by excess unlabeled insulin indicating the specificity of the interaction.

All the above observations point to a marked similarity between the Golgi and plasma membrane receptors. This similarity includes binding properties, antigenicity, and apparent molecular size. An interesting difference between the two receptor populations is depicted in Fig. 5. When subcellular fractions were preincubated at 30°C to evaluate receptor stability we observed a more rapid decrease in the binding capacity of plasmalemma than Golgi for insulin and hGH. The Golgi insulin receptor was

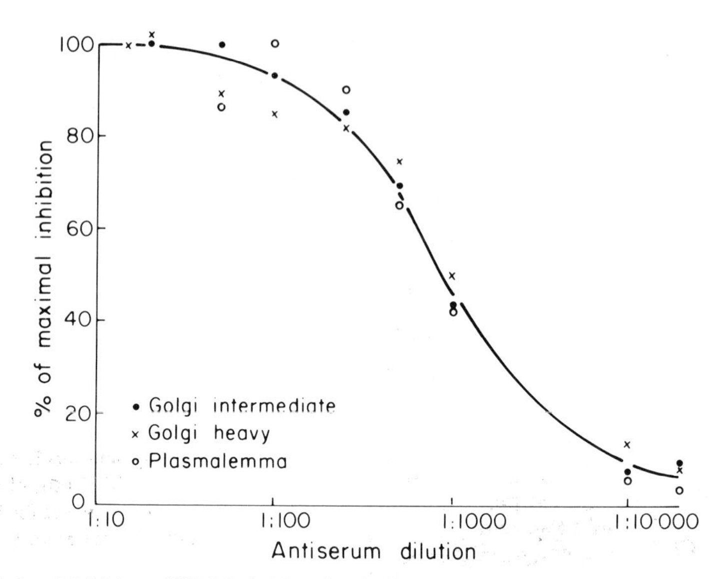

FIG. 3. Inhibition of ^{125}I-labeled insulin binding to subcellular fractions as a function of insulin antireceptor serum concentration. Subcellular fractions were incubated for 22 hours at 4°C with the various dilutions of antiserum. After rinsing with buffer at 4°C the membranes were incubated with ^{125}I-labeled insulin for 48 hours in the presence and absence of excess unlabeled insulin (50 μg) to determine specific binding. Maximum inhibition of binding at antiserum dilution of 1 : 10 was: Golgi intermediate, 54.6%; Golgi heavy, 49.2%; and plasmalemma, 56.6%. Data were normalized to maximum inhibition of 100% to facilitate comparison. From B. I. Posner, B. A. Patel, D. Baldwin, and D. P. Steiner (unpublished).

remarkably stable. If the Golgi fractions consisted, to a significant extent, of lysosome-like elements, one would have expected to see reduced not greater receptor stability than that observed in plasmalemma.

C. RECEPTORS IN OTHER INTRACELLULAR COMPARTMENTS

The observation of insulin binding to nuclei from rat liver has been controversial. The initial study demonstrated binding to Triton-treated nuclei (Goldfine and Smith, 1976). Since this procedure appears to strip away the nuclear membrane (Bergeron *et al.*, 1978b) (nuclear integrity is presumably maintained by fibrous laminae) it is difficult to visualize where the receptor might be located. Furthermore Triton treatment does not rule out plasmalemma contamination. This could still occur via actual transfer of solubilized insulin receptors to the fibrous laminae of the nuclei (Bergeron *et al.*, 1978b). More recently several investigators have reported insulin binding to nuclei isolated without Triton treatment from rat (Vigneri *et al.*, 1978) and mouse (Goidl, 1979) liver. Insulin binding to nuclear mem-

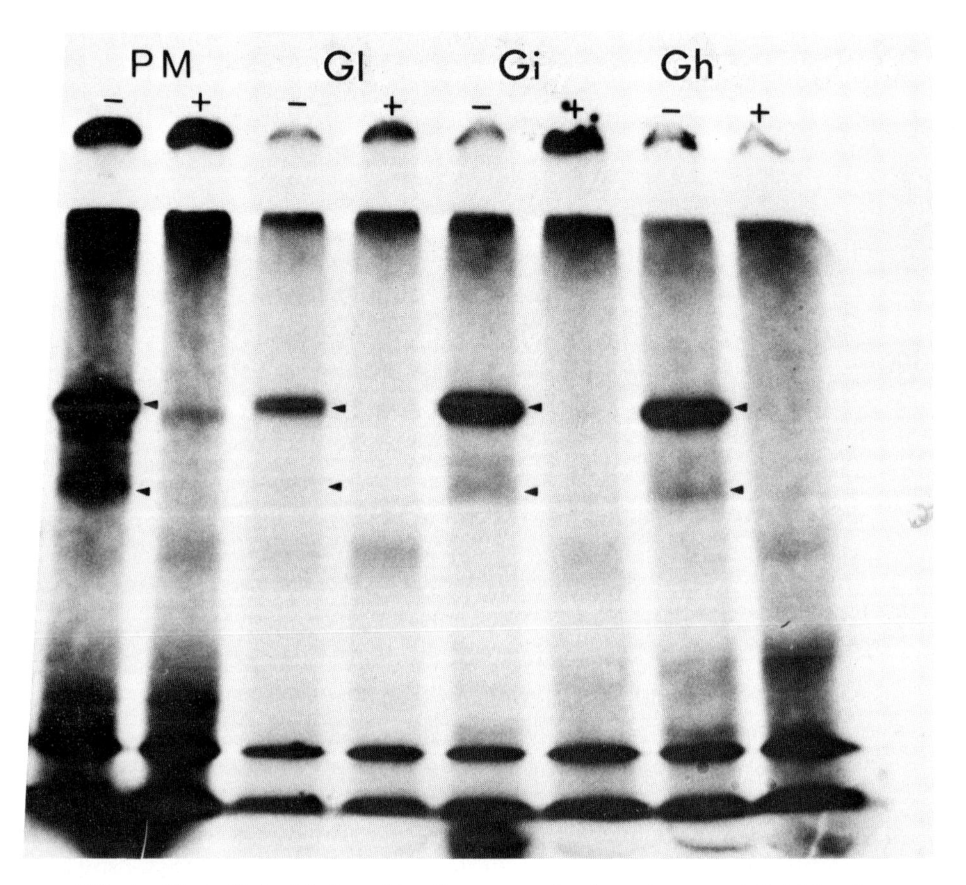

FIG. 4. Photoaffinity labeling of insulin receptor in plasmalemma and Golgi fractions. Radioiodinated $N^{\epsilon B29}$-monoazidobenzoyl insulin was incubated with the various membrane fractions and then photolyzed and analyzed by autoradiography after electrophoresis in SDS–polyacrylamide slab gels as previously described (Yip *et al.*, 1980). The amount of protein used was respectively: plasma membrane (PM), 350 μg; Golgi light (Gl), 190 μg; Golgi intermediate (Gi), 470 μg; Golgi heavy (Gh), 560 μg. The arrows point to the M_r 130K and 90K bands, respectively, which were specifically labeled by the photoreactive insulin. The photolabeling of these two bands was abolished by excess unlabeled insulin (+).

branes was much lower than to plasmalemma (Vigneri *et al.*, 1978b), was not inhibited by antibody to plasmalemma receptors (Goldfine *et al.*, 1977), and appeared to have different properties from those of plasmalemma (e.g., different affinity profiles, pH optima, and responses to 2 *M* NaCl) (Vigneri *et al.*, 1978b). Using an immunofluorescent technique Horvat (1978) showed binding of insulin to intact nuclei. We have examined ^{125}I-labeled hormone binding to rat liver nuclei prepared in various

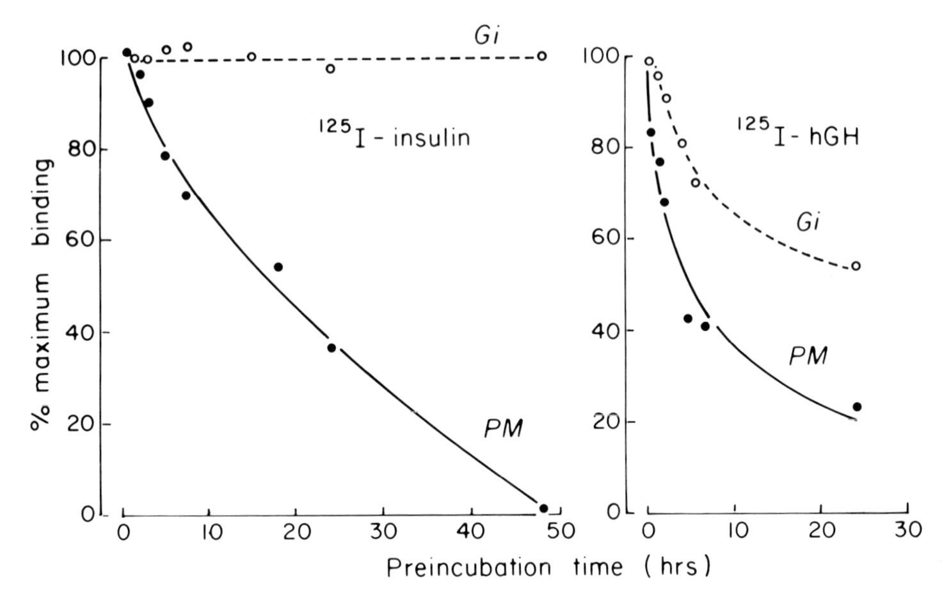

FIG. 5. Loss of binding activity following incubation of subcellular fractions at 30°C. At each time point ^{125}I-labeled hormone in the presence and absence of excess unlabeled hormone was added to the incubation and specific binding was determined after further incubation at 4°C for 48 hours (insulin) or 24 hours (hGH). The data on Golgi intermediate (Gi) and plasmalemma (PM) fractions are depicted but Golgi light and heavy fractions behaved similar to Gi. For details see Posner *et al.* (1978, 1979b).

ways and have not been impressed by the low level of binding seen (Table III). Furthermore we have employed *in vitro* autoradiography to visualize direct binding of ^{125}I-labeled insulin to subcellular fractions (Sikstrom *et al.*, 1980). Whereas we were successful in visualizing specific binding to Golgi and plasmalemma we could not detect ^{125}I-labeled insulin binding to nuclei. We thus suggest that the existence of insulin receptors in nuclei remains unsettled probably because current methods for detection are insufficiently sensitive to give unambiguous results. The same problem in respect to Triton treatment of nuclei (vide supra) could apply to the observation that nuclei from chick dorsal root neurons contain NGF binding sites (Andres *et al.*, 1977).

Recently we have looked for receptors in other vacuolar components of the cell. Table IV summarizes studies made upon Golgi fractions and lysosomes. As noted before (Bergeron *et al.*, 1973a) the Golgi fractions are highly enriched in galactosyltransferase (GT) and only slightly enriched in acid phosphatase (AP). In contrast the lysosomal elements are very enriched in AP and contain low levels of GT. The high level of [^{125}I]hGH and ^{125}I-labeled insulin binding seen in the lysosomal elements cannot be ac-

TABLE III

Binding of ^{125}I-Labeled Insulin and [^{125}I]hGH to Isolated Liver Nuclei and Control Membrane Preparations[a]

Preparation	Protein (mg/ml)	Specific binding insulin (%)	Specific binding hGH (%)
Nuclei, Method A	1.06	0.0	1.0
Nuclei, Method B	0.90	0.8	0.2
Nuclei, Method C	0.80	0.6	0.0
Pregnant rabbit liver (microsomes)	0.30		17.8
Human placenta (microsomes)	0.22	16.2	

[a] Nuclei (Method A) were prepared by the procedure of Blobel and Potter (1966). Some aliquots were treated with 1% Triton X-100 (Method B), and others with 0.5% Triton X-100 (Method C) before assaying for binding. For details see Bergeron *et al.* (1978b).

counted for by GT-containing structures since the ratio of specific binding to GT (C/B and D/B) is much greater than in Golgi. Though this observation supports the notion that peptide hormone receptors are in lysosomal elements two points indicate that the situation is somewhat more complex. First, the binding observed in tritosomes can be largely accounted for by Golgi contamination. Second, the lysosomal subfraction which had the highest hGH and insulin binding was not the one showing the highest concentration of acid phosphatase. This lack of conformity between the distribution of enzyme activity and hormone binding raises the possibility that there are other structures besides galactosyltransferase (Golgi) and acid phosphatase (lysosomes) enriched vesicles which are enriched in receptor content.

III. The Origin and Significance of Intracellular Receptors

The origin of the intracellular receptors is not clear. Several possibilities merit consideration: (1) they may be *precursors* synthesized within the cell on their way via the Golgi apparatus to the plasmalemma, or (2) they could represent receptor internalized to the vacuolar system of the cell subsequent to the formation of hormone–receptor complexes at the cell surface. It is emphasized that the existence of the intracellular vacuolar pool may be a consequence of both internalization on the one hand and

TABLE IV

Enzyme Activity and Binding of [^{125}I]hGH and ^{125}I-Labeled Insulin in Golgi and Lysosomal Fractions from Female Rat Liver[a]

Cell fraction	Relative specific activity		Percentage specific binding			
	Acid phosphatase (A)	Galactosyl-transferase (B)	hGH (C)	Insulin (D)	C/B	D/B
Golgi[b]						
Light	2.9 ± 0.3	37.3 ± 1.8	44.9 ± 3.5	8.9 ± 1.2	1.3 ± 0.1	0.2 ± 0.0
Intermediate	4.0 ± 0.1	33.4 ± 1.5	42.5 ± 3.9	10.7 ± 0.7	1.3 ± 0.1	0.3 ± 0.0
Heavy	2.1 ± 0.1	17.7 ± 1.4	8.8 ± 1.3	4.6 ± 0.6	0.6 ± 0.1	0.3 ± 0.0
Lysosomes[c]						
Total L fraction	5.7 ± 1.2	0.4 ± 0.2	4.1 ± 2.8	6.3 ± 3.4		
Subfractions						
L1	12.2 ± 1.2	2.0 ± 0.2	38.8 ± 7.6	23.4 ± 3.0	20.3 ± 6.0	11.2 ± 0.1
L2	24.1 ± 2.8	0.7 ± 0.2	16.7 ± 5.5	13.9 ± 1.5	27.2 ± 9.6	22.8 ± 0.5
L3	18.3 ± 2.0	0.7 ± 0.2	10.9 ± 2.5	17.1 ± 3.6	17.0 ± 4.8	29.7 ± 12.5
L4	3.8 ± 1.0	0.3 ± 0.1	3.4 ± 1.1	3.5 ± 1.3	18.0 ± 4.6	16.7 ± 4.4
Tritosomes	38.1 ± 2.7	7.5 ± 1.8	15.1 ± 2.0	2.9 ± 0.5	2.6 ± 0.5	0.5 ± 0.2

[a] Golgi fractions were prepared as described by Ehrenreich *et al.* (1973). Lysosomes were purified by the procedure of Wattiaux *et al.* (1978). Tritosomes were as described by Dean (1977). Acid phosphatase was assayed using β-glycerophosphate as substrate (Barrett and Heath, 1977). Galactosyltransferase was assayed by the method of Bretz and Staubli (1977).

[b] Mean ± SE of 6 fractionations.

[c] Mean ± SE of 3 fractionations.

biosynthesis on the other with the magnitude of the contribution for each process varying with circumstances. The possible role(s) of the intracellular receptors would include the following: (1) the biosynthetic precursors for those of the plasmalemma, (2) enroute to degrading sites for hormone and receptor with recycling of a portion of the latter to the plasmalemma, and (3) sites of intracellular hormone action(s).

A. PRECURSOR FOR THE PLASMALEMMA

It has been well established that secretory proteins, after being synthesized on the rough endoplasmic reticulum, pass through the Golgi complex to the plasmalemma where they are secreted via the process of exocytosis (Palade, 1975). This sequence has been worked out in particular detail in the exocrine pancreas but may apply to the hepatocyte as well (Bergeron *et al.*, 1978a). It has been suggested that membrane proteins, in general, and peptide hormone receptors, in particular, follow the same intracellular route (Bergeron *et al.*, 1973b; Palade, 1975). Thus receptors synthesized on the rough endoplasmic reticulum would be transferred to and concentrated within the Golgi apparatus and pass via secretory vesicles to the plasmalemma. We have tested this hypothesis by examining the sequence of events during the induction of the rat hepatic lactogen receptor (Posner *et al.*, 1979b). Earlier work had shown that this receptor was present at high concentration in female rat liver and at low concentration in male rat liver (Posner *et al.*, 1974a). Furthermore, the receptor was readily induced in male animals by estrogen administration (Posner *et al.*, 1974b). When the time course of receptor appearance subsequent to induction was studied in Golgi fractions and plasmalemma a clear sequence was observed. Receptors rapidly increased (by 12 hours) in Golgi vesicles and attained high levels before a significant increase was noted in plasmalemma (3 days) (Fig. 6). Though this sequence is compatible with a precursor–product relationship it is fully possible that it reflects the changes in receptor level in two independent cellular compartments. Studies of acetylcholine receptor synthesis suggest that a substantial part of the intracellular receptor pool remains sequestrated within the cell and does not readily exchange with the plasmalemma compartment (Gardner and Fambrough, 1979). It is also difficult to see why a receptor with a half life of several hours (Kelly *et al.*, 1975) should require several days to exit from Golgi to plasmalemma. Assuming the validity of the precursor–product hypothesis this latter finding would imply that translocation from the intracellular to plasmalemma compartment is not regulated by simple thermodynamic considerations alone.

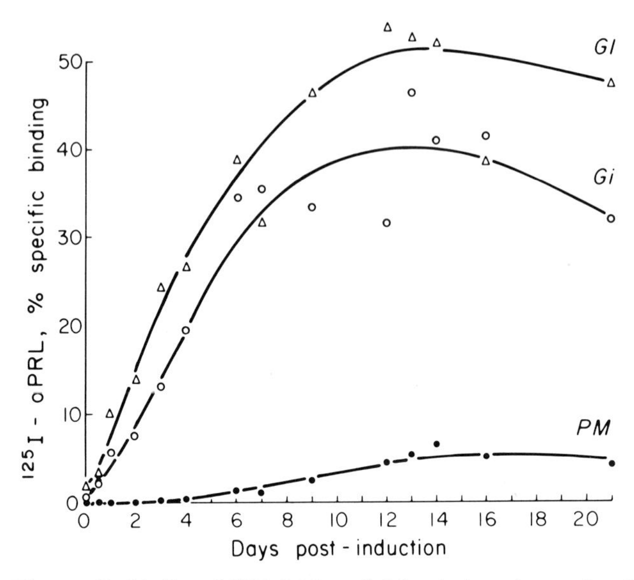

FIG. 6. The specific binding of [^{125}I]oPRL to Golgi and plasmalemma fractions of male rat liver at different times after prolactin receptor induction by estrogen. Each male rat received a single subcutaneous injection of 1.0 mg estradiol valerate at time zero. At each time thereafter 7 to 15 animals were killed and Golgi light (Gl), Golgi intermediate (Gi), and plasmalemma (PM) fractions were simultaneously prepared from the pooled livers. Specific binding was determined as described elsewhere (Posner *et al.*, 1979b).

B. RECEPTOR REGULATION

With the above considerations in mind we have examined insulin binding in Golgi fractions and plasmalemma from the liver of obese, hyperglycemic, insulin-resistant mice (Posner *et al.*, 1978a). Two different genetically obese mouse strains (ob/ob and db/db) were studied. In preliminary studies it was shown that all 3 Golgi fractions (i.e., Golgi light, intermediate, and heavy) showed saturable insulin binding sites with specificities identical to that of plasmalemma. Insulin binding to subcellular fractions from lean versus obese littermate mice was compared (Table V). The level of insulin binding to plasmalemma was greatly reduced in the hyperinsulinemic obese mice as previously established (Kahn *et al.*, 1973). There was less of a reduction in insulin binding to Golgi vesicles from obese mice versus lean animals. In contrast, binding to Golgi heavy elements was the same (ob/ob) or higher (db/db) in obese compared to lean littermates. These differences reflected changes in receptor number not difference in affinity and were the same when expressed in terms of

TABLE V
Percentage Specific Binding of ^{125}I-Labeled Insulin to Subcellular Fractions from Livers of Obese and Lean Mice[a]

	ob/ob		db/db	
Cell fraction	Obese	Lean	Obese	Lean
Plasmalemma	1.5 ± 0.2[b]	7.2 ± 0.4	1.3 ± 0.3[b]	9.5 ± 0.1
Golgi vesicles	5.7 ± 1.1[b]	14.7 ± 1.6	3.2 ± 0.7[b]	11.9 ± 2.3
Golgi heavy	18.6 ± 2.8	18.3 ± 0.7	23.8 ± 2.8[c]	19.7 ± 2.5
Insulin (ng/ml)	20.9 ± 6.6	0.9 ± 0.1	14.6 ± 7.3	1.5 ± 0.5

[a] All values are mean ± SE of 3 different experiments in each of which 9 to 12 animals of each type were used. Golgi vesicles consisted of Gl and Gi combined. Insulin values are mean ± SE of determinations on pooled sera from each experiment.
[b] $p < 0.01$ by t test for paired data.
[c] $p < 0.025$ by t test for paired data. From Posner *et al.* (1978a).

galactosyltransferase (Posner *et al.*, 1979a). As with the data of Fig. 6 these observations indicate that the intracellular receptor concentration (at least in particular pools) is regulated differently from that of the plasmalemma. This is in contrast to observations showing a parallel change of insulin binding to putative nuclear and plasma membranes (Vigneri *et al.*, 1978a).

There are two major possibilities to consider in interpreting these data. Which is correct hinges on the nature of the Golgi heavy fraction. This fraction contains both small vesicles of uncertain origin as well as VLDL-filled vesicles and flattened saccular elements. We have suggested that the small vesicles might be endocytotic in nature (Josefsberg *et al.*, 1979). The maintenance or augmentation of insulin receptors in the Golgi heavy fraction from hyperinsulinemic obese mice could be due to the accumulation of internalized surface receptors in endocytotic vesicles—a process perhaps augmented by the hyperinsulinemia. In support of this is the rapid internalization of ^{125}I-labeled insulin and prolactin into the Golgi heavy fraction (vide infra). Alternatively the receptors may lie on true cisternal elements and thus be more intimately associated with the sites of biosynthesis than those receptors on the plasmalemma. To explain how Golgi cisternal receptor concentration remains unchanged or increased in the face of a marked reduction of plasmalemma receptors we have suggested a bimodal influence of ligand on its own receptor (Posner *et al.*, 1978a). In our proposal the binding of hormone to its receptor evokes two distinct though perhaps related changes: (a) an acceleration of receptor loss from the cell surface, probably by ligand-induced internalization, and (b) an increased production of new receptors intracellularly (Fig. 7). The net effect of such interactions could be an increase or decrease of tissue receptor levels depending upon whether receptor production or loss was more markedly affected. This could vary with hormone target tissue and other physiologic modulators. The virtue of the hypothesis is that it provides a general explanation for polypeptide hormone receptor regulation. In particular it explains the inductive effect of prolactin (Posner *et al.*, 1975; Manni *et al.*, 1978) and the down-regulating effect of insulin (Gavin *et al.*, 1974; Blackard *et al.*, 1978) on their respective hepatic receptor levels within one framework where only kinetic differences in the two opposing processes determine the final result.

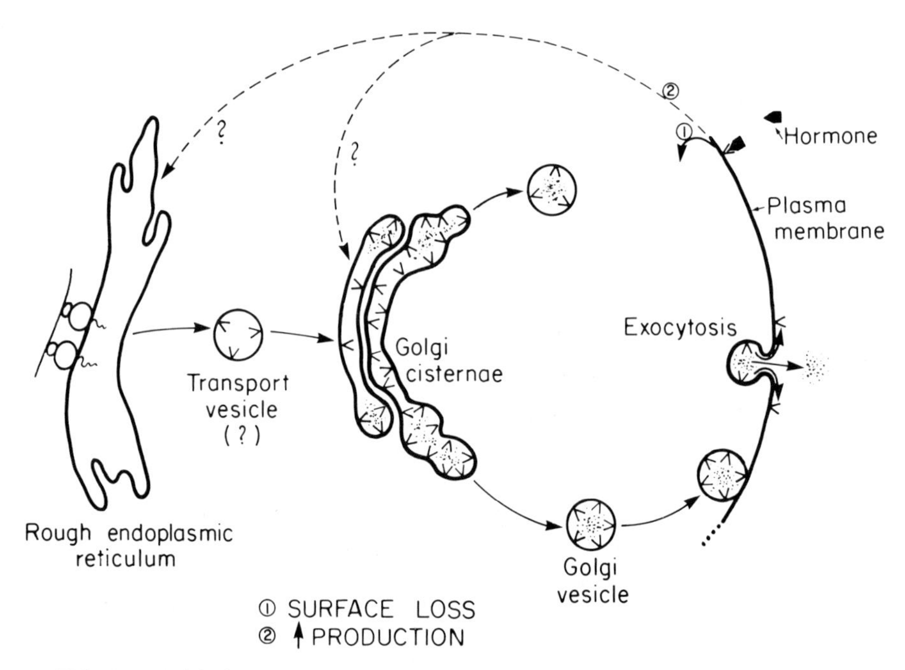

FIG. 7. Model of receptor regulation by hormone. The formation of hormone–receptor complex at the plasma membrane leads to internalization with the loss of receptors (1). It also is postulated to lead to the increased production of new receptors (2) which are synthesized on the RER, concentrated in the Golgi, and transferred via Golgi vesicles and exocytosis to the plasma membrane.

IV. Internalization of Polypeptide Hormones

Until recently studies of the interaction of peptide hormones with their target tissues have focused on hormone–receptor complex formation at the cell surface. A number of earlier observations have suggested however that peptide hormones may enter cells. Thus, Lee and Williams (1954) administered ^{131}I-labeled insulin to living rats and observed an association of radiolabel with various subcellular fractions of rat liver. It was later shown that intravenously administered [^{3}H]ACTH was taken up into a number of subcellular fractions of rat adrenal (Muller and Scriba, 1969), and that [^{3}H]acetyl-hGH was concentrated in a variety of subcellular fractions (especially mitochondrial) of hypox rat liver (Maddaiah *et al.*, 1970). The distribution of [^{131}I]bGH administered *in vivo* was examined in subcellular fractions and by autoradiography in rat liver and kidney, and a preferential association of label with mitochondria was found (Groves *et al.*, 1972). These studies were not definitive due to uncertainty about plasmalemma contamination of subcellular fractions, the quality of labeled hormone as a ligand, or the failure to evaluate the specificity of uptake.

Somewhat more convincing perhaps were the observations that [^{125}I]NGF was taken up, by a NGF-specific process, in synaptic terminals of autonomic neurons, and concentrated in the cell bodies after retrograde axonal transport (Hendry *et al.*, 1974; Stockel *et al.*, 1974). In studies of [^{125}I]EGF binding to cultured human fibroblasts it was shown that bound hormone, by means of a temperature-dependent energy-requiring process, became progressively less available for interaction with specific antibody and for digestion by trypsin (Carpenter and Cohen, 1976). Similar observations were made more recently on the interaction of ^{125}I-labeled insulin with rat adipocytes (Kahn and Baird, 1978). Both sets of observations are compatible with internalization. An even more compelling observation was the demonstration by fluorescence microscopy and autoradiography of specific uptake of [^{125}I]PTH and [^{3}H]PTH into renal proximal tubular cytoplasm (Nordquist and Palmieri, 1974). This study was limited by the lack of quantitative analysis of the morphologic findings and uncertainty about the integrity of the apparently internalized radiolabel. Using an immunohistochemical approach Nolin and Witorsch (1976) suggested that endogenous prolactin could be identified in rat mammary epithelial cells.

Recently the employment of more sophisticated morphological approaches and refined subcellular fractionation procedures has led to an unambiguous proof that internalization of peptide hormones is a rapid, quantitatively significant process. Our preliminary data, obtained by a combination of quantitative autoradiography and subcellular fractionation, demonstrated a receptor-mediated uptake and concentration of intact hormone into vesicular structures, primarily Golgi, of the rat hepatocyte (Posner *et al.*, 1977; Bergeron *et al.*, 1977b).

A. *IN VIVO* AUTORADIOGRAPHIC STUDIES

Autoradiography has been developed into a powerful tool for studying the relationship between cell function and structure (Leblond, 1965). In recent years it has been employed to localize receptors for peptide hormones *in vivo* (de Kretser *et al.*, 1969; Mayberry *et al.*, 1971; Rajaniemi and Vanha-Perttula, 1972; Birkinshaw and Falconer, 1972; Nordquist and Palmieri, 1974). These early qualitative studies demonstrated the feasibility of applying this technique to the study of hormone receptors. In parallel with Orth and Christensen (1977) we have developed an *in vivo* autoradiographic approach to evaluate quantitatively receptor distribution in various tissues (Bergeron *et al.*, 1977a; Bergeron and Posner, 1979). In our procedure ^{125}I-labeled hormone is injected intravenously alone or with excess unlabeled hormone and at various times thereafter the animals undergo whole-body perfusion with buffer to washout unbound hormone. This is followed by perfusion with a fixative solution to attach irreversibly the bound hormone to its receptors. After suitable processing the distribution of radioactivity in tissue sections is determined by light or electron microscope autoradiography. In analogy with *in vitro* procedures specific binding is the difference in the concentration of radioactivity (grains per unit area) between tissue sections from animals receiving ^{125}I-labeled hormone alone (total binding) and sections from animals receiving ^{125}I-labeled hormone and excess unlabeled hormone (nonspecific binding). This procedure has led to the mapping of receptor distribution for a number of peptide hormones including insulin (Bergeron *et al.*, 1980b), prolactin (Walsh *et al.*, 1978), calcitonin (Warshawsky *et al.*, 1980), and parathormone (Tchervenkov *et al.*, 1980).

The procedure has the unique capacity to identify potential target tissues for peptide hormones, and within multicellular complex tissues to delineate the particular cell types bearing hormone receptors. In respect to insulin quantitatively important receptor concentrations have been located in tissues and structures not usually considered as insulin target tissues, such as the exocrine pancreas (Bergeron *et al.*, 1980a), the adrenal gland, and GI tract (Bergeron *et al.*, 1980b), and the circumventricular organs and microvessels of the brain (van Houten *et al.*, 1979; van Houten and Posner, 1979).

One of the powerful extensions of this technology has been the visualization of ^{125}I-labeled hormone binding at the ultrastructural level. We have followed the time course of association of injected ^{125}I-labeled insulin with rat liver (Table VI). Specific binding of the labeled hormone was seen in hepatocytes but not endothelial cells of the sinusoids (Bergeron *et al.*, 1977b). An analysis of electron microscope autoradiographs by the line source method indicated that at 3 minutes postinjection a high proportion of grains was on the plasmalemma whereas by 10 minutes this percentage had gone from 66 to $<10\%$. Concomitantly there was a significant concentration of grains over intracellular vacuolar elements (Table VI). By 20 minutes the remaining grains showed an increase in proportion on the plasmalemma, suggesting recycling of hormone, presumably in the form of hormone–receptor complexes. Figure 8 depicts the kinds of structures with which radiolabel become associated. At early times label was observed over small vesicles, some of them coated vesicles. At later times label was strikingly concentrated in the Golgi region of the cell, particularly in vesicular structures. A number of these structures at 10 minutes looked like fairly typical Golgi vesicles with VLDL content whereas others did not look like classical Golgi vesicles. These latter vesicles did not appear to contain acid phosphatase as assessed cytochemically and we have hence referred to them as lysosome-like (Bergeron *et al.*, 1979). It is interesting that at 20 minutes postinjection there was a significantly higher concentration of grains over these structures than over classical Golgi

TABLE VI

Electron Microscope Autoradiographic Analysis of Hepatic Radiolabel Distribution at 3, 10, and 20 Minutes after ^{125}I-Labeled Insulin[a]

Structures	Percentage of total grains		
	3 minutes	10 minutes	20 minutes
Plasmalemma	66.9	7.6	17.0
Subplasmalemmal vesicles	11.1	2.0	9.9
Cytoplasm	8.3	29.6	19.3
Golgi apparatus	0.6	15.3	5.8
Lysosome-like vacuoles	0.6	17.3	27.0
Endoplasmic reticulum (smooth and rough)	1.5	9.2	8.0
Mitochondria	3.9	6.6	3.1
Nucleus	1.3	1.5	1.3
Others	—	0.5	1.8
All structures	94.2	89.6	93.2

[a] The number of grains analyzed at each time was 318 at 3 minutes, 196 at 10 minutes, and 223 at 20 minutes. The table is a composite of data from Bergeron *et al.* (1977b, 1979).

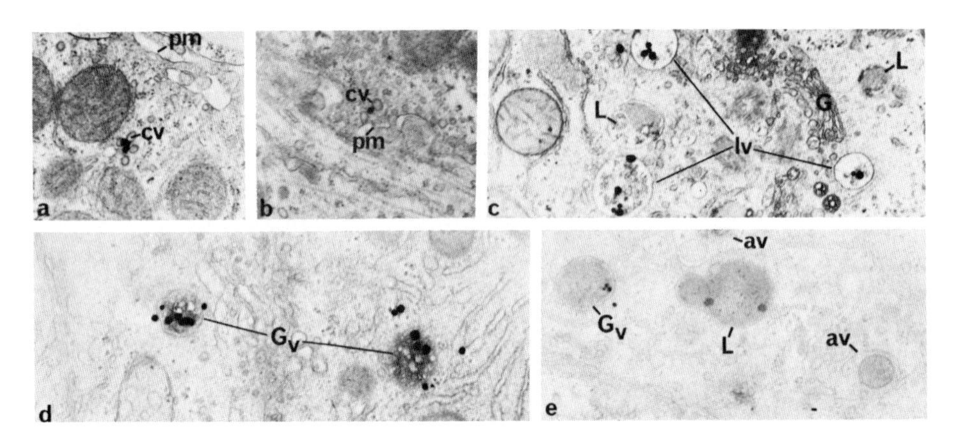

FIG. 8. Major *in vivo* sites of accumulation of radioactivity 10 minutes after injection of ^{125}I-labeled insulin as determined by fine grain autoradiography (a) and (b) show coated vesicles (cv) near the plasmalemma (pm), which are overlaid by silver (2–5% of grains). (c) shows lysosome-like vacuoles (lv) within the Golgi (G) region (17.3% of grains). (d) depicts trans Golgi vacuoles (Gv) identified by VLDL content (15.3% of grains). (e) shows Golgi vesicle (Gv) with VLDL content surrounded by autophagic vacuoles (av) and a classical dense body lysosome (L). Magnification ×22,000 (a, b, e) and ×30,000 (c, d). From Posner *et al.* (1980).

vesicles (Table VI). Only a few grains were observed over Golgi cisternal elements and none over typical secondary lysosomes enriched in acid phosphatase.

Figure 9 illustrates grains over vacuolar elements of a neuronal cell body in the area postrema of the rat brain. It thus emphasizes that the internalization process seen in liver is very likely a general phenomenon in all receptor-bearing mammalian cells.

B. UPTAKE INTO SUBCELLULAR FRACTIONS

Studies of both [^{125}I]oPRL and ^{125}I-labeled insulin (Josefsberg *et al.*, 1979; Posner *et al.*, 1980c) have shown a rapid uptake of radiolabel by the liver with concentration in Golgi > total microsomes > homogenate. The time course of ^{125}I-labeled insulin uptake into these fractions is depicted in Fig. 10 and was maximal at 2 minutes. Uptake into a purified nuclear fraction was low and radiolabel concentration was less than 5% that of total microsomes and therefore only about 0.5% that of Golgi (Posner *et al.*, 1980c). These observations paralleled those on [^{125}I]oPRL which also showed a marked concentration in Golgi fractions compared to all other subcellular fractions examined (Josefsberg *et al.*, 1979). The concentration of radioactivity in Golgi at an early (3 minutes) time is high according to

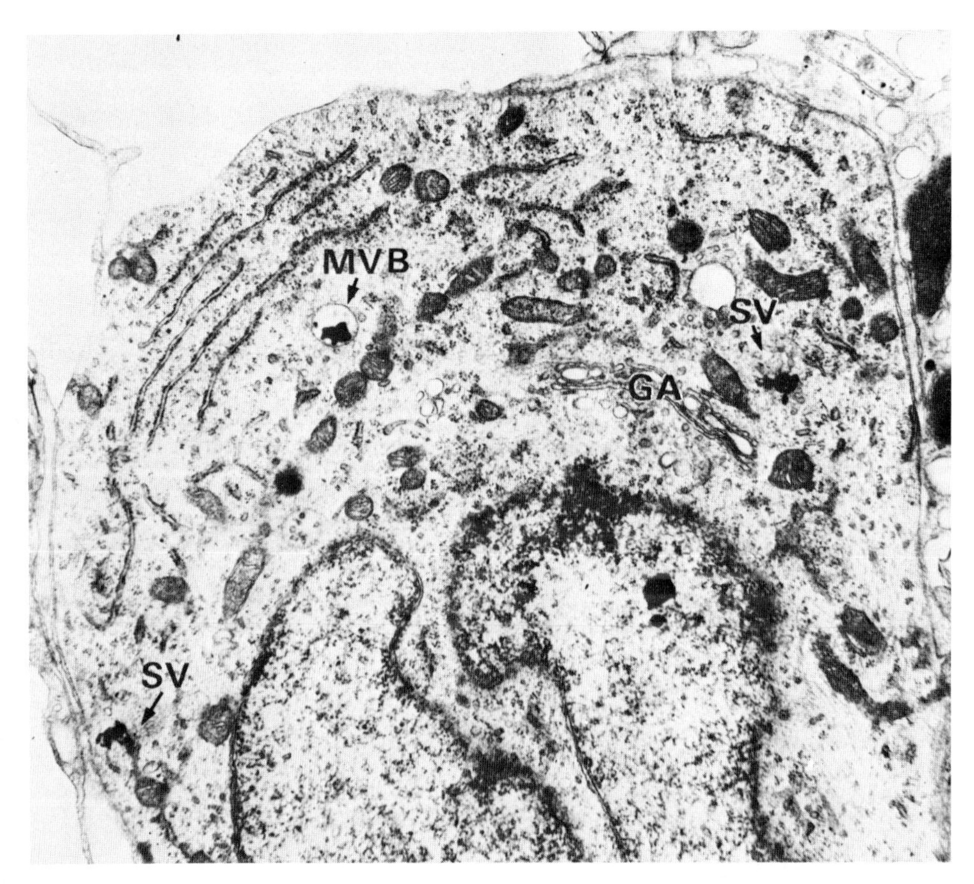

FIG. 9. Electron microscope autoradiograph showing the sequestration of internalized radiolabel within clusters of vesicular and saccular elements (SV) and a multivesicular body (MVB) of a neuron from the area postrema 5 minutes after the systemic injection of ^{125}I-labeled insulin. Magnification ×5300. From M. van Houten and B. I. Posner. (unpublished).

subcellular fractionation (Fig. 10) but low as determined by *in vivo* autoradiography (Fig. 8). Our explanation for this discrepancy is as follows: At early times the total radioactivity in Golgi fractions is largely due to uptake into Golgi heavy elements (Fig. 13) wherein most of the radioactivity is associated with small vesicles (Posner *et al.*, 1980c). We have tentatively interpreted this as reflecting internalization to endocytotic vesicles. Thus the time course of uptake into Golgi depicted in Fig. 10 probably represents the composite phenomena of internalization into endocytotic vesicles at early times and into typical Golgi vesicles at later times.

The uptake process appeared to be receptor dependent. Thus the up-

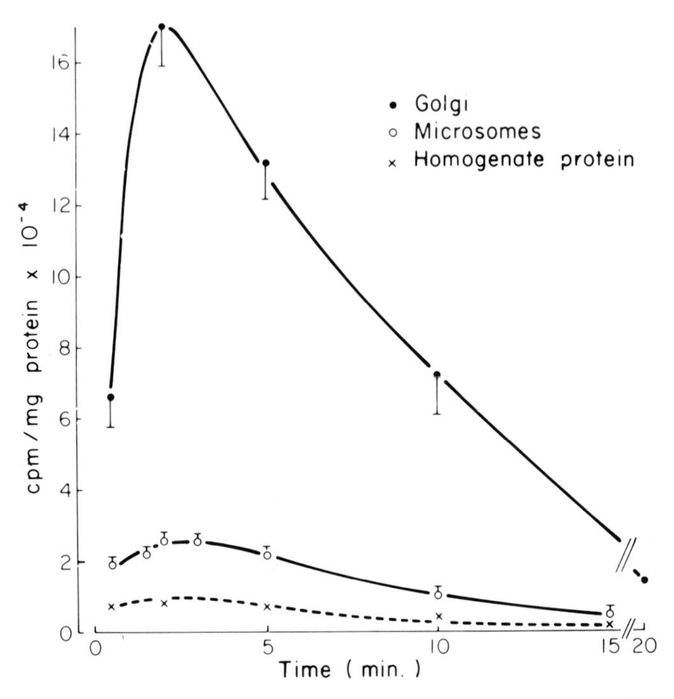

FIG. 10. Time course of uptake of ^{125}I-labeled insulin into homogenate, microsomes, and total Golgi fraction. Specific activity of the total Golgi fraction was calculated from the radioactivity and protein content of the individual Golgi light, intermediate, and heavy fractions. Each point is the mean ± SE of 4 to 10 experiments in each of which 3 animals were used. Each animal received about 12×10^6 cpm of ^{125}I-labeled insulin. From Posner *et al.* (1980c).

take of ^{125}I-labeled insulin was inhibited by unlabeled insulin in a dose-dependent manner, and by analogs of insulin in parallel with their ability to block the binding of ^{125}I-labeled insulin to receptors *in vitro* (Fig. 11). Structurally unrelated peptide hormones had no inhibitory effect. Though these experiments were done on microsomes it was shown that the inhibition of uptake into microsomes was fully reflected in the Golgi fractions prepared therefrom. Similar observations were made on prolactin uptake. Of particular interest here was the much lower uptake of [^{125}I]oPRL into male compared to female rat liver. This was predictable for a receptor-mediated process since receptor levels in male liver are much lower than those in female liver (Posner *et al.*, 1974a).

Detailed studies were performed to show that the process of homogenization and fractionation would not redistribute label from one compartment to another. The addition of ^{125}I-labeled insulin to the liver just prior

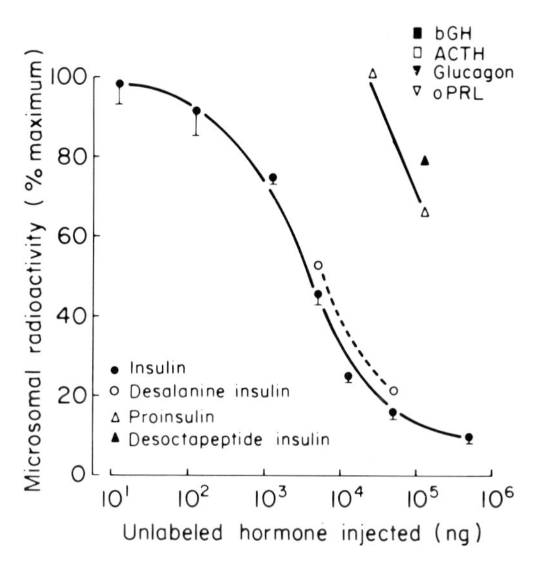

FIG. 11. Specificity of uptake of ^{125}I-labeled insulin into rat liver microsomes. Animals were sacrificed 2 minutes after ^{125}I-labeled insulin was injected with or without the indicated quantity of unlabeled hormone. Maximal microsomal radioactivity refers to the uptake when ^{125}I-labeled insulin was injected without unlabeled hormone (8.0, 12.1, and 14.4 × 106 cpm/animal in each of 3 experiments, respectively). Each point on the insulin uptake-inhibition curve is the mean ± SE of the determinations in 3 animals. The variation of the other measurements was similar. From Posner *et al.* (1980c).

to homogenization led to much lower concentrations of radiolabel in all subcellular fractions especially Golgi, and a different pattern of radiolabel distribution than seen following *in vivo* administration (Posner *et al.*, 1980c).

C. INTACT HORMONE IN GOLGI VESICLES

The association of radiolabel with the Golgi fractions while presumptive is not definitive evidence of internalization into these vacuolar structures. It was conceivable that the radiolabel was selectively associated with contaminating vesicles of lysosomal nature. We thus resorted to electron microscrope autoradiography of Golgi fractions at times of peak labeling after *in vivo* ^{125}I-labeled hormone. In the case of both insulin and prolactin autoradiographic grains were localized to VLDL-containing vesicles and tubules in Golgi light and intermediate fractions (Fig. 12). The situation with the Golgi heavy fraction, as noted above, was more complex and the majority of grains were associated with small vesicles of probable endocytotic origin. The analysis of grain distribution in the morphologically

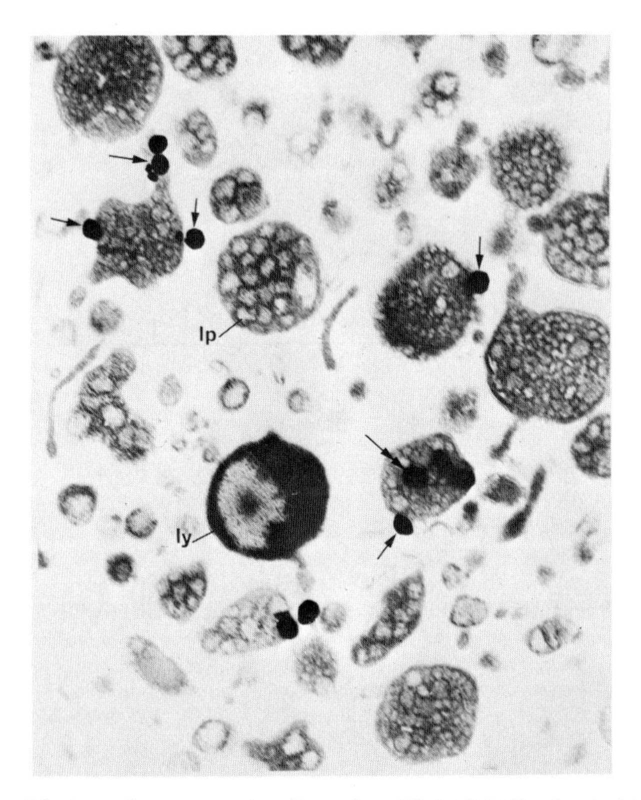

FIG. 12. Electron microscope autoradiography of Golgi light fraction isolated at 2 minutes after the injection of ^{125}I-labeled insulin into the portal vein of rats. Autoradiographic silver grains (arrows) mark the periphery of the Golgi vesicles clearly identified by their characteristic very low density lipoprotein particle content (lp). A rare secondary lysosomal contaminant is indicated (ly). At no time were silver grains found in association with secondary lysosomes. Magnification ×50,000. From Posner *et al.* (1980c).

typical Golgi vesicles of the light and intermediate fractions showed a high proportion of grains over the vesicle membrane supporting the view that the radiolabeled material was still attached to receptors following internalization (Table VII).

It was also possible that the internalized hormone was no longer intact but rather partially degraded or otherwise altered so as to be biologically inert. We thus extracted radiolabel from the isolated subcellular fractions and evaluated its integrity by chromatography and by measuring its capacity to interact with receptors. By these criteria at early times a high percentage of the radiolabel was on intact molecules. Even at later times integrity was not less than 50% of the native ^{125}I-labeled hormone (Table VIII).

TABLE VII
Grain Distribution in Golgi Vesicle Fractions[a]

Fraction	Location	Percentage distribution	
		Insulin	Prolactin
Golgi light	Over membrane	60.0	50.1
	Inside vesicles	32.4	38.2
	Outside vesicles	7.6	11.7
Golgi intermediate	Over membrane	51.2	52.3
	Inside vesicles	43.1	36.8
	Outside vesicles	5.7	10.9

[a] Autoradiographic fine grains as shown in Fig. 12 were counted as over membrane if any part of the grain was over membrane. Adapted from Josefsberg *et al.* (1979) and Posner *et al.* (1980c).

D. TIME COURSE OF UPTAKE INTO GOLGI AND COMPARISON WITH LYSOSOMAL FRACTIONS

The time course of ^{125}I-labeled insulin uptake after *in vivo* administration was studied in plasmalemma and the individual Golgi fractions (Fig. 13). Uptake into plasmalemma was maximal at the earliest time examined and declined thereafter. Uptake was more rapid in Golgi heavy than in the other Golgi fractions, and showed a sharp peak at 2 minutes with subsequent rapid decline to low levels by 20 minutes. The time course of uptake into Golgi intermediate was shifted somewhat to later times and radiolabel declined less rapidly from peak values which were close to twice those seen in the other two fractions. The time course of radiolabel incorpora-

TABLE VIII
Integrity of Radiolabeled Insulin and Prolactin Extracted from Rat Liver Golgi Fractions[a]

Time after injection (min)	Specific binding (% control)					
	Gl		Gi		Gh	
	Insulin	PRL	Insulin	PRL	Insulin	PRL
2	87.3	104.2	75.0	83.3	79.0	100.2
10	52.0	81.7	53.6	73.4	75.3	155.4
20	44.0	n.p.	50.5	n.p.[b]	55.0	n.p.
30	n.p.	106.4	n.p.	74.4	n.p.	126.2

[a] Radioactivity extracted from the Golgi fractions was evaluated for integrity by rebinding to female rat liver ([^{125}I]oPRL) or human placental (^{125}I-labeled insulin) membranes. Insulin data are from Posner *et al.* (1980c). Prolactin data are from Verma *et al.* (1978).
[b] n.p., not performed.

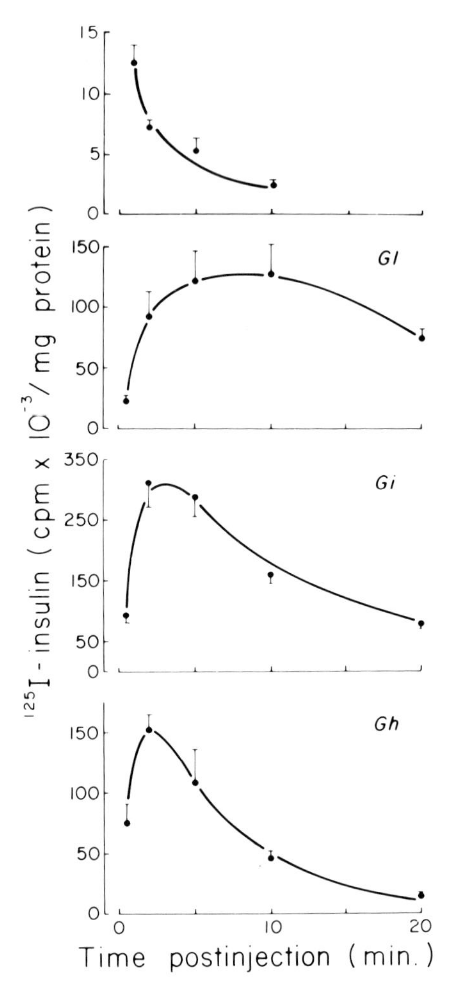

FIG. 13. Time course of association of radioactivity with plasmalemma and individual Golgi fractions following the injection of ^{125}I-labeled insulin. At various times after the injection of ^{125}I-labeled insulin (12×10^6 cpm/animal) the subcellular fractions were prepared from 6 to 12 animals and radioactivity per mg fraction protein was determined as described in Posner *et al.* (1980c).

tion into Golgi light was quite different with a more extended plateau rather than a peak maximum value (Posner *et al.*, 1980c). These data are compatible with the uptake sequence plasmalemma → Golgi heavy → Golgi intermediate → Golgi light. This sequence, the small vesicle content of the Golgi heavy fraction, and the *in vivo* autoradiographic data have led us to suggest that uptake into the Golgi heavy fraction largely reflects internalization into endocytotic vesicle (vide supra). Though the sequence of uptake was the same for prolactin and insulin the latter hormone was cleared more rapidly through the Golgi fractions.

In view of a number of studies claiming internalization of labeled peptides into lysosomes (reviewed in Gorden *et al.*, 1980) we examined ^{125}I-labeled insulin uptake into lysosomal fractions. Suitably pure lysosomal fractions were obtained by the technique of Wattiaux *et al.* (1978) in which the lysosome-enriched L fraction from rat liver was subfractionated on a discontinuous metrizamide gradient (Table IV). Since we wished to reduce lysosomal processing in order to magnify uptake into this compartment we examined the effect of chloroquine on the uptake of ^{125}I-labeled insulin into both Golgi and lysosomal fractions. Chloroquine augmented uptake into lysosomal subfractions but also greatly increased the radioactivity associated with the Golgi elements (Posner *et al.*, 1980a). The relative extent of radiolabel concentrated in the individual Golgi and lysosomal subfractions at 20 minutes after ^{125}I-labeled insulin administration is depicted in Table IX. It is evident that there is a far lower concentration of radiolabel in the lysosomal subfractions than in the Golgi fractions from both chloroquine-treated and control animals. This difference was maintained throughout the time course of uptake (Posner *et al.*, 1980a). We have shown that the radiolabeled material retained consequent to chloroquine treatment largely reflects intact hormone. Furthermore autoradiography of Golgi fractions from chloroquine-treated animals after ^{125}I-labeled insulin administration showed grains heavily concentrated in

TABLE IX
Effect of Chloroquine on Concentration of ^{125}I-Labeled Insulin in Golgi and Lysosomal Elements[a]

	Control	+ Chloroquine
Gl	18,035 ± 5,321	104,154 ± 22,416
Gi	32,387 ± 3,615	209,712 ± 39,332
Gh	8,580 ± 1,237	24,586 ± 2,252
L2	1,804 ± 490	10,767 ± 4,672
L3	577 ± 97	3,637 ± 315

[a] Each animal received 12×10^6 cpm of ^{125}I-labeled insulin by internal jugular vein 20 minutes before sacrifice. Chloroquine treatment was 10 and 5 mg/100 gm body wt. 2 and 1 hours, respectively, before ^{125}I-labeled insulin injection. All values are mean ± SE of four fractionations. From Posner *et al.* (1980a).

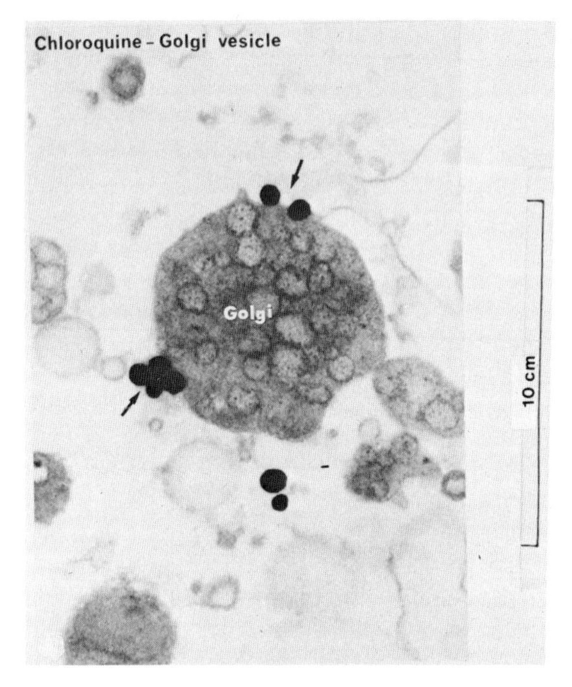

FIG. 14. Electron microscope autoradiograph of Golgi light fraction isolated 10 minutes after the injection of ^{125}I-labeled insulin into chloroquine-treated rats. The micrograph illustrates a Golgi vesicle filled with characteristic very low density lipoprotein secretory content. Silver grains (arrows) are closely apposed to the vesicle's periphery. Magnification ×50,000. From Posner *et al.* (1980a).

classical VLDL-filled Golgi vesicles (Fig. 14). We conclude that internalized hormone is rapidly concentrated in Golgi vesicles and, only minimally in typical, biochemically defined lysosomes. Chloroquine seems to act by retarding the processing of internalized hormone resulting in its augmented accumulation in Golgi elements.

E. VESICLE HETEROGENEITY AND TRAFFIC

Our analysis has focused upon receptors and internalized hormones inside intracellular vesicles. We have examined two kinds of vesicles: (1) lysosomes, enriched in acid phosphatase (de Duve *et al.*, 1955), and (2) Golgi vesicles identified by their VLDL content and high galactosyltransferase activity (Ehrenreich *et al.*, 1973; Bergeron *et al.*, 1973b; Bergeron, 1979). The intracellular vesicle population is more complex than these distinctions would indicate. Thus, there is a large body of data which point to the existence of different populations of lysosomes (Davies, 1975; Rome *et al.*, 1979). Recent studies have shown that in the Golgi light and intermediate fractions there are vesicles filled with VLDL which are not highly enriched in galactosyltransferase (Ito and Palade, 1978). Preliminary evidence had indicated to us that hormone binding is not concentrated in Golgi and lysosomes exclusively. Thus, maximum binding in lysosomal subfractions did not correspond to maximum acid phosphatase. Nor was it accounted for by Golgi as judged by galactosyltransferase activity (Table IV). This prompted us to fractionate the L fraction by density gradient centrifugation using Percoll, a colloidal silica sol coated with polyvinylpyrrolidone. The individual gradient fractions were assayed for enzyme activity and hormone binding (Fig. 15). It is evident that the galactosyltransferase activity sediments at low and the acid phosphatase activity at high density. 5′-nucleotidase was evenly dispersed throughout the gradient. Binding of [^{125}I]hGH was maximal in the intermediate region and did not coincide with the acid phosphatase profile. It was thus likely contained in structures not conforming to lysosomal particles.

A similar analysis of the different Golgi fractions was undertaken to evaluate heterogeneity here as well. Highly purified galactosyltransferase structures sedimented at low density whereas acid phosphatase enriched elements sedimented at high density. The bulk of the binding sites cosedimented in the galactosyltransferase region. However specific binding sites were highly concentrated in heavier elements including structures of density intermediate between that of galactosyltransferase and acid phosphatase components. The profiles for the Golgi heavy fraction were very similar. Those for the Golgi light revealed exclusively galactosyltransferase components and no intermediate structures or acid phosphatase-enriched elements. Therefore these studies have confirmed the existence of a high concentration of hormone receptors in galactosyltransferase-enriched Golgi structures. In addition the data indicate the presence of receptors in heavier elements, structures of intermediate density, not especially enriched in either galactosyltransferase or acid phosphatase (M. N. Khan, B. I. Posner, R. J. Khan, and J. J. M. Bergeron, unpublished data).

The time course of ^{125}I-labeled insulin corporation into the different components of the Golgi intermediate fraction was studied (Fig. 16). Radiolabel was first taken up into the lighter galactosyltransferase-enriched region and later appeared in heavier structures. This time-dependent shift in density of incorporated radioactivity suggests to us that the initial uptake into Golgi vesicles is followed by the transfer of material to progressively heavier lysosomal-like structures perhaps in the course of processing the internalized hormone. It is interesting to note the rough

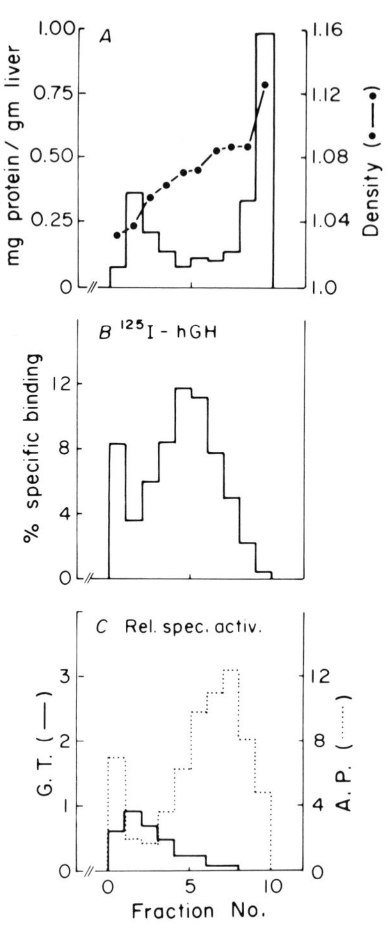

FIG. 15. The distribution of protein, [^{125}I]hGH binding, and marker enzymes after Percoll gradient centrifugation of a rat liver L fraction. The lysosome-enriched L fraction was prepared as described by Wattiaux *et al.* (1978) and suspended in 0.25 *M* sucrose. A homogeneous suspension (density 1.07 gm/ml) was diluted with an isoosmotic Percoll solution and centrifuged at 40,000 g_{av} for 60 minutes at 4°C. Fractions of 2 to 3 ml were obtained by pumping in a concentrated sucrose solution. Density was determined and each fraction was diluted with 25 m*M* Tris HCl–10 m*M* $MgCl_2$ (pH 7.4) and centrifuged at 82,000 g_{av} for 120 minutes. The particulate material above the Percoll pellet was removed, diluted with Tris-Mg buffer, and assayed for protein (A), [^{125}I]hGH specific binding per 50 μg protein (B) as noted in Posner *et al.* (1978), and enzyme activities (C) (methods referenced in Table IV). From M. N. Khan, B. I. Posner, R. J. Khan, and J. J. M. Bergeron (unpublished).

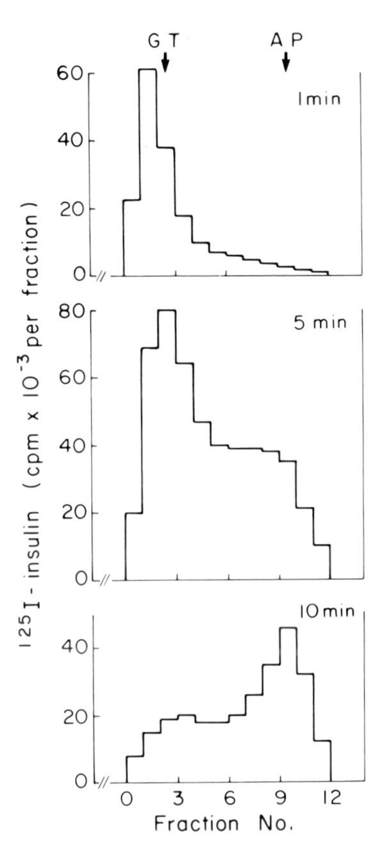

FIG. 16. The distribution of radioactivity as a function of time after ^{125}I-labeled insulin injection in a Golgi intermediate fraction subfractionated on an isopycnic Percoll gradient. The injection of ^{125}I-labeled insulin and the preparation of the Golgi fraction are described elsewhere (Posner *et al.*, 1980c). The Golgi intermediate fraction was suspended in 0.25 *M* sucrose, diluted with Percoll to a density of 1.05 mg/ml, and centrifuged at 60,000 g_{av} for 30 minutes. Fractions were collected (legend of Fig. 15) and assayed for protein and radioactivity. The position of the peaks for two marker enzymes, acid phosphatase (AP) and galactosyltransferase (GT), are indicated in the top panel. From M. N. Khan, B. I. Posner, R. J. Khan, and J. J. M. Bergeron (unpublished).

parallelism between these observations and those obtained by *in vivo* autoradiography (Fig. 8 and Table VI).

One other intracellular vacuolar element bears mention. This is the GERL system as defined by Novikoff (1976). In liver it has been considered to be distributed among VLDL-containing vesicles and saccules at the trans face of the Golgi apparatus (Novikoff and Yam, 1978). The difficulty in ascribing a unique morphologic or biochemical marker to

GERL (Hand, 1979) has not enabled us to distinguish between internalization into GERL or trans Golgi elements (Bergeron *et al.*, 1979).

V. The Sequence and Significance of Internalization

A. THE SEQUENCE

The sequence of internalization which we visualize is depicted in Fig. 17. Our data indicate that uptake is a receptor-mediated process and that it occurs consequent to the formation of the hormone–receptor complex at the cell surface. It would appear from studies using fluorescent derivatives of hormones (Varga *et al.*, 1976; Schlessinger *et al.*, 1978), and ferritin complexed LDL (Anderson *et al.*, 1976), EGF (Haigler *et al.*, 1979),

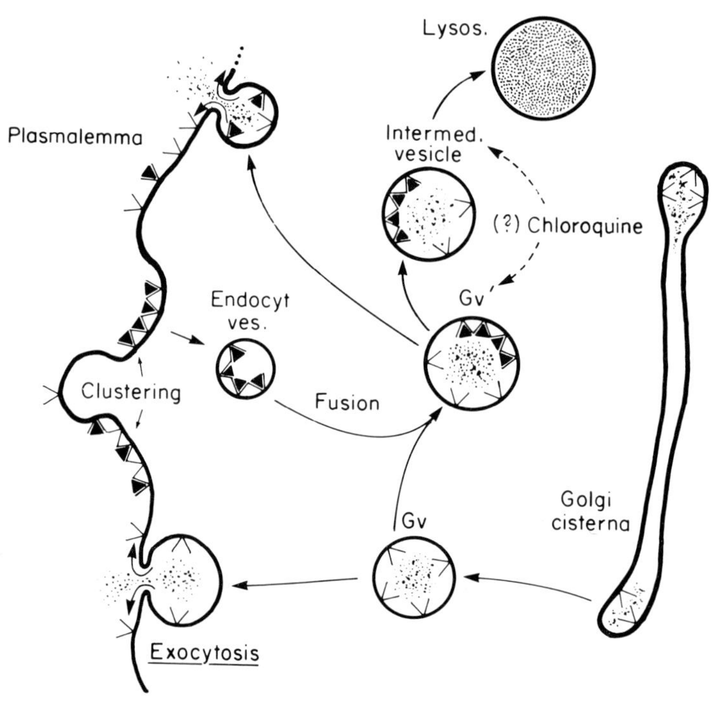

FIG. 17. Schematic depiction of the internalization and postulated intracellular fate of a polypeptide hormone. The endocytotic vesicle fuses with a Golgi vesicle (Gv) to form a modified element (Gv′) which may participate in exocytosis (and hence recycle hormone–receptor complexes) or undergo transformation to an intermediate vesicle similar in appearance to a Golgi vesicle. We suggest that this latter vesicle may go on to become a secondary lysosome. Possible points of chloroquine action are depicted.

and insulin (Nelson *et al.*, 1978) that the aggregation of hormone–receptor complexes occurs prior to pinocytosis. The degree to which aggregation in coated pits and endocytosis via coated vesicles occurs appears to vary with the cell type and peptide studied (Carpentier *et al.*, 1979; Bilheimer *et al.*, 1978). Our own data indicate that the association of internalized peptide with coated vesicles does occur but infrequently (Fig. 8). It is generally agreed that the internalized peptide is concentrated in vacuolar elements of the cell. The contention that insulin is internalized into the cell nucleus (Goldfine *et al.*, 1978) has not been confirmed either by our own observations (Bergeron *et al.*, 1979; Posner *et al.*, 1980b) or the studies of others (Carpentier *et al.*, 1978, 1979). A number of investigators have concluded that endocytosed peptide is concentrated in lysosomes (Carpentier *et al.*, 1978, 1979; Amsterdam *et al.*, 1979; Haigler *et al.*, 1978, 1979; Gorden *et al.*, 1978; Hubbard and Stukenbrok, 1979). We have, in keeping with the classical definition (de Duve *et al.*, 1955), regarded the lysosome as an acid phosphatase-enriched vesicle. In no instance have we, using either autoradiography and cytochemistry (Bergeron *et al.*, 1979) or biochemical techniques (Posner *et al.*, 1980a) observed internalized peptide in these structures. The ultimate destination of internalized hormone may well be lysosomal but the acid pH and hydrolytic activity in these components should lead to ready dissociation of hormone from receptor, and rapid degradation into small molecules, with the consequent failure to localize peptides therein. As detailed above, our observations indicate that the vacuolar elements initially receiving internalized peptide hormones are Golgi vesicles. This determination is based upon: (1) the *in vivo* autoradiographic demonstration of internalized radiolabel in typical Golgi vesicles, (2) the uptake and concentration of radiolabel in highly purified Golgi vesicle fractions (light and intermediate) which are minimally contaminated by plasmalemma and lysosomes, (3) the demonstration by autoradiography that radiolabel in the Golgi vesicle fractions is associated with bona fide VLDL-containing vesicles—the morphological criterion used in identifying Golgi vesicles (Ehrenreich *et al.*, 1973), and (4) the observation that internalized radiolabeled peptide is first incorporated into low density galactosyltransferase-enriched components and only later appears in heavier structures with higher acid phosphatase and lower galactosyltransferase content (Fig. 16). This latter observation is the basis for our suggestion, as delineated in Fig. 17, that the formation of a fused structure is followed by its stepwise transformation via an intermediate vesicle to a lysosome in the course of which the vesicle becomes denser and the hormone is metabolized. It is not clear whether the transition involves successive vesicle fusions or other mechanisms for acquiring new properties. The intermediate vesicle is depicted as somewhere between a Golgi and lysosomal vesicle in its properties. However, this abstraction may describe a range of vesicles with more or less of either Golgi or lysosomal features, perhaps in a reciprocal relationship to one another. It is worth noting that this sequence is not exclusive of other kinds of transitions but appears to be a prominent pathway judging from our data and that of others (Desbuquois *et al.*, 1979; Varga *et al.*, 1976; Pertoft *et al.*, 1978). Thus Golgi vesicles containing internalized hormone could engage in exocytosis during which hormone–receptor complexes might be externalized (i.e., recycled to the cell surface). Something like this could explain the higher proportion of plasmalemma-associated radiolabel at 20 minutes than at 10 minutes following ^{125}I-labeled insulin injection (Table VI). Having said all this it should nevertheless be noted that even the galactosyltransferase-enriched Golgi vesicles containing VLDL may be heterogeneous. Some components may be involved exclusively in secretion and biogenesis of receptors and others exclusively in concentrative internalization of hormone–receptor complexes. Future studies will have to determine if there is this kind of compartmentalization or if the internalization and biogenetic pathways meet within the same structure, as we have suggested in Fig. 17.

We have depicted internalization as involving the hormone–receptor complex. The notion that receptor is internalized with the ligand is supported by our observation that a high porportion of radiolabel in typical Golgi vesicles was on the membrane of these structures (Josefsberg *et al.*, 1979; Posner *et al.*, 1980c). Cointernalization of ligand and receptor is further supported by the studies of McKanna *et al.* (1979) on ferritin-EGF uptake, Debuquois *et al.* (1979) on insulin-induced receptor redistribution, and Das and Fox (1978) on the fate of the covalent [^{125}I]EGF–receptor complex in mouse 3T3 fibroblasts.

Finally, our data indicate that chloroquine acts prior to the lysosome in retarding the processing of internalized material. The exact site of action is uncertain but may involve the transition from intermediate components to lysosomes and/or the transition from Golgi vesicles to intermediate elements. An effect of chloroquine on the Golgi can be inferred from the work of Wibo and Poole (1974).

B. THE SIGNIFICANCE

A link between internalization and hormonal degradation is implied in the sequence of Fig. 17. This relationship was first suggested by the studies of Terris and Steiner (1975, 1976) who showed that in both perfused liver and isolated hepatocytes the degradation of ^{125}I-labeled insulin was coupled to its binding to the insulin receptor. The observed decrease in the integrity of Golgi-associated radiolabel after ^{125}I-labeled insulin injection (Table VIII), along with our observations on chloroquine-induced retention of radiolabel, would appear to indicate that processing of peptide is initiated in the Golgi vesicular fractions. Whether this occurs in true Golgi vesicles or intermediate elements is not at present clear. The observations of preferential degradation of cell bound [^{125}I]EGF (Carpenter and Cohen, 1976; Amsterdam *et al.*, 1979), the inhibiting effect of lysosomotropic agents on degradation (Marshall and Olefsky, 1979; Ascoli and Puett, 1978), and the accumulation of ferritin cores in lysosomes following the internalization of ferritin–EGF (McKanna *et al.*, 1979) further substantiate the thesis that internalized peptide is subjected to degradative processing. The processing of receptor consequent to internalization of the hormone–receptor complex is suggested by the observed correlation between ligand-induced down-regulation and pinocytosis (Haigler *et al.*, 1979a; Gorden *et al.*, 1979), and by the studies of Das and Fox (1978) on the fate of the photoaffinity labeled EGF receptor.

The possibility has been mooted of some kind of intracellular hormonal action. The view that peptide hormones may, in analogy with steroid hormones, alter nuclear function directly (Goldfine, 1977) seems less compelling in the face of little evidence for the accumulation of internalized peptide hormones in the cell nucleus. It has been suggested that insulin, or more likely a fragment of insulin, might act directly on the intracellular machinery (Steiner, 1977). This seems unlikely in view of the ability of antireceptor antibody to mimic insulin action (Van Obberghen *et al.*, 1979). The possibility that a modified ligand or ligand product can act intracellulary still receives attention in view of the demonstration that the metabolism of internalized LDL yields products which exert an intracellular regulatory role on cholesterol metabolism (Brown and Goldstein, 1979).

We suggest that the concentrative internalization of substantially intact peptide hormones, very likely as hormone–receptor complexes, into characteristic Golgi vesicular elements reflects more than a degrading pathway for hormones. It seems less than coincidental that lactogen–receptor complexes are internalized into the same subcellular elements in which lactogen receptors first appear during receptor induction (Fig. 6). To us this suggests a regulatory role of the internalized hormone–receptor complex on Golgi function, at least in respect to receptor regulation.

There is evidence that Golgi function may be broadly influenced by hormones. In diabetic rats bearing hepatic pancreatic islet transplants those hepatocytes adjacent to an islet showed enlarged Golgi-derived secretory vesicles whereas distant hepatocytes showed less prominent Golgi vacuoles with smaller lipoprotein particles (Eder *et al.*, 1979). Insulin has been shown to stimulate the translocation of glucose transport sites from an intracellular to plasmalemma location (Cushman and Wardzala, 1980; Suzuki and Kono, 1980), and the intracellular location appears to be Golgi vesicles (Suzuki and Kono, 1980). Insulin has also been shown, by morphometric methods, to diminish rapidly the hepatic concentration of autophagic vacuoles which are thought to be derived from the Golgi apparatus (Pfeifer, 1978). It therefore appears that the Golgi apparatus is subject to peptide hormone modulation, and we suggest that this modulation is effected via internalized hormone–receptor complexes.

There are two general, not mutually exclusive, ways by which hormone–receptor complexes could regulate Golgi function. First, in analogy with the effect of hormone–receptor complexes on the cell surface, internalized complexes could couple to unique Golgi membrane effectors (viz. enzymes) and thus modulate their activities. This in turn might influence Golgi function and other features of the internal milieu. Second, the internalization of hormone–receptor complexes coupled with exocytosis may be a means of redistributing membrane constituents between the plasmalemma and intracellular vacuoles. This redistributive process need not be restricted to the ligand's receptor but may involve other membrane proteins with a proclivity to interact with the hormone–receptor complex (viz. various effectors). Such a model could explain the effect of insulin on redistributing not only its own receptors but such effectors as the glucose transport sites.

VI. Summary

1. Receptors for insulin, growth hormone, prolactin, and insulin-like growth factors have been identified in Golgi fractions of rat liver. The Golgi complex seems to be a region of receptor enrichment generally exceeding that of plasmalemma.

2. Golgi receptors are very similar to those of the plasma membrane in respect to binding properties, antigenicity, and apparent molecular size, but are more stable on preincubation than those of plasmalemma.

3. Internalization of intact peptide hormone into rat hepatocytes has been demonstrated using both quantitative *in vivo* autoradiography and subcellular fractionation techniques. Hormone is internalized by a receptor-mediated process in accordance with the sequence plasmalemma → Golgi heavy → Golgi intermediate → Golgi light. Uptake into Golgi heavy probably largely reflects incorporation into endocytotic vesicles.

4. Golgi receptors probably derive from formation of new receptors within the cell and from internalization of surface receptors to this region.

Evidence for receptor recycling between Golgi elements and plasmalemma has been presented.

5. A second pool of intracellular binding sites has been described. The components contained in these sites are low in galactosyltransferase activity and are intermediate in density between galactosyltransferase-enriched vesicles and typical lysosomes.

6. Internalized peptide hormone appears to undergo a sequence of intracellular transitions. Peptide concentrates first in galactosyltransferase-enriched vesicles and subsequently in heavier elements. This sequence suggests a transfer of internalized peptide from Golgi vesicles via intermediate components to lysosomes.

7. The concentration of identifiable peptide in lysosomes was much lower than in Golgi elements even in the presence of chloroquine given to inhibit degradation. In fact chloroquine resulted in augmented accumulation of radiolabeled peptide in apparently bona fide Golgi vesicles suggesting that it inhibits intracellular degradation by retarding the intracellular transfer of hormone to degrading sites.

8. The concentrative internalization of hormones to apparently true Golgi vesicles prior to subsequent intracellular processing suggests a role for peptide hormones in regulating Golgi function. This could involve the influence of internalized hormone–receptor complexes on the activity of unique Golgi effectors and/or an effect of hormone–receptor complexes on membrane protein distribution between the surface and vacuolar compartments of the cell.

ACKNOWLEDGMENTS

This work was supported by grants M.T.-4182 and M.T.5605 from the Medical Research Council of Canada and by Grant 1 R01 AM 19573 from the U.S. Public Health Service. Drs. Posner and Bergeron are chercheurs boursiers du Québec.

We thank Dr. B. Kopriwa for her invaluable and kind help with the autoradiography. We also acknowledge the fine technical assistance of Mrs. J. Fournel and Miss D. Raquidan.

REFERENCES

Amsterdam, A., Nimrod, A., Lamprecht, S. A., Burstein, L., and Lindner, H. R. (1979). *Am. J. Physiol.* **5** (2), E 129.

Anderson, R. G. W., Goldstein, J. W., and Brown, M. S. (1976). *Proc. Natl. Acad. Sci. U.S.A.* **73,** 2434.

Andres, R. Y., Jeng, I., and Bradshaw, R. A. (1977). *Proc. Natl. Acad. Sci. U.S.A.* **74,** 2785.

Ascoli, M., and Puett, O. (1978). *J. Biol. Chem.* **253,** 4892.

Baldwin, D., Jr., Terris, S., and Steiner, D. F. (1980). *J. Biol. Chem.* **255,** 4028.

Barrett, A. J., and Heath, M. F. (1977). *In* "Lysosomes: A Laboratory Handbook" (J. T. Dingle, ed.), p. 36. North-Holland Publ., Amsterdam.

Bergeron, J. J. M. (1979). *Biochim. Biophys. Acta* **555,** 493.
Bergeron, J. J. M., and Posner, B. I. (1975). *J. Cell Biol.* **67,** 30a.
Bergeron, J. J. M., and Posner, B. I. (1979). *J. Histochem. Cytochem.* **27,** 1512.
Bergeron, J. J. M., Ehrenreich, J. H., Siekevitz, P., and Palade, G. E. (1973a). *J. Cell Biol.* **59,** 45.
Bergeron, J. J. M., Evans, W. H., and Geschwind, I. I. (1973b). *J. Cell Biol.* **59,** 771.
Bergeron, J. J. M., Levine, G., Sikstrom, R., O'Shaughnessy, D., Kopriwa, B., Nadler, N. J., and Posner, B. I. (1977a). *Proc. Natl. Acad. Sci. U.S.A.* **74,** 5051.
Bergeron, J. J. M., Levine, G., Sikstrom, R., Nadler, N. J., Kopriwa, B., and Posner, B. I. (1977b). *J. Cell Biol.* **75,** 182a.
Bergeron, J. J. M., Borts, D., and Cruz, J. (1978a). *J. Cell Biol.* **76,** 548.
Bergeron, J. J. M., Posner, B. I., Josefsberg, Z., and Sikstrom, R. A. (1978b). *J. Biol. Chem.* **253,** 4058.
Bergeron, J. J. M., Sikstrom, R. A., Hand, A. R., and Posner, B. I. (1979). *J. Cell Biol.* **80,** 427.
Bergeron, J. J. M., Rachubinski, R., Searle, N., Borts, D., Sikstrom, R., and Posner, B. I. (1980a). *J. Histochem. Cytochem.* **28,** 824.
Bergeron, J. J. M., Rachubinski, R., Searle, N., Sikstrom, R., Borts, D., Bastian, P., and Posner, B. I. (1980b). *Endocrinology* (in press)
Berson, S. A., and Yalow, R. S. (1959). *J. Clin. Invest.* **38,** 1996.
Bilheimer, D. W., Ho, Y. K., Brown, M. S., Anderson, R. G. W., and Goldstein, J. L. (1978). *J. Clin. Invest.* **61,** 678.
Birkinshaw, M., and Falconer, I. R. (1972). *J. Endocrinol.* **55,** 323.
Blackard, W. G., Guzelian, P. S., and Small, M. E. (1978). *Endocrinology* **103,** 548.
Blobel, G., and Potter, V. R. (1966). *Science* **154,** 1662.
Bretz, R., and Staubli, W. (1977). *Eur. J. Biochem.* **77,** 181.
Brown, M. S., and Goldstein, J. L. (1979). *Proc. Natl. Acad. Sci. U.S.A.* **76,** 5905.
Carpenter, G., and Cohen, S. (1976). *J. Cell Biol.* **71,** 159.
Carpentier, J.-L., Gorden, P., Amherdt, M., Van Obberghen, E., Kahn, C. R., and Orci, L. (1978). *J. Clin. Invest.* **61,** 1057.
Carpentier, J.-L., Gorden, P., Freychet, P., LeCam, A., and Orci, L. (1979). *J. Clin. Invest.* **63,** 1249.
Catt, K. J., Harwood, J. P., Agiulera, G., and Dufau, M. L. (1979). *Nature (London)* **280,** 109.
Cuatrecasas, P. (1969). *Proc. Natl. Acad. Sci. U.S.A.* **63,** 450.
Cuatrecasas, P. (1974). *Annu. Rev. Biochem.* **43,** 169.
Cushman, S. W., and Wardzala, L. J. (1980). *J. Biol. Chem.* **255,** 4758.
Das, M., and Fox, C. F. (1978). *Proc. Natl. Acad. Sci. U.S.A.* **75,** 2644.
Davies, M. (1975). *In* "Lysosomes in Biology and Pathology" (J. T. Dingle and R. T. Dean, eds.), Vol. 4, p. 305. North-Holland Publ., Amsterdam.
Dean, R. T. (1977). *In* "Lysosomes: A Laboratory Handbook" (J. T. Dingle, ed.), p. 1. North-Holland Publ., Amsterdam.
de Duve, C., Pressman, B. C., Gianetto, R., Wattiaux, R., and Appelmans, F. (1955). *Biochem. J.* **60,** 604.
de Kretser, D. M., Martin, T. J., and Melick, R. A. (1969). *J. Endocrinol.* **46,** 507.
Desbuquois, B., Willeput, J., and Huet de Froberville, A. (1979). *FEBS Lett.* **106,** 338.
Eder, H. A., Novikoff, P. M., Novikoff, A. B., Yam, A., Beyer, M., and Gidez, L. I. (1979). *Proc. Natl. Acad. Sci. U.S.A.* **76,** 5905.
Ehrenreich, J. H., Bergeron, J. J. M., Siekevitz, P., and Palade, G. E. (1973). *J. Cell Biol.* **59,** 45.

Fambrough, D. M., and Devreotes, P. N. (1978). *J. Cell Biol.* **76,** 237.
Farquhar, M. G., Bergeron, J. J. M., and Palade, G. E. (1974). *J. Cell Biol.* **60,** 8.
Gardner, J. M., and Fambrough, D. M. (1979). *Cell* **16,** 661.
Gavin, J. R., III, Roth, J., Neville, D. M., Jr., DeMeyts, P., and Buell, D. N. (1974). *Proc. Natl. Acad. Sci. U.S.A.* **71,** 84.
Goidl, J. A. (1979). *Biochemistry* **18,** 3674.
Goldfine, I. (1977). *Diabetes* **26,** 148.
Goldfine, I. D., and Smith, G. J. (1976). *Proc. Natl. Acad. Sci. U.S.A.* **73,** 1427.
Goldfine, I. D., Vigneri, R., Cohen, D., Pliam, N. B., and Kahn, C. R. (1977). *Nature (London)* **269,** 698.
Goldfine, I. D., Jones, A. L., Hradek, G. T., Wong, K. Y., and Mooney, J. S. (1978). *Science* **202,** 760.
Goodfriend, T. L., and Lin, S.-Y. (1970). *Circ. Res.* **26–27,** Suppl. I, 163.
Gorden, P., Carpentier, J.-L., Cohen, S., and Orci, L. (1978). *Proc. Natl. Acad. Sci. U.S.A.* **75,** 5025.
Gorden, P., Carpentier, J.-L., Van Obberghen, E., Barazzone, P., Roth, J., and Orci, L. (1979). *J. Cell Sci.* **39,** 77.
Gorden, P., Carpentier, J.-L., Freychet, P., and Orci, L. (1980). *Diabetologia* **18,** 263.
Groves, W. E., Houts, G. E., and Bayse, G. S. (1972). *Biochim. Biophys. Acta* **264,** 472.
Haigler, H., Ash, J. F., Singer, S. J., and Cohen, S. (1978). *Proc. Natl. Acad. Sci. U.S.A.* **75,** 3317.
Haigler, H. T., McKanna, J. A., and Cohen, S. (1979a). *J. Cell Biol.* **83,** 82.
Haigler, H. T., McKanna, J. A., and Cohen, S. (1979b). *J. Cell Biol.* **81,** 382.
Hand, A. R. (1980). *J. Histochem. Cytochem.* **28,** 82.
Hendry, I. A., Stockel, K., Thoenen, H., and Iversen, L. L. (1974). *Brain Res.* **68,** 103.
Horvat, A. (1978). *J. Cell Physiol.* **97,** 37.
Horvat, A., Li, E., and Katsoyannis, P. G. (1975). *Biochim. Biophys. Acta* **382,** 609.
Hubbard, A. L., and Stukenbrok, H. (1979). *J. Cell Biol.* **83,** 65.
Ito, A., and Palade, G. E. (1978). *J. Cell Biol.* **79,** 590.
Josefsberg, Z., Posner, B. I., Patel, B., and Bergeron, J. J. M. (1979). *J. Biol. Chem.* **254,** 209.
Kahn, C. R., and Baird, K. (1978). *J. Biol. Chem.* **253,** 4900.
Kahn, C. R., Neville, D. M., Jr., and Roth, J. (1973). *J. Biol. Chem.* **248,** 244.
Kelly, P. A., Posner, B. I., and Friesen, H. G. (1975). *Endocrinology* **97,** 1408.
Kono, T., and Barham, F. W. (1971). *J. Biol. Chem.* **246,** 6210.
Leblond, C. P. (1965). *Am. J. Anat.* **116,** 1.
Lee, N. D., and Williams, R. H. (1954). *Endocrinology* **54,** 5.
Lefkowitz, R. J., Roth, J., and Pastan, I. (1970). *Proc. Natl. Acad. Sci. U.S.A.* **65,** 745.
McKanna, J. A., Haigler, H. T., and Cohen, S. (1979). *Proc. Natl. Acad. Sci. U.S.A.* **76,** 5689.
Maddaiah, V. T., Rezvani, I., Chen, S. Y., and Collipp, P. J. (1970). *Biochem. Med.* **4,** 492.
Manni, A., Chambers, M. J., and Pearson, O. H. (1978). *Endocrinology* **103,** 2168.
Marshall, S., and Olefsky, J. M. (1979). *J. Biol. Chem.* **254,** 10153.
Mayberry, H. E., Van den Brande, J. L., Van Wyk, J. J., and Waddell, W. J. (1971). *Endocrinology* **88,** 1309.
Mitra, S., and Rao, C. V. (1978). *Arch. Biochem. Biophys.* **191,** 331.
Muller, O. A., and Scriba, P. C. (1969). *Acta Endocrinol.* **60,** 463.
Nelson, D. M., Smith, R. M., and Jarett, L. (1978). *Diabetes* **27,** 530.
Nolin, J. M., and Witorsch, R. J. (1976). *Endocrinology* **99,** 949.
Nordquist, R. E., and Palmieri, G. M. A. (1974). *Endocrinology* **95,** 229.

Novikoff, A. B. (1976). *Proc. Natl. Acad. Sci. U.S.A.* **73,** 2781.
Novikoff, P. M., and Yam, A. (1978). *J. Cell Biol.* **76,** 1.
Orth, J., and Christensen, A. K. (1977). *Endocrinology* **101,** 262.
Palade, G. E. (1975). *Science* **189,** 347.
Patel, B., Posner, B. I., Baldwin, D., Jr., and Steiner, D. F. (1980). *Clin. Res.* **28,** 675.
Pertoft, H., Warmegrad, B., and Hook, M. (1978). *Biochem J.* **174,** 309.
Pfeiffer, U. (1978). *J. Cell Biol.* **78,** 152.
Posner, B. I. (1974). *Diabetes* **23,** 209.
Posner, B. I. (1975). *Can. J. Physiol. Pharmacol.* **53,** 689.
Posner, B. I. (1976). *Endocrinology* **99,** 1168.
Posner, B. I., and Bergeron, J. J. M. (1975). *Clin. Res.* **23,** 617.
Posner, B. I., and Bergeron, J. J. M. (1980). *Proc. Cong. Int. Diabetes Fed., 10th, Vienna* (in press)
Posner, B. I., Kelly, P. A., Shiu, R. P. C., and Friesen, H. G. (1974a). *Endocrinology* **95,** 521.
Posner, B. I., Kelly, P. A., and Friesen, H. G. (1974b). *Proc. Natl. Acad. Sci. U.S.A.* **71,** 2407.
Posner, B. I., Kelly, P. A., and Friesen, H. G. (1975). *Science* **187,** 57.
Posner, B. I., Josefsberg, Z., Patel, B., and Bergeron, J. J. M. (1977). *J. Cell Biol.* **75,** 191a.
Posner, B. I., Raquidan, D., Josefsberg, Z., and Bergeron, J. J. M. (1978a). *Proc. Natl. Acad. Sci. U.S.A.* **75,** 3302.
Posner, B. I., Josefsberg, Z., and Bergeron, J. J. M. (1978). *J. Biol. Chem.* **253,** 4067.
Posner, B. I., Josefsberg, Z., and Bergeron, J. J. M. (1979a). *Pediat. Adolesc. Endocrinol.* **7,** 382.
Posner, B. I., Josefsberg, Z., and Bergeron, J. J. M. (1979b). *J. Biol. Chem.* **254,** 12494.
Posner, B. I., Patel, B., and Bergeron, J. J. M. (1980a). *Clin. Res.* **28,** 521.
Posner, B. I., Gonzales, R., and Guyda, H. J. (1980b). *Can. J. Biochem.* **58,** 1075.
Posner, B. I., Patel, B., Verma, A. K., and Bergeron, J. J. M. (1980c). *J. Biol. Chem.* **255,** 735.
Pricer, W. E., and Ashwell, G. (1976). *J. Biol. Chem.* **251,** 7539.
Rajaniemi, H., and Vanha-Pertrulla, T. (1972). *Endocrinology* **90,** 1.
Rome, L. H., Garvin, A. J., Attietta, M. M., and Neufeld, E. F. (1979). *Cell* **17,** 143.
Roth, J. (1973). *Metabolism* **22,** 1059.
Schlessinger, J., Schecter, Y., Willingham, M. C., and Pastan, I. (1978). *Proc. Natl. Acad. Sci. U.S.A.* **75,** 2659.
Sikstrom, R. A., Posner, B. I., and Bergeron, J. J. M. (1980). *Cell Biol. Int. Rep.* **4,** 15.
Steiner, D. F. (1977). *Diabetes* **26,** 322.
Stockel, K., Paravocini, U., and Thoenen, H. (1974). *Brain Res.* **76,** 413.
Sutherland, E. W., Robison, G. A., and Butcher, R. W. (1968). *Circulation* **37,** 279.
Suzuki, K., and Kono, T. (1980). *Proc. Natl. Acad. Sci. U.S.A.* **77,** 2542.
Terris, S., and Steiner, D. F. (1975). *J. Biol. Chem.* **250,** 8389.
Terris, S., and Steiner, D. F. (1976). *J. Clin. Invest.* **57,** 885.
Tchervenkov, S., Goltzman, D., Rouleau, M. F., Rosenblatt, M., and Bergeron, J. J. M. (1980). *Annu. Meet. Endocrinol. Soc., 62nd* Abstr. No. 200, p. 224.
Van Houten, M., and Posner, B. I. (1979). *Nature (London)* **282,** 623.
Van Houten, M., Posner, B. I., Kopriwa, B., and Brawer, J. (1979). *Endocrinology* **105,** 666.
Van Obberghen, E., Spooner, P. M., Kahn, C. R., Chernick, S. S., Garrison, M. M., Karlsson, F. A., Greenfeld, C. (1979). *Nature (London)* **280,** 500.
Varga, J. M., Moellmann, G., Fritsch, P., Godawska, E., and Lerner, A. B. (1976). *Proc. Natl. Acad. Sci. U.S.A.* **73,** 559.

Verma, A. K., and Posner, B. I. (1979). *Annu. Meet. Endocrinol. Soc.*, 61st Abstr. No. 30, p. 20.
Verma, A. K., Posner, B. I., and Bergeron, J. J. M. (1978). *J. Cell Biol.* **83,** 2460.
Vigneri, R., Pliam, N. B., Cohen, D. C., Pezzino, V., Wong, K. Y., and Goldfine, I. D. (1978a). *J. Biol. Chem.* **253,** 8192.
Vigneri, R., Goldfine, I. D., Wong, K. Y., Smith, G. J., and Pezzino, V. (1978b). *J. Biol. Chem.* **253,** 2098.
Walsh, R., Posner, B. I., Kopriwa, B., and Brawer, J. (1978). *Science* **201,** 1041.
Wattiaux, R., Wattiaux-de Coninck, S., Ronveaux-Dupal, M.-F., and Dubois, F. (1978). *J. Cell Biol.* **78,** 349.
Warshawsky, H., Goltzman, D., Rouleau, M. F., and Bergeron, J. J. M. (1980). *J. Cell Biol.* **85,** 682.
Wibo, M., and Poole, B. (1974). *J. Cell Biol.* **63,** 430.
Yip, C. C., Yeung, C. W. T., and Moule, M. L. (1980). *Biochemistry* **19,** 70.
Young, M. E. M., Moscarello, M. A., and Riordan, J. R. (1976). *J. Biol. Chem.* **251,** 5860.

DISCUSSION

A. Amsterdam: I have two questions. The first concerns the redistribution of ^{125}I-labeled insulin. Have studies been done on this? The second is does the injection of one hormone influence the distribution of another?

B. Posner: We've done detailed studies, looking at the redistribution of ^{125}I-labeled insulin [*J. Biol. Chem.* (1980) **255,** 735] where we, fairly convincingly, showed that redistribution was of minimal significance. Thus, the addition of ^{125}I-labeled insulin to rat liver just prior to homogenization did not result in the association of significant radioactivity with the subsequently prepared Golgi fractions.

The second question is, does the injection of one hormone influence in any way the distribution of another? We haven't studied that in great detail. At least at early times this appears unlikely since a large excess of unrelated hormone coinjected with labeled hormone in no way influenced the uptake of labeled hormone. We have not examined whether there might be an influence on radiolabel distribution within various subfractions. Our major efforts have been in trying to delineate the actors in this rather complicated process.

M. Postel-Vinay: I would like to give you more evidence of the internalization of the receptors in parallelism to the hormone internalization. This is from the work of Bernard Desbuquois and myself in Paris. Using subcellular fractionation techniques, we have examined the changes in the distribution of the receptors for insulin, growth hormone, and glucagon in rat liver that occur following *in vivo* injection of native hormone. We found that, in insulin-injected rats, the insulin-binding activity decreases by 2-fold in the plasma membranes and concomitantly increases by 2- to 3-fold in the Golgi fractions. These changes occur as early as 90 seconds after injection, are maximal between 4 and 16 minutes, and persist for at least 80 minutes; by 2–3 hour the binding activity is restored in plasma membranes whereas it decreases below control values in Golgi fractions. We believe that these data are compatible with the concept that, at least with insulin, internalization of the receptors accompanies and presumably mediates that of the ligand.

B. Posner: I'm aware of such data from the group at Hôpital Enfant Malade in Paris [*FEBS Lett.* (1979) **106,** 338]. Your data certainly would qualify as one of the pieces of evidence supporting hormone-induced internalization of receptors. The only caveat I raise is whether, since the Golgi compartment probably reflects newly synthesized receptor as well as internalized receptor, you may not be looking at new receptors.

C. Kahn: I found your talk very interesting, there was a lot of new data and I'm glad to see that Canadians studying insulin action are as long-winded as the Americans studying insulin action. However, I have a couple of questions which I'm really trying to resolve in my mind as to whether the pathway which you are describing for the hormone, the fate of the hormones bound to the cell, is a unique type and how it might fit in with the observations of Carpentier and Gorden, as well as observations concerning other internalized ligands. I have two rather related questions in this regard. The first is that while I'm really not sure of the details of the methodology, I imagine that to show the presence of the Golgi vesicles filled with lipoprotein, one must give the animals either alcohol or some sort of lipid meal before the sacrifice, or were these studies in basal state.

B. Posner: Because of criticisms that were made to us about the use of alcohol and the influence that it might have in stimulating crinophagy and other processes, we excluded alcohol from all our latter studies. All our animals have been starved overnight and are in a basal state.

C. Kahn: The second point is related to the generality of the model you have developed. The model or paradigm that Gorden and Carpentier have been following is very similar to that that has been developed for LDL and for α_2-macroglobulin and some other internalized molecules. I was wondering if you apply the same types of technology and the same criteria which you are applying for the hormones, would you now conclude that these other ligands are following the same pathway of internalization, or is the pathway, through the Golgi unique for the hormonal ligands which are internalized?

B. Posner: I don't think we can say the pathway is unique for hormones. What we can say is that this is the predominant pathway we observe. Why others are not seeing this in their systems I'm not sure? The problem may be more in the interpretation of data than in what is actually observed. There is the possibility of direct access to the lysosomal system as with bulk phase endocytosis. Let me point out that when you examine hepatocytes and lymphocytes in culture it is not clear how you distinguish between a Golgi vesicle and a lysosome. One of the virtues of working with the living animal is that you can identify Golgi vesicles on morphological grounds by virtue of their VLDL content. It is difficult to be sure on strictly morphological grounds, what is the nature of a vesicle in fibroblasts and other cells in culture. Now there is the added problem of heterogeneity of the Golgi vesicles, thus VLDL markers may not be unique to galactosyltransferase-enriched structures. In summary, I think the problem of sorting out vesicle traffic is a central one and we will have to use every tool we possibly can in order to solve it.

C. Kahn: If you apply the same criteria to the evaluation of the data on LDL would you say, at this point, that we could safely say that LDL goes directly to the lysosome or does this issue also need further investigation?

B. Posner: Yes, I think this should be reconsidered and investigated with the view to thinking about LDLs going through the Golgi apparatus.

J. E. Rall: If I can come back to the first question, so much depends on the precision of subcellular fractionation. I have two questions. One is, have you done affinity labeling of the surface receptors and then done your purification. I notice you did use a photoaffinity label of insulin but I was not sure whether that had been done before or after disruption of the cell. Have you done it before with any kind of affinity label or even with something like lactoperoxidase iodination of any tyrosine group available on the cell surface. Second, on some of your autoradiographs I saw what I thought were black dots and I didn't see the familar black snakes. Could you tell me why you get more dots and less snakes?

B. Posner: In respect to the latter question, the compact grains seen on autoradiography were developed by the use of special procedures developed by Dr. Beatrice Kopriwa at McGill University [*Histochemistry* (1975) **44,** 201]. This permits increased ease of identification of structures underlying the grains, especially if the structures are small. The first question referred to affinity labeling of the receptor. Our studies are all *in vivo* and this renders affinity labeling impractical. This problem should be approached using cells in culture.

R. Chatterton: My question is somewhat peripheral to your main discussion, but I'd hope you could shed some light on it because I have an interest in the area. Glucocorticoids, as we know, inhibit many of the effects on the long list that Dr. Kahn presented; some of the earliest as well as some of the last acting such as those on proliferation of cells. We also know that glucocorticoids, particularly in lysosomes, stabilize membranes. I wondered if you'd done any studies on sites of action in the process where glucocorticoids might act, or whether you could speculate on where they could act.

B. Posner: We have not studied the internalization of glucocorticoids. We did look at triiodothyronine and observed no significant concentration of this small molecule in vacuolar elements of the hepatocyte.

R. Fellows: In order to separate the contributions of biosynthesis of receptor and internalization of receptor to the Golgi binding activity, have you carried out experiments to inhibit biosynthesis with various agents?

B. Posner: In collaboration with Paul Kelly and Henry Friesen [*Endocrinology* (1975) **97,** 1408] we showed that in animals treated with cyclohexamide there was a rapid decline in the hepatic prolactin receptor level. Some preliminary studies are underway to define whether this decline occurs more rapidly in the Golgi compartment.

J. Nolin: I have a question that may bear some relationship to Dr. Kahn's question. It may also be particularly appropriate. I'm curious about your use of the ethanol-treated rat. To what extent have your studies involved sober rats? I ask this particularly in view of some data presented by W. V. Moore, P. Leppert, and J. A. Fix (*Proc. Endocrine Soc. June 1980*, Abstract 675 p. 243) at the Endocrine Meetings this June indicating that some of the parameters you have described are quite different when they are studied in the non-alcohol-treated rat.

B. Posner: Well, we actually got rid of the drunk rats because they were tearing up the place. Seriously, we decided to avoid the use of alcohol because of criticisms like yours. John Bergeron recently published a study where he compared the properties of Golgi elements isolated from ethanol-treated and control rats. He showed a virtual identity of properties [*Biochim. Biophys. Acta* (1979) **555,** 493]. Even so we decided to stay away from ethanol and in all our recent studies we've not used ethanol-treated animals. We have also repeated a number of the insulin uptake studies in non-ethanol-treated animals and have found the same pattern and sequence of uptake. So I don't think that ethanol treatment has introduced a problem in our studies.

S. Cohen: I'm not surprised that there are receptors in the Golgi apparatus. All of the receptors must be synthesized within the cell and they have to be transported to outside of the cell. The mechanism of transport is the Golgi apparatus, just as it is for the release of insulin. What I'm wondering is if insulin is not getting in by the reverse exocytosis, endocytosis, just accidently, and once it's within the cell it would combine with receptors already there. Does your data exclude this possibility?

B. Posner: Well there are data that I didn't show you on the effect of colchicine on the internalization process. When we treat rats with colchicine in doses which have been shown to inhibit exocytosis to a significant extent, perhaps 40–50%, we see no or very little effect on the internalization of insulin. So we don't think that it's coupled to the exocytotic process as such. We cannot be completely sure; there may be other changes that compensate for the lack of coupling but it does seem on the basis of this kind of study not to be coupled.

S. Cohen: Does colchicine affect the number of receptors that are on the cell membrane?

B. Posner: No it does not, in the time periods in which we have looked.

H.-C. Blossey: There may be two pools of receptors within the cell, one of the newly synthesized receptor and one is the internalized receptor. What about the quantitative relationship between these two pools of receptors within the cell in steady-state conditions.

B. Posner: I'm not sure what the quantitative relationship is and to what extent the two pools are mixed. Our data to date suggest mixing though they are not completely definitive.

Z. Naor: Can you distinguish in your morphological studies between Golgi and GERL in view of the report that GERL might resemble the lysosome?

B. Posner: You are right. We should really refer to Golgi-GERL. I don't think we can exclude GERL from being involved especially since we are not sure what it constitutes in the rat hepatocyte.

C. Raj: Is aggregation of and capping of receptors in these tissues an essential prerequisite for internalization?

B. Posner: From our data we can say nothing about that. From the data in the literature it appears that capping and macroaggregation are not required for internalization.

H. Friesen: Do you find any fragmentation at all of the prolactin that is internalized in the liver?

B. Posner: To the extent that we've looked, no. However, we have not examined this with detailed chromatographic–electrophoretic methods as yet.

Studies on the Structure and Function of the Chicken Progesterone Receptor

WILLIAM T. SCHRADER, MARIA E. BIRNBAUMER, MARK R. HUGHES, NANCY L. WEIGEL, WAYNE W. GRODY, AND BERT W. O'MALLEY

Department of Cell Biology, Baylor College of Medicine, Houston, Texas

I. Introduction

A. SUMMARY

The chicken oviduct progesterone receptor is shown to consist of two nonidentical subunits, each able to bind hormone. The subunits are each single polypeptide chains, with discrete, separable functional domains. The two subunits are separate gene products, probably arising from different genes. The intact complex manifests the chromatin-binding activity of the larger B subunit but not the DNA-binding activity of the smaller A subunit. The latter activity is expressed only upon dissociation of A from the complex. This protein binds DNA from any source with high affinity, preferring single-stranded structures. From its effect upon double-stranded DNA, a role is proposed for this protein as a helix-destabilizing protein. On the basis of the known interaction of B and A with nuclear constituents and as a result of chromatin transcription studies a hypothesis is advanced for the mechanism by which the progesterone receptor may regulate gene transcription. In this hypothesis we envision an initial interaction of the intact AB complex with chromatin mediated by the chromatin site on B, followed by liberation of A which can interact with DNA to potentiate RNA synthesis.

This article is not intended to be a comprehensive review on steroid receptors, nor even a review of work on the chick progesterone receptor. Rather, it presents work from this laboratory.

B. BACKGROUND REVIEW OF EARLIER WORK BY OUR LABORATORY

For a number of years, we have been studying the mechanism of steroid hormone regulation of gene expression in the chick oviduct (for reviews,

ISBN 0-12-571137-9

see O'Malley *et al.,* 1969; Vedeckis *et al.,* 1978). This work has been aided by the development of specific gene probes for the major egg white proteins regulated in the gland, a topic in a preceding issue of this series (O'Malley *et al.,* 1979).

The salient features of this reproductive system are shown in Fig. 1. The immature oviduct consists of a tube of undifferentiated cells. Administration of estrogen causes growth and differentiation of the gland with inpocketing of the surface epithelium to produce structures called tubular glands. These tubular glands eventually comprise almost 90% of the cell population in the mature laying hen oviduct. These cells synthesize ovalbumin, conalbumin, lysozyme, ovomucoid, and a variety of other egg white proteins. In the differentiated cells, estrogen causes *de novo* synthesis of messenger RNA for these proteins in a very rapid process which follows the accumulation of the steroids in the cell nuclei (Swaneck *et al.,* 1979; Tsai *et al.,* 1976). Progesterone administration to the undifferentiated tissue does not cause growth or differentiation. However, when this hormone is administered to estrogenized chicks, surface epithelial goblet cells synthesize and secrete the protein avidin (O'Malley, 1967). If estrogen administration is discontinued to produce what is called the "withdrawn state," a regressed structure is seen in which none of the egg white proteins is synthesized and there is a concomitant cessation of synthesis of their respective messenger RNAs. Curiously, administration

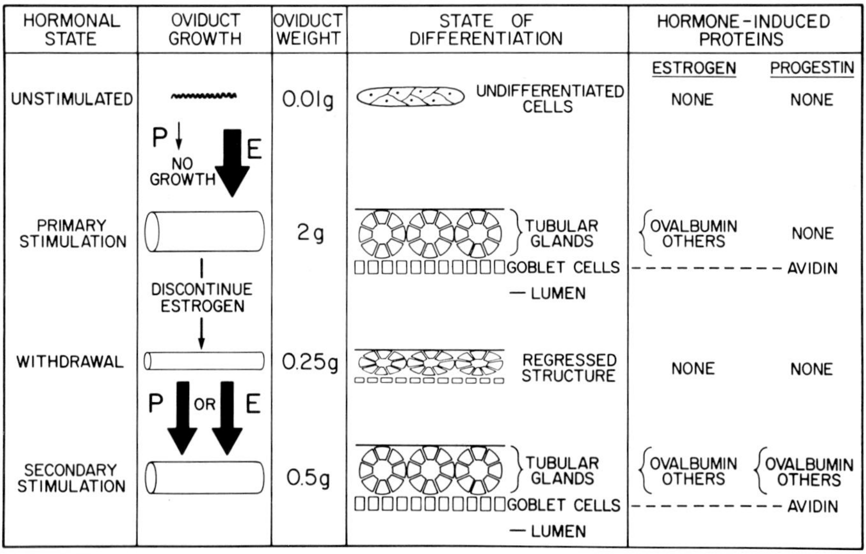

HORMONAL STATE	OVIDUCT GROWTH	OVIDUCT WEIGHT	STATE OF DIFFERENTIATION	HORMONE-INDUCED PROTEINS	
				ESTROGEN	PROGESTIN
UNSTIMULATED		0.01g	UNDIFFERENTIATED CELLS	NONE	NONE
	P ↓ NO GROWTH; E ↓				
PRIMARY STIMULATION		2g	TUBULAR GLANDS	OVALBUMIN OTHERS	NONE
			GOBLET CELLS		AVIDIN
			— LUMEN		
	DISCONTINUE ESTROGEN				
WITHDRAWAL		0.25g	REGRESSED STRUCTURE	NONE	NONE
	P OR E				
SECONDARY STIMULATION		0.5g	TUBULAR GLANDS	OVALBUMIN OTHERS	OVALBUMIN OTHERS
			GOBLET CELLS		AVIDIN
			— LUMEN		

FIG. 1. Schematic representation of steroid hormonal events in regulation of chick oviduct cell function.

of either progesterone or estrogen (a process referred to as "secondary stimulation") causes the renewed onset of synthesis of ovalbumin and the other egg white proteins (Palmiter, 1973). For reasons which remain completely unclear, progesterone is equally as potent as estrogen in inducing ovalbumin synthesis in this stage. The process is not due to peripheral or target cell conversion of progesterone to estrogen.

Our interest in progesterone receptors began with the observations of a number of laboratories that radioactive steroids administered *in vivo* accumulate in target cell nuclei. In the oviduct, the time course for progesterone's appearance in nuclei was consistent with its putative role in modulation of gene expression (O'Malley *et al.*, 1971). For this reason the progesterone receptor seemed a likely candidate as a gene regulatory protein in this organism. Since specific endpoint gene DNAs destined for regulation by this agent had been cloned in our laboratory, we have been attempting to elucidate both the structure and function of the progesterone receptor protein in molecular terms.

The progesterone receptor was also a good choice for study since the tissue can be grown and differentiated to produce progesterone receptor without requiring administration of progesterone itself. Thus oviduct cells in the estrogenized gland contain progesterone receptor unoccupied by the ligand and thus accessible to binding *in vitro* by radioactive hormone. Our earlier studies both *in vivo* and *in vitro* had shown that radioactive progesterone–receptor complexes accumulated in the target cell nuclei. These studies were completed some time ago and the results of these investigations were summarized in numerous review articles (O'Malley *et al.*, 1970; Buller and O'Malley, 1976). Of particular importance was the observation that there appeared to be a finite number of sites in oviduct cell nuclei to which the receptors would bind (Buller *et al.*, 1975). An example of this sort of study is shown in Fig. 2. Here progesterone receptors of oviduct cytosol labeled *in vitro* with tritiated progesterone were used to titrate oviduct nuclei. The Scatchard plot of the binding data is shown in the figure. The binding is a saturable phenomenon, with an apparent equilibrium constant of about 10^{-8} molar and a limited number of sites per cell nucleus. In this case about 3600 sites per nuclei were detected.

II. Studies of Progesterone Receptor Structure

A. HORMONE BINDING SITE ANALYSIS

It was of interest to understand the biochemistry of the receptor protein, and specifically the sort of interactions with nuclear constituents which account for this observation. First we studied the nature of interac-

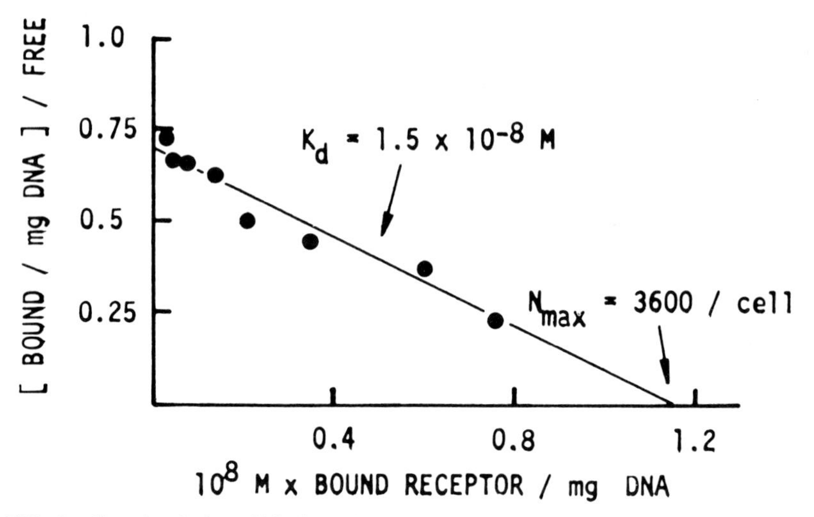

FIG. 2. Scatchard plot of binding of cytoplasmic progesterone receptor hormone complexes to oviduct nuclei at 0°C. Oviduct nuclei were titrated *in vitro* with chick oviduct cytosol containing progesterone receptor saturated with tritiated progesterone. The hyperbolic binding curves were converted to the Scatchard plot representation shown here and corrected for the DNA concentration of the nuclei.

tion of progesterone receptor with its ligand. Titration of progesterone receptor with a variety of ligands revealed that only compounds known to be biologically active in the chicken showed significant binding to the protein. Dissociation rate experiments such as that shown in Fig. 3 were done. Figure 3 shows an Arrhenius plot, in which the dissociation rate constant was found to vary exponentially with temperature. The plot is linear, indicating that there is no evident conformational change in the protein involved in the dissociation process. Similar titration experiments done with receptor adsorbed to a variety of ion-exchange resins showed that adsorption of the protein to these resins did not significantly alter the hormone-binding site, as evidenced by the fact that both the association and dissociation rate constants were not detectably perturbed by these interactions (Hansen *et al.*, 1976). These studies suggested that the hormone's interaction with the protein probably involved interactions with a hydrophobic domain on the receptor different from the ionic environment involved in receptor binding to the resins.

We measured the dissociation rate by dialysis, and found that the progesterone–receptor complex had an apparent half-life at zero degrees of approximately 80 hours. However when nonradioactive progesterone was added in excess to the incubations the half-life was reduced to approximately 12 hours (Schrader *et al.*, 1975a). From this and other observations we conclude that there is apparently a complex dissociation reac-

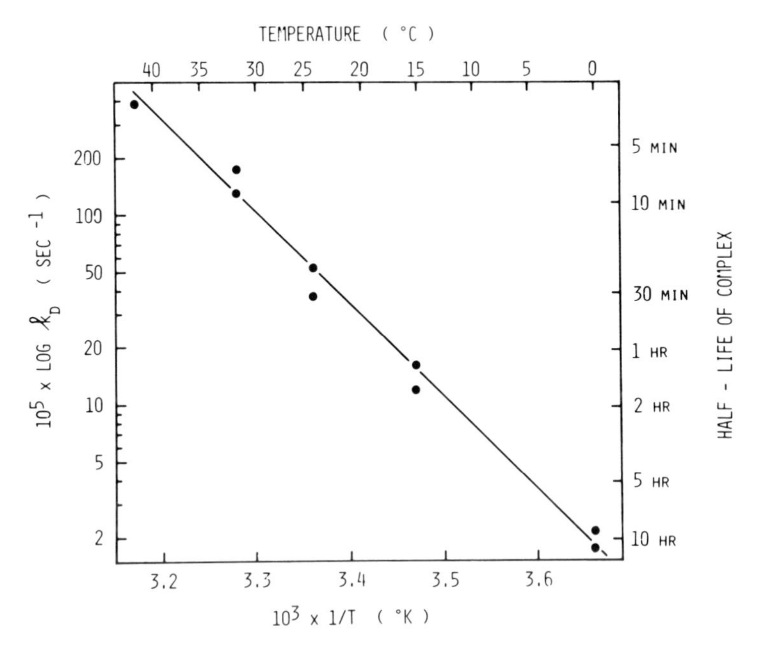

FIG. 3. Arrhenius plot of the progesterone receptor dissociation reaction. Labeled progesterone receptor complexes were prepared by ammonium sulfate precipitation of cytosol and redissolved in low ionic strength buffer. For each point an excess of nonradioactive progesterone was added and the time course of dissociation of the complexes was determined at each temperature indicated. From the half-time of the complexes at each temperature appropriate dissociation rate constants were determined and plotted as shown.

tion going on by which the ligand induces alterations of receptor structure. Such a mechanism may involve existence of a secondary or "helper" ligand site on the protein. This experimental evidence would be entirely consistent with the steric–allosteric model for hormone–receptor interaction proposed by Sherman (1970). Finally, a variety of studies of the effect of pH, ionic strength, and the presence of cofactors for the hormone-binding reaction has been undertaken in our laboratory. To date no definitive example exists for the involvement of any cofactors in the hormone-binding reaction.

B. CHARACTERIZATION OF PROTEINS A AND B

1. *Chromatographic Behavior*

In order to evaluate the involvement of other cytoplasmic proteins in modulating the hormone-binding reaction we performed a partial purification of the protein by gel filtration as shown in Fig. 4. In Fig. 4A is shown

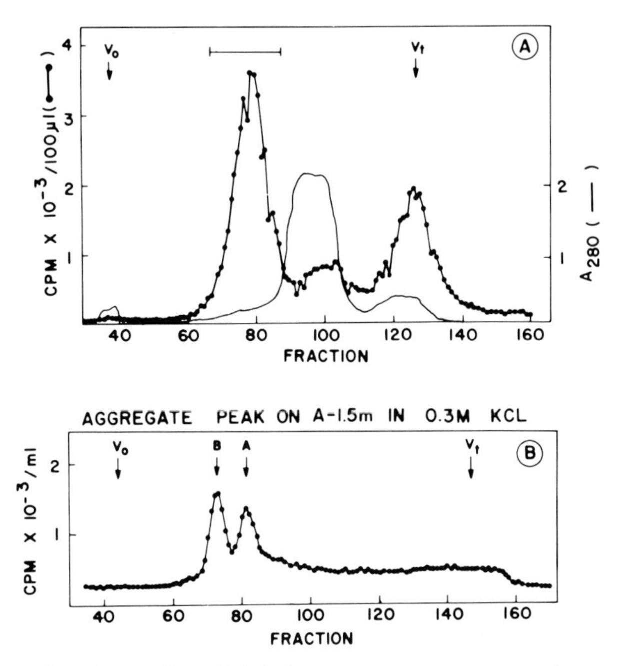

FIG. 4. Gel filtration profiles of labeled progesterone receptor complexes at low and high ionic strength. (A) Gel filtration on Agarose A-15m in low ionic strength. V_0 and V_t denote the void and total volumes of the column, respectively. Aliquots were counted for radioactivity (●—●). The solid line denotes the protein profile determined by absorbe nce at 280 nm. The bars from fraction 65–85 denote the fraction of receptor pooled, concentrated and rechromatographed as shown in B. (B) is A-1.5m chromatography in 0.3 *M* KCl. The arrows at B and A denote the elution locations of authentic receptor B and A prepared by ion-exchange chromatography.

the elution profile of radioactive cytoplasmic progesterone–receptor complexes run under conditions of low ionic strength. The receptor elutes as a radioactive peak ahead of the major cytoplasmic proteins with an apparent molecular weight of about 225,000. This material was pooled and rechromatographed in high ionic strength on another gel filtration column. The radioactivity was resolved into two smaller components termed B and A which from their relative peak heights appear to be present in approximately equal amounts. Peak B, in fraction 72, and peak A, in fraction 80, had apparent molecular weights of about 114,000 and 71,000, respectively. We predicted they were present in the larger complex in equal amounts, from the assumption that each bound a single molecule of labeled progesterone, and the fact that their molecular weights sum to less than that of the larger complex.

These individual components were shown not to be merely the product of *in vitro* preparation methods. Exactly the same profile was obtained when the apo-protein (that is, the protein lacking hormone) was chromatographed. Second, there was no evidence for precursors in this process since no higher molecular weight progesterone binding molecules were detected (Vedeckis *et al.*, 1979). Addition of protease inhibitors similarly had no effect on the profile. Thus we concluded that neither was the product of a proteolytic degradation of an intact larger molecule.

Since B and A were not clearly resolved by the gel filtration method, ion-exchange chromatography was used to resolve the two proteins more completely. This has been accomplished using either DEAE cellulose, phosphocellulose, or hydroxylapatite (Schrader, 1975). On all three of these resins adequate resolution can be obtained in order to perform hormone-binding studies on the individual A and B proteins (Schrader and O'Malley, 1972). When protein A and protein B were examined individually their hormone-binding specificity and kinetics of progesterone binding were found to be identical and indistinguishable from the starting cytoplasmic material. Thus we concluded that both A and B were authentic progesterone receptor proteins and that their isolation into individual fractions did not demonstrably alter their hormone-binding characteristics. A summary of a number of chemical and physical parameters of the A and B proteins obtained over the past few years is shown in Table I. This table summarizes the values obtained for Stokes radius, sedimentation coefficient, and the apparent molecular weight calculated for these components from these two values. The molecular weights determined under denaturing conditions were made from the purified proteins obtained as shown below. In addition, Table I summarizes the hormone-binding characteristics of the two proteins.

2. *Interaction with Nuclear Constituents*

Of great interest was the question of whether both of these proteins occurred in oviduct nuclei. We showed by both *in vivo* and *in vitro* tissue slice experiments that both A and B could be extracted from nuclei in approximately equal amounts. When characterized by both gel filtration and ion-exchange chromatography, no differences have been found in the chromatographic behavior of A and B from the nucleus as compared to their behavior from the cytoplasm. Thus at the present time there is no evidence for a conversion of these proteins from a cytoplasmic to a nuclear form.

In studying the nuclear-binding reaction two interesting features were observed. The first is shown in Fig. 5. When DNA cellulose chromatography was used to evaluate the binding of these proteins to DNA, we observed that only the A protein showed DNA-binding activity (Schrader

TABLE I

Molecular Properties of Receptor Forms

Parameter	Method	A	B	Intact complex	Units
Sedimentation coefficient	Sucrose gradient	3.6	4.2	6	S
Stokes radius (R_s)	Gel filtration	46	63	80	A
Frictional ratio (f/f_0)	S and Rs	1.74	1.9	—	
Axial ratio (prolate)	S and Rs	14	18	—	
Partial specific volume	Bouyancy in NaBr	0.73	0.73	—	cm^3/gm
Molecular weight	S and Rs	71K	114K	225K	gm/mole
	SDS Gels	79K	108K	—	gm/mole
Association rate constant	$k_a \times 10^{-5}$	2.8	6.3	7.0	M^{-1} sec^{-1}
Dissociation rate constant	$k_d \times 10^5$	1.9	2.4	2.1	sec^{-1}
Equilibrium constant	$k_d \times k_a$	0.07	0.04	0.03	nM
	Scatchard plot	5.0	5.0	5.0	nM
N-terminus	Protein sequencing	Blocked	Blocked	—	
Number of hormone sites	UV spectroscopy	1	1	2	
Percentage α-helix	Circular dichroism	—	12	—	
Nuclear binding preference	Titration	DNA	Chromatin	Chromatin	
Number of peptide chains	SDS gels	1	1	—	

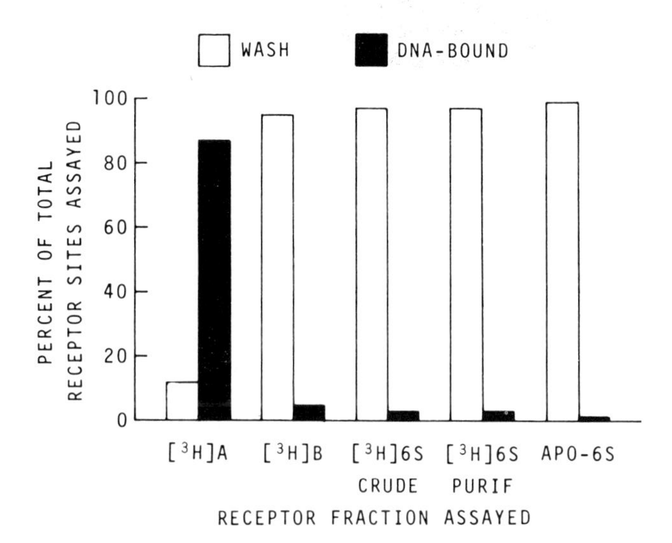

FIG. 5. DNA cellulose chromatography of partially purified receptors prepared by ion-exchange chromatography. DNA cellulose columns were prepared in low ionic strength. The receptors were applied at 0.05 *M* KCl and washed with this buffer. Then DNA-bound material was eluted at 0.4 *M* KCl, and samples of each fraction were counted for radioactivity. A, B, and 6S refer to receptors A, B, and intact complex, respectively.

et al., 1972). Protein B, although extractable from nuclei, did not show detectable DNA-binding activity at ionic strengths greater than 0.05 *M* KCl (Vedeckis *et al.*, 1980b).

Since a larger complex containing A and B was observed on both gel filtration and sucrose gradients in low ionic strength, we tested that larger complex for its binding to these nuclear constituents also, as shown in Fig. 5. The 6 S complex did not bind to DNA cellulose. From this result we speculated that the receptor aggregate had a masked DNA-binding site on the A protein which was exposed only upon a conformational change or upon its dissociation from the larger complex (O'Malley *et al.*, 1972; Coty *et al.*, 1979).

The second interesting feature was that chromatin-binding activity was found to reside in the receptor B protein (Schrader *et al.*, 1972). It is this protein which appears to interact with target cell-specific nuclear "acceptor" sites. These sites are comprised of nuclear nonhistone proteins (Spelsberg *et al.*, 1972) and are presumed to be required for binding the intact receptors within chromatin (Spelsberg *et al.*, 1977).

The intact large receptor complexes, containing both proteins B and A, bind to oviduct nuclei (Buller *et al.*, 1975) with an apparent equilibrium constant of 10^{-8} to 10^{-9} *M*. Thus we conclude that the chromatin-binding site on protein B is not occluded in the large complex.

Our studies of receptor B's interaction with chromatin have not been carried further recently; the reader is directed to Vedeckis *et al.* (1978) for review.

C. PURIFICATION OF THE PROTEINS

1. Studies by Steroid Photoaffinity Labeling

In order to study receptors A and B in greater detail, we developed a method for labeling both covalently with radioactive steroid. The method involves photoaffinity labeling of receptor proteins in crude extracts using a synthetic progestin, [^{3}H]R5020 (Dure *et al.*, 1980). This ligand binds with somewhat better affinity to oviduct progesterone receptors than does authentic progesterone. Because of the presence of a double bond in the B ring, the absorption maximum is shifted toward the visible and irradiation can be performed at wavelengths above 300 nm. Thus irradiation of this compound does not cause detectable damage to the protein structure itself. When the progesterone receptors in cytosol were complexed with tritiated R5020 and then irradiated with UV light, analysis of the protein mixture by SDS–polyacrylamide gels showed the results in Fig. 6. Here radioactive R5020 peaks were observed by counting gel slices at apparent molecular weights of 106,000 and 78,000. Approximately equal peak heights were observed as shown in the top portion of the figure. As shown on the bottom, the resolution of receptor A and B protein by DEAE cellulose chromatography after irradiation successfully resolved these two peaks. Thus we determined that the larger peak was protein B and the smaller peak at 78,000 was protein A.

The method can be applied to these crude mixtures with good specificity as shown in Fig. 7. Here the receptor A protein was photoaffinity labeled as in Fig. 6 after partial purification by ion exchange and DNA-cellulose chromatography. Then the sample was applied to an SDS–polyacrylamide slab gel and the tritium was detected by autofluorography of the gel. The staining of the gel shown on the left with Coomassie blue revealed that the preparation has been partially purified but no stained band could be detected at 79,000 molecular weight. However, the autofluorograph on the right shows a major radioactive band at that molecular weight along with a satellite band at 64,000. It is not yet clear whether the secondary band is a breakdown product of the receptor or represents the labeling of a nonspecific component in the mixture. Similar experiments have been carried out following partial purification of the receptor

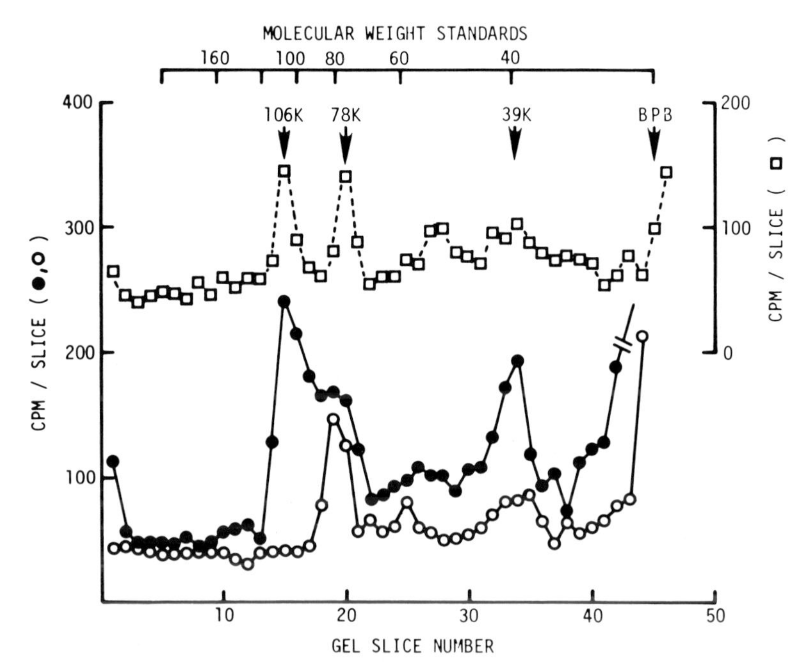

FIG. 6. SDS–polyacrylamide gel electrophoresis analysis of tritiated R5020 coupled to progesterone receptors and then precipitated at 35% saturation of ammonium sulfate. The redissolved precipitates were then UV irradiated for 30 minutes. The samples were then collected, lyophilized, and subjected to SDS–polyacrylamide gel electrophoresis in 7.5% polyacrylamide gels. Upper panel, Molecular weight determinations of the two hormone binding peaks. Lower panel, SDS gels of receptor A and B protein separated by DEAE cellulose chromatography following irradiation. Open circles, DEAE receptor A fraction prepared by stepwise elution of DEAE cellulose at 0.15 *M* KCl. Closed circles, DEAE B protein fraction obtained by stepwise elution of the column with 0.3 *M* KCl.

B protein. In these cases a band of approximately 108,000 molecular weight is labeled.

From the results of Figs. 6 and 7, we can conclude that the progesterone receptor A and B proteins are large polypeptide chains, with the hormone-binding sites contained within these structures. As will be further detailed below, there is no evidence at present for involvement of additional polypeptides held noncovalently for any of the known activities of these proteins.

2. *Purification of A and B*

We proceeded to purify the receptor A protein by the method developed by Coty and co-workers (1979), using differential chromatography. This method involves passage of crude receptor extracts through columns of

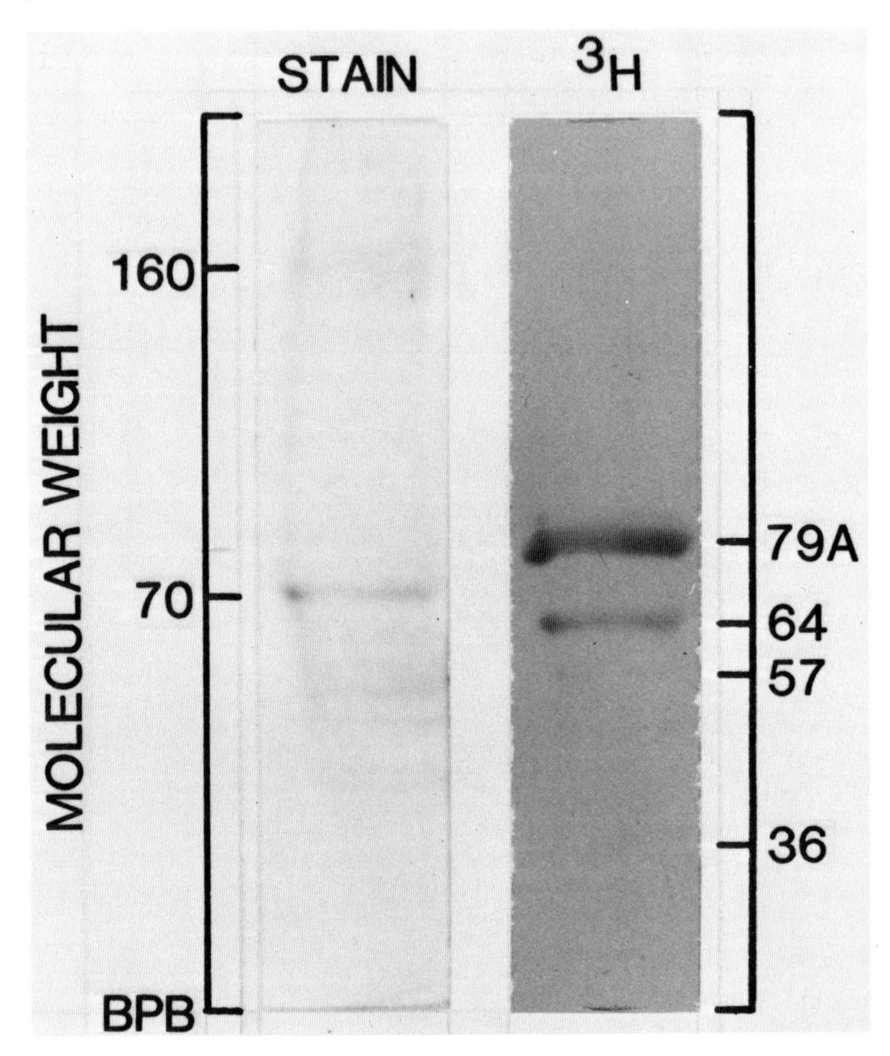

FIG. 7. SDS–polyacrylamide gel electrophoresis autofluorogram of [^{3}H]R5020-labeled A protein after partial purification of labeled ammonium sulfate precipitate by DEAE cellulose and DNA cellulose chromatography. The labeled material was run on a 7.5% polyacrylamide slab gel. The Coomassie blue-stained gel pattern of this material is shown on the left. On the right is the autofluorogram of this lane after impregnation of the slab gel with Enhance (New England Nuclear). Molecular weight standards were run in adjacent lanes and shown for comparison.

phosphocellulose and DNA cellulose to which the aggregate receptor does not adsorb. However, the receptor A protein itself will adsorb to both resins following dissociation of the large complex to its subunits. By this method, about a 5000-fold purification was obtained. A single band of stained protein was seen by SDS–polyacrylamide gel electrophoresis with the molecular weight at 79,000. The protein obtained in this fashion retains its ability to bind to DNA as shown in Fig. 8. In this figure sucrose gradient ultracentrifugation was used to examine the binding of [^{3}H]progesterone-labeled A protein to a ^{32}P-labeled bacterial plasmid pBR322 DNA. When sedimented independently, the two materials behaved as shown on the left. On the right is shown the behavior when the receptor was mixed with an excess of the ^{32}P-labeled DNA. Figure 8 shows that the majority of the receptor A protein sedimented with the plasmid DNA, evidence that the purified protein had retained its DNA-binding activity.

Receptor B protein was purified from oviducts of laying hens by the method of Schrader *et al.* (1977). This protein was complexed with endogenous progesterone and was only labeled to the extent of 2% by the addition of radioactive hormone to the extract. The B protein was also purified about 5000-fold and gave a single band with a molecular weight of about 110,000. It was shown to be receptor B by the criteria listed in Table II. This protein had also retained its nuclear-binding activity as shown by chromatin titration experiments similar to that presented in Fig. 9. Here saturable binding to oviduct chromatin was observed with an equilibrium constant of about 10^{-9} molar. Thus these techniques which have been

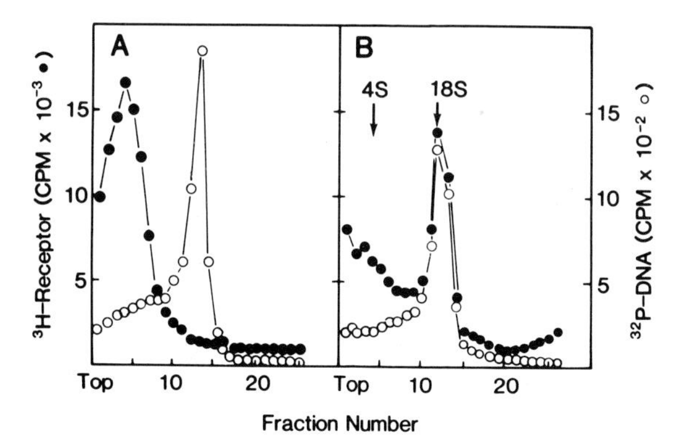

FIG. 8. DNA-binding activity of the purified progesterone receptor A subunit studied by sedimentation in 5% to 20% sucrose gradients. Closed circles, receptor–hormone complexes. Open circles, linear end-labeled [^{32}P]plasmid pBR322 DNA following *Eco*RI digestion. (A) Sedimentation of the individual reactants. (B) Cosedimentation of receptor with the DNA peak when the two were mixed together.

TABLE II
Purification of Hen Progesterone Receptor B Subunit

Parameter	Method	Comments
Purity	1. SDS gel electrophoresis	1 Band; 108 K
	2. Acid–urea gel electrophoresis	1 Band
	3. Peptide mapping of ^{125}I-labeled receptor	Number of tyrosines correlates with amino acid analysis
	4. Gel filtration in guanidine HCl	1 A_{235} peak
Protein is receptor B	1. Nondenaturing gel electrophoresis	1 Band; coincident staining and ^{3}H
	2. UV spectroscopy	1 mol hormone/mol protein
	3. Gas chromatography–mass spectrometry of bound ligand from protein	Progesterone only; 0.35 mol/mol protein
	4. Photoaffinity labeling with ^{3}H-steroid	Purified protein has bound ^{3}H on SDS gels

presented in detail elsewhere satisfactorily purified both A and B receptor proteins to near homogeneity, with retention of some of the desired biologic characteristics.

We have had occasion to examine the potential enzymatic activities which might be present in these proteins as shown in Table III. Although

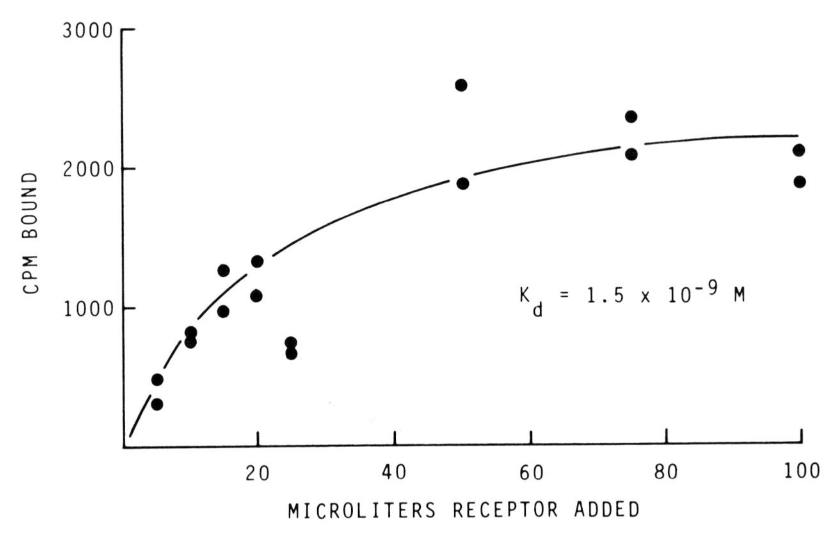

FIG. 9. Binding of purified hen receptor B subunit to chick oviduct chromatin. Chick oviduct chromatin was titrated with receptor as shown on the abscissa. After 60 minutes incubation at 0°C chromatin receptor complexes were collected by precipitation and the precipitates counted for radioactivity. The equilibrium constant shown on the figure was calculated by a Scatchard plot treatment of the data.

TABLE III
Enzyme Activities Not Detectable in Progesterone Receptors

Enzyme	Substrate	Assay condition
Ribonuclease	HnRNA	Gel electrophoresis
	Adenovirus mRNAs	TCA solubility
	Ovalbumin mRNA	DNA transcription
DNA exonuclease	5′ or 3′ end labeled DNA	Nitrocellulose filter binding, sedimentation
DNA endonuclease	Nick-translated DNA	Same
	ϕX174 RFI	Denaturation of closed circles
Protease	Receptor autolysis	SDS–PAGE
	Histone H1	Receptor + chromatin
	Azocasein	Spectrophotometric
RNA polymerase	Oviduct chromatin	RNA synthesis *in vitro*
	DNA	Same
	ATP + [^{32}P]pyrophosphate	Pyrophosphate exchange
DNA gyrase	Plasmid DNA	No ATP requirement

certainly not a complete list, this table summarizes a variety of enzyme tests which have been performed in our laboratories. To date, no additional enzymatic activity has been detected in either receptor A or receptor B nor in their intact aggregate. Thus, the potential for additional functional activities, while attractive due to the size of these proteins, remains an unproven concept.

D. COMPARISON OF THE PURIFIED PROTEINS

1. Limited Proteolysis

Due to the similarities of hormone-binding kinetics for the receptor A and B proteins we asked whether or not the two proteins might bear a precursor–product relationship. The first attempts to answer this question were undertaken by proteolytic digestion studies using endogenous proteases. Incubations of receptor under a variety of conditions in both crude and purified states with oviduct extracts, oviduct tissue, and with various purified proteases failed to show any conversion of the larger receptor B protein to receptor A, the smaller protein.

To test this question by a more direct structural determination progesterone receptors B and A covalently labeled with [^{3}H]R5020 were studied by SDS–polyacrylamide gel electrophoresis. The individual A and B proteins were partially digested in the native state using *Staphylococcus aureus* V8 protease. SDS–polyacrylamide gel electrophoresis of the digest showed the results of Fig. 10. This figure shows that the meroproteins (i.e., the hormone-binding fragments) of B and A differed slightly in molecular weight following digestion with this enzyme. This was consistent with the notion that the two proteins are not identical.

2. Peptide Mapping

A more definitive test was undertaken using the purified receptors A and B from hen oviduct. The receptor protein bands were sliced out of SDS–polyacrylamide gels and iodinated *in situ* by the chloramine T procedure (Weigel *et al.*, 1981a). Then the proteins were digested completely with trypsin. A map of the ^{125}I-labeled tyrosyl tryptic peptides of A and B is shown in Fig. 11. This figure is a schematic representation of the map obtained when A and B digest were mixed. Analysis of individual A or B digests allowed assignment of the peptides shown to the appropriate source, as shown on the figure.

Figure 11 shows that the A and B proteins do not show similar tryptic maps. In fact, there is surprisingly little homology between the two, although there are some potential overlapping peptides. A number of pep-

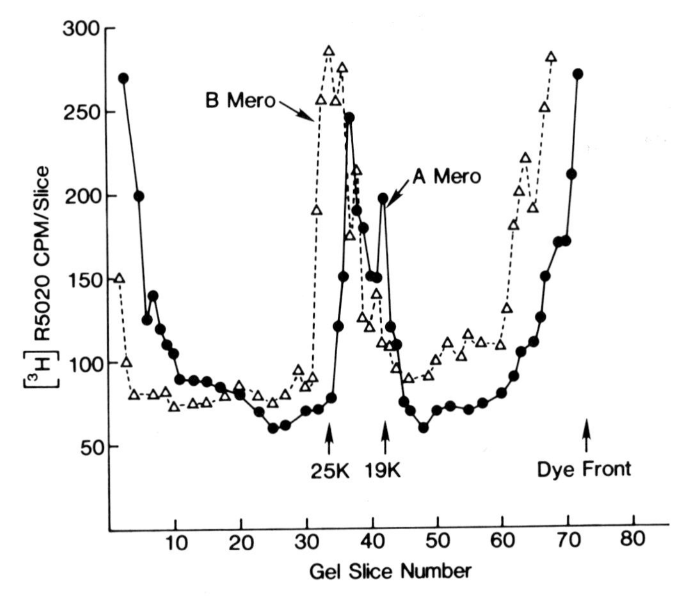

FIG. 10. SDS–polyacrylamide gel analysis of [^{3}H]R5020-labeled receptor A and B mero-proteins obtained by digestion of partially purified receptors with *Staphylococcus aureus* protease. Digests were run on 12% polyacrylamide gels sliced and counted for tritium following solubilization of the slices with hydrogen peroxide. Molecular weight standards are shown by the arrows on the figure.

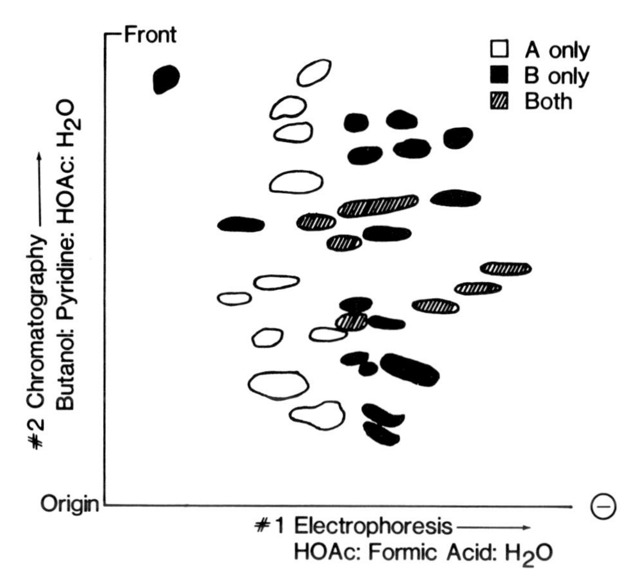

FIG. 11. Tryptic map of iodinated peptides in the hen receptors A and B. The clear peptides are those derived from the A protein alone. The filled regions are those peptides present only in B. The hatched peptides are those which could not be resolved and which may be common to the two proteins.

tides are present in A and lacking in B; the inverse is also true. Thus we conclude that B protein cannot be converted to A, that both proteins can be digested to yield hormone-binding mero-proteins, and finally that they appear to be the products of different messenger RNAs and thus probably are separate gene products as well.

E. SUBUNIT STRUCTURE OF THE NATIVE COMPLEX

Next we turned our attention to whether receptors A and B are indeed subunits of a larger complex. The initial sedimentation studies of the receptor had shown behavior similar to that observed for all other steroid receptors, namely, a reversible association and dissociation from a 4 S sedimenting material to a higher aggregate with a sedimentation coefficient of 8–10 S (Sherman *et al.*, 1970). When the aggregate was isolated by either gel filtration or sucrose gradient ultracentrifugation, subsequent dissociation of this aggregate and analysis for A and B proteins by phosphocellulose chromatography showed the presence in the extract of equal peaks of both B and A (Schrader *et al.*, 1975b). This was consistent with but did not prove A and B were in fact subunits of a complex.

1. Use of Bifunctional Cross-Linking Agents

To test this idea more fully a protein bifunctional cross-linking agent was used, called methylmercaptobutyrimidate (Birnbaumer *et al.*, 1979). This compound has been used to cross-link proximal ribosomal proteins. It reacts with an amino group on one subunit and can then make a disulfide link with the second subunit, if it has a nearby free sulfhydryl. These studies were undertaken using progesterone receptor in crude cytoplasmic extracts labeled with progesterone. After amidination and oxidation, a stable high-molecular-weight 7 S aggregate was obtained in about 50% yield. It resisted dissociation at high ionic strength as shown in Fig. 12. This complex has an apparent Stokes radius and sedimentation coefficient giving a molecular weight of about 225,000. Its behavior is identical to the native material shown in Fig. 4A.

Since the cross-link used in these studies contains a disulfide bond, the reaction is reversible by the addition of a reducing agent. Thus in order to analyze the composition of the cross-linked large receptor complexes, we isolated them by sucrose gradient ultracentrifugation in high ionic strength. Under these conditions, the cross-linked material can be isolated free of unreacted receptors A and B. The pooled aggregates were then reduced with β-mercaptoethanol. They were subjected to gel filtration in

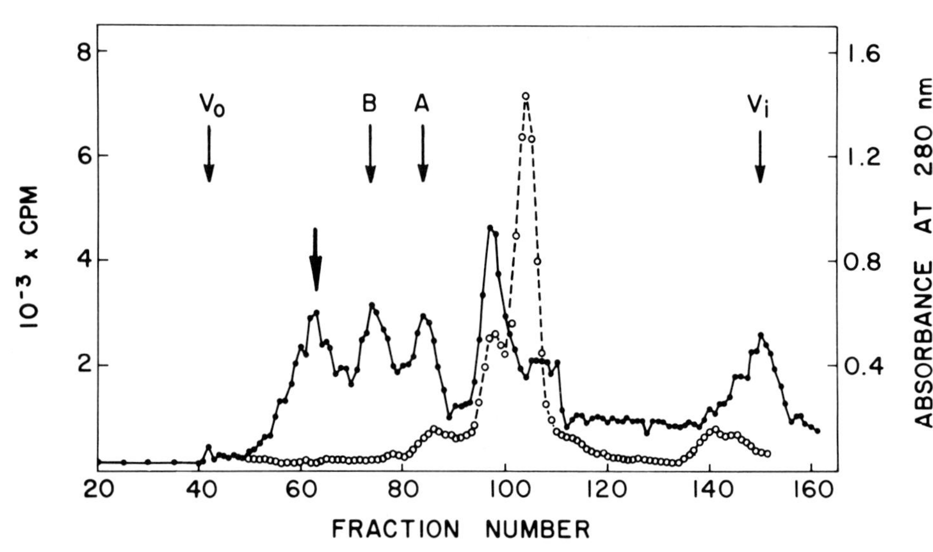

FIG. 12. Gel filtration on Agarose A-1.5m in 0.3 *M* KCl of progesterone receptors cross-linked with methylmercaptobutyrimidate. Arrows at the top show elution locations of authentic receptors B and A. The large arrow in fraction 62 denotes the elution peak of the cross-linked material which resists dissociation. (●— —●), [^{3}H]Progesterone elution profile. (○---○), Protein profile.

high ionic strength as shown in Fig. 13. When the complexes thus obtained were analyzed in this fashion a pair of peaks corresponding to receptors A and B were obtained, again in approximately equal amounts. Thus the cross-linking studies were consistent with the notion that the native receptor complex contained both receptors A and B as subunits.

2. Reconstitution Studies

To test this idea further, reconstitution studies were undertaken using the isolated A and B proteins. Our earlier experiments of this sort had been largely unsuccessful, leading to the notion that perhaps receptor A or B had been altered during the dissociation reactions such that reversible reassociation could not occur (Schrader *et al.*, 1975b). In order to dissociate the complexes and yet prevent this irreversible denaturation process, the receptor aggregates were dissociated by treatment with 5 mM pyridoxal phosphate. This agent causes dissociation of the intact receptors to their A and B proteins. Pyridoxal phosphate forms a Schiff base with epsilon amino groups on lysine residues of proteins, thus also establishing the potential involvement of these residues in the subunit association reaction. Pyridoxal phosphate can be covalently coupled to lysines by reduction with sodium borohydride. Alternatively, it can be removed from the protein by titration with another source of amino groups such as

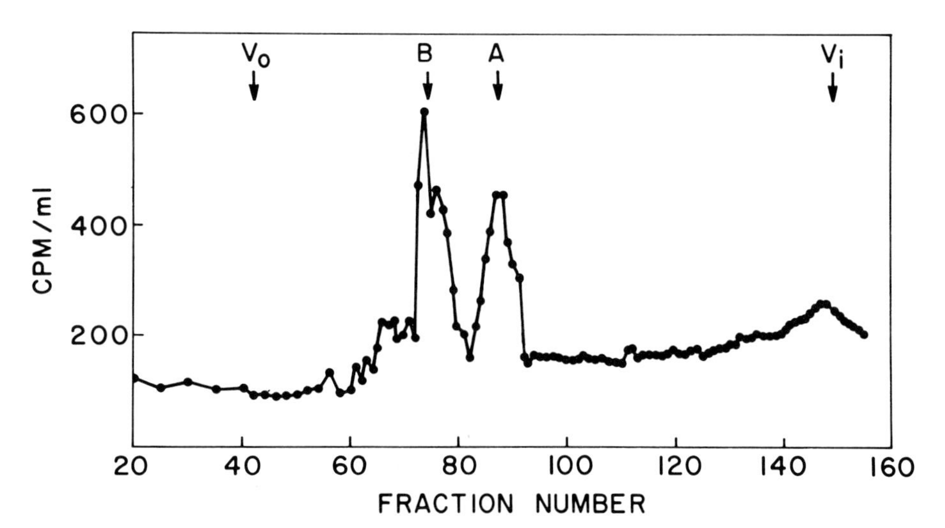

FIG. 13. Gel filtration of products released from cross-linked receptor by 2-mercaptoethanol reduction. Cross-linked material was collected by sucrose gradient ultracentrifugation, reduced and analyzed for B and A content on Agarose A-1.5m run in 0.3 M KCl. Arrows at B and A denote elution positions of authentic B and A used to calibrate the column. From Birnbaumer *et al.* (1979).

ethanolamine. The reversibility of this reaction was then tested as shown in Fig. 14. Here receptors in crude cytoplasmic extracts were analyzed by sucrose gradient ultracentrifugation in low ionic strength. In panel a is shown the behavior of the untreated extract. Following treatment with

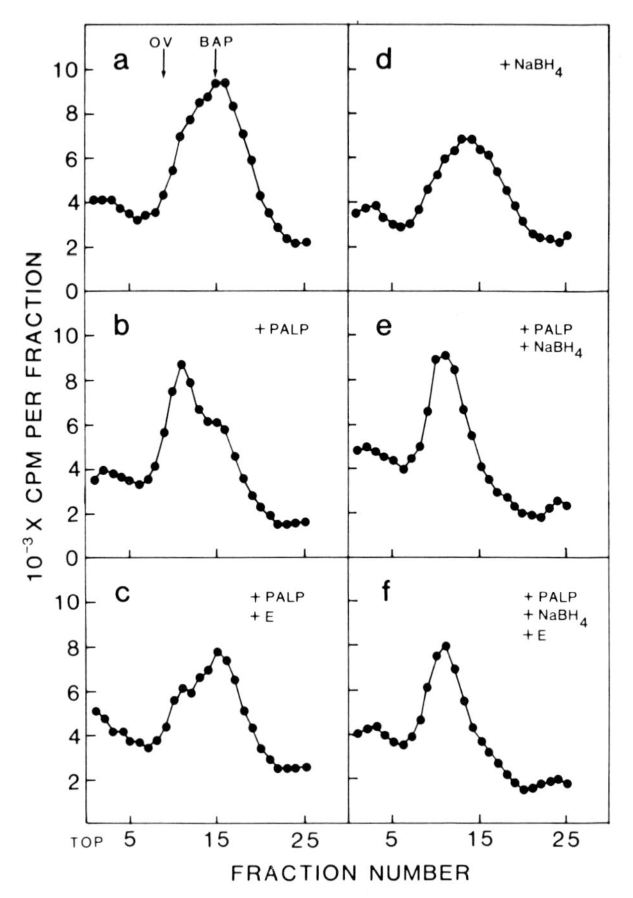

FIG. 14. Reversible assembly of receptor monomers by use of pyridoxal phosphate (PALP) treatment. Analysis of receptor sedimentation coefficients was done by sucrose gradient ultracentrifugation at low ionic strength in comparison with ovalbumin (OV) and bacterial alkaline phosphatase (BAP) which sediment at 3.67 S and 6.3 S, respectively. (a) Labeled cytoplasmic progesterone receptors alone. (b) Same material after treatment in 10 m*M* pyridoxal phosphate. (c) Material after PALP was treated with ethanolamine (E) in excess before analysis. (d–f) Same as companion panels (a–c) on left but samples also treated with sodium borohydride to couple PALP covalently. (d) Cytosol treated only with sodium borohydride. (e) Borohydride treatment after PALP. (f) Same as (e) except ethanolamine added after sodium borohydride.

pyridoxal phosphate the results in panel b were obtained. About 50% of the receptors were dissociated to 4 S subunits. Subsequent treatment of the extract before sucrose gradient analysis with ethanolamine revealed the profile shown in panel c. This treatment caused a partial reversal of the dissociation reaction and the partial restoration of the aggregated complex with concomitant consumption of the 4 S monomers. Panels d, e, and f show the effects of covalent attachment of pyridoxal phosphate to the protein. Treatment with sodium borohydride in panel d had no effect on the unreacted complex. However, if pyridoxal phosphate treatment was followed by borohydride reduction, sucrose gradient centrifugation showed a quantitative conversion of the complexes to the 4 S mixture of subunits shown in panel e. If reduction with borohydride was done there was no reversal upon treatment with ethanolamine as shown in panel f. Thus we concluded that the pyridoxal phosphate treatment and its reversal with ethanolamine was a suitable method for studying reversibility of the subunit assembly reaction.

To test for the involvement of both the receptors A and B in the aggregate formation, partially purified receptors A and B were prepared using ion-exchange chromatography following treatment with pyridoxal phosphate. When receptor A or receptor B alone was treated with ethanolamine, the results in the left two panels in Fig. 15 were obtained. There was no conversion to heavier material. However, when A and B were mixed in equal molar mixture and then treated with ethanolamine, the results shown in the right hand panel were seen. Here the 4 S peak was consumed and an aggregate peak was produced.

These results on reconstitution thus demonstrate that A and B are both subunits of a larger complex. They are present apparently in equal amounts in the complex and both of them are required for complex formation. In view of the partial purification used to prepare the subunits for these experiments it also appears by these studies but there are no additional cofactors required at least to produce this 6 S complex.

3. Prosthetic Groups

We have undertaken a study of possible prosthetic groups required for receptor action by studying the involvement of heavy metals and phosphorylation reactions in receptor structure and function. In earlier studies we showed that chelators of divalent cations had no effect on the sedimentation profile of progesterone receptor. However, as shown in Fig. 16A, sodium molybdate at 10 m*M* concentration stabilizes the progesterone receptor as an 8–10 S complex (Grody *et al.*, 1980). This is not an irreversible stabilization of the complex, as shown in Fig. 16B. Sedimentation of

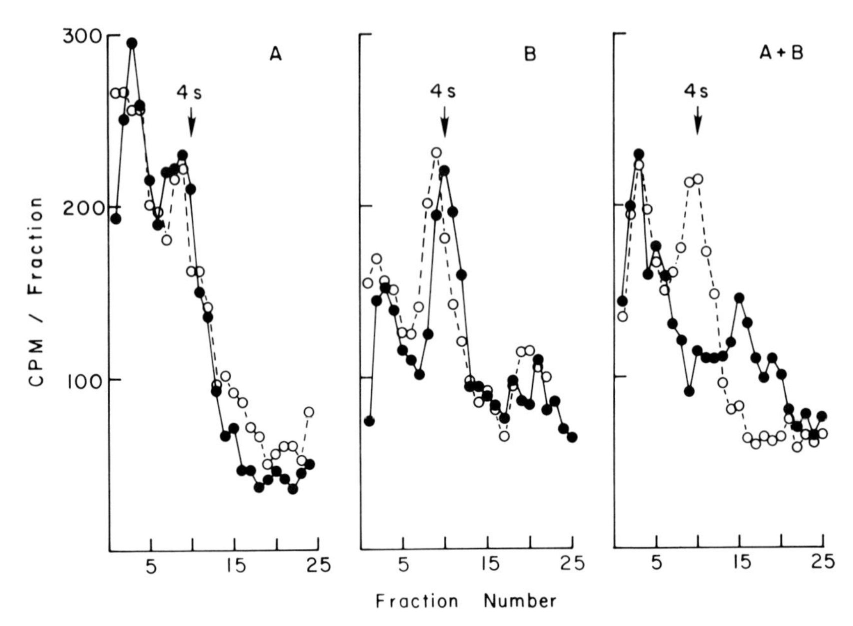

FIG. 15. Reconstitution of receptors A and B using ethanolamine treatment (closed circles) of A only (left), B only (middle), or a mixture of equal amounts of A and B (right). Analysis was by sucrose gradient ultracentrifugation, with the top of each gradient to the left. Free, dissociated [^{3}H]progesterone ran in fraction 3. Receptors without ethanolamine (open circles) were prepared by pyridoxal phosphate treatment and chromatography as described by Grody *et al.* (1981).

receptors in sucrose gradients containing 0.3 *M* potassium chloride showed the expected mixture of 4 S subunits. The reaction was not reversed by the presence of molybdate in the experiments. Similar results have been shown using calcium (Schrader *et al.*, 1977). Since molybdate is a known inhibitor of phosphatases, others have suggested that steroid receptors may be phosphoproteins and the effects of molybdate on their function may be due to their regulation of receptor phosphorylation. In studies presented elsewhere (Grody *et al.*, 1980) we have been unable to detect a phosphorylation–dephosphorylation reaction of the receptors. Rather, we speculate that the molybdate affects the stabilization of the subunits. This agent may simply stabilize receptors by virtue of the fact that the hormone-binding activity is inherently more stable in the intact A · B complex than it is in the separated subunits. Thus our present view is that there are no known prosthetic groups on the receptors although the potential function of metal cations in subunit assembly cannot be ruled out at this time.

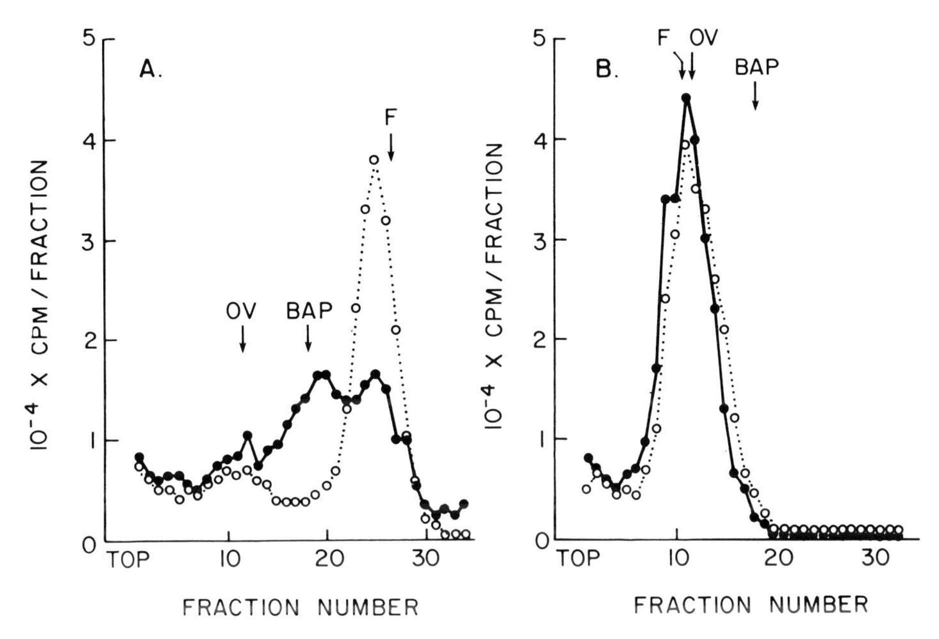

FIG. 16. Effect of metal ions on receptor sedimentation behavior in low (A) and high (B) ionic strength. Symbols OV and BAP are sedimentation standards as in Fig. 14. Solid circles, profile of [^{3}H]progesterone-labeled cytosol receptors. Open circles, profile obtained when 10 m*M* sodium molybdate was included in the gradient. Arrows labeled F denote location of receptor peak in equivalent experiment using sodium fluoride. From Grody *et al.* (1980).

F. RESOLUTION OF FUNCTIONAL DOMAINS

1. Hormone-Binding Site

Next we turned to the question of the arrangement of functional domains on the proteins. Both steroid receptor subunits have hormone-binding sites and both of them appear to be required for assembly of the intact complex. Thus it was of interest to ask whether or not these functional domains and the functional domains concerned with DNA-binding activity on the A subunit could be localized within specific portions of the proteins. For these studies proteolytic digestion of the native receptor proteins was undertaken using a crude endogenous calcium-activated neutral protease present in oviduct tissue (Vedeckis *et al.*, 1980a). This enzyme is present in high concentration in oviduct nuclei, and was used as shown in Fig. 17. Here gel filtration in Sephadex G-100 was used to assay a mixture of receptors A and B for smaller proteolytic fragments retaining bound hormone. The column does not resolve A from B. Upon incubation

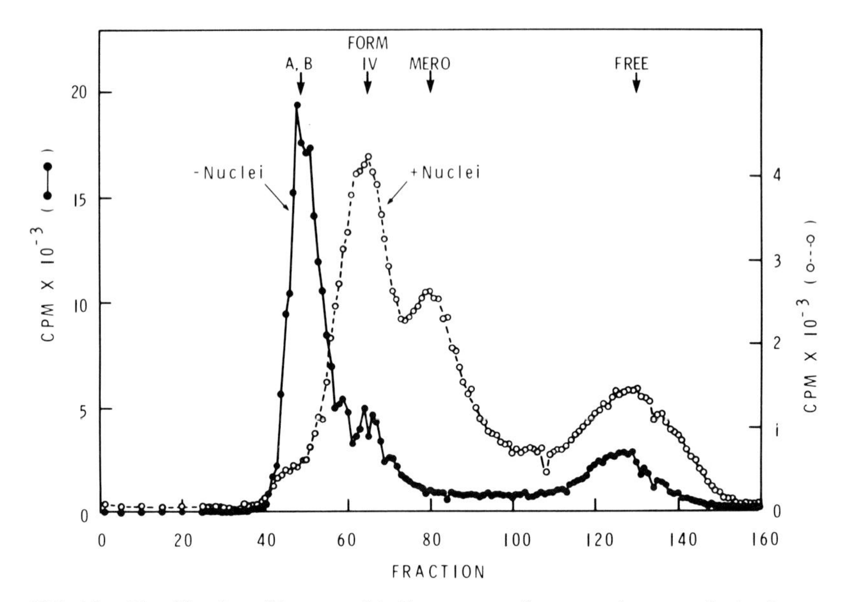

FIG. 17. Identification of hormone-binding receptor fragments by proteolysis of receptor subunits A and B using an endogenous calcium-activated protease. Analysis of receptor fragments was by Sephadex G-100 gel filtration in 0.3 *M* KCl. Closed circles, profile of an equimolar mixture of undigested A and B subunits. Open circles, profile obtained following 25 minute incubation with oviduct nuclei at 25°C as source of enzyme. Arrows at Form IV and mero denote elution locations of proteolytic hormone-binding fragments identified in separate experiments using purified enzyme.

at 25°C with nuclei as a source of the enzyme, two smaller peaks were obtained of receptor-derived hormone-binding activity. The peak labeled Form IV is an intermediate in the digestion (Vedeckis *et al.,* 1980b) and has an apparent molecular weight of about 43,000. The limit digest of the reactions is the mero-protein peak with an apparent molecular weight of about 23,000 in these experiments. This material is actually a mixture of mero-B and mero-A. This fact is borne out by the experiment presented earlier in Fig. 10, using a different enzyme. In experiments not presented here, we prepared mero-B and mero-A independently using the endogenous enzyme, and found that they have indistinguishable isoelectric points. Thus, the native mero fragments are very similar to each other. We conclude that the enzyme liberates the hormone-binding domains as discrete entities from both proteins.

2. *DNA-Binding Site*

Similarly, we tested the meroproteins for DNA binding and found that neither mero showed this activity (Vedeckis *et al.,* 1980b). We therefore speculated that the DNA domain resided elsewhere on the protein and attempted to locate it. For this purpose we studied first the receptor A Form IV. Under conditions of mild proteolysis, Form IV can be produced as the predominant product, using any of the proteases we have tested. More extensive digestion converts Form IV quantitatively to the meroprotein. The DNA-binding activity was studied using *Staphylococcus aureus* V8 protease, as shown in Fig. 18. After mild digestion of a labeled, partially purified receptor preparation, the digest was applied to a DNA–

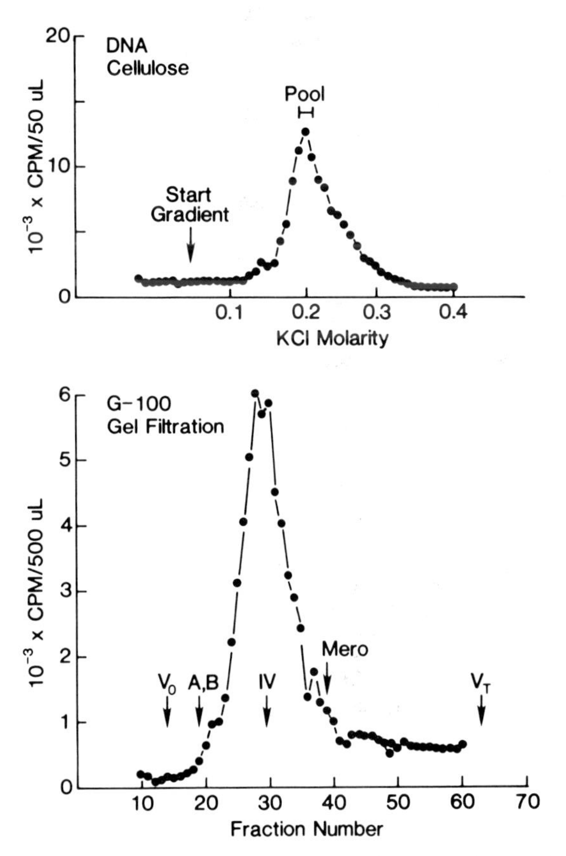

FIG. 18. Assignment of the DNA-binding domain of receptor A to its Form IV fragment. Labeled cytosol receptors were precipitated by ammonium sulfate (35% saturation) and the redissolved pellet subjected to mild digestion with *Staphylococcus aureus* V8 protease. The digest was passed through a small DNA-cellulose column and DNA-bound material eluted with a KCl gradient as shown in the top panel. The pooled peak was then analyzed by Sephadex G-100 gel filtration as shown on the bottom in 0.3 *M* KCl. Arrows on the lower panel denote elution locations of authentic receptors and fragments described in Fig. 17.

cellulose column as shown in the top panel. The adsorbed peak eluted at a KCl molarity equivalent to that required for intact receptor A to elute. The peak was then analyzed as shown in the bottom panel for its content of intact subunits and Form IV. This figure shows clearly that the DNA-positive material was Form IV. In experiments not shown, we demonstrated that this is the receptor A-derived Form IV; Form IV from B does not show equivalent DNA-binding activity.

Thus we conclude that the DNA site lies within the Form IV fragment of receptor A. This result is not in agreement with our earlier published conclusion on the placement of this site (Vedeckis *et al.*, 1980b). This is due to an experimental manipulation in the former work, in which digestion of the native receptors was done under conditions which permit receptor subunits to remain associated. Digestion of the crude material under these conditions yields receptor Form IV fragments still complexed to each other. As shown in Fig. 5, the associated subunits do not bind to DNA. Thus, our observation that Form IV did not contain the DNA site was due to this association of the fragments. We showed in subsequent unpublished work that upon treatment with KCl, the Form IV digest could bind to DNA. Coincidentally, this Form IV DNA experiment also establishes that the subunit-interaction or assembly domain also resides at least partially within Form IV.

A more sensitive method for detecting the receptor fragments which contain DNA-binding activity was to perform digestion of native receptor A protein purified as described above, using either *Staphylococcus aureus* protease or trypsin. Analysis is carried out by the method of Bowen *et al.* (1980). The digests first were subjected to SDS–polyacrylamide gel electrophoresis on 7.5% polyacrylamide gels and washed free of the bulk of the SDS. The peptides were transferred to a nitrocellulose filter by a blotting procedure. Then the nitrocellulose filters were incubated with ^{32}P-labeled DNA, washed, and subjected to autoradiography. As shown in Fig. 19, distinct bands of DNA-binding activity were found for the intact receptor A starting material at the appropriate molecular weight of 78,000. Subsequent digestion products with either enzyme also had DNA-binding activity. The band at about 40,000 molecular weight for the *Staphylococcus aureus* protease digest appears to be the Form IV fraction. The smallest identified fragment of the protein containing DNA-binding activity was a band at a molecular weight of 15,000. In other experiments not shown here we found that this fragment does not contain the hormone-binding activity. Thus the DNA-binding activity of the A protein can be isolated as a 15,000 molecular weight fragment which is separate from the hormone-binding activity. Thus we conclude that the DNA- and hormone-binding activities reside in separate domains of the protein.

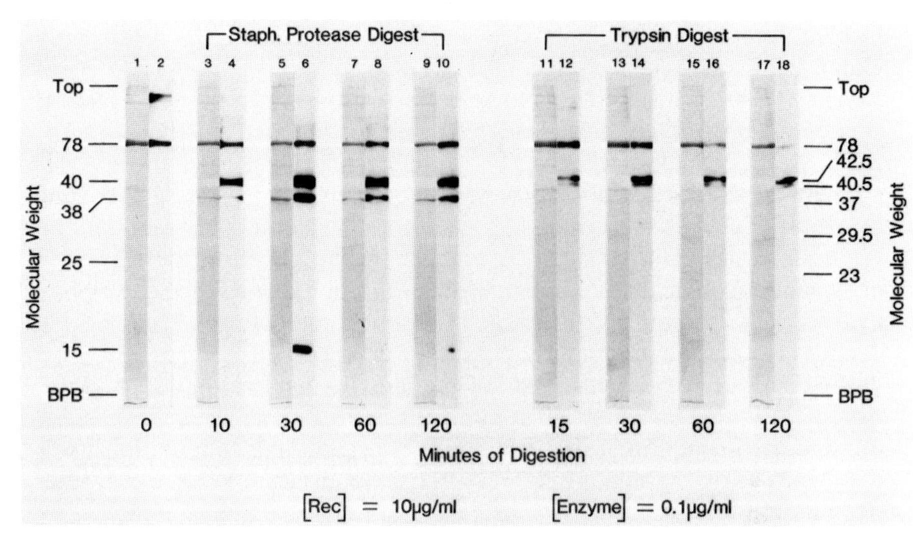

FIG. 19. Detection of purified receptor A DNA-binding activity following proteolysis of receptor with *Staphylococcus aureus* V8 protease (lanes 1–10) or trypsin (lanes 11–18). Purified hen receptor A protein or digests were subjected to SDS–polyacrylamide gel electrophoresis in 12% slab gels. The gels were washed free of excess SDS and proteins transferred nonquantitatively to nitrocellulose filter sheets in dilute buffer for 2 days. Then the filters were incubated for several hours with ^{32}P-labeled DNA (Sp Act = 10^7 cpm/μg). After extensive washing the filters were autoradiographed to reveal bound DNA. Right-hand lane of each pair is the ^{32}P autoradiograph. Residual protein left in the gel after blotting was detected by Coomassie blue staining, as shown by the left-hand lane of each pair.

3. *Immunologic Domain*

Finally, the immunologic reactivity of A and B was compared. For reasons that are not clear we have been unable to raise antibodies to either progesterone receptor A or B from either chick or hen by repeated injection of up to 500 μg into a variety of animals using a variety of routes of injection and a variety of adjuvant techniques. However there exists in sheep a weak immunoglobin of the IgG class which reacts specifically with progesterone receptors from chick oviduct. It is not clear why this spontaneous activity should be present in sheep; however the levels of activity are very low. An injection of the animals with receptor proteins does not affect the titer in these animals of this antibody material. It is an IgG class of antibody due to the fact that the anti-receptor activity will adsorb to *Staphylococcus aureus* cell wall protein A. This fact has been used as an assay for the activity using *Staphylococcus aureus* protein A adsorbed to Sepharose. When this is used in small columns the [^{3}H]progesterone-labeled receptor antigen can be adsorbed to the resin and subsequently eluted with acetic acid (Weigel *et al.*, 1981b).

Using this assay the immunologic cross-reactivity of receptors A and B was compared, and the immunologic domain mapped on the proteins. Both receptor A and receptor B are equivalently reactive toward this antibody. The location of this immunologic domain was sought following digestion of the receptor with the endogenous calcium-activated neutral protease as shown in Fig. 20. As shown by the panel on the right, the mero-receptor hormone-binding fragment did not adsorb to the antibody and was not retained by the protein A-Sepharose column. Under these conditions the intact receptor mixture was adsorbed as shown by the dashed line. However as shown on the left the immunologic domain resists digestion by this enzyme. A competition study was used as an assay. In this experiment undigested receptor was present in a competition along with nonradioactive intact receptors (the solid circles) or the nonradioactive receptor digests (the open circles). Both materials were equivalently antigenic in the competition assay.

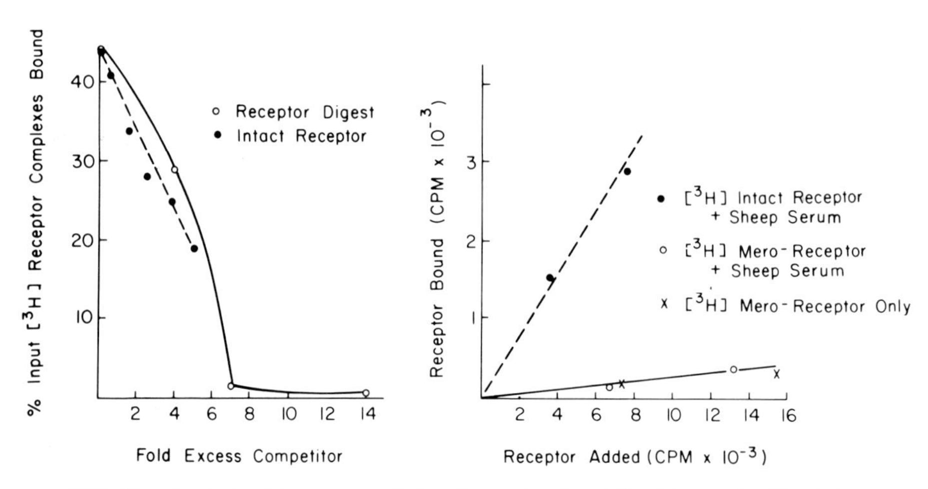

FIG. 20. Analysis of immunoreactivity of receptor A and B mixture using *Staphylococcus aureus* protein A-Sepharose mini-column adsorption assay. Right-hand panel shows the direct adsorption study. (●---●) Adsorption of [^{3}H]progesterone–receptor complexes bound to sheep serum IgG spontaneous antibody. Adsorbed ^{3}H was eluted from the column with acetic acid. (○—○) Adsorption of ^{3}H-labeled mero-receptors after addition of sheep serum. (×—×) Background adsorption of mero-receptors without added serum IgG fraction. Left panel, competition assay for resistance of immunoreactive domain to digestion by calcium-activated protease. Labeled receptors were incubated with sheep IgG antibody together with various amounts of nonradioactive intact progesterone–receptor complexes (●--●) or with protease-digested nonradioactive complexes (○—○).

Thus we conclude that the immunologic domain lies on a portion of the receptor external to the mero-protein fragment. In studies to be presented elsewhere, we observed that the intact receptor A–B aggregate is not immunoreactive. We therefore presume (but have not yet proven) that this spontaneous sheep antibody recognizes a determinant on A and B near or at the subunit assembly domain, possibly in Form IV.

In summary, our proteolytic digestion studies so far have identified discrete functional domains on A and B for hormone and immunologic reactivity. They have shown gross similarities between the two, but the two are clearly separate proteins. It is tempting to speculate that A and B may be products of two closely related genes, which may have evolved from a common progenitor gene and then diverged.

III. Studies of Progesterone Receptor Function

A. EFFECTS ON RNA SYNTHESIS IN CHROMATIN

1. *Tissue Specificity*

Next we turned our attention to the functional characteristics of the progesterone receptors. As was mentioned above, progesterone affects ovalbumin RNA synthesis under conditions of secondary stimulation. Under these conditions the tissue is already differentiated and primed to respond to a hormonal stimulus. As shown in Table IV this can be seen as an effect of progesterone *in vivo* upon ovalbumin mRNA levels as measured by cell-free translation. Similarly, the hormone affects the RNA template capacity of oviduct chromatin. Initiation sites for RNA synthesis

TABLE IV

Effects of Progesterone Administration on Transcription Activity of Oviducts during Secondary Stimulation

Time after injection of progesterone (hours)	Antibody-precipitable [^{35}S]ovalbumin in cell-free translation assay (cpm/μg poly(A)-RNA)	RNA initiation sites in isolated oviduct chromatin (sites/pg DNA)
0	0	8,100
0.5	—	16,800
1	—	23,600
4	300	—
6	—	14,200
10	1200	—
24	2700	13,800

in chromatin detected *in vitro* rise within 30 minutes of hormone administration *in vivo*. These changes in template activity and mRNA are consistent with other studies of receptor accumulation in the nucleus (O'Malley *et al.*, 1971).

In earlier studies using purified progesterone receptor complexes prepared by affinity chromatography (Kuhn *et al.*, 1975) we titrated oviduct and nontarget chromatins with receptor and measured RNA initiation sites (Schwartz *et al.*, 1976). This technique amounts to a glorified chromatin template assay, and was criticized for its use of a prokaryotic RNA polymerase. As we have pointed out on a number of occasions, the initiation site assay was not designed to measure promoter-mediated *in vivo* initiation sites for RNA synthesis. Rather, it was constructed as a means of probing receptor-mediated changes in chromatin conformation. However, the important aspect of the studies is shown in Table V. This table shows that the purified receptor preparation containing no other proteins stimulated target-chromatin transcription but not transcription from nontarget chromatin such as liver. Furthermore, the process was saturable, with an apparent equilibrium constant and time course consistent with the binding of receptors to chromatin.

2. *Relative Activities of Intact Complex and Subunits*

We also used this assay to investigate the functional requirements for both receptor subunits A and B (Buller *et al.*, 1976). For this purpose, we isolated partially purified intact complex and also individual A and B subunits. A sample experiment of this sort is shown in Fig. 21. Here a half-maximum stimulation of RNA initiation sites by the intact receptor occurred at a receptor concentration of about 5 n*M*, consistent with the

TABLE V
Tissue Specificity of Purified Receptor Effects on RNA Initiation Sites in Chromatin

Chromatin source	Addition of receptor	RNA sites/pg DNA
Withdrawn	0	9,800
oviduct	10^{-8} *M*	13,600
Estrogenized	0	24,800
oviduct	10^{-8} *M*	18,700
Liver	0	14,300
	10^{-8} *M*	15,000
Erythrocyte	0	2,600
	10^{-8} *M*	2,900
Purified	0	190,000
DNA	10^{-8} *M*	191,000

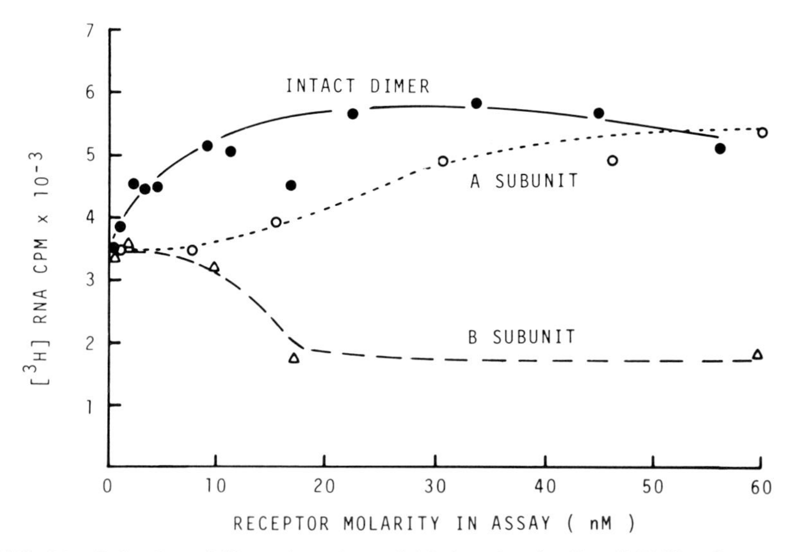

FIG. 21. Induction of rifamycin-resistant initiation sites for *E. coli* RNA polymerase in oviduct chromatin *in vitro*. Progesterone receptor–hormone complexes were added at the indicated molarities. Intact dimer A and B subunits prepared as described in Buller *et al.* (1976) and assayed as described in Schwartz *et al.* (1976).

equilibrium constant for the binding of receptors to chromatin. The B protein by itself was not stimulatory and may even inhibit the reaction. However, the A protein by itself *in vitro* caused a stimulation but only at much greater concentrations of added receptor.

We proposed a hypothesis to explain these findings (Buller *et al.*, 1976). We suggested that the intact complex had to interact with specific chromatin acceptor sites consisting of chromosomal proteins able to interact with the receptors through the B subunit's chromatin-binding domain. Then there must occur an exposure of the DNA-binding activity of the A subunit either through a conformational change of the intact complex or by dissociation of the complex to liberate the DNA-binding A subunit. Then there was the potential for the A protein to interact directly with the DNA and somehow to affect the transcription reaction itself.

B. RECEPTOR A PROTEIN INTERACTION WITH DNA

From such an analysis it was clear that it was necessary to study the DNA-binding reaction of the A protein more directly. With the availability of this purified protein we began studies of DNA binding to ask two fundamental questions. First, was there evidence for nucleotide sequence specificity in the binding of the receptor to DNA? Second, was the receptor capable of altering DNA structure? In view of the fact that the A protein activity appeared to be expressed only upon dissociation of A complexes, either of these alternatives could account for the apparent biologic activity of the intact receptor when added to the chromatin.

To analyze the receptor interaction with DNA more quantitatively the nitrocellulose filter adsorption assay of Riggs *et al.* (1970) was used. In this assay radioactive ^{32}P-labeled DNA is mixed with the purified receptor protein and then incubation mixtures are filtered through nitrocellulose filters to which the receptor proteins bind quantitatively. Double-stranded DNA in the absence of protein does not bind to the filter. However, if the DNA is bound to the protein, then the ^{32}P-labeled DNA is retained on the filter. In this way a rapid and sensitive assay can be developed as a quantitative method for measuring receptor–DNA interaction. The only absolute requirement is that the receptor be uncontaminated by other DNA-binding proteins, a condition met by the purification protocol. A partial proof of this is seen in Fig. 19.

1. *Binding Kinetics*

We measured the kinetics of interaction of receptor with DNA at 0°C as shown in Fig. 22. Receptors were added to DNA in low ionic strength buffer (60 m*M* KCl). Figure 22A shows that the association time to reach steady state for receptor–DNA interaction was on the order of 30–40 minutes. Upon addition of nonradioactive DNA in excess to labeled receptor–DNA complexes, the dissociation reaction was studied and was found to have a half-time of between 40 and 180 minutes as shown in Fig. 22B. Since the nitrocellulose filter method requires only 45 seconds to complete, it appeared by these criteria that the method was indeed an equilibrium technique suitable for use in studying progesterone receptor–DNA interaction.

2. *Nucleotide Sequence Specificity Studies*

We then prepared a number of fragments of the ovalbumin natural gene which had been cloned into bacterial plasmids in our laboratory (Woo *et al.*, 1981). A schematic diagram of the fragments tested for receptor binding is shown in Fig. 23. Each of these fragments was prepared individually and end-labeled with radioactive ^{32}P to high specific activity. Binding experiments using these fragments are shown in Fig. 24. As is evident from this figure, there is no detectable difference among any of the DNA fragments tested. In Fig. 24A are shown various restriction fragments of the gene extending to both the left and right of the transcription unit (Roop *et al.*, 1978, 1980). Also shown is a companion experiment using pure receptor B as a control. Here again, this protein failed to demonstrate

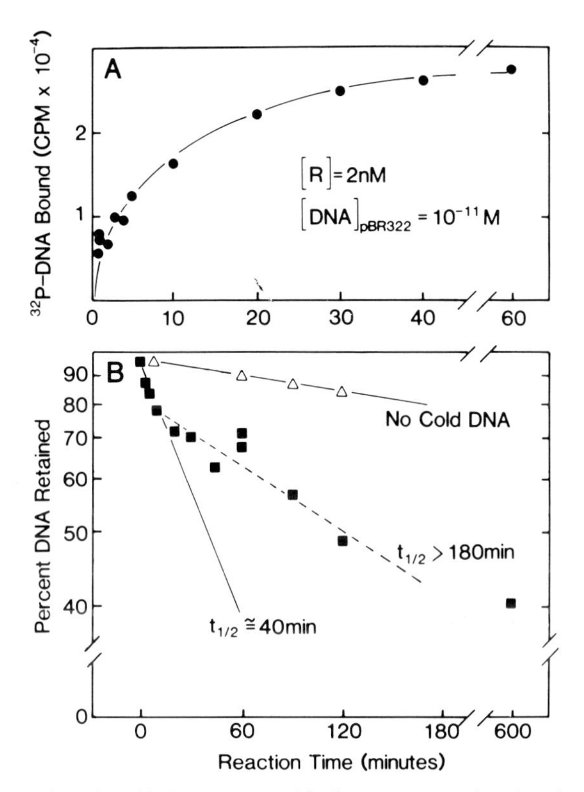

FIG. 22. Kinetics of purified receptor A binding to DNA using the nitrocellulose filter assay. ^{32}P-labeled DNA from plasmid pBR322 was labeled by nick translation and mixed with receptors at zero time. (A) Aliquots were taken and filtered on nitrocellulose to obtain the association reaction curve. (B) Dissociation reaction obtained by adding excess non-radioactive DNA to the 60 minute point of (A), and then collecting filtrates at the times shown. (■——■), dissociation in presence of cold DNA. (△——△), no excess DNA. Half-lives shown are calculated from the two straight lines drawn through the solid squares.

detectable DNA binding at this ionic strength (60 m*M* KCl). This protein contains a weak DNA-binding activity (Vedeckis *et al.*, 1980b) but it is not expressed above 30–40 m*M* KCl.

In Fig. 24B are results using two fragments of ovalbumin DNA which had particular interest. The 583 bp piece encompasses the 5′ end of the ovalbumin gene and contains the promoter sequence for the gene and also the first exon. The 750 bp piece is an internal fragment which contains a number of intron–exon junctions. This figure shows that neither fragment bound the receptor preferentially. These experiments have been substantiated by numerous competition experiments. Thus to date there is no

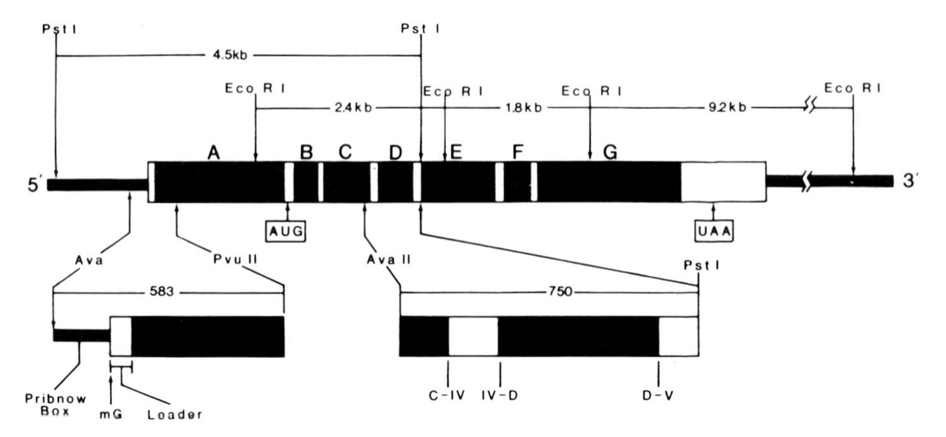

FIG. 23. Partial restriction endonuclease map of the chicken ovalbumin gene showing relevant *Pst*I and *Eco*RI sites used to clone various fragments. Exploded view below shows *Ava*II–*Pvu*II and *Ava*II–*Pst*I double digest sites used to excise the fragments shown. Letters A–G refer to the intervening DNA sequences (■); open regions are the structural sequences.

evidence for nucleotide sequence specificity in the receptor's interaction with DNA.

3. *Effects on DNA Structure*

Thus we turned our attention to the nature of the interaction of receptor with DNA in topological terms. In initial studies we showed by DNA competition that the progesterone receptor binds preferentially to single-stranded DNA as compared to double-stranded DNA. This preference for single-stranded regions of the DNA was further documented as shown in Fig. 25. In this experiment linear, double-stranded plasmid pBR322 was end-labeled with ^{32}P and then subjected to limited digestion using pancreatic DNase. At various intervals of the digestion aliquots of the DNA were taken and isolated. The effect of this digestion on the sedimentation coefficient of the DNA is indicated on the figure. Then receptor titration of these various DNAs was performed. Three representative examples of a family of binding curves are shown. The full-length plasmid DNA bound receptor but only a small fraction of the DNAs was retained on the filters (compare to Fig. 24). With more extensively digested DNA, the binding became more extensive also. Eventually as a highly nicked DNA was tested, the binding was no longer saturable. Thus DNA with single-stranded character was the preferred substrate for receptor A binding. It is not clear from such an experiment whether the receptor prefers long, single-stranded regions or prefers binding to nicks or single-stranded extended ends. This latter possibility was addressed by receptor binding to

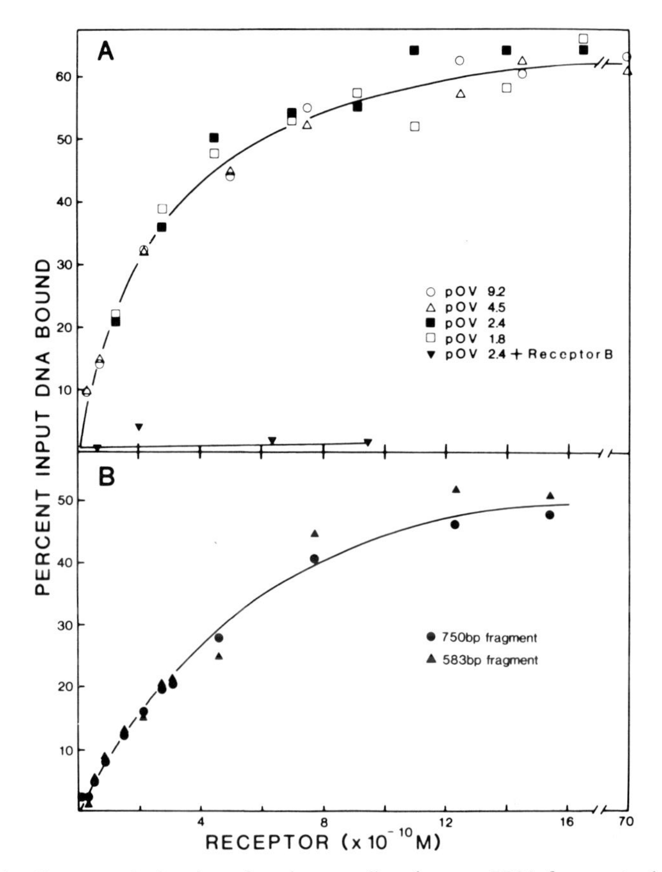

FIG. 24. Receptor A titration of various ovalbumin gene DNA fragments described in Fig. 23. (A) Binding data obtained using plasmid DNAs labeled by nick translation and purified chick oviduct receptor A. DNA–protein complexes were recovered by nitrocellulose filter adsorption. (B) Same experiment using two special DNA fragments excised as shown in Fig. 23.

plasmid pBR322 DNA linearized with restriction endonuclease *Eco*RI, which leaves 5′-extended ends four nucleotides long. When the 5′ ends were labeled, receptor binding was extensive. However, when these ends were filled in by resynthesis of blunt ends with subtilisin-treated DNA polymerase I, binding was considerably reduced. We conclude tentatively from this finding that single-stranded ends are indeed efficient binding sites for receptor. They are not obligatory, however, since receptor also binds extensively to relaxed, circular pBR322 DNA containing a single nick in one strand only. In sedimentation studies, receptor also binds extensively to single-stranded circular DNA which contains no ends. Fi-

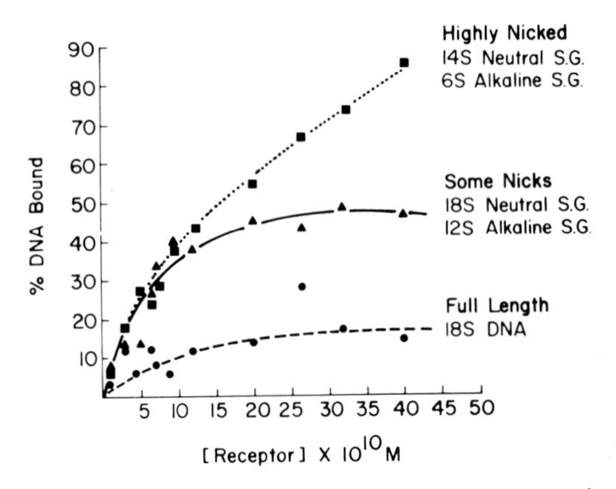

FIG. 25. Effect of DNase nicking of linear duplex DNA upon the receptor binding reaction. Plasmid pBR322 DNA was linearized with *Eco*RI, then the ends were filled by 3′-extending with proteolytic large fragment of DNA polymerase I to repair the AATT tails, using [α-^{32}P]dATP and dTTP as substrates. A subsequent time course of nicking by DNase I was done recovering ^{32}P-labeled DNA at various times. Sedimentation coefficients for these DNAs are listed (S.G. = sucrose gradient). The curves show three sample binding curves at various degrees of nicking. Nitrocellulose assay as in Fig. 22.

nally, in DNA "footprinting" experiments, receptor does not preferentially protect 5′-extended single-stranded sequences. Thus, we conclude from experiments such as these that any single-stranded region of the DNA can be a particularly effective binder of the receptor. This is the expected behavior for DNA binding proteins which are helix-destabilizing proteins, that is, those which shift the helix-coil transition of the DNA in favor of the random coil (Alberts and Sternglanz, 1977). This notion was tested further by comparing the binding of receptor to DNA in the nitrocellulose filter assay and simultaneously assaying for the effect of the receptor on the sensitivity of the DNA to digestion by a single-strand specific nuclease as shown in Fig. 26. In this figure receptor titration of linear plasmid DNA labeled by nick translation showed saturation in the nitrocellulose filter assay at less than 1 n*M* receptor. The receptor had no effect upon the sensitivity of the DNA to digestion by S1 nuclease until concentrations in excess of 8 n*M* were reached. At this concentration and above the DNA became progressively more and more sensitive to S1 nuclease digestion until at very high concentrations of receptor about 70% of the DNA was digestible by the enzyme. This is consistent with the notion that the receptor when bound to DNA causes it to extend into a more single-stranded conformation. We conclude from our present studies that the receptor A subunit has no detectable nucleotide sequence specificity, but that it is probably a helix-destabilizing protein able to unwind the DNA.

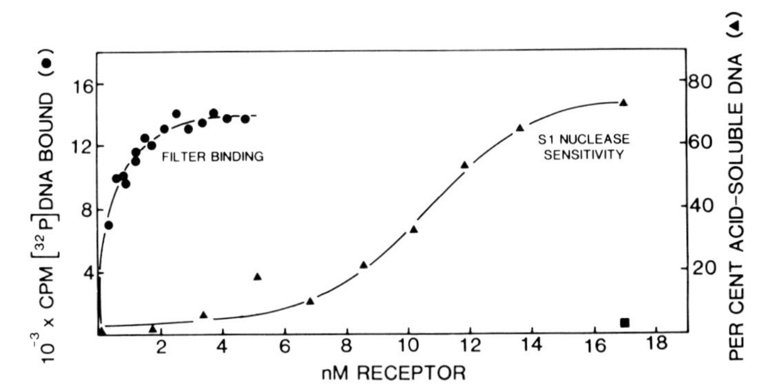

FIG. 26. Effect of purified receptor A on labeled DNA sensitivity to single-strand specific nuclease S1. Incubations of [^{32}P]plasmid DNA and receptor A at the concentrations shown were assayed in companion aliquots for nitrocellulose filter binding and S1 sensitivity by extent of DNA solubility in cold acid. (●—●) Nitrocellulose filter binding data. (▲—▲) S1 nuclease sensitivity. (■) Extent of DNA solubilization by receptor A with no added nuclease.

C. A HYPOTHESIS REGARDING THE MECHANISM OF GENE REGULATION BY THE PROGESTERONE RECEPTOR

1. Local Effects

Our current working hypothesis regarding the mechanism by which the chick progesterone receptor may function is shown in Fig. 27. The intact protein appears to be a complex of receptor A and receptor B subunits, which interacts with certain target-cell nuclear sites termed acceptor sites by virtue of the chromatin-binding activity of the B subunit. We speculate that these acceptor sites are proximal to genes destined to be regulated by these hormones, although at present there is no experimental evidence for the location of these chromosomal proteins near regulated genes. We propose that there must then be a dissociation to liberate the DNA-binding subunit A. This protein can in some way become associated with a region of the DNA where stimulation of RNA synthesis can occur. In view of the potential helix-destabilization activity shown above, we speculate finally that this reaction may play a key role in the initiation of RNA synthesis, possibly by facilitating entry of RNA polymerase into the DNA duplex. At the present time studies are under way in our laboratory using the purified receptors described here to study this process in detail using *in vitro* transcription of the ovalbumin gene as a test system (Tsai *et al.*, 1981).

2. Remote Effects

Recently, studies of chromatin organization have revealed aspects of gene expression which may require some alteration or extension of the

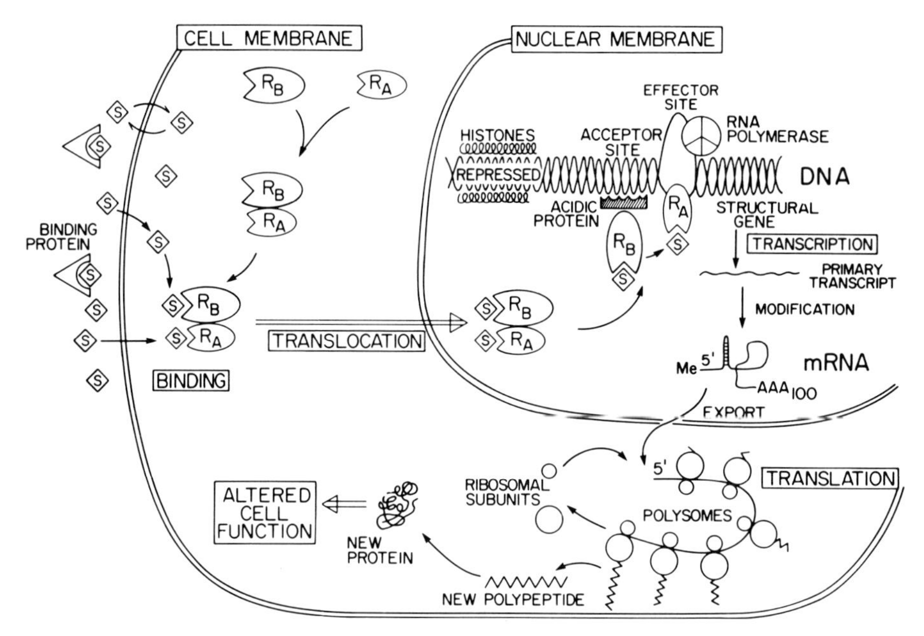

FIG. 27. A hypothesis to explain the mechanism of progesterone receptor action in chick oviduct. Receptors, R_B and R_A; steroid, S.

hypothesis above. Other workers have reported that potentially expressible eukaryotic genes are preferentially digestible in chromatin by the enzyme DNase I, as compared to their digestion rates in cells where these genes are never expressed (Weintraub and Groudine 1976; Stalder *et al.*, 1980). In a series of experiments reported elsewhere (Lawson *et al.*, 1980), we have investigated the relationship between oviduct gene expression and chromatin structure. We found that the ovalbumin gene is more sensitive to DNase I in oviduct than it is in spleen, liver, or erythrocyte nuclei. In contrast, the β-globin gene is resistant to digestion in oviduct, spleen, and liver nuclei but is sensitive in erythrocyte nuclei.

Two other genes, designated X and Y (Royal *et al.*, 1979), are located adjacent to the ovalbumin gene. These two are also inducible by steroids, but at only 1 and 6%, respectively, of the induction of ovalbumin (Colbert *et al.*, 1980). We found that genes X and Y also exhibit preferential DNase I sensitivity in oviduct nuclei.

Moreover, the DNase I-sensitive region includes the intergenic spacer regions, and extends over at least an 80 kb segment of this DNA (Lawson *et al.*, 1981). These data suggest that those aspects of chromatin structure which confer DNase I sensitivity to expressible genes are not necessarily confined within the immediate transcription unit of the genes. Rather, it appears that the DNA is organized into polygenic domains in which an entire region containing transcribed genes and nontranscribed spacer elements can exist in the DNase I-sensitive conformation.

It is tempting to speculate that the recruitment of these polygenic domains into a DNase I-sensitive conformation may be a control step in the process of differentiation. Within this DNase I-sensitive (and potentially expressible) domain, effectors such as steroid receptors could then operate on this primed network to modulate the expression of individual genes. This concept is illustrated in Fig. 28. Within a given chromosomal segment common to distinct cell types I and II, the sequestering of different regions of the DNA into DNase-sensitive domains results in the potentiation of

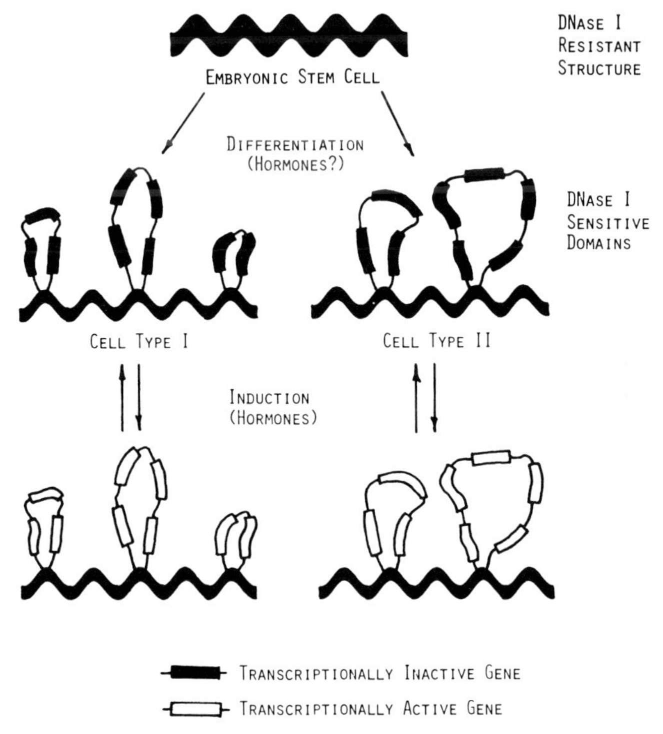

FIG. 28. Possible implications for gene expression derived from studies of chromatin structure. Differentiation is pictured here as a process which renders certain gene sets sensitive to digestion by DNase I, which correlates with expressibility of those genes. Different groups of gene clusters are shown affected in two different cell types. By a separate process gene clusters appearing in such DNase-sensitive structures are then affected by the process labeled induction.

unique sets of genes whose ultimate expression characterizes the observed phenotype.

If this be the case, we must consider the possibility that steroid hormone receptors may not influence gene expression directly at promoters immediately flanking a gene, but may act at regions distant from the induced genes to alter their chromatin organization. For instance, steroid hormones might exert a structural effect at the boundaries of DNase I-sensitive loops. This action could then be transduced by some conformational effect on the DNA contained in the loop region, so that RNA polymerase could initiate transcription of each gene. Although it would serve no further purpose to speculate on how this might occur, it is interesting to us that estrogen receptors in mammalian systems have been found associated both with DNase-sensitive regions (Scott and Frankel, 1980) and with the highly DNase-resistant nuclear matrix (Barrack *et al.*, 1977). Thus it is reasonable to keep such a model in mind as we search for DNA binding "effector" sites for steroid receptor function.

3. Caveats

There remain, of course, numerous alternatives to the scheme outlined in Fig. 27. Of particular concern is the possibility that progesterone receptor actually regulates genes other than ovalbumin and the major egg white proteins normally controlled by estrogen. There may in fact be progesterone receptor-specific DNA loci elsewhere in the genome for which we currently have no probe. Also, since the mechanism by which these proteins act is still completely unknown, one cannot rule out the possibility that the interactions of receptors so far described with nuclear constituents are merely artifacts, or partial reactions of the actual *in situ* events. We expect that *in vitro* studies of specific gene regulation will be required to evaluate these possibilities. It would also be useful to be able to work with the estrogen receptor as well. The similarities of structure and function it may have to the progesterone receptor are presently unclear, although the estrogen receptor also seems to consist of a pair of distinguishable components (Kon *et al.*, 1980; Taylor and Smith, 1979). In the broader sense, we would like to be able to compare the chick progesterone receptor with other steroid receptors from nonavian sources. In our laboratory, limited studies of other receptors indicate considerable structural similarities among all receptors tested (Schrader *et al.*, 1980). This notion of receptor function mediated through subunits of dissimilar structure is by no means an accepted one in the field; hopefully as others begin to study the purified receptors by the techniques outlined here this discrepancy will be clarified.

IV. Future Directions and Problems in Steroid Receptor Biochemistry

The hypothesis set forth above, and depicted in Fig. 27, is still undergoing tests in our laboratories. It should not be interpreted as fact; however, we are not aware of any information on chick progesterone receptor function which is inconsistent with this scheme. There are several aspects of this model, as it relates to steroid hormone action in general, to which we will now turn.

A. LOCATION OF UNOCCUPIED RECEPTORS

It has been customary for us to depict progesterone receptors before binding of the hormone as being located in the cell cytoplasm. An axiom in the field is that the receptor proteins bind steroid in the cytoplasm and then migrate to the nucleus. Cell fractionation studies are consistent with this view, but may be entirely incorrect. Due to the low affinity of the aporeceptors (those lacking hormone) for the nucleus, it is probable that the receptors can in fact reside within the nucleus (or anywhere else) in the absence of ligand. It is difficult, in fact, to visualize the mechanism by which these proteins could be excluded from the nucleus. We stress the need for direct, immunocytochemical or autoradiographic tests of this translocation step. Until such a test is done conclusively, it is not clear where the aporeceptors reside. Only the occupied receptors (i.e., holoreceptors) have been shown by cell fractionation and autoradiographic studies to be confined to one compartment, the nucleus.

B. THE NATURE OF RECEPTOR ACTIVATION

Nearly every laboratory studying steroid receptors has reported, using *in vitro* methods, that receptors in crude cytoplasmic extracts do not bind to nuclei or DNA efficiently unless either warmed (25°C 30 minutes) or treated with high ionic strength (usually ammonium sulfate precipitation). Our own studies along these lines (Buller *et al.*, 1975) were consistent with the prevailing view. However, all of these tests were *in vitro* experiments, for which no satisfactory mechanistic explanation has emerged. Progesterone binding does not change the charge or conformation of these proteins in a detectable way. DNA binding of the A subunit occurs whether hormone is present or not (Coty *et al.*, 1979). Thus, it is not clear what "activation" is, nor is it clear whether this phenomenon occurs *in vivo*. Obviously, the ligand must be having some effect on the protein, and that effect may properly be termed activation. But we would caution that the *in vitro* experiments can all be explained if one assumes that cell disruption has exposed receptors *in vitro* to other factors not active *in vivo*. Pyridoxal phosphate, for example, appears to bind to the receptors *in vitro* and block "activation." Perhaps this ligand is only exposed to the receptors upon cell disruption. We suggest that the notion of receptor "activation" be treated cautiously until some mechanistic explanation is found.

C. RECEPTOR MODIFICATION

Progesterone receptor, as others, has been investigated for evidence of phosphorylated residues, presence of carbohydrate, binding of ATP, cyclic AMP, and processing by cellular proteases. This aspect remains open to debate in the future, but we have been unable to detect either phosphorylation or carbohydrate in either crude or purified preparations. The purified proteins are also not efficient substrates for cyclic AMP-dependent protein kinase. Treatment of receptor preparations with molybdate ion, a phosphatase inhibitor, stabilizes the receptor's hormone-binding activity as has been found for glucocorticoids (Sando *et al.,* 1977). But we find that the metal ion appears to be acting not as an inhibitor of phosphatase, but rather it stabilizes the receptor A · B complex in its 8–9 S conformation. The hormone-binding sites are inherently more stable in the intact complex than they are when the subunits are dissociated (Grody *et al.,* 1980).

Binding of ATP to receptors has also been reported (Moudgil and Toft, 1975). These studies have only been successful using ATP-Sepharose, where the ATP concentrations are enormously high. All of our attempts to measure ATP-receptor binding by direct double-label experiments using [γ-^{32}P]ATP and [^{3}H]progesterone have failed. We feel it is likely the ATP-Sepharose test reflects occupancy of the DNA-binding sites of the receptors, with some nucleotide specificity. Preferential binding of progesterone receptor to poly(dA · dT) is consistent with this interpretation. It is unlikely, though, from our studies, that ATP is a prosthetic group on receptors *in vivo*.

Proteolytic modification of receptors certainly takes place *in vitro*. The primary enzyme involved is a calcium-activated neutral protease, which has a strong K_m for receptor and is present in all chick tissues tested (Vedeckis *et al.,* 1980a). It is not clear, however, if the enzyme has any *in vivo* relevance. Both cytoplasmic and nuclear receptors have the same electrostatic charge and Stokes' radii, and thus there is no obligatory role known for the enzyme in nuclear uptake. However, the enzyme is particularly abundant in oviduct nuclei. It is thus possible that the receptors undergo internal proteolysis in the nucleus, perhaps as a means of producing inactive receptors to be released from their sites of action. Since the nuclear progesterone receptor has not yet been purified and subjected to analysis under denaturing conditions, this possibility remains open. This is a fruitful area for future experimentation.

D. RECEPTOR ENZYMATIC ACTIVITY

The receptor proteins are sufficiently large in molecular weight for them to have multiple activities in addition to their hormone-binding and nuclear-binding domains. Several of the more likely enzymatic activities have been tested, and found to be absent, as shown in Table III. We also have tested receptors for metabolism of progesterone. By several criteria no reductase, hydroxylase, or isomerase activities were detectable. Second, the receptors have no endogenous ribonuclease or deoxyribonuclease activity toward either single- or double-stranded substrates. DNA nicking activity is also absent. Receptors are devoid of protein kinase activity and also of histone H1 protease or autoproteolytic activity. Finally, progesterone receptors do not have RNA polymerase activity, and cannot perform the subreaction of ATP-pyrophosphate exchange. This list is of course a brief one; potential enzymatic pathways such as histone acetylase, or a specific protein kinase activity, have not been tested.

E. RECEPTOR ASSOCIATION WITH SPECIFIC GENES

Our earlier chromatin transcription studies described above had shown that purified receptors could stimulate RNA transcription from oviduct chromatin preferentially. The effect was saturable, and reproduced roughly the degree of change in template activity brought about by treatment of the animal itself with progesterone. However, the assay method used measured RNA synthesis grossly, and did not distinguish whether the same RNAs were stimulated *in vitro* as were known to occur *in vivo*. In fact, since *E. coli* RNA polymerase was used, incorrect transcripts were probably the rule rather than the exception.

Thus, it remains to be established whether the ovalbumin gene, for example, can be preferentially stimulated by progesterone receptor *in vitro*. Our early attempts at this were not conclusive, since the assay method was subject to errors due to presence of ovalbumin mRNA fragments in the receptor preparation. Second, progesterone is not the natural inducer of ovalbumin *in vivo:* estradiol is required except in the specialized case of the oviduct following acute withdrawal of hormonal support. Under that condition, progesterone will substitute for estradiol *in vivo* as an inducer.

F. EFFECT OF ACCEPTOR SITES ON RATES OF GENE INDUCTION

A perplexing aspect of steroid induction of gene activity has been the kinetics argument: if a great number of unique-sequence genes are to be induced by the stimulus, how can differential rates of induction be achieved? Second, if the genes really are unique sequences in the DNA, by what mechanism do receptors search the genome rapidly and arrive at the desired genes? Third, if receptors have general DNA-binding affinity, how can the receptors avoid interaction with the wrong DNA sequences?

The answers to these questions are unknown, but some speculation can be done based upon our hypothesis in Fig. 27. We shall consider these three questions in reverse order.

First, how can the receptors avoid association with the DNA of genes not under the hormone's control? This problem is exactly analogous to that faced by the *lac* repressor protein in *E. coli,* for example. In that case, in fact, the repressors *in vivo* are largely adsorbed to nonoperator DNA (Von Hippel *et al.,* 1974). Binding sites of the nonoperator type outnumber the operator by about 10^6 to 1. The *lac* system partly compensates for this by having developed an extremely strong affinity of the repressor for the operator DNA, about 10^6 times stronger than its binding constant to the nonoperator DNA. In the hormone-responsive cell, we have not succeeded in detecting such extraordinarily strong binding sites for receptors. Yet since receptors do stimulate specific genes, some mechanism must exist for preventing interaction at undesired loci. It is our present view that the receptor dimerization process is the key element in this compensation. As mentioned above, the receptor A subunit's DNA-binding site is blocked in the dimer, thus preventing incorrect DNA associations. We speculate that the receptor B "specifier" subunit is functional in guiding the A · B complexes to specific sites in the nucleus, defined by the presence of nonhistone "acceptor" proteins. Only then is the highly reactive DNA-binding A subunit liberated in functional form in the vicinity of the DNA it is to regulate. Since we find the K_{diss} for receptor A-DNA binding to be about 100 times stronger than receptor B-chromatin binding, this reactive receptor A would immediately bind to the DNA.

Second, how do the receptors search the genome rapidly enough to encounter unique-sequence genes in a matter of minutes or less? There is enough DNA in a typical cell for perhaps 10^6 genes, of which only perhaps 10^4 are expressed, and even fewer regulated by a given hormone. If we consider one gene in the tissue and ask the question: in what time will that gene be turned on in half of the cells? We define, then, a half-time for induction of that gene. It is well-established that the half-time for induction can vary under different physiological states. If the gene DNA is present as only a single copy and is not amplified, and if the receptor titer per cell is fixed, by what mechanism can the half-time be shortened? One possibility is if the *acceptor* sites at the gene can be repeated many-fold. Under this condition, if receptor dimers have a short lifetime, the acceptor site redundancy will determine the reaction rate. Thus, a gene could be turned on very rapidly if the acceptor sites associated with that gene were able to bind multiple receptors. It is interesting to point out that a class of nuclear proteins has been detected which appears able to "mask" acceptors in chromatin (Spelsberg *et al.*, 1972). If these factors are themselves regulated, then perhaps the redundancy of acceptors is not only real but also controlled by the cell.

This brings us to point three: how to account for differential rates of induction of various genes? A possibility lies in the answer to question 2 above. If the rates of induction of two genes are controlled by their respective acceptor sites, then the degree of redundancy of acceptors with each would determine independently the rate for each. Thus in this way one might imagine that the same, common signal (the receptor complex) might induce two different genes at different rates by exactly the same biochemical mechanism. Cell differentiation, if it changed acceptor site availability or redundancy, might also affect gene induction in this manner.

These ideas regarding Figs. 27 and 28 do not, of course, adequately explain all of the effects of steroids. Secondary gene effects, due to action of earlier gene products, probably exist and bear on the overall physiologic response. But we are struck by the notion that the very earliest primary inductions by steroids may be fitted to such a scheme.

REFERENCES

Alberts, B., and Sternglanz, R. (1977). *Nature (London)* **269,** 655.

Barrack, E. R., Hawkins, E. F., Allen, S. L., Hicks, L. L., and Coffey, D. S. (1977). *Biochem. Biophys. Res. Commun.* **79,** 829–836.

Birnbaumer, M. E., Schrader, W. T., and O'Malley, B. W. (1979). *Biochem. J.* **181,** 201–213.

Bowen, B., Steinberg, J., Laemmli, U. K., and Weintraub, H. (1980). *Nucleic Acids. Res.* **8,** 1–20.

Buller, R. E., and O'Malley, B. W. (1976). *Biochem. Pharmacol.* **25,** 1.

Buller, R. E., Schrader, W. T., and O'Malley, B. W. (1975). *J. Biol. Chem.* **250,** 809–818.

Buller, R. E., Schwartz, R. J., Schrader, W. T., and O'Malley, B. W. (1976). *J. Biol. Chem.* **251,** 5178–5186.

Colbert, D. A., Knoll, B. J., Woo, S. L. C., Mace, M. L., Tsai, M. J., and O'Malley, B. W. (1980). *Biochemistry* **19,** 5586–5592.

Coty, W. A., Schrader, W. T., and O'Malley, B. W. (1979). *J. Steroid Biochem.* **10,** 1–12.

Dure, L. S., IV, Schrader, W. T., and O'Malley, B. W. (1980). *Nature* (*London*) **283,** 784–786.

Grody, W. W., Compton, J. G., Schrader, W. T., and O'Malley, B. W. (1980). *J. Steroid Biochem.* **12,** 115–120.

Grody, W. W., Schrader, W. T., and O'Malley, B. W. (1981). *Biochem. Biophys. Res. Commun.* (Submitted).

Hansen, P. E., Schrader, W. T., and O'Malley, B. W. (1976). *J. Steroid Biochem.* **7,** 723–732.

Hughes, M. R., Compton, J. G., Schrader, W. T., and O'Malley, B. W. (1981). *Biochemistry* (in press)

Kon, O. L., Webster, R. A., and Spelsberg, T. C. (1980). *Endocrinology* **107,** 1182–1191.

Kuhn, R. W., Schrader, W. T., Smith, R. G., and O'Malley, B. W. (1975). *J. Biol. Chem.* **250,** 4220–4228.

Kuhn, R. W., Schrader, W. T., Coty, W. A., Conn, P. M., and O'Malley, B. W. (1977). *J. Biol. Chem.* **252,** 308–317.

Lawson, G. M., Tsai, M. J., and O'Malley, B. W. (1980). *Biochemistry* **19,** 4403–4411.

Lawson, G. M., Tsai, M. J., Knoll, B. J., and O'Malley, B. W. (1981). *Biochemistry* (Submitted).

Moudgil, V. K., and Toft, D. O. (1975). *Proc. Natl. Acad. Sci. U.S.A.* **72,** 901–905.

O'Malley, B. W. (1967). *Biochemistry* **6,** 2546.

O'Malley, B. W., McGuire, W. L., Kohler, P. O., and Korenman, S. G. (1969). *Recent Prog. Horm. Res.* **25,** 105–160.

O'Malley, B. W., Sherman, M. R., Toft, D. O., Spelsberg, T. C., Schrader, W. T., and Steggles, A. W. (1970). *In* "Advances in the Biosciences" (G. Raspe, ed.), Vol. 7, pp. 213–234. Pergamon, Oxford.

O'Malley, B. W., Toft, D. O., and Sherman, M. R. (1971). *J. Biol. Chem.* **246,** 1117–1122.

O'Malley, B. W., Spelsberg, T. C., Schrader, W. T., Chytil, F., and Steggles, A. W. (1972). *Nature* (*London*) **235,** 141–144.

O'Malley, B. W., Roop, D. R., Lai, E. C., Nordstrom, J. L., Catterall, J. F., Swaneck, G. E., Colbert, D. A., Tsai, M. J., Dugaiczyk, A., and Woo, S. L. C. (1979). *Recent Prog. Horm. Res.* **35,** 1–46.

Palmiter, R. D. (1973). *J. Biol. Chem.* **248,** 8260.

Riggs, A. D., Suzuki, H., and Bourgeois, S. (1970). *J. Mol. Biol.* **48,** 67–83.

Roop, D. R., Nordstrom, J. L., Tsai, S. Y., Tsai, M. J., and O'Malley, B. W. (1978). *Cell* **15,** 671.

Roop, D. R., Tsai, M. J., and O'Malley, B. W. (1980). *Cell* **19,** 63–68.

Royal, A., Garapin, A., Cami, B., Perrin, F., Mandel, J. L., Lemeur, M., Bregergegre, F., Gannon, F., LePennec, J. P., Chambon, P., and Kovilsky, P. (1979). *Nature* (*London*) **279,** 125–132.

Sando, J. J., Nielsen, C. J., and Pratt, W. B. (1977). *J. Biol. Chem.* **252,** 7568–7578.

Schrader, W. T. (1975). *Methods Enzymol.* **36,** 187–211.

Schrader, W. T., and O'Malley, B. W. (1972). *J. Biol. Chem.* **247,** 51–59.

Schrader, W. T., and O'Malley, B. W. (1978). *In* "Receptors and Hormone Action" (B. W. O'Malley, ed.), Vol. 2, p. 189. Academic Press, New York.

Schrader, W. T., Toft, D. O., and O'Malley, B. W. (1972). *J. Biol. Chem.* **247,** 2401–2407.

Schrader, W. T., Buller, R. E., Kuhn, R. W., and O'Malley, B. W. (1975a). *J. Steroid Biochem.* **5,** 1–8.

Schrader, W. T., Heuer, S. S., and O'Malley, B. W. (1975b). *J. Biol. Chem.* **250,** 809–818.

Schrader, W. T., Coty, W. A., Smith, R. G., and O'Malley, B. W. (1977). *Ann. N.Y. Acad. Sci.* **286,** 64–80.

Schrader, W. T., Seleznev, Y., Vedeckis, W. V., and O'Malley, B. W. (1980). *In* "Gene Regulation by Steroid Hormones" (A. K. Roy and J. H. Clark, eds.), pp. 78–88. Springer-Verlag, Berlin and New York.

Schwartz, R. J., Kuhn, R. W., Buller, R. E., Schrader, W. T., and O'Malley, B. W. (1976). *J. Biol. Chem.* **251,** 5166–5177.

Scott, R. W., and Frankel, F. R. (1980). *Proc. Natl. Acad. Sci. U.S.A.* **77,** 1291–1295.

Sherman, M. R. (1970). *In* "Advances in the Biosciences" (G. Raspe, ed.), Vol. 7, p. 369. Pergamon, Oxford.

Sherman, M. R., Corvol, P. L., and O'Malley, B. W. (1970). *J. Biol. Chem.* **245,** 6085–6096.

Spelsberg, T. C., Steggles, A. W., Chytil, F., and O'Malley, B. W. (1972). *J. Biol. Chem.* **247,** 1369–1374.

Spelsberg, T. C., Webster, R., Pikler, G., Thrall, C., and Wells, D. (1977). *Ann. N.Y. Acad. Sci.* **286,** 43–63.

Stalder, J., Larsen, A., Engel, J. D., Dolan, M., Groudine, M., and Weintraub, H. (1980). *Cell* **20,** 451–460.

Swaneck, G. E., Kreuzaler, F., Tsai, M. J., and O'Malley, B. W. (1979). *Biochem. Biophys. Res. Commun.* **88,** 1412–1418.

Taylor, R. N., and Smith, R. G. (1979). *Biochem. Biophys. Res. Commun.* **91,** 136.

Tsai, S. Y., Tsai, M. J., Schwartz, M. J., Kalimi, M., Clark, J. H., and O'Malley, B. W. (1975). *Proc. Natl. Acad. Sci. U.S.A.* **72,** 4228–4232.

Tsai, S. Y., Tsai, M. J., and O'Malley, B. W. (1981). *Proc. Natl. Acad. Sci. U.S.A.* (in press)

Vedeckis, W. V., Schrader, W. T., and O'Malley, B. W. (1978). *In* "Biochemical Actions of Hormones" (G. Litwack, ed.), Vol. 5, p. 321. Academic Press, New York.

Vedeckis, W. V., Schrader, W. T., and O'Malley, B. W. (1979). *In* "Steroid Hormone Receptor Systems" (W. W. Leavitt and J. H. Clark, eds.), pp. 309–327. Plenum, New York.

Vedeckis, W. V., Freeman, M. R., Schrader, W. T., and O'Malley, B. W. (1980a). *Biochemistry* **19,** 335–343.

Vedeckis, W. V., Schrader, W. T., and O'Malley, B. W. (1980b). *Biochemistry* **19,** 343–349.

Von Hippel, P. H., Revzin, A., Gross, C. A., and Wang, A. C. (1974). *Proc. Natl. Acad. Sci. U.S.A.* **71,** 4808–4812.

Weigel, N. L., Birnbaumer, M. E., Fahnestock, M., Schrader, W. T., and O'Malley, B. W. (1981a) *Nature (London)* (submitted)

Weigel, N. L., Pousette, A., Schrader, W. T., and O'Malley, B. W. (1981b). *Biochemistry* (Submitted)

Weintraub, H., and Groudine, M. (1976). *Science* **193,** 848–856.

Woo, S. L. C., Beattie, W. G., Catterall, J. F., Dugaiczyk, A., Stader, R., Brownlee, G. G., and O'Malley, B. W. (1981). *J. Biol. Chem.* (Submitted)

DISCUSSION

B. Robaire: I'd like to know whether you have looked in the oviduct for the nuclear matrix that D. S. Coffey has found in mammalian cells and whether you can demonstrate any binding of the progesterone receptor to such a complex.

W. Schrader: We haven't done those experiments.

A. K. Roy: Several years ago you suggested that all steroid receptors possess A and B subunits and the activation process represents subunit aggregation—would you like to share your recent thoughts about this?

W. Schrader: I think there are more similarities among steroid receptors than there are differences. I have looked at the chromatographic properties of a number of steroid receptors and have seen the same sort of behavior that I outlined at the start of my talk. I don't think that there is any compelling evidence that the progesterone receptor in the oviduct is structurally unique among the steroid receptors.

P. B. Naylor: I was looking forward to your being able to tell us that there was a specific fragment of the cloned DNA that bound the receptor. Would you care to speculate as to the reason you were not successful? Is this a technical problem or is it really not there?

W. Schrader: There is still a great potential that we simply are not using the right methods to look for nucleotide sequence specificity. The second pitfall is that we simply may not have the right piece of DNA. We are hoping that if a high-affinity binding site exists for progesterone receptor near the ovalbumin gene that it would be within DNA which we have cloned. In the case of the ovalbumin gene, the gene is 7.8 kilobases from the start of initiation to the 3′ end of the transcript. The largest single fragment which we have tested is 12 kilobases in length so that it goes a couple of kilobases to the left and a little bit to the right of the natural gene. We are hoping that if such a high-affinity site were to exist that it would be someplace in that vicinity, but we cannot exclude the possibility that there is a completely unforeseen mechanism by which receptor regulation might occur some distance away. In that case, we simply don't have the right DNA yet. We're continuing to look at that and I think we'll just have to wait and see.

H. G. Friesen: I was very interested in your remark that sheep have natural antibodies to the progesterone receptor—could you elaborate on that somewhat—is this a high-affinity antibody—do both rams and ewes have it—do other species exhibit it or is it unique to the sheep?

W. Schrader: This was following up on the work of Thomas Fox in Boston who reported that a number of hyperimmunized animals contain sera which react with the estrogen receptor in the mouse. He was pointing this out more or less as a caution that these sort of antibodies exist. We thought we had raised an antibody to the chick progesterone receptors in sheep. In the process of trying to nail that down, we found out that the activity was actually a general activity which was present in many different sheep. The sheep we have checked all happen to be male sheep; about 20 sheep have been looked at and they have a range of titers of this material, but it's always very low. It's active only at about a dilution of 1 : 40, and its equilibrium constant is around 10^{-9} molar for the interaction of that material with the receptor. It's apparently an IgG as evidenced by the fact that it binds to *Staphylococcus aureus* protein A and also it's precipitated by a rabbit anti-sheep IgG antibody. I tried to figure out why in the world a sheep would be walking around with a spontaneous antibody to the chicken oviduct progesterone receptor and your guess is as good as mine. I simply have no idea.

C. Kahn: I would like to ask a couple of questions about the comparative structure in the A and B receptor subunits. My impression is that your impression is that these are really very distinct polypeptide chains and yet they have many functions in common including the progesterone binding, the reactivity with the antibody, and so forth; I wondered in this particular case if you could tell us a little bit more about your thinking in this regard. Is it possible, for example, that there are common peptide X fragments to both subunits which are the overlapping spots in the peptide map? One of these might be the progesterone-binding site. Could you look at this using your affinity label or using the antibody which occurs in these sheep? A second correlative question would be—is there evidence that this sheep natural antibody recognizes some of these common regions or is it, in fact, recognizing different regions of the A and B subunits?

W. Schrader: That's a very good point. First of all, we don't know which of those tryptic peptides is the hormone-binding domain. We're trying to do those experiments at the present time. The problem with such experiments is that the tryptic peptide with R5020 bound covalently to it is probably not going to behave the same in the tryptic map. Thus we may have some problems identifying the fragment, but we're trying to do exactly what you propose. Second, as far as the antibody work is concerned, the antibody is of such a low titer that we cannot use it to work on the purified proteins. We haven't been able to clean it up enough. Despite a fair amount of effort we have been unable to raise decent antibodies as has been done for glucocorticoid receptors and for estrogen receptors. I have no idea why. As far as my interpretation of the gross similarity between A and B and their actually being completely separate proteins, all I can do is speculate. One possibility is that the two receptor proteins arise from two different genes which have diverged a bit. Thus they may have retained a common hormone-binding site, but may have diverged elsewhere. Such an idea has been seen for the globin gene family, for example. There is an overall similarity among the various fetal and adult globin genes, but their protein products are not identical.

C. Lazier: Many people now seem to be adding molybdate to stabilize their cytoplasmic receptor preparations. What is your experience with molybdate and what do you think its mechanism of action might be?

W. Schrader: Molybdate has become very popular following the work of W. Pratt and his colleagues at Michigan. Those workers found that when sodium molybdate was present, the cytosol glucocorticoid receptor was considerably stabilized as far as its hormone-binding activity was concerned. Every laboratory which has tried those experiments has found that the addition of sodium molybdate at about 10–20 mM stabilizes the hormone-binding activity of the aporeceptor fraction. The mechanism of this stabilization is not clear. My view from the work which we've done is that the molybdate probably binds to the receptor and stabilizes the receptor aggregate so it doesn't dissociate to monomers. I believe that the unoccupied hormone-binding site is intrinsically less stable in the isolated monomers than it is in the aggregate. Thus any influence which causes receptor aggregation would stabilize. Furthermore any influence which destabilized the aggregate would cause the hormone-binding activity to become less stable.

C. Lazier: Have you done tryptic maps on the A and B proteins from nuclear receptor preparations and compared them with those for the cytosol A and B proteins?

W. Schrader: No, we have not done that. Both the hen and the chick receptors which I've described here are prepared from cytoplasm not from nuclei. We have done no purification of the nuclear progesterone receptor so I cannot compare the two. In the chromatographic studies of the nuclear receptors which have been done in my lab over the years, we have never found a difference between the nuclear and the cytoplasmic materials on the basis of size or charge. But the covalent R5020 technique is a much more sensitive method since SDS gels can be used; and now we're trying to ask that question using this method.

W. R. Moyle: From the structure of DNA one would predict that regions of DNA rich in AT pairs might favor binding of the receptor to DNA better than those rich in GC pairs. Have you tried comparing inhibition by binding by synthetic DNA pieces that have high contents of AT pairs as opposed to GC pairs? Are there regions in ovalbumin rich in AT pairs near where you expect initiation to start?

W. Schrader: Yes, that is correct—since AT pairs had only two hydrogen bonds per pair they breathe to a greater extent than GC pairs. That's why a helix-destabilizing protein would be expected to associate preferentially with AT-rich regions. We've tried those experiments and found the synthetic oligo-deoxynucleotide poly(dA · dT) to be a better competitor than poly(dG · dC). The problem with those experiments is that commercially available oligonucleotides are pretty short and they are heterodisperse in length. Thus it is very difficult to know exactly how to do those experiments so you can interpret them. A second and I think perhaps more informative experiment has been done using the recombinant bacterial plasmid pOV230 which is an ovalbumin cDNA clone. This plasmid was constructed using A-T linkers at either end of the inserted cDNA. Thus, this DNA has two fairly long stretches of AT sequences in it. But this DNA does not bind the receptor any better under our conditions than does any other DNA. Finally, yes, there is a short AT-rich region near the ovalbumin gene proximal to the site of initiation. This is called the Hogness box, which in the ovalbumin gene has the nucleotide sequence TATATAT. It is located 26 nucleotides to the left of the first coding nucleotide in the primary transcript.

W. R. Moyle: If both A and B subunits of the receptor are synthesized by different genes one might expect to find free A and free B present in the cytoplasm. Have you looked for either of these?

W. Schrader: Yes, actually that work has been done. From my earliest studies I had found that there was always a certain amount of free A and free B in any cytoplasmic extract. This line of work has also been continued recently by Thomas C. Spelsberg and his collaborators at the Mayo Clinic. They found an annual rhythm in the receptor content and in the A to B ratio in the hen oviduct throughout the growing year. The B protein concentration of the chick oviduct cytosol is virtually a constant throughout the year. However, the A protein's titer goes from being equal to that of B to being very much lowered. It's tempting to speculate that perhaps that may represent varying expressions of two different genes. I don't want to push this business about two different genes—it is also possible to construct a plausible map which would allow one to construct both A and B from a common gene, so I only throw that out as a suggestion. What I wish to stress is the fact that the evidence is now clear that B and A cannot arise from the same mature messenger RNA. Thus they are not precursor–product, and A cannot simply be a proteolytic artifact arising *in vitro*.

S. W. Spaulding: Does the helix-destabilizing A subunit of the receptor potentiate transcription of double-stranded DNA by eukaryotic polymerase II?

W. Schrader: We have not been able to show that activity thus far—that work is just getting started and so far I don't have anything to say about it.

J. E. Rall: I can see why you were disappointed that there was no difference in binding between ovalbumin gene and a large series of nucleotides upstream of it versus unfractionated DNA. But maybe that really is telling us something—maybe the regulators of gene expression don't do something as simple as interact with the promoter side or an RNA polymerase binding site—perhaps they do something differently. There may be something to what Davidson has always been saying about repetitive sequences. I am always impressed that when you do a digest of DNA with restriction enzymes and run it out on a gel and then hybridize it with DNA complementary to a message you get 2 or 3 lines. Is there any way you can do this with your affinity labeled receptor protein—to see if it bound specifically to any DNA fragment? Have you done anything like that, and have you looked at repetitive DNA, which isn't too hard to isolate, to see whether there's any difference in binding to it versus unique sequence DNA?

W. Schrader: Detection of binding specificity depends upon the relative equilibrium constants for binding to a specific site compared to total DNA. Let's take the case of the *lac* repressor protein: it binds to its operator with a particular equilibrium constant and it binds to every other DNA with a 10,000-fold weaker equilibrium constant. Even with this huge difference in affinity, one cannot detect the binding of *lac* repressor to its operator unless you eliminate most of the nonoperator DNA from the DNA fragment that you use. You can't find it just by taking the total *E. coli* DNA and trying to bind repressor. So I don't think those experiments you proposed are presently possible. As far as the reiterated DNA—no, we have not looked at that.

E. J. Rall: Yes, I know about the problems of a protein which binds well to nonspecific DNA and better to some specific sequences. I thought, however, that in an equilibrium experiment with immobilized DNA fragments that even a 100-fold difference in affinity constant might show specific binding.

W. Schrader: I haven't thought through that experiment perhaps carefully enough—I would be happy to talk about it with you privately.

B. I. Posner: In your picture of the A and B subunits being held together in a complex, you had positive charges on both subunits facing one another. By what forces do you imagine this complex being maintained?

W. Schrader: What I was trying to indicate there was that the subunit-interaction regions of the two proteins have a net positive charge, not that those were the only charges that are present. There's probably something on the order of 120 lysine residues for example in the B protein and a greater number of acidic residues than that—so there is considerable charge distributed around the protein. I'm just saying that by virtue of the DEAE and phosphocellulose binding profiles of these various digests it looks like certain regions have expressed certain preponderances of charge. Obviously if the binding is electrostatic (and to the present time all the evidence says that the binding is not covalent) since it can be dissociated by high ionic strength, I would predict that there must be concomitant negative charges to make such an electrostatic interaction possible. The nature of that interaction is not known.

B. I. Posner: You describe how interaction with the DNA may take place during the course of "breathing" of the DNA. That is, the subunit binds to the exposed single strand and shifts the equilibrium toward the single-stranded material leading, in effect, to an unwinding. If this is physiologically important and perhaps involved in the initiation of transcription, in what way do you visualize such a process being reversed?

W. Schrader: There certainly is no evidence that such a mechanism is functioning *in vivo* or even in the isolated nuclei. All I'm saying is that I think this subreaction can occur *in vitro*. I didn't mean to imply that this DNA helix destabilization reaction has been detected under any sort of *in situ* conditions. Now with that disclaimer let me say something about an off reaction. I can think of several possibilities. It turns out that this calcium activated neutral protease which we used in the initial digests is present in the nucleus. One intriguing possibility is that the receptor protein is digested in the nucleus by the protease and thus its half-life in the nucleus is limited by that enzyme. A second possibility is that the hormone simply comes off the protein and the protein loses its DNA-binding activity. The bad news for that latter possibility is that we have shown that the receptor A protein binds just fine to DNA cellulose with or without hormone. Thus, there's no requirement for the hormone to get DNA binding to DNA cellulose. However, we cannot prepare the apo-protein to homogeneity and hence cannot do the studies on the uncomplexed protein by the nitrocellulose method. So whether or not an effect of the hormone on DNA binding will ultimately be found is anyone's guess.

L. E. Faber: You said there's no evidence of a cofactor in the formation of the AB complex?

W. Schrader: That's correct—we can perform what appears to be the A plus B reconstitution reaction without adding any cofactors. For example, we don't have to add magnesium, we don't have to add ATP, and we don't have to add reducing agents. That does not mean that no such cofactors exist—I tried to make that clear—just that we're not aware of any at this time. Since the preparations of A and B were only at best 50-fold purified in the reconstitutions I showed, it is of course equally possible that such cofactors are still present in these crude preparations. That will become clear only as we try to reconstitute the highly purified receptors.

The Role of Guanine Nucleotides in Regulation of Adenylate Cyclase Activity

ALLEN M. SPIEGEL, ROBERT W. DOWNS, JR., MICHAEL A. LEVINE, MORTON J. SINGER, JR., WOLFGANG KRAWIETZ, STEPHEN J. MARX, CHARLES J. WOODARD, SHARON A. REEN, AND G. D. AURBACH

Metabolic Diseases Branch, National Institute of Arthritis, Metabolism, and Digestive Diseases, National Institutes of Health, Bethesda, Maryland

I. Introduction

The adenylate cyclase (AC) complex plays a key role in the transfer of information from extracellular first messengers such as hormones to the interior of the cell. The activated enzyme catalyzes formation of the second messenger, cyclic 3′,5′-adenosine monophosphate (cAMP), which in turn regulates diverse intracellular processes (in most, if not all, cases by acting upon cAMP-dependent protein kinases).

Robison and Sutherland (1971) summarized available knowledge concerning AC structure (Fig. 1). Subcellular fractionation studies showed that the enzyme is located on the plasma membrane. The catalytic portion of the enzyme was presumed to face the cytoplasm and convert Mg^{2+}-ATP to cAMP. A receptor portion of the enzyme, located on the external surface of the plasma membrane, was the presumed site of hormone binding. Agonist binding to the receptor leads to increased catalytic activity, but the mechanism of hormone action as well as the nature of the connection between receptor and catalytic portion of the enzyme were not known. Membrane lipids were thought to be important in coupling receptor to the catalytic portion of the enzyme, since detergent solubilization leads to loss of hormone responsiveness. The fluoride ion (F^-) was found to activate particulate AC from all tissues. F^- also activates the detergent-solubilized enzyme and thus F^- was presumed to bypass the receptor and act directly on the catalytic part of the enzyme.

The structure of the AC complex and the mechanism of hormone activation have been the subjects of intensive investigation by many laboratories over the last decade. As a result, the enzyme is now known to consist of at least 3 components: the hormone receptor (R), the catalytic unit (C),

ISBN 0-12-571137-9

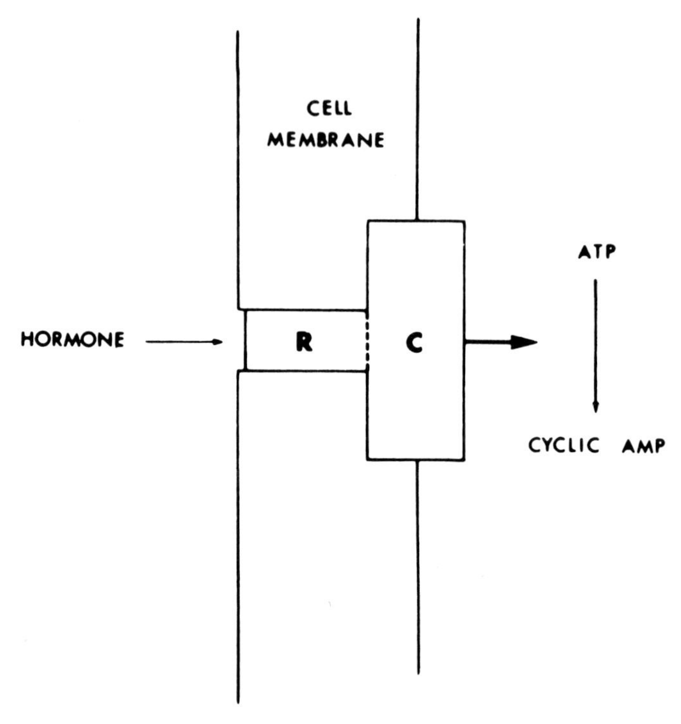

FIG. 1. Model of adenylate cyclase complex. R, Hormone receptor; C, catalytic portion of enzyme. From Robison and Sutherland (1971).

and a recently discovered guanine nucleotide-binding protein (G).[1] R has been shown to be a separate component by biochemical (Orly and Schramm, 1976; Limbird and Lefkowitz, 1977), genetic (Insel *et al.*, 1976), and developmental (Bilezikian *et al.*, 1977) studies. Considerable progress has been made in purification of R, particularly for the β-adrenergic receptor. Studies on R structure and function have been recently reviewed (Caron *et al.*, 1979) and will not be discussed here. C is an intrinsic membrane protein located on the inner surface of the plasma membrane (Neer, 1978) and has not yet been well characterized. The G unit is also an intrinsic membrane protein located on the cytoplasmic side of the plasma membrane (Kaslow *et al.*, 1980). In this article, we will review data on the separation of the G unit from the AC complex, describe the role of guanine nucleotides (GN) in mediating AC activation by hor-

[1] The guanine nucleotide-binding protein has been variously designated G, N, G/F, etc. Since no general consensus exists as yet, we will continue to refer to it as G in this article.

mones, F^-, and cholera toxin, and discuss clinical abnormalities involving the G unit.[2]

II. Role of GN in Hormonal Activation of AC

The studies of Rodbell and co-workers (1971), demonstrating a requirement for GTP for glucagon activation of hepatic AC, provided the first evidence that GN play a critical role in hormonal stimulation of the enzyme. The GTP requirement was not appreciated in previous studies in part because: (1) very low concentrations (K_m for GTP $\sim 10^{-7}$ M) of GN satisfy the requirement, (2) ATP and crude membrane preparations (used as enzyme substrate and enzyme source, respectively) were contaminated with GN, and (3) a nucleoside triphosphate-regenerating system (e.g., creatine phosphate–creatine phosphokinase), routinely employed in AC assay to prevent ATP depletion, forms GTP from contaminating GN. Utilizing appropriate assay conditions and employing nonhydrolyzable GTP analogs such as Gpp(NH)p[3] (see later), several laboratories showed that GN involvement in hormonal regulation of AC is a general phenomenon, not limited to glucagon stimulation of hepatic AC (Londos *et al.*, 1974).

For our studies on GN regulation of AC, the turkey erythrocyte proved to be a very useful model system. Turkey erythrocytes represent a readily obtained, homogeneous cell population from which purified plasma membranes are readily prepared by hypotonic lysis. A typical β-receptor (β_1 subtype, about 400 sites/cell) was identified in turkey erythrocyte plasma membranes with the radioiodinated high-affinity β-adrenergic blocker, hydroxybenzylpindolol (Aurbach *et al.*, 1974; Brown *et al.*, 1976). The β-receptor in turkey erythrocytes, as in other cell types, is linked to AC; agonists increase intracellular cAMP which in turn regulates Na^+ and K^+ transport (Gardner *et al.*, 1976), possibly by controlling phosphorylation of a membrane protein (M_r = 240,000) termed goblin by Greengard and co-workers (Beam *et al.*, 1979). The evidence supporting the aforementioned conclusions was presented by Gardner at a previous Laurentian Hormone Conference (1975).

Several GTP analogs (Fig. 2) facilitated investigation of the role of GTP in hormonal stimulation of AC from turkey erythrocytes. Analogs such as

[2] GN also show important effects on hormone receptor binding and may be involved in inhibitory control of AC activity (reviewed in Rodbell, 1980), but these effects are beyond the scope of this article.

[3] Abbreviations of GN analogs: Gpp(NH)p, guanylyl 5′-imidodiphosphate; Gp(CH_2)pp, guanylyl 5′-α-β-methylene triphosphate; GTP-γ-S, guanosine 5′(γ-thio)-triphosphate; GDP-β-S, guanosine 5′ (β-thio)-diphosphate.

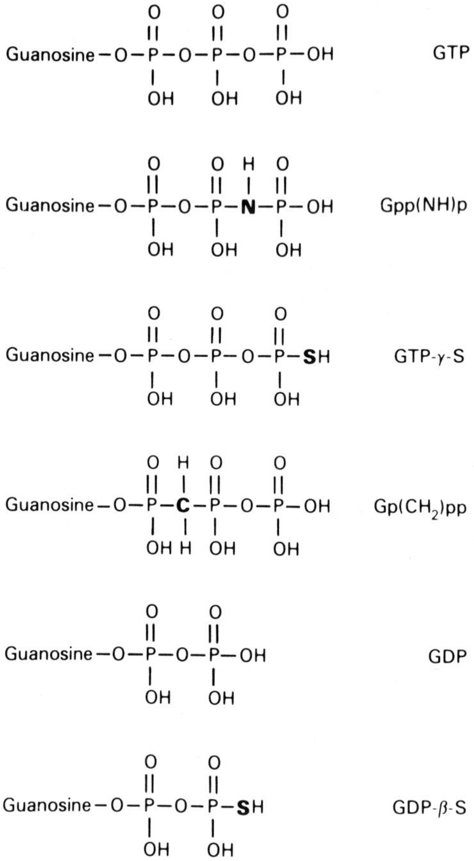

```
                 O     O     O
                 ||    ||    ||
Guanosine—O—P—O—P—O—P—OH                GTP
                 |     |     |
                 OH    OH    OH

                 O     O  H  O
                 ||    || |  ||
Guanosine—O—P—O—P—N—P—OH                Gpp(NH)p
                 |     |     |
                 OH    OH    OH

                 O     O     O
                 ||    ||    ||
Guanosine—O—P—O—P—O—P—SH                GTP-γ-S
                 |     |     |
                 OH    OH    OH

                 O  H  O     O
                 || |  ||    ||
Guanosine—O—P—C—P—O—P—OH                Gp(CH2)pp
                 |  |  |     |
                 OH H  OH    OH

                 O     O
                 ||    ||
Guanosine—O—P—O—P—OH                    GDP
                 |     |
                 OH    OH

                 O     O
                 ||    ||
Guanosine—O—P—O—P—SH                    GDP-β-S
                 |     |
                 OH    OH
```

FIG. 2. Structures of GN analogs. Substitution of P–N–P and P–C–P for P–O–P, and P–SH for P–OH renders the involved P relatively resistant to enzymatic cleavage.

Gpp(NH)p and GTP-γ-S have a structure sufficiently similar to that of GTP to enable them to bind to GTP-specific sites but unlike GTP, the γ-phosphate of the analogs is relatively resistant to hydrolysis. We initially compared the effects of GTP and Gpp(NH)p in turkey erythrocyte AC with and without added β-adrenergic agonist. The data (Fig. 3) are notable in several respects: (1) Gpp(NH)p is a more effective stimulator than GTP both with and without added isoproterenol (ISO); (2) Gpp(NH)p + ISO stimulate the enzyme much more effectively than either agent alone; (3) the synergistic response to Gpp(NH)p + ISO is effectively blocked by the β-adrenergic antagonist, propranolol; (4) Gpp(NH) p + ISO produces greater stimulation than F^-; the latter was previously thought to produce "maximal" enzyme stimulation.

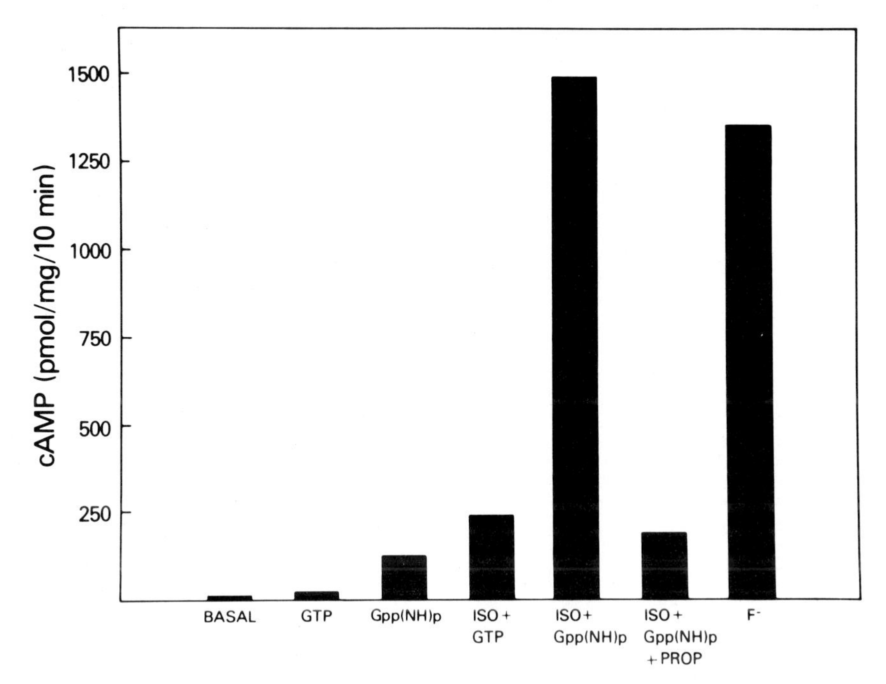

FIG. 3. GN effects on turkey erythrocyte AC. Turkey erythrocyte membrane AC activity expressed as pmol/mg protein was assayed for 10 minutes at 37°C with the additions shown. Concentrations of GN = 10 μM, of ISO and propranolol = 50 μM.

The ability of GTP to inhibit competitively Gpp(NH)p-mediated stimulation (Fig. 4) showed that Gpp(NH)p and GTP share a common site of action on AC (Spiegel and Aurbach, 1974). The GTP binding site is specific for GN and distinct from the substrate binding site for ATP; other purine and pyrimidine nucleotides, e.g., ITP, bind with much lower affinity or are ineffective (Spiegel and Aurbach, 1974). Gpp(NH)p not only stimulated AC to a much greater degree than GTP but, unlike GTP, formed a persistently activated state of the enzyme we termed holocatalytic (Spiegel *et al.*, 1976) (Table I). Formation of the holocatalytic state requires the simultaneous action of β-adrenergic agonists and Gpp(NH)p. Once formed, the holocatalytic state is not inhibitable by propranolol but β-adrenergic blockers prevent formation of the holocatalytic state. Mg^{2+} is also required for formation of the holocatalytic state, since EDTA (but not EGTA) blocks its formation and this inhibition is overcome by added Mg^{2+} (Spiegel *et al.*, 1976). We interpreted these data to suggest that Mg^{2+} is necessary for binding of Gpp(NH)p to the GN binding site on AC.

Gpp(NH)p (but not GTP) leads to a 10-fold left shift in the dose–response curve for β-adrenergic stimulation of turkey erythrocyte AC.

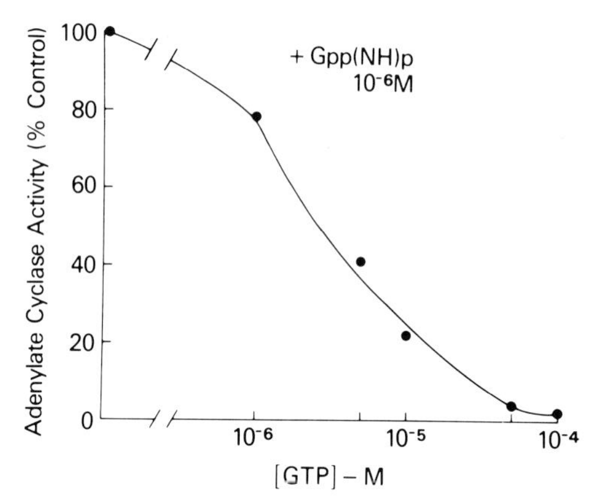

FIG. 4. Inhibition of Gpp(NH)p-stimulated AC activity by GTP. Turkey erythrocyte AC was assayed in the presence of 1 μM Gpp(NH)p and increasing concentrations of GTP. Activity is plotted as percentage of control without GTP.

This increase in apparent potency of β-adrenergic agonists is a consequence of the persistently activated state of the enzyme achieved with Gpp(NH)p + ISO (Spiegel and Aurbach, 1974).

The ability of Gpp(NH)p to stimulate AC excluded the possibility that GN activation of the enzyme involves transfer of the γ-phosphate of GTP to a component of AC. Since Gpp(NH)p is susceptible to cleavage at the α–β phosphate bond, the possibility remained that transfer of a pyrophosphate group accounts for AC activation. Cuatrecasas and co-workers (1975) postulated such a mechanism; they suggested that the ability of Gpp(NH)p (and not GTP) to persistently activate AC could be accounted

TABLE I
Formation of the Holocatalytic State[a]

Incubation additions	Assay additions	cAMP formed (pmol/mg/10 min)
None	Gpp(NH)p + ISO	2600
Gpp(NH)p	ISO	390
ISO	Gpp(NH)p	80
ISO + Gpp(NH)p	None	1270
ISO + Gpp(NH)p	Prop	1340
ISO + Gpp(NH)p + prop	None	50

[a] Turkey erythrocyte membranes were incubated with additions detailed in column 1 and then washed 3 times with a 10-fold excess of buffer. Subsequent additions during adenylate cyclase assay are shown in column 2. Concentrations used were Gpp(NH)p + ISO 10 μM, and propranolol 100 μM. (Modified from Spiegel *et al.*, 1976.)

for by the greater resistance to subsequent cleavage of the imidodiphosphate transferred from Gpp(NH)p compared with the pyrophosphate transferred from GTP. We were able to exclude a pyrophosphorylation mechanism by showing that Gp(CH_2)pp, a GTP analog resistant to cleavage at the α–β postion, is nonetheless a quite effective stimulator of AC from turkey erythrocytes and rat reticulocytes (Spiegel *et al.*, 1977). Gp(CH_2)pp, like Gpp(NH)p, forms the holocatalytic state; this was explained by the resistance of the γ-phosphate of Gp(cH_2)pp to cleavage by either turkey erythrocyte or rat reticulocyte membranes (Spiegel *et al.*, 1977).

Elimination of phosphorylation and pyrophosphorylation mechanisms made it likely that GN effects on AC are not due to a covalent modification of a component of the enzyme but rather to allosteric change caused by binding of GN to a specific site(s). The greater efficacy of nonhydrolyzable GTP analogs suggested that hydrolysis of GTP to GDP could be responsible for enzyme deactivation. Thus hydrolysis-resistant analogs would result in persistent activation. Cassel and Selinger (1976) provided evidence for this hypothesis by demonstrating β-adrenergic stimulation of a high-affinity GTPase in turkey erythrocyte membranes. β-adrenergic stimulation of GTP hydrolysis is consistent with a role for β-adrenergic agonists in facilitating binding of GTP to a GN site related to AC.

The action of β-adrenergic agonists involves release of tightly bound GDP from the AC-associated GN binding site on turkey erythrocyte membranes. This was directly demonstrated by Cassel and Selinger (1978) and Downs *et al.* (1980a). [^{3}H]GTP was incubated with turkey erythrocyte membranes in the presence and absence of β-adrenergic agonist. A second incubation with unlabeled GN and propranolol removed [^{3}H]GTP from hormone-independent binding sites. In the final "release" phase of the experiment, GN was added with and without ISO and the amount of [^{3}H]GN released measured (Table II). Note that ISO is required both in the initial incubation to permit binding to specific sites and during the release phase (Fig. 5). Anion-exchange chromatography of released [^{3}H]GN revealed that $>$ 90% of ISO-dependent GN released was GDP even though [^{3}H]GTP was initially bound [nonspecific hydrolysis of GTP was prevented by including App(NH)p and sodium pyrophosphate in the assay medium]. The data are compatible with the scheme depicted in Fig. 6.

GN effects on turkey erythrocyte AC differ in certain respects from effects on mammalian receptor-cyclase systems such as the rat reticulocyte (Fig. 7). Hormone-independent stimulation by Gpp(NH)p is greater in rat reticulocytes than in turkey erythrocytes. This may reflect greater exchangeability at the GN binding site of rat reticulocytes, either because

TABLE II
β-Adrenergic-Dependent Release of [³H]GN from Turkey Erythrocyte Membrane-Binding Sites[a]

	[³H]GN released (fmol/mg)		
First incubation	−ISO	+ISO	Δ
[³H]GTP	77	85	8
[³H]GTP + ISO	53	164	111

[a] [³H]GTP was bound to membranes in the presence and absence of ISO and that bound to hormone-independent sites exchanged for unlabeled GTP. [³H]GN was then released with and without isoproterenol. The difference (Δ) represents [³H]GN released from ISO-dependent sites. (Modified from Downs *et al.*, 1980a.)

GDP does not remain bound after GTP hydrolysis or because GDP is less tightly bound. The ratio of ISO + GTP to ISO + Gpp(NH)p stimulation is much higher in rat reticulocytes than in turkey erythrocytes. This could reflect a slower GTPase reaction in rat reticulocytes but direct verification of this hypothesis is not available. The differences in GN effect are likely quantitative rather than qualitative; even in systems characterized by substantial hormone-independent Gpp(NH)p stimulation, addition of hormone eliminates a characteristic lag phase and augments Gpp(NH)p stimulation (Salomon *et al.*, 1975). ISO + GTP, moreover, does not activate persistently, even in systems characterized by a high ISO + GTP/ISO + Gpp(NH)p ratio. Quantitative differences in GN effects in various receptor-cyclase systems are determined by the G unit rather than the

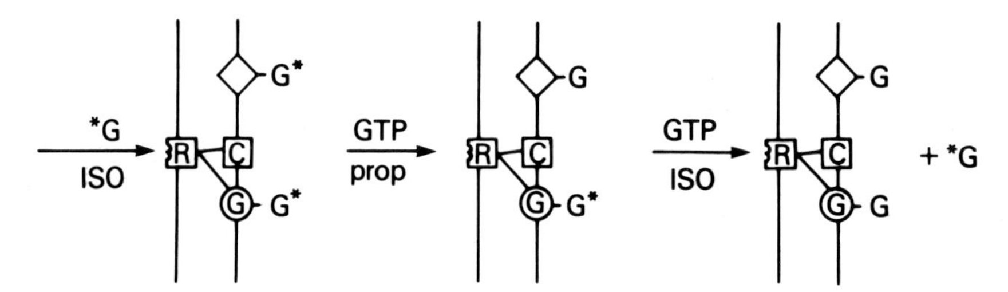

FIG. 5. Schematic diagram of ISO-dependent [³H]GN binding and release from turkey erythrocyte membranes. G* represents labeled and G represents unlabeled GN. The diamond represents non-AC-related ("nonspecific") GN binding sites. In the presence of ISO, G* binds to specific and nonspecific sites. Unlabeled GTP (G) added in the absence of ISO (propranolol is added to prevent any residual β-adrenergic agonist from binding to β-receptor) exchanges for G* at nonspecific sites only. In the final release phase of the experiment, GTP and ISO cause release of G* from specific (i.e., AC-related) sites.

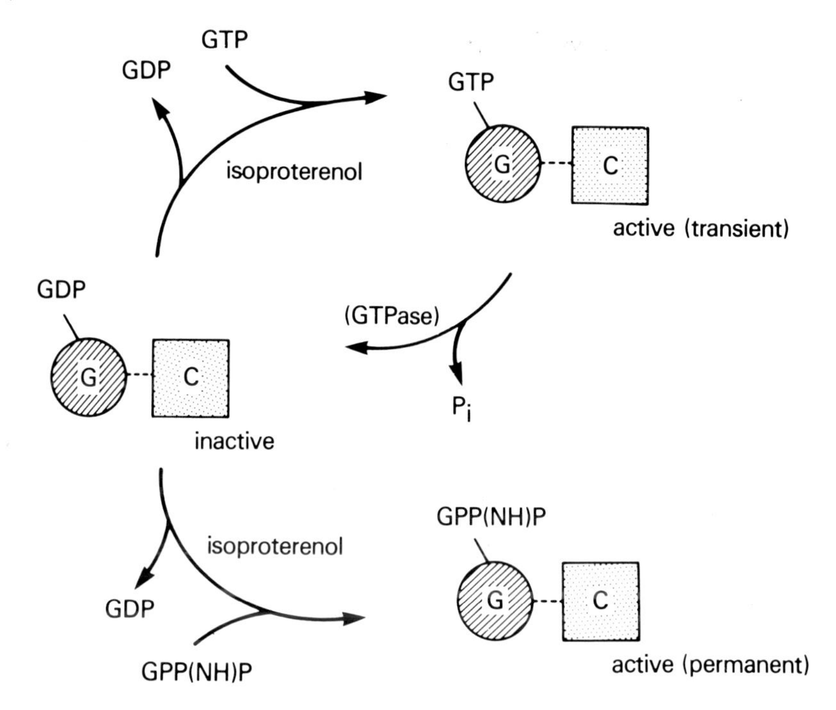

FIG. 6. Schematic model of GN exchange cycle (modified from Cassel and Selinger, 1978). The GDP-bound G unit represents the inactive state of the AC complex. In the presence of ISO, tightly bound GDP is released from the turkey erythrocyte G unit. ISO facilitates GTP binding to the G unit; this results in a transient activation of AC that is terminated by GTPase action. The system with GDP bound returns to the basal (inactive) state. With Gpp(NH)p and ISO, Gpp(NH)p (nonhydrolyzable GTP analog) becomes bound to the G unit and the system is persistently activated.

receptor or catalytic units (Kaslow *et al.*, 1979), but the structural basis for these differences is unknown. From a purely experimental point of view, the strict dependence upon β-adrenergic agonists that characterizes GN effects on turkey erythrocyte AC provides a useful control to ascertain the specificity of various GN-related events.

III. Role of GN in F^- Activation of AC

Recognition of the importance of GN in regulation of AC activity prompted a reevaluation of the mechanism of F^- activation. The observation that F^-, unlike hormone, stimulation was not dependent on exogenous GN appeared to confirm the hypothesis that F^- acted directly on C. The effects of ISO + GMP on turkey erythrocyte AC provided evidence that

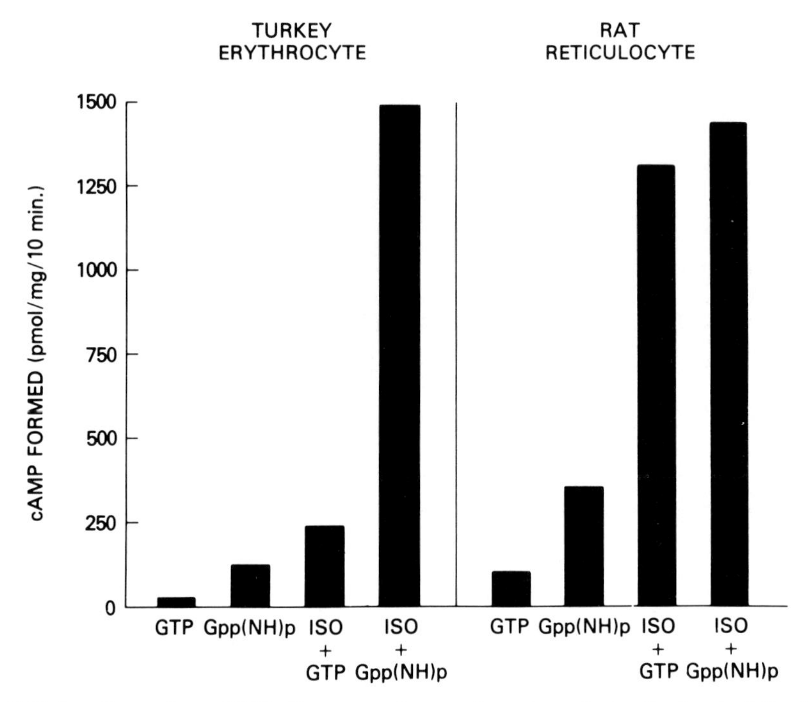

FIG. 7. Comparison of GN effects on turkey erythrocyte and rat reticulocyte AC activity. Membranes were incubated with GN (10 μM) with and without ISO (50 μM) and assayed for AC activity for 10 minutes at 37°C.

GN could influence F^- stimulation (Downs *et al.,* 1980a). Incubation of turkey erythrocyte membranes with ISO + GMP clears a portion of the GN binding sites of tightly bound GDP. Because GMP shows a low affinity for the GN site, high concentrations (1 mM) are required but the effect is specific for GMP (as opposed to other nucleoside monophosphates) and, as expected, absolutely depends on the presence of a β-adrenergic agonist, i.e., GMP (1 mM) alone is without effect (Downs *et al.,* 1980a). ISO + GMP treatment creates a unique state of the turkey erythrocyte AC characterized by hormone-independent GN exchange. Thus Gpp(NH)p now stimulates substantially without ISO; F^- stimulation is reduced but can be restored to control with GTP or GDP (Fig. 8).

Further evidence for a role of GN in F^- stimulation was provided by studies with the GDP analog, GDP-β-S (Eckstein *et al.,* 1979; Downs *et al.,* 1980a). The ability of GDP-β-S to block Gpp(NH)p stimulation (Fig. 9) suggests it can bind to the GN site; despite this, and its close similarity in structure to GDP, GDP-β-S does not restore F^- stimulation after ISO + GMP treatment (Fig. 9). Indeed, GDP-β-S itself was found to block F^-

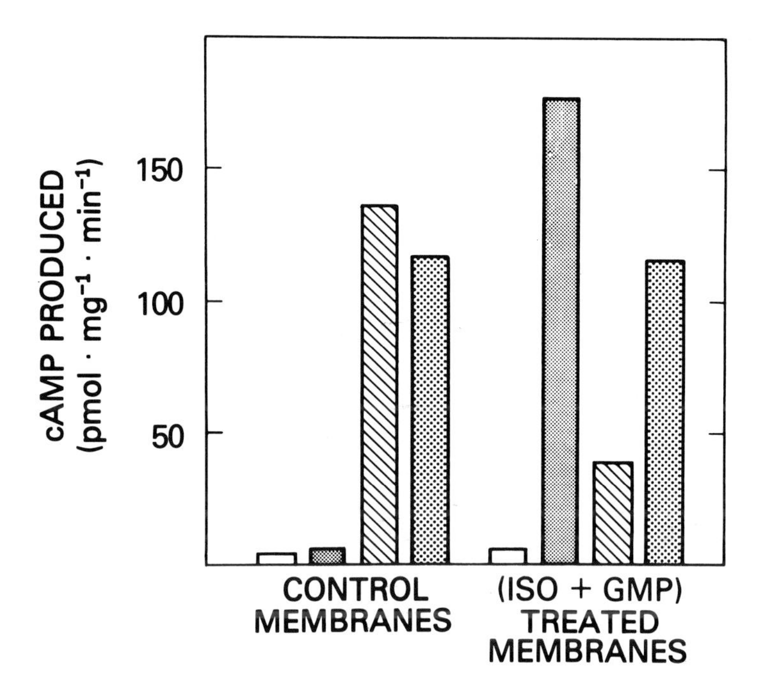

FIG. 8. Effect of ISO + GMP treatment on turkey erythrocyte membrane AC activity. Membranes were incubated with ISO (50 μM) and GMP (1 mM) at 37°C for 30 minutes, washed, and then assayed for AC activity with no additions (open bars), 0.1 mM Gpp(NH)p (shaded bars), 10 mM F^- (hatched bars), or 10 mM F^- plus 0.1 mM GTP (stippled bars). Propranolol (0.1 mM) was also added to the assay medium to preclude effects of residual ISO. (From Downs *et al.*, 1980a.)

stimulation (Table III). This effect of GDP-β-S specifically depends upon β-adrenergic agonists. The effect of GDP-β-S, moreover, is reversible, again in a β-adrenergic dependent manner. Thus F^- + GTP does not restore F^- stimulation following ISO + GDP-β-S treatment but a second incubation with ISO + GTP does (Table III). This shows that F^- stimulation does not involve exchange at the GN binding site.

Restoration of F^- stimulation by GDP after ISO + GMP treatment and inhibition of F^- stimulation by GDP-β-S (which is not readily phosphorylated to a triphosphate) suggested that F^- stimulation involves phosphorylation of GDP to GTP or maintenance of GTP on the GN binding site. To test this hypothesis directly, we analyzed the [^{3}H]GN specifically released by β-adrenergic agonists in the presence and absence of F^-. With F^- present, AC as expected was activated but GDP accounted for over 90% of the GN specifically released whether or not F^- was present throughout the experiment (Downs *et al.*, 1980a). This result (Fig. 10) was obtained

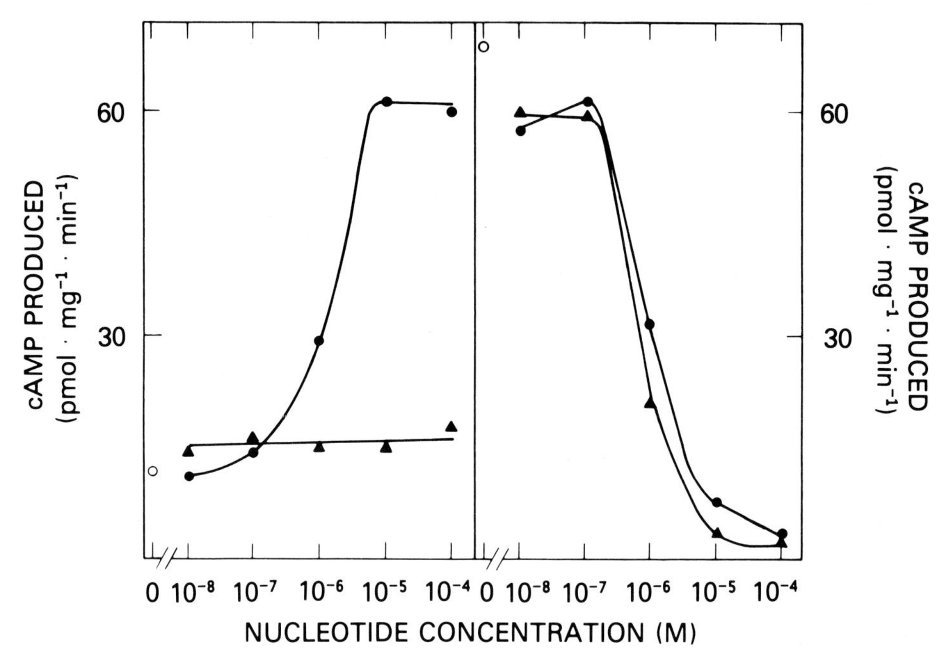

FIG. 9. The effect of GDP-β-S on membranes preincubated with ISO + GMP. Membranes were incubated with ISO + GMP, washed with buffer, and then assayed for AC activity. Enzyme activity was determined with F^- (10 m*M*) (left) or with Gpp(NH)p (0.1 m*M*) (right) and increasing concentrations of GDP (●) or GDP-β-S (▲). (From Downs *et al.*, 1980a.)

with either [^{3}H]GDP or [^{3}H]GTP as the GN present during initial incubation. Thus, under these conditions, there was no evidence for F^--dependent formation or maintenance of GTP at the GN binding site.

Since binding of GN to the GN site on turkey erythrocyte membranes requires Mg^{2+} (Spiegel *et al.*, 1976), ISO + EDTA treatment of membranes releases bound GN and presumably results in formation of an "empty site" (Cassel and Selinger, 1978). F^- stimulation is not altered by ISO + EDTA treatment. This suggests that F^- can stimulate AC without a GN bound at the GN site. The data up to this point suggest that F^- stimulation may be influenced by the nature of the GN bound to the G unit, e.g., GDP-β-S blocks F^- stimulation; data to be presented later provide direct evidence for participation of the G unit in F^- stimulation of AC.

IV. Role of GN in Cholera Toxin Activation of AC

Cholera intoxication is characterized clinically by a severe, often lethal, secretory diarrhea. The observation that treatment of small intestinal

TABLE III
Effect of GDP-β-S on AC Activity[a]

Assay additions[b]	TM treated with: ISO + GDP-β-S	GDP-β-S
	(pmol cAMP/mg/min)	
None	0	0.9
F^-	0.8	19.4
F^- + GTP	0.7	22.3
Additions during second incubation[c]	**Additions during assay, cAMP produced (pmol/mg/min): None**	**F^-**
None	0	0
GTP	0	0
GTP + ISO	0	15.0
Gpp(NH)p + ISO	23.4	—

[a] Modified from Downs *et al.* (1980a).

[b] Turkey erythrocyte membranes were incubated with GDP-β-S (10^{-4} *M*) with or without ISO (10^{-4} *M*) for 30 minutes at 37°C. The membranes were then washed with buffer and assayed for AC activity with additions shown in column 1.

[c] Turkey erythrocyte membranes were incubated with ISO + GDP-β-S and washed as in (*b*) and then incubated a second time with additions shown in column 1. Following washing, membranes were assayed for AC activity with or without NaF.

segments with exogenous cAMP mimicked the effect of cholera toxin suggested that cholera toxin acts by raising cAMP in mucosal cells of the intestine (reviewed in Moss and Vaughan, 1979). Not only was this suggestion confirmed, but it was shown that cholera toxin *in vitro* causes an increase in intracellular cAMP in any of a variety of cell types tested.

Studies on cholera toxin structure and binding to cells have been reviewed recently (Moss and Vaughan, 1979) and will not be discussed here. Instead, we will focus on the mechanisms whereby the active A_1 fragment of cholera toxin, having entered the cell, proceeds to activate adenylate cyclase. Studies on particulate membranes prepared from cells exposed to cholera toxin showed a persistently activated AC with an enhanced sensitivity to hormonal stimulation (Flores and Sharp, 1975). Turkey erythrocytes treated with cholera toxin showed a leftward shift in the dose–response curve for isoproterenol-mediated increase in cAMP accumulation (Rudolph *et al.*, 1977) comparable to the Gpp(NH)p-induced shift in sensitivity of turkey erythrocyte plasma membrane AC to isoproterenol stimulation. The similarity of these effects to those of Gpp(NH)p prompted speculation concerning a role for GN in cholera toxin action.

Gill (1975) then made the critical observation that cholera toxin (specifi-

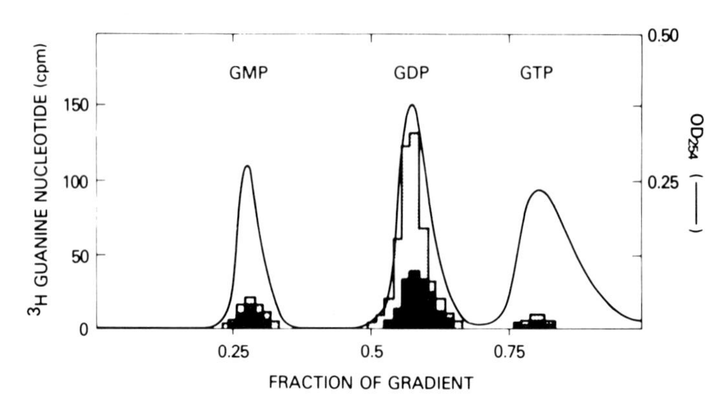

Guanine Nucleotide Released
(% total released)

	GMP	GDP	GTP
Control Δ	9	91	0
+ F Δ	6	92	2

FIG. 10. Identity of the GN released by ISO with or without F^-. ISO-dependent [^{3}H]GN release was determined (as described in Fig. 5 and Table III) with (F^-) or without (control) 10 m*M* F^-. The top panel shows the anion-exchange chromatographic profile of [^{3}H]GN released. The smooth curves represent unlabeled marker nucleotides (OD_{254}). The black bars represent [^{3}H]GN released without ISO and the open bars ISO-dependent [^{3}H]GN released. The bottom panel shows the percentage of each GN (GMP, GDP, GTP) specifically released with or without F^-. GDP is the predominant nucleotide released in either instance. (Modified from Downs *et al.*, 1980a.)

cally the A_1 fragment) could activate particulate AC if NAD were added as a cofactor. Cholera toxin was shown to possess NAD glycohydrolase activity and also transferred ADP-ribose from NAD to arginine (Moss and Vaughan, 1977).

Cholera toxin activation might therefore involve ADP-ribosylation of a component of the AC complex. As a consequence of this putative covalent modification, AC activity in turkey erythrocyte membranes is altered in several important respects. ISO + GTP stimulation is increased significantly and approaches the effect of ISO + Gpp(NH)p; F^- stimulation is sharply reduced (Fig. 11).

Cassel and Selinger (1977) showed that cholera toxin treatment reduced catecholamine-stimulated GTPase and thus increased the efficacy of GTP. The effect of cholera toxin on F^-, however, cannot be explained by GTPase inhibition. An additional effect of cholera toxin treatment of avian

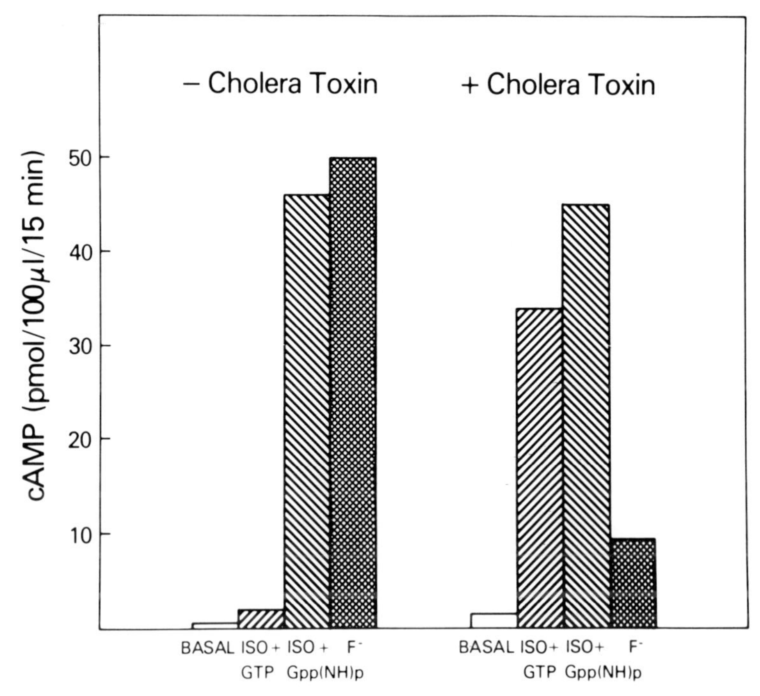

FIG. 11. Effect of cholera toxin on turkey erythrocyte adenylate cyclase activity. Turkey erythrocyte membranes were incubated with NAD (1 m*M*) with or without 100 μg/ml of cholera toxin (pretreated with 20 m*M* dithiothreitol). The membranes were then washed and assayed for AC activity with the agents shown.

erythrocyte membranes is an increase in hormone-independent stimulation by Gpp(NH)p or GTP-γ-S (Lad *et al.*, 1980); this effect, too, cannot be accounted for by GTPase inhibition. All three effects could represent consequences of covalent modification (ADP-ribosylation) of the G unit. Direct evidence for such a mechanism has been obtained in several laboratories and will be presented later.

V. Isolation of the G Unit

The evidence presented thus far points to a critical role for GN in regulation of AC activity by hormones, F^-, and cholera toxin. In this section, we will describe the experiments that clarified the relationship between the GN binding site and the components of the AC complex. The occurrence in plasma membranes of a large number of GN binding sites unrelated to AC activity complicated the experimental approach to this problem (Spiegel and Aurbach, 1974; Pfeuffer and Helmreich, 1975).

Employing GTP affinity chromatography, Pfeuffer (1977) and our group (Spiegel *et al.*, 1979) showed that the GN binding site is located on a component of the AC complex distinct from the catalytic unit. Specific binding of the G unit to a GTP matrix required linkage of GTP to the matrix via the γ-phosphate; only nonspecific protein binding was obtained with GTP linked to agarose via periodate cleavage and hydrazinolysis of the ribose ring (Spiegel *et al.*, 1979). Binding of the G unit to GTP-γ-agarose also required membrane treatment with β-adrenergic agonist (e.g., ISO) + GMP before solubilization. As noted earlier, the resultant clearing of tightly bound GDP from a portion of GN binding sites permits subsequent hormone-independent exchange at the GN site; thus solubilized (and hence no longer hormonally responsive) G units, cleared of tightly bound GDP by ISO + GMP, can bind to GTP-γ-agarose. Residual GDP bound units following ISO + GMP treatment are incapable of binding. Without ISO + GMP treatment essentially all G units retain GDP and are not adsorbed to GTP-γ-agarose. Thus incubation of control (untreated) solubilized preparation of turkey erythrocyte membranes with GTP-γ-agarose does not alter adenylate cyclase response (Fig. 12); by contrast, incubation of an ISO + GMP treated preparation with the affinity matrix depletes the bulk of the Gpp(NH)p stimulatable activity as well as the GTP-induced increment in F^- response. Both of these activities are dependent upon G units cleared of GDP, and it is just these units that are retained by GTP-γ-agarose. Addition of Gpp(NH)p to the ISO + GMP-treated preparation before incubation with the affinity matrix prevents binding to the matrix (Fig. 12); instead of binding to GTP-γ-agarose, the G units bind Gpp(NH)p and AC is activated. This competition experiment shows that GTP-γ-agarose depletion of AC activity is not a nonspecific effect.

The next question was: could the depleted Gpp(NH)p stimulated AC activity be recovered from the affinity matrix? After washing the matrix with buffer alone, we eluted with buffer containing Gpp(NH)p (0.2 m*M*). The eluate, itself, showed minimal AC activity. A substantial portion of the Gpp(NH)p-stimulated activity could be recovered by adding the eluate to the supernate derived from incubating the solubilized preparation with GTP-γ-agarose (Table IV). An eluate prepared from GTP-γ-agarose that had been incubated with control (no ISO + GMP treatment) solubilized preparation does not restore AC activity when added to depleted supernate. We interpreted these data as follows: (1) The GN binding site is located on a distinct component of the AC complex, the G unit; (2) after detergent solubilization the G unit and catalytic unit may be separated by affinity chromatography; (3) binding of the G unit to the affinity matrix depends upon ISO + GMP treatment of membranes before

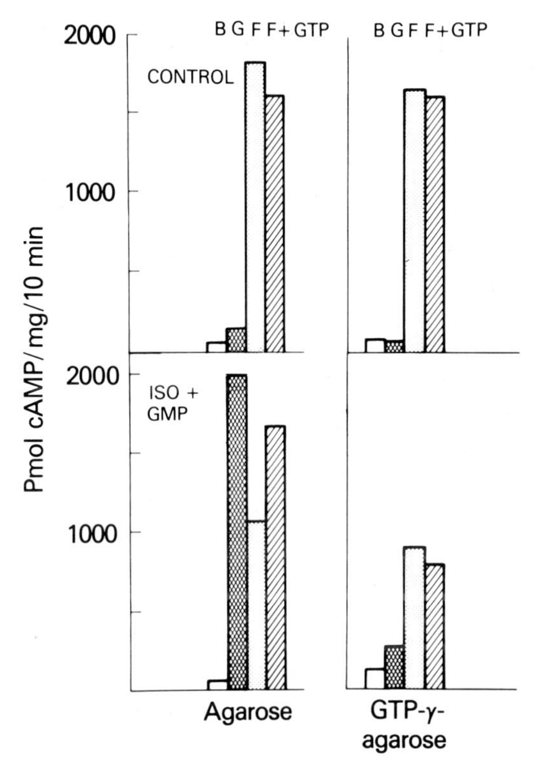

FIG. 12. Interaction of solubilized AC with agarose and GTP-γ-agarose. Turkey erythrocyte membranes were treated with GMP alone (top) or with ISO + GMP (bottom) and then solubilized. Soluble extracts were incubated with agarose (left) or GTP-γ-agarose (right), centrifuged, and the supernates assayed for AC activity with the following additions: B, none; G, 0.1 mM Gpp(NH)p; F, 10 mM F^-; F + GTP, 10 mM F^- + 0.1 mM GTP.

solubilization; (4) G units eluted from the matrix and catalytic units not retained by the matrix recombine to form an active AC complex. It is of interest that using identical experimental conditions we were unable to show binding to GTP-γ-agarose of G units derived from solubilized cardiac, hepatic, or brain plasma membranes. The reason(s) for this difference is unclear; it may relate to the aforementioned difference in tightness of binding of GN to the G unit from avian erythrocytes vs mammalian AC systems.

The G unit eluted from GTP-γ-agarose with Gpp(NH)p increased AC activity of either solubilized or particulate turkey erythrocyte membrane preparations. The AC complex of unfractionated solubilized and particulate turkey erythrocyte membranes consists of C units and G units with tightly bound GDP; the latter prevents significant hormone-independent

TABLE IV
Recombination of Solubilized Adenylate Cyclase Components[a]

Preparation assayed (in presence of 0.1 m*M* Gpp(NH)p)	Adenylate cyclase activity (pmol cAMP/75 μl/10 min)	Percentage of control activity
a. Supernatant after ISO + GMP prep incubation with agarose	35.3	100
b. Supernatant after ISO + GMP prep incubation with GTP-γ-agarose	2.9	8
c. Eluate from GTP-γ-agarose beads previously incubated with ISO + GMP prep	1.8	—
d. Eluate from GTP-γ-agarose beads previously incubated with GMP prep	0.5	—
e. Recombination of b + c	17.7	50
f. Recombination of b + d	4.8	13

[a] Solubilized membrane preparations (GMP prep or ISO + GMP prep) were incubated with agarose or GTP-γ-agarose. After incubation, suspensions were centrifuged and the supernatant fractions were removed for assay. Packed beads were washed with buffer and eluted with buffer containing 0.1 m*M* Gpp(NH)p. The elution suspension was then centrifuged and the eluates removed for assay. In a and b the agarose-treated and GTP-γ-agarose-treated supernatants were diluted 1:1 (vol/vol) with buffer just before assay. In c and d eluates were assayed directly. In e and f, the GTP-γ-agarose-treated supernatant was combined 1:1 with eluates c and d, respectively just before assay. (Modified from Spiegel *et al.*, 1979.)

response to Gpp(NH)p. Apparently endogenous GDP-bound G units do not prevent interaction of added Gpp(NH)p-bound G units with C units to form an active AC complex.

We next sought to determine if the turkey erythrocyte-derived G unit could interact with heterologous C units to increase AC activity. For these experiments, the CYC$^-$ mutant clone of S49 mouse lymphoma cells proved a very useful tool. In a series of elegant studies, Gilman and co-workers showed that the CYC$^-$ mutant lacked F$^-$, hormone, GN, and cholera toxin stimulated AC activity but did contain a C unit (as evidenced by conversion of Mn^{2+}-ATP to cAMP) (Ross *et al.*, 1978). Detergent extracts of wild type S49 cells (devoid of AC activity) restored F$^-$ and GN responsive AC activity to CYC$^-$ plasma membranes. This suggested that the CYC$^-$ mutant lacked the component(s) necessary for AC response to F$^-$ and GN.

We eluted the turkey erythrocyte-derived G unit from GTP-γ-agarose with various GN and tested the ability of the eluates to restore CYC$^-$ AC activity (Table V) (Nielsen *et al.*, 1980). Eluates prepared with nonhydrolyzable GTP analogs, e.g., Gpp(NH)p, restored CYC$^-$ AC activity,

TABLE V
Hormone-Dependent Recovery of G Unit in Affinity Eluates[a,b]

Incubation	Additions to assay	cAMP (pmol/20 min/100 μl)	
		Control	ISO + GMP
Gpp(NH)p eluate + CYC$^-$	Gpp(NH)p	0.2	8.1
GTP eluate + CYC$^-$	GTP	0.1	0.2
GTP eluate + CYC$^-$	GTP + F$^-$	0.4	2.5

[a] Assay by activation of AC in CYC$^-$ membranes.

[b] Turkey erythrocyte membranes were incubated with GMP (control) or ISO + GMP, washed, and solubilized. Soluble extracts were incubated with GTP-γ-agarose and affinity eluates prepared with either Gpp(NH)p or GTP (both 0.2 m*M*). Affinity eluates were mixed with CYC$^-$ membranes and assayed for AC activity with additions shown in column 2. (Modified from Nielsen *et al.*, 1980.)

while eluates prepared with GTP[4] or GDP did not. Addition of F$^-$ to the assay medium, however, allowed activation of CYC$^-$ AC with GTP and GDP eluates. Restoration of both GN and F$^-$ responsive AC activity to CYC$^-$ plasma membranes by affinity eluates depends upon β-adrenergic agonist pretreatment of turkey erythrocyte membranes. Addition of affinity purified G units to human erythrocyte membranes (which lack functional C units) does not restore AC activity; thus nonspecific membrane effects are insufficient to explain restoration of CYC$^-$ AC activity by affinity purified G units.

The preceding experiments showed that heterologous G and C units can combine to form an active AC complex; this implies evolutionary conservation of structure of the components of the AC system. Restoration of F$^-$ activity to CYC$^-$ membranes by affinity purified G units provided direct evidence that F$^-$ activity depends on the G unit. Studies by Pfeuffer (1979) and Howlett and Gilman (1980) suggest that F$^-$ acts directly on the G unit to convert it from an inactive form to a form that combines with C to produce an active AC complex. The precise mechanisms of the F$^-$ effect, as well as the basis for its inhibition by GDP-β-S and by cholera toxin, remain unclarified.

VI. Cholera Toxin-Dependent ADP-Ribosylation of the G Unit

Gill's report (1975) that NAD is a requisite cofactor for cholera toxin activation of AC suggested that cholera toxin ADP-ribosylated the G unit

[4] Elution of the G unit with GTP probably results in a GDP-bound G unit as a consequence of GTP hydrolysis at the GN binding site; direct evidence for this has, however, not yet been obtained.

in a manner analogous to the action of diphtheria toxin on a different GTPase, i.e., elongation factor II (Collier, 1975). Gill and Meren (1978) showed that cholera toxin caused ^{32}P incorporation (from α-^{32}P-labeled NAD) into a pigeon erythrocyte membrane protein of M_r = 42,000 on SDS–gel electrophoresis. Cassel and Pfeuffer (1978) demonstrated that the cholera toxin-dependent-labeled protein (also from pigeon erythrocyte membranes) bound to GTP-γ-agarose and could be eluted specifically with GN. They showed, moreover, that the labeling (as well as altered AC activity) could be reversed in a cholera toxin catalyzed reaction at pH 6.1 with added nicotinamide. Since Pfeuffer (1977) had previously shown that a GTP photoaffinity analog bound primarily to a 42,000 M_r protein of pigeon erythrocyte membranes, the preceding experiments provided evidence that cholera toxin indeed ADP-ribosylated the G unit.

In turkey erythrocyte membranes, by contrast, cholera toxin independent labeling of multiple proteins obscured specific toxin-dependent protein labeling (Cassel and Pfeuffer, 1978). By using conditions that suppressed toxin independent labeling, Downs *et al.* (1981) showed that a 42,000 M_r protein was the predominant toxin-dependent-labeled band in turkey erythrocyte membranes. The 42K-labeled protein could be extracted from membranes with detergent, adsorbed to GTP-γ-agarose, and eluted with GN (Fig. 13). Adsorption of the cholera toxin-labeled G unit to the affinity matrix was still dependent upon ISO + GMP treatment.

Cholera toxin-dependent ADP-ribosylation provides a convenient tool to monitor the G unit independently of AC activity. Thus we were able (Downs *et al.*, 1981) to show that GDP-β-S eluted the G unit from GTP-γ-agarose even though the GDP-β-S eluate does not restore activity to CYC^- membranes (even, as expected, with F^- added to the AC assay).

Using toxin-dependent labeling, as well as assays based on restoration of AC activity to CYC membranes, several groups (Pfeuffer, 1979; Howlett and Gilman, 1980; Kaslow *et al.*, 1980) have studied the hydrodynamic properties of the G unit. In Lubrol PX solubilized extracts the protein has an apparent molecular weight of about 130,000. Treatment with F^- or Gpp(NH)p appears to cause a reduction in size of the G unit. The 42,000 M_r protein observed on SDS–gel electrophoresis appears to represent a subunit of a G unit oligomer. Answers to critical questions regarding GTPase activity of the G unit, the site of cholera toxin catalyzed ADP-ribosylation, and the structure of the GN binding site await complete purification of the G unit. Affinity chromatography of turkey or pigeon erythrocyte G units results in an approximate 50-fold purification over detergent-solubilized extract. A recent preliminary report (Sternweiss *et al.*, 1980) describes 3000-fold purification of the G unit from rabbit liver; the purified protein reportedly consists of two major polypeptides (M_r = 35,000 and 45,000) on SDS–gel electrophoresis.

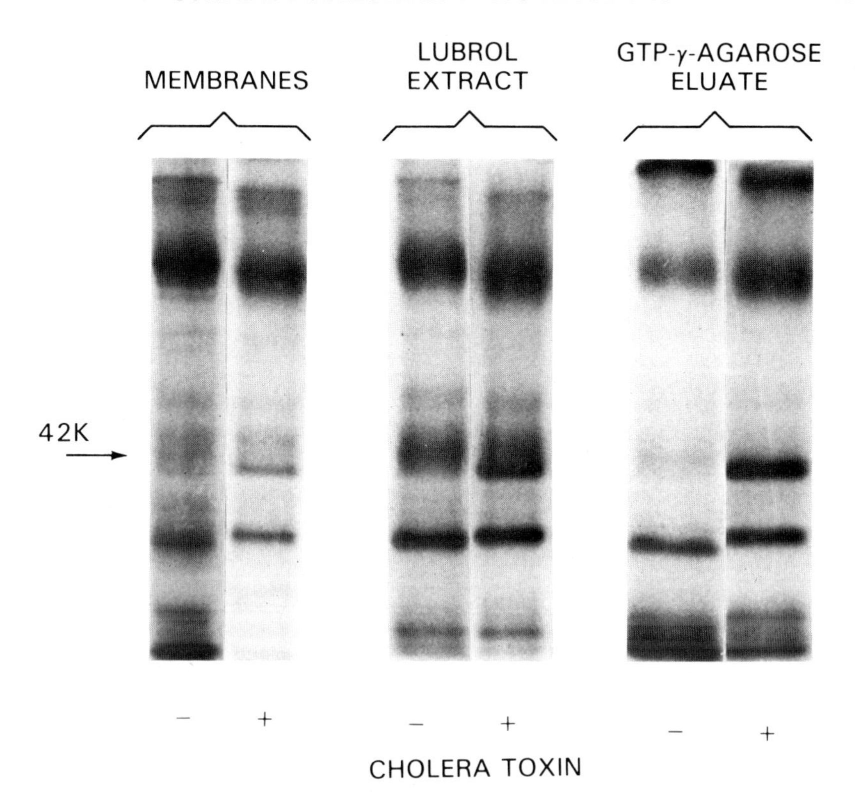

FIG. 13. Cholera toxin-dependent labeling of a 42K protein band from turkey erythrocyte membranes. Membranes were incubated with or without cholera toxin (100 μg/ml) and with α-^{32}P-labeled NAD (10 μ*M*) and thymidine for 20 minutes at 30°C. The membranes were then washed and either directly subjected to SDS–gel electrophoresis (left), solubilized and analyzed on SDS gels (middle), or treated with ISO + GMP and then solubilized. Solubilized ISO + GMP-treated extracts were incubated with GTP-γ-agarose, the resin washed with buffer alone and eluted with 0.2 m*M* Gpp(NH)p, and the eluate concentrated on Amicon CF-25 cones. The concentrated eluate was then analyzed on SDS–gel electrophoresis (right). Autoradiograms were prepared from stained dried gels. The marker indicates 42K determined with MW standards. (From Downs *et al.*, 1981.)

VII. Deficiency of G Units in Pseudohypoparathyroidism (PHP)

The profound alteration in AC responsiveness of G unit defective mutants (e.g., CYC^-) of S49 mouse lymphoma cells raised the possibility that abnormal hormone response in humans might involve G unit defects. PHP, described by Albright *et al.* (1942), is a prototypical hormone-resistance disorder. Patients with PHP show the biochemical features of hypoparathyroidism despite apparently normal parathyroid hormone (PTH) secretion. Chase *et al.* (1969) showed that patients with PHP lacked the normal rise in urinary cAMP excretion that follows PTH infusion. The implication was that a defect existed in the receptor–AC system of patients with this disorder. Although hypoparathyroidism is the most commonly recognized endocrine deficiency in PHP, careful study of patients with PHP revealed a high incidence of primary hypothyroidism (Marx *et al.*, 1971; Werder *et al.*, 1975); in some cases, resistance to multiple hormones acting via cAMP was observed (Wolfsdorf, 1978). This led us to speculate that a defect in a component of the AC complex common to all tissues, i.e., the G unit, might be present in patients with PHP.

To test this hypothesis, we measured the G unit in erythrocyte membranes from patients with PHP and from control individuals. The human erythrocyte is readily obtained and while it lacks functional β-receptor or C units, it does contain functional G units (Kaslow *et al.*, 1980). We assayed the G unit after detergent extraction with two different C unit acceptors, CYC^- membranes and solubilized turkey erythrocyte membranes. In both assay systems, patients with PHP showed a significant reduction in G units compared with controls (Fig. 14). No alteration in affinity for GN was observed (Levine *et al.*, 1980a). All of the subjects with PHP depicted in Fig. 14 show the somatic abnormalities collectively termed Albright's hereditary osteodystrophy (AHO). These abnormalities

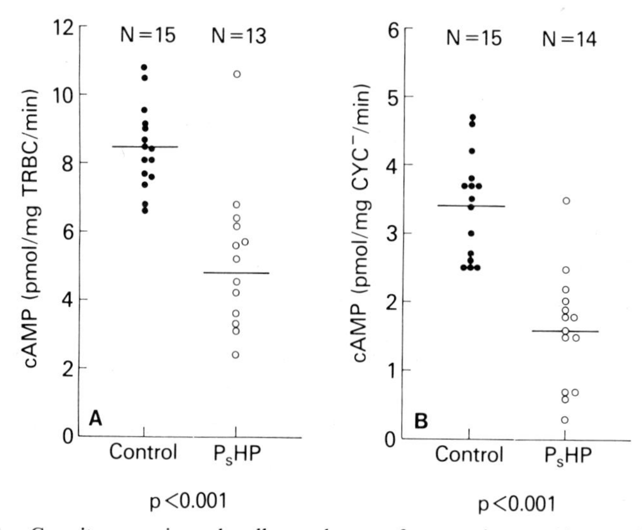

FIG. 14. G unit assay in red cell membranes from patients with pseudohypoparathyroidism (PsHP) and from normal controls. Red cell membranes were prepared by hypotonic lysis, solubilized with Lubrol PX, and incubated with GTP-γ-S (10^{-4} *M*) for 20 minutes at 37°C. Extracts were added to (A) solubilized turkey erythrocyte membranes or (B) CYC^- membranes and assayed for AC activity. Each point represents the mean of triplicate determinations for individual subjects; the horizontal lines show the group means. (From Levine *et al.*, 1980a.)

(brachydactyly, obesity, dwarfism, etc.) were present in the patients originally described by Albright. Other individuals have been found who lack AHO but show the other features of PHP, i.e., resistance to exogenous and endogenous PTH. Measurement of red cell membrane G units in such patients disclosed no abnormality. Farfel *et al.* (1980) have recently made similar observations. One individual with AHO showed consistently normal red cell G units on repeated testing (Fig. 14). All of these observations suggest that PHP is a heterogeneous disorder. The data support the hypothesis that in at least one group of patients with PHP and AHO, a deficiency of functional G units may represent the underlying defect and may account for resistance to PTH.

If indeed G unit deficiency is the basic defect in PHP, the question arises as to why the disorder manifests clinically primarily as hypoparathyroidism. Although no entirely satisfactory explanation exists, several points should be made. First, hypoparathyroidism (hypocalcemia and hyperphosphatemia) is not an obligatory feature of the disease. Two of the patients we studied (a mother and daughter) with classical AHO and resistance to exogenous PTH nonetheless are consistently normocalcemic without vitamin D therapy. The second point, alluded to above, is that careful study of patients with PHP discloses multiple defects in functions mediated by cAMP (Levine *et al.*, 1980b). Overt hypothyroidism and/or hyperresponsiveness to TRH is an extremely common feature (present in the two normocalcemic patients referred to above). The picture is compatible with primary hypothyroidism although goiter is absent. The likely explanation is resistance to TSH action.

Gonadal function likewise is abnormal. Primary amenorrhea or oligomenorrhea has commonly been observed in our series. In some patients elevated gonadotropins, suggesting primary gonadal resistance, has been found (Wolfsdorf *et al.*, 1978). Although prolactin deficiency in PHP has been reported (Farfel *et al.*, 1980), normal prolactin secretion has been observed in our series. Thus it is clear that PHP (at least in patients with reduced G units) is a multihormonal resistance disorder, not limited to PTH target tissues.

What determines the pattern and severity of expression in each individual case is unclear. The average reduction in red cell G units was 50%. The overall physiological consequences of such a G unit deficiency cannot be adequately formulated at this stage of understanding of the receptor–AC complex. The precise details of the stoichiometry and interaction of R, G, and C units are unknown. One can only speculate that even a partial reduction in G units may impair hormone responsiveness. Numerous other factors (which may vary from tissue to tissue) such as increased trophic hormone secretion, cAMP phosphodiesterase activity, cAMP-dependent protein kinase activity, etc., may all interact to determine the final physiologic response. Thus, it is clear that in some tissues, cAMP response to hormone greatly exceeds the amount necessary to fully activate protein kinase and mediate a full physiologic response. Preliminary studies on glucagon responsiveness in our patients with PHP are compatible with this formulation, i.e., the glycemic response to 0.5 mg glucagon (intravenous bolus) is normal in PHP but plasma cAMP (a more proximal response) may be blunted.

VIII. Summary and Conclusions

We have reviewed data demonstrating the critical role GN play in regulating AC activity. GN bind to a site located on a distinct component of the AC complex termed the G unit. In the intact cell, GTP binds to the G unit and permits it to interact with the C unit to increase AC activity. Hydrolysis of GTP to GDP deactivates the enzyme presumably because the GDP-bound form of the G unit has much lower affinity for C. Hormones appear to regulate AC activity by facilitating binding of GTP to the G unit. Enzyme deactivation as a result of GTP hydrolysis permits rapid fluctuation in enzyme activity in response to changes in hormone concentration. The G unit thus serves to transduce hormone–receptor interactions into alterations in AC catalytic activity.

In vitro, the enzyme may be activated by F^- without the participation of the hormone receptor. F^- activation does depend on the G unit; F^- promotes interaction of an inactive, e.g., GDP bound, G unit with C to cause an increase in AC activity. The mechanism by which F^- leads to G and C unit interaction still must be clarified.

Cholera toxin also activates AC by acting on the G unit. In this instance covalent modification, ADP-ribosylation, of the G unit is involved. The cholera toxin catalyzed modification in G unit structure alters the response to GTP so that the latter's action resembles that of the nonhydrolyzable GTP analogs such as Gpp(NH)p. As a result enzyme activation is more persistent and the cell is more sensitive to hormones. In clinical cholera, persistent enzyme activation leads to increased cAMP production in the small intestine (the site of toxin production) and severe secretory diarrhea. Cholera intoxication thus represents an example of increased AC activity as a result of G unit modification, and emphasizes that one cannot view target organ response merely in terms of quantity of trophic hormone secreted or solely in terms of hormone receptor concentration. It is theoretically possible that other disorders involving overproduction of cAMP may also involve alterations in the G unit.

The converse situation, i.e., defective target organ response secondary to G unit alteration, is also theoretically possible. In at least one situation, the inherited disorder PHP, deficiency of functional G unit may account for inadequate response to trophic hormones. Further studies, both basic and clinical, will undoubtedly increase our understanding of the role of the G unit in normal and abnormal cell function.

ACKNOWLEDGMENTS

We gratefully acknowledge the collaboration of Thor Nielsen and Martin Rodbell (LNE, NIAMDD) in experiments involving CYC⁻ S49 cells. We are especially appreciative of Mrs. L. Perry for excellent secretarial assistance.

REFERENCES

Albright, F., Burnett, C. H., Smith, P. H., and Parson, W. (1942). *Endocrinology* **30,** 922.
Aurbach, G. D., Fedak, C. H., Woodard, C. J. Palmer, J. S., Hauser, D., and Troxler, F. (1974). *Science* **186,** 1223.
Beam, K. G., Alper, S. L., Palade, G. E., and Greengard, P. (1979). *J. Cell Biol.* **83,** 1.
Bilezikian, J. P., Spiegel, A. M., Brown, E. M., and Aurbach, G. D. (1977). *Mol. Pharmacol.* **13,** 775.
Brown, E. M., Gardner, J. D., and Aurbach, G. D. (1976). *Endocrinology* **99,** 1370.
Caron, M. G., Limbird, L. E., and Lefkowitz, R. J. (1979). *Mol. Cell. Biochem.* **28,** 45.
Cassel, D., and Pfeuffer, T. (1978). *Proc. Natl. Acad. Sci. U.S.A.* **75,** 2669.
Cassel, D., and Selinger, Z. (1976). *Biochim. Biophys. Acta* **452,** 538.
Cassel, D., and Selinger, Z. (1977). *Proc. Natl. Acad. Sci. U.S.A.* **74,** 3307.
Cassel, D., and Selinger, Z. (1978). *Proc. Natl. Acad. Sci. U.S.A.* **75,** 4155.
Chase, L. R., Melson, G. L., and Aurbach, G. D. (1969). *J. Clin. Invest.* **48,** 1832.
Collier, R. J. (1975). *Bacteriol. Rev.* **39,** 54.
Cuatrecasas, P., Jacobs, S., and Bennett, V. (1975). *Proc. Natl. Acad. Sci. U.S.A.* **72,** 1739.
Downs, R. W., Jr., Spiegel, A. M., Singer, M., Reen, S., and Aurbach, G. D. (1980). *J. Biol. Chem.* **255,** 949.
Downs, R. W., Jr., Reen, S. A., Levine, M. A., Aurbach, G. D., and Spiegel, A. M. (1981). *Arch. Biochem. Biophys.* (in press).
Eckstein, F., Cassel, D., Levkovitz, H., Lowe, M., and Selinger, Z. (1979). *J. Biol. Chem.* **254,** 9829.
Farfel, Z., Brickman, A. S., Kaslow, H. R., Brothers, V. M., and Bourne, H. R. (1980). *N. Engl. J. Med.* **303,** 237.
Flores, J., and Sharp, G. W. G. (1975). *J. Clin. Invest.* **56,** 1345.
Gardner, J. D., Aurbach, G. D., Spiegel, A. M., and Brown, E. M. (1976). *Recent Prog. Horm. Res.* **32,** 567.
Gill, D. M. (1975). *Proc. Natl. Acad. Sci. U.S.A.* **72,** 2064.
Gill, D. M., and Meren, R. (1978). *Proc. Natl. Acad. Sci. U.S.A.* **75,** 3050.
Howlett, A. C., and Gilman, A. G. (1980). *J. Biol. Chem.* **255,** 2861.
Insel, P. A., Maguire, M. E., Gilman, A. G., Bourne, H. R., Coffino, P., and Melmon, K. L. (1976). *Mol. Pharmacol.* **12,** 1062.
Kaslow, H. R., Farfel, Z., Johnson, G. L., and Bourne, H. R. (1979). *Mol. Pharmacol.* **15,** 472.

Kaslow, H. R., Johnson, G. L., Brothers, V. M., and Bourne, H. R. (1980). *J. Biol. Chem.* **255,** 3736.
Lad, P. M., Nielsen, T. B., Preston, M. S., and Rodbell, M. (1980). *J. Biol. Chem.* **255,** 988.
Levine, M. A., Downs, R. W., Jr., Singer, M., Marx, S. J., Aurbach, G. D., and Spiegel, A. M. (1980a). *Biochem. Biophys. Res. Commun.* **94,** 1319.
Levine, M. A., Downs, R. W., Jr., Marx, S. J., Lasker, R. D., Aurbach, G. D., and Spiegel, A. M. (1980b). *Proc. Int. Conf. Calcium Regulat. Horm., 7th Excerpta Medica, Amsterdam.*
Limbird, L. E., and Lefkowitz, R. J. (1977). *J. Biol. Chem.* **252,** 799.
Londos, C., Salomon, Y., Lin, M. C., Harwood, J. P., Schramm, M., Wolff, J., and Rodbell, M. (1974). *Proc. Natl. Acad. Sci. U.S.A.* **71,** 3087.
Marx, S. J., Hershman, J. M., and Aurbach, G. D. (1971). *J. Clin. Endocrinol. Metab.* **33,** 822.
Moss, J., and Vaughan, M. (1977). *J. Biol. Chem.* **252,** 2455.
Moss, J., and Vaughan, M. (1979). *Annu. Rev. Biochem.* **48,** 581.
Neer, E. J. (1978). *J. Biol. Chem.* **253,** 1498.
Nielsen, T. B., Downs, R. W., Jr., and Spiegel, A. M. (1980). *Biochem. J.* **190,** 439.
Orly, J., and Schramm, M. (1976). *Biochemistry* **73,** 4410.
Pfueffer, T. (1977). *J. Biol. Chem.* **252,** 7224.
Pfeuffer, T. (1979). *FEBS Lett.* **101,** 85.
Pfeuffer, T., and Helmreich, E. J. M. (1975). *J. Biol. Chem.* **250,** 867.
Robison, G. A., and Sutherland, E. W. (1971). *Ann. N.Y. Acad. Sci.* **1,** 185.
Rodbell, M. (1980). *Nature (London)* **284,** 17.
Rodbell, M., Krans, H. M. J., Pohl, S. L., and Birnbaumer, L. (1971). *J. Biol. Chem.* **246,** 1872.
Ross, E. M., Howlett, A. C., Ferguson, K. M., and Gilman, A. G. (1978). *J. Biol. Chem.* **253,** 6401.
Rudolph, S., A., Schafer, D. E., and Greengard, P. (1977). *J. Biol. Chem.* **252,** 7132.
Salomon, Y., Lin, M. C., Londos, C., Rendell, M., and Rodbell, M. (1975). *J. Biol. Chem.* **250,** 4239.
Spiegel, A. M., and Aurbach, G. D. (1974). *J. Biol. Chem.* **249,** 7630.
Spiegel, A. M., Brown, E. M., Fedak, S. A., Woodard, C. J., and Aurbach, G. D. (1976). *J. Cyclic Nucleotide Res.* **2,** 47.
Spiegel, A. M., Downs, R. W., Jr., and Aurbach, G. D. (1977). *Biochem. Biophys. Res. Commun.* **76,** 758.
Spiegel, A. M., Downs, R. W., Jr., and Aurbach, G. D. (1979). *J. Cyclic Nucleotide Res.* **5,** 3.
Sternweis, P. C., Northup, J. K., Schleifer, L. S., Smigel, M. D., Garrison, J. C., and Gilman, A. G. (1980). *Fed. Proc. Fed. Am. Soc. Exp. Biol.* (Abstract No. 1870).
Werder, E. A., Illig, R., Bernasconi, S., Kind, H., and Prader, A. (1975). *Pediat. Res.* **9,** 12.
Wolfsdorf, J. I., Rosenfield, R. L., Fang, V. S., Kobayashi, R., Razdan, A. K., and Kim, M. H. (1978). *Acta Endocrinol.* **88,** 321.

DISCUSSION

L. Birnbaumer: I should like to add to your excellent presentation, some recent data obtained in collaboration with Dr. Ravi Iyengar. We studied the role of Mg ion in the action of guanine nucleotides. As you surely know, a commonly present component in all of the incubations that test for GMP-p(NH)p (and other guanine nucleotide) effects is Mg ion. In its absence no nucleotide effect is observed in any adenylyl cyclase. We tested whether this requirement is due to interaction of Mg with the nucleotide binding regulatory component, and found this to be so. Briefly, we extracted the regulatory component from liver membranes, inactivated the coextracted catalytic component by heat treatment, and then incubated the extract with varying concentrations of Mg (0.5–20 m*M*) in the presence of 5 μM GMP-p(NH)p. After various times at 32.5°C we diluted the mixtures 50-fold into adenylyl cyclase reagent containing media with cyc^- S49 cell membranes keeping Mg ion concentrations constant, but reducing the GMP-p(NH)p concentration to 0.1 μM, a concentration that under the conditions used would lead to very little reconstitution of cyc^- adenylyl cyclase even at 20 m*M* Mg ion. We found that the preincubation step resulted in activation of the regulatory component that was dependent on time and concentration of Mg. Further, the rate of activation of the regulatory component (seen by elevated cyc^- reconstituted activities) was increased by increasing concentrations of Mg ion. Activation of adenylyl cyclase by Mg ion and guanine nucleotides is therefore primarily the result of activation of the regulatory component.

Within this context and with respect to your determination of a defective or lowered level of the regulatory component in PSP patients, I wonder whether you looked at the Mg regulation of their regulatory component. It may be that rather than dealing with a lowered level of regulatory component, you are dealing with normal levels of a defective regulatory component; defective in its interaction with Mg ion.

A. M. Spiegel: I have certainly learned a great deal from you over the years, Dr. Birnbaumer, and I appreciate the comment and question. First, as regards the studies on pseudohypoparathyroidism (PHP), we have not looked at magnesium as a variable; a fixed concentration of magnesium is included in all the reconstitution assays we performed. I think the possibility that the G unit in some patients with PHP shows an abnormality in magnesium regulation is a very interesting one. As I have tried to emphasize, PHP is a heterogeneous disorder and, while most of the patients we tested showed a decrease in functional G units, some did not. It is possible that variations in magnesium concentration during assay would bring out a defect in some of the latter group of patients. A further point is that in the studies of Farfel *et al.* (*N. Eng. J. Med.* **303,** 237, 1980) the G unit was quantitated by labeling with ^{32}P-NAD in a cholera toxin catalyzed reaction, as well as by adenylate cyclase assay. The former method also shows a reduction in G unit amount in the group of PHP patients with reduced G unit by reconstitution assay. Thus, at least in this group, it is unlikely that abnormal magnesium regulation is responsible for the G unit defect.

The second point is a more general one regarding the importance of magnesium in guanine nucleotide-G unit interactions. We agree wholeheartedly with you on this point. Indeed, in a paper we published several years ago (Spiegel *et al., J. Cyclic Nucleotide Res.* **2,** 47, 1976), we showed that persistent activation of turkey erythrocyte adenylate cyclase by isoproterenol + Gpp(NH)p could be blocked by EDTA (1 m*M*) but not by EGTA, and that the effect of EDTA could be overcome by additional Mg^{2+}. We interpreted these data to mean that Mg^{2+} is critically required for binding of guanine nucleotides to the G unit. Cassel and Selinger extended our observations by showing that incubation of turkey erythrocyte membranes with isoproterenol + EDTA apparently leads to a G unit with an "empty site," i.e., isoproterenol causes release of bound guanine nucleotide and the lack of magnesium prevents rebinding to the G unit (Cassel and Selinger, *Proc. Natl. Acad. Sci. U.S.A.* **75,** 4155, 1978).

B. Robaire: Do you have any evidence that the ratio of GTP + ½ GDP/GTP + GDP + GMP can regulate the activity of the G subunit? i.e., Do you think that there is something analogous to the adenylate energy charge that Dr. Atkinson has talked about for years.

A. M. Spiegel: This is a very interesting question but one that I am incapable of answering with any "hard" data. First, it should be obvious that virtually all of the evidence for the role of guanine nucleotides in the regulation of adenylate cyclase has been obtained in broken cell preparations rather than in intact cells. What is the evidence in intact cells that guanine nucleotides are important? There are two lines of evidence: (1) Treatment of intact cells with cholera toxin leads to profound changes in intracellular cAMP content and hormone responsiveness. Since it has been clearly shown that cholera toxin acts by covalently modifying the G unit in a way that causes GTP to be more effective, it is highly probable that the effects of cholera toxin in intact cells reflect this alteration in GTP efficacy. (2) More direct evidence comes from experiments with mycophenolic acid. This compound interferes with GMP (but not AMP) synthesis and thereby depletes the intracellular guanine nucleotide pool by about 80%. Two groups (T. J. Franklin and P. A. Wose, *Eur. J. Biochem.* **77,** 113–117, 1977; G. S. Johnson and V. R. Mukku, *J. Biol. Chem.* **254,** 95–100, 1979) have shown that mycophenolic acid leads to a 50–70% reduction in cAMP response to hormones in intact cells. This suggests that hormone response is indeed influenced by the availability of intracellular GTP. Since intracellular GTP concentrations are approximately 0.5 m*M* and since GTP-dependent hormone stimulation of broken cell adenylate cyclase preparations is already maximal at 0.1 m*M* GTP, it is surprising that an 80% reduction of intracellular GTP would have any effect on hormone stimulation of intracellular cAMP content. The effect of mycophenolic acid on hormone response has been cited as evidence for the existence of a specific pool of guanine nucleotides involved in adenylate cyclase regulation (Johnson and Mukku, 1979). These experiments, however, do not offer insight into whether or not the intracellular GTP/GDP ratio per se influences hormone response. An answer to this question would require a method to manipulate specifically the GTP/GDP ratio; I am not sure such a method is currently available.

A. Broadus: A couple of questions which I didn't see answered in those figures you ran through briefly. One is that there is an old observation which is perhaps known to many in this audience but not all, and, therefore, I'll describe briefly. That is, in practically every system of study *in vivo* and *in vitro,* if one gives massive pharmacologic doses of hormone, one sees a peak response of 30-fold or so over baseline and within minutes it's down to 2 to 4 × response. It is as though one has induced a hormone-resistant state. I can't help thinking about the data that you've just shown as they might apply to the observations I've cited. Can you speculate?

A. M. Spiegel: I can only speculate at this time. The question is a very important one and again points to the difficulty of extrapolating from broken cell to intact cell experiments. As you have mentioned, when one studies the intracellular cAMP response to PTH (and indeed to most other agonists capable of stimulating adenylate cyclase), one observes a "peak-trough" type of response usually occurring over a time course measured in minutes. There are probably several factors responsible for the rapid decline in cAMP that is observed despite continued presence of agonist. Extracellular release of cAMP and increase in cAMP phosphodiesterase activity may both play a role, although the latter probably occurs with a more delayed time course. The overall phenomenon has often been termed "desensitization." Some groups suggest that alteration in hormone receptor number and/or affinity may be involved but events distal to the receptor probably also play a role. At this time, an unequivocal role for guanine nucleotides and the G unit in this process has not been demonstrated. Recently Ezra and Salomon (*J. Biol. Chem.* **255,** 653–658, 1980) have shown that desensitization of rat ovarian plasma membrane adenylate cyclase is a hormone (LH or HCG) *and* GTP [but not Gpp(NH)p]-dependent process. The effects they observed in a broken cell preparation paralleled intact cell observations, i.e., a time-dependent loss of hormone (not not NaF) responsiveness. They postulated that hormone-stimulated and

GTP-dependent phosphorylation of an unidentified membrane component may play a key role in the desensitization process. Further studies in various tissues will be needed to verify this hypothesis and to determine if it is generally applicable.

A. Broadus: Patients with pseudohypoparathyroidism fall into two general visual camps, those who are phenotypically completely normal and those with the classical osteodystrophic presentation. In our own experience, it's been roughly 50–50, and I don't know whether that experience is biased or not. Is there any difference in those with the classical syndrome and those who might easily be misjudged as having idiopathic hypoparathyroidism without testing in terms of your own results?

A. M. Spiegel: As you suggest, there is definite heterogeneity within the group of patients said to have pseudohypoparathyroidism (PHP). If one defines PHP as a disease in which the biochemical features of hypoparathyroidism (hypocalcemia, hyperphosphatemia) are present despite adequate endogenous PTH secretion and in which there is resistance to exogenous PTH (a deficient urinary cAMP response), two groups of patients may be immediately distinguished on the basis of their physical appearance. One group has normal features; the other shows the somatic features (brachydactyly, decreased height, etc.) termed Albright's hereditary osteodystrophy (AHO). The relative incidence of either type is difficult to judge since the disease is rare. In our experience, the "classic" type, i.e., patients exhibiting AHO, is far more common but this may reflect bias in ascertainment.

Our studies on the G unit in red cells from patients with PHP show an important difference between the two groups of patients. Those without AHO show normal G unit in every case. All but one of our group with AHO show a reduced G unit number. Farfel *et al.* (*New Eng. J. Med.* **303,** 237, 1980) report the same findings, and in their patient group there were more cases without AHO. The presence of AHO per se, however, does not imply a G unit abnormality. Patients with so-called pseudopseudohypoparathyroidism by definition have AHO but are not resistant to PTH. The G unit was not significantly reduced in at least one such case we have studied.

C. R. Kahn: Despite an exceptionally clear presentation, I would like to ask you to clarify a few points regarding the interaction of the guanyl nucleotides with the G components. Most of the data which you have presented are based on the final biological response, that is activation or lack of activation in the cyclase.

A. M. Spiegel: The direct binding studies necessary to answer detailed kinetic questions regarding association and dissociation of guanine nucleotides cannot readily be done in the plasma membrane or solubilized preparations of the enzyme available. Unlike typical hormone–receptor studies, here one is dealing with a ligand for which there is a huge excess of nonadenylate cyclase related binding sites and these are not necessarily of lower affinity than the sites on the G unit. It will be necessary to purify the G unit before one can answer the detailed kinetic questions you raise. At this point, we *can* say that various guanine nucleotides differ in intrinsic activity, i.e., ability to stimulate adenylate cyclase (cf. GTP-γ-S, a potent stimulator, vs GDP, relatively ineffective) and in *apparent* affinity, e.g., while the apparent K_m for most guanine nucleotides is approximately 0.5 μM, the K_m for GMP appears to be much higher. There are also examples of what one might term "partial agonists," e.g., Gpp(CH_2)p, but the precise basis for this is not known.

C. R. Kahn: That's true. The point is, however, that it's a little difficult from these observations to directly model the binding affinities of the various guanine nucleotides for the guanyl nucleotide sites. For example, you have frequently suggested that you are exchanging one guanine nucleotide or one sort of guanine nucleotide for another. From the direct binding sites, can one really say that during these types of experiments there is dissociation and association kinetics of the various guanine nucleotides, and affinities which are consistent with this being related to their affinity for the guanine nucleotide site or do they differ in intrinsic activity? Second, the point related to the ability to put the GMPPND onto the site after GMP loading seems particularly confusing to me since, from a thermodynamic consideration, the total free energy to get the nucleotide bound would be the same whether the site was preoccupied or not preoccupied, unless, of course, the GMP was acting as some sort of alosteric regulation. Finally, is the GTPase able to hydrolize the different types of substrates while they're on the G component, or do they have to first dissociate? From what you have said this would also affect the kinetics of association–dissociation.

A. M. Spiegel: I am unable to offer in molecular terms an explanation for the effects of GMP on the G unit. Our and other's data clearly show that GMP profoundly alters the responsiveness of adenylate cyclase in turkey erythrocyte membranes and this alteration almost certainly involves the G unit. The effect is specific for GMP as opposed to AMP, IMP, or XMP; it is time, temperature, and concentration dependent, and most importantly it absolutely depends on the simultaneous addition of a β-adrenergic agonist. We have no direct evidence that GMP actually remains bound to the G unit, although this is certainly a possibility. The effect of GMP may be to alter the conformation of the G unit in a way that permits hormone-independent exchange of guanine nucleotides, but at this point this is pure speculation.

C. R. Kahn: The second one was specifically related to the postulated exchange between the GMP.

A. M. Spiegel: Defining the precise relationship between GTPase activity and the G unit will likewise require study of purified components. In a series of elegant experiments, Cassel and Selinger (*Biochim. Biophys. Acta* **452,** 538, 1976) were able to demonstrate a β-adrenergic agonist stimulated GTPase in turkey erythrocyte membranes despite the presence of high "nonspecific" GTPase activity. The key evidence for the relevance of the measured GTPase to adenylate cyclase is its ability to be modified in a specific manner by catecholamines. The available evidence does not permit the conclusion that the GTPase activity is a property of the G unit itself. My speculation would be that this is likely. Cholera toxin, which as we have seen covalently modifies the G unit, appears to alter the GTPase activity. If we elute the G unit from the affinity matrix with GTP, the eluted unit behaves as if it has bound GDP and not GTP. But these observations do not prove that the G unit itself is the GTPase and such proof must await G unit purification.

F. Auletta: It appears that one of the major effects of cholera toxin is the activation of prostaglandins E and F (synthesis and/or release). I was wondering whether you've tried any of the prostaglandins or inhibitors of prostaglandin in your system. Also, could you speculate about the role of prostaglandins in your *in vitro* turkey erythrocyte model?

A. M. Spiegel: As far as I know, there is nothing unique about the effects of cholera toxin on prostaglandin-mediated responses. Receptors for prostaglandins, particularly of the E-type, are often coupled to adenylate cyclase. Cholera toxin, as discussed, increases responsiveness of cells to agonists coupled to adenylate cyclase and this would be true for prostaglandins as well as β-adrenergic agonists and peptide hormones. Inhibition of prostaglandin synthesis does not have any effect I know of on cholera toxin action. In the system we have discussed, turkey erythrocyte adenylate cyclase is not stimulated by prostaglandin but that of S49 mouse lymphoma cells is.

W. P. VanderLaan: My question is clinically based on and stimulated by the distressing amount of gastroenteritis afflicting the present conference. Does bismuth exert its beneficial effects through the mechanism you describe, or is its mode of action known?

A. M. Spiegel: Is bismuth in fact the active ingredient in peptobismol? I can only respond by saying that in addition to cholera, there is another form of severe diarrhea caused by an exotoxin secreted by certain *E. coli* which may be responsible for some cases of so-called traveler's diarrhea. This toxin has been shown to act in an identical fashion to cholera toxin, that is, by covalently modifying the G unit and activating adenylate cyclase. Not being a gastroenterologist, I would hesitate to make a diagnosis in the current situation.

As to bismuth, heavy metals, particularly those with a high affinity for sulfhydryl groups, inhibit adenylate cyclase. I have no idea whether the effect of peptobismol involves such a mechanism.

Nephrogenous Cyclic AMP

ARTHUR E. BROADUS

Department of Internal Medicine,
Yale University School of Medicine, New Haven, Connecticut

I. Introduction

The studies described in this article were begun in 1967, at which time I was a graduate student with Joel Hardman and Earl Sutherland. I remember clearly my initial converation with Dr. Sutherland concerning the initiation of human and clinical studies; he was not only enthusiastic but expressed a certain disappointment, perhaps even annoyance, that the clinical implications of his work had not previously been explored. He understood intuitively the cross-fertilizing interrelationship between good basic and clinical investigation, and he remained keenly interested and involved in the human studies as they progressed. We initiated a collaboration with Grant Liddle, who shared Dr. Sutherland's enthusiasm and perception, and the group was joined by Neil Kaminsky in 1968. Although the work described in this article evolved over more than a decade and involves studies performed in a variety of institutions and laboratories, much of the information that has accrued over the years was anticipated by the early work at Vanderbilt. I am sorry that Dr. Sutherland isn't here today to share in the growth of this aspect of the field.

In 1967, the second messenger function of cyclic AMP (cAMP) in mediating the action of a wide variety of hormones was appreciated, but there were few studies of cAMP content in extracellular fluids. Cyclic AMP was known to occur in high concentrations in urine, and Joel Hardman was in the process of studying the effects of a number of agents on cyclic nucleotide excretion in rats (Hardman *et al.*, 1969). In 1966, a report (never subsequently confirmed) appeared concerning the effects of antidiuretic hormone (ADH) on cAMP excretion in humans (Takahashi *et al.*, 1966), and, in 1967, Chase and Aurbach published their classic paper on the effects of parathyroid hormone (PTH) on cAMP excretion in rats (Chase and Aurbach, 1967). Although the implications of these studies were clear, the central dogma of the mid-1960s was that membranes were poorly, if at all, permeable to cAMP. Thus, our initial working hypothesis was that the cAMP in urine probably reflected the effects of

ISBN 0-12-571137-9

hormones acting directly on the kidney and that the extrusion of cAMP across renal tubular cell membranes might represent a relatively unique phenomenon. At that time, I was modifying existing assay techniques for the measurement of cyclic nucleotides in plasma and other extracellular fluids. The initial determination of cAMP in plasma began with 250 ml of my own plasma, involved three chromatographic steps, and yielded a final assay sample of 500 μl with a recovery of approximately 20%. The cAMP concentration in that painful sample was 14.7 nM. A quick calculation revealed that filtration of that plasma concentration of cAMP would result in the excretion of approximately 2.5 μmol per day, approximately one-half of the cAMP excretion rate we had measured in normal human subjects. There followed another working hypothesis, that urinary cAMP might be derived from multiple sources, and these several working hypotheses led to the studies described below.

II. Physiology of Cyclic AMP Metabolism and Excretion

The initial questions we posed were (1) what is the mechanism of renal plasma clearance of cAMP and (2) what are the sources of cAMP in human urine? The study design involved the simultaneous infusion of inulin and [^{3}H]cAMP, with determination of the clearances of inulin, [^{3}H]cAMP, and endogenous cAMP (Broadus *et al.*, 1970). In all individuals studied, the clearance of [^{3}H]cAMP was identical to inulin clearance, indicating that the mechanism of renal plasma clearance of cAMP was simple glomerular filtration. However, in all studies, the clearance of endogenous cAMP exceeded that of inulin and [^{3}H]cAMP, or, stated in another fashion, the specific radioactivity of cAMP in urine was considerably diluted with respect to that in plasma. This could only have occurred if a quantity of cAMP formed *de novo* in the kidney was added to that filtered from plasma. The term nephrogenous cAMP was introduced to describe this renal component and to emphasize that the observed mechanism of net cAMP clearance was novel and could not be described in terms of conventional mechanisms of renal clearance.

The metabolism and excretion of cAMP in man are summarized in Fig. 1. As noted above, the total amount of cAMP excreted is the sum of that derived from two sources: (a) the filtered load of the nucleotide and (b) nephrogenous cAMP. On the average, each component accounts for approximately 50% of the total quantity of cAMP excreted by normal individuals (Broadus *et al.*, 1977). The same mechanism of cAMP clearance has been confirmed in the dog and the rat, although the relative quantities of cAMP from each source in these species differ somewhat from the findings in man (Broadus, 1977).

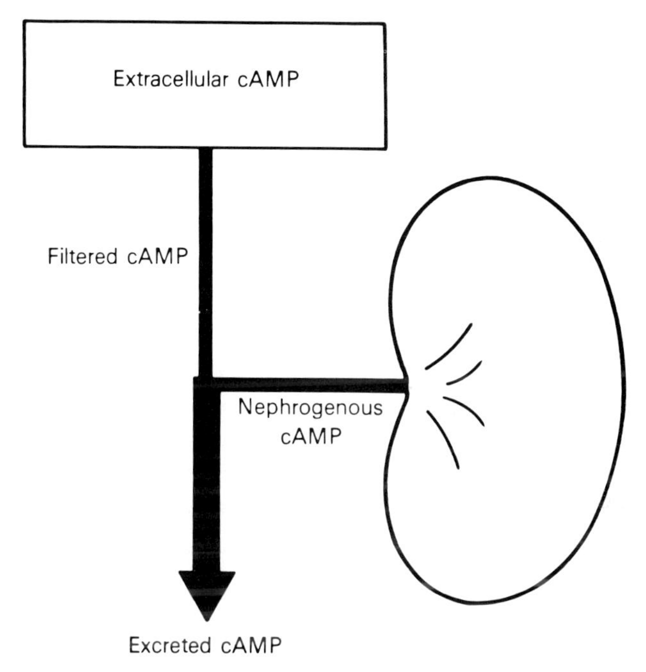

FIG. 1. Schematic representation of the sources of cAMP in human urine. From Broadus (1977).

The filtered load of cAMP is derived from the extracellular or "miscible" pool of the nucleotide (i.e., plasma and the extracellular and cellular compartments which are in equilibrium). During the [^{3}H]cAMP infusion studies, it was possible to evaluate the pharmacokinetics of this pool. Cyclic AMP was found to distribute into a space severalfold larger than the extracellular volume and to turn over rapidly, with a half-time of approximately 25 minutes and a metabolic clearance rate of about 650 ml/minute. Clearly, only some one-fifth of the metabolic clearance could be accounted for by cAMP filtration into the urine. Although pharmacological doses of several agents have been reported to increase the plasma concentration of cAMP (Broadus, 1977), the sources of cAMP in the extracellular pool and the site of its metabolism under basal conditions remain largely unknown. It is likely that a variety of tissues participate in the systemic production and metabolism of cAMP.

In spite of the limited knowledge concerning cAMP metabolism in the extracellular pool, the kinetic information described above had important implications which anticipated the findings of subsequent studies. First, the dynamics of cAMP distribution and turnover would imply that a substantial stimulus would be required to significantly alter the concentration of cAMP in plasma; it was subsequently found that physiological amounts of agents such as glucagon, ACTH, and PTH did not produce discernible changes in the plasma concentration of cAMP (Broadus, 1977). Second, the concentration of cAMP in plasma in normal individuals was found to vary over a relatively narrow range, with approximately 90% of observed values being between 12 and 20 n*M* (Broadus, 1979). Moreover, the plasma concentration of the nucleotide was found to rise with progressive renal impairment, such that the filtered load of the nucleotide remained relatively constant when expressed as a function of the glomerular filtration rate (over a range of GFR from 20 to 140 ml/minute) (Broadus *et al.*, 1977). The principal conclusions of these findings are (1) urinary cAMP provides a particularly crude and insensitive index of alterations in metabolism of the compound in the miscible pool and (2) the filtered load of cAMP provides a relatively constant "background" of excreted cAMP upon which the nephrogenous component is superimposed. That is, the principal determinant of variations in the total cAMP excretion rate between individuals is the quantity of nephrogenous cAMP.

Nephrogenous cAMP is the only specific pool of the nucleotide easily measured *in vivo*. The findings of Chase and Aurbach (Chase and Aurbach, 1967) were rapidly confirmed in our laboratory, and it was shown that the PTH-induced increases in cAMP excretion were of nephrogenous origin (Kaminsky *et al.,* 1970a). Such changes in plasma cAMP as occurred in response to pharmacological doses of the hormone also appeared to be derived from the kidney rather than bone (Kaminsky *et al.*, 1970a; Broadus, 1977). Although a number of agents, including calcitonin and ADH, have been reported to stimulate cAMP generation in kidney preparations *in vitro*, these agents do not influence nephrogenous cAMP excretion *in vivo* (Broadus, 1977; Kaminsky *et al.*, 1970b). Pharmacological doses of calcitonin are associated with increases in the plasma concentration of cAMP and the filtered load of the nucleotide but do not influence nephrogenous cAMP (Kaminsky *et al.*, 1970b). In studies carefully performed with inulin clearance and maximal antidiuretic and pressor doses of ADH, the hormone was unassociated with discernible changes in cAMP in any pool (Kaminsky *et al.*, 1970b). In addition, perfectly normal values for total cAMP excretion (3.48 ± 0.90 nmol/100 ml GF, mean ± SD) and nephrogenous cAMP (1.71 ± 0.50 nmol/100 ml GF, mean ± SD) were observed in six well-characterized patients with the syndrome of inappropriate secretion of ADH (Forrest and Broadus, 1979). The failure of ADH to influence nephrogenous cAMP remains unexplained; it has been speculated that the distal nephron may be sufficiently impermeable that alterations in intracellular cAMP concentrations in the cells in this region are not reflected in the urine (Broadus, 1977).

In the final analysis, the effects of PTH appear to account for 90–100% of the nephrogenous component of cAMP excretion. In patients with idiopathic hypoparathyroidism, who are generally regarded as having complete functional aparathyroidism, values for nephrogenous cAMP are reproducibly in the range of zero.

III. Methods and Expression of Data

The measurement of cAMP in urine is extremely simple. Both the protein-binding and radioimmunoassay give highly reproducible results in samples simply diluted in assay buffer and assayed directly. Urine samples should be collected into hydrochloric acid or another suitable preservative (we employ 20 ml 6 *N* HCl for 24-hour specimens and 1 ml 6 *N* HCl per estimated hour of collection in spot or timed urine specimens). Infected urine produces spuriously low results because of bacterial phosphodiesterase content, but patients with staghorn calculi or acute urinary tract infections may be studied reliably if samples are collected into HCl.

The measurement of cAMP in plasma is not simple, and a number of investigators expressed a degree of consternation with regard to the plasma determination at the recent cyclic nucleotide meeting in Colorado. The difficulty presumably relates to the relatively low content of cAMP in plasma vis-à-vis that of other potentially interfering substances.

Blood samples should be obtained under basal, unstressed conditions, in order to avoid the modest effects of exertion and catecholamines on plasma levels of cAMP (Broadus, 1977). Samples are drawn into standard anticoagulent amounts of EDTA, which inhibits the magnesium-requiring phosphodiesterase activity in plasma (commercial vacutainer tubes containing EDTA in liquid form are ideal). Blood samples are centrifuged at top speed in a tabletop unrefrigerated clinical centrifuge for 10–15 minutes, and the plasma is removed with care to leave the buffy coat undisturbed.

We presently employ a relatively simple chromatographic step using a 5.5 cm column of prewashed AG 1-X8 (200–400 mesh) in the formate form, prepared in short Pasteur pipets. A tracer dose (approximately 20,000 dpm) of [^{3}H]cAMP is added to 1 ml of plasma, and the sample is deproteinized with 4 ml of 5% trichloroacetic acid. The supernatant is neutralized with 400 μl of 2.5 *M* Tris buffer, pH 11.5, and added to the column. The column is washed sequentially with 1 ml water, 2 ml water, 3 ml water, and 2 ml 1 *N* formic acid. Cyclic AMP is then eluted and the next 5 ml of 1 *N* formic acid, and the sample is lyophilized or dried under air. The sample is reconstituted in 0.75 ml assay buffer; an aliquot is counted for recovery, and triplicate 100-μl aliquots are assayed for cAMP content using an immunoassay and nonacylated samples.

Several laboratories are currently attempting to measure cAMP by immunoassay in unpurified acetylated plasma samples, but an extensive data base with this method has not been published. There has long been a suspicion, never systematically confirmed, that specific antisera may differ in the degree of interference produced by nonspecific factors in plasma (e.g., ionic strength, protein concentration, etc.).

Results for both nephrogenous cAMP and total cAMP excretion should be expressed as a function of the glomerular filtration rate. The filtered load of cAMP is, by definition, a direct function of the filtration rate. The nephrogenous component is an indirect function of the GFR, where the filtration rate serves as an index of functional renal tubular mass. The units derived from actual clearance calculations are nmol/minute/100 ml GFR; however, these units are mathematically redundant (i.e., they express two rates) and reduce by unit analysis to nmol/100 ml GF (where GF is glomerular filtrate). In actual practice, data for total cAMP excretion or nephrogenous cAMP are computed with a simple shorthand clearance calculation. For example, given respective concentrations of cAMP and creatinine in urine of $6.0 \times 10^{-6}\,M$ and 100 mg/dl, one initially computes total cAMP excretion on a creatinine basis (i.e., $6.0 \times 10^{-6}\,M \div 100$ mg/dl $= 6$ nmol/ml $\div 1$ mg/ml $= 6$ nmol/mg creatinine). The expression of total cAMP excretion as a function of GFR is achieved simply by multiplying this value by the serum creatinine concentration, in mg/dl (i.e., 6 nmol/mg creatinine $\times$ 0.8 mg/dl $=$ 4.80 nmol/100 ml GF). Given a plasma cAMP concentration of 15 nM, which corresponds to 1.5 nmol of cAMP per deciliter of glomerular filtrate, nephrogenous cAMP is computed simply by subtracting the filtered load of cAMP from the total cAMP excretion rate (i.e., 4.8 nmol/100 ml GF $-$ 1.5 nmol/100 ml GF $=$ 3.3 nmol/100 ml GF).

The proper expression of data is of tremendous importance to the correct interpretation of results. This issue has escaped the attention of some investigators and all of the commercial laboratories, several of which have persisted in reporting urinary cAMP results in meaningless terms. The expression of cAMP data on a creatinine basis (e.g., nmol/mg creatinine) is clearly suboptimal, in that it is physiologically irrational and is associated with spurious "elevations" and cAMP excretion in a variety of circumstances (e.g., thyrotoxicosis, cachexia, etc.). The only difficulty with the expression of cAMP data on a GFR basis is the requirement for the accurate measurement of serum creatinine; this determination becomes progressively imprecise at values <0.8 mg/dl and is the limiting factor in studying pediatric patients. The expression provides reliable results down to a level of GFR in the 20–30 ml/minute range but has never been validated in patients with more advanced azotemia (Broadus *et al.*, 1977).

Although a number of studies have appeared concerning a putative diurnal variation of plasma and/or urinary cAMP, there is little agreement among these studies as to the pattern or extent of the diurnal variation observed (Broadus, 1977). In the author's experience, the diurnal variation of cAMP in plasma and urine is minimal and does not represent a significant issue in the collection of samples or interpretation of results.

IV. Clinical Studies

In 100 normal subjects, nephrogenous cAMP averaged 1.59 ± 0.59 nmol/100 ml GF (mean ± SD), with a normal range of 0.34–2.70 nmol/100 ml GF (mean ± 2 SD).[1] The mean plasma cAMP concentration in these subjects was 16.08 ± 2.98 n*M* (range 10.13–22.03 n*M*).

In 16 patients with well-characterized chronic hypoparathyroidism (untreated serum calcium < 7.5 mg/dl), nephrogenous cAMP averaged 0.29 ± 0.16 nmol/100 ml GF (Fig. 2). Four of these patients had idiopathic hypoparathyroidism (mean untreated serum calcium 6.3 mg/dl) and an average nephrogenous cAMP of 0.07 nmol/100 ml GF. In five additional patients with partial postoperative hypoparathyroidism (untreated serum calcium >7.5 mg/dl), nephrogenous cAMP averaged 0.60 ± 0.31 nmol/100 ml GF. In four untreated and one treated patient with pseudohypoparathyroidism (mean serum calcium 8.2 mg/dl, range 6.4–9.7 mg/dl; each patient had increased serum iPTH at the time of study), nephrogenous cAMP averaged 0.40 ± 0.31 nmol/100 ml GF (range 0.04–0.80 nmol/100 ml GF, data not shown in Fig. 2). These data indicate that the defect in patients with pseudohypoparathyroidism is not necessarily absolute. In 18 patients with nonparathyroid hypercalcemia (malignancy with local osteolysis, sarcoidosis, vitamin D intoxication, etc.), nephrogenous cAMP averaged 0.34 ± 0.18 nmol/100 ml GF.

It should be emphasized that values of zero or near-zero for nephrogenous cAMP are as easily and reproducibly measured as are values which are severalfold elevated. This allows the determination to provide an accurate index of parathyroid function over the entire range of parathyroid activity, accounting for the truly bimodal distribution of results in hypercalcemic patients and the usefulness of the measurement and assessing degrees of clinical hypoparathyroidism.

In 175 patients with primary hyperparathyroidism, nephrogenous cAMP averaged 4.48 ± 1.70 nmol/100 ml GF (Fig. 2). Results of nephrogenous cAMP were elevated (>2.7 nmol/100 ml GF) in 160 (91%) of these 175 patients. There was a significant positive correlation between

[1] Unless otherwise specified, all data in this article are given as mean ± SD and normal ranges as mean ± 2 SD.

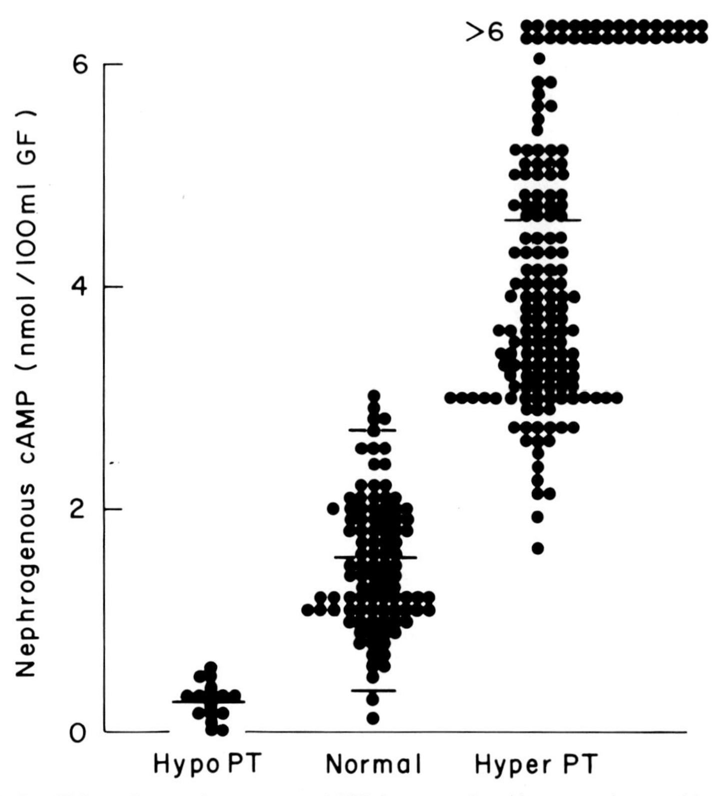

FIG. 2. Values for nephrogenous cAMP in control subjects, patients with chronic hypoparathyroidism (HypoPT), and patients with primary hyperparathyroidism (HyperPT). The horizontal lines denote mean values in the patients and mean ± 2 SD in the control subjects.

the serum calcium levels and the values for nephrogenous cAMP in the patients with primary hyperparathyroidism ($r = 0.45$, $p < 0.001$). Eighty-three of these patients had mild hypercalcemia (serum calcium ≤ 11.0 mg/dl), and 24 patients had associated moderate renal impairment (mean creatinine clearance 40 ml/minute, range 12–50 ml/minute). Nephrogenous cAMP was 4.34 ± 1.79 nmol/100 ml GF in 10 nonazotemic patients with secondary hyperparathyroidism. Results for nephrogenous cAMP were disproportionately low vis-à-vis the degree of hypercalcemia in nine patients with familial hypocalciuric hypercalcemia (mean serum calcium 12.0 ± 1.4 mg/dl, mean nephrogenous cAMP 2.37 ± 1.42 nmol/100 ml GF, with a range of 1.25–5.78 nmol/100 ml GF and seven of nine values <2.7 nmol/100 ml GF), in agreement with the findings of other investigators (Marx *et al.*, 1978).

Although there was clearly an increased scatter of data, the simple measurement of total cAMP excretion (Fig. 3) provided results that were almost as useful diagnostically as those provided by the technically more demanding measurement of nephrogenous cAMP (Fig. 2). The normal range for total cAMP excretion was 1.83–4.47 nmol/100 ml GF. The mean value in the patients with primary hyperparathyroidism was 6.26 ± 1.91 nmol/100 ml GF, and elevated values were observed in 155 of the patients (89%). In the 16 patients with chronic hypoparathyroidism, total cAMP excretion averaged 2.02 ± 0.31 nmol/100 ml GF (range 1.36–2.66 nmol/100 ml GF).

The mechanisms responsible for the hypercalcemia of malignancy are extremely controversial (Rodman and Sherwood, 1978). Two general

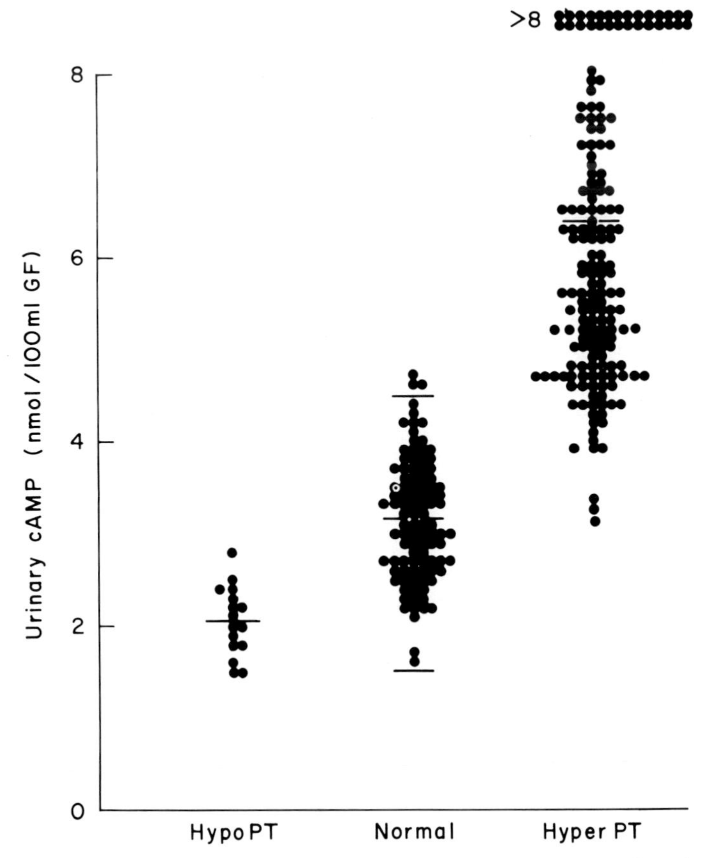

FIG. 3. Values for total cAMP excretion in control subjects and patients with hypoparathyroidism and primary hyperparathyroidism. The construction of the figure is identical to Fig. 2.

mechanisms are usually invoked to explain malignancy-associated hypercalcemia: local osteolytic hypercalcemia (hypercalcemia resulting from the local osteolytic effects of primary tumor cells in bone or those metastatic to bone) and humoral hypercalcemia of malignancy (hypercalcemia resulting from the effects of a humoral substance(s) produced by tumors remote from bone). The relative frequency of these mechanisms, sound criteria for invoking one or another mechanism, and the nature of the putative humoral mediator(s) remain largely unknown.

We studied 50 unselected patients with malignancy-associated hypercalcemia with measurements of routine chemistries, renal tubular phosphorus threshold (TmP/GFR), fractional calcium excretion, nephrogenous cAMP, plasma 1,25-dihydroxyvitamin D (1,25-$(OH)_2D$), and serum immunoreactive PTH (iPTH) as determined by four region-specific antisera (amino-terminal, carboxy-terminal, multivalent, and "intact"). The data were compared to those from 15 patients with primary hyperparathyroidism selected for a similar degree of hypercalcemia and to those from 15 control (nonhypercalcemic) patients with cancer. The findings in the latter group were normal and will not be further discussed.

The results for nephrogenous cAMP segregated the patients with malignancy-associated hypercalcemia into two clearly bimodal subpopulations (Fig. 4). Those patients with elevated nephrogenous cAMP values were regarded as having a humoral basis for their hypercalcemia (humoral hypercalcemia of malignancy or HHM), and those patients with suppressed nephrogenous cAMP were regarded as having local osteolytic hypercalcemia (LOH). The mean values for TmP/GFR were 1.7 ± 0.5 and 2.7 ± 1.0 mg/dl in these two groups, respectively. The remaining determinations in the patients with primary hyperparathyroidism, humoral hypercalcemia of malignancy, and local osteolytic hypercalcemia are summarized in Fig. 5. In comparison to patients with primary hyperparathyroidism, patients with humoral hypercalcemia of malignancy had markedly increased fractional calcium excretion, low or undetectable plasma 1,25-$(OH)_2D$ concentrations, and low or undetectable serum iPTH with each of the four assays. Similar results were observed in the patients with local osteolytic hypercalcemia. All three groups were clearly and easily distinguished biochemically.

These results suggest that patients with humoral hypercalcemia of malignancy have a circulating humoral substance(s) which shares with native PTH the ability to stimulate proximal tubular adenylyl cyclase activity and phosphorous excretion but which differs from native PTH in its relative inability to stimulate calcium readsorption in the distal nephron, its inability to stimulate renal 1-hydroxylase activity, and its poor reactivity with a variety of anti-PTH antisera. The humoral syndrome is com-

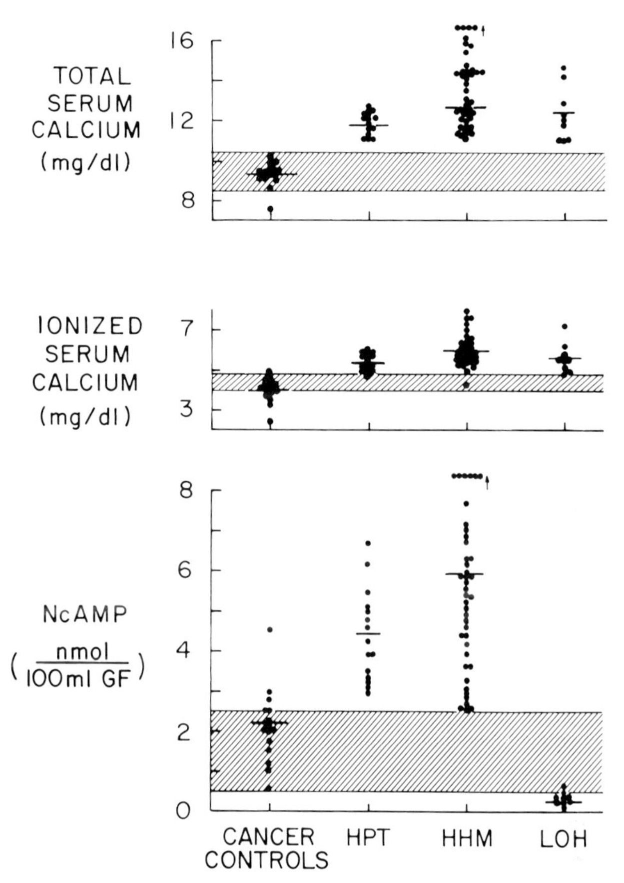

FIG. 4. Total serum calcium, ionized serum calcium, and nephrogenous cAMP in normocalcemic patients with a malignancy (cancer controls), patients with primary hyperparathyroidism and moderate hypercalcemia (HPT), and patients with humoral (HHM) and local osteolytic (LOH) mechanisms of malignancy-associated hypercalcemia. From Stewart *et al.* (1980).

mon, being identified in 40 of our initial series of 50 patients. Although the nature of the circulating material in patients with humoral hypercalcemia of malignancy remains unknown, the classification of patients with malignancy-associated hypercalcemia into humoral and nonhumoral subpopulations on the basis of results for nephrogenous cAMP has recently been independently corroborated by the newly introduced cytochemical bioassay (CBA) for PTH (Goltzman *et al.*, 1980). Mean CBA activity was 12-fold higher in patients with the humoral syndrome than in those with the local osteolytic syndrome (Stewart *et al.*, 1980b).

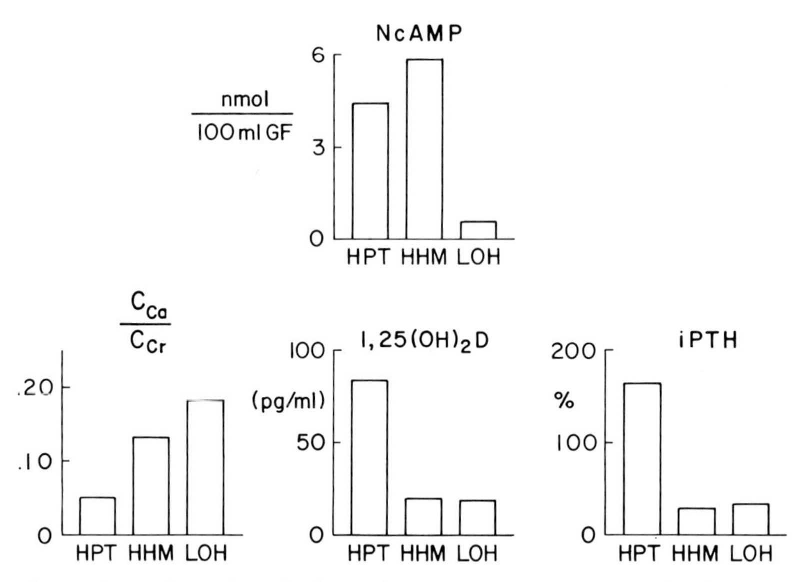

FIG. 5. Comparison of results for nephrogenous cAMP (NcAMP), fractional calcium excretion (C_{Ca}/C_{Cr}), plasma 1,25-$(OH)_2D$, and serum iPTH determined with a multivalent antiserum in patients with primary hyperparathyroidism (HPT), patients with humoral hypercalcemia of malignancy (HHM), and patients with local osteolytic hypercalcemia (LOH).

V. Acute Studies: Parathyroid Suppression Tests and the Oral Calcium Tolerance Test

One of the major consequences of the difficulty posed by the immunoheterogeneity of the circulating forms and fragments of PTH has been the general unavailability of viable parathyroid suppression tests similar to those used to evaluate other endocrine axes (Martin *et al.*, 1979). The measurement of nephrogenous cAMP presumably provides an index of the effects of the circulating native or active peptide, which is generally regarded as representing only some 10% of the total circulating immunoreactive material (Martin *et al.*, 1979). Therefore, it was proposed that the determination of nephrogenous cAMP might allow for the development of valid parathyroid suppression tests. The ability of the determination to accurately reflect parathyroid function over the entire range of parathyroid activity was discussed previously.

The question was initially studied using a standard calcium infusion technique (4 mg/calcium/kg/body weight/hour). In 10 normal volunteers, calcium infusion was associated with a rapid suppression of nephrogenous cAMP into the hypoparathyroid range (Broadus *et al.*, 1978a). The intravenous calcium challenge was then simplified to the "calcium injection" technique, employing 3 mg/calcium/kg/body weight administered over 10 minutes (Fig. 6). In normal volunteers, this modest challenge produced calcemic responses which generally occurred within the normal range, yet nephrogenous cAMP was reproducibly suppressed into the hypoparathyroid range (Fig. 6). As anticipated, the induced decreases in circulating iPTH as determined with a multivalent antiserum were smaller and inconsistent (Fig. 6). The calcium infusion and injection techniques have been used to evaluate parathyroid suppressibility in patients with adenomatous hyperparathyroidism and parathyroid hyperplasia (Brown *et al.*, 1979) and as diagnostic techniques in patients with "subtle" primary hyperparathyroidism (Broadus *et al.*, 1978a), although the diagnostic use of these tests has been largely supplanted by the oral calcium tolerance test (see below).

The best single example of the sensitivity provided by the measurement of nephrogenous cAMP is the effect produced in normal subjects by the oral administration of the amount of calcium (350 mg) in a normal calcium-containing meal (Broadus *et al.*, 1978b). This physiological oral challenge produces a 30% suppression of nephrogenous cAMP in the face of induced increases in serum calcium which are in the range of 0.2 mg/dl.

Figure 7 is a schematic representation of the oral calcium tolerance test. The test consists of three sequential 2-hour urine collections, with midpoint blood samples drawn during the first and third collection periods. The first collection period serves as the fasting control period, the second collection as the lag time required for peak calcium absorption to occur (no data are derived from this period), and the third collection period as the experimental period demonstrating the maximal systemic and physiological effects of the absorbed calcium. The test is conceptually similar to the oral calcium challenge techniques introduced by Peacock *et al.* (1968) and Pak *et al.* (1975) but embodies a number of significant modifications from these earlier techniques. These modifications include altered timing to reflect the effects of peak calcium absorption, assessment of the calcemic response, the measurement of nephrogenous cAMP, the expression of calcium and cAMP data as a function of GFR rather than creatinine excretion, and the expression of the calciuric response as the induced change or "delta" in calcium excretion from the wide range of values for fasting calcium excretion (Broadus *et al.*, 1978b, 1980a). The data base derived from the test listed in Fig. 7 is that which may be obtained for research purposes; in its simplest diagnostic form, the test requires measurement of only serum calcium and creatinine and urinary calcium, creatinine, and cAMP, with proper calculation and expression of data. Valid results may be obtained from both outpatient and inpatient studies

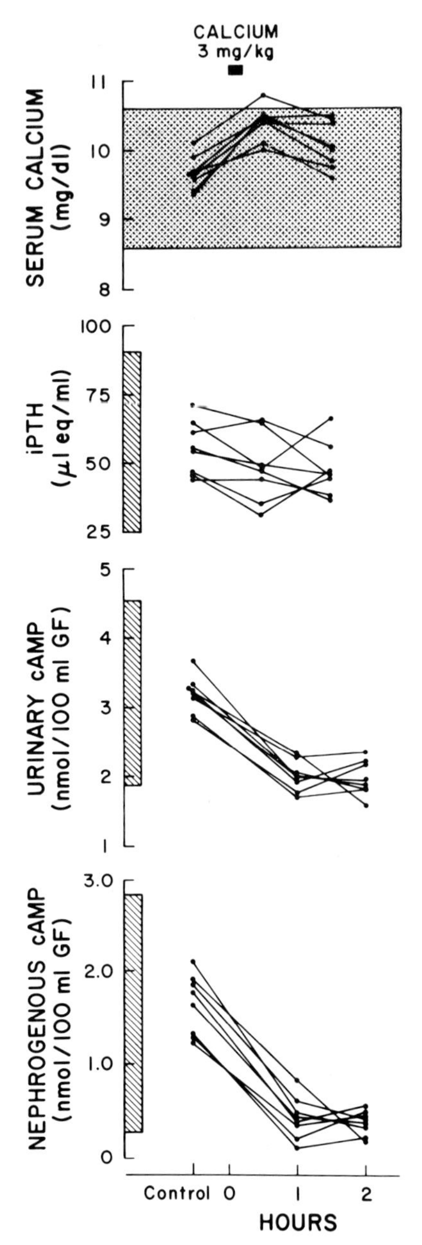

FIG. 6. The results of "calcium injection" (3 mg elemental calcium/kg body weight administered over 10 minutes) in 8 normal subjects. The mean total serum calcium rose by 0.7 mg/dl at + 20 minutes and 0.3 mg/dl at + 80 minutes. The cross-hatched bars (bottom 3 panels) and stippled area (top panel) denote normal ranges. From Broadus *et al.* (1978a).

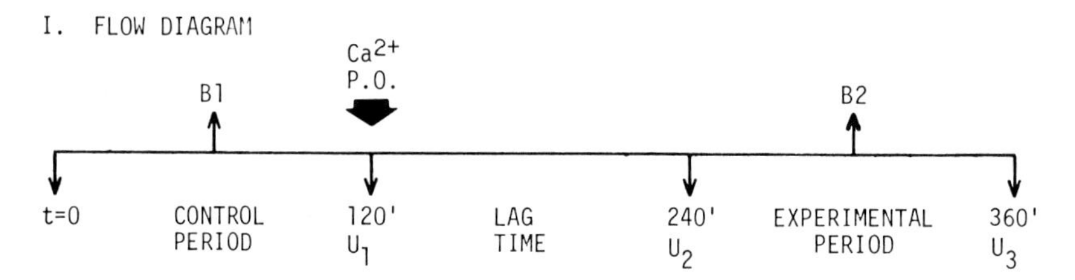

II. DATA BASE

A. STATIC MEASUREMENTS (CONTROL PERIOD)

1. BASAL SERUM CALCIUM & PHOSPHORUS
2. FASTING CALCIUM EXCRETION
3. FASTING TMP/GFR
4. BASAL NEPHROGENOUS OR TOTAL cAMP EXCRETION
5. BASAL VITAMIN D METABOLITES

B. DYNAMIC MEASUREMENTS (EXPERIMENTAL VS CONTROL PERIOD)

1. CALCEMIC RESPONSE AS INDEX OF "CALCIUM TOLERANCE"
2. CALCIURIC RESPONSE (Δ mg CALCIUM/100 ML GF) AS INDEX OF GI ABSORPTION
3. SUPPRESSIBILITY OF NEPHROGENOUS OR TOTAL cAMP EXCRETION

FIG. 7. Flow diagram and data base derived from the oral calcium tolerance test. See text for details.

but require that subjects be on a restricted (approximately 400 mg) calcium diet for 7–10 days prior to testing.[2]

The two principal uses of the calcium tolerance test are in diagnosis (see below) and in assessing the status of intestinal calcium absorption in a given patient population. The test assumes that the calciuric response to the oral calcium challenge provides an accurate index of intestinal calcium absorption, an assumption that has been validated in a number of patient groups but which may not be valid under all circumstances.

Figure 8 depicts the relationship between circulating 1,25-$(OH)_2D$ (the fully activated vitamin D steroid hormone which regulates intestinal calcium absorption) and the calciuric response to the tolerance test in 80 patients with primary hyperparathyroidism (Broadus *et al.*, 1980b). There was a strong positive correlation between the plasma level of 1,25-$(OH)_2D$ and the calciuric response to the test in these patients (Fig. 8). There was

[2] Standard outpatient instructions and nursing instructions for the calcium tolerance test can be obtained from the author by written request.

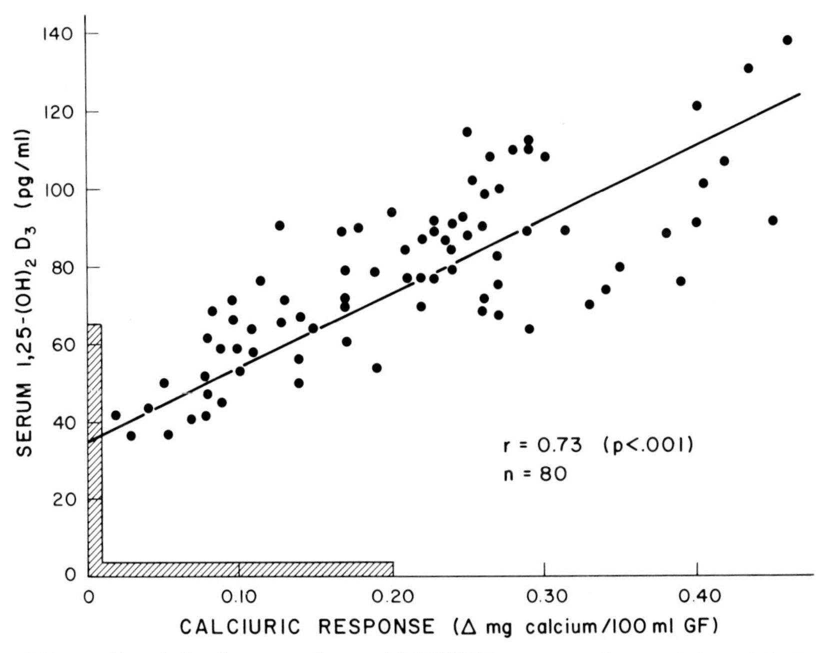

FIG. 8. Correlation between plasma 1,25-$(OH)_2D$ concentrations and the calciuric response to the calcium tolerance test in 80 patients with primary hyperparathyroidism. The cross-hatched bars denote normal ranges. Modified from Broadus *et al.* (1980b).

also a strong positive correlation between plasma 1,25-$(OH)_2D$ and 24-hour calcium excretion determined on an unrestricted calcium diet (data not shown). These and other data suggested that 1,25-$(OH)_2D$-mediated intestinal calcium absorption serves as the principal source of the calcium excreted by patients with primary hyperparathyroidism.

When considered as a whole, however, the patient population demonstrated considerable heterogeneity with respect to the plasma level of 1,25-$(OH)_2D$, the status of intestinal calcium absorption, and the presence and/or degree of hypercalciuria. In order to further examine pathophysiological correlates, the patients were subdivided into "absorptive" (n = 45) and "nonabsorptive" (n = 35) subpopulations based on whether or not they displayed a hyperabsorptive response to the calcium tolerance test (calciuric response $\Delta > 0.20$ mg calcium/100 mg GF). Patients in the absorptive subpopulation displayed markedly elevated circulating 1,25-$(OH)_2D$, intestinal hyperabsorption of calcium, an accentuated calcemic response or calcium "intolerance" associated with a mean 24% suppression in nephrogenous cAMP, striking hypercalciuria (mean 499 mg/day) on an unrestricted calcium intake, and a high incidence

(58%) of renal stones. Patients in the nonabsorptive subpopulation displayed normal or near-normal results for circulating $1,25\text{-}(OH)_2D$ and responses to the calcium tolerance test, predominate normocalciuria, and a low incidence (14%) of renal stones.

As illustrated schematically in Fig. 9, the pattern of calcium absorption and excretion in individuals in the absorptive subpopulation of patients with primary hyperparathyroidism is remarkably similar to the pattern observed in patients with so-called absorptive hypercalciuria (compare Figs. 9 and 11). A key element in the pathophysiological sequence leading to hypercalciuria in the "absorptive" patients with primary hyperparathyroidism was the degree of parathyroid suppression noted after oral calcium administration (results for nephrogenous cAMP were within the normal range in more than 40% of patients during the experimental period). A similar degree of suppression was also revealed by the measurement of 24-hour total cAMP excretion on an unrestricted calcium diet in these patients (see below). This degree of parathyroid suppression was unanticipated and further strengthens the analogy to the pathophysiological pattern of calcium absorption and excretion in absorptive hypercalciuria.

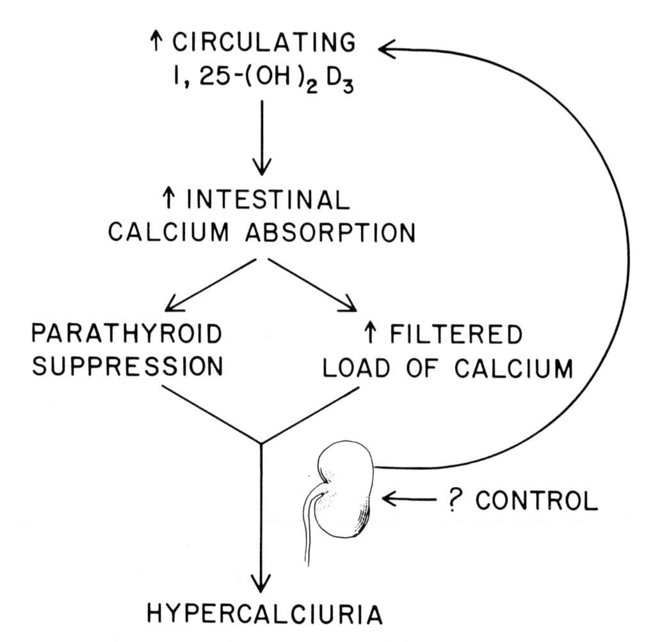

FIG. 9. Schematic representation of the pathophysiological sequence leading to hypercalciuria in the absorptive subpopulation of patients with primary hyperparathyroidism.

When the patients were examined for variables (e.g., degrees of biochemical hyperparathyroidism and hypophosphatemia, status of renal function and vitamin D repletion, etc.) which might influence the rate-limiting step in 1,25-$(OH)_2D$ synthesis in the kidney, no explanation for the 4-fold range in circulating 1,25-$(OH)_2D$ in the patient population as a whole could be found. Our present inability to explain the wide range of observed 1,25-$(OH)_2D$ results presumably reflects imperfect knowledge concerning the control of renal 1-hydroxylase activity but could represent a more fundamental observation implying polymorphism of the basic disease process.

In addition to the insight into the pathophysiological spectrum of primary hyperparathyroidism provided by the studies summarized above, an appreciation of the importance of 1,25-$(OH)_2D$ in the clinical expression of the disease process has both therapeutic and diagnostic implications. Oral phosphorus therapy has long been used empirically in the treatment of certain patients with primary hyperparathyroidism. Although we were unable to define the factor(s) responsible for the elevations in circulating 1,25-$(OH)_2D$ in the absorptive subpopulation with primary hyperparathyroidism, hypophosphatemia is a recognized stimulus of renal 1-hydroxylase activity, and it seemed reasonable to hypothesize that phosphorus replacement therapy might short-circuit the PTH–1,25-$(OH)_2D$ axis or otherwise inhibit 1,25-$(OH)_2D$ synthesis in these patients. Accordingly, 10 well-characterized patients in the absorptive subpopulation of patients with primary hyperparathyroidism were placed on a trial of oral phosphorus therapy (1250–1500 mg elemental phosphorus daily) for 12 or more months. Phosphorus therapy was associated with a mean reduction in circulating 1,25-$(OH)_2D$ from 79 to 53 pg/ml, with corresponding decreases in the calciuric response to the tolerance test and 24-hour calcium excretion and without a discernible "rebound" increase in parathyroid function (Broadus *et al.*, 1979). The long-term implications of this therapeutic approach remain unknown.

Patients with "subtle" primary hyperparathyroidism (other terms in usuage include "normocalcemic primary hyperparathyroidism" and "primary hyperparathyroidism with intermittent hypercalcemia") represent a difficult problem in differential diagnosis, and the literature generated in connection with these patients is justly regarded as controversial. The controversy is not a recent one and dates from the initial description of idiopathic hypercalciuria as a separate entity; indeed, it is interesting to recall that nearly one-third of the patients described in Henneman's classic paper on idiopathic hypercalciuria had undergone prior negative parathyroid explorations (Henneman *et al.*, 1958). It has since been widely observed and reported that mild hypercalcemia is the rule rather than the exception in patients with primary hyperparathyroidism and stone disease and that a pattern of intermittent hypercalcemia is not infrequently observed in these patients (persistent normocalcemia is very rare). Although the controversy continues in certain quarters, recent studies have clarified the pathophysiological pattern of abnormalities in this subtle clinical variant of primary hyperparathyroidism and have provided a sound conceptual approach to diagnosis. The important observations in these patients are four: (1) although the serum calcium fluctuates over a rather wide range, the abnormality in parathyroid function is persistent (i.e., the term "intermittent hyperparathyroidism" is a misnomer); (2) the patients demonstrate a marked "intolerance" to exogenous calcium; (3) although parathyroid function is not autonomous, abnormal parathyroid suppressibility can be easily demonstrated, and (4) plasma concentrations of 1,25-$(OH)_2D$ are typically markedly elevated (Broadus *et al.*, 1978a, 1980a). In a sense, the typical patient with subtle primary hyperparathyroidism is a forme fruste of the average patient in the absorptive subpopulation of primary hyperparathyroidism and represents an extreme example of the disproportionality which may be observed in this subpopulation between measured abnormalities in serum calcium and urinary calcium excretion. This disproportionality has long puzzled investigators, in that it could not be explained by prevailing concepts concerning the filtered load of calcium (under fasting conditions) and the effects of PTH on calcium reabsorption in the distal nephron; it is now clear that the disproportionate hypercalciuria in these patients results entirely from the 1,25-$(OH)_2D$-mediated intestinal hyperabsorption of calcium and the sequence of events illustrated in Fig. 9. This pathophysiological pattern both predicts and explains the striking abnormalities displayed by patients with subtle primary hyperparathyroidism when studied with the oral calcium tolerance test (Fig. 10). In these patients, the tolerance test reveals a combination of induced-hypercalcemia (mean serum calcium 11.4 ± 0.5 mg/dl from a fasting baseline value of 10.2 ± 0.2 mg/dl) and abnormal parathyroid suppressibility (mean nephrogenous cAMP 2.66 ± 0.57 nmol/100 ml GF during the experimental collection period) which makes diagnosis a relatively simple matter. Clearly, in this patient population, the calcium tolerance test serves as a rather classical endocrine suppression test. Occasional patients with mild hyperparathyroidism are observed who have normal circulating 1,25-$(OH)_2D$ and who do not hyperabsorb calcium (one such patient is illustrated in Fig. 10), but even in these patients the tolerance test usually induces a sufficiently clear pattern of abnormalities to prove diagnostic. Occasionally, we will fall back on the calcium injection technique to corroborate the diagnosis in such a patient (Broadus *et al.*, 1978a).

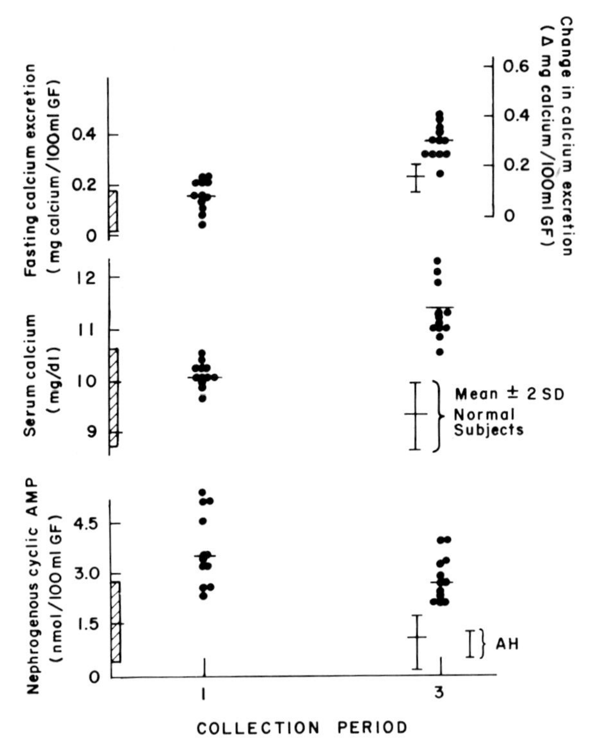

FIG. 10. Calcium tolerance test results in 12 patients with subtle primary hyperparathyroidism. The figure contains data from the first (control) and third (experimental) collection periods. The cross-hatched bars adjoining the ordinates to the left denote normal ranges. In the upper panel, fasting calcium excretion is represented by the ordinate to the left, and the calciuric response, expressed as the change (Δ mg calcium/100 ml GF) from fasting values, is represented by the ordinate to the right. The responses (mean ± 2 SD) of 18 normal subjects to the test are shown by vertical bars in the experimental collection period. Also shown in the bottom panel is the range of nephrogenous cAMP results in patients with absorptive hypercalciuria who developed mild hypercalcemia during the tolerance test (mean 10.8 mg/dl, range 10.6–11.0 mg/dl). From Broadus *et al.* (1980a).

Since the initial description of idiopathic hypercalciuria nearly three decades ago, a number of hypotheses have been advanced to explain the normocalcemic hypercalciuria and tendency to hypophosphatemia displayed by these patients. These various hypotheses were considered in the initial series of Henneman *et al.* (1958), and a variety of indirect data have been gathered over the ensuing years in support of one or another hypothesis. In recent years, more sophisticated investigative and laboratory techniques have been employed in studying these patients, and it has become clear that the existing hypotheses are not mutually exclusive.

	CALCIUM ABSORPTION	EXTRACELLULAR CALCIUM	PT FUNCTION	CALCIUM EXCRETION FL	CALCIUM EXCRETION Reab	$1,25\text{-}(OH)_2D_3$	SERUM P_i
ABSORPTIVE HC	[↑]	N, ↑	N, ↓	↑	↓	↑	N, [↓]*
RENAL HC	↑	↓	↑	↓	[↓]	↑	N, ↓
PRIMARY HPT	↑	N, ↑	[↑]	↑	↑	↑	N, ↓

FIG. 11. Pathophysiological features in patients with absorptive hypercalciuria, renal hypercalciuria, and subtle primary hyperparathyroidism. The putative primary defect in each syndrome is enclosed in an open square. *, denotes "renal phosphate leak"; HC, hypercalciuria; HPT, hyperparathyroidism; PT, parathyroid; FL, filtered load; Reab, tubular reabsorption.

Rather, the consensus opinion of current investigators is that there are several distinct mechanistic categories or subtypes of idiopathic hypercalciuria within the general hypercalciuric population, although there is substantial disagreement between investigators with regard to valid criteria for differential diagnosis and the frequency of the individual hypercalciuric subtypes (Pak, 1979; Coe *et al.*, 1973; Lemann, 1980; Broadus *et al.*, 1978b).

Figure 11 presents a classification of idiopathic hypercalciuria and summarizes the pathophysiological features of the three principal subtypes of idiopathic hypercalciuria: absorptive hypercalciuria, renal hypercalciuria, and subtle primary hyperparathyroidism (the latter patients were discussed in detail previously and are included in the classification on the grounds of historical precedent and in order to compare and contrast diagnostic criteria with the other hypercalciuric subtypes).[3] Patients with absorptive hypercalciuria have an increase in gastrointestinal calcium absorption which is associated with postprandial increases in the

[3] The term "resorptive" hypercalciuria has been employed by some investigators in reference to patients with primary hyperparathyroidism. However, according to the findings discussed previously concerning the predominant intestinal source of urinary calcium in patients with primary hyperparathyroidism, this term is somewhat of a misnomer. Most patients for whom the term would appear to be valid are actually examples of secondary hypercalciuria (e.g., immobilization) and are not included in the idiopathic category. In the author's view, the semantics in the field have often tended to cloud rather than clarify important pathophysiological issues.

serum level and filtered load of calcium, an induced-decrease in parathyroid function (with an attendant decrease in PTH-mediated calcium reabsorption in the distal nephron), and spillage of the absorbed load of calcium into the urine. Recent evidence suggests that patients subclassified as having absorptive hypercalciuria may actually harbor as many as three basic pathogenetic mechanisms: one group is regarded as having a primary defect in renal tubular phosphorus reabsorption, hypophosphatemia with a reduction in TmP/GFR, and secondary increases in circulating 1,25-$(OH)_2D$ and intestinal calcium absorption; another group presents with increases in circulating 1,25-$(OH)_2D$ and intestinal calcium absorption in the setting of clearly normal serum phosphorus concentrations and values for TmP/GFR, and a third group manifests intestinal hyperabsorption of calcium in the presence of normal circulating levels of 1,25-$(OH)_2D$ (Pak, 1979; Lemann, 1980). Patients with renal hypercalciuria have a primary defect in renal tubular calcium reabsorption, associated with secondary hyperparathyroidism and attendant increases in 1,25-$(OH)_2D$ synthesis and intestinal calcium absorption and a tendency to hypophosphatemia. The pathophysiological basis of hypercalciuria in patients with subtle primary hyperparathyroidism was discussed previously.

In addition to the pathophysiological insight gained from an understanding of the features summarized in Fig. 11, it is intuitively apparent that accurate differential diagnosis must be based on the demonstration of one or a combination of features that can be considered to be unique for each syndrome. For example, a tendency to hypophosphatemia and increases in circulating 1,25-$(OH)_2D$ and intestinal calcium absorption are features which are shared by each hypercalciuric subtype and are of no differential value (Fig. 11). Differential diagnosis must, therefore, be based on measures of serum calcium, calcium excretion, and parathyroid function under fasting conditions and/or after manipulating the system with exogenous calcium in order to make subtle abnormalities more apparent.

The oral calcium tolerance test is an extremely useful test in differential diagnosis, in that it embodies a number of independent diagnostic criteria (Figs. 7 and 12). The measurement of fasting calcium excretion is of limited diagnostic utility, and all three patient subgroups display abnormal calciuric responses, denoting intestinal hyperabsorption of calcium (upper panel of Fig. 12). The crux of differential diagnosis lies in the calcemic responses and the appropriateness of the coincident parathyroidal response. Patients with absorptive hypercalciuria display a marked calcemic response (mild hypercalcemia is induced in about one-quarter of patients) associated with an appropriate suppression of nephrogenous cAMP into the low-normal range (Fig. 12). Patients with renal hypercal-

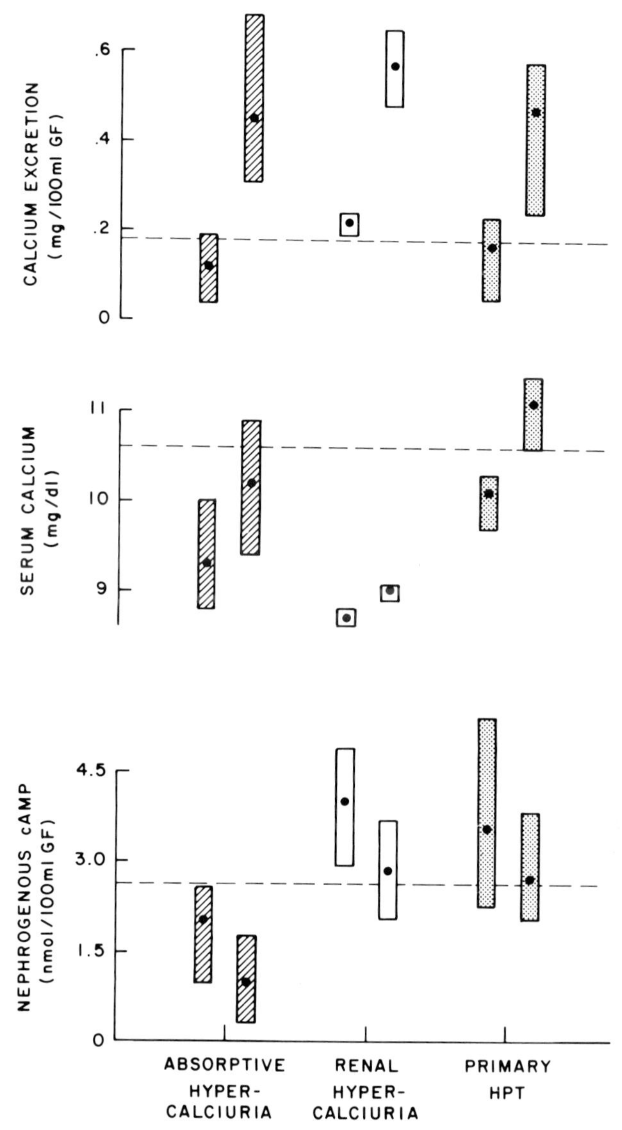

FIG. 12. Calcium tolerance test results in patients with absorptive hypercalciuria, renal hypercalciuria, and subtle primary hyperparathyroidism. For each patient group, the bar to the left corresponds to the control period and the bar to the right to the experimental period. The dashed lines denote upper normal limits under fasting, control conditions. The solid dots represent mean values, and the vertical height of the bars the range of values. From Broadus and Thier (1977).

ciuria display a minimal calcemic response associated with a slight but appropriate suppression in nephrogenous cAMP. The combination of induced hypercalcemia and abnormal suppressibility of nephrogenous cAMP is diagnostic of subtle primary hyperparathyroidism, as discussed above. Although the determination of nephrogenous cAMP provides an index of parathyroid suppressibility which is approximately twice as sensitive as that provided by the simple measurement of total cAMP excretion, the latter measurement is adequate for diagnostic purposes in the vast majority of cases. Thus, in its simplest diagnostic form, the calcium tolerance test is well within the technical reach of a routine endocrine laboratory.

Figure 13 contains results for 24-hour calcium and total cAMP excretion in patients with absorptive and renal hypercalciuria studied on both a low-normal (400 mg) and high-normal (1000 mg) calcium intake. The figure illustrates two important points. First, the increase in dietary calcium intake had a marked influence on calcium excretion in the hypercalciuric patients (upper panel of Fig. 13), in contrast to the minimal influence of calcium intake on calcium excretion in normal subjects (Broadus *et al.*, 1981). The importance of employing a high-normal calcium diet in screening patients for hypercalciuria has been repeatedly stressed (Broadus *et al.*, 1978b; Broadus and Thier, 1977). Clearly, the pathophysiological basis of this approach is the increase in intestinal calcium absorption which is common to each of the hypercalciuric subtypes. Second, results obtained on the 1000-mg calcium intake may serve as a "poor man's" calcium tolerance test. That is, patients with absorptive hypercalciuria demonstrated rather marked suppression in total cAMP excretion on the high-normal calcium intake (to a value < 3.5 nmol/100 ml GF in each patient), such that they could be clearly segregated from the patients with renal hypercalciuria (bottom panel of Fig. 13). These data constitute the simplest conceivable office or clinic practice approach to accurate differential diagnosis of the hypercalciurias, assuming patients with subtle primary hyperparathyroidism are excluded by other criteria (in the Renal Stone Clinic at Yale, our rule-of-thumb is to seriously consider the possibility of subtle primary hyperparathyroidism in a patient with a mean serum calcium $\geq$ 10.0 mg/dl on three determinations performed fasting and with scrupulous blood drawing and analytical technique).

Figure 14 illustrates results for 24-hour calcium and total cAMP excretion in 50 patients with primary hyperparathyroidism studied on both 400-mg and 1000-mg calcium diets. Again, a steep slope of calcium excretion on calcium intake was observed, associated with a significant decrease in total cAMP excretion on the 1000-mg calcium intake. The diet-

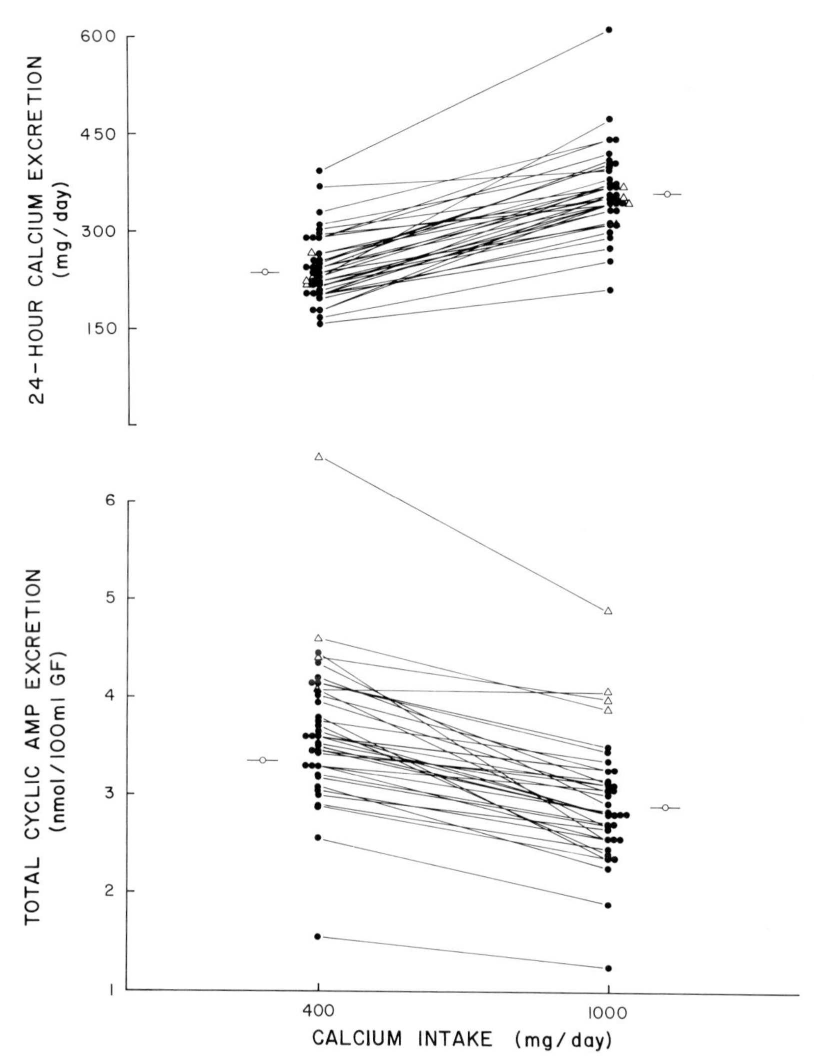

FIG. 13. Results for calcium and total cAMP excretion in patients with absorptive (●) and renal (△) hypercalciuria studied on both a 400-mg and a 1000-mg calcium diet. The open circles and bars denote mean values. From Broadus *et al.* (1981).

induced increase in calcium excretion and suppression of total cAMP excretion were particularly impressive in the patients in the absorptive subpopulation with the disorder, as anticipated. These data have obvious pathophysiological significance, in that the degree of parathyroid suppression observed occurred well within the normal range of dietary calcium intake. In addition, the data are of diagnostic significance, in that values for

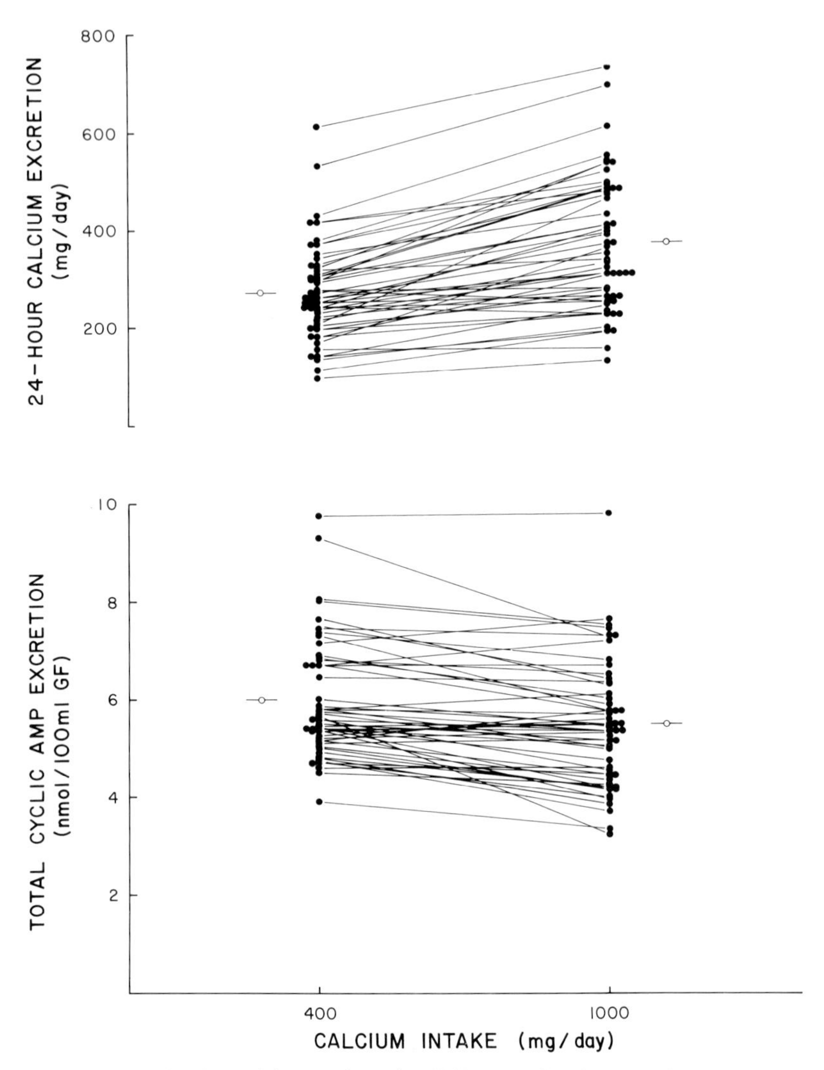

FIG. 14. Results for calcium and total cAMP excretion in 50 patients with primary hyperparathyroidism studied on both a 400-mg and a 1000-mg calcium diet. The open circles and bars denote mean values. Note that the scales differ from those in Fig. 13. From Broadus *et al.* (1981).

total cAMP excretion were within the normal range in 28% of the 50 patients studied on the high-normal calcium diet. Clearly, patients suspected of having primary hyperparathyroidism should be evaluated fasting or on a restricted calcium diet (values < 4.5 nmol/100 ml GF were observed in only two of the 50 patients on the 400-mg calcium diet).

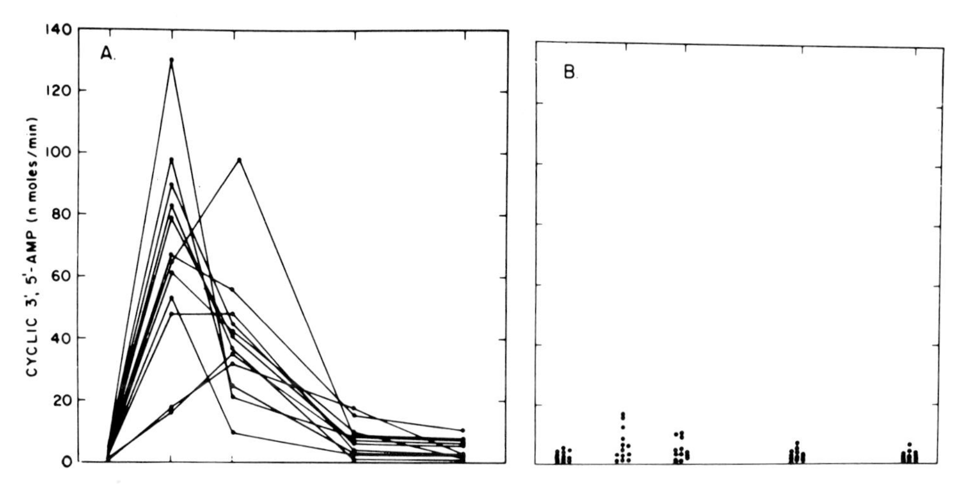

FIG. 15. Total urinary cAMP responses to PTH infusion in normal subjects (A) and patients with pseudohypoparathyroidism (B). Modified from Chase *et al.* (1969).

VI. Additional Uses of the Cyclic AMP Analyses

Figure 15 illustrates the effects of PTH infusion on total cAMP excretion in normal subjects and patients with pseudohypoparathyroidism. Chase and Aurbach initially reported the blunted or absent cAMP response in patients with pseudohypoparathyroidism in 1969, and their protocol has since become the established technique for diagnosis of the disorder. Since increasing numbers of patients with pseudohypoparathyroidism who lack the typical phenotypic features of the condition are being observed, PTH infusion should be considered in any chemically hypoparathyroid patient who lacks a history of prior neck surgery. The most recent data concerning the nature of the defect in pseudohypoparathyroidism are summarized by Dr. A. Spiegel (this volume).

Results for nephrogenous cAMP or total cAMP excretion can be used to assess the success of parathyroid exploration, as a guide in managing postparathyroidectomy hypocalcemia, and even as an intraoperative monitor of the progress of parathyroid surgery (Spiegel *et al.* 1977, 1978).

VII. Summary

In this article, I have presented the details of the physiology of cAMP excretion in man and have sketched the evolution of the use of determinations of nephrogenous cAMP and total cAMP excretion as indices of parathyroid function. I have reemphasized my concerns regarding the proper expression and interpretation of cAMP data. I have deliberately presented the cAMP data within the context of a discussion of a wide and complex variety of disorders of mineral metabolism, in order to emphasize the clinical and experimental versatility of the measurements. In spite of this versatility, it should be clear from the foregoing discussion that the cAMP determinations should not be regarded as a panacea. In the final analysis, there are a number of available parathyroid function tests (i.e., the measurement of TmP/GFR, serum iPTH, nephrogenous cAMP or total cAMP excretion, and PTH-like activity by cytochemical bioassay), and the choice of methodology should be based on an intelligent assessment of the complexity and requirements of the problem facing the individual clinician and/or investigator.

ACKNOWLEDGMENTS

A large number of individuals participated in the various studies described in this manuscript. Dr. Andrew Stewart was the prime mover in the malignancy-associated hypercalcemia studies, and Drs. Leonard Deftos, David Goltzman, and Ronald Horst provided important aspects of the analytical data base in these studies. I am particularly indebted to the members of the Renal Stone Clinic at Yale: Mrs. Alice Ellison and Drs. Cecil Hodson, Alan Kliger, and Robert Lang and to Mrs. Pat Behrends, Mrs. Toni Ziyadeh, and the staff of Hunter 5. Dr. Howard Rasmussen lent insight and encouragement in many of the studies. Ms. Kathy Joy's dedication and expertise touched all aspects of the studies described, and Mrs. Nancy Canetti provided superb secretarial assistance. The studies were supported in part by NIH grants RR 125 and AM 20570.

REFERENCES

Broadus, A. E. (1977). *In* "Advances in Cyclic Nucleotide Research" (P. Greengard and G. A. Robison, eds.), p. 509. Raven, New York.

Broadus, A. E. (1979). *Nephron* **23,** 136.

Broadus, A. E., and Thier, S. O. (1977). *N. Engl. J. Med.* **300,** 839.

Broadus, A. E., Kaminsky, N. I., Hardman, J. G., Sutherland, E. W., and Liddle, G. W. (1970). *J. Clin. Invest.* **49,** 2222.

Broadus, A. E., Mahaffey, J. E., Bartter, F. C., and Neer, R. M. (1977). *J. Clin. Invest.* **60,** 771.

Broadus, A. E., Deftos, L. J., and Bartter, F. C. (1978a). *J. Clin. Endocrinol. Metab.* **46,** 477.

Broadus, A. E., Dominguez, M., and Bartter, F. C. (1978b). *J. Clin. Endocrinol. Metab.* **47,** 751.

Broadus, A., Horst, R., Lang, R., and Rasmussen, H. (1979). *Clin. Res.* **27,** 363A.

Broadus, A. E., Horst, R. L., Littledike, E. T., Mahaffey, J. E., and Rasmussen, H. (1980a). *Clin. Endocrinol.* **12,** 225.

Broadus, A. E., Horst, R. L., Lang, R., Littledike, E. T., and Rasmussen, H. (1980b). *N. Engl. J. Med.* **302,** 421.

Broadus, A. E., Lang, R., Kliger, A., and Rasmussen, H. (1981). *J. Clin. Endocrinol. Metab.* (in press).

Brown, E. M., Broadus, A. E., Brennan, M. F., Gardner, D. G., Marx, S. J., Spiegel, A. M.,

Downs, R. W., Attie, M., and Aurbach, G. D. (1979). *J. Clin. Endocrinol. Metab.* **48,** 604.
Chase, L. R., and Aurbach, G. D. (1967). *Proc. Natl. Acad. Sci. U.S.A.* **58,** 518.
Chase, L. R., Melson, G. L., and Aurbach, G. D. (1969). *J. Clin. Invest.* **48,** 1832.
Coe, F. L., Canterbury, J. M., Firpo, J. J., and Reiss, E. (1973). *J. Clin. Invest.* **52,** 134.
Forrest, J. N., and Broadus, A. E. (1979). *Am. Soc. Nephrol.* **12,** 186A.
Goltzman, D., Henderson, B., and Loveridge, N. (1980). *J. Clin. Invest.* **65,** 1309.
Gray, R. W., Wilz, D. R., and Lemann, A. E. (1977). *J. Clin. Endocrinol. Metab.* **45,** 299.
Hardman, J. G., Davis, J. W., and Sutherland, E. W. (1969). *J. Biol. Chem.* **244,** 6354.
Henneman, P. H., Benedict, P. H., Forbes, A. P., and Dudley, H. R. (1958). *N. Engl. J. Med.* **259,** 802.
Kaminsky, N. I., Broadus, A. E., Hardman, J. G., Jones, D. J., Ball, J. H., Sutherland, E. W., and Liddle, G. W. (1970a). *J. Clin. Invest.* **49,** 2387.
Kaminsky, N. I., Ball, J. H., Broadus, A. E., Hardman, J. G., Sutherland, E. W., and Liddle, G. W. (1970b). *Trans. Assoc. Am. Physicians* **83,** 235.
Lemann, J. (1980). *In* "Nephrolithiasis, Contemporary Issues in Nephrology" (F. L. Coe, B. M. Brenner, and J. H. Stein, eds.), Vol. 5, p. 86. Churchill, London.
Martin, K. J., Hruska, K. A., Freitag, J. J., Klahr, S., and Slatopolsky, E. (1979). *N. Engl. J. Med.* **301,** 1092.
Marx, S. J., Spiegel, A. M., Brown, E. M., Windeck, R., Gardner, D. G., Downs, R. W., Attie, M., and Aurbach, G. D. (1978). *J. Clin. Endocrinol. Metabolism* **47,** 1190.
Pak, C. Y. C. (1979). *Am. J. Physiol.* **237,** F415.
Pak, C. Y. C., Kaplan, R., Bone, H., Townsend, J., and Waters, O. (1975). *N. Engl. J. Med.* **292,** 497.
Peacock, M., Knowles, F., and Nordin, B. E. C. (1968). *Br. Med. J.* **2,** 729.
Rodman, J. S., and Sherwood, L. M. (1978). *In* "Metabolic Bone Disease" (L. V. Avioli and S. M. Krane, eds.), Vol. II, p. 555. Academic Press, New York.
Spiegel, A. M., Marx, S., Brennan, M., Brown, E., Koehler, J., and Aurbach, G. (1977). *Clin. Res.* **25,** 401A.
Spiegel, A. M., Marx, S. J., Brennan, M. F., Brown, E., Koehler, J., and Aurbach, G. (1978). *J. Clin. Endocrinol. Metab.* **47,** 537.
Stewart, A. F., Horst, R., Deftos, L. J., Cadman, E. C., Lang, R., and Broadus, A. E. (1980). *N. Engl. J. Med.* **303,** 1377.
Stewart, A. F., Goltzman, D., Deftos, L. J., Vignery, A., Horst, R., Kirkwood, J., and Broadus, A. (1980b). *Clin. Res.* **28,** 407A.
Takahashi, K., Kamimura, M., Shinko, T., and Tsuji, S. (1966). *Lancet* **2,** 967.

DISCUSSION

G. Campbell: I have several questions. It's been my understanding that PTH has at least three functions in the kidney. In the proximal tubule, it decreases the reabsorption of sodium, chloride, calcium, and bicarbonate. In the distal tubule, it increases the reabsorption of calcium and it participates in regulating the hydroxylases in the interconversions of the vitamin Ds. Could you tell me which of these are mediated through the generation of cyclic AMP? The second question is, is the adenyl cyclase located on the luminal surface of the tubular cell or basal surface or completely around the membrane of the tubular cell?

A. Broadus: Let me handle the second question first. The most recent evidence is that the cyclase-receptor complex is on the interstitial side of the cell, the basal-lateral side. The step mediating phosphate transport is on the luminal border, and it is the cascade of events involving the kinase, phosphorylation, and so on that mediates events across the cell. The implication would be that something having to do with the phosphate transport mechanism in the luminal membrane is phosphorylated; its activity is decreased and phosphate is spilled into the urine. That is the polarity of the cell as I understand it and its biochemical components. Your first point which I would answer second is actually a very tough one. I think there would be little question in anyone's mind that the parathyroid hormone-dependent regulation of phosphorus reabsorption in the proximal tubular is cyclic AMP-mediated, so the answer to that is yes. There are a number of biological situations in which alterations in cyclic AMP generation in the kidney do not correspond with hydroxylase activity. One classic example would be the humoral syndrome of malignancy-associated hypercalcemia, as discussed in my presentation. There are other observations that suggest that cyclic AMP may not regulate the hydroxylase. Finally, yes, there is a PTH-sensitive adenylyl cyclase in the distal nephron. An interesting observation we made, and I meant to ask Alan about this; we have seen a number of patients with pseudohypoparathyroidism whose calcium excretion is, in fact, low in the untreated state. That and a series of other observations make me question whether or not cyclic AMP really mediates the effects of PTH on calcium reabsorption in the distal nephron. I would differ with one of the points you made in asking the question to the extent that PTH and cyclic AMP have anything to do with calcium reabsorption in the proximal nephron. PTH decreases sodium and phosphate reabsorption in the proximal tubule, and it is the unreabsorbed sodium that flushes the calcium through the proximal tubule. I don't think there are any direct effects of PTH on calcium transport at that level.

G. Campbell: May I ask another question. PTH does have a natriuretic effect in the proximal tubule. Did you imply that the effects on sodium reabsorption are indirect effects of the action of PTH on phosphorus.

A. Broadus: No, no, I'm sorry, PTH has a natriuretic effect, and it's the natriuretic effect which induces the calciuretic effect in the proximal nephron.

G. Campbell: And, you said the adenyl cyclase and receptor were on the interstitial and lateral sides. Does the cyclic AMP then diffuse through the cell to the luminal surface or is this some sort of shuttle mechanism in the membrane of the cell?

A. Broadus: I don't know the answer to that, in fact, I don't think it is known. I don't know whether it is an orderly sequence of transfer or simple diffusion. It is clear, however, that the cyclic AMP that we measure in plasma and urine leaks out of both sides of the cell. For example, if one gives a real blast of parathyroid hormone, one sees a rather substantial increase in plasma cyclic AMP. This cyclic AMP comes from the kidney and not bone.

T. Bigos: I wondered whether you might speculate on the feasibility of using urinary cyclic AMP measurements for screening patients with osteopenia for possible abnormal parathyroid function. In our own clinical experience, on one occasion in particular, we encountered a menopausal patient with serum calciums in the range of 10 to 10.2 mg%. By means other than urinary cAMP, we were able to show that the patient in fact had hyperparathyroidism (vitamin D and thiazide challenges with subsequent hypercalcemia and PTH-nonsuppressibility and later surgical proof with removal of an adenoma). This raised the lingering question of how many patients with normocalcemic osteopenia that might be called osteoporosis in fact have correctable underlying parathyroid disease?

A. Broadus: Well, that's just about as tough a question as it is to ferret these patients out of the stone population. It obviously comes up much more frequently than it is found. I would feel much better in dealing with the answer to that question if I felt I understood osteopenia as it occurs in hyperparathyroidism. What was described in 1926, osteitis fibrosa cystica, was hardly a subtle bone disease. The patients had multiple fractures and ultimately died of their severe disease process. Through the early 10 to 15 years of collections of series of patients with hyperparathyroidism, which was then regarded as a rare disease, there was a predominance of patients with the so-called bone presentation. In modern series, the percentage of such patients has decreased to the extent that even relatively mild osteitis is present in no more than 5% of the patients I see. However, one does see a 30 to 40% incidence of so-called osteopenia. What is this? Well, it is what appears on X-ray to be simple osteoporosis; it is diffuse. This is the patient that T. Bigos was asking about. Now it isn't yet clear in my mind what the histological or histomorphometric equivalent of osteopenia in hyperparathyroidism is, to what extent is it parathyroid-related, is it progressive, does it regress postoperatively, and so on? That information is not available. We're just beginning to try to look at this. For example, does our subdivision of patients in any way imply differences in terms of bony lesions? I don't know. I don't know how to make a diagnosis in such a patient apart from conventional means. Did you have any index of vitamin D status or absorption of calcium in your patient? Do I assume correctly that it was a postmenopausal female, first of all?

T. Bigos: We had normal 25-hydroxyvitamin D levels and 24-hour urinary calcium excretion in the range of 115 mg per gram of creatinine, so it didn't seem that we had, at least by those parameters, vitamin D deficiency, nor did we have significant hypercalciuria.

A. Broadus: Well this is really the key question, we are discussing the postmenopausal female with a serum calcium of about 11 and radiographic osteopenia. What do you do? Is the osteopenia specific? Is it indeed related to the hyperparathyroidism? I simply do not know the answers to these questions. Bob Neer at the MGH has a large series of patients with hyperparathyroidism who are being followed, and they are being followed very carefully. He has mentioned that he has seen in that category of the postmenopausal female, a progressive decrease in bone density as a function of time. He regards this as an indication for surgery. I can only pass that along as his own statement.

J. Parsons: I was very interested in your observations of the importance of intestinal hyperabsorption of calcium in the hyperparathyroidism syndrome. I think there must be very major individual variations in the sensitivity of that response to a given level of parathyroid hormone excess. It may be, I quite agree with you, that we won't really understand that until this other chemical bioassay becomes easy enough to handle the number of samples involved in looking at diurnal changes, for example. But there is one particular category that you might be interested in; we've been looking at responses to exogenous parathyroid hormone fragment as you may know in patients with osteoporosis, and when given in small spiked doses, it is capable of stimulating bone formation in virtually all patients, but the group as a whole has not shown corresponding increases in intestinal calcium absorption. One or two individual patients did show quite clear increases and animals always show such increases in both 1,25-dihydroxyvitamin D levels and intestinal calcium absorption. But many of the hyperparathyroid osteoporotic patients have not. Bob Mueller has done some direct challenge tests with one 1,34-PTH fragment and has shown in four of those patients so far that their 1,25 levels did not rise whereas, in normals, both in his own hands and in published series, a very clear rise is always seen in 1,25-$(OH)_2D$.

A. Broadus: I think that is very interesting. We now have 80 or 100 patients completely studied (Table A). Within that population we tried to look at all the variables that might relate to 1,25-dihydroxyvitamin D production. As you can see, if one subdivides the patients on the basis of the presence or absence of intestinal hyperabsorption of calcium, one winds up with two subpopulations with strikingly different mean circulating concentrations of 1,25-dihydroxyvitamin D. Yet between these subpopulations there are no significant differences in the status of vitamin D repletion, the degree of hypophosphatemia, and so on. So I have no explanation for the 4-fold range of 1,25-dihydroxyvitamin D levels we observed. I quite frankly thought we would be able to sort this out. I was thinking, in fact, of some old data that you had published about calcium balance versus the severity of hypercalcemia. I thought

TABLE A

Features of Absorptive and Nonabsorptive Patients with Primary Hyperparathyroidism[a]

	Serum 25-OHD (ng/ml)	Serum calcium (mg/dl)	Serum phos-phorous (mg/dl)	TmP/GFR (mg/dl)	GFR (ml/min)	Serum iPTH (μl eq/ml)	Nephrogenous cyclic AMP (nmol/100 ml GF)	Age (years)	Sex (M/F)
Absorptive (n = 30)	20 ± 9	11.0 ± 0.7	2.6 ± 0.5	2.3 ± 0.5	91 ± 18	129 ± 58	4.13 ± 1.14	49 ± 12	8/22
Nonabsorptive (n = 20)	22 ± 10	11.3 ± 1.2	2.7 ± 0.5	2.3 ± 0.3	100 ± 27	123 ± 44	3.60 ± 1.01	55 ± 14	8/12

[a] All data are shown as mean ± SD.

we would see perhaps an inverse correlation between serum calcium and 1,25-dihydroxyvitamin D. We didn't see it, and we have looked at twice as many patients and we still haven't seen it. I think that either we don't fully understand the regulation of 1,25-dihydroxyvitamin D or we're dealing with heterogeneity in this population at a very fundamental level.

H. Friesen: I wonder if you or Dr. Goltzman have had an opportunity to examine tumor extracts from those patients with humorally mediated hypercalcemia and malignancy to determine whether the nature of the factor that gives a positive response in the cytochemical assay is present in the tumor extracts and whether its characteristics are identical to what you see in the plasma.

A. Broadus: What I showed here was *in vivo* data which are as recent as even a couple of weeks ago; this work was just present this Spring. Obviously, our major goal is to go *in vitro* at this point. I think we have probably exhausted what we could or should do *in vivo*. We did culture one cell line from a patient with an ovarian carcinoma, and in the medium from that cell line we were able to see both striking bone resorbing activity and striking CBA activity. There was no PTH immunoreactivity in this medium, and only a small amount of the CBA activity could be eliminated by prior incubation with an excess of anti-PTH antiserum. We are now establishing a fairly wide ranging effort to pursue the material *in vitro*. It isn't that easy, as probably some investigators in this room know, to come by tissue from these patients, in the sense that hypercalcemia is a late complication of malignancy. There are few primary operations done in such patients, and it is very difficult to deal with autopsy material.

B. Posner: Did you look at the activity of this humoral factor in an adenyl cyclase assay?

A. Broadus: One thing that I didn't make clear is that one of the things that recommends the CBA technique is its exquisite sensitivity. In theory we are talking about a technique that is sensitive to 10^{-15} *M;* in practice, it is in the range of 10^{-12} *M*. We have set up a more sensitive canine renal cortical cyclase system than anybody has ever published, but this system is not sensitive enough to see what Dr. Goltzman saw in the medium. We hope to have enough material to use the cyclase system as a "tag" because it is a much simpler technique than the CBA technique.

C. Kahn: I was going to ask about a slightly different area. A few years ago it was suggested that nephrogenic cyclic AMP was also somewhat elevated by vasopressin and that perhaps one could use nephrogenic cyclic AMP as a diagnostic test in patients with vasopressin-resistent diabetes insipidus. I've heard from others, however, that this has been difficult to reproduce. I wonder if you have had any experience with this disease using your assay and whether you thought one could measure more than parathyroid hormone action with this test.

A. Broadus: I personally wouldn't really question the effects of ADH *in vitro* because I think these effects have been demonstrated in a number of laboratories. However, I have never seen any convincing evidence that vasopressin *in vivo* does anything to nephrogenous cyclic AMP. We have done very, very careful vasopressin infusion studies. We saw no increase in nephrogenous cyclic AMP in response to huge doses of the hormone. We also looked at a group of six patients with the inappropriate ADH syndrome who were well characterized. One of the critical issues here is the issue of data expression. Some of the older studies which expressed their values as nmoles of cyclic AMP per milligram of creatinine reported elevated values in patients with SIADH. But we're dealing mostly with patients with cancer who are wasted, who are putting out small amounts of creatinine, and I would submit that anything you would measure and express on that basis is going to appear elevated. Within our series, 3 of 6 patients were elevated in terms of total cyclic AMP excretion expressed on that basis; however, that is in the face of perfectly normal plasma values, perfectly normal nephrogenous cyclic AMP values, and perfectly normal total cyclic AMP excretion. So its all a phenomenon of expressing one's data inappropriately. That area of the nephron is impermeable to everything, and perhaps it is impermeable to cyclic AMP as well; I have no other explanation for the absence of demonstrable effects of ADH *in vivo*.

T. Murray: I'd like to get you to speculate a little bit on the nature of this humoral factor that's produced in these hypercalcemic cancer patients—apparently it interacts with PTH receptors although the activity seen by the cytochemical bioassay is larger than PTH by gel chromatography. On the other hand, it doesn't increase 1,25-$(OH)_2D$ levels. The speculation that comes most easily is that it's a biosynthetic precursor to parathyroid hormone, although several immunoassays directed at different portions of the molecule don't show up any immunoreactivity which is against that possibility. My questions are: do you know anything about the effects of the biosynthetic precursors pro-PTH or pre-pro-PTH on either the 1,25-$(OH)_2D$ response in patients or on the cytochemical bioassay. I know that pro-PTH is not terribly active in most usable bioassays but there might be something different in the cytochemical system.

A. Broadus: That's a multifaceted question. I'll speculate a little bit but not widely. I don't think it's worth your time to listen to wide speculation at this point. My bias would be that the material is a peptide, and I base that on precedent in the field of ectopic humoral syndromes in general. It would be appealing to think of it as perhaps a precursor. You just noted that in several biological assays pro-PTH has very limited activity, and I'm told by Joel Habener that pre-pro-PTH has absolutely none. If we were dealing with a precursor, then we would be presumably dealing with some sort of conversion at the site of action. I suppose this is conceivable. However, I think I would favor that we are dealing with a large protein that simply shares with PTH some forms of biological activity but not others. I didn't really emphasize some of the points in my presentation but we're seeing proximal tubular effects which are similar to those of PTH. We are not seeing hydroxylase stimulatory activity; we're not seeing distal tubular effects; we are seeing bony effects which are both similar and dissimilar. It's a very strange pattern that we're developing, but this is all phenomenology at this level. The whole thrust at this point is to try to isolate the material *in vitro*.

T. Murray: Do you know if David Goltzman has put pro-PTH in his cytochemical system?

A. Broadus: No, David has not looked at precursors in his system. He has looked at prostaglandins of the E series, and these do not demonstrate CBA activity.

J. Geller: Does thyroid hormone increase urinary cyclic AMP?

A. Broadus: No, it does not.

J. Geller: What percentage of your patients with calcium problems require the measurement of nephrogenous cyclic AMP. I just wonder how to fit this assay into clinical medicine. Most of the time we can recognize primary hyperparathyroidism and hypercalcemic malignancy with PTH assays, calcium assays, and vitamin D assays. I've wondered and read about your nephrogenous cyclic AMP test for a long time and I don't know practically speaking, what percentage of patients you find necessary to do this test in?

A. Broadus: Well, we use the cyclic AMP determinations as our front line clinical tool because that's what we have set up in our institution. We find this tool to be very reliable and versatile. A couple of years ago there was a presentation of diagnostic methods at the Endocrine Society, and Grant Liddle got up and said that's all quite wonderful but I thought I did pretty well with these patients 20 years ago before we had all these new determinations. What can you do that I can't? That was a fairly lucid comment, I think. My own feeling is that a combination of clinical experience and judgment is the most important single diagnostic test in existence. I could very easily with most patients get along simply with measurements of TmP/GFR and serum calcium. I think the determination of total cyclic AMP excretion is diagnostic in the vast majority of patients, and that determination is extraordinarily simple. I like to have some index of increased parathyroid function in my patients before I will make that diagnosis because I know that lurking out there are 10% or so of patients who are tough. So I like to have something I can lean on to take me from my 90% clinical diagnosis to a 100% biochemical one.

F. C. Bartter: Doctor Broadus, I believe, as you do, that the effect of vasopressin on nephrogenous cyclic AMP is negligible, at least in man. I question, however, your means of illustrating this. In the syndrome of inappropriate secretion of ADH, the vast majority of the plasma vasopressin values, which are now available in profusion, are normal. The important point is that they are inappropriately normal in the face of hyponatremia and hypotonicity of plasma, which should have lowered them to below normal or to zero. There are relatively few patients with SIADH who, because of a tumor producing vasopressin from an ectopic site, have elevated plasma vasopressin. In the series of patients you showed a normal value would almost surely have been found for plasma vasopressin.

A. Broadus: I think that's a very good point, and certainly we did not have immunoreactive vasopressin measured in these patients. I was making more of a general clinical point. That point is that the clinical diagnosis SIADH is not associated with the increases in nephrogenous cyclic AMP or total cyclic AMP excretion. I regard the negative ADH infusion studies as a far more definitive examination of this question.

Discussion to "The Neuroendocrine Control of the Menstrual Cycle"[1]

ERNST KNOBIL

Department of Physiology, University of Pittsburgh School of Medicine, Pittsburgh, Pennsylvania

DISCUSSION

R. F. Weick: Dr. Knobil, these are elegant experiments which demonstrate actions of estrogen on the pituitary. I, too, have been working on some of the effects of estrogen on gonadotropin secretion in the rhesus monkey, and some of my results are difficult to reconcile with the hypothesis that estrogen acts only on the pituitary. In one set of experiments, crystalline estradiol-17β was placed directly into different areas of the hypothalamus. In ovariectomized animals, placement of estradiol into the medial basal hypothalamus was followed by a negative feedback effect and an LH surge, as is seen following systemic administration of estrogen. Estrogen in the anterior hypothalamus was without effect, which is consistent with your lesioning experiments. The effective implants were at the level of the arcuate nucleus, probably in the third ventricle. Placement of the estradiol 0.75 mm dorsal or 2 mm lateral to this position resulted in only the negative feedback effect without an LH surge. Estrogen placed 2 mm dorsal to the arcuate nucleus on the midline had no apparent effect on LH secretion. It is possible that the estrogen from the implants is gaining access to the portal system and having its effect on the pituitary. Although I cannot document this with hard evidence, the dramatic changes in gonadotropin secretion which accompany rather small changes in position of the estrogen implant seem more consistent with a local, rather than a distant, site of action.

In another series of experiments I have been testing the acute response of the pituitary to exogenous LHRH at various stages of the estrogen-induced LH surge in the ovariectomized monkey. The effects of subcutaneous implantation of Silastic capsules containing estradiol-17β on serum LH levels are shown in the bottom panel of Fig. A: an initial inhibition followed by the LH surge. Panel A shows the increase in LH following LHRH injection 1 hour prior to implantation of the estrogen capsules. As seen in panel B, the response to the same dose of LHRH 24 hours later was unchanged, although LH secretion at this time was inhibited by the estrogen. The response to the same dose of LHRH during the LH surge, shown in panel C, is smaller than during either previous test, although this is confounded by the fact that this injection occurred at different stages of the LH surge in different animals. These results suggest that estrogen can influence LH secretion by some manner other than by merely changing the sensitivity of the pituitary to LHRH.

A third point, for which I have no fresh data, involves the conundrum of the actions of progesterone. Experiments from your laboratory have shown that progesterone does not block pulsatile discharges of LH in the ovariectomized monkey but that it does block the LH

[1] For article see Knobil, E. (1980). *Recent Prog. Hormone Res.* **36**, 53.

ISBN 0-12-571137-9

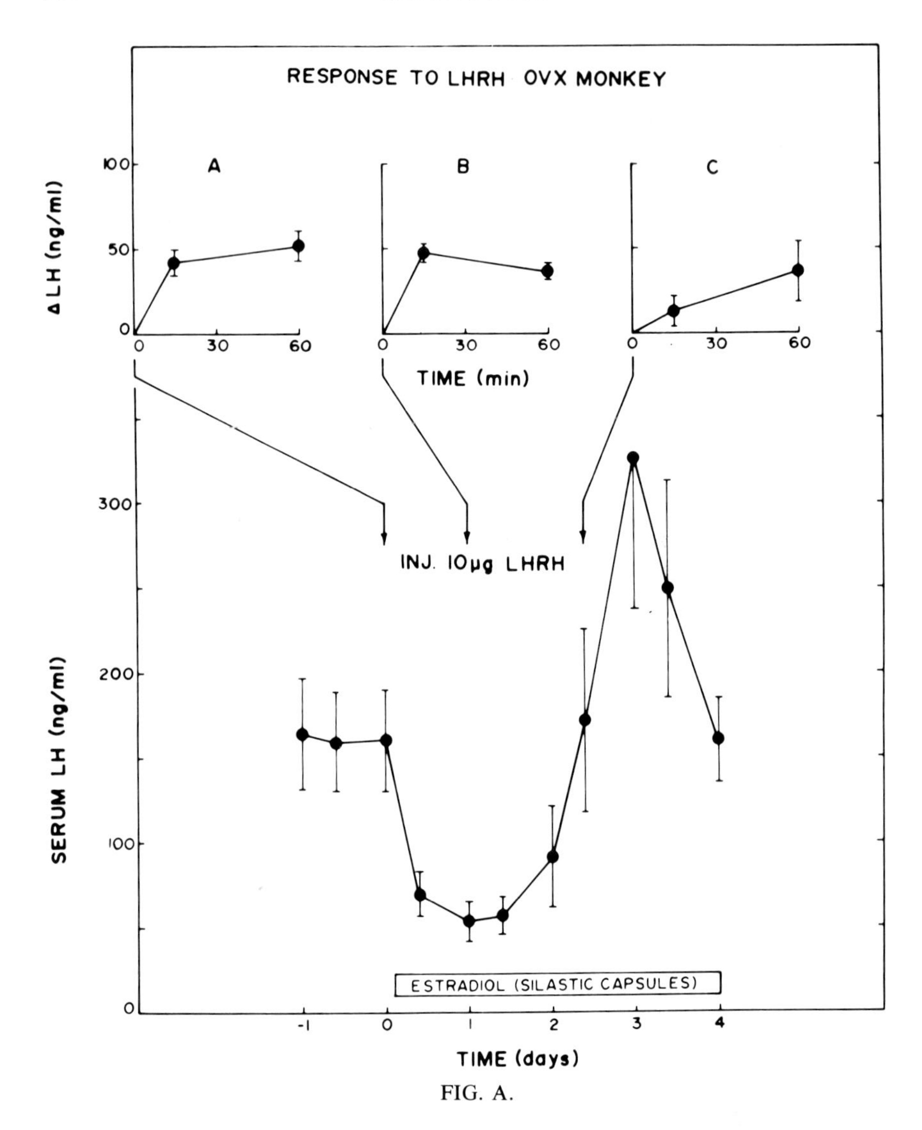

FIG. A.

surge. I previously interpreted this to mean that progesterone inhibits the neural regions controlling the LH surge, but not those controlling tonic LH secretion. Your pituitary model of the regulation of LH secretion would seem to require inhibition by progesterone at the level of the pituitary, but only under certain conditions.

E. Knobil: To address your last point first, we have recently established using the hypophysiotropic clamp technique that progesterone appears to act at the level of the hypothalamus to block estrogen-induced gonadotropin surges. Its well known facilitatory effect in this regard, however, seems to be exerted at the pituitary (see Wildt *et al.*, *Proc. 6th Int. Congr. Endocrinol.*, 1980).

When we gave single injections of GnRH throughout the menstrual cycle you may recall that we also found that the response to this stimulus was least when estrogen was the highest, before the actual initiation of the LH surge. The response was highest during the surge [Krey *et al.*, *in* "Hypothalamic Hypophysiotropic Hormones" (C. Gual and E. Rosemberg, eds.). Excerpta Medical International Congress Series 263, 1973]. I believe that the experiments illustrated in Fig. 8 speak for themselves. Similar results were obtained in the same study (Plant *et al.*, *Endocrinology* **102,** 1015, 1978) when the estrogen was given as a constant infusion rather than a single intravenous pulse. It is difficult to interpret these findings in terms other than a pituitary site of estrogen action. At least we failed in the attempt.

Lastly, I really do think that it is very difficult to be certain that the estrogen you introduced into the hypothalamus of your monkeys, at varying distances from the pituitary portal vasculature, did not act directly at the level of the pituitary gland.

F. Naftolin: I think that data from Drs. Lincoln and Short (*Recent Prog. Hormone Res.* **36,** 1, 1980) and yours given today showed us some clues for the control of gonadotropins in the menopausal individual. Their data, which is consistent with a little bit too much LRF, and your data, which is consistent with advertent administration of an oversupply of LRF, show that under those conditions FSH can go up disproportionate to LH in the castrate or pseudocastrate animal. I think it could be a useful model for menopause.

Second, I would like to say a word for our students who have to deal with the concept of "negative" and "positive" feedback. Data such as yours which so elegantly show that you don't get "positive" feedback without a preceding "negative" feedback is much more easily discussed in terms of "biphasic feedback." I'd put in a pitch for the use of that term.

E. Knobil: The menopause question is an interesting one. It should be easy to find the answer but I don't know it at the moment. In any case, a slowing in the frequency of endogenous GnRH pulses would readily explain the change in FSH : LH ratios observed in premenopausal women.

The use of the phrases negative and positive feedback has bothered many of us from time to time, but for different reasons. The problem is that we don't have any understanding of the mechanisms whereby estrogens either inhibit or stimulate gonadotropin secretion although I am confident, at long last, that these actions are exerted at the level of the pituitary gonadotrophs, at least in the rhesus monkey. For the moment, all we can do is find the most felicitous descriptions of the phenomenology in question. The choice will remain a matter of taste until we really understand what estrogens are doing, in this regard, at the cellular and subcellular levels.

E. M. Bogdanove: I have a comment and a question. The comment has to do with the point Dr. Weick raised. I am sure you would agree that the absence of evidence can never be taken as evidence of absence. Consequently, although you have demonstrated very beautifully that you can closely mimic the behavior of the spontaneously running system without any variation in the output of your hypothalamic prosthesis, this need not mean that the free-running system actually operates in the same way, without any variation in hypothalamic secretory patterning.

The question has to do with prolactin. When you put a radio frequency lesion directly into the arcuate nucleus and eliminated LH and FSH secretion, was there really no change in prolactin? From the figure, this appeared to be the case even after you had given estrogen, which I found rather surprising. I wonder if you have evidence or an opinion regarding whether the action of estrogen on prolactin secretion is via the hypothalamus. Or is there some other explanation for the failure of prolactin to rise in this situation?

E. Knobil: Of course I agree that our experiments have not excluded changes in hypothalamic activity during the normal menstrual cycle. In fact such changes are known to occur as I have indicated in the formulation of our model. Our studies unequivocally demonstrate, however, that the system *can* function normally, as best we can determine, in the face of a rigidly controlled, unvarying GnRH input. The onus now is on those who believe that an increment in GnRH release normally initiates the preovulatory gonadotropin surge, to demonstrate that this, in fact, occurs.

While changes in the frequency of GnRH pulses are clearly observable during the menstrual cycle as I have mentioned, particularly during the luteal phase, the functional significance of this eludes me at the moment. The hourly frequency of GnRH administration yielded a time course of progesterone indistinguishable from that observed in monkeys with intact nervous systems in which the frequency of hypothalamic input is presumably less than that. I believe that whatever the significance of the alteration in GnRH pulse frequency during the normal menstrual cycle may be, they probably represent modulatory rather than primary components of the basic control system which can perform its entire task without a change in frequency.

Prolactin secretion in the rhesus monkey, in contrast to that in the rat and sheep, is quite insensitive to acute changes in estrogen levels. The system does respond, however, to prolonged alterations in circulating estrogen concentrations, but its sites of action in this regard remain to be established.

R. B. Jaffe: These were very elegant experiments, very lucidly presented. Perhaps there is a species difference among primates. In normally cycling women, when we administer estradiol very early in the cycle (a time when endogenous gonadotropins and estradiol are low) in amounts which simulate the periovulatory estradiol concentrations for an appropriate duration we are able to effect a spontaneous surge of LH unaccompanied by a surge of FSH. If, in contrast, we superimpose small doses of progesterone in amounts which simulate those normally seen in the periovulatory period, namely 1 to 2 ng/ml, we can maximize and regularize the LH surge and can effect an FSH surge as well (R. J. Chang and R. B. Jaffe, *J. Clin. Endocrinol. Metab.* **47,** 119, 1978).

E. Knobil: Yes, I agree that there seems to be a difference between the human and the monkey in this regard. In the latter one can initiate very respectable LH and FSH surges with estrogen alone. It seems, however, that this species difference is quantitative rather than qualitative in that there appears to be general agreement that the initiation of the surge in both instances is due to an estrogen increment but progesterone is required in the human female for the full development of both the LH and FSH surges. A modulatory influence of the steroid if you will.

W. F. Crowley: I have some confirmatory data in that regard. We have administered LHRH in a very similar fashion to female Kallman's Syndrome patients and have been able to induce both follicular ripening and endogenous LH surges employing a 2-hourly frequency of administration, but at a dosage of 25–50 ng/kg, i.e., one-fortieth the doses you've used. This may well represent one of the quantitative species difference that you are talking about. My questions relate to the extremes of your AM/FM program. In the animals that you administered the LHRH every 8 hours and observed a monotrophic increase in FSH, were the gonads intact and if so, what was the response? The second question is when you keep the frequency the same and increased the dosage 10-fold you said you achieved high LH levels but "down-regulated" the FSH. These observations sound to me very reminiscent of the gonadotropin pattern observed in the polycystic ovary syndrome. I wonder if you followed the animals long enough to see if any such changes in ovarian morphology occurred.

E. Knobil: All of our frequency experiments were conducted in ovariectomized monkeys, hence we could not ascertain the ovarian responses to changing LH : FSH ratios. This is a critically important question which we are currently addressing in identically prepared animals but with their ovaries *in situ*.

F. J. Karsch: The control system you described is based on a pulsatile output of GnRH from the hypothalamus. Yet so far as I am aware, pulsatile secretion of gonadotropin is not demonstrable during the menstrual cycle of the rhesus monkey. I have two questions related to that. First, why is pulsatile gonadotropin secretion not demonstrable during the monkey menstrual cycle? Second, does pulsatile gonadotropin secretion occur in ovary-intact monkeys with arcuate nucleus lesions that are induced to have menstrual cycles by pulsatile delivery of GnRH?

E. Knobil: You are quite correct. Circhoral gonadotropin pulses are not readily demonstrable in the peripheral circulation of intact rhesus monkeys who differ from most other species in this regard. The reason for this has become apparent recently and is illustrated in Fig. 8 and in similar studies (see Plant *et al., Endocrinology* **102,** 1015, 1978). We can replicate the circhoral pulses seen in ovariectomized but otherwise normal monkeys by the pulsatile administration of GnRH to ovariectomized monkeys with hypothalamic lesions. When physiological increments of estrogen are produced in these animals the LH pulses are completely obtunded and can no longer be readily detected in the peripheral circulation despite the continued, pulsatile administration of the GnRH. It seems that the negative feedback loop between the ovary and the pituitary is particularly sensitive in the rhesus monkey although my guess is that if we could sample the pituitary effluent directly, before it is diluted by the remainder of the circulation, we could probably detect gonadotropin pulses with sensitive radioimmunoassays.

An interesting consequence of this unusual behavior of the rhesus monkey is that it permits the conclusion that the ovary, in contrast to the pituitary, is able to respond quite nicely to nonpulsatile, tropic hormone stimulation.

L. Bullock: To return to the question of differential responses of gonadotropins, it appeared to me that when you gave GnRH to immature monkeys you induced very nice LH spikes but I did not see much change in FSH. I wonder if this is really true or if it is an artifact of how the data were presented.

E. Knobil: What you noted is a function of the way the data are plotted. In fact, there is no difference between the gonadotropic levels of normal menstrual cycles and those induced in immature monkeys by intermittent GnRH administration.

K. Sterling: I have a comment and a question. The comment concerns my experiences in breeding Siberian husky dogs. Every so often when I don't want them mating one of the males (who are very ingenious) undoes the padlock and gets in with a bitch in heat. I have found a highly reliable way to prevent conception in a 40-pound bitch is to give an intramuscular injection of 1 to 2 mg of estradiol valerate followed the same day and for five consecutive days by 1 mg of oral diethylstilbestrol. This method is not known by all veterinarians; but some do employ it. What I want to know is, since it has worked 100% in my hands with no endonetritis, what do you suppose is going on—is *everything* flattened? I didn't bother to measure the FSH or LH or for that matter, and needless to say, not the GnRH. I assume everything is suppressed including the implantation. What's your guess about it?

E. Knobil: I would tend to agree that your 40-pound bitch was completely flattened by the inundation of estrogen to which you subjected her. In ovariectomized monkeys, constant exposure to even low estrogen levels will, in time, close the negative feedback loop so "tightly" that gonadotropin synthesis is totally inhibited.

INDEX